Aids to Learning

Chapter Zero: Learning How to Learn

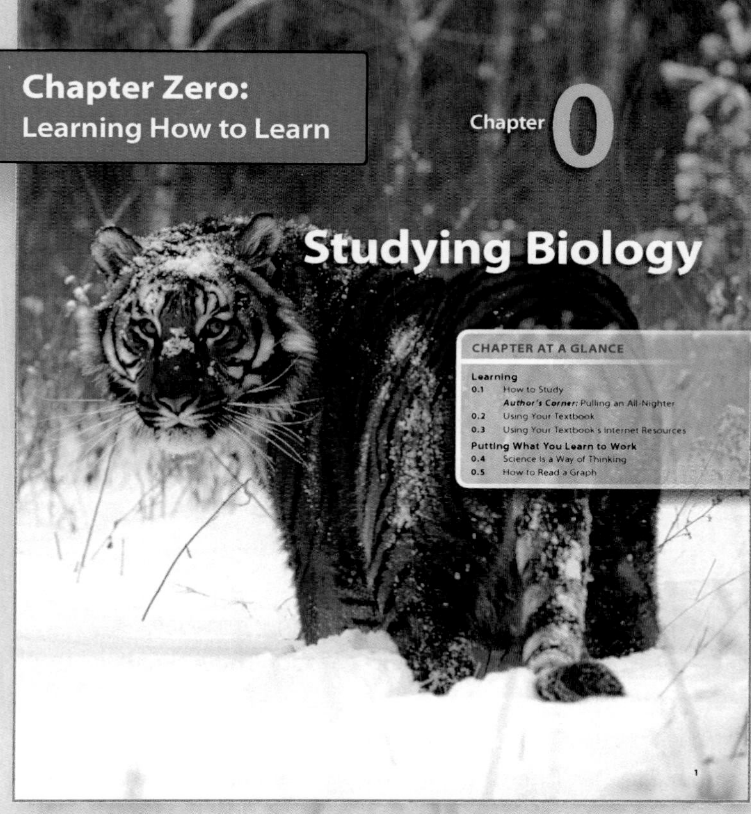

Targeted Learning Objectives: Defining a Learning Path

Control

...on entirely in terms of proteins that ...ing or activating the "reading" of a ...hin the last decade, however, it has ...cules also regulate gene expression, ...lly important level of control.

...in 2008 was completely cured of AIDS. How? First, his immune system was wiped out with radiation and drugs, then he received blood stem cells (which make both circulating blood cells and immune system cells) from a person homozygous for a gene mutation known as *delta 32*. This mutation destroys the cell surface receptor called CCR5 that allows HIV to invade the immune system, so that people homozygous for it are immune to HIV infection and AIDS. Because the patient's own blood stem cells had been destroyed, these new ones reconstituted his blood supply and immune system with *delta 32* cells. He has been free of the HIV virus for 20 months and it appears he has been permanently cured of AIDS. Wiping out a person's immune system is far too dangerous as a general therapy (10%–30% die), but the success in this instance has encouraged researchers to try using RNA "scissors" as described on this page to cut out the *delta 32* gene from a patient's own blood stem cells and reinject them after wiping out only the patient's blood stem cells, not the entire immune sy... ...chers report that the concept is working in...

Discovery of RNA Interference

LEARNING OBJECTIVE 12.7.1 Define RNA interference.

As will be discussed in detail in chapter 13, the bulk of the eukaryotic genome is not translated into proteins. This finding was puzzling at first, but began to make sense in 1998, when a simple experiment was carried out, for which Americans Andrew Fire and Craig Mello later won the Nobel Prize in Physiology or Medicine in 2006. These investigators injected double-stranded RNA molecules into the nematode worm *Caenorhabditis elegans*. This resulted in the silencing of the gene whose sequence was complementary to the double-stranded RNA, and of no other gene. The investigators called this very specific effect **gene silencing, or RNA interference.** What is going on here? A group of viruses called RNA viruses, those that contain RNA as their hereditary storage molecule rather than DNA, replicate themselves through double-stranded intermediates. RNA interference may have evolved as a cellular defense mechanism against these viruses with double-stranded viral RNAs being targeted for destruction by RNA interference machinery. Without intending to do so, the nematode researchers had stumbled across this defense.

Putting the Concept to Work
...g double-stranded DNA provide a defense ...ses?

...rference Works

...OBJECTIVE 12.7.2 Explain how small RNA mol... ...ut RNA interference.

...rence, researchers noted that in the process of silencing ...duced short RNA molecules (ranging in length from 21 ... that matched the gene being silenced. Earlier researchers ...rger messenger RNA (mRNA), transfer RNA (tRNA), and ... (rRNA) had not noticed these far smaller bits, tossing them out during experiments. These bits of RNA are called "small interfering RNA" or siRNA. How do these small fragments of RNA silence the activity of specific genes? In a complex way we are just beginning to understand clearly, the small RNA fragments bind to any mRNA molecules in the cell that have a complementary sequence. Silencing of the gene that produced this mRNA is achieved in one of two ways (figure 12.18): either the expression of the mRNA is inhibited by blocking its translation into protein, or the mRNA is simply destroyed. In either case, the specific gene that produced that mRNA fails to be expressed—it is silenced.

Putting the Concept to Work
If RNA is not double-stranded, how can siRNA bind to mRNA?

D1529700

siRNA/target mRNA duplex
Translation is blocked
mRNA is destroyed

Figure 12.18 RNA interference.
RNA interference stops gene expression either by blocking the translation of the gene (on the left) or by targeting the mRNA for destruction before it can be translated.

Applications (Apps): Biology in Your World

Links: Arrows that Link Ideas

...of respira... ...rbon dioxide ...ving organ... ...sms or deep underground. The cycle is begun by plants that use CO_2 in photosynthesis to build organic molecules—in effect, they trap the carbon atoms of CO_2 within the living world. The carbon atoms are returned to the atmosphere's pool of CO_2 through respiration, combustion, and erosion, as shown in figure 20.9.

Respiration

Carbon dioxide is generated at two points during cellular respiration. First, two molecules of CO_2 are produced in the oxidation of pyruvate to acetyl-CoA, discussed on page 121. Another four molecules of CO_2 are produced in the Krebs cycle, discussed on page 122.

All organisms in ecosystems respire—that is, they extract energy from organic food molecules, which involves stripping away the carbon atoms and combining them with oxygen to form CO_2. This end product of respiration is released into the atmosphere.

Combustion

Plants that become buried in sediment may be transformed by pressure into coal or oil. The carbon originally trapped by these plants is only released back into the atmosphere when the coal or oil (called **fossil fuels**) is burned.

Human activity is causing the carbon cycle to become unbalanced. As described on page 454, the influx of large amounts of carbon dioxide into the atmosphere from the burning of fossil fuels is causing atmospheric temperatures to rise, a process called global warming.

...again in oceans.

Putting the Concept to Work
How is carbon released into the atmosphere from plants?

BIOLOGY & YOU

You and the Carbon Cycle. You and every American make a contribution to global warming, because the way we live each day adds a lot of carbon dioxide to the earth's atmosphere. Your "carbon footprint" is a measure of the amount of carbon dioxide produced to fuel your daily life. In the diagram below, your carbon footprint is the sum of two parts: the *primary footprint* over which you have direct control, and the *secondary footprint* which measures the CO_2 emissions associated with the manufacture and breakdown of products we use. The average worldwide carbon footprint is about 4 tons per year. The average footprint of people in the United States is five times that, over 20 tons per year! The worldwide target to combat global warming is 2 tons per year. Imagine what your life would be like with your carbon footprint reduced 90%. The world's future depends upon it.

Car manufacture & delivery 7%
Clothes & personal effects 4%
Food & drink 5%
House-buildings & furnishings 9%
Air travel 6%
Public transportation 3%
Recreation & leisure 14%
Private transportation 10%
Financial services 3%
Home-electricity 12%
Share of public services 12%
Home-gas, oil, & coal 15%

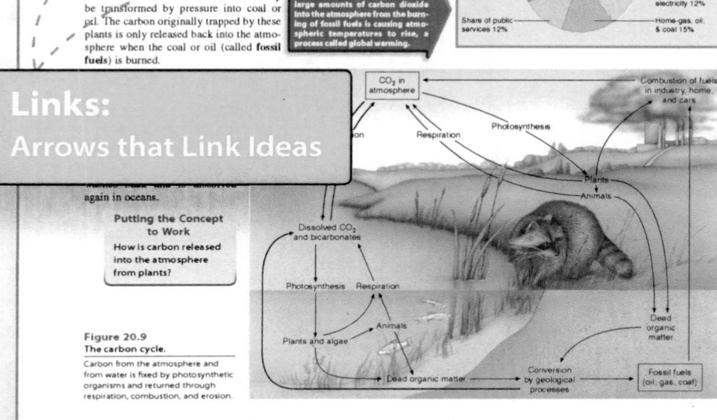

Figure 20.9
The carbon cycle.
Carbon from the atmosphere and from water is fixed by photosynthetic organisms and returned through respiration, combustion, and erosion.

Experiments: Thinking Like a Scientist

Inquiry & Analysis

...in tissue culture, such as those growing in culture flasks in the photo below, will divide only a certain number of times. After about 50 population doublings cell division stops (a doubling is a round of cell division producing two daughter cells for each dividing cell, for example going from a population of 30 cells to 60 cells). If a cell sample is taken after 20 doublings and frozen, when thawed it resumes growth for 30 more doublings, and then stops. An explanation of the "Hayflick limit" was suggested in 1986 when researchers first glimpsed an extra length of DNA at the end of chromosomes. Dubbed *telomeres*, these lengths proved to be composed of the simple DNA sequence TTAGGG, repeated nearly a thousand times. Importantly, telomeres were found to be substantially shorter in the cells of older body tissues. This led to the hypothesis that a run of some 16 TTAGGGs was where the DNA replicating enzyme, called polymerase, first sat down on the DNA (16 TTAGGGs being the size of the enzyme's "footprint"), and because of being its docking spot, the polymerase was unable to copy that bit. Thus a 100-base portion of the telomere was lost by a chromosome during each doubling as DNA replicated. Eventually, after some 50 doubling cycles, each with a round of DNA replication, the telomere would be used up and there would be no place for the DNA replication enzyme to sit. The cell line would then enter senescence, no longer able to proliferate.

This hypothesis was tested in 1998. Using genetic engineering, researchers transferred into newly established human cell cultures a gene that leads to expression of an enzyme called *telomerase* that all cells possess but no body cell uses. This enzyme adds TTAGGG sequences back to the end of telomeres, in effect rebuilding the lost portions of the telomere. Laboratory cultures of cell lines with (telomerase plus) and without (normal) this gene were then monitored for many generations. The graph above displays the results.

Effect of Telomerase on Cell Culture Growth

Population doublings: 30 60 90 120 150
Normal
Telomerase plus
Relative growth rate
Months: 0 3 6 9 12 15 18 21 24 27 30 33

TTAGGG TTAGGG TTAGGG TTAGGG TTAGGG.......

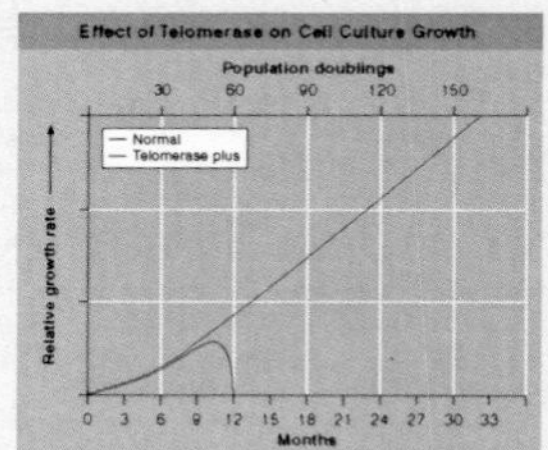

Analysis

1. **Applying Concepts** Comparing continuous processes, how do normal skin cells (blue line) differ in their growth history from telomerase plus cells with the telomerase gene (red line)?
2. **Interpreting Data** After how many doublings do the normal cells cease to divide? the telomerase plus cells?
3. **Making Inferences** After 9 population doublings, would the rate of cell division be different between the two cultures? after 15? Why?
4. **Drawing Conclusions** How does the addition of the telomerase gene affect the senescence (death by old age) of skin cells growing in culture? Does this result confirm the telomerase hypothesis this experiment had set out to test?

Brief Contents

Chapter 0 Studying Biology 1

Part 1 The Study of Life

Chapter 1 The Science of Biology 15

Part 2 The Living Cell

Chapter 2 The Chemistry of Life 33
Chapter 3 Molecules of Life 49
Chapter 4 Cells 65
Chapter 5 Energy and Life 91
Chapter 6 Photosynthesis: Acquiring Energy from the Sun 103
Chapter 7 How Cells Harvest Energy from Food 117

Part 3 The Continuity of Life

Chapter 8 Mitosis 133
Chapter 9 Meiosis 147
Chapter 10 Foundations of Genetics 159
Chapter 11 DNA: The Genetic Material 189
Chapter 12 How Genes Work 205

Part 4 The Evolution and Diversity of Life

Chapter 14 Evolution and Natural Selection 249

Part 5 The Living Environment

Chapter 19 Populations and Communities 375
Chapter 20 Ecosystems 403
Chapter 22 Human Influences on the Living World 451

Part 6 Animal Life

Chapter 23 The Animal Body and How It Moves 473
Chapter 26 The Path of Food Through the Animal Body 515
Chapter 29 The Nervous System 561
Chapter 30 Chemical Signaling Within the Animal Body 583
Chapter 31 Reproduction and Development 597
Chapter 13 The New Biology 223

Appendix A 651
Glossary 653
Credits 664
Index 667
Applications Index 684

Selected material from

Essentials of The Living World

Fourth Edition

George B. Johnson
Washington University

Cedarville University

Mc Graw Hill Education

3 4 5 6 7 8 9 10 DIG/DIG 15 14 13

ISBN-13: 978-1-259-20735-8
ISBN-10: 1-259-20735-8

Learning Solutions Consultant: Jennifer Harrington
Associate Project Manager: Mark Bodensteiner
Cover Photo Credits: © Alan and Sandy Carey/Getty Images

Contents

Preface x

0 Studying Biology 1

Learning 2

0.1 How to Study 2
0.2 Using Your Textbook 6
0.3 Using Your Textbook's Internet Resources 8

Putting What You Learn to Work 10

0.4 Science Is a Way of Thinking 10
0.5 How to Read a Graph 12

Part 1
The Study of Life

1 The Science of Biology 15

Biology and the Living World 16

1.1 The Diversity of Life 16
1.2 Properties of Life 17
1.3 The Organization of Life 18
1.4 Biological Themes 20

The Scientific Process 22

1.5 Stages of a Scientific Investigation 22
1.6 Theory and Certainty 24

Core Ideas of Biology 26

1.7 Four Theories Unify Biology as a Science 26

Part 2
The Living Cell

2 The Chemistry of Life 33

Some Simple Chemistry 34

2.1 Atoms 34
2.2 Ions and Isotopes 36
2.3 Molecules 37

Water: Cradle of Life 42

2.4 Unique Properties of Water 42
2.5 Water Ionizes 44

3 Molecules of Life 49

Forming Macromolecules 50

3.1 Building Big Molecules 50

Types of Macromolecules 52

3.2 Proteins 52
3.3 Nucleic Acids 56
3.4 Carbohydrates 58
3.5 Lipids 60

4 Cells 65

The World of Cells 66

4.1 Cells 66

Kinds of Cells 69

4.2 Prokaryotic Cells 69
4.3 Eukaryotic Cells 70

Tour of a Eukaryotic Cell 72

4.4 The Plasma Membrane 72
4.5 The Nucleus: The Cell's Control Center 74
4.6 The Endomembrane System 76
4.7 Organelles That Harvest Energy 78
4.8 The Cytoskeleton: Interior Framework of the Cell 80

Transport Across Plasma Membranes 82

4.9 Diffusion and Osmosis 82
4.10 Bulk Passage into and out of Cells 84
4.11 Selective Permeability 85

5 Energy and Life 91

Cells and Energy 92

5.1 The Flow of Energy in Living Things 92
5.2 The Laws of Thermodynamics 93

Cell Chemistry 94

5.3 Chemical Reactions 94

Enzymes 95

5.4 How Enzymes Work 95
5.5 How Cells Regulate Enzymes 97

How Cells Use Energy 98

5.6 ATP: The Energy Currency of the Cell 98

6 Photosynthesis: Acquiring Energy from the Sun 103

Photosynthesis 104

6.1 An Overview of Photosynthesis 104
6.2 How Plants Capture Energy from Sunlight 108
6.3 How Photosystems Convert Light to Chemical Energy 110
6.4 Building New Molecules 112

Photorespiration 113

6.5 Photorespiration: Putting the Brakes on Photosynthesis 113

7 How Cells Harvest Energy from Food 117

An Overview of Cellular Respiration 118

7.1 Where Is the Energy in Food? 118

Respiration Without Oxygen: Glycolysis 120

7.2 Using Coupled Reactions to Make ATP 120

Respiration with Oxygen: The Krebs Cycle 121

7.3 Harvesting Electrons from Chemical Bonds 121
7.4 Using the Electrons to Make ATP 124

Harvesting Electrons Without Oxygen: Fermentation 127

7.5 Cells Can Metabolize Food Without Oxygen 127

Other Sources of Energy 128

7.6 Glucose Is Not the Only Food Molecule 128

Part 3
The Continuity of Life

8 Mitosis 133

Cell Division 134

8.1 Prokaryotes Have a Simple Cell Cycle 134
8.2 Eukaryotic Cell Cycle 135
8.3 Chromosomes 136
8.4 Cell Division 138

Cancer and the Cell Cycle 141

8.5 What Is Cancer? 141

9 Meiosis 147

Meiosis 148

9.1 Discovery of Meiosis 148
9.2 The Sexual Life Cycle 149
9.3 The Stages of Meiosis 150

Comparing Meiosis and Mitosis 154

9.4 How Meiosis Differs from Mitosis 154

10 Foundations of Genetics 159

Mendel 160

10.1 Mendel and the Garden Pea 160
10.2 What Mendel Observed 162
10.3 Mendel Proposes a Theory 164
10.4 Mendel's Laws 167

From Genotype to Phenotype 168

10.5 How Genes Influence Traits 168
10.6 Why Some Traits Don't Show Mendelian Inheritance 170

Chromosomes and Heredity 174

10.7 Chromosomes Are the Vehicles of Mendelian Inheritance 174
10.8 Human Chromosomes 176

Human Hereditary Disorders 178

10.9 Studying Pedigrees 178
10.10 The Role of Mutations in Human Heredity 180
10.11 Genetic Counseling and Therapy 184

11 DNA: The Genetic Material 189

Genes Are Made of DNA 190

11.1 The Griffith Experiment 190
11.2 The Hereditary Material 191
11.3 Discovering the Structure of DNA 192

DNA Replication 194

11.4 How DNA Copies Itself 194

Altering the Genetic Message 198

11.5 Mutation 198

12 How Genes Work 205

From Gene to Protein 206

12.1 The Central Dogma 206
12.2 Transcription 207
12.3 Translation 208
12.4 Gene Expression 211

Regulating Gene Expression 214

12.5 Transcriptional Control in Prokaryotes 214
12.6 Transcriptional Control in Eukaryotes 216
12.7 RNA-Level Control 218

Part 4
The Evolution and Diversity of Life

14 Evolution and Natural Selection 249

Evolution 250

14.1 Darwin's Voyage on HMS *Beagle* 250
14.2 Darwin's Evidence 252
14.3 The Theory of Natural Selection 253

Darwin's Finches: Evolution in Action 255

14.4 The Beaks of Darwin's Finches 255
14.5 How Natural Selection Produces Diversity 257

Preface

No one who teaches biology today can fail to appreciate how important a subject it has become for our modern world. From global warming to stem cell initiatives to teaching intelligent design in classrooms, biology permeates the news, and in large measure will define students' futures. As a teacher, I have stood in front of classrooms for over 30 years and attempted to explain biology to puzzled and sometimes uninterested students, an experience that has been both fun and frustrating: Fun because biology is a joy to teach, rich in ideas and interesting concepts, and increasingly key to many important public issues; frustrating because in every biology class there are always some students who will not pay attention, who not only miss out on the fun but also fail to acquire a tool that will be essential to their futures.

This text, *Essentials of The Living World*, is my attempt to address this problem. It is short enough to use in one semester, without a lot of technical details to intimidate wary students. I have tried to write it in an informal, friendly way, to engage as well as to teach. The focus of the book is on the biology that plays an important role in each student's life. I have at every stage addressed ideas and concepts, rather than detailed information, trying to teach *how* things work and *why* things happen the way they do rather than merely naming parts or giving definitions.

Following a Learning Path

In setting out to improve this edition of *Essentials of The Living World*, my focus has been on improving it as a learning tool. I have made many changes, some obvious, others more subtle, all of them aimed at making it easier for students using this text to understand and appreciate what they learn in lecture, and so do better in the course.

Anyone familiar with this text will see at a glance the major change: Each chapter is now broken into conceptual blocks, each block introduced with a **targeted learning objective** that pinpoints the concept or process that is the focus of the block. Each block is completed with a "putting the concept to work" question that requires the student to draw a conclusion from what he or she has learned—to put the learning objective to work, and in that way to reinforce its retention.

Each chapter's learning objectives thus define a "learning path," introducing a series of ideas and information in an order designed to erect a conceptual framework that a student can use to organize his or her understanding. By incorporating learning objectives directly into the text where they arise, rather than isolating them at the head of sections, *Essentials of The Living World* places the bull's-eye (the learning objective) right on its target (the text to be understood and learned).

218 Part 3 The Continuity of Life

IN THE NEWS

Silencing AIDS. After decades of searching unsuccessfully for an effective AIDS vaccine, researchers are turning to other approaches. One of the most promising centers on a 42-year-old American resident of Germany, who in 2008 was completely cured of AIDS. How? First, his immune system was wiped out with radiation and drugs, then he received blood stem cells (which make both circulating blood cells and immune system cells) from a person homozygous for a gene mutation known as *delta 32*. This mutation destroys the cell surface receptor called CCR5 that allows HIV to invade the immune system, so that people homozygous for it are immune to HIV infection and AIDS. Because the patient's own blood stem cells had been destroyed, these new ones reconstituted his blood supply and immune system with *delta 32* cells. He has been free of the HIV virus for 20 months and it appears he has been permanently cured of AIDS. Wiping out a person's immune system is far too dangerous as a general therapy (10%–30% die), but the success in this instance has encouraged researchers to try using RNA "scissors" as described on this page to cut out the *delta 32* gene from a patient's own blood stem cells and reinject them after wiping out only the patient's blood stem cells, not the entire immune system. Researchers report that the concept is working in monkeys.

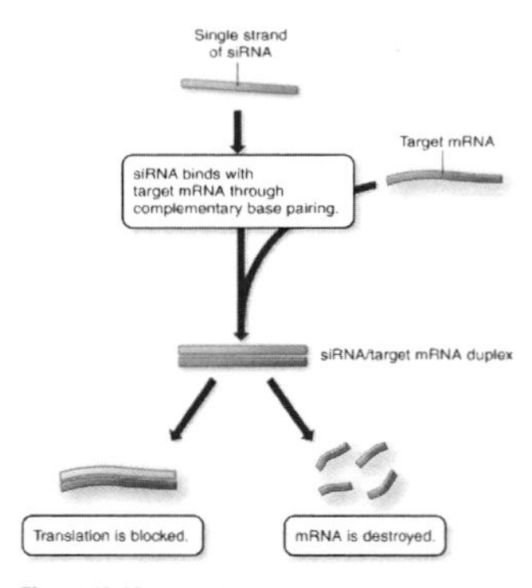

Figure 12.18 RNA interference.
RNA interference stops gene expression either by blocking the translation of the gene (on the left) or by targeting the mRNA for destruction before it can be translated.

12.7 RNA-Level Control

Thus far we have discussed gene regulation entirely in terms of proteins that regulate the start of transcription by blocking or activating the "reading" of a particular gene by RNA polymerase. Within the last decade, however, it has become increasingly clear that RNA molecules also regulate gene expression, acting after transcription as a second equally important level of control.

Discovery of RNA Interference

LEARNING OBJECTIVE 12.7.1 Define RNA interference.

As will be discussed in detail in chapter 13, the bulk of the eukaryotic genome is not translated into proteins. This finding was puzzling at first, but began to make sense in 1998, when a simple experiment was carried out, for which Americans Andrew Fire and Craig Mello later won the Nobel Prize in Physiology or Medicine in 2006. These investigators injected double-stranded RNA molecules into the nematode worm *Caenorhabditis elegans*. This resulted in the silencing of the gene whose sequence was complementary to the double-stranded RNA, and of no other gene. The investigators called this very specific effect **gene silencing,** or **RNA interference.** What is going on here? A group of viruses called RNA viruses, those that contain RNA as their hereditary storage molecule rather than DNA, replicate themselves through double-stranded intermediates. RNA interference may have evolved as a cellular defense mechanism against these viruses with double-stranded viral RNAs being targeted for destruction by RNA interference machinery. Without intending to do so, the nematode researchers had stumbled across this defense.

Putting the Concept to Work
How can attacking double-stranded DNA provide a defense against RNA viruses?

How RNA Interference Works

LEARNING OBJECTIVE 12.7.2 Explain how small RNA molecules carry out RNA interference.

Investigating interference, researchers noted that in the process of silencing a gene, plants produced short RNA molecules (ranging in length from 21 to 28 nucleotides) that matched the gene being silenced. Earlier researchers focusing on far larger messenger RNA (mRNA), transfer RNA (tRNA), and ribosomal RNA (rRNA) had not noticed these far smaller bits, tossing them out during experiments. These bits of RNA are called "small interfering RNA" or siRNA. How do these small fragments of RNA silence the activity of specific genes? In a complex way we are just beginning to understand clearly, the small RNA fragments bind to any mRNA molecules in the cell that have a complementary sequence. Silencing of the gene that produced this mRNA is achieved in one of two ways (figure 12.18): either the expression of the mRNA is inhibited by blocking its translation into protein, or the mRNA is simply destroyed. In either case, the specific gene that produced that mRNA fails to be expressed—it is silenced.

Putting the Concept to Work
If RNA is not double-stranded, how can siRNA bind to mRNA?

Learning objectives define a learning path.

At its most basic level, a student's learning path through each chapter is a journey that attempts to convert learning objectives into **realized learning outcomes**. The success of this transformation is assessed not only at the end of each learning objective's text block, but also again at the end of the chapter, where each learning objective is linked to a specific learning outcome summarized at the end of the chapter, and to Bloom-based end-of-chapter questions, each linked to a specific learning outcome. Students using **McGraw-Hill Connect® Biology** (discussed on page xiii) will find each Connect assessment question linked to a specific learning objective, rather than simply to a chapter or section.

Focusing on the Essential Concepts

More than most subjects, biology is at its core a set of ideas, and if students can master these basic ideas, the rest comes easy. Unfortunately, while most of today's students are very interested in biology, they are put off by the terminology. When you don't know what the words mean, it's easy to slip into thinking that the content is difficult, when actually the ideas are simple, easy to grasp, and fun to consider. It's the terms that get in the way, that stand as a wall between students and science. With this text I have tried to turn those walls into windows, so that readers can peer in and join the fun.

Analogies have been my tool. In writing *Essentials of The Living World*, I have searched for simple analogies that relate the matter at hand to things we all know. As science, analogies are not exact, but I do not count myself compromised. Analogies trade precision for clarity. If I do my job right, the key idea is not compromised by the analogy I use to explain it, but rather revealed.

There is no way to avoid the fact that some of the important ideas of biology are complex. No student encountering photosynthesis for the first time gets it all on the first pass. To aid in learning the more difficult material, I have given special attention to key concepts and processes like photosynthesis and osmosis that form the core of biology. The essential processes of biology are not optional learning. A student must come to understand every one of them if he or she is to master biology as a science. A student's learning goal should be not simply to memorize a list of terms, but rather to be able to visualize and understand what's going on. With this goal in mind, I have prepared nearly two dozen "this is how it works" *Essential Biological Process* illustrations explaining the important concepts and processes that students encounter in introductory biology. Each of these *Essential Biological Process* illustrations walks the student through a complex process, one step at a time, so that the central idea is not lost in the details.

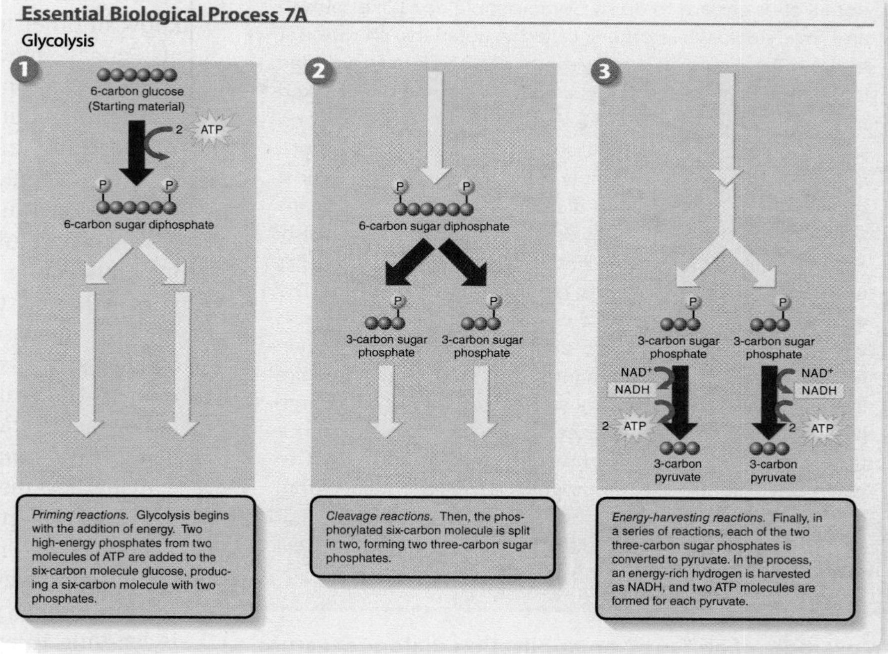

Essential Biological Process

Teaching Biology as an Evolutionary Journey

This text, and its companion concepts text *The Living World*, were the first texts to combine evolution and diversity into one continuous narrative. Traditionally, students had been exposed to weeks of evolution before being dragged through a detailed tour of the animal phyla, the two areas presented as if unrelated to each other. I chose instead to combine these two areas, presenting biological diversity as an evolutionary journey. This has proven a very powerful way to teach evolution's role in biology, and today you would be hard pressed to find a text that does not organize the material in this way.

Evolution not only organizes biology, it explains it. It is not enough to say that a frog is an amphibian, transitional between fish and reptiles. This correctly organizes frogs on the evolutionary spectrum, but fails to explain *why* frogs are the way they are, with a tadpole life stage and wet skin. Only when the student is taught that amphibians evolved as highly successful land animals, often as big as ponies and armor plated, can students get the point: Of 37 families of amphibians, all but the three that lived in water (frogs, salamanders, and caecilians) were driven extinct with the advent of reptiles. A frog has evolved to invade water, not escape it. It is in this way that evolution explains biology, and that is how I have tried to use evolution in this text, to explain.

A red-eyed tree frog.

BIOLOGY & YOU

Vegans. We humans are omnivores, meaning we can eat a broad range of plant and animal tissues—but not all of us choose to do so. Some people don't like spinach and love steak, while others, called vegetarians, choose not to eat meat. Some become vegetarians because they judge it a more healthy diet—plants are low in saturated fats linked to heart disease. Others make the choice for ethical reasons, sensitive to the animal rights issues associated with livestock agriculture. Still others simply don't like meat. The most extreme form of vegetarian diet is the "vegan" diet. Vegans avoid all animal proteins. They don't eat red meat, poultry, fish, eggs, or milk. Instead, they obtain all protein and nutrients from grains, vegetables, fruits, legumes, nuts, and seeds. The vegan diet, mirroring that of our early human ancestors, is very challenging, because no single fruit, vegetable, or grain contains all the essential amino acids that humans require in their diet. Vegetal foods must be eaten in particular combinations to provide this necessary balance. Beans and rice together provide a balanced diet, but neither food does so when eaten alone. For calcium, which is usually obtained from milk, vegans must eat green leafy vegetables like broccoli or spinach. In practice it is not difficult to achieve this balance if a vegan eats a variety of plants.

An example of an "app," an application dialogue feature.

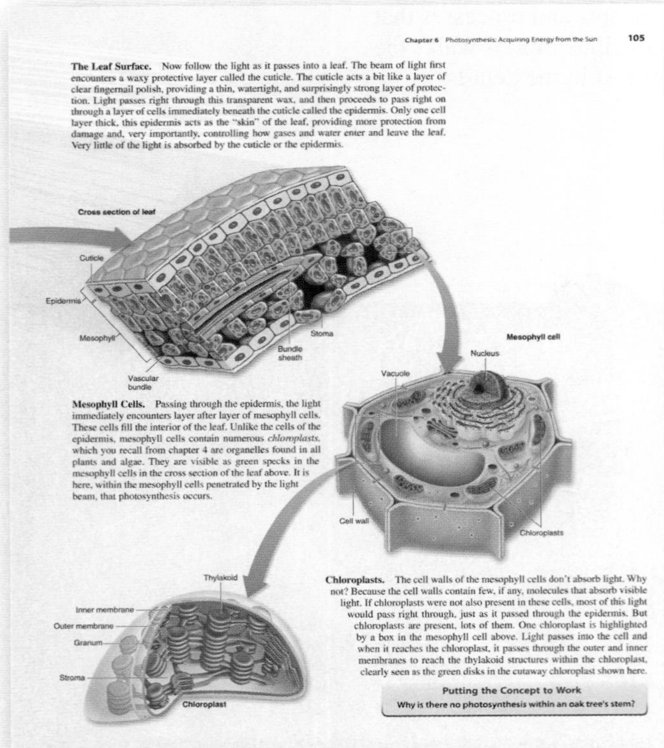

Chapter 6 Photosynthesis: Acquiring Energy from the Sun 105

The Leaf Surface. Now follow the light as it passes into a leaf. The beam of light first encounters a waxy protective layer called the cuticle. The cuticle acts a bit like a layer of clear fingernail polish, providing a thin, watertight, and surprisingly strong layer of protection. Light passes right through this transparent wax, and then proceeds to pass right on through a layer of cells immediately beneath the cuticle called the epidermis. Only one cell layer thick, this epidermis acts as the "skin" of the leaf, providing more protection from damage and, very importantly, controlling how gases and water enter and leave the leaf. Very little of the light is absorbed by the cuticle or the epidermis.

Mesophyll Cells. Passing through the epidermis, the light immediately encounters layer after layer of mesophyll cells. These cells fill the interior of the leaf. Unlike the cells of the epidermis, mesophyll cells contain numerous *chloroplasts*, which you recall from chapter 4 are organelles found in all plants and algae. They are visible as green specks in the mesophyll cells in the cross section of the leaf above. It is here, within the mesophyll cells penetrated by the light beam, that photosynthesis occurs.

Chloroplasts. The cell walls of the mesophyll cells don't absorb light. Why not? Because the cell walls contain few, if any, molecules that absorb visible light. If chloroplasts were not also present in these cells, most of this light would pass right through, just as it passed through the epidermis. But chloroplasts are present, lots of them. One chloroplast is highlighted by a box in the mesophyll cell above. Light passes into the cell and when it reaches the chloroplast, it passes through the outer and inner membranes to reach the thylakoid structures within the chloroplast, clearly seen as the green disks in the cutaway chloroplast shown here.

Putting the Concept to Work
Why is there no photosynthesis within an oak tree's stem?

Integration of art into the text.

Linking Essential Concepts to Everyday Life

One of the principal roles of nonmajor biology courses is to create educated citizens. In writing *Essentials of The Living World* I have endeavored to relate what the student is learning to the biology each student ought to know in order to live as an informed citizen in the 21st century. Students also engage much more actively in the course when they can see how what they are studying relates to their own everyday lives.

Throughout the text, *Essentials of The Living World* presents full-page **connections**, readings written by the author that make connections between a chapter's contents and the everyday world: *Biology and Staying Healthy* discusses health issues that impact each student; *Today's Biology* examines advances in biology that importantly affect society; *A Closer Look* examines interesting points in more detail; and *Author's Corner* takes a more personal view (the author's) of how science relates to our everyday lives.

It is impossible to thumb through the pages of this text without seeing another way *Essentials of The Living World* links what a student is learning to the world that the student knows. In the margins of many pages are short **apps**—application dialogues: *In the News* relates a page's content to today's news; *Evolution* points to evolutionary connections; and *Biology & You* explains how the page's content is linked to something in a student's everyday life. These short essays do not attempt to teach the content of the page, but rather to relate it to something the student knows or cares about. There are several apps in every chapter, some of them surprising, all of them interesting.

A third way *Essentials of The Living World* links what the student is learning to everyday life is the **Implication For You questions** found below key illustrations in each chapter. These questions are directed not at assessing the student's understanding of the illustration, but rather at pushing students to think about the implications of the illustration to their own lives. Many are open-ended, probing a student's own opinions on a subject. All of them link the illustration to the student's everyday life.

Using Visuals to Teach Concepts

Art has always been a core component of this text, as today's students are visual learners. To help students learn, *Essentials of The Living World* has a clean and simple art style that focuses on concepts and minimizes detail. In recent editions I have sought to amplify the power of illustrations to teach concepts by linking the interior content of illustrations directly to the text that describes that part of the illustration. I have set about doing this in three ways: **1. Bubble numbers.** In complex diagrams where there is a lot going on, I have placed numbers (set off in colored balls) at key positions, and the same "bubble numbers" at those locations in the text where that element of the illustration is being described. This makes it much easier for a student to use the illustration as it was intended, to walk through the process and see how the parts are related. **2. Integration of art into text.** In some places, like the introduction to photosynthesis (treated on pages 104 to 107), many different processes are covered, each with its own illustration. In these instances, bouncing back and forth between illustration and text makes it difficult for a student to gain or retain perspective, and so I have chosen in these instances to integrate the illustrations directly into the text, providing a single narrative. **3. Phylum facts.** The biggest problem students encounter in studying animal diversity is the mass of detail filling every page. To ease the student's task of sorting through all this, I have constructed "Phylum Facts" illustrations that highlight the key points.

Learning How to Learn

In over 30 years of teaching I have seen students do well and others do poorly, and one of the best predictors of who would do well has been how well a student is prepared to learn. Entering a large freshman course, does a student know how to take notes? Does a student know how to use these notes effectively with the textbook? Can a student read a graph? *Essentials of The Living World* tackles this problem head-on, with a "chapter 0" at the beginning of the text to help students with these very basic but essential learning tools.

Inquiry & Analysis

One of the most useful things a student can take away from his or her biology class is the ability to judge scientific claims that they encounter as citizens, long after college is over. As a way of teaching that important skill, I have expanded the *Inquiry & Analysis* features I introduced in previous editions. All chapters now end with a full-page presentation of an actual scientific investigation that requires the student to analyze the data and reach conclusions. These pages in this text provide more bang for the buck in learning that lasts.

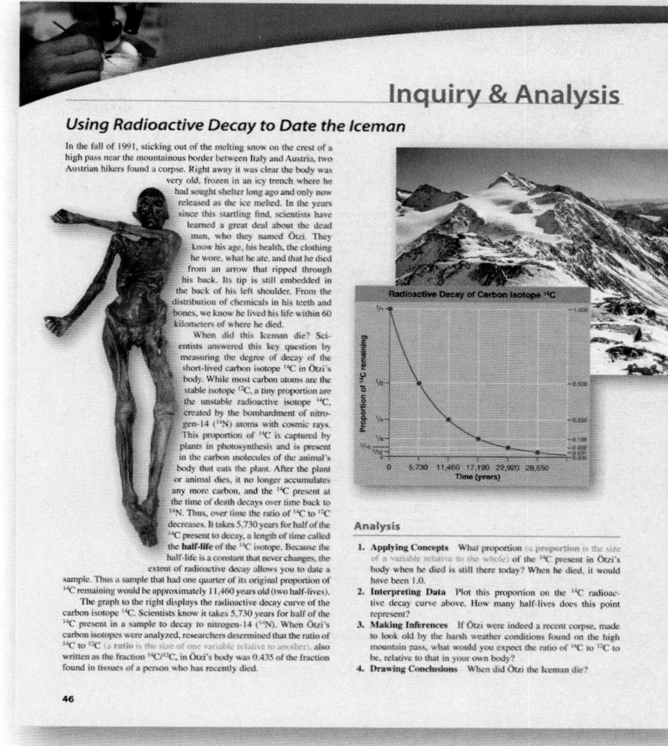

Inquiry & Analysis

Using Radioactive Decay to Date the Iceman

In the fall of 1991, sticking out of the melting snow on the crest of a high pass near the mountainous border between Italy and Austria, two Austrian hikers found a corpse. Right away it was clear the body was very old, frozen in an icy trench where he had sought shelter long ago and only now released as the ice melted. In the years since this startling find, scientists have learned a great deal about the dead man, who they named Ötzi. They know his age, his health, the clothing he wore, what he ate, and that he died from an arrow that ripped through his back. Its tip is still embedded in the back of his left shoulder. From the distribution of chemicals in his teeth and bones, we know he lived his life within 60 kilometers of where he died.

When did this Iceman die? Scientists answered this key question by measuring the degree of decay of the short-lived carbon isotope ^{14}C in Ötzi's body. While most carbon atoms are the stable isotope ^{12}C, a tiny proportion are the unstable radioactive isotope ^{14}C, created by the bombardment of nitrogen-14 (^{14}N) atoms with cosmic rays. This proportion of ^{14}C is captured by plants in photosynthesis and is present in the carbon molecules of the animal's body that eats the plant. After the plant or animal dies, it no longer accumulates any more carbon, and the ^{14}C present at the time of death decays over time back to ^{14}N. Thus, over time the ratio of ^{14}C to ^{12}C decreases. It takes 5,730 years for half of the ^{14}C present to decay, a length of time called the **half-life** of the ^{14}C isotope. Because the half-life is a constant that never changes, the extent of radioactive decay allows you to date a sample. Thus a sample that had one quarter of its original proportion of ^{14}C remaining would be approximately 11,460 years old (two half-lives).

The graph to the right displays the radioactive decay curve of the carbon isotope ^{14}C. Scientists know it takes 5,730 years for half of the ^{14}C present in a sample to decay to nitrogen-14 (^{14}N). When Ötzi's carbon isotopes were analyzed, researchers determined that the ratio of ^{14}C to ^{12}C (a ratio is the size of one variable relative to another), also written as the fraction $^{14}C/^{12}C$, in Ötzi's body was 0.435 of the fraction found in tissues of a person who has recently died.

Analysis

1. **Applying Concepts** What proportion (a proportion is the size of a variable relative to the whole) of the ^{14}C present in Ötzi's body when he died is still there today? When he died, it would have been 1.0.
2. **Interpreting Data** Plot this proportion on the ^{14}C radioactive decay curve above. How many half-lives does this point represent?
3. **Making Inferences** If Ötzi were indeed a recent corpse, made to look old by the harsh weather conditions found on the high mountain pass, what would you expect the ratio of ^{14}C to ^{12}C to be, relative to that in your own body?
4. **Drawing Conclusions** When did Ötzi the Iceman die?

46

An example of an Inquiry & Analysis feature.

Connect® and *LearnSmart*™

Every year, more and more students using *Essentials of The Living World* do so on their laptop computers or iPads. This use opens up an exciting possibility not available using printed books: the text can be interactive. Embedded throughout the *eBook* version of *Essentials of The Living World* are animations and videos that a student can use to explore further. The interactivity also allows students to be in one-to-one contact with their instructors, which helps in clarifying schedules and taking exams.

Much more profoundly important, an interactive text using the *ConnectPlus*® text-integrated assessment program allows both the instructor and student to assess progress through each chapter's learning path. In *Connect*®, instructors can assign a class a series of interactive questions. As the student completes the interactives, *Connect* grades each answer. If a student has trouble with a question, the program connects that question to the learning objective in the *eBook* where the question is answered. By the time a student has successfully navigated the series of instructor-assigned questions, he or she is well on the way to mastering the assignment.

Connect-assigned quizzes are instructor-driven, typically with the same set of questions selected by the instructor for the entire class. However, not all students come to a freshman biology class equally well prepared. For many, it is their first science course. For others, high school science class seems in the distant past. For still others, they are right on top of the material and eager to charge ahead.

LearnSmart™, which is delivered through *Connect*, addresses this problem in a direct way, tailoring its questions to each student individually. Using artificial intelligence, *LearnSmart* examines a student's answers to a series of questions, pinpoints concepts and information the student does not yet understand, and maps out a study plan for what that student needs to learn. The power of this approach is that it adapts directly to a particular student. As a student moves through his or her individualized study plan, "timeouts" take the student to the *eBook* text page to sharpen hazy understanding. A student and *LearnSmart* constitute a one-person biology course, with a learning path contoured to that individual's needs and speed of learning.

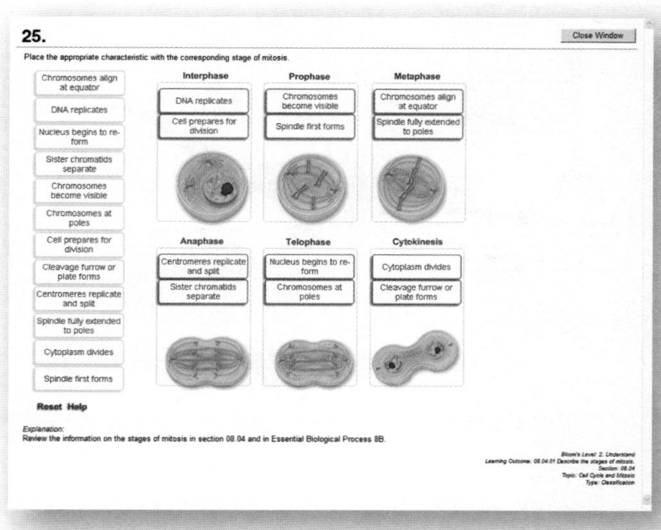

A *Connect* question.

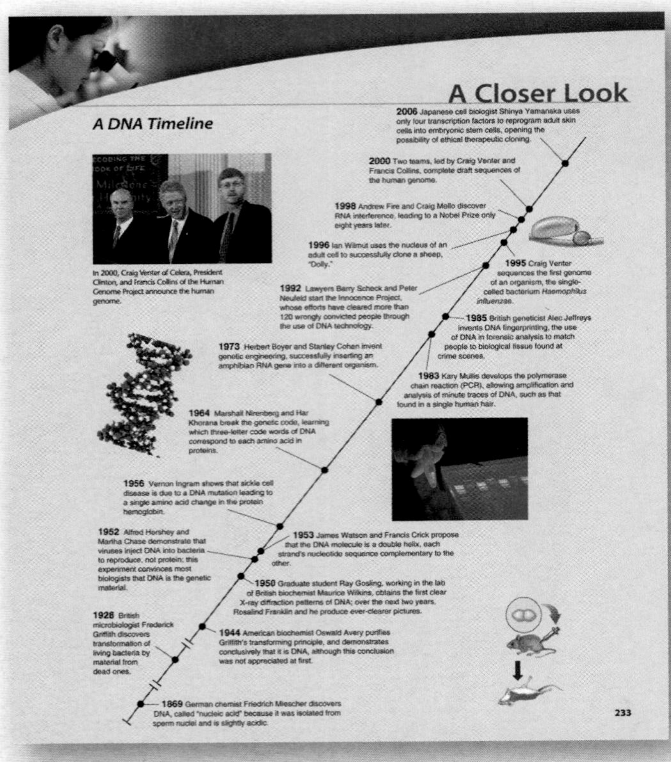

A Closer Look

A DNA Timeline

In 2000, Craig Venter of Celera, President Clinton, and Francis Collins of the Human Genome Project announce the human genome.

2006 Japanese cell biologist Shinya Yamanaka uses only four transcription factors to reprogram adult skin cells into embryonic stem cells, opening the possibility of ethical therapeutic cloning.

2000 Two teams, led by Craig Venter and Francis Collins, complete draft sequences of the human genome.

1998 Andrew Fire and Craig Mello discover RNA interference, leading to a Nobel Prize only eight years later.

1996 Ian Wilmut uses the nucleus of an adult cell to successfully clone a sheep, "Dolly."

1995 Craig Venter sequences the first genome of an organism, the single-celled bacterium *Haemophilus influenzae*.

1992 Lawyers Barry Scheck and Peter Neufeld start the Innocence Project, whose efforts have cleared more than 120 wrongly convicted people through the use of DNA technology.

1985 British geneticist Alec Jeffreys invents DNA fingerprinting, the use of DNA in forensic analysis to match people to biological tissue found at crime scenes.

1983 Kary Mullis develops the polymerase chain reaction (PCR), allowing amplification and analysis of minute traces of DNA, such as that found in a single human hair.

1973 Herbert Boyer and Stanley Cohen invent genetic engineering, successfully inserting an amphibian RNA gene into a different organism.

1964 Marshall Nirenberg and Har Khorana break the genetic code, learning which three-letter code words of DNA correspond to each amino acid in proteins.

1956 Vernon Ingram shows that sickle cell disease is due to a DNA mutation leading to a single amino acid change in the protein hemoglobin.

1953 James Watson and Francis Crick propose that the DNA molecule is a double helix, each strand's nucleotide sequence complementary to the other.

1952 Alfred Hershey and Martha Chase demonstrate that viruses inject DNA into bacteria to reproduce, not protein; this experiment convinces most biologists that DNA is the genetic material.

1950 Graduate student Ray Gosling, working in the lab of British biochemist Maurice Wilkins, obtains the first clear X-ray diffraction patterns of DNA; over the next two years, Rosalind Franklin and he produce ever-clearer pictures.

1944 American biochemist Oswald Avery purifies Griffith's transforming principle, and demonstrates conclusively that it is DNA, although this conclusion was not appreciated at first.

1928 British microbiologist Frederick Griffith discovers transformation of living bacteria by material from dead ones.

1869 German chemist Friedrich Miescher discovers DNA, called "nucleic acid" because it was isolated from sperm nuclei and is slightly acidic.

233

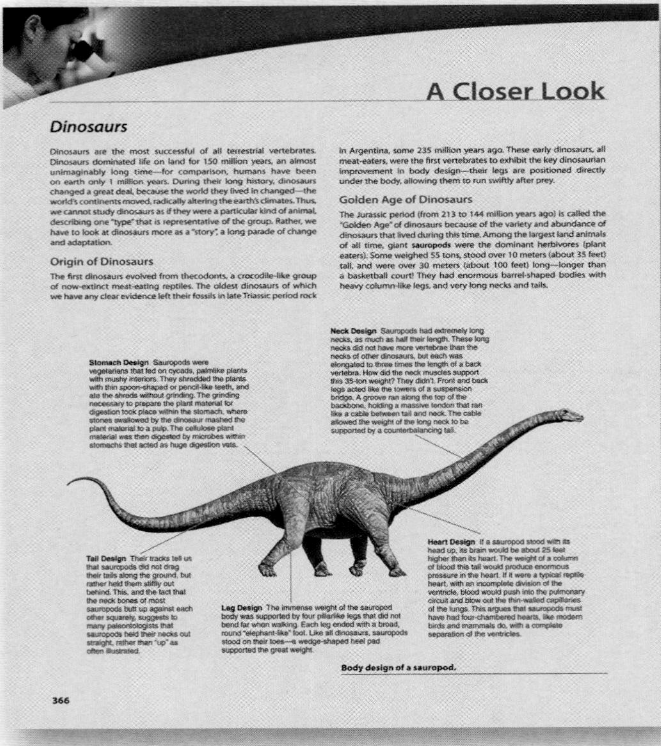

A Closer Look

Dinosaurs

Dinosaurs are the most successful of all terrestrial vertebrates. Dinosaurs dominated life on land for 150 million years, an almost unimaginably long time—for comparison, humans have been on earth only 1 million years. During their long history, dinosaurs changed a great deal, because the world they lived in changed—the world's continents moved, radically altering the earth's climates. Thus, we cannot study dinosaurs as if they were a particular kind of animal, describing one "type" that is representative of the group. Rather, we have to look at dinosaurs more as a "story", a long parade of change and adaptation.

Origin of Dinosaurs

The first dinosaurs evolved from thecodonts, a crocodile-like group of now-extinct meat-eating reptiles. The oldest dinosaurs of which we have any clear evidence left their fossils in late Triassic period rock in Argentina, some 235 million years ago. These early dinosaurs, all meat-eaters, were the first vertebrates to exhibit the key dinosaurian improvement in body design—their legs are positioned directly under the body, allowing them to run swiftly after prey.

Golden Age of Dinosaurs

The Jurassic period (from 213 to 144 million years ago) is called the "Golden Age" of dinosaurs because of the variety and abundance of dinosaurs that lived during this time. Among the largest land animals of all time, giant **sauropods** were the dominant herbivores (plant eaters). Some weighed 55 tons, stood over 10 meters (about 35 feet) tall, and were over 30 meters (about 100 feet) long—longer than a basketball court! They had enormous barrel-shaped bodies with heavy column-like legs, and very long necks and tails.

Stomach Design Sauropods were vegetarians that fed on cycads, palmlike plants with mushy interiors. They shredded the plants with thin spoon-shaped or pencil-like teeth, and ate the shreds without grinding. The grinding necessary to prepare the plant material for digestion took place within the stomach, where stones swallowed by the dinosaur mashed the plant material to a pulp. The cellulose plant material was then digested by microbes within stomachs that acted as huge digestion vats.

Neck Design Sauropods had extremely long necks, as much as half their length. These long necks did not have more vertebrae than the necks of other dinosaurs, but each was elongated to three times the length of a back vertebra. How did the neck muscles support this 35-ton weight? They didn't. Front and back legs acted like the towers of a suspension bridge. A groove ran along the top of the backbone, holding a massive tendon that ran like a cable between tail and neck. The cable allowed the weight of the long neck to be supported by a counterbalancing tail.

Tail Design Their tracks tell us that sauropods did not drag their tails along the ground, but rather held them stiffly out behind. This, and the fact that the neck bones of most sauropods butt up against each other squarely, suggests to many paleontologists that sauropods held their necks out straight, rather than "up" as often illustrated.

Leg Design The immense weight of the sauropod body was supported by four pillarlike legs that did not bend far when walking. Each leg ended with a broad, round "elephant-like" foot. Like all dinosaurs, sauropods stood on their toes—a wedge-shaped heel pad supported the great weight.

Heart Design If a sauropod stood with its head up, its brain would be about 25 feet higher than its heart. The weight of a column of blood this tall would produce enormous pressure in the heart. If it were a typical reptile heart, with an incomplete division of the ventricle, blood would push into the pulmonary circuit and blow out the thin-walled capillaries of the lungs. This argues that sauropods must have had four-chambered hearts, like modern birds and mammals do, with a complete separation of the ventricles.

Body design of a sauropod.

366

Updating the Content

Biology as a science has advanced rapidly in the years since I first wrote *Essentials of The Living World*. Four examples serve to make the point clearly:

RNA Interference (page 218) This discovery, so important that it won a Nobel Prize in the shortest length of time ever, has totally altered our view of how genes are regulated, and is revolutionizing medicine.

Ethanol and Biofuels (pages 467 to 468) A topic very much in the news, a careful explanation is needed for a student to understand the issue.

Curing Cancer (pages 142 to 143) The families of many students are affected by cancer, and one quarter of all students will someday experience it.

Genetic Engineering (pages 224 to 245) Advances in the field of genetic engineering are in the forefront of today's biology, from genomic studies and the development of cancer vaccines to stem cell research and gene therapy.

A Closer Look at Content Changes. Many chapters of this revision of *Essentials of The Living World* have been updated to reflect these advances, and to improve the text as a learning tool:

Part 1

- Added "Using Your Textbook's Internet Resources" to chapter 0, where the use of new *Connect* and *LearnSmart eBook* learning programs has been integrated into the discussion of how to study biology.

Part 2

- Expanded the treatment of chemical bonds, and added a new "Ice, Carbon Dioxide, and Polar Bears" feature to chapter 2.
- Added new integrated art illustrations of the plasma membrane and the cytoskeleton to chapter 4.

Part 3

- Added new section "Studying Pedigrees" to chapter 10.
- Added new sections to chapter 12 expanding the discussion and illustration of the central dogma of gene expression, transcription, and an overview of gene expression.
- In chapter 13, updated discussions of DNA cancer vaccines, stem cell research, and new gene therapy vectors, and added a discussion of curing hemophilia using zinc fingers to guide the placement of the corrective gene.

Part 4

- Added sections on "Prokaryotic Lifestyles" and "How Viruses Infect Organisms" to chapter 16.
- Added a new "A Closer Look" reading on "Dinosaurs" and a section on "Human Evolution" to chapter 18.

Part 5

- Added new sections "Population Range" and "Population Distribution" and the feature "The War Against Urban Deer" to chapter 19.

Part 6

- Revised the treatment of USDA nutrition guidelines in chapter 26.
- Streamlined the treatment of the brain, sensory perception, and vision in chapter 29.
- Updated the statistics on cancer in chapters 25 and 30.

Part 7

- Streamlined the treatment of plant hormones in chapter 33.

Acknowledgments

Every author knows that he or she labors on the shoulders of many others; the text you see is the result of hard work by an army of "behind-the-scenes" editors, spelling and grammar checkers, photo researchers, and artists that perform their magic on our manuscript; and an even larger army of production managers and staff that then transform this manuscript into a bound book. I cannot thank them all. Eric Weber and Rose Koos were my editorial team, with whom I worked every day. Publisher Michael Hackett solved the many management problems his author inadvertently created in his excess of enthusiasm, and provided valuable advice and support. I don't think I have ever enjoyed working with a publisher as much. Marty Lange, the editor-in-chief, oversaw all of this with humor and consistent support. Kelly Heinrichs spearheaded our production team, which for several editions now has made a habit of working miracles with a tight schedule. Wendy Nelson copy edited all the way from Texas. The photo program was carried out by Lori Hancock, who as always has done a super job. The art program, conceived several editions ago by William Ober, M.D., and Claire Garrison, R.N., continues to develop with the clarity and excitement they had envisioned. Laurie Janssen has again done a great job with the design—she really seems to "get" tigers. This edition was produced by Lachina Publishing Services.

My long-time, off-site developmental editor and right arm, Megan Berdelman, has again played an invaluable role in overseeing every detail of a complex revision. Every *Connect* question associated with this text has her fingerprints on it. Her intelligence and perseverance continue to play a major role in the quality of this book.

The marketing of this new edition was again planned and supervised by Tamara Maury, a battle-wise general not afraid to fight in the trenches alongside the many able sales reps who present our book to instructors.

George Johnson

Reviewers

I have authored other texts, and all of my writing efforts have taught me the great value of reviewers in improving my texts. Scientific colleagues from around the country have provided numerous suggestions on how to improve the content of the fourth edition of *Essentials,* and many instructors and students using the third edition have suggested ways to clarify explanations, improve presentations, and expand on important topics. The instructors listed below provided detailed comments. I have tried to listen carefully to all of you. Every one of you has my thanks!

Sylvester Allred
Northern Arizona University
Thomas H. Alton
Western Illinois University
Lena Ballard
Rock Valley College
Dennis Bell
University of Louisiana–Monroe
Linda L. Bergen-Losee
Saint Leo University
Lisa L. Boggs
Southwestern Oklahoma State University
Cheryl Boice
Lake City Community College
Sergiy Borysov
University of Tampa
Nancy Bowers
Park University
Bob Boykin
Bossier Parish Community College
Carol A. Britson
University of Mississippi
Steven G. Brumbaugh
Green River Community College
Steven Brumbaugh
Green River Community College
Lisa Bryant
Arkansas State University
Matthew Burnham
Jones County Junior College

Chantae M. Calhoun
Lawson State Community College
Jocelyn Cash
Central Piedmont Community College
Aaron Cassill
University of Texas at San Antonio
Bane W. Cheek
Polk Community College
Denise L. Chung
Long Island University–Brooklyn Campus
Craig W. Clifford
Northeastern State University
Yvonne E. Cole
Florissant Valley Community College
Michael Collins
Rhodes College
George R. Davis
Minnesota State University–Moorhead
Chris Davison
Long Beach City College
Buffany DeBoer
Wayne State College
Kristiann Dougherty
Valencia Community College
Michael J. Dougherty
Hampden–Sydney College
Tcherina Duncombe
Palm Beach State College
William E. Dunscombe
Union County College
Paula Edgar
John Wood Community College
Bruce Edinger
West Liberty State College
Jeff E. Engel
Western Illinois University
Marirose T. Ethington
Genesee Community College
Tracy M. Felton
Union County College
Tullio Ferretti
Hinds Community College
Victor Fet
Marshall University
Teresa G. Fischer
Indian River College
Melanie Florence
Dixie State College
Brandon L. Foster
Wake Technical Community College
Debra L. Foster
Park University
Nancy A. Freeman
El Camino Community College
Dennis W. Fulbright
Michigan State University
Michael D. Gottlieb
LaGuardia Community College
Tammy Greene
Arkansas State University–Beebe
Carla Guthridge
Cameron University
Sue Habeck
Tacoma Community College
Richard Hanke
Rose State College
Nixie Hnetkovsky
Frontier Community College
Dale A. Holen
Pennsylvania State University
Pavla Hoyer
Los Angeles Valley College
Michael E. S. Hudspeth
Northern Illinois University
Amy G. Hurst
Rose State College
Jeremiah N. Jarrett
Central Connecticut State University
Adeline Jasinski
Bristol Community College
Roishene Johnson
Bossier Parish Community College
Angela Jones
California State University–Long Beach
Anthony Jones
Tallahassee Community College
Robyn Jordan
University of Louisiana–Monroe
Judy Kaufman
Monroe Community College
Ronald Keiper
Valencia Community College
Amy Kennedy
Central Carolina Community College
Amine Kidane
Columbus State Community College
Karl Kleiner
York College of Pennsylvania
Roger C. Klockziem
Martin Luther College
Todd Kostman
University of Wisconsin Oshkosh
Pramod Kumar
The University of Texas at San Antonio
John Landers
LaGuardia Community College
Mary Lehman
Longwood University
Susan Lewandowski
Westmoreland County Community College
Suzanne Long
Monroe Community College
Eric Lovely
Arkansas Tech University
Richard Maloof
County College of Morris
Mark Manteuffel
St. Louis Community College
Roy J. Marler
Cascade College
Darlene Martin
Excelsior College
Kamau W. Mbuthia
Bowling Green State University
Melissa Meador
Arkansas State University–Beebe
Linda Meeks
Lake Michigan College
Judith Megaw
Indian River State College
Eric R. Myers
South Suburban College
Steven Mark Norris
California State University–Channel Islands
Igor V. Oksov
Union County College
Theodore J. O'Tanyi
Widener University
Usha R. Palaniswamy
Excelsior College
Robert P. Patterson
North Carolina State University
Joe Petti
Albertus Magnus College
Mary Phillips
Tulsa Community College
Crystal Pietrowicz
Southern Maine Community College
Barbara Pleasants
Iowa State University
Karen Plucinski
Missouri Southern State University
Wendy M. Rappazzo
Harford Community College
Pamela Riddell
Macomb Community College
Carlton Rockett
Bowling Green State University
Neil Romney
Skagit Valley College—Whidbey Island Campus
Sydha Salihu
West Virginia University
Eric Saliim
North Carolina Central University
Hope Sasway
Suffolk County Community College
Robert J. Schodorf
Lake Michigan College
Roy D. Schodtler
Lake Land College
Roger Seeber, Jr.
West Liberty State College
William A. Shear
Hampden–Sydney College
Greg Sievert
Emporia State University
William Simcik
Lone Star College–Tomball
Beatrice Sirakaya
Pennsylvania State University
Larry D. Spears
St. Louis University
Erika Stephens
Arkansas State University–Beebe
Judith L. Stewart
College of Southern Nevada
Irina Stroup
Shasta College
Lavon Sumption
Columbus State Community College
Sue Trammell
John A. Logan College
William Unsell
University of Central Oklahoma
George E. Veomett
University of Nebraska–Lincoln
Adil M. Wadia
The University of Akron Wayne College
Timothy S. Wakefield
John Brown University
Suzanne Wakim
Butte–Glenn Community College District
Jamie Welling
South Suburban College
Kenneth Welling
North Carolina Central University
Jennifer Wiatrowski
Pasco–Hernando Community College
Daniece Williams
Hinds Community College–Rankin Campus
David Williams
Valencia Community College
Harry E. Womack
Salisbury University
Calvin Young
Fullerton College
Kevin V. Young
Utah State University–Brigham City

Teaching and Learning Tools

The **Best** of **Both Worlds**

McGraw-Hill Higher Education and Blackboard® Have Teamed Up

Blackboard®, the Web-based course-management system, has partnered with McGraw-Hill to better allow students and faculty to use online materials and activities to complement face-to-face teaching. Blackboard features exciting social learning and teaching tools that foster more logical, visually impactful, and active learning opportunities for students. You'll transform your closed-door classrooms into communities where students remain connected to their educational experience 24 hours a day.

This partnership allows you and your students access to McGraw-Hill's Connect® and McGraw-Hill Create™ right from within your Blackboard course—all with one single sign-on.

Not only do you get single sign-on with Connect and Create, you also get deep integration of McGraw-Hill content and content engines right in Blackboard. Whether you're choosing a book for your course or building Connect assignments, all the tools you need are right where you want them—inside of Blackboard.

Gradebooks are now seamless. When a student completes an integrated Connect assignment, the grade for that assignment automatically (and instantly) feeds your Blackboard grade center.

McGraw-Hill and Blackboard can now offer you easy access to industry leading technology and content, whether your campus hosts it or we do. Be sure to ask your local McGraw-Hill representative for details.

McGraw-Hill LearnSmart™

McGraw-Hill LearnSmart™ is available as an integrated feature of McGraw-Hill Connect® Biology and provides students with a GPS (Guided Path to Success) for your course. Using artificial intelligence, LearnSmart intelligently assesses a student's knowledge of course content through a series of adaptive questions. It pinpoints concepts the student does not understand and maps out a personalized study plan for success. This innovative study tool also has features that allow instructors to see exactly what students have accomplished and a built-in assessment tool for graded assignments. Visit the following site for a demonstration.

www.mhlearnsmart.com

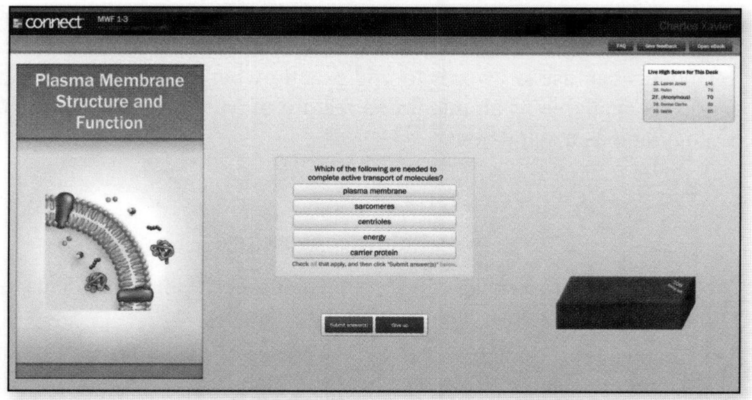

McGraw-Hill LabSmart™

Mc Graw Hill LabSmart™

THE Virtual Lab Experience

Based on the same world-class super-adaptive technology as LearnSmart, McGraw-Hill LabSmart is a must-see, outcomes-based lab simulation. It assesses a student's knowledge and adaptively corrects deficiencies, allowing the student to learn faster and retain more knowledge with greater success.

First, a student's knowledge is adaptively leveled on core learning outcomes: Questioning reveals knowledge deficiencies that are corrected by the delivery of content that is conditional on a student's response. Then, a simulated lab experience requires the student to think and act like a scientist: Recording, interpreting, and analyzing data using simulated equipment found in labs and clinics. The student is allowed to make mistakes - a powerful part of the learning experience! A virtual coach provides subtle hints when needed; asks questions about the student's choices; and allows the student to reflect upon and correct those mistakes. Whether your need is to overcome the logistical challenges of a traditional lab, provide better lab prep, improve student performance, or make your online experience one that rivals the real world, LabSmart accomplishes it all.

To learn more, visit
www.mhlabsmart.com

McGraw-Hill Connect® Biology

McGraw-Hill Connect® Biology provides online presentation, assignment, and assessment solutions. It connects your students with the tools and resources they'll need to achieve success.

With Connect Biology, you can deliver assignments, quizzes, and tests online. A robust set of questions and activities are presented and aligned with the textbook's learning outcomes. As an instructor, you can edit existing questions and author entirely new problems. Track individual student performance—by question, assignment, or in relation to the class overall—with detailed grade reports. Integrate grade reports easily with Learning Management Systems (LMS), such as WebCT and Blackboard—and much more.

ConnectPlus® Biology provides students with all the advantages of Connect Biology, plus 24/7 online access to an eBook. This media-rich version of the book is available through the McGraw-Hill Connect platform and allows seamless integration of text, media, and assessments.

To learn more, visit
www.mcgrawhillconnect.com

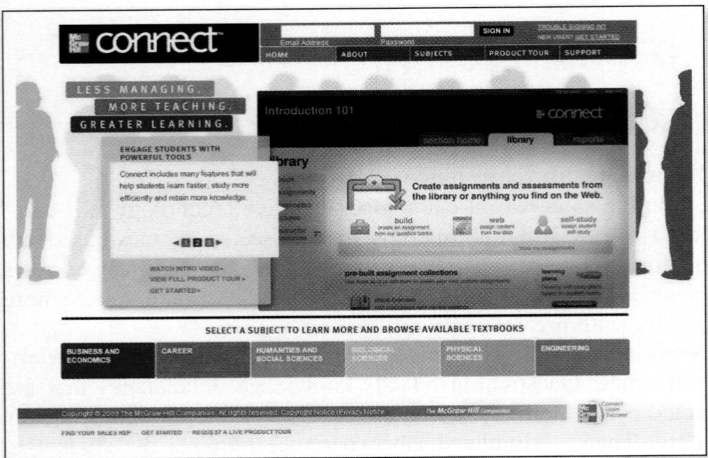

Animations for a New Generation

Dynamic, 3D animations of key biological processes bring an unprecedented level of control to the classroom. Innovative features keep the emphasis on teaching rather than entertaining.

- An options menu lets you control the animation's level of detail, speed, length, and appearance, so you can create the experience you want.
- Draw on the animation using the whiteboard pen to highlight important areas.
- The scroll bar lets you fast-forward and rewind while seeing what happens in the animation, so you can start at the exact moment you want.
- A scene menu lets you instantly jump to a specific point in the animation.
- Pop-ups add detail at important points and help students relate the animation back to concepts from lecture and the textbook.
- A complete visual summary at the end of the animation reminds students of the big picture.
- Animation topics include: Cellular Respiration, Photosynthesis, Molecular Biology of the Gene, DNA Replication, Cell Cycle and Mitosis, Meiosis, Muscle Contraction, Neural Transmission, Membrane Transport, and Plant Transport.

McGraw-Hill Create™

With **McGraw-Hill Create™**, you can easily rearrange chapters, combine material from other content sources, and quickly upload content you have written, like your course syllabus or teaching notes. Find the content you need in Create by searching through thousands of leading McGraw-Hill textbooks. Arrange your book to fit your teaching style. Create even allows you to personalize your book's appearance by selecting the cover and adding your name, school, and course information. Order a Create book and you'll receive a complimentary print review copy in 3–5 business days or a complimentary electronic review copy (eComp) via e-mail in minutes. Go to www.mcgrawhillcreate.com today and register to experience how McGraw-Hill Create empowers you to teach *your* students *your* way.

www.mcgrawhillcreate.com

Presentation Tools

Everything you need for outstanding presentations in one place.

www.mhhe.com/esstlw4

- *FlexArt Image Powerpoints*—including every piece of art that has been sized and cropped specifically for superior presentations, as well as labels that can be edited and flexible art that can be picked up and moved on key figures. Also included are tables, photographs, and unlabeled art pieces.
- *Lecture PowerPoints with Animations*—animations illustrating important processes are embedded in the lecture material.
- *Animation PowerPoints*—animations only are provided in PowerPoint.
- *Labeled JPEG Images*—full-color digital files of all illustrations that can be readily incorporated into presentations, exams, or custom-made classroom materials.
- *Base Art Image Files*—unlabeled digital files of all illustrations.

Presentation Center

In addition to the images from your book, this online digital library contains photos, artwork, animations, and other media from an array of McGraw-Hill textbooks.

Computerized Test Bank

A comprehensive bank of test questions is provided within a computerized test bank powered by McGraw-Hill's flexible electronic testing program, **EZ Test Online.** A new tagging scheme allows you to sort questions by Bloom's difficulty level, learning outcome, topic, and section. With EZ Test Online, instructors can select questions from multiple McGraw-Hill test banks or author their own, and then either print the test for paper distribution or give it online.

Instructor's Manual

The instructor's manual contains chapter outlines, lecture enrichment ideas, and discussion questions.

My Lectures—Tegrity®

McGraw-Hill Tegrity® records and distributes your class lecture with just a click of a button. Students can view anytime/anywhere via computer, iPod, or mobile device. It indexes as it records your PowerPoint® presentations and anything shown on your computer so students can use keywords to find exactly what they want to study. Tegrity is available as an integrated feature of McGraw-Hill Connect Biology and as a standalone.

Companion Website

www.mhhe.com/esstlw4

The *Essentials of The Living World* companion website allows students to access a variety of free digital learning tools that include

- Chapter-level quizzing
- Animations and videos
- Vocabulary flashcards
- Virtual labs

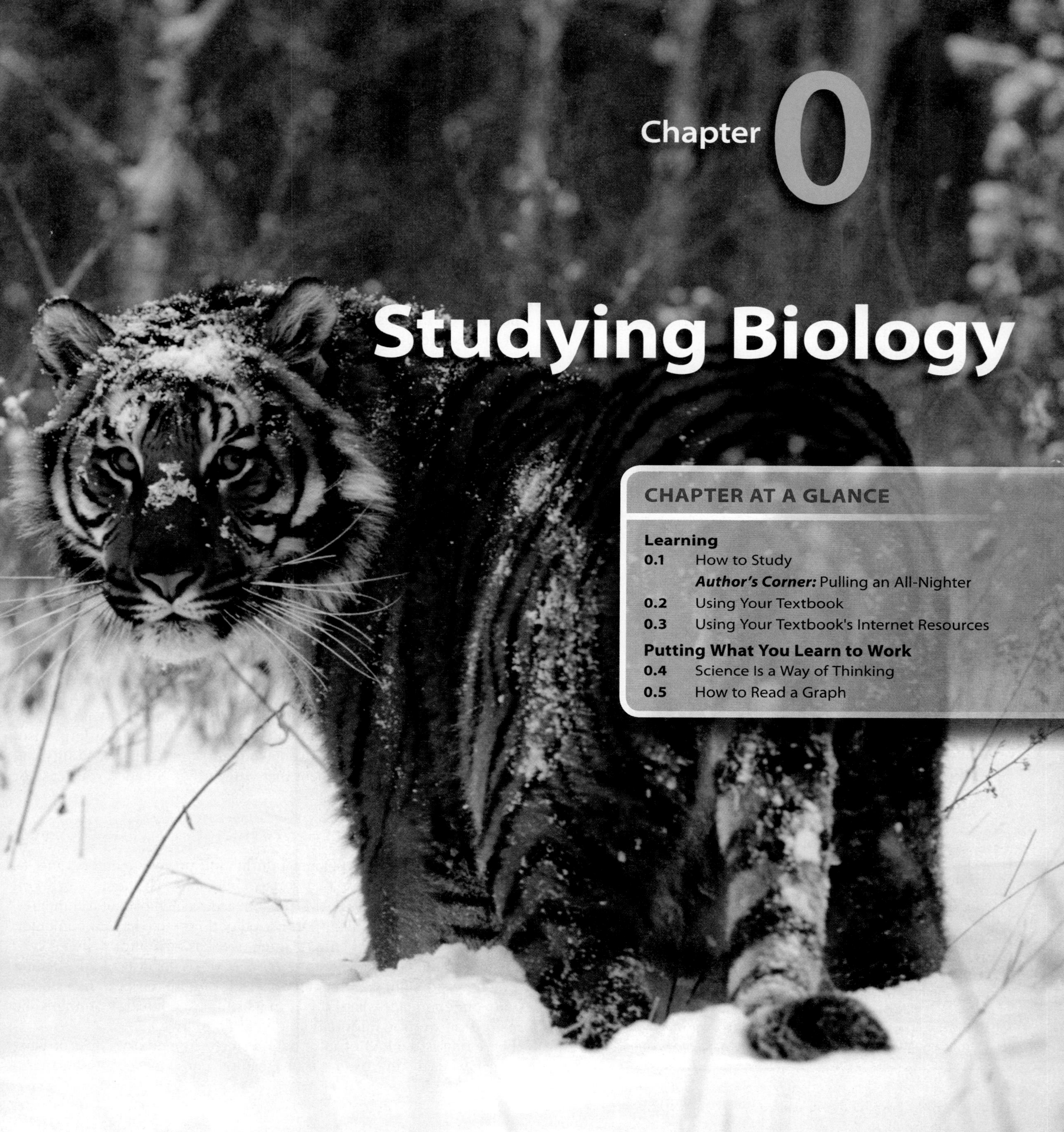

Chapter 0

Studying Biology

CHAPTER AT A GLANCE

Learning

0.1 How to Study

Author's Corner: Pulling an All-Nighter

0.2 Using Your Textbook

0.3 Using Your Textbook's Internet Resources

Putting What You Learn to Work

0.4 Science Is a Way of Thinking

0.5 How to Read a Graph

Learning

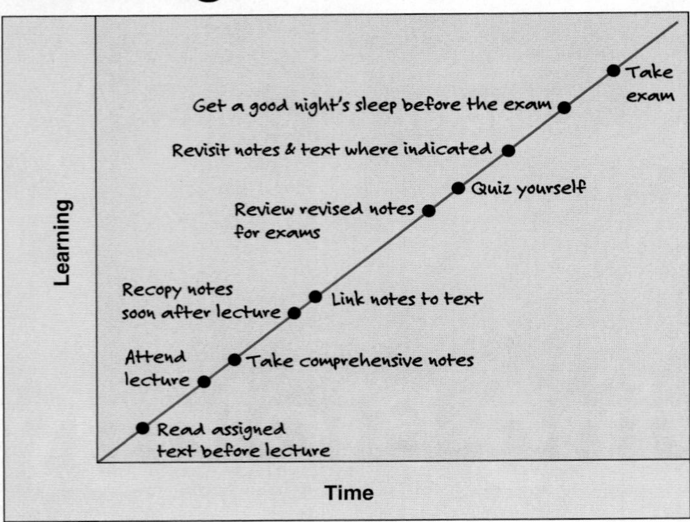

Figure 0.1 **A learning timeline.**

0.1 How to Study

Taking Notes

Listening to lectures and reading the text are only the first steps in learning enough to do well in a biology course. The key to mastering the mountain of information and concepts you are about to encounter is to take careful notes. Studying from poor-quality notes that are sparse, disorganized, and barely intelligible is not a productive way to approach preparing for an exam.

There are three simple ways to improve the quality of your notes:

1. **Take many notes.** Always attempt to take the most complete notes possible during class. If you miss class, take notes yourself from a tape of the lecture, if at all possible. It is the process of taking notes that promotes learning. Using someone else's notes is but a poor substitute. When someone else takes the notes, that person tends to do most of the learning as well.
2. **Take paraphrased notes.** Develop a legible style of abbreviated note taking. Obviously, there are some things that cannot be easily paraphrased (referred to in a simpler way), but using abbreviations and paraphrasing will permit more comprehensive notes. Attempting to write complete organized sentences in note taking is frustrating and too time consuming—people just talk too fast!
3. **Revise your notes.** As soon as possible after lecture, you should decipher and revise your notes. Nothing else in the learning process is more important, because this is where most of your learning will take place. By revising your notes, you meld the information together and put it into a context that is understandable to you. As you revise your notes, organize the material into major blocks of information with simple "heads" to identify each block. Add ideas from your reading of the text and note links to material in other lectures. Clarify terms and concepts that might be confusing with short notes and definitions. Thinking through the ideas of the lecture in this organized way will crystallize them for you, which is the key step in learning. Also, simply rewriting your notes to make them legible, neat, and tidy can be a tremendous improvement that will further enhance your ease of learning (figure 0.1).

Remembering and Forgetting

Learning is the process of placing information in your memory. Just as in your computer, there are two sorts of memory. The first, *short-term memory*, is analogous to the RAM (random access memory) of a computer, holding information for only a short period of time. Like in your computer, this memory is constantly being "written over" as new information comes in. The second kind of memory, *long-term memory*, consists of information that you have stored in your memory banks for future retrieval, like storing files on your computer's hard drive. In its simplest context, learning is the process of transferring information to your hard drive.

Forgetting is the loss of information stored in memory. Most of what we forget when taking exams is the natural consequence of short-term

BIOLOGY & YOU

Improving Memory. There is an active market on the Internet for commercial products that claim to improve your memory. Many of these products involve repetitive games or other gimmicks; few have any lasting impact on memory. Psychologists have carried out considerable research on this subject, and have found that the best way to improve memory seems to be to increase the supply of oxygen to the brain. How do you do this? These researchers recommend aerobic exercise. Walking for three hours each week significantly increases brain oxygen levels, as does swimming or cycling. One study found that chewing gum while studying will supply the brain with enough oxygen to improve memorizing items simply because of the muscle movement.

memories not being effectively transferred to long-term memory. Forgetting occurs very rapidly, dropping to below 50% retention within one hour after learning and leveling off at about 20% retention after 24 hours.

There are many things you can do to slow down the forgetting process. Here are two important ones:

1. **Recopy your notes as soon as possible after lecture.** Remember, there is about a 50% memory loss in the first hour. You should use your textbook as well when recopying your notes.
2. **Establish a purpose for reading.** When you sit down to study your textbook, have a definite goal to learn a particular concept. Each chapter begins with a preview of its key concepts—let them be your guides. Do not try and learn the entire contents of a chapter in one session; break it up into small pieces that are "easily digested."

Learning

Learning may be viewed as the efficient transfer of information from your short-term memory to your long-term memory. Learning strategists refer to this transfer as *rehearsal*. As its name implies, rehearsal always involves some form of repetition. There are four general means of rehearsal in the jargon of education called "critical thinking skills" (**figure 0.2**).

Repeating. The most obvious form of rehearsal is repetition. To learn facts, the sequence of events in a process, or the names of a group of things, you write them down, say them aloud, and mentally repeat them over and over until you have "memorized" them. This often is a first step on the road to learning. Many students mistake this as the only step. It is not, as it involves only rote memory instead of understanding. If all you do in this course is memorize facts, you will not succeed.

Organizing. It is important to organize the information you are attempting to learn, because the process of sorting and ordering increases retention. For example, if you place a sequence of events in order, like the stages of mitosis, you will be able to recall the entire sequence if you can remember what gets the sequence started.

Linking. Biology has a natural hierarchy of information, with terms and concepts nested within other terms and concepts. You will learn facts and concepts more easily if you attempt to connect them with something you already know, linking them to some information that is already stored in your memory. Throughout this textbook, you will see arrows, like the one in **figure 0.3**, indicating such links. Use them to check back over concepts and processes you have already learned. You will be surprised how much doing this will help you learn the new material.

Connecting. You will learn biology much more effectively if you relate what you are learning to the world around you. The many challenges of living in today's world are often related to the information presented in this course, and understanding these relationships will help you learn. In each chapter of this textbook you will encounter several Apps (Application dialogs) in the outer margins (there is a "BIOLOGY & YOU" App on the facing page) that allow you to briefly explore a "real-world" topic related to what you are learning. Read them. You may not be tested on these Apps, but reading them will provide you with another "hook" to help you learn the material on which you will be tested.

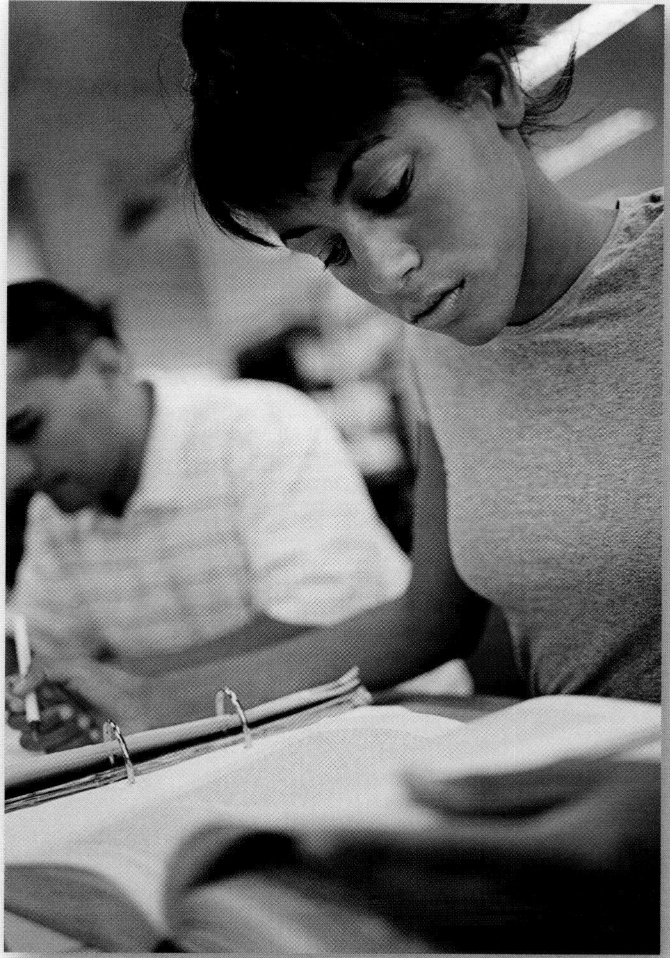

Figure 0.2 Learning requires work.

Learning is something you do, not something that happens to you.

IMPLICATION FOR YOU If you are honest with yourself, how many of the four rehearsal techniques (critical thinking skills) do you use when you take a science course like this one? Do you think they are as important in non-science classes like English or history? Why?

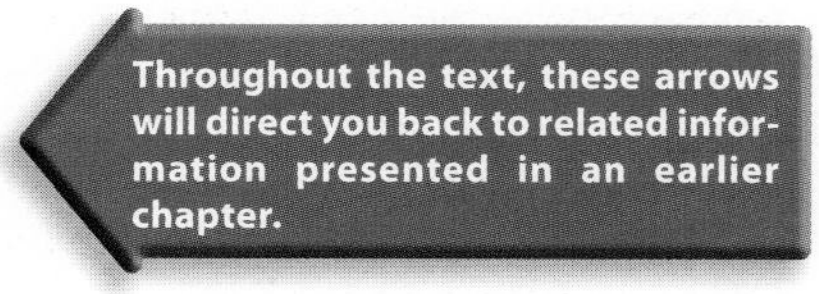

Throughout the text, these arrows will direct you back to related information presented in an earlier chapter.

Figure 0.3 Linking concepts.

These linking arrows, found throughout the text, will help you to form connections between seemingly discrete topics covered earlier in the text.

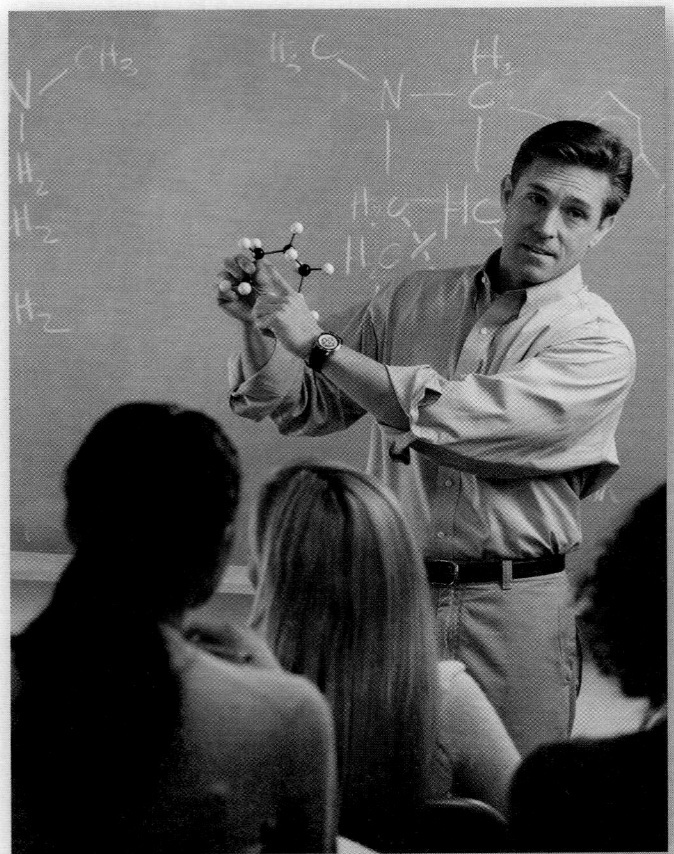

Figure 0.4 Critical learning occurs in the classroom.

Learning occurs in at least four distinct stages: doing assigned textbook readings before lecture; attending class; listening and taking notes during lecture; and recopying notes shortly after lecture. If you are diligent in these steps, then studying lecture notes and text assignments before exams is much more effective. Skipping any of these stages makes it far less likely that you will learn successfully.

Studying to Learn

If I have heard it once, I have heard it a thousand times, "Gee, Professor Johnson, I studied for 20 hours straight and I still got a D." By now, you should be getting the idea that just throwing time at the material does not ensure a favorable outcome. Many students treat studying for biology like penance: If you do it, you will be rewarded for having done so. Not always.

The length of time spent studying, and the spacing between study or reading sessions, directly affects how much you learn. If you had 10 hours to spend studying, you would be better off if you broke it up into 10 one-hour sessions, than to spend it all in one or two sessions. There are two good reasons for this:

First, we know from formal cognition research (as well as from our everyday life experiences) that we remember "beginnings" and "endings" but tend to forget "middles." Thus, the learning process can benefit from many "beginnings" and "endings."

Second, unless you are unusual, after 30 minutes or an hour your ability to concentrate is diminished. Concentration is a critical component of studying to learn. Many short, topic-focused study sessions maximize your ability to concentrate effectively. For most of us, effective concentration also means a comfortable, quiet environment with no outside distractions like loud music or conversations.

Learning Is an Active Process

It is important to realize that learning biology is not something you can do passively. Many students think that simply possessing a lecture video or a set of class notes will get them through. In and of themselves, videos and notes are no more important than the Nautilus machine an athlete works out on. It is not the machine *per se*, but what happens when you use it effectively, that is of importance.

Common sense will have a great deal to do with your success in learning biology, as it does in most of life's endeavors. Your success in this biology course will depend on simple, obvious things (**figure 0.4**):

- *Attend class.* Go to all the lectures and be on time.
- *Read the assigned readings before lecture.* If you have done so, you will hear things in lecture that will be familiar to you, a recognition that is a vital form of learning reinforcement. Later you can go back to the text to check details.
- *Take comprehensive notes.* Recognizing and writing down lecture points is another form of recognition and reinforcement. Later, studying for an exam, you will have already forgotten lecture material you did not record, and so even if you study hard you will miss exam questions on this material.
- *Revise your notes soon after lecture.* Actively interacting with your class notes while you still hold much of the lecture in short-term memory provides perhaps the most powerful form of reinforcement, and will be a key to your success.

As you proceed through this textbook, you will encounter a blizzard of terms and concepts. Biology is a field rich with ideas and the technical jargon needed to describe them. What you discover reading this textbook is intended to support the lectures that provide the core of your biology course. Integrating what you learn here with what you learn in lecture will provide you with the strongest possible tool for successfully mastering the basics of biology. The rest is just hard work.

Author's Corner

Pulling an All-Nighter

At some point in the next months you will face that scary rite, the first exam in this course. As a university professor, I get to give the exams rather than take them, but I can remember with crystal clarity when the shoe was on the other foot. I didn't like exams a bit as a student—what student does? But in my case I was often practically paralyzed with fear. What scared me about exams was the possibility of unanticipated questions. No matter how much I learned, there was always something I didn't know, some direction from which my teacher could lob a question I had no chance of answering.

I lived and died by the all-nighter. Black coffee was my closest friend in final exam week, and sleep seemed a luxury I couldn't afford. My parents urged me to sleep more, but I was trying to cram enough in to meet any possible question, and couldn't waste time sleeping.

Now, driven by time (often kicking and screaming), I find I did it all wrong. In work published over the last few years, researchers at Harvard Medical School have demonstrated that our memory of newly learned information improves only after sleeping at least six hours. If I wanted to do well on final exams, I could not have chosen a poorer way to prepare. The gods must look after the ignorant, as I usually passed.

Learning is, in its most basic sense, a matter of forming memories. The Harvard researchers' experiments showed that a person trying to learn something does not improve his or her knowledge until after they have had more than six hours of sleep (preferably eight). It seems the brain needs time to file new information and skills away in the proper slots so they can be retrieved later. Without enough sleep to do all this filing, new information does not get properly encoded into the brain's memory circuits.

To sort out the role of sleep in learning, the Harvard Medical School researchers used Harvard undergrads as guinea pigs. The undergraduates were trained to look for particular visual targets on a computer screen, and to push a button as soon as they were sure they had seen one. At first, responses were relatively sluggish—it typically took 400 milliseconds for a target to reach a student's conscious awareness. With an hour's training, however, many students were hitting the button correctly in 75 milliseconds.

How well had they learned? When retested from 3 to 12 hours later on the same day, there was no further improvement past a student's best time in the training session. If the researchers let a student get a little sleep, but less than six hours, then retested the next day, the student still showed no improvement in performing the target identification.

For students who slept more than six hours, the story was very different. Sleep greatly improved performance. Students who achieved 75 milliseconds in the training session would reliably perform the target identification in 62 milliseconds after a good night's sleep! After several nights of ample sleep, they often got even more proficient.

Why six or eight hours, and not four or five? The sort of sleeping you do at the beginning of a night's sleep and the sort you do at the end are different, and both, it appears, are required for efficient learning.

The first two hours of sleeping are spent in deep sleep, what psychiatrists call slow-wave sleep. During this time, certain brain chemicals become used up, which allows information that has been gathered during the day to flow out of the memory center of the brain, the hippocampus, and into the cortex, the outer covering of the brain where long-term memories are stored. Like moving information in a computer from active memory to the hard drive, this process preserves experience for future reference. Without it, long-term learning cannot occur.

Over the next hours, the cortex sorts through the information it has received, distributing it to various locations and networks. Particular connections between nerve cells become strengthened as memories are preserved, a process that is thought to require the time-consuming manufacturing of new proteins.

If you halt this process before it is complete, the day's memories do not get fully "transcribed," and you don't remember all that you would have, had you allowed the process to continue to completion. A few hours are just not enough time to get the job done. Four hours, the Harvard researchers estimate, is a minimum requirement.

The last two hours of a night's uninterrupted sleep are spent in rapid-eye-movement (rem) sleep. This is when dreams occur. The brain shuts down the connection to the hippocampus and runs through the data it has stored over the previous hours. This process is also important to learning, as it reinforces and strengthens the many connections between nerve cells that make up the new memory. Like a child repeating a refrain to memorize it, the brain goes over what it has learned, until practice makes perfect.

That's why my college system of getting by on three or four hours of sleep during exam week and crashing for 12 hours on weekends didn't work. After a few days, all of the facts I had memorized during one of my "all-nighters" faded away. Of course they did. I had never given them a chance to integrate properly into my memory circuits.

As I look back, I now see that how well I did on my exams probably had far less to do with how hard I studied than with how much I slept. It doesn't seem fair that after all these years, with my own kids now in college pulling all-nighters, I have to admit that my parents were right all along.

0.2 Using Your Textbook

A Textbook Is a Tool

A student enrolled in an introductory biology course, as you are, almost never learns everything from the textbook. Your text is a tool to explain and amplify what you learn in lecture. No textbook is a substitute for attending lectures, taking notes, and studying them. Success in your biology course is like a stool with three legs: lectures, class notes, and text reading—all three are necessary. Used together, they will take you a long way toward success in the course.

When to Use Your Text. While you can glance at your text at any time to refresh your memory or answer a question that pops into your mind, your use of your text as a learning tool should focus on providing support for the other two "legs" of course success, lectures and class notes.

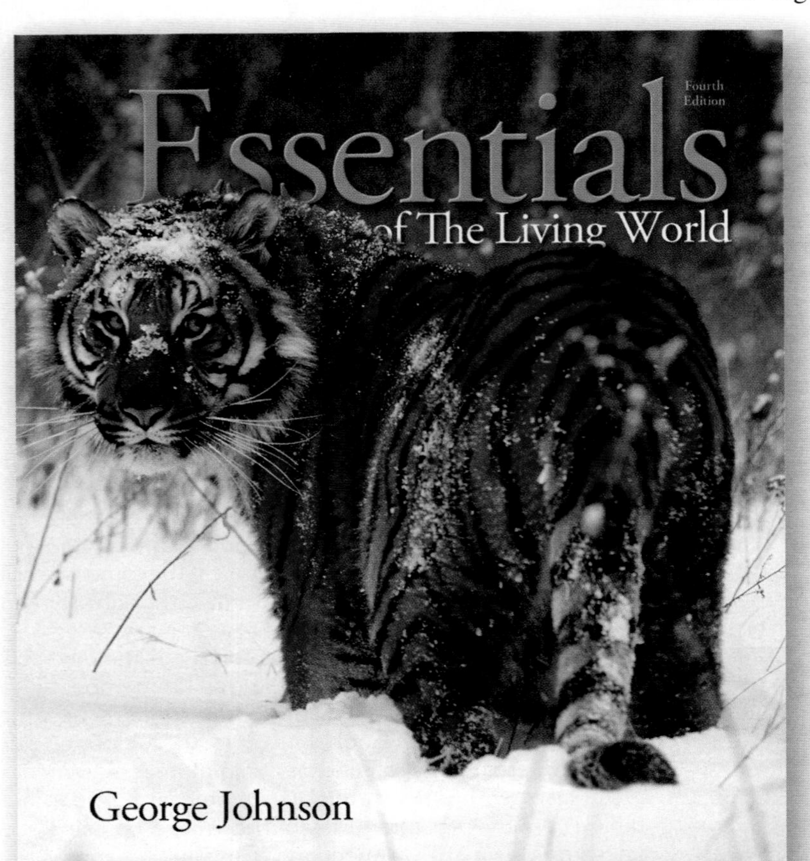

Do the Assigned Reading. Many instructors assign reading from the text, reading that is supposed to be done before lecture. The timing here is very important: If you already have a general idea of what is being discussed in lecture, it is much easier to follow the discussion and take better notes.

Link the Text to Your Lecture Notes. Few lectures cover exactly what is in the text, and much of what is in the text may not be covered in lecture. That said, much of what you will hear in lecture is covered in your text. This coverage provides you with a powerful tool to reinforce ideas and information you encounter in lecture. Text illustrations and detailed explanations can pound home an idea quickly grasped in lecture, and answer any questions that might occur to you as you sort through the logic of an argument. Thus it is absolutely essential that you follow along with your text as you recopy your lecture notes, keying your notes to the textbook as you go. Annotating your notes in this way will make them far better learning tools as you study for exams later.

Review for Exams. It goes without saying that you should review your recopied lecture notes to prepare for an exam. But that is not enough. What is often missed in gearing up for an exam is the need to also review that part of the text that covers the same material. Reading the chapter again, one last time, helps place your lecture notes in perspective, so that it will be easier to remember key points when a topic explodes at you off the page of your exam.

How to Use Your Text. The single most important way to use your text is to read it. As your biology course proceeds and you move through the text, read each assigned chapter all the way through at one sitting. This will give you valuable perspective. Then, guided by your lecture notes, go back through the chapter, one *learning objective* at a time, and focus on the concepts in each learning objective as you recopy your notes. Pay attention to the "linking" arrows in the text, as using them will reinforce what you are learning. As discussed earlier, building a bridge between text and lecture notes is a very powerful way to learn. Remember, your notes don't take the exam, and neither does the textbook; you do, and the learning that occurs as you integrate text pages and lecture notes in your mind will go a long way toward your taking it well.

Learning Tools at Your Disposal

A textbook is more than just words. What do you see when you flip through the pages of this text? Pictures, lots of them. And questions, scattered through each chapter and clustered at chapter's end. The pictures and quiz questions you will encounter within each chapter can be an important part of your learning experience.

Let the Illustrations Teach You. All introductory biology texts are rich with colorful photographs and diagrams. They are there not to decorate, but to aid your comprehension of ideas and concepts. When the text refers you to a specific figure, look at it—the visual link will help you remember the idea much better than restricting yourself to cold words on a page.

Three sorts of illustrations offer particularly strong reinforcement:

Essential Biological Process Illustrations. While you will be asked to learn many technical terms in this course, learning the names of things is not your key goal. Your goal is to master a small set of concepts. There are several essential biological processes that explain how organisms work the way they do. When you have understood these processes, much of the heavy lifting in learning biology is done. Every time you encounter one of these essential biological processes in the text, you will be provided with an illustration to help you better understand. These *Essential Biological Process* illustrations break the process down into easily understood stages, so that you can grasp how the overall process works without being lost in a forest of details (**figure 0.5*a***).

Bubble Links. Illustrations teach best when they are simple. Unfortunately, some of the structures and processes being illustrated just aren't simple. Every time you encounter a complex diagram in the text, it will be "predigested" for you—the individual components of the diagram will each be identified with a number in a colored circle, or bubble. This same number is also placed in the text narrative right where that component is discussed. These bubble links allow the text to step you through the illustration, explaining what is going on at each stage—the illustration is a feast you devour one bite at a time.

Phylum Facts. Not all of what you will learn are concepts. Sometimes you will need to soak up a lot of information, painting a picture with facts. Nowhere is this more true than when you study animal diversity. In chapter 18 you will encounter a train of animal phyla (a phylum is a major category of organisms) with which you must become familiar. In such a sea of information, what should you learn? Every time you encounter a phylum in chapter 18, you will be provided with a *Phylum Facts* illustration that selects the key bits of information about the body and lifestyle of that kind of animal (**figure 0.5*b***). If you learned and understood only the items highlighted there, you would have mastered much of what you need to know.

Check What You Know. As you move through a chapter, addressing first one topic and then another, it will be important that you monitor your progress—not only what you have read, but how well you have understood it.

Putting Concepts to Work. At the end of each learning objective within a chapter, you will encounter a "putting the concept to work" question you can use to reinforce what you are learning. If you can't answer it, you should go back and have another look at that section.

End-of-Chapter Questions. When you complete a chapter, you can gauge how well you have learned the material by answering the questions at the end of the chapter, each linked to a learning objective. If you get a question wrong, you can revisit the learning objective within that chapter. You can further test your knowledge with the *LearnSmart* questions provided by *ConnectPlus* if your class utilizes this program (discussed in the next section).

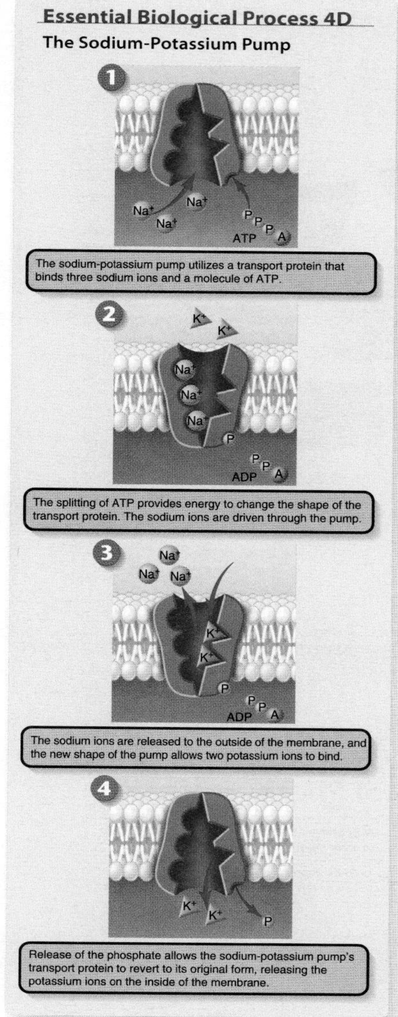

Essential Biological Process 4D
The Sodium-Potassium Pump
1
The sodium-potassium pump utilizes a transport protein that binds three sodium ions and a molecule of ATP.
2
The splitting of ATP provides energy to change the shape of the transport protein. The sodium ions are driven through the pump.
3
The sodium ions are released to the outside of the membrane, and the new shape of the pump allows two potassium ions to bind.
4
Release of the phosphate allows the sodium-potassium pump's transport protein to revert to its original form, releasing the potassium ions on the inside of the membrane.

(a)

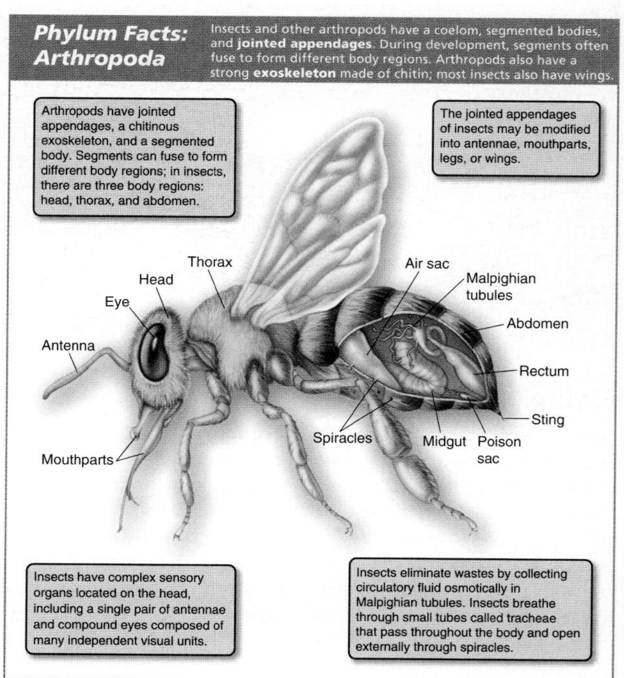

Phylum Facts: Arthropoda
Insects and other arthropods have a coelom, segmented bodies, and jointed appendages. During development, segments often fuse to form different body regions. Arthropods also have a strong exoskeleton made of chitin; most insects also have wings.
Arthropods have jointed appendages, a chitinous exoskeleton, and a segmented body. Segments can fuse to form different body regions; in insects, there are three body regions: head, thorax, and abdomen.
The jointed appendages of insects may be modified into antennae, mouthparts, legs, or wings.
Head
Thorax
Eye
Antenna
Mouthparts
Air sac
Malpighian tubules
Abdomen
Rectum
Sting
Spiracles
Midgut
Poison sac
Insects have complex sensory organs located on the head, including a single pair of antennae and compound eyes composed of many independent visual units.
Insects eliminate wastes by collecting circulatory fluid osmotically in Malpighian tubules. Insects breathe through small tubes called tracheae that pass throughout the body and open externally through spiracles.

(b)

Figure 0.5 Visual learning tools.

(a) An example of an *Essential Biological Process* illustration.
(b) An example of a Phylum Facts illustration.

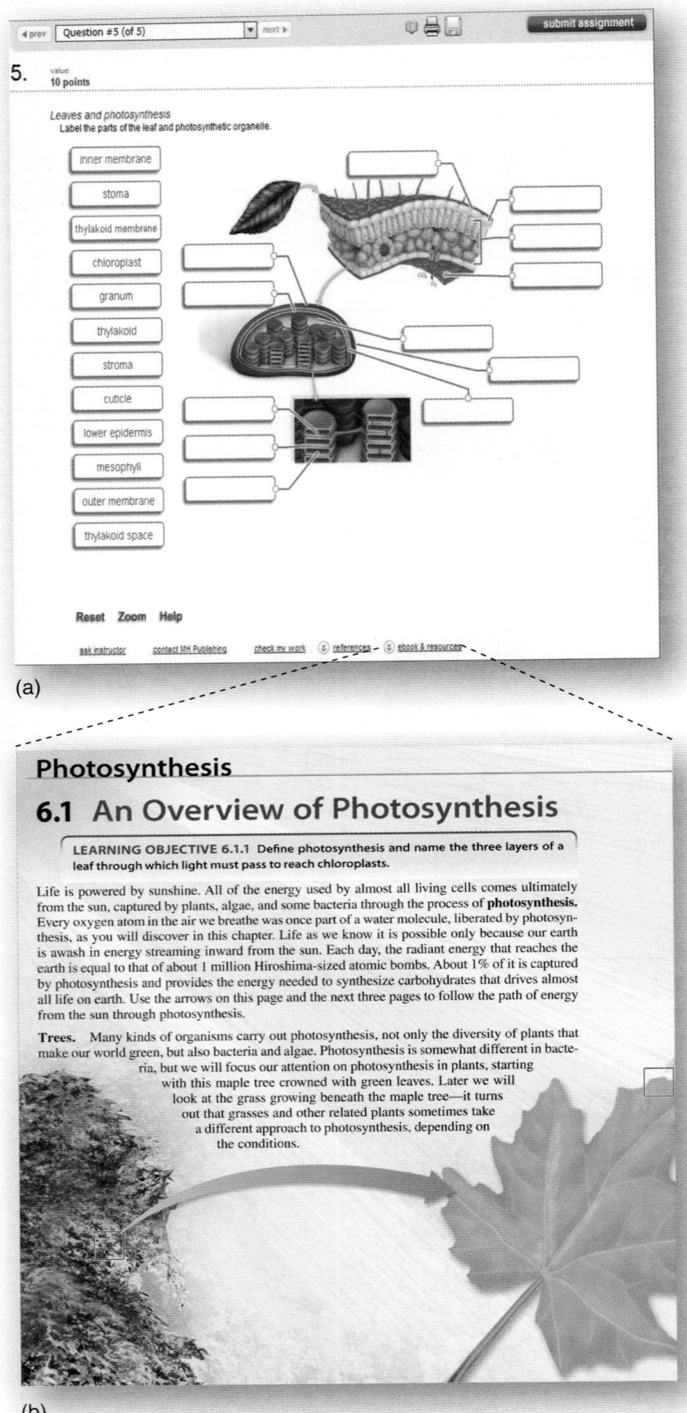

Photosynthesis

6.1 An Overview of Photosynthesis

LEARNING OBJECTIVE 6.1.1 Define photosynthesis and name the three layers of a leaf through which light must pass to reach chloroplasts.

Life is powered by sunshine. All of the energy used by almost all living cells comes ultimately from the sun, captured by plants, algae, and some bacteria through the process of **photosynthesis.** Every oxygen atom in the air we breathe was once part of a water molecule, liberated by photosynthesis, as you will discover in this chapter. Life as we know it is possible only because our earth is awash in energy streaming inward from the sun. Each day, the radiant energy that reaches the earth is equal to that of about 1 million Hiroshima-sized atomic bombs. About 1% of it is captured by photosynthesis and provides the energy needed to synthesize carbohydrates that drives almost all life on earth. Use the arrows on this page and the next three pages to follow the path of energy from the sun through photosynthesis.

Trees. Many kinds of organisms carry out photosynthesis, not only the diversity of plants that make our world green, but also bacteria and algae. Photosynthesis is somewhat different in bacteria, but we will focus our attention on photosynthesis in plants, starting with this maple tree crowned with green leaves. Later we will look at the grass growing beneath the maple tree—it turns out that grasses and other related plants sometimes take a different approach to photosynthesis, depending on the conditions.

Figure 0.6 Using *Connect*.

Using a text-integrated assessment program called *Connect*, your instructor is able to provide you with a series of interactive questions that test your understanding of key concepts and information. (a) In the question about leaves and photosynthesis you see above, for example, your job is to correctly label the parts of a leaf and its chloroplasts. (b) By clicking on the "*eBook* and resources" button below the question, you can at any point review the learning objective in the *eBook* where this material is discussed.

0.3 Using Your Textbook's Internet Resources

Connect

It probably came as no surprise to you that you were instructed in the previous section to read your text in order to learn the material on which you will be tested, using its illustrations to fortify your understanding. It thus came as something of a surprise to education researchers when they found that most successful students do exactly the opposite. Watching how college students actually use their textbooks, they repeatedly observed students going first to the illustrations, then to the captions beneath them, and only later to the words of the text, using the text to clarify their understanding of the illustrations! Said simply, successful students are often visual learners.

A visual learner is best tested with visual and interactive questions. If your class is utilizing an instructor-guided learning program called *ConnectPlus*, just such an approach is available to you. As a platform for tackling such interactive assessment of how you are doing, *ConnectPlus* provides you with a fully interactive *eBook* version of this text, with embedded animations and videos, as well as notes and highlights added by your instructor. For each class assignment, the instructor then assigns you a series of interactive questions, such as the one you see in figure 0.6. *ConnectPlus* grades each answer for you. If you have trouble with a question, the program connects that question to the learning objective in the *eBook* where the question is answered.

How *Connect* Helps You to Learn. *Connect* is not simply a testing machine, used by the instructor to look over your shoulder and spy on how you are studying. Far from it. It is a powerful learning platform that you can use to help understand instructor-assigned material. By the time you have successfully navigated the series of questions assigned by your instructor, you will be well on the way to mastering the assignment. Also, you can search out the answer to any question that stumps you, using visual tools to guide the process.

Connect is no substitute for reading your text and linking it to your lecture notes. Make no mistake about it—your text and lecture notes are the only sure road to success in this course. The great utility of *Connect* is that it provides a way for you to check how you are doing. The visual and interactive questions you access through *Connect* are self-study questions fully integrated with the text. They provide you with a powerful—and fun—way to identify holes in your understanding of an assignment, and the means to fill them in. Why wait until an exam to find out what you don't know? Your course grade will be far superior if you find and solve these problems before the exam. And should quizzes and exams be administered to you as unlinked *Connect* questions, it will be like meeting an old friend, a familiar face you have met many times before.

Kinds of *Connect* Questions. *Connect* presents you with five kinds of interactive questions: *Labeling questions,* such as figure 0.6, challenge you to drag terms to correctly label an illustration. *Composition questions* ask you to place words into a paragraph to correctly finish a sentence. *Sequence questions* have you arrange a series of images or process steps into the proper order. *Classification questions* require you to place a set of terms or characteristics into their appropriate categories. Lastly, *Inquiry and Analysis questions* ask you to select the graph that best portrays the results expected when an experiment is modified in a particular way.

LearnSmart

While *Connect* is a powerful learning tool that any student will profit from using, it is instructor-driven, typically with the same set of questions selected by the instructor for the entire class. Not all students come to a biology class, however, with the same level of preparation, or remember equally well what they learned in high school. *LearnSmart,* which is delivered through *Connect,* addresses this problem in a direct way, tailoring its questions to each student individually. Using artificial intelligence, *LearnSmart* examines your answers to a series of questions, pinpoints concepts and information you do not yet understand, and maps out a study plan personalized for what you need to learn.

The power of *LearnSmart* is that it adapts directly to you. While all students are given the same initial set of questions, the questions that follow are directed specifically to you, selected by *LearnSmart's* artificial intelligence to focus on areas where your performance on the initial set of questions was weak. When you get one of these questions wrong, *LearnSmart* calls a "timeout" and takes you to the page in the *eBook* where that topic is discussed. You are then able to sort out the answer to the question you missed and then resume quizzing to see if you mastered the point. As you can imagine, *LearnSmart* contains a lot of questions—any chapter of this text may have from one to 300 associated *LearnSmart* questions!

At any point as you move along your own individual learning path through a chapter, you can call up a *LearnSmart* report like the one you see in figure 0.7 to see how you are doing. You can even look at the "Tree of Knowledge" to see your current learning status: what portions of the chapter's web of concepts you have mastered, and which others still need attention. You and *LearnSmart* constitute a one-person biology course, with *LearnSmart* devising a learning path contoured to your own needs and speed of learning.

As your own private instructor, *LearnSmart* can see into what you are learning in surprising ways. Using its "self-assessment" feature, a *LearnSmart* report will allow you to view how aware you were of whether or not you knew the answers. This awareness can help you study more effectively, by identifying areas of a chapter where you are not doing so.

LearnSmart can only help you if you use it. As you address the individual learning objectives of a chapter, let *LearnSmart* focus your study of each learning objective on those aspects of it you have not yet mastered. Later, when you come back to a chapter to review for a test or exam, let *LearnSmart* guide your review, making for you specialized quizzes to sharpen your memory of key points and practice for the upcoming exam.

Website Resources

The website for this textbook *(www.mhhe.com/esstlw4)* provides you with a variety of resources to help you master key concepts:

Study On The Fly. This application allows you to download particular videos and animations (this website provides a blizzard of them) to your iPad or other mobile device, so you can study "on the run."

Explorations. There are 33 *Explorations,* like the one illustrating drug addiction in figure 0.8, that allow you to explore a key concept by manipulating key variables and examining the impact of your actions.

Virtual Labs. For many chapters, there is a *Virtual Lab* that allows you to closely examine a real experiment reported in a published paper. You can then devise and carry out your own parallel experiment, and evaluate its results. You can even interview the investigating scientist, and read his or her published paper reporting the study and its outcome.

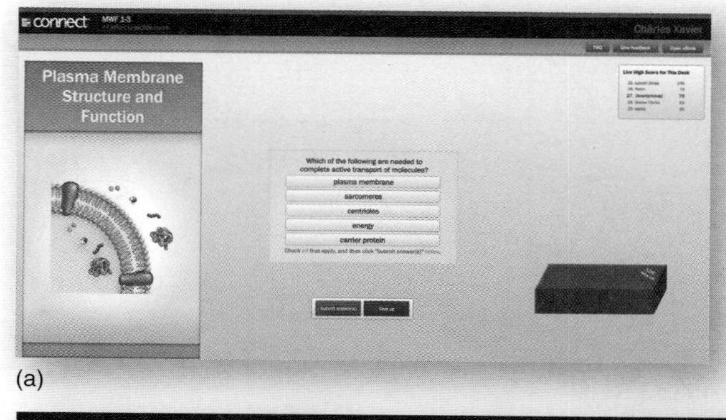

(a)

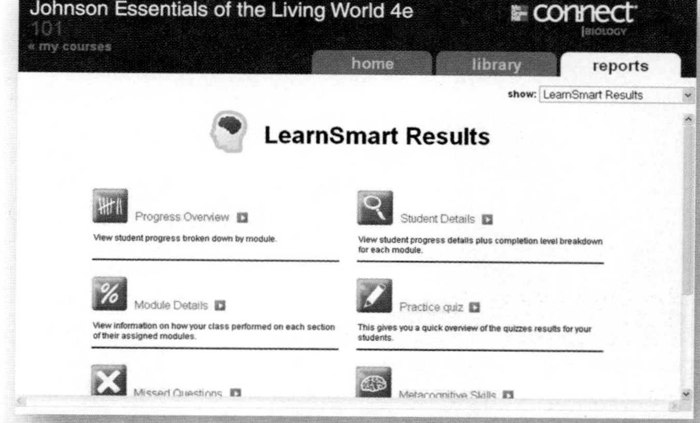

(b)

Figure 0.7 Using *LearnSmart.*

LearnSmart is an artificial intelligence program that initially quizzes you with a battery of questions like the one above on plasma membrane components (a), issues reports like the one you see here that identify what you do not yet understand (b), and then continues to probe those areas until you do understand them.

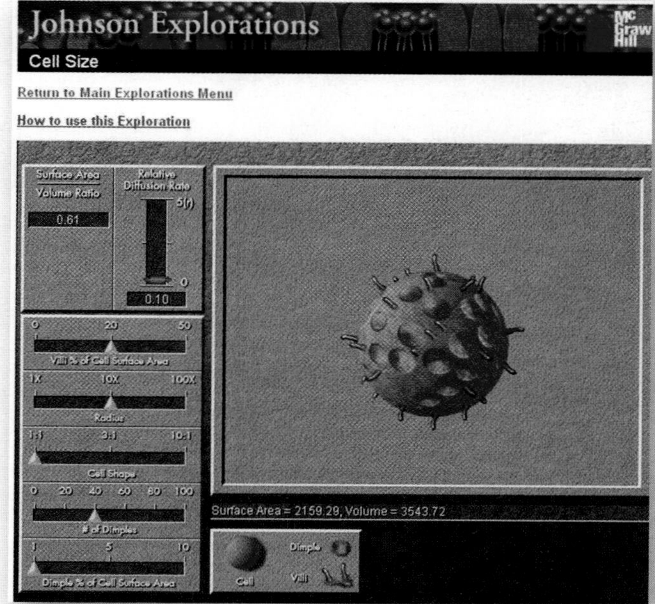

Figure 0.8 Using *Explorations.*

Some two dozen *Explorations* allow you to manipulate variables that affect a process, like drug addiction, and observe the results.

Putting What You Learn to Work

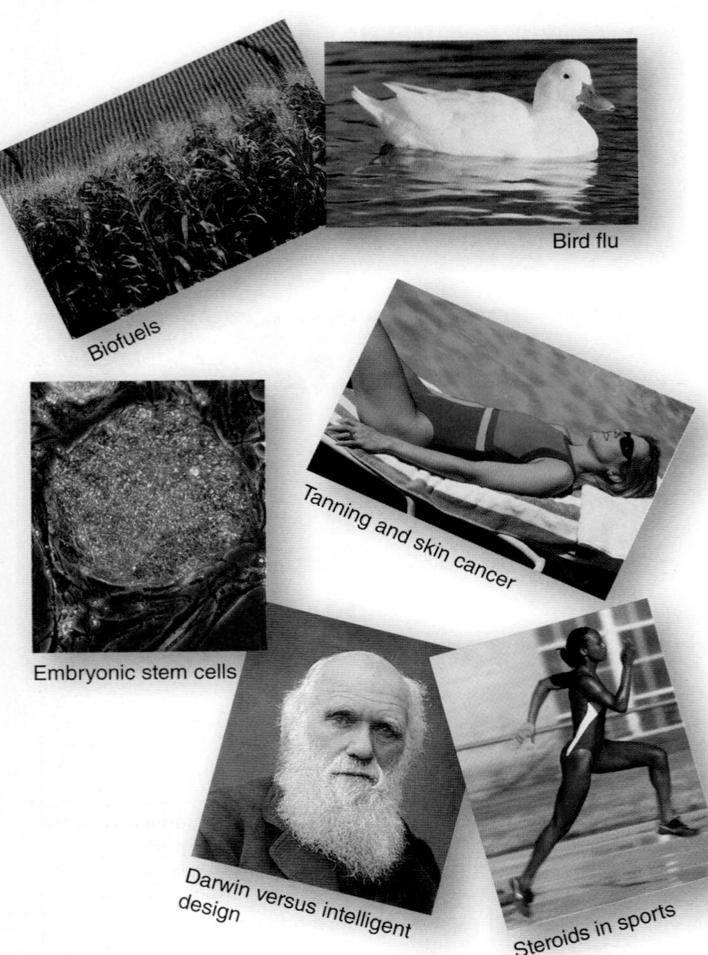

Figure 0.9 Biology in the news.

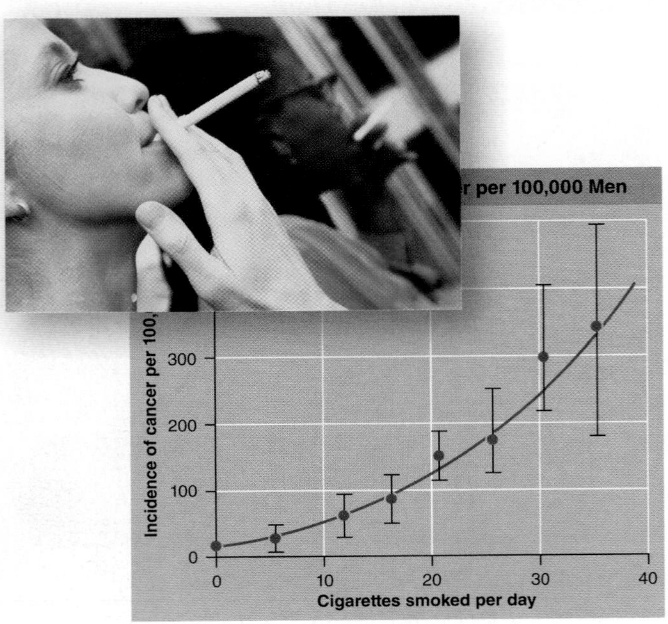

Figure 0.10 Does smoking cause lung cancer?

0.4 Science Is a Way of Thinking

In the study of biology you will encounter a great deal of information, a forest of new terms and definitions, and a lot of descriptions of how things work—body processes, evolutionary relationships, interactions within ecosystems, and many others. In all of this, you will be asked to accept that what you are being taught is "true," that it accurately reflects reality. In fact, what it accurately reflects is what we know about reality. Of the things that you learn in this course, some will be altered by future scientists as they learn more. As we will discuss in chapter 1, our knowledge of science is always incomplete, the picture of reality we construct always a rough draft.

One of the most important things you can learn in a biology course is how these adjustments are made. Long after this class is completed, you will be making decisions that involve biology, and they will be better, more informed decisions if you have acquired the skill to evaluate scientific claims for yourself. Because it is printed in the newspaper or cited on a web site doesn't make a scientific claim valid. **Figure 0.9** illustrates the sorts of biology you encounter today in the news—and this is just a small sample. They are, all of them, important issues that will affect your own life. How do you reach informed opinions about them?

You do it by asking the question, "How do we know this?" Science is a way of thinking that demands to see the evidence, that challenges the validity of every claim. If you can learn to do this, to apply this skill in the future to personal decisions about biology as it impacts your life, you will have taken from this course a valuable lesson.

How Do We Know What We Know?

A useful way to learn how scientists think, how they constantly check and question what they know, is to look at real cases. What follows are four instances where biologists have come to a conclusion. These conclusions will be taught in this textbook, reflecting the world about us as best as science can determine. All four of these cases will be treated at length in later chapters—here they serve only to introduce the process of scientific questioning.

Does Cigarette Smoking Cause Lung Cancer? According to the American Cancer Society, 571,950 Americans died of cancer in 2011. Fully one in four of the students using this textbook can be expected to die of it. Twenty-seven percent of these cancer victims, almost a third, die of lung cancer.

As you might imagine, something that kills so many of us has been the subject of much research. The first step biologists took was to ask a simple question: "Who gets lung cancer?" The answer came back loud and clear: Fully 87% of those who die from lung cancer are cigarette smokers. Delving into this more closely, researchers looked to see if the incidence of lung cancer (that is, how many people contract it per 100,000 people) can be predicted by how many cigarettes a person smokes each day. As you can see in the graph in **figure 0.10** (which is shown again on page 594), it can. The more cigarettes smoked, the higher the occurrence of lung cancer. Based on this study, and lots of others like it, examined in more detail on pages 200 and 510, biologists concluded that smoking cigarettes causes lung cancer.

Does Carbon Dioxide Cause Global Warming? Our world is getting warmer—a lot warmer. The great ice caps that cover Antarctica and Greenland are melting, and sea levels are rising. Looking for the cause, atmospheric scientists soon began to suspect what might at first seem an unlikely culprit: carbon dioxide (CO_2), a gas that is a minor component (0.03%) of the air we breathe. As you will learn in this course, burning coal and other fossil fuels releases CO_2 into the atmosphere. Problems arise because CO_2 traps heat. As the modern world industrializes, more and more CO_2 is released. Does this lead to a hotter earth? To find out, researchers looked to see if the rise in global temperature reflected a rise in the atmosphere's CO_2. As you can see in the graph in figure 0.11 (which is shown again on page 454), it does. After these and other careful studies, which we will explore in detail on pages 454 and 470, scientists concluded that rising CO_2 levels are indeed the cause of global warming.

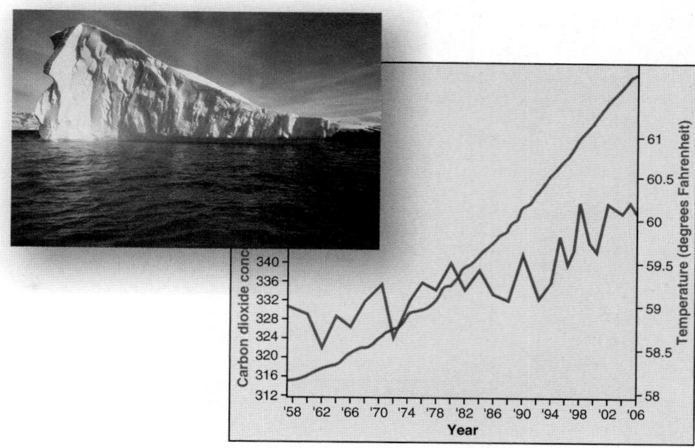

Figure 0.11 **Does carbon dioxide cause global warming?**

Does Obesity Lead to Type 2 Diabetes? The United States is in the midst of an obesity epidemic. From 1991 to 2007, the percentage of Americans who were obese almost tripled, from 12% to over 34%. Coincidentally (or was it a coincidence?), the number of Americans suffering from type 2 diabetes (a disorder in which the body loses its ability to regulate glucose levels in the blood, often leading to blindness and amputation of limbs) more than tripled over the same 16-year period, from 7 million to more than 23 million (that's one in every 14 Americans!).

What is going on here? When researchers compared obesity levels with type 2 diabetes levels, they found a marked correlation, clearly visible in the graph in figure 0.12 (which is shown again on page 591). Investigating more closely, the researchers found that an estimated 80% of people who develop type 2 diabetes are obese. Detailed investigations described on page 591 have now confirmed the relationship that these early studies hinted at: Overeating triggers changes in the body that lead to type 2 diabetes.

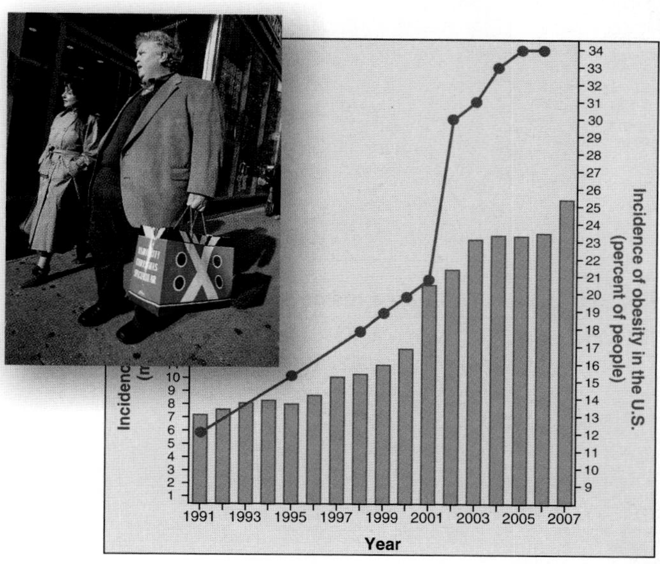

Figure 0.12 **Does obesity lead to type 2 diabetes?**

What Causes the Ozone Hole? Twenty-five years ago, atmospheric scientists first reported a loss of ozone (O_3 gas) high in the atmosphere over Antarctica. This was scary, because ozone in the upper atmosphere absorbs ultraviolet radiation from the sun, protecting the earth's surface from these harmful rays. Trying to understand the reason for this "ozone hole," researchers considered many possibilities, and one of them seemed a good candidate: chlorofluorocarbons, or CFCs. CFCs are supposedly inert chemicals that are widely used as heat exchangers in air conditioners. However, further studies, detailed on pages 23 and 457, indicated that CFCs are not inert after all—in the intense cold temperatures high over Antarctica, they cause O_3 to be converted to O_2. Scientists concluded that CFCs were indeed causing the ozone hole over Antarctica. This finding led to international treaties beginning in 1990 blocking the further manufacture of CFC chemicals. As you can see in the graph in figure 0.13, the size of the ozone hole seems to have stopped expanding.

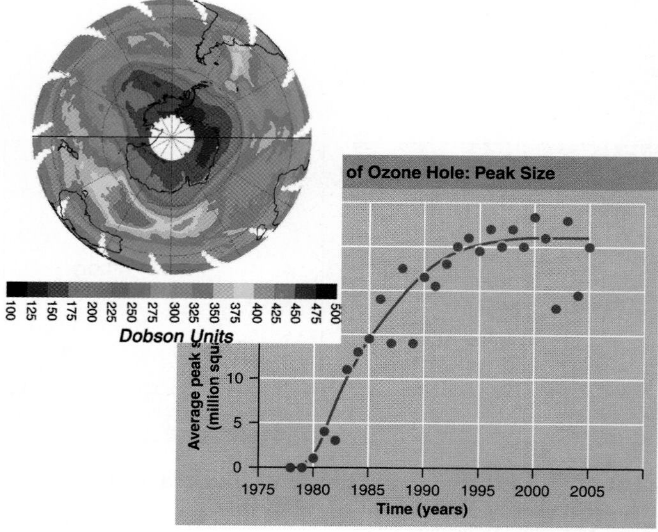

Figure 0.13 **What causes the ozone hole?**

Looking at the Evidence

One thing these four cases have in common is that in each, scientists reached their conclusion not by applying established rules but rather by looking in detail at what was going on and then testing possible explanations. In short, they gathered data and analyzed it. If you are going to think independently about scientific issues in the future, then you will need to learn how to analyze data and understand what it is telling you. In each case above, the data is presented in the form of a graph. Said simply, you will need to learn to read a graph.

0.5 How to Read a Graph

Variables and Graphs

In the previous section you encountered four graphs illustrating what happened to variables, such as global temperature, size of the ozone hole, incidence of obesity, and incidence of lung cancer, when other variables changed. A **variable,** as its name implies, is something that can change. Variables are the tools of science, and you will encounter many different kinds as you proceed through this text. Many of the variables biologists study are examined in graphs like the ones you saw on the previous pages. A **graph** shows what happens to one variable when another one changes.

There are two types of variables. The first kind, an **independent variable,** is one that a researcher deliberately changes—for example, the concentration of a chemical in a solution, or the number of cigarettes smoked per day. The second kind, a **dependent variable,** is what happens in response to the changes in the independent variable—for example, the intensity of a solution's color, or the incidence of lung cancer. Importantly, the change in a dependent variable that is measured in an experiment is not predetermined by the investigator.

In science, all graphs are presented in a consistent way. The independent variable is always presented and labeled across the bottom, called the *x axis.* The dependent variable is always presented and labeled along the side (usually the left side), called the *y axis* (**figure 0.14**).

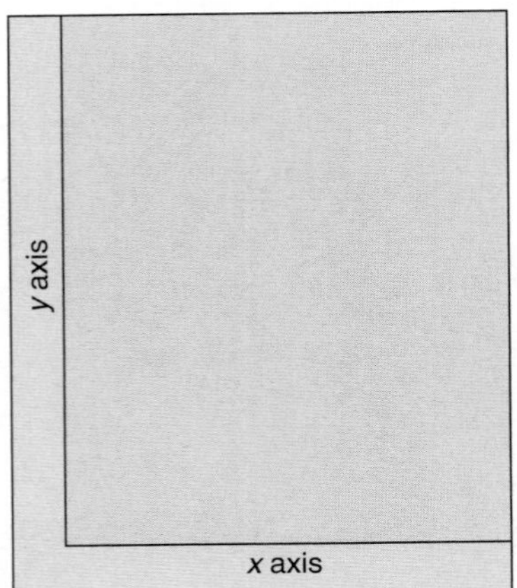

Figure 0.14 The two axes of a graph.

The independent variable is almost always presented along the *x* axis, and the dependent variable is usually shown along the *y* axis.

Some research involves examining correlations between sets of variables, rather than the deliberate manipulation of a variable. For example, a researcher who measures both diabetes and obesity levels (as described in the previous section) is actually comparing two dependent variables. While such a comparison can reveal correlations and so suggest potential relationships, ***correlation does not prove causation***. What is happening to one variable may actually have nothing to do with what happens to the other variable. Only by manipulating a variable (making it an independent variable) can you test for causality. Just because people that are obese tend to also have diabetes does not establish that obesity *causes* diabetes. Other experiments are needed to determine causation.

Using the Appropriate Scale and Units

A key aspect of presenting data in a graph is the selection of proper scale. Data presented in a table can utilize many scales, from seconds to centuries, with no problems. A graph, however, typically has a single scale on the *x* axis and a single scale on the *y* axis, which might consist of molecular units (for example, nanometers, microliters, micrograms) or macroscopic units (for example, feet, inches, liters, days, milligrams). In each instance, a scale must be chosen that fits what is being measured. Changes in centimeters would not be obvious in a graph scaled in kilometers. Also, if a variable changes a great deal over the course of the experiment, it is often useful to use an expanding scale. A **log** or **logarithmic scale** is a series of numbers plotted as powers of 10 (1, 10, 100, 1,000,...) rather than in the linear progression seen on most graphs (2,000, 4,000, 6,000,...). Consider the two graphs in **figure 0.15**, where the *y* axis is plotted on a linear scale on the left and on a log scale on the right. You can see that the log scale more clearly displays changes in the dependent variable (the *y* axis) for the upper values of the independent variable (the *x* axis, values 2, 3, and 4). Notice that the interval *between* each *y* axis number is not linear either—the

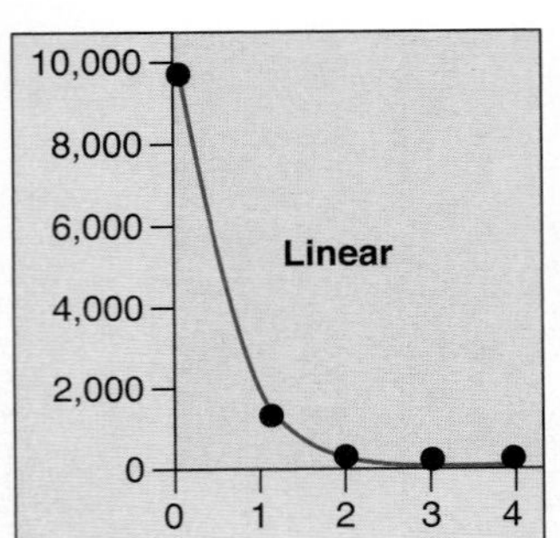

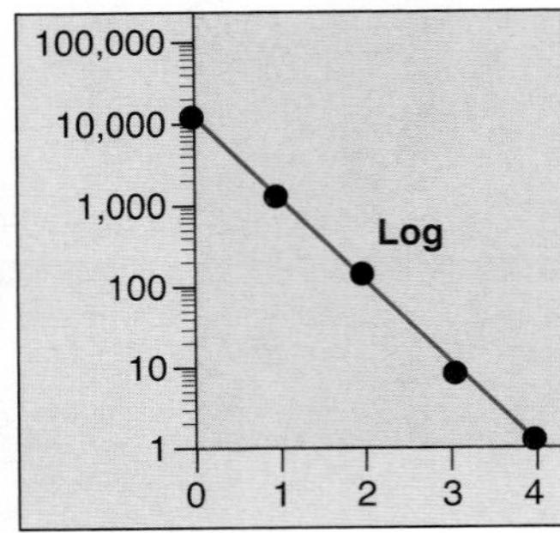

Figure 0.15 Linear and log scale: two ways of presenting the same data.

interval between each number is itself subdivided on a log scale. Thus, 50 (the fourth tick mark between 10 and 100) is plotted much closer to 100 than to 10.

Individual graphs use different units of measurement, each chosen to best display the experimental data. By international convention, scientific data are presented in **metric units,** a system of units expressed as powers of 10. For example, weight is expressed in units called *grams*. Ten grams make up a decagram, and 1,000 grams is a kilogram. Smaller weights are expressed as a portion of a gram—for example, a centigram is a hundredth of a gram, and a milligram is a thousandth of a gram. The units of measurement employed in a graph are by convention indicated in parentheses next to the independent variable label on the *x* axis and the dependent variable label on the *y* axis.

Drawing a Line

Most of the graphs that you will find in this text are **line graphs,** which are graphs composed of data points and one or more lines. Line graphs are typically used to present *continuous data*—that is, data that are discrete samples of a continuous process. An example might be data measuring how quickly the ozone hole develops over Antarctica in August and September of each year. You could in principle measure the area of the ozone hole every day, but to make the project more manageable in time and resources, you might actually take a measurement only once a week. Measurements reveal that the ozone hole increases in area rapidly for about six weeks before shrinking, yielding six data points during its expansion. These six data points are like individual frames from a movie—frozen moments in time. The six data points might indicate a very consistent pattern, or they might not.

Consider the hypothetical data in the graphs of figure 0.16. The data points on the left graph are changing in a very consistent way, with little variation from what a straight line (drawn in red) would predict. The graph in the middle shows more experimental variation, but a straight line still does a good job of revealing the overall pattern of how the data are changing. Such a straight "best-fit line" is called a **regression line** and is calculated by estimating the distance of each point to possible lines, adding the values, and selecting the line with the lowest sum. The data points in the graph on the right are randomly distributed and show no overall pattern, indicating that there is no relationship between the dependent and the independent variables.

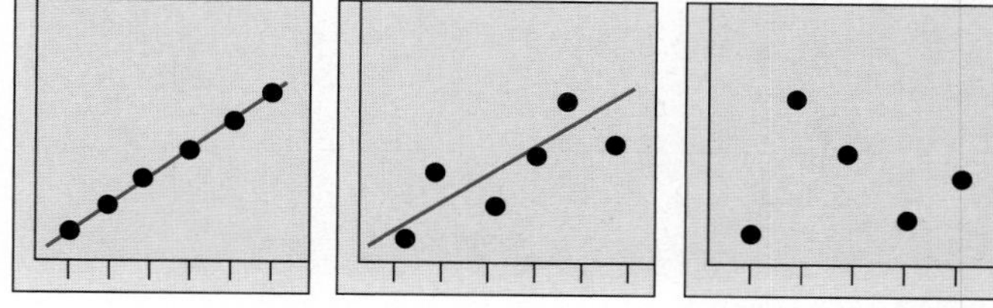

Figure 0.16 Line graphs: hypothetical growth in size of the ozone hole.

Other Graphical Presentations of Data

Sometimes the independent variable for a data set is not continuous but rather represents discrete sets of data. A line graph, with its assumption of continuity, cannot accurately represent the variation occurring in discrete sets of data, where the data sets are being compared with one another. In these cases, the preferred presentation is that of a **histogram,** a kind of bar graph. For example, if you were surveying the heights of pine trees in a park, you might group their heights (the independent variable) into discrete "categories" such as 0 to 5 meters tall, 5 to 10 meters, and so on. These categories are placed on the *x* axis. You would then count the number of trees in each category and present that dependent variable on the *y* axis, as shown in figure 0.17.

Some data represent proportions of a whole data set, for example the different types of trees in the park as a percentage of all the trees. This type of data is often presented in a **pie chart** (figure 0.18).

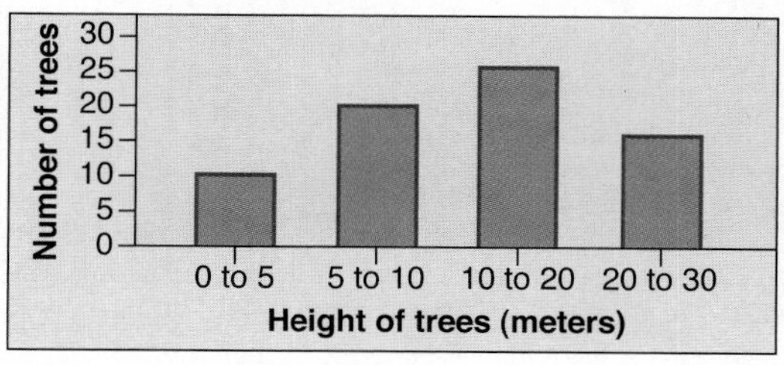

Figure 0.17 Histogram: the frequency of tall trees.

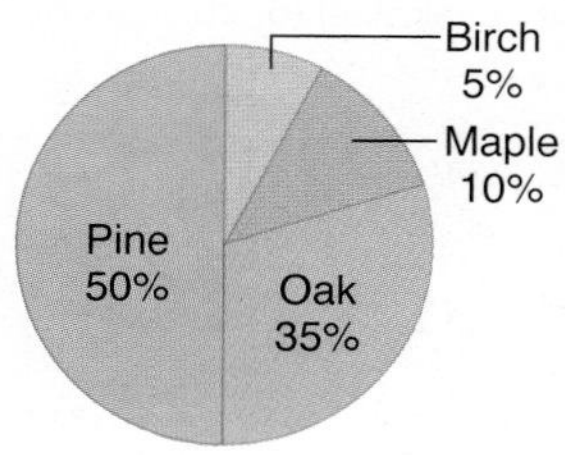

Figure 0.18 Pie chart: the composition of a forest.

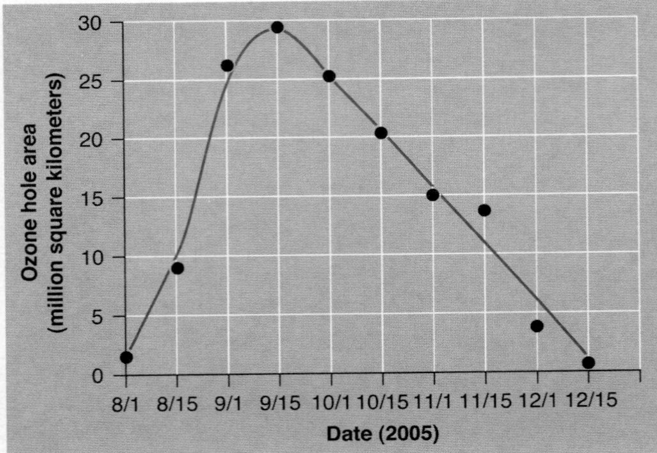

Figure 0.19 Changes in the size of the ozone hole over one year.

This graph shows how the size of the ozone hole changes over time, first expanding in size and then getting smaller.

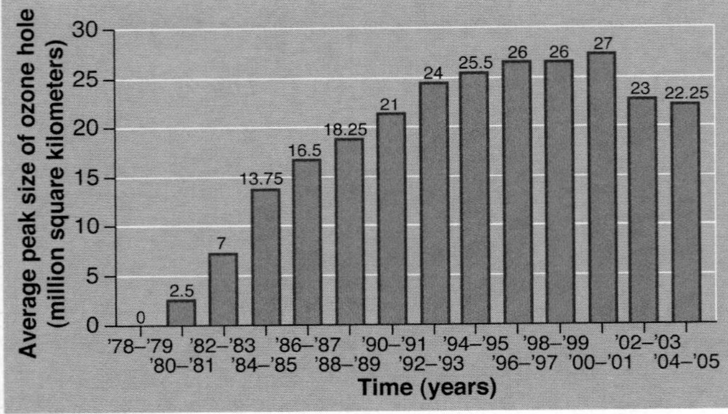

Figure 0.20 The peak sizes of the ozone hole.

This histogram shows how the size of the ozone hole increased in size (determined by its peak size) for 20 years before it then started to decrease.

Putting Your Graph-Reading Skills to Work: Inquiry & Analysis

The sorts of graphs you have encountered here in this brief introduction are all used frequently by scientists in analyzing and presenting their experimental results, and you will encounter them often as you proceed through this text.

Learning to read a graph and understanding what it does and does not tell you is one of the most important things you can take away from a biology course. To help you develop this skill, every chapter of this text ends with a full-page ***Inquiry & Analysis*** feature. Each of these end-of-chapter features describes a real scientific investigation. You will be introduced to a question, and then given a hypothesis posed by a researcher (a hypothesis is a kind of explanation) to answer that question. The feature will then tell you how the researcher set about evaluating his or her hypothesis with an experiment and will present a graph of the data the researcher obtained. You are then challenged to analyze the data and reach a conclusion about the validity of the hypothesis.

As an example, consider research on the ozone hole. What sort of graph might you expect to see? A *line graph* can be used to present data on how the size of the ozone hole changes over the course of one year. Because the dependent variable is the size of the ozone hole measured continuously over a single season, a smooth curve accurately portrays what is actually going on. In this case, the regression line is not a straight line, but rather a curve (figure 0.19).

Can line graphs and histograms be used to present the same data? In some cases, yes. The mode of its presentation does not alter the data; it only serves to emphasize the point being investigated. The *histogram* in figure 0.20 presents data on how the peak size of the ozone hole has changed in two-year intervals over the past 26 years. However, this same data could also have been presented as a line graph (see figure 0.13).

Presented with a graph of the data obtained in the investigation of the *Inquiry & Analysis*, it will be your job to analyze it. Every analysis of a graph involves four distinct steps, some more complex than others but all essential to the process.

Applying Concepts. Your first task is to make sure you understand the nature of the variables, and the scale at which they are being presented in the graph. As a self-test, it is always a good idea to ask yourself to identify the dependent variable.

Interpreting Data. Look at the graph. What is changing? How much? How quickly? Is the change continuous? Progressive? What in fact has happened?

Making Inferences. Looking at what has happened, can you logically infer that the independent variable has caused the change you see in the dependent variable?

Drawing Conclusions. Does the inference you were able to make support the hypothesis that the experiment set out to test?

This process of inquiry and analysis is the nuts and bolts of science, and by mastering it, you will go a long way toward learning how a scientist thinks.

Chapter 1

The Science of Biology

CHAPTER AT A GLANCE

Biology and the Living World
1.1 The Diversity of Life
1.2 Properties of Life
1.3 The Organization of Life
1.4 Biological Themes
The Scientific Process
1.5 Stages of a Scientific Investigation
1.6 Theory and Certainty
Author's Corner: Where Are All My Socks Going?
Core Ideas of Biology
1.7 Four Theories Unify Biology as a Science
Inquiry & Analysis: Does the Presence of One Species Limit the Population Size of Others?

Biology and the Living World

1.1 The Diversity of Life

"Flash-back" arrow

"Flash-forward" arrow

What are these? Throughout this text you will encounter blue and green linking arrows. These "Flash-back" and "Flash-forward" concept links will direct you to related material in earlier chapters or in later chapters. Using them will help you master the interconnected nature of concepts in biology.

LEARNING OBJECTIVE 1.1.1 List the six kingdoms of life.

In its broadest sense, biology is the study of living things—the science of life. The living world is teeming with a breathtaking variety of creatures—whales, algae, mushrooms, bacteria, pine trees—all of which can be categorized into six groups, or **kingdoms,** of organisms (figure 1.1). Organisms that are placed into a kingdom possess similar characteristics with all other organisms in that same kingdom and are very different from organisms in the other kingdoms. Biologists study the diversity of life in many different ways. They live with gorillas, collect fossils, isolate bacteria, and study molecules of heredity. In the midst of all this diversity, it is easy to lose sight of the key lesson of biology, which is that all living things have much in common.

Putting the Concept to Work

Identify the kingdom to which you belong.

Figure 1.1 The six kingdoms of life.

Biologists assign all living things to six major categories called *kingdoms*. Each kingdom is profoundly different from the others.

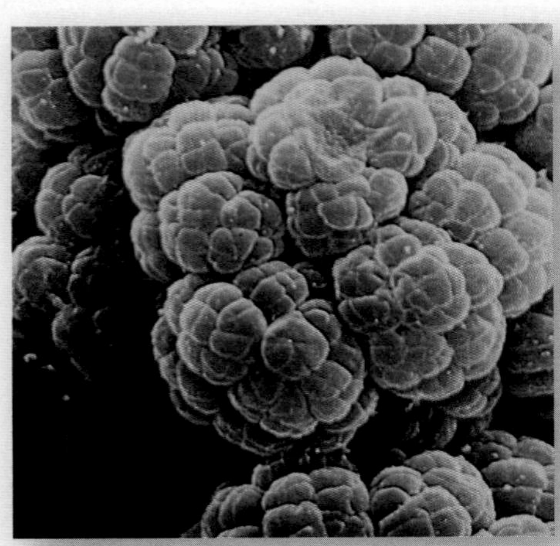

Archaea. This kingdom of prokaryotes (simple cells that do not have nuclei) includes this methanogen, which manufactures methane.

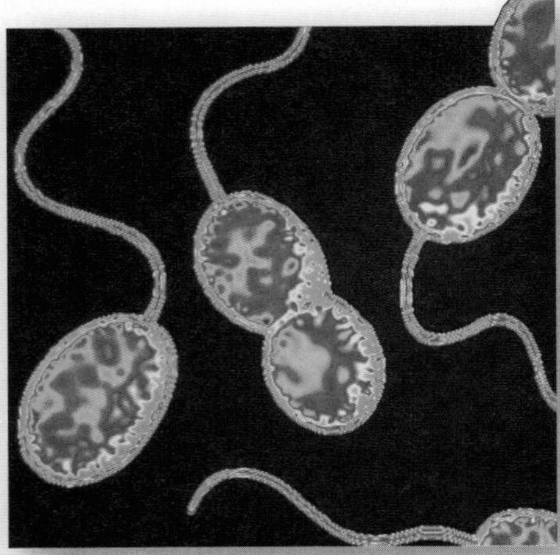

Bacteria. This group is the second of the two prokaryotic kingdoms. Shown here are purple sulfur bacteria, which are able to convert light energy into chemical energy.

Protista. Most of the unicellular eukaryotes (those whose cells contain a nucleus) are grouped into this kingdom, and so are the multicellular algae pictured here.

Fungi. This kingdom contains nonphotosynthetic organisms, mostly multicellular, that digest their food externally, such as these mushrooms.

Plantae. This kingdom contains photosynthetic multicellular organisms that are primarily terrestrial, such as the flowering plant pictured here.

Animalia. Organisms in this kingdom are nonphotosynthetic multicellular organisms that digest their food internally, such as this ram.

1.2 Properties of Life

LEARNING OBJECTIVE 1.2.1 Name and describe the five basic properties shared by all living things.

Biology is the study of life—but what does it mean to be alive? What are the properties that define a living organism? This is not as simple a question as it seems because some of the most obvious properties of living organisms are also properties of many nonliving things—for example, *complexity* (a computer is complex), *movement* (clouds move in the sky), and *response to stimulation* (a soap bubble pops if you touch it). To appreciate why these three properties, so common among living things, do not help us define life, imagine a mushroom standing next to a television: The television seems more complex than the mushroom, the picture on the television screen is moving while the mushroom just stands there, and the television responds to a remote control device while the mushroom continues to just stand there—yet it is the mushroom that is alive. All living things share five basic properties:

1. **Cellular organization.** All living things are composed of one (figure 1.2) or more cells. A cell is a tiny compartment with a thin covering called a *membrane*. Some cells have simple interiors, while others are complexly organized, but all are able to grow and reproduce. A human body contains about 10–100 trillion cells (depending on how big you are)—that is a lot, a string 100 trillion centimeters long could wrap around the world 1,600 times!
2. **Metabolism.** All living things use energy. Moving, growing, thinking—everything you do requires energy. Where does all this energy come from? It is captured from sunlight by plants, algae, and certain bacteria through photosynthesis. To get the energy that powers our lives, we extract it from plants or from animals that eat plants or that eat plant-eating animals (figure 1.3). The transfer of energy from one form to another in cells is an example of *metabolism*.
3. **Homeostasis.** While the environment often varies a lot, organisms act to keep their interior conditions relatively constant using a process called *homeostasis*. For example, your body acts to maintain an internal temperature of about 37°C (98.6°F), regardless of how hot or cold the weather might be. Stable internal conditions allow other complex body processes to be better coordinated.
4. **Growth and reproduction.** All living things grow and reproduce. Bacteria increase in size and simply split in two, as often as every 15 minutes. More complex organisms grow by increasing the number of cells and reproduce sexually by producing gametes that combine giving rise to offspring.
5. **Heredity.** All organisms possess a genetic system that is based on a long molecule called *DNA* (*deoxyribonucleic acid*). The information that determines what an individual organism will be like is contained in a code that is dictated by the order of the subunits making up the DNA molecule, just as the order of letters on this page determines the sense of what you are reading. Each set of instructions within the DNA is called a *gene*. DNA is faithfully copied from one generation to the next, and so any change in a gene is preserved and passed on to future generations. The transmission of characteristics from parent to offspring is a process called *heredity*.

Putting the Concept to Work

Explain why complexity, movement, and response to stimuli are not properties that define life.

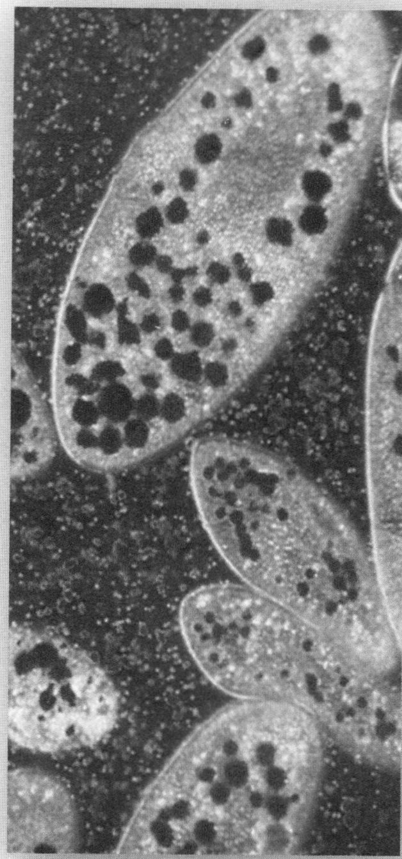

Figure 1.2 Cellular organization.

These paramecia are complex single-celled protists that have just ingested several yeast cells. Like these paramecia, many organisms consist of just a single cell, while others are composed of trillions of cells.

IMPLICATION FOR YOU In your body, bacterial cells outnumber the body's own cells by a 10 to 1 ratio. What do you imagine these billions of bacteria are doing?

Figure 1.3 Metabolism.

This kingfisher obtains the energy it needs to move, grow, and carry out its body processes by eating fish that eat algae. The bird metabolizes this food using chemical processes that occur within cells.

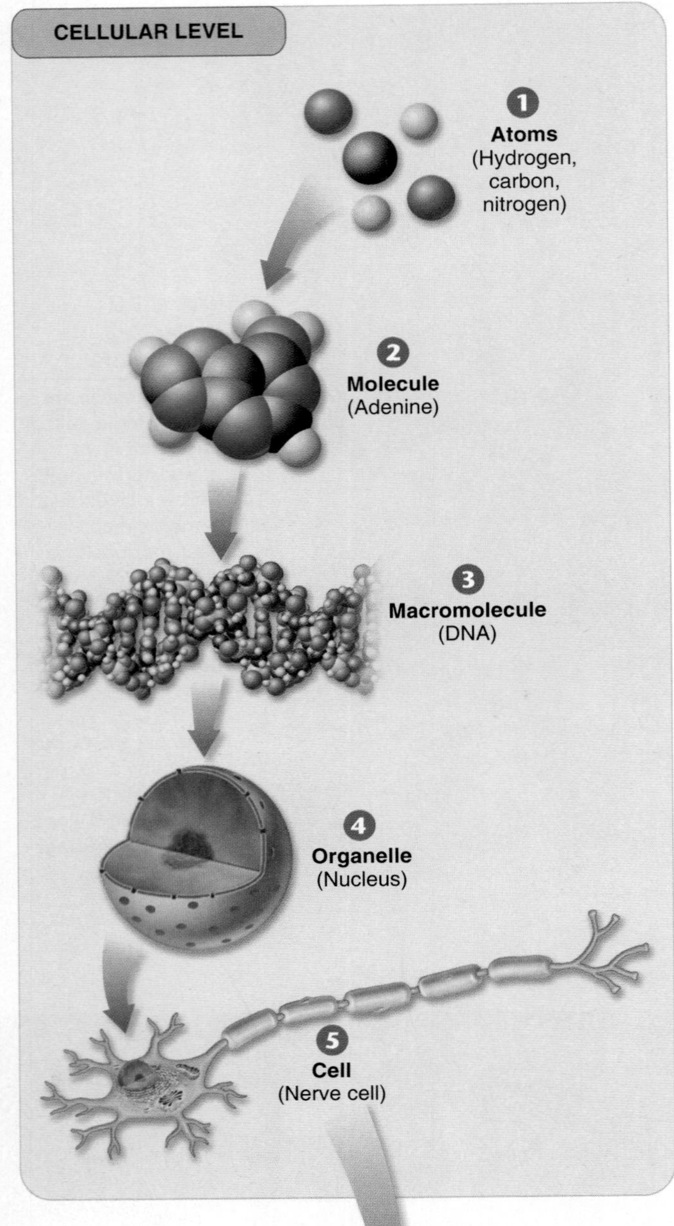

1.3 The Organization of Life

A Hierarchy of Increasing Complexity

LEARNING OBJECTIVE 1.3.1 **List the 13 hierarchical levels of the organization of life, and factor them into three general levels of complexity.**

A key factor in organizing living things is the degree of complexity. We will examine the complexity of life at three levels: cellular, organismal, and populational.

This text follows this hierarchy of increasing complexity. The cellular level is discussed in chapters 2 through 13; the organismal level is discussed in chapters 23 through 33; and the population level is discussed in chapters 14 through 22.

Cellular Level. Following down the first section of figure 1.4, you can see that structures within cells get more and more complex—that there is a *hierarchy* of increasing complexity within cells.

1. **Atoms.** The fundamental elements of matter are atoms.
2. **Molecules.** Atoms are joined together into complex clusters called molecules.
3. **Macromolecules.** Large complex molecules are called macromolecules, such as DNA that stores hereditary information.
4. **Organelles.** Complex biological molecules are assembled into tiny compartments within cells called organelles, such as the nucleus within which the cell's DNA is stored.
5. **Cells.** Organelles and other elements are assembled into membrane-bounded units we call cells. Cells are the smallest level of organization that can be considered alive.

Figure 1.4 Levels of organization.

A traditional and very useful method of sorting through the many ways in which the organisms of the living world interact is to arrange them in terms of levels of organization, proceeding from the very small and simple to the very large and complex. Here we examine organization within the cellular, organismal, and populational levels.

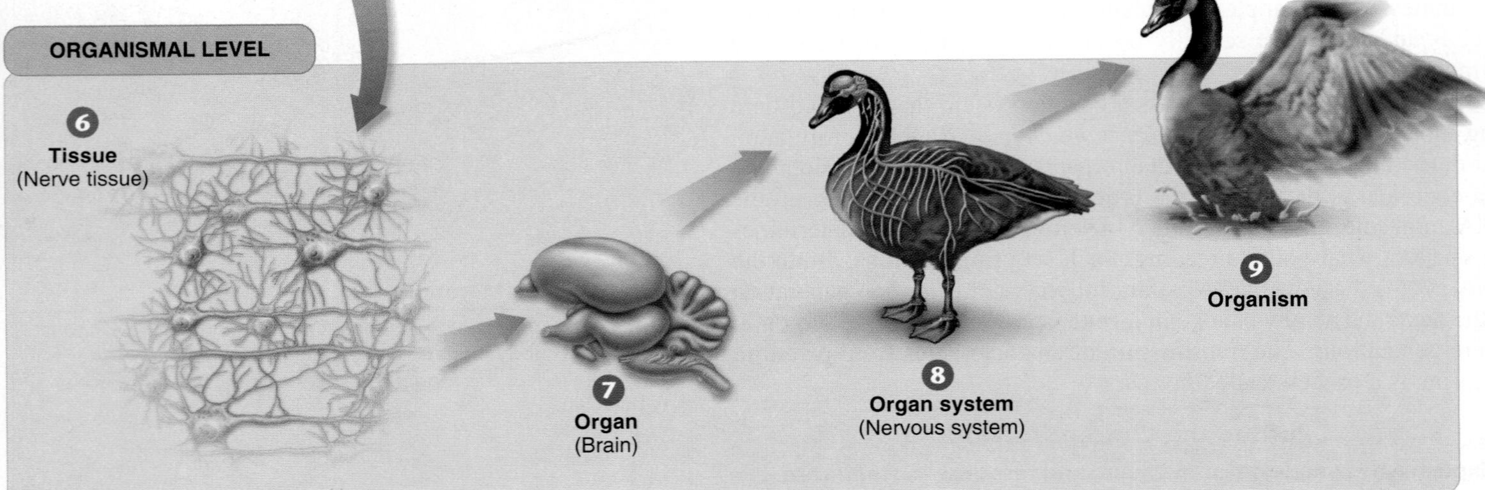

Organismal Level. At the organismal level, in the second section of figure 1.4, cells are organized into four levels of complexity.

6 **Tissues.** The most basic level is that of tissues, which are groups of similar cells that act as a functional unit. Nerve tissue is one kind of tissue, composed of cells called neurons that carry electrical signals.

7 **Organs.** Tissues, in turn, are grouped into organs, which are body structures composed of several different tissues that form a structural and functional unit. Your brain is an organ composed of nerve cells and a variety of tissues that form protective coverings and distribute blood.

8 **Organ systems.** At the third level of organization, organs are grouped into organ systems. The nervous system, for example, consists of sensory organs, the brain and spinal cord, neurons that convey signals throughout the body, and supporting cells.

9 **Organism.** Organ systems function together to form an organism.

Populational Level. Organisms are further organized into several hierarchical levels within the living world, as you can see to the right.

10 **Population.** The most basic of these is the population, which is a group of organisms of the same species living in the same place. A flock of geese living together on a pond is a population.

11 **Species.** All the populations of a particular kind of organism together form a species, its members similar in appearance and able to interbreed. All Canada geese are members of the species *Branta canadensis.* Sandhill cranes are a different species.

12 **Community.** At a higher level of biological organization, a community consists of all the populations of different species living together in one place. Geese, for example, may share their pond with ducks, fish, grasses, and many kinds of insects.

13 **Ecosystem.** At the highest tier of biological organization, a biological community and the soil and water within which it lives together constitute an ecological system, or ecosystem.

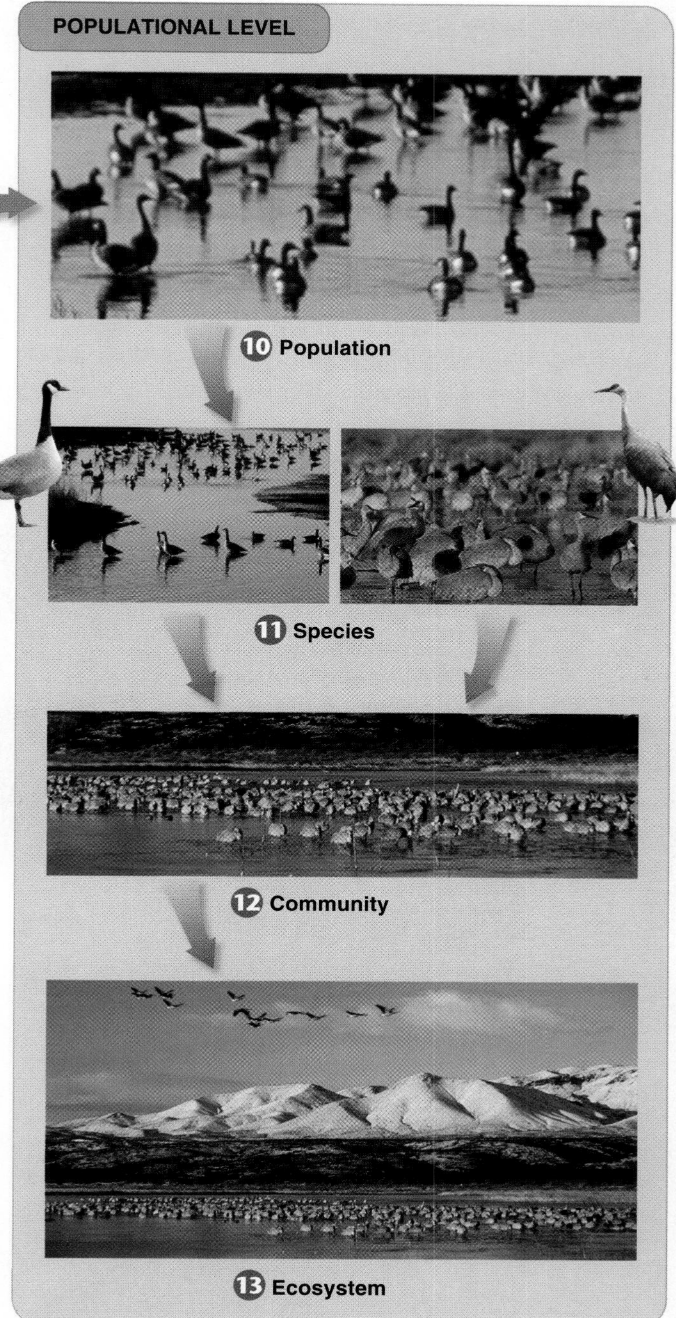

Putting the Concept to Work

The nucleus of one of your skin cells is bounded by a membrane and contains DNA. Why is it not considered to be alive?

Emergent Properties

LEARNING OBJECTIVE 1.3.2 Explain the origin of emergent properties.

At each higher level in the living hierarchy, novel properties emerge, properties that were not present at simpler levels. These **emergent properties** result from the way in which components interact and are the natural consequence of the hierarchy and structural organization of life. Functional properties emerge from more complex organization. Metabolism is an emergent property of life. The chemical reactions within a cell arise from interactions between molecules that are orchestrated by the orderly environment of the cell's interior. Consciousness is an emergent property of the brain that results from the interactions of many neurons in different parts of the brain.

Putting the Concept to Work

Describe an emergent property for each of the three general levels of life's complexity.

EVOLUTION

Computer Games Evolve. In 2008 the designer of the best-selling video game of all time (THE SIMS) unveiled his new creation, SPORE. In this computer game, players experience life unfolding across billions of years, its course guided by evolutionary biology. The game starts with single-celled bacteria living in the ocean, and follows their evolution into intelligent multicelled creatures that populate the land. Based on the mathematics of game theory, SPORE performs a digital version of natural selection, and challenges the player to survive by adapting to a changing world.

1.4 Biological Themes

LEARNING OBJECTIVE 1.4.1 List and explain the five general themes that define biology as a science.

Just as a house is organized into thematic areas such as bedroom, kitchen, and bathroom, so the living world is organized by major *themes,* such as how energy flows within the living world from one part to another. As you study biology in this text, five general themes will emerge repeatedly, themes that serve to both unify and explain biology as a science.

Evolution

Evolution is genetic change in a species over time. Charles Darwin was an English naturalist who, in 1859, proposed the idea that this change is a result of a process called **natural selection.** Simply stated, those organisms whose characteristics make them better able to survive the challenges of their environment live to reproduce, passing their favorable characteristics on to their offspring. Darwin was thoroughly familiar with variation in domesticated animals (in addition to many nondomesticated organisms). He knew that varieties of pigeons could be selected by breeders to exhibit exaggerated characteristics, a process called *artificial selection.* You can see some of these extreme-looking pigeons pictured here. We now know that the characteristics selected are passed on through generations because DNA is transmitted from parent to offspring. Darwin visualized how selection in nature could be similar to that which had produced the different varieties of pigeons. Thus, the many forms of life we see about us on earth today, and the way we ourselves are constructed and function, reflect a long history of natural selection.

The Flow of Energy

All organisms require energy to carry out the activities of living—to build bodies and do work and think thoughts. All of the energy used by most organisms comes from the sun and is passed in one direction through ecosystems. The simplest way to understand the flow of energy through the living world is to look at who uses it. The first stage of energy's journey is its capture by green plants, algae, and some bacteria by the process of photosynthesis. This process uses energy from the sun to synthesize sugars that photosynthetic organisms like plants store in their bodies. Plants then serve as a source of life-driving energy for animals that eat them. Other animals, like the eagle shown here, may then eat the plant eaters. At each stage, some energy is used for the processes of living, some is transferred, and much is lost primarily as heat. The flow of energy is a key factor in shaping ecosystems, affecting how many and what kinds of organisms live in a community.

Cooperation

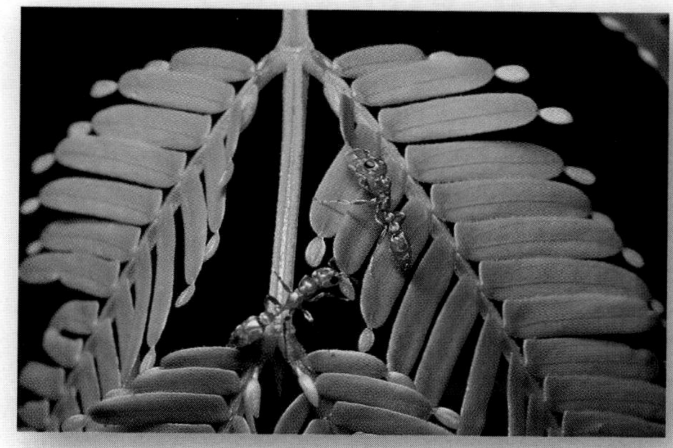

The ants cooperating in the photo on the right protect the plant on which they live from predators and shading by other plants, while the plant returns the favor by providing the ants with nutrients (the yellow structures at the tips of the leaves). This type of cooperation has played a critical role in the evolution of life on earth. For example, organisms of two different species that live in direct contact, like the ants and the plant on which they live, form a type of relationship called **symbiosis.** Many types of cells possess organelles that are the descendants of symbiotic bacteria, and symbiotic fungi helped plants first invade land from the sea. The coevolution of flowering plants and insects—where changes in flowers influenced insect evolution and in turn, changes in insects influenced flower evolution—has been responsible for much of life's great diversity.

Structure Determines Function

One of the most obvious lessons of biology is that biological structures are very well suited to their functions. You will see this at every level of organization: Enzymes, which are macromolecules that cells use to carry out chemical reactions, are precisely structured to match the shapes of the chemicals the enzymes must manipulate. Within the many kinds of organisms in the living world, body structures seem carefully designed to carry out their functions—the long tongue with which the moth to the right sucks nectar from deep inside a flower is one example. The superb fit of structure to function in the living world is no accident. Life has existed on earth for over 2 billion years, a long time for evolution to favor changes that better suit organisms to meet the challenges of living. It should come as no surprise to you that after all this honing and adjustment, biological structures carry out their functions well.

Homeostasis

The high degree of specialization we see among complex organisms is possible only because these organisms act to maintain a relatively stable internal environment, a process introduced earlier called homeostasis. Without this constancy, many of the complex interactions that need to take place within organisms would be impossible. Maintaining homeostasis in a body as complex as yours requires a great deal of signaling back-and-forth between cells. For example, homeostasis often involves water balance to maintain proper blood chemistry. All complex organisms need water—some, like this hippo, luxuriate in it. Others, like the kangaroo rat that lives in arid conditions where water is scarce, obtain water from food and never actually drink.

You will encounter these five biological themes repeatedly in this text. But just as a budding architect must learn more than the parts of buildings, so your study of biology should teach you more than a list of themes, concepts, and parts of organisms. Biology is a dynamic science that will affect your life in many ways, and that lesson is in a very fundamental respect the most important you will learn.

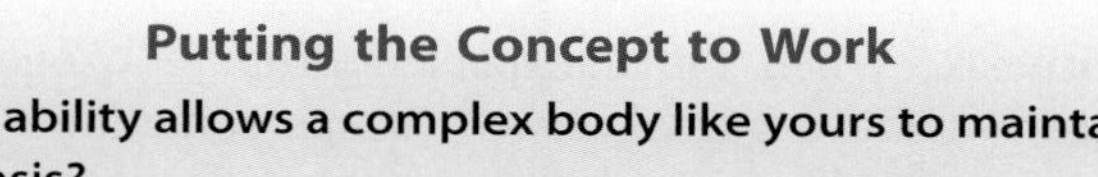

Putting the Concept to Work

What key ability allows a complex body like yours to maintain homeostasis?

The Scientific Process

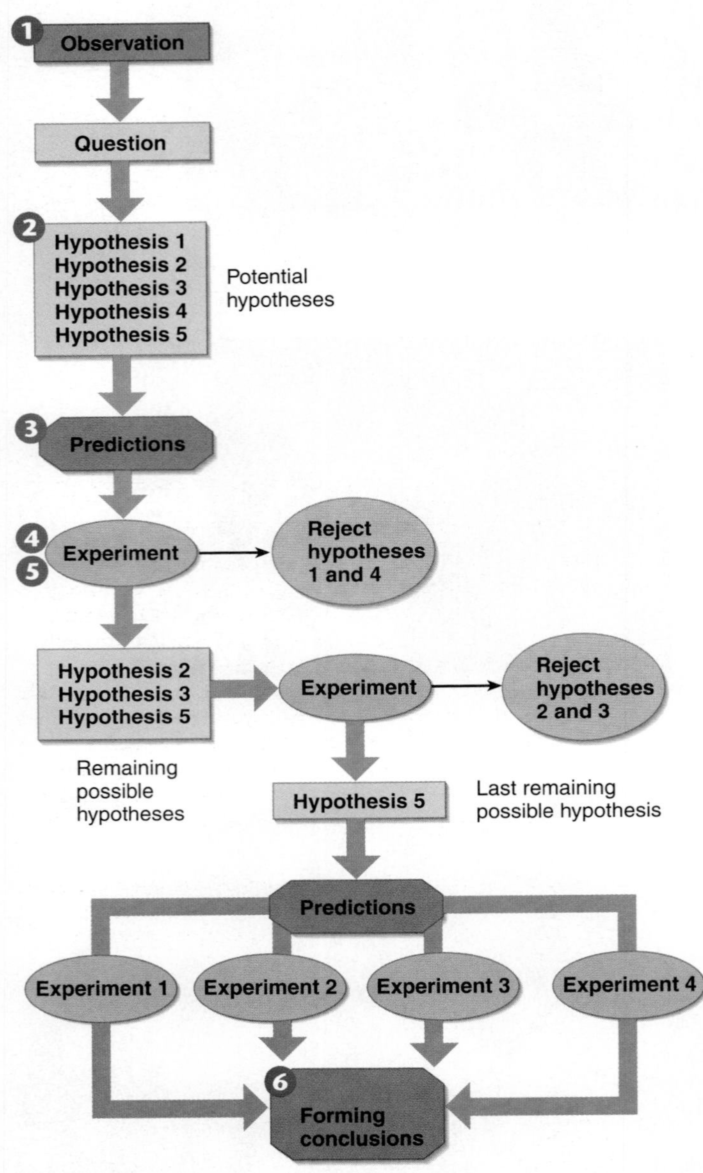

Figure 1.5 The scientific process.

This diagram illustrates the stages of a scientific investigation. First, observations are made that raise a particular question. Then a number of potential explanations (hypotheses) are suggested to answer the question. Next, predictions are made based on the hypotheses, and several rounds of experiments (including control experiments) are carried out in an attempt to eliminate one or more of the hypotheses. Finally, any hypothesis that is not eliminated is retained. Further predictions can be made based on the accepted hypothesis and tested with experiments. If a hypothesis is validated by numerous experiments and stands the test of time, it may eventually become a theory.

1.5 Stages of a Scientific Investigation

LEARNING OBJECTIVE 1.5.1 Explain how the six stages of a scientific investigation allow biologists to discover general principles by careful examination of specific cases.

How Science Is Done

Scientists establish general principles as a way to explain the world around us, but how do scientists determine which general principles are true from among the many that might be? They do this by systematically testing alternative proposals. If these proposals prove inconsistent with experimental observations, they are rejected as untrue. After making careful observations concerning a particular area of science, scientists construct a hypothesis, which is a suggested explanation that accounts for those observations, an "educated guess." A hypothesis is a proposition that might be true. Those hypotheses that have not yet been disproved are retained. They are useful because they fit the known facts, but they are always subject to future rejection in the light of new information.

We call the test of a hypothesis an experiment. To evaluate alternative hypotheses, you would conduct an experiment designed to eliminate one or more of the hypotheses. Note that this does not prove that any of the other hypotheses are true; it merely demonstrates that one of them is not. A successful experiment is one in which one or more of the alternative hypotheses is demonstrated to be inconsistent with the results and is thus rejected.

In this text, you will encounter a great deal of information, often accompanied by explanations. These explanations are hypotheses that have withstood the test of experiment. Many will continue to do so; others will be revised as new observations are made. Biology, like all science, is in a constant state of change, with new ideas appearing and replacing old ones.

The Scientific Process

Scientific investigations can be said to have six stages as illustrated in figure 1.5: ❶ observing what is going on; ❷ forming a set of hypotheses; ❸ making predictions; ❹ testing them and ❺ carrying out controls, until one or more of the hypotheses have been eliminated; and ❻ forming conclusions based on the remaining hypothesis. To better understand how a scientist progresses through these stages, let's examine an actual scientific investigation, the discovery and analysis of the ozone hole.

1. **Observation.** The key to any successful scientific investigation is careful *observation.* Scientists had studied the skies over the Antarctic for many years, noting a thousand details about temperature, light, and levels of chemicals. Had these scientists not kept careful records of what they observed, they might not have noticed that levels of the atmospheric gas ozone were dropping.
2. **Hypothesis.** When the unexpected drop in ozone was reported, scientists made a guess why—perhaps something was destroying the ozone; maybe the culprit was chlorofluorocarbons (CFCs), an industrial chemical used as a coolant in air conditioners, propellants in aerosols, and foaming agents in making Styrofoam. Of course, this

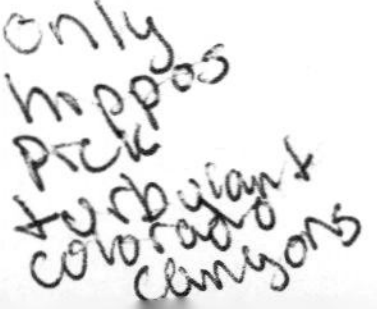

was not a guess in the true sense; scientists had some working knowledge of CFCs and what they might be doing in the upper atmosphere. We call such a guess a **hypothesis.** What the scientists guessed was that chlorine from the breakdown of CFCs was reacting chemically with ozone over the Antarctic (figure 1.6), converting ozone (O_3) into oxygen gas (O_2) and removing the ozone shield from our earth's atmosphere. Often, scientists will form *alternative hypotheses* if they have more than one guess about what they observe. In this case, there were several other hypotheses advanced to explain the ozone hole. One suggestion explained it as a normal consequence of the spinning of the earth, the ozone spinning away from the polar regions much as water spins away from the center as a clothes washer moves through its spin cycle. Another hypothesis was that the ozone hole was simply due to sunspots, and would soon disappear.

3. **Predictions.** If the CFC hypothesis is correct, then several consequences can reasonably be expected. We call these expected consequences *predictions.* A prediction is what you expect to happen if a hypothesis is true. The CFC hypothesis predicts that if CFCs are responsible for producing the ozone hole, then it should be possible to detect CFCs in the upper Antarctic atmosphere as well as the chlorine released from CFCs that attack the ozone.
4. **Testing.** Scientists set out to test the CFC hypothesis by attempting to verify some of its predictions. We call the test of a hypothesis an *experiment.* To test the hypothesis, atmospheric samples were collected from the stratosphere over 6 miles up by a high-altitude balloon. Analysis of the samples revealed the presence of CFCs, as predicted. Were the CFCs interacting with the ozone? The samples contained free chlorine and fluorine, confirming the breakdown of CFC molecules. The results of the experiment thus support the hypothesis.
5. **Controls.** Events in the upper atmosphere can be influenced by many factors. We call each factor that might influence a process a **variable.** To evaluate alternative hypotheses about one variable, all the other variables must be kept constant so that we do not get misled or confused by these other influences. This is done by carrying out two experiments in parallel: In the first experimental test, we alter one variable in a known way to test a particular hypothesis; in the second, called a *control experiment,* we do *not* alter that variable. In all other respects, the two experiments are the same. To further test the CFC hypothesis, scientists carried out control laboratory experiments in which they detected no drop in ozone levels in the absence of CFCs. The result of the control was consistent with the predictions of the hypothesis.
6. **Conclusion.** A hypothesis that has been tested and not rejected is tentatively accepted. The hypothesis that CFCs released into the atmosphere are destroying the earth's protective ozone shield is now supported by a great deal of experimental evidence and is widely accepted. A collection of related hypotheses that have been tested many times and not rejected is called a **theory.** A theory indicates a higher degree of certainty; however, in science, nothing is "certain." For example, the theory of the ozone shield—that ozone in the upper atmosphere shields the earth's surface from harmful UV rays by absorbing them—is supported by a wealth of observation and experimentation and is widely accepted.

Putting the Concept to Work

If no theory is certain, can you propose a future discovery that if confirmed would disprove the theory of the ozone shield?

Figure 1.6 Living under the ozone hole.

These Adelie penguins share many properties with you and all living things. Their bodies are made up of cells, just as your body is. They have families, with offspring that resemble their parents, just as your parents do. They grow by eating, as you do, although their diet is limited to fish and krill they catch in the cold Antarctic waters. The sky above them shields them from the sun's harmful UV radiation, just as the sky above you shields you. Not in the summer, however. In the Antarctic summer an "ozone hole" appears, depleting the ozone above these penguins and exposing them to the danger of UV radiation. It appears that human activities far to their north are having a serious impact on the environment of these penguins.

IMPLICATION FOR YOU If the ozone hole above these penguins extends only over Antarctica (and sometimes the tip of South America), why should people living in the United States worry about it?

BIOLOGY & YOU

Ozone Therapy. Ozone is claimed by some to have remarkable healing properties and holistic health benefits. For example, it is asserted that ozone inhibits the growth of lung and breast cancer cells. Like other claims of health benefits, this claim is widely discounted by the medical community. Most states prohibit the medical use of ozone and consider the marketing of ozone generators as dangerous (ozone has toxic effects on the lungs) and providing no medical benefit.

The theory that the Earth was flat—the idea that the Earth was flat was generally accepted until about 330 B.C. when Aristotle provided observational evidence for a spherical Earth using constellations. About 100 years later Eratosthenes provided quantitative evidence by estimating the circumference of the Earth.

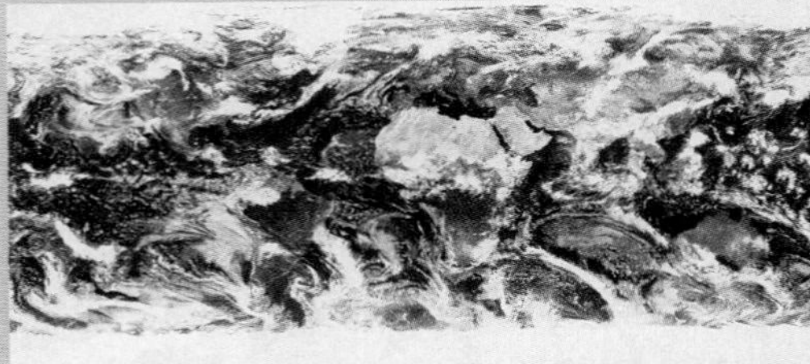

The theory that the sun circles Earth—this geocentric view of the universe was accepted as fact until Copernicus first proposed a sun-centered solar system in the 16th century, which was supported by quantitative evidence in the early 1600s by Galileo.

The theory of creationism—this explanation of the origin and diversity of life on Earth following the account presented in the Bible was widely accepted, although other explanations that proposed that life evolved on Earth were also put forth. The theory of creationism was questioned and then dispelled in 1859, when Charles Darwin proposed an explanation for evolution, a process called natural selection, which is the widely accepted scientific explanation of the origin and diversity of life on Earth.

The theory of acquired traits—Jean-Baptiste Lamarck, a predecessor of Darwin, proposed an explanation of evolution. He stated that traits were acquired during one's life and were then passed on to offspring. Darwin later proposed the explanation of natural selection as the driving force of evolution.

The hypothesis of cold nuclear fusion—the experimental results that led to this hypothesis, that nuclear reactions could be performed at near room temperature and pressure, were presented in 1989. The results could have revolutionized the energy industry, but the results could not be duplicated and widespread support for the hypothesis never developed.

Figure 1.7 Rejected theories.

To illustrate how experimentation changes scientific thought, consider these scientific theories that were once accepted as true, but have since been rejected.

IMPLICATION FOR YOU The theory of global warming was controversial when first proposed, but has gained widespread support in recent years. How has the acceptance of this theory affected your own life, or has it?

1.6 Theory and Certainty

LEARNING OBJECTIVE 1.6.1 Define hypothesis and theory, and distinguish between them.

A theory is a unifying explanation for a broad range of observations. Thus, we speak of the theory of gravity, the theory of evolution, and the theory of the atom. Theories are the solid ground of science, that of which we are the most certain. However, there is no absolute truth in science, only varying degrees of uncertainty. A scientist's acceptance of a theory is always provisional, because the possibility always remains that future evidence will cause a theory to be revised; some "once-accepted" theories are discussed in figure 1.7.

The word "theory" is thus used very differently by scientists than by the general public. To a scientist, a theory represents that of which he or she is most certain; to the general public, the word theory implies a *lack* of knowledge or a guess. How often have you heard someone say, "It's only a theory!"? As you can imagine, confusion often results. In this text the word theory will always be used in its scientific sense, in reference to a generally accepted scientific principle.

The Scientific "Method"

It was once fashionable to claim that scientific progress is the result of applying a series of steps called the *scientific method;* that is, a series of logical "either/or" predictions tested by experiments to reject one alternative. The assumption was that trial-and-error testing would inevitably lead one through the maze of uncertainty that always slows scientific progress. If this were indeed true, a computer would make a good scientist—but science is not done this way! If you ask successful scientists how they do their work, you will discover that without exception they design their experiments with a pretty fair idea of how they will come out. Environmental scientists understood the chemistry of chlorine and ozone when they formulated the CFC hypothesis, and they could imagine how the chlorine in CFCs would attack ozone molecules. A hypothesis that a successful scientist tests is not just any hypothesis. Rather, it is a "hunch" or educated guess in which the scientist integrates all that he or she knows, in an attempt to get a sense of what *might* be true. It is because insight and imagination play such a large role that some scientists are so much better at science than others—just as Beethoven and Mozart stand out among composers.

The Limitations of Science

Scientific study is limited to organisms and processes that we are able to observe and measure. Supernatural and religious hypotheses are beyond the realm of scientific analysis because they cannot be scientifically studied, analyzed, or explained. Supernatural hypotheses can be used to explain any result, and cannot be disproven by experiment or observation. Scientists in their work are limited to objective interpretations of observable phenomena.

A nonscientific argument called Intelligent Design has been suggested as an alternative to evolution. The ability to study and test this argument versus a scientific one is discussed in chapter 14 on pages 264-265.

Putting the Concept to Work

Why don't computers, which are good at trial-and-error testing, make good scientists?

Where Are All My Socks Going?

All my life, for as far back as I can remember, I have been losing socks. Not pairs of socks, mind you, but single socks. I first became aware of this peculiar phenomenon when as a young man I went away to college. When Thanksgiving rolled around that first year, I brought an enormous duffle bag of laundry home. My mother, instead of braining me, dumped the lot into the washer and dryer, and so discovered what I had not noticed—that few of my socks matched anymore.

That was over forty years ago, but it might as well have been yesterday. All my life, I have continued to lose socks. This last Christmas I threw out a sock drawer full of socks that didn't match, and took advantage of sales to buy a dozen pairs of brand-new ones. Last week, when I did a body count, three of the new pairs had lost a sock!

Enough. I set out to solve the mystery of the missing socks. How? The way Sherlock Holmes would have, scientifically. Holmes worked by eliminating those possibilities that he found not to be true. A scientist calls possibilities "hypotheses" and, like Sherlock, rejects those that do not fit the facts. Sherlock tells us that when only one possibility remains unrejected, then—however unlikely—it must be true.

Hypothesis 1: It's the socks. I have four pairs of socks bought as Christmas gifts but forgotten until recently. Deep in my sock drawer, they have remained undisturbed for five months. If socks disappear because of some intrinsic property (say the manufacturer has somehow designed them to disappear to generate new sales), then I could expect at least one of these undisturbed ones to have left the scene by now. However, when I looked, all four pairs were complete. Undisturbed socks don't disappear. Thus I reject the hypothesis that the problem is caused by the socks themselves.

Hypothesis 2: Transformation, a fanciful suggestion by science fiction writer Avram Davidson in his 1958 story "Or All the Seas with Oysters" that I cannot get out of the quirky corner of my mind. I discard the socks I have worn each evening in a laundry basket in my closet. Over many years, I have noticed a tendency for socks I have placed in the closet to disappear. Over that same long period, as my socks are disappearing, there is something in my closet that seems to multiply—COAT HANGERS! Socks are larval coat hangers! To test this outlandish hypothesis, I had only to move the laundry basket out of the closet. Several months later, I was still losing socks, so this hypothesis is rejected.

Hypothesis 3: Static cling. The missing single socks may have been hiding within the sleeves of sweat shirts or jackets, inside trouser legs, or curled up within seldom-worn garments. Rubbing around in the dryer, socks can garner quite a bit of static electricity, easily enough to cause them to cling to other garments. Socks adhering to the outside of a shirt or pant leg are soon dislodged, but ones that find themselves within a sleeve, leg, or fold may simply stay there, not "lost" so much as misplaced. However, after a diligent search, I did not run across any previously lost socks hiding in the sleeves of my winter garments or other seldom-worn items, so I reject this hypothesis.

Hypothesis 4: I lose my socks going to or from the laundry. Perhaps in handling the socks from laundry basket to the washer/dryer and back to my sock drawer, a sock is occasionally lost. To test this hypothesis, I have pawed through the laundry coming into the washer. No single socks. Perhaps the socks are lost after doing the laundry, during folding or transport from laundry to sock drawer. If so, there should be no single socks coming out of the dryer. But there are! The singletons are first detected among the dry laundry, before folding. Thus I eliminate the hypothesis that the problem arises from mishandling the laundry. It seems the problem is in the laundry room.

Hypothesis 5: I lose them during washing. Perhaps the washing machine is somehow "eating" my socks. I looked in the washing machine to see if a sock could get trapped inside, or chewed up by the machine, but I can see no possibility. The clothes slosh around in a closed metal container with water passing in and out through little holes no wider than a pencil. No sock could slip through such a hole. There is a thin gap between the rotating cylinder and the top of the washer through which an errant sock might escape, but my socks are too bulky for this route. So I eliminate the hypothesis that the washing machine is the culprit.

Hypothesis 6: I lose them during drying. Perhaps somewhere in the drying process socks are being lost. I stuck my head in our clothes dryer to see if I could see any socks, and I couldn't. However, as I look, I can see a place a sock could go—behind the drying wheel! A clothes dryer is basically a great big turning cylinder with dry air blowing through the middle. The edges of the turning cylinder don't push hard against the side of the machine. Just maybe, every once in a while, a sock might get pulled through, sucked into the back of the machine.

To test this hypothesis, I should take the back of the dryer off and look inside to see if it is stuffed with my missing socks. My wife, knowing my mechanical abilities, is not in favor of this test. Thus, until our dryer dies and I can take it apart, I shall not be able to reject hypothesis 6. Lacking any other likely hypothesis, I take Sherlock Holmes' advice and tentatively conclude that the dryer is the culprit.

Core Ideas of Biology

Figure 1.8 Life in a drop of pond water.

All organisms are composed of cells. Some organisms, including these protists, are single celled, while others, such as plants, animals, and fungi, consist of many cells.

1.7 Four Theories Unify Biology as a Science

The Cell Theory: Organization of Life

LEARNING OBJECTIVE 1.7.1 State the cell theory, and describe how it was formulated in stages.

All organisms are composed of cells, life's basic units. Cells were discovered by Robert Hooke in England in 1665. Hooke was using one of the first microscopes, one that magnified 30 times. Looking through a thin slice of cork, he observed many tiny chambers, which reminded him of monks' cells in a monastery. Not long after that, the Dutch scientist Anton van Leeuwenhoek used microscopes capable of magnifying 300 times, and discovered an amazing world of single-celled life in a drop of pond water like you see in **figure 1.8**. In 1839, the German biologists Matthias Schleiden and Theodor Schwann, summarizing a large number of observations by themselves and others, concluded that all living organisms consist of cells. Their conclusion forms the basis of what has come to be known as the *cell theory*. Later, biologists added the idea that all cells come from other cells. The cell theory, one of the basic ideas in biology, is the foundation for understanding the reproduction and growth of all organisms. You will learn much more about cells in chapter 4.

Putting the Concept to Work

Why was it not possible to develop the cell theory until the end of the 17th century?

The Gene Theory: Molecules and Inheritance

LEARNING OBJECTIVE 1.7.2 State the gene theory, and define the term *gene*.

Even the simplest cell is incredibly complex, more intricate than a computer. The information that specifies what a cell is like—its detailed plan—is encoded in a long cablelike molecule called **DNA** (**deoxyribonucleic acid**). Each DNA molecule is formed from two long chains of building blocks, called nucleotides, wound around each other. You can see in **figure 1.9** that the two chains face each other, like two lines of people holding hands. The chains contain information in the same way this sentence does—as a sequence of letters. There are four different nucleotides in DNA (symbolized as A, T, C, and G in the figure), and the sequence in which they occur encodes the information. Specific sequences of several hundred to many thousand nucleotides make up a *gene*, a discrete unit of hereditary information. All organisms encode their genes in strands of DNA. The *gene theory*, illustrated in **figure 1.10**, states that the proteins and RNA molecules encoded by an organism's genes determine what it will be like. Genes are the subject of chapters 12 and 13.

How DNA functions in the cell is directly related to its structure and is discussed in detail in chapter 3, pages 56 and 57 and again in chapter 11, page 192.

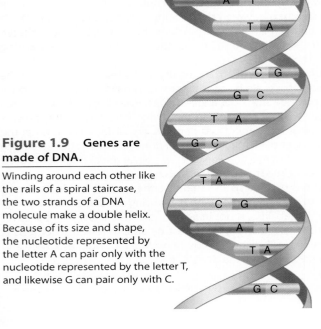

Figure 1.9 Genes are made of DNA.

Winding around each other like the rails of a spiral staircase, the two strands of a DNA molecule make a double helix. Because of its size and shape, the nucleotide represented by the letter A can pair only with the nucleotide represented by the letter T, and likewise G can pair only with C.

Putting the Concept to Work

Do you imagine that all the cells of an organism contain the same genes? If so, how can its body have different kinds of cells?

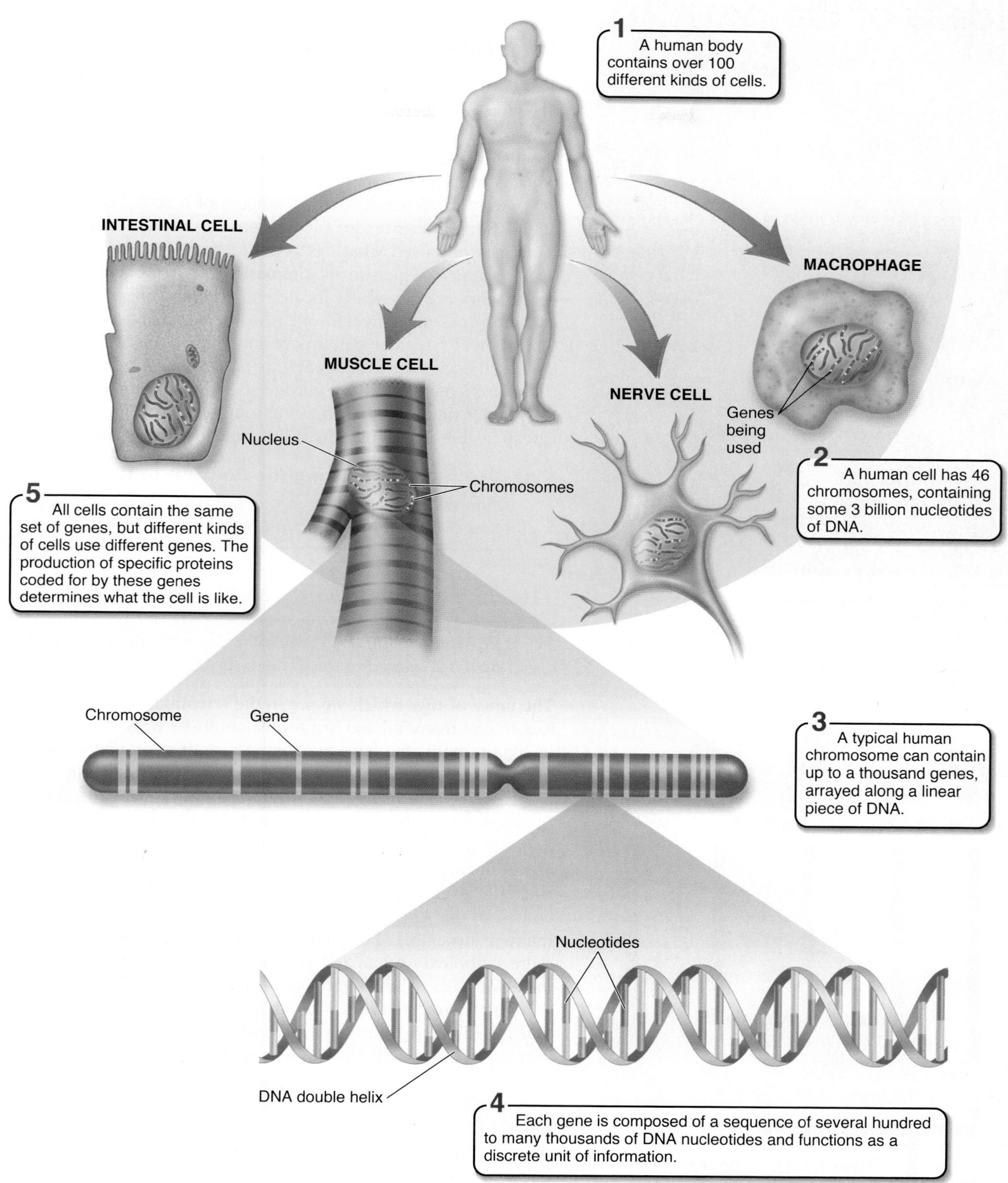
1
A human body contains over 100 different kinds of cells.
INTESTINAL CELL
MUSCLE CELL
NERVE CELL
MACROPHAGE
Genes being used
Nucleus
Chromosomes
2
A human cell has 46 chromosomes, containing some 3 billion nucleotides of DNA.
5
All cells contain the same set of genes, but different kinds of cells use different genes. The production of specific proteins coded for by these genes determines what the cell is like.
Chromosome
Gene
3
A typical human chromosome can contain up to a thousand genes, arrayed along a linear piece of DNA.
Nucleotides
DNA double helix
4
Each gene is composed of a sequence of several hundred to many thousands of DNA nucleotides and functions as a discrete unit of information.

Figure 1.10 The gene theory.

The gene theory states that what an organism is like is determined in large measure by its genes. Here you see how the many kinds of cells in the body of each of us are determined by which genes are used in making each particular kind of cell.

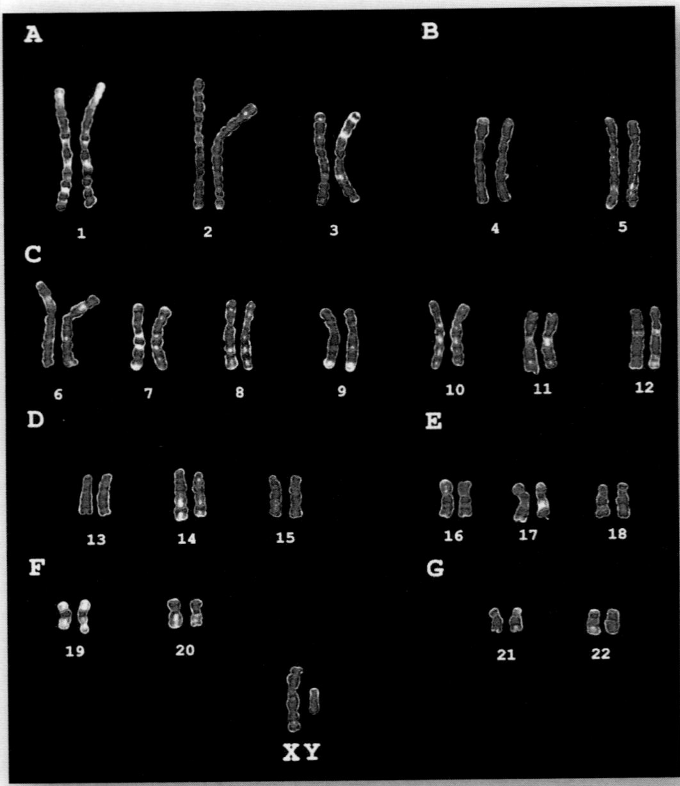

Figure 1.11 Human chromosomes.

The chromosomal theory of inheritance states that genes are located on chromosomes. This human karyotype (an ordering of chromosomes) shows banding patterns on chromosomes that represent clusters of genes.

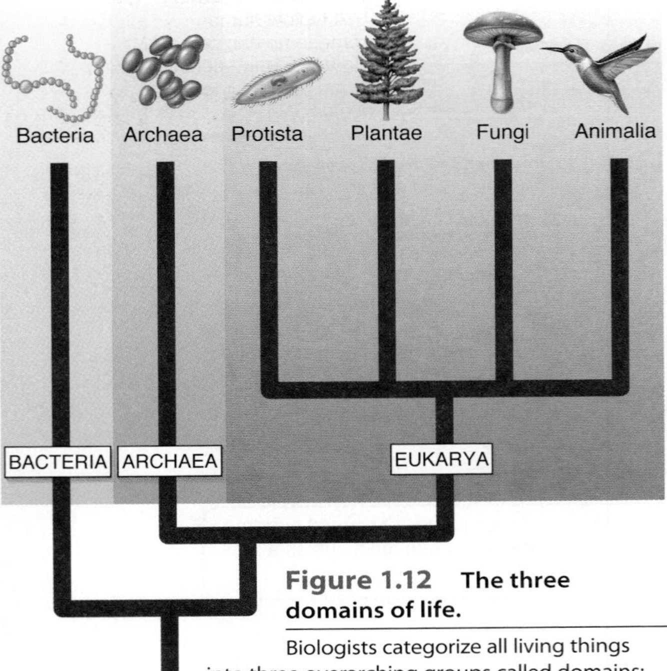

Figure 1.12 The three domains of life.

Biologists categorize all living things into three overarching groups called domains: Bacteria, Archaea, and Eukarya. Domain Bacteria contains the kingdom Bacteria, and domain Archaea contains the kingdom Archaea. Domain Eukarya is composed of four more kingdoms: Protista, Plantae, Fungi, and Animalia.

The Theory of Heredity: Unity of Life

LEARNING OBJECTIVE 1.7.3 State the theory of heredity and explain how it is related to the chromosomal theory of inheritance.

The storage of hereditary information in genes composed of DNA is common to all living things. The *theory of heredity* first advanced by Gregor Mendel in 1865 states that the genes of an organism are inherited as discrete units. A triumph of experimental science developed long before genes and DNA were understood, Mendel's theory of heredity is the subject of chapter 10. Soon after Mendel's theory gave rise to the field of genetics, other biologists proposed what has come to be called the *chromosomal theory of inheritance,* which in its simplest form states that the genes of Mendel's theory are physically located on chromosomes, and that it is because chromosomes are parceled out in a regular manner during reproduction that Mendel's regular patterns of inheritance are seen. In modern terms, the two theories state that genes are a component of a cell's chromosomes (like the 23 pairs of human chromosomes you see in figure 1.11), and that the regular duplication of these chromosomes during sexual reproduction is responsible for the pattern of inheritance we call Mendelian segregation.

Putting the Concept to Work

If genes are located on chromosomes, does it necessarily follow that chromosomes contain DNA?

The Theory of Evolution: Diversity of Life

LEARNING OBJECTIVE 1.7.4 State the theory of evolution and how it is related to the gene theory.

The unity of life, which we see in the retention of certain key characteristics among many related life-forms, contrasts with the incredible diversity of living things that have evolved. These diverse organisms are sorted by biologists into six kingdoms, as you learned in section 1.1. Organisms placed in the same kingdom have in common some general characteristics. In recent years, biologists have added a classification level above kingdoms, based on fundamental differences in cell structure. The six kingdoms are each now assigned into one of three great groups called *domains:* Bacteria, Archaea, and Eukarya (figure 1.12). Bacteria and Archaea each consist of one kingdom of prokaryotes (single-celled organisms with little internal structure). Four more kingdoms composed of organisms with more complexly-organized cells are placed within the domain Eukarya, the eukaryotes. The kingdoms of life are discussed in detail in chapter 15.

The **theory of evolution,** advanced by Charles Darwin in 1859, attributes the diversity of the living world to natural selection. Those organisms best able to respond to the challenges of living will leave more offspring, he argued, and thus their traits become more common in the population. It is because the world offers diverse opportunities that it contains so many different life-forms. Today scientists can decipher all the genes (the genome) of an organism. One of the great triumphs of science in the century and a half since Darwin is the detailed understanding of how Darwin's theory of evolution is related to the gene theory—of how changes in life's diversity result from changes in individual genes (figure 1.13).

Putting the Concept to Work

Of what domain are you a member?

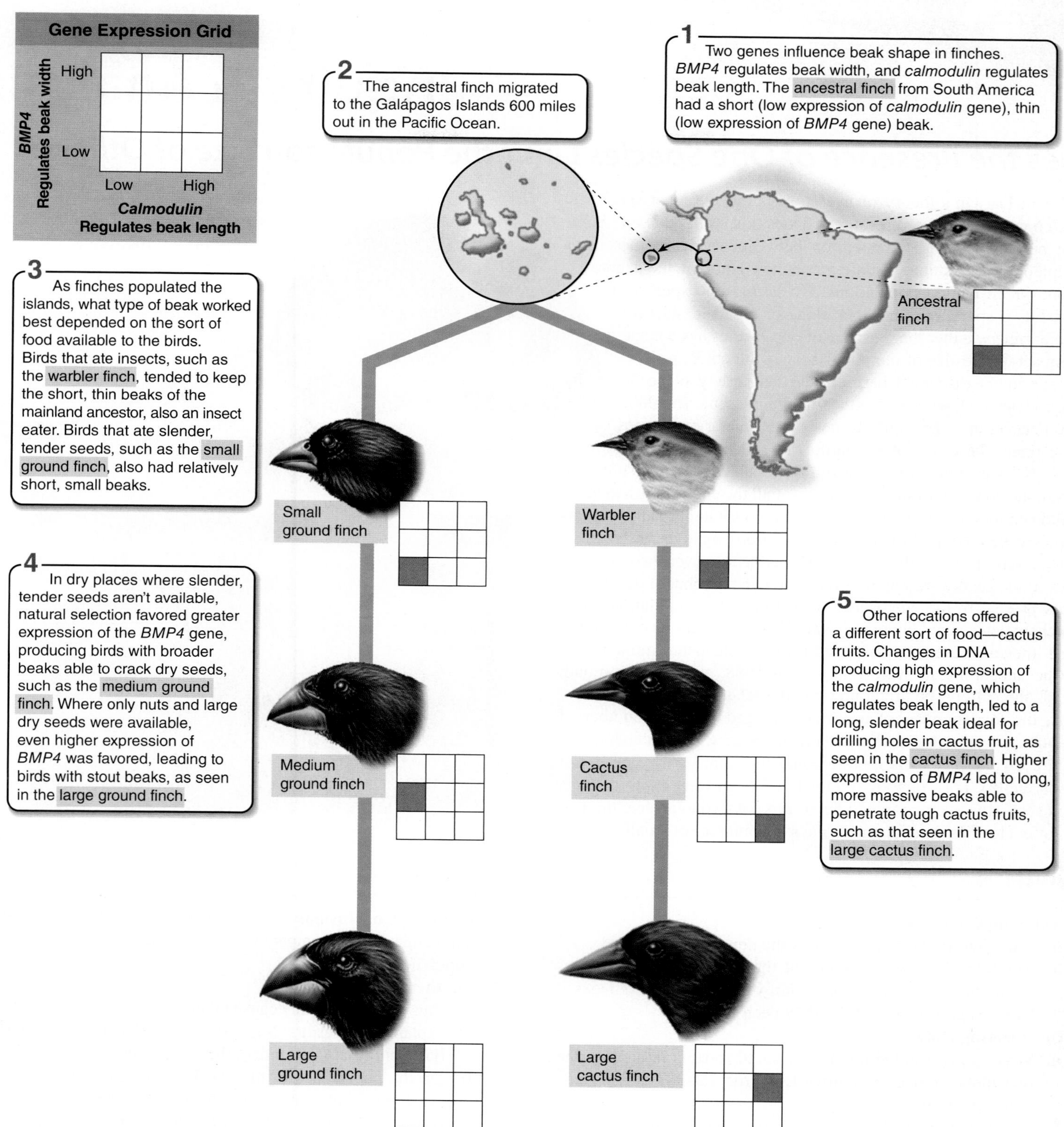

Gene Expression Grid
BMP4
Regulates beak width
High
Low
Low
High
Calmodulin
Regulates beak length
1 Two genes influence beak shape in finches. BMP4 regulates beak width, and calmodulin regulates beak length. The ancestral finch from South America had a short (low expression of calmodulin gene), thin (low expression of BMP4 gene) beak.
2 The ancestral finch migrated to the Galápagos Islands 600 miles out in the Pacific Ocean.
Ancestral finch
3 As finches populated the islands, what type of beak worked best depended on the sort of food available to the birds. Birds that ate insects, such as the warbler finch, tended to keep the short, thin beaks of the mainland ancestor, also an insect eater. Birds that ate slender, tender seeds, such as the small ground finch, also had relatively short, small beaks.
Small ground finch
Warbler finch
4 In dry places where slender, tender seeds aren't available, natural selection favored greater expression of the BMP4 gene, producing birds with broader beaks able to crack dry seeds, such as the medium ground finch. Where only nuts and large dry seeds were available, even higher expression of BMP4 was favored, leading to birds with stout beaks, as seen in the large ground finch.
5 Other locations offered a different sort of food—cactus fruits. Changes in DNA producing high expression of the calmodulin gene, which regulates beak length, led to a long, slender beak ideal for drilling holes in cactus fruit, as seen in the cactus finch. Higher expression of BMP4 led to long, more massive beaks able to penetrate tough cactus fruits, such as that seen in the large cactus finch.
Medium ground finch
Cactus finch
Large ground finch
Large cactus finch

Figure 1.13 The theory of evolution.

Darwin's theory of evolution proposes that many forms of a gene may exist among members of a population, and that those members with a form better suited to their particular habitat will tend to reproduce more successfully, and so their traits become more common in the population, a process Darwin dubbed "natural selection." Here you see how this process is thought to have worked on two pivotal genes that helped generate the diversity of finches on the Galápagos Islands, visited by Darwin in 1831 on his round-the-world voyage on HMS *Beagle*. This example of evolution was a key to Darwin's thinking. The way in which modern knowledge of genes has expanded our understanding of evolution among Darwin's finches is examined in greater detail in chapter 14.

Inquiry & Analysis

Does the Presence of One Species Limit the Population Size of Others?

Implicit in Darwin's theory of evolution is the idea that species in nature compete for limited resources. Does this really happen? Some of the best evidence of competition between species comes from experimental field studies, studies conducted not in the laboratory but out in natural populations. By setting up experiments in which two species occur either alone or together, scientists can determine whether the presence of one species has a negative impact on the size of the population of the other species. The experiment discussed here concerns a variety of seed-eating rodents that occur in North American deserts. In 1988, researchers set up a series of 50-meter × 50-meter enclosures to investigate the effect of kangaroo rats on smaller seed-eating rodents. Kangaroo rats were removed from half of the enclosures, but not from the other enclosures. The walls of all the enclosures had holes that allowed rodents to come and go, but in plots without kangaroo rats the holes were too small to allow the kangaroo rats to enter.

The graph to the right displays data collected over the course of the next three years as researchers monitored the number of the smaller rodents present in the enclosures. To estimate the population sizes, researchers determined how many small rodents could be captured in a fixed interval. Data were collected for each enclosure immediately after the kangaroo rats were removed in 1988, and at three-month intervals thereafter. The graph presents the relative population size—that is, the total number of captures averaged over the number of enclosures (an **average** is the numerical mean value, calculated by adding a list of values and then dividing this sum by the number of items in the list. For example, if a total of 30 rats were captured from 3 enclosures, the average would be 10 rats). As you can see, the two kinds of enclosures do not contain the same number of small rodents.

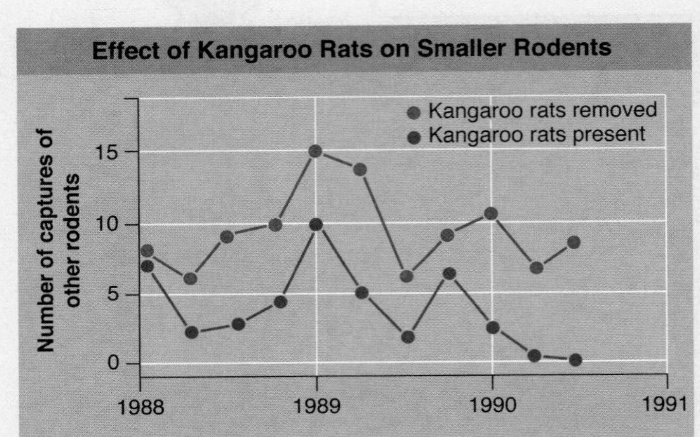

Analysis

1. **Applying Concepts**
   a. **Variable.** In the graph, what is the dependent variable?
   b. **Relative Magnitude.** Which of the two kinds of enclosures maintains the highest population of small rodents? Does it have kangaroo rats or have they been removed?
2. **Interpreting Data**
   a. What is the average number of small rodents in each of the two plots immediately after kangaroo rats were removed? After one year? After two?
   b. At what point is the difference between the two kinds of enclosures the greatest?
3. **Making Inferences**
   a. What precisely is the observed impact of kangaroo rats on the population size of small rodents?
   b. Examine the magnitude of the difference between the number of small rodents in the two plots. Is there a trend?
4. **Drawing Conclusions** Do these results support the hypothesis that kangaroo rats compete with other small rodents to limit their population sizes?
5. **Further Analysis**
   a. Can you think of any cause other than competition that would explain these results? Suggest an experiment that could potentially eliminate or confirm this alternative.
   b. Do the populations of the two kinds of enclosures change in synchrony (that is, grow and shrink at the same times) over the course of a year? If so, why might this happen? How would you test this hypothesis?

Summary of Learning Outcomes

Biology and the Living World

The Diversity of Life

1.1.1 Biology is the study of life. While the living world is astonishingly diverse, all living organisms share common characteristics. Organisms are categorized by biologists into six groups called kingdoms. The six kingdoms are Bacteria, Archaea, Protista, Fungi, Plantae, and Animalia.

Properties of Life

1.2.1 All living organisms share five basic properties:

Cellular organization: All living organisms are composed of cells.

Metabolism: All living organisms, like the kingfisher shown here from figure 1.3, use energy.

Homeostasis: All living organisms maintain stable internal conditions.

Growth and reproduction: All living organisms grow in size and reproduce.

Heredity: All living organisms possess genetic information in DNA that determines how each organism looks and functions, and this information is passed on to future generations.

The Organization of Life

1.3.1 Living organisms exhibit increasing levels of complexity within their cells (cellular level), within their bodies (organismal level), and within ecosystems (populational level).

1.3.2 Life's hierarchical organization is responsible for novel emergent properties that characterize the living world. These properties are the natural consequences of ever more complex structural organization.

Biological Themes

1.4.1 Five themes emerge from the study of biology: (1) evolution, (2) the flow of energy, (3) cooperation, (4) structure determines function, and (5) homeostasis.

The Scientific Process

Stages of a Scientific Investigation

1.5.1 In their studies, scientists systematically eliminate hypotheses that are not consistent with observation. Hypotheses are possible explanations that are used to form predictions. These predictions are tested experimentally. Some hypotheses are rejected based on experimental results, while others are tentatively accepted.

- Scientific investigations often use a series of stages, called the scientific process, to study a scientific question. These stages are observations, forming hypotheses, making predictions, testing, establishing controls, and drawing conclusions.
- The discovery of the hole in the ozone required careful observations of data collected from the atmosphere. Based on these observations, scientists proposed an explanation of what caused a decrease in the levels of ozone over the Antarctic. This explanation is called a hypothesis. They then formed predictions and tested the hypothesis against controls. The hypothesis that CFCs released into the atmosphere were causing the breakdown of ozone to oxygen gas was supported by the data. Further experimentation allowed scientists to form the conclusion that CFCs were responsible for the loss of ozone over the Antarctic.

Theory and Certainty

1.6.1 Hypotheses that hold up to testing over time are combined into statements called theories. Theories carry a higher degree of certainty, although no theory in science is absolute.

- The process of science was once viewed as a series of "either/or" predictions that were tested experimentally. Now, this discrete series of steps, which used to be referred to as the "scientific method," is often modified to take into account the role of judgment and intuition.
- Science can only study what can be tested experimentally. A hypothesis can be established through science only if it can be tested and potentially disproven.

Core Ideas of Biology

Four Theories Unify Biology as a Science

1.7.1 The cell theory states that all living organisms are composed of cells, which grow and reproduce to form other cells.

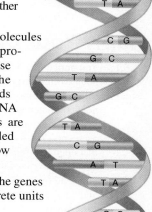

1.7.2 The gene theory states that long molecules of DNA carry instructions for producing cellular components. These instructions are encoded in the nucleotide sequences in the strands of DNA, like this section of DNA from figure 1.9. The nucleotides are organized into discrete units called genes, and the genes determine how an organism looks and functions.

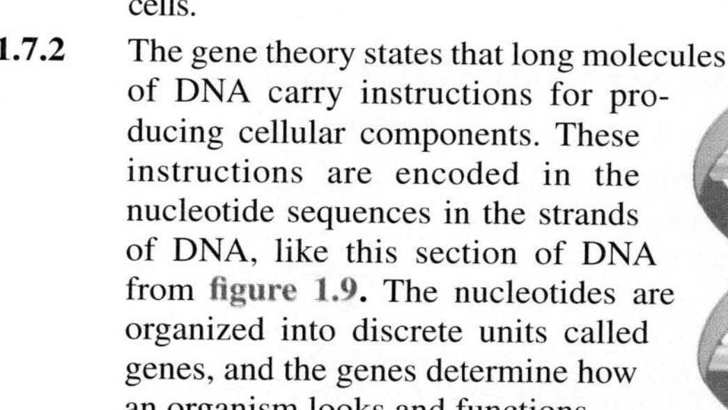

1.7.3 The theory of heredity states that the genes of an organism are passed as discrete units from parent to offspring.

1.7.4 Organisms are organized into kingdoms based on similar characteristics. The organisms within a kingdom show similarities but exhibit differences from those of other kingdoms. The kingdoms are further organized into three major groups called domains based on their cellular characteristics. The three domains are Bacteria, Archaea, and Eukarya.

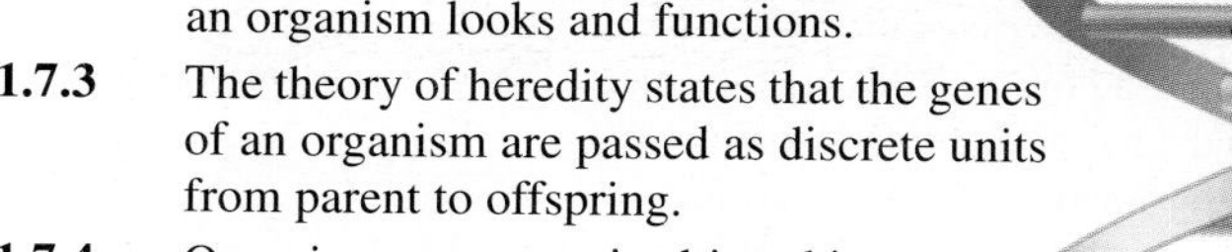

- The theory of evolution states that modifications in genes that are passed from parent to offspring result in changes in future generations. Today's biological diversity is the product of a long evolutionary journey.

Test Your Understanding

1.1.1 Biologists categorize all living things based on related characteristics into large groups, called
a. kingdoms.
b. species.
c. populations.
d. ecosystems.

1.2.1 Living things can be distinguished from nonliving things because they have
a. complexity.
b. movement.
c. cellular organization.
d. response to a stimulus.

1.3.1 Living things are organized. Choose the answer that illustrates this organization and that is arranged from smallest to largest.
a. cell, atom, molecule, tissue, organelle, organ, organ system, organism, population, species, community, ecosystem
b. atom, molecule, organelle, cell, tissue, organ, organ system, organism, population, species, community, ecosystem
c. atom, molecule, organelle, cell, tissue, organ, organ system, organism, community, population, species, ecosystem
d. atom, molecule, cell wall, cell, organ, organelle, organism, species, population, community, ecosystem

1.3.2 At each level in the hierarchy of living things, properties occur that were not present at the simpler levels. These are referred to as
a. novelistic properties.
b. complex properties.
c. incremental properties.
d. emergent properties.

1.4.1 The five general biological themes are
a. evolution, energy flow, competition, structure determines function, and homeostasis.
b. evolution, energy flow, cooperation, structure determines function, and homeostasis.
c. evolution, growth, competition, structure determines function, and homeostasis.
d. evolution, growth, cooperation, structure determines function, and homeostasis.

1.5.1 When trying to figure out explanations for observations, you usually construct a series of possible hypotheses. Then you make predictions of what will happen if each hypothesis is true, and
a. test each hypothesis, using appropriate controls, to determine which hypothesis is true.
b. test each hypothesis, using appropriate controls, to rule out as many as possible.
c. use logic to determine which hypothesis is most likely true.
d. reject those that seem unlikely.

1.5.1 Which of the following is correct regarding a hypothesis?
a. After sufficient testing, you can conclude that it is true.
b. If it explains the observations, it doesn't need to be tested.
c. After sufficient testing, you can accept it as probable, being aware that it may be revised or rejected in the future.
d. You never have any degree of certainty that it is true; there are too many variables.

1.7.1 Cell theory states that
a. all organisms have cell walls that come from other cell walls.
b. all cellular organisms undergo sexual reproduction.
c. all living organisms use cells for energy, either their own or cells they ingest from other organisms.
d. all living organisms consist of cells, and all cells come from other cells.

1.7.2 The gene theory states that all the information that specifies what a cell is and what it does
a. is different for each cell type in the organism.
b. is passed down, unchanged, from parents to offspring.
c. is contained in a long molecule called DNA.
d. All of the above.

1.7.4 The theory of evolution is based on the hypothesis put forth by
a. Mendel.
b. Watson and Crick.
c. Darwin.
d. Schleiden and Schwann.

Apply Your Understanding

1.5.1 You notice that on cloudy days people often carry umbrellas, folded or in a case. You also note that when umbrellas are open there are many more car accidents. You hypothesize that open umbrellas cause car accidents. Explain the reasoning you used to reach this conclusion and why this sort of reasoning can sometimes lead to incorrect conclusions, as here. [Hint: From chapter 0, what is a dependent variable?]

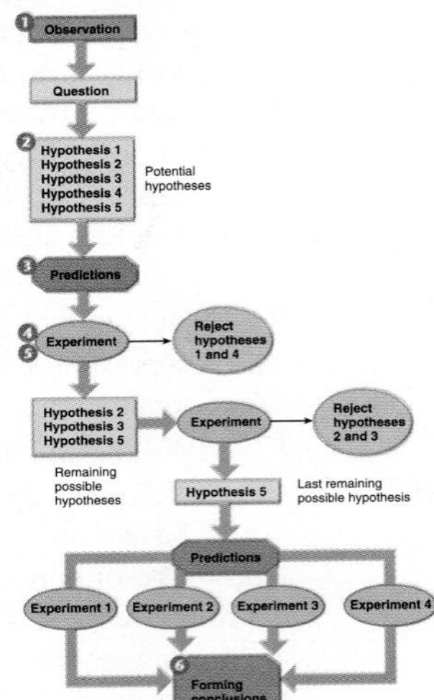

1.6.1 For over two centuries global temperatures have been warming, and over this same period of time the number of pirate ship attacks has steadily decreased. Does this graph support the conclusion that the number of pirate ship attacks has decreased because of warmer temperatures? [Hint: Read section 0.5 in chapter 0 to help answer the question.]

Synthesize What You Have Learned

1.2.1 You are the biologist in a group of scientists who have traveled to a distant star system and landed on a planet. You see an astounding array of shapes and forms. You have three days to take samples of living things before returning to earth. How do you decide what is alive?

1.5.1 St. John's wort is an herb that has been used for hundreds of years as a remedy for mild depression. How might a modern-day scientist research its effectiveness?

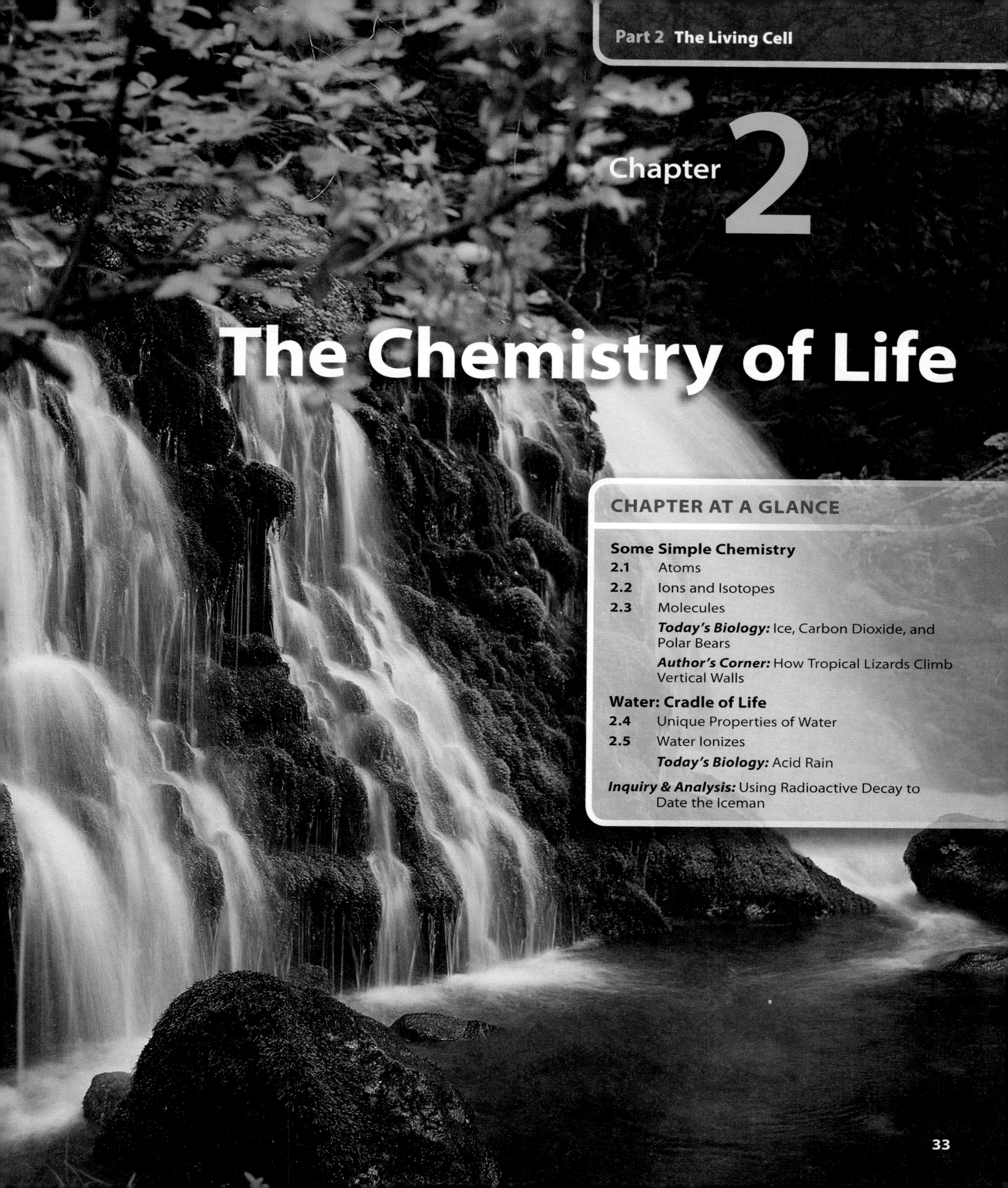

Chapter 2

The Chemistry of Life

CHAPTER AT A GLANCE

Some Simple Chemistry
2.1 Atoms
2.2 Ions and Isotopes
2.3 Molecules
Today's Biology: Ice, Carbon Dioxide, and Polar Bears
Author's Corner: How Tropical Lizards Climb Vertical Walls
Water: Cradle of Life
2.4 Unique Properties of Water
2.5 Water Ionizes
Today's Biology: Acid Rain
Inquiry & Analysis: Using Radioactive Decay to Date the Iceman

Some Simple Chemistry

Figure 2.1 Replacing electrolytes.

During extreme exercise, athletes will often consume drinks that contain "electrolytes," chemicals such as calcium, potassium, and sodium that play an important role in muscle contraction. Electrolytes can also be depleted in other types of dehydration.

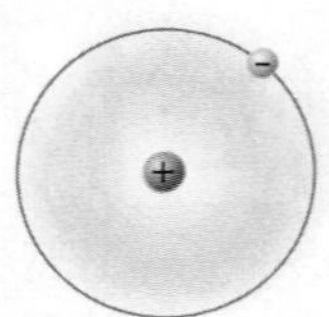

Figure 2.2 Basic structure of an atom.

All atoms have a nucleus consisting of protons and neutrons, except hydrogen, the smallest atom, which has only one proton and no neutrons in its nucleus. Carbon, for example, has six protons and six neutrons in its nucleus. Electrons spin around the nucleus in orbitals a far distance away from the nucleus. The electrons determine how atoms react with each other.

TABLE 2.1 Elements Common in Living Organisms

Element	Symbol	Atomic Number	Mass Number
Hydrogen	H	1	1.008
Carbon	C	6	12.011
Nitrogen	N	7	14.007
Oxygen	O	8	15.999
Sodium	Na	11	22.989
Phosphorus	P	15	30.974
Sulfur	S	16	32.064
Chlorine	Cl	17	35.453
Potassium	K	19	39.098
Calcium	Ca	20	40.080
Iron	Fe	26	55.847

2.1 Atoms

LEARNING OBJECTIVE 2.1.1
Describe the basic structure of an atom in terms of three subatomic particles.

Biology is the science of life, and all life, in fact even all nonlife, is made of substances. Chemistry is the study of the properties of these substances. So, while it may seem tedious or unrelated to examine chemistry in a biology text, it is essential. Organisms are chemical machines (figure 2.1), and to understand them we must learn a little chemistry.

Any substance in the universe that has mass and occupies space is defined as matter. All matter is composed of extremely small particles called **atoms.** An atom is the smallest particle into which a substance can be divided and still retain its chemical properties.

Every atom has the same basic structure you see in figure 2.2. At the center of every atom is a small, very dense nucleus formed of two types of subatomic particles, **protons** (illustrated by purple balls) and **neutrons** (the pink balls in the figure). Whizzing around the nucleus is an orbiting cloud of a third kind of subatomic particle, the **electron** (depicted by yellow balls on concentric rings). Neutrons have no electrical charge, whereas protons have a positive charge and electrons have a negative one. In a typical atom, there is an orbiting electron for every proton in the nucleus. The electron's negative charge balances the proton's positive charge so that the atom is electrically neutral.

An atom is typically described by the number of protons in its nucleus or by the overall mass of the atom. The terms *mass* and *weight* are often used interchangeably, but they have slightly different meanings. Mass refers to the amount of a substance, whereas weight refers to the force gravity exerts on a substance. Hence, an object has the same mass whether it is on the earth or the moon but its weight will be greater on the earth, because the earth's gravitational force is greater than the moon's. For example, an astronaut weighing 180 pounds on earth will weigh about 30 pounds on the moon. He didn't lose any significant mass during his flight to the moon, there is just less gravitational pull on his mass.

The number of protons in the nucleus of an atom is called the **atomic number.** For example, the atomic number of carbon is 6 because it has six protons. Atoms with the same atomic number (that is, the same number of protons) have the same chemical properties and are said to belong to the same **element.** Formally speaking, an element is any substance that cannot be broken down into any other substance by ordinary chemical means.

Neutrons are similar to protons in mass, and the number of protons and neutrons in the nucleus of an atom is called the **mass number.** A carbon atom that has six protons and six neutrons has a mass number of 12. An electron's contribution to the overall mass of an atom is negligible. The atomic numbers and mass numbers of some of the most common elements in living organisms are shown in table 2.1.

Putting the Concept to Work

Each of the elements in table 2.1 has a mass number that is about double its atomic number. Why?

Electrons Determine What Atoms Are Like

LEARNING OBJECTIVE 2.1.2 Explain why electrons determine the chemical behavior of atoms.

Electrons have very little mass (only about 1/1,840 the mass of a proton). Of all the mass contributing to your weight, the portion that is contributed by electrons is less than the mass of your eyelashes. And yet electrons determine the chemical behavior of atoms because they are the parts of atoms that come close enough to each other in nature to interact. Almost all the volume of an atom is empty space. Protons and neutrons lie at the core of this space, while orbiting electrons are very far from the nucleus. If the nucleus of an atom were the size of an apple, the orbit of the nearest electron would be more than a mile out!

Putting the Concept to Work

How much of the mass of the earth (6×10^{24} kg) is electrons?

Electrons Carry Energy

LEARNING OBJECTIVE 2.1.3 Explain how electrons carry energy.

Because electrons are negatively charged, they are attracted to the positively charged nucleus, but they also repel each other's negative charge. It takes work to keep them in orbit, just as it takes work to hold an apple in your hand when gravity is pulling the apple down toward the ground. The apple in your hand is said to possess **energy,** the ability to do work, because of its position—if you were to release it, the apple would fall. Similarly, electrons have energy of position, called *potential energy*. It takes work to oppose the attraction of the nucleus, so moving the electron farther out away from the nucleus, as shown by the set of arrows on the right side of figure 2.3, requires an input of energy and results in an electron with greater potential energy. Cells use the potential energy of atoms to drive chemical reactions.

Potential energy is discussed in more detail on page 92, and chapters 6 and 7 discuss how the potential energy from electrons is used in biological systems.

The volume of space around a nucleus where an electron is most likely to be found is called the *orbital* of that electron. Each energy level of an atom, called an *electron shell*, has a specific number of orbitals, and each orbital can hold up to two electrons. The first shell in any atom contains one orbital. Helium, shown in figure 2.4*a*, has one electron shell with one orbital that corresponds to the lowest energy level. The orbital contains two electrons, shown above and below the nucleus. In atoms with more than one electron shell, the second shell contains four orbitals and holds up to eight electrons. Nitrogen, shown in figure 2.4*b*, has two electron shells; the first one is completely filled with two electrons, but three of the four orbitals in the second electron shell are not filled because nitrogen's second shell contains only five electrons (openings in orbitals are indicated with dotted circles). In atoms with more than two electron shells, subsequent shells also contain up to four orbitals with a maximum of eight electrons. Atoms with unfilled electron orbitals tend to be more reactive because they lose, gain, or share electrons in order to fill their outermost electron shell. An atom with a completely filled outermost shell is more stable.

Putting the Concept to Work

Why don't electrons, which carry a negative charge, simply crash into the positively charged nucleus?

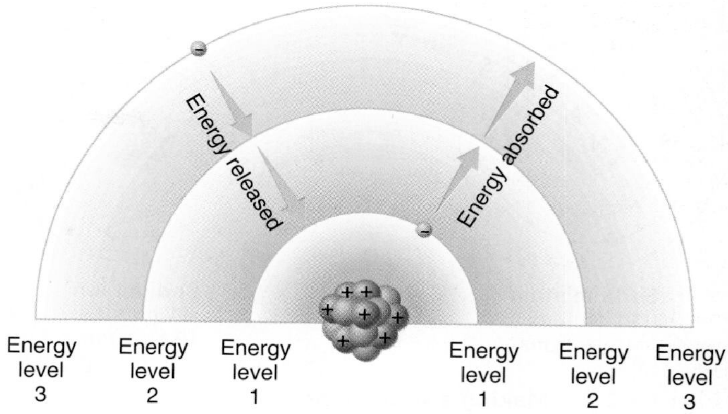

Figure 2.3 The electrons of atoms possess potential energy.

Electrons that circulate rapidly around the nucleus contain energy, and depending on their distance from the nucleus, they may contain more or less energy. Energy level 1 is the lowest potential energy level because it is closest to the nucleus. When an electron absorbs energy, it moves from level 1 to the next higher energy level (level 2). When an electron loses energy, it falls to a lower energy level closer to the nucleus.

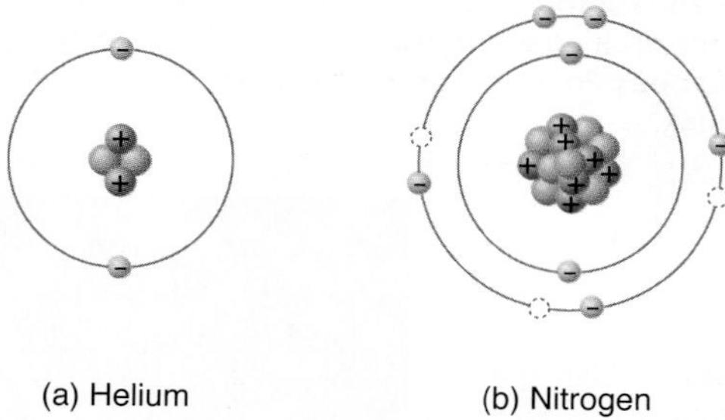

Figure 2.4 Electrons in electron shells.

(a) An atom of helium has two protons, two neutrons, and two electrons. The electrons fill the one orbital in its one electron shell, the lowest energy level. (b) An atom of nitrogen has seven protons, seven neutrons, and seven electrons. Two electrons fill the orbital in the innermost electron shell, and five electrons occupy orbitals in the second electron shell (the second energy level). The orbitals in the second electron shell can hold up to eight electrons; therefore there are three vacancies in the outer electron shell of a nitrogen atom.

IMPLICATION FOR YOU Helium gas is often used to inflate party balloons, and if you release these balloons they rise up into the air. If you fill the party balloons with nitrogen gas, they don't rise. Why this difference in party balloon behavior?

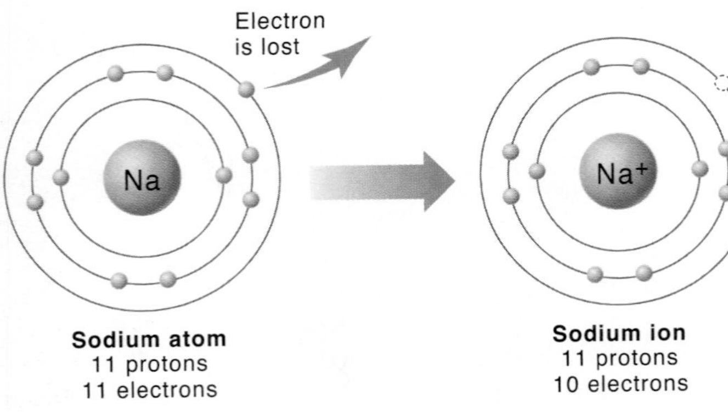

Figure 2.5 Making a sodium ion.

An electrically neutral sodium atom has 11 protons and 11 electrons. Sodium ions bear a positive charge when they ionize and lose one electron. Sodium ions have 11 protons and only 10 electrons.

2.2 Ions and Isotopes

Ions

LEARNING OBJECTIVE 2.2.1 Differentiate between a cation and an anion.

Sometimes an atom may gain or lose an electron from its outer shell (we will look at why this happens in the next section). Atoms in which the number of electrons does not equal the number of protons because they have gained or lost one or more electrons are called **ions.** All ions are electrically charged. For example, an atom of sodium (on the left in figure 2.5) becomes a positively charged ion (Na^+), called a *cation*, when it loses an electron (on the right); one proton in the nucleus is left with an unbalanced charge (11 positively charged protons and only 10 negatively charged electrons). Negatively charged ions, called *anions*, form when an atom gains one or more electrons from another atom.

Putting the Concept to Work

Does table salt contain more cations or anions?

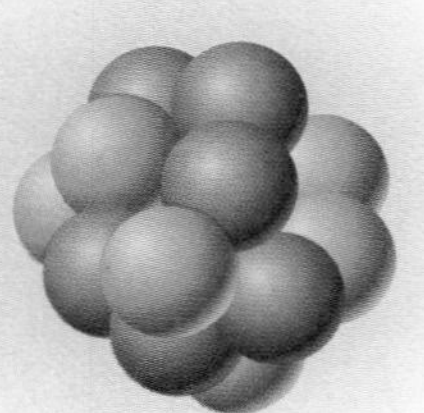

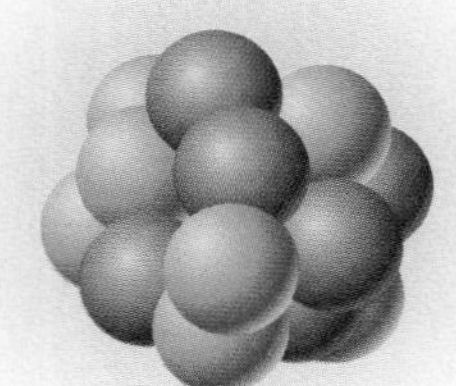

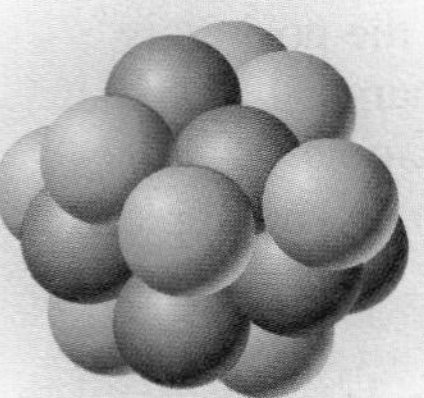

Figure 2.6 Isotopes of the element carbon.

The three most abundant isotopes of carbon are carbon-12, carbon-13, and carbon-14. The yellow "clouds" in the diagrams represent the orbiting electrons, whose numbers are the same for all three isotopes. Protons are shown in purple, and neutrons are shown in pink.

Isotopes

LEARNING OBJECTIVE 2.2.2 Differentiate between an ion and an isotope.

The number of neutrons in an atom of a particular element can vary without changing the chemical properties of the element. Atoms that have the same number of protons but different numbers of neutrons are called **isotopes.** Isotopes of an atom have the same atomic number but differ in their mass number. Most elements in nature exist as mixtures of different isotopes. For example, there are three isotopes of the element carbon, all of which possess six protons (the purple balls in figure 2.6). The most common isotope of carbon (99% of all carbon) has six neutrons (the pink balls). Because its mass number is 12 (six protons plus six neutrons), it is referred to as carbon-12 (on the left). The isotope carbon-14 (on the right) is rare (1 in 1 trillion atoms of carbon) and unstable, such that its nucleus tends to break up into particles with lower atomic numbers, a process called **radioactive decay.** Radioactive isotopes are used in dating fossils, as discussed in the "Inquiry & Analysis" feature at the end of the chapter, and in medicine.

Medical Uses of Radioactive Isotopes. Radioactive isotopes are used in many medical procedures. Short-lived isotopes, those that decay fairly rapidly and produce harmless products, are commonly used as *tracers,* a radioactive substance that is taken up and used by the body. Emissions from the radioactive isotope tracer are detected using special laboratory equipment, and can reveal key diagnostic information about the functioning of the body. For example, PET and PET/CT (positron emission tomography/computerized tomography) imaging procedures can be used to identify a cancerous area in the body (figure 2.7).

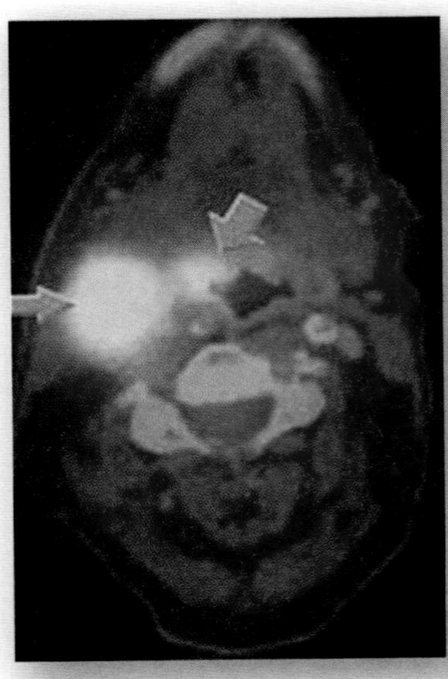

Figure 2.7 Using a radioactive tracer to identify cancer.

In certain medical imaging procedures, the patient is injected intravenously with a radioactive tracer that is absorbed in greater amounts by cancer cells. The tracer emits radioactivity that is detected using PET and PET/CT equipment. A cancerous area in the neck is seen as bright yellow glowing areas.

Putting the Concept to Work

Why do the three abundant isotopes of carbon all form the same types of chemical bonds?

2.3 Molecules

Nature of the Chemical Bond

LEARNING OBJECTIVE 2.3.1 Define a chemical bond and describe the three principal kinds.

A **molecule** is a group of atoms held together by energy. The energy acts as "glue," ensuring that the various atoms stick to one another. The energy or force holding two atoms together is called a **chemical bond.** There are three principal kinds of chemical bonds: ionic bonds, where the force is generated by the attraction of oppositely charged ions; covalent bonds, where the force results from the sharing of electrons; and hydrogen bonds, where the force is generated by the attraction of opposite partial electrical charges. Another important type of chemical attraction called van der Waals forces will be discussed later, but keep in mind that this type of weak interaction is not considered a chemical bond.

Putting the Concept to Work

Can you name an atom that is *not* part of a molecule?

Ionic Bonds

LEARNING OBJECTIVE 2.3.2 Explain how ionic bonds promote crystal formation.

Chemical bonds called **ionic bonds** form when atoms are attracted to each other by opposite electrical charges. Just as the positive pole of a magnet is attracted to the negative pole of another, so an atom can form a strong link with another atom if they have opposite electrical charges. Because an atom with an electrical charge is an ion, these bonds are called ionic bonds.

Everyday table salt is built of ionic bonds. The sodium and chlorine atoms that make up table salt are ions. The sodium you see in the yellow panels of figure 2.8*a* gives up the sole electron in its outermost shell (leaving a filled outer shell) and chlorine, in the light green panels, gains an electron to complete its outermost shell. Recall from section 2.1 that an atom is more stable when its outermost electron shell is filled. As a result of this electron hopping, sodium atoms in table salt are positive sodium ions and chlorine atoms are negative chloride ions. Because each ion is electrically attracted to all surrounding ions of opposite charge, they form an elaborate matrix of ionic bonds between alternating sodium and chloride ions—a crystal (figure 2.8*b*). That is why table salt is composed of tiny crystals and is not a powder.

The two key properties of ionic bonds that make them form crystals are that they are strong (although not as strong as covalent bonds) and that they are *not* directional. An ion is attracted to the electrical field contributed by all nearby ions of opposite charge. Ionic bonds do not play an important part in most biological molecules because of this lack of directionality. Biological molecules require the more specific associations made possible by directional bonds.

Putting the Concept to Work

In figure 2.8*b*, how many sodium ions interact with an individual chloride ion?

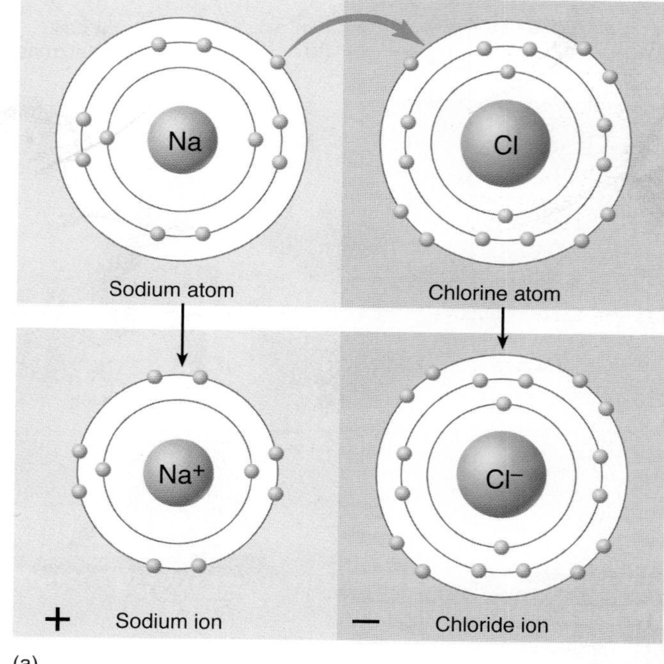

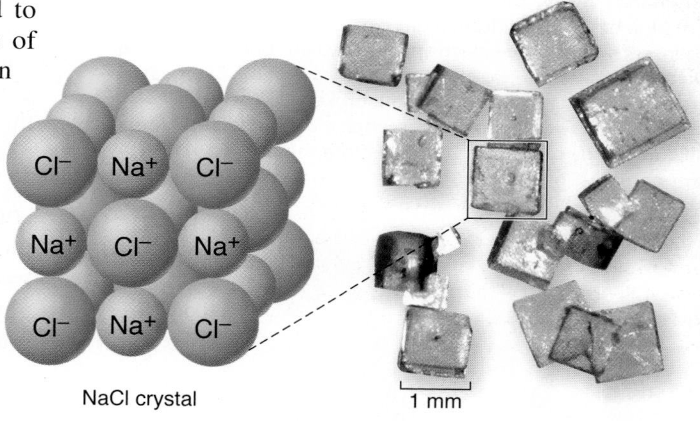

Figure 2.8 The formation of ionic bonds in table salt.

(a) When a sodium atom donates an electron to a chlorine atom, the sodium atom, lacking that electron, becomes a positively charged sodium ion. The chlorine atom, having gained an extra electron, becomes a negatively charged chloride ion. (b) Sodium chloride forms a highly regular lattice of alternating sodium ions and chloride ions. You are familiar with these crystals as everyday table salt.

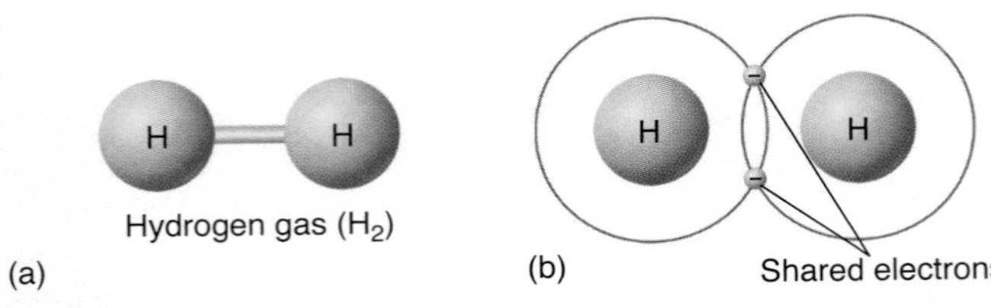

Figure 2.9 A covalent bond forms hydrogen gas.

Covalent bonds involve the sharing of electrons, indicated by the light blue bar in (a). Hydrogen gas consists of two atoms of hydrogen, each having one electron. The covalent bond forms when the two atoms share the two electrons, as shown in (b). Energy is often released when covalent bonds are broken. (c) The *Hindenberg* dirigible was filled with hydrogen gas when it exploded and burned in 1937; the energy of the inferno came from the breaking of H_2 covalent bonds.

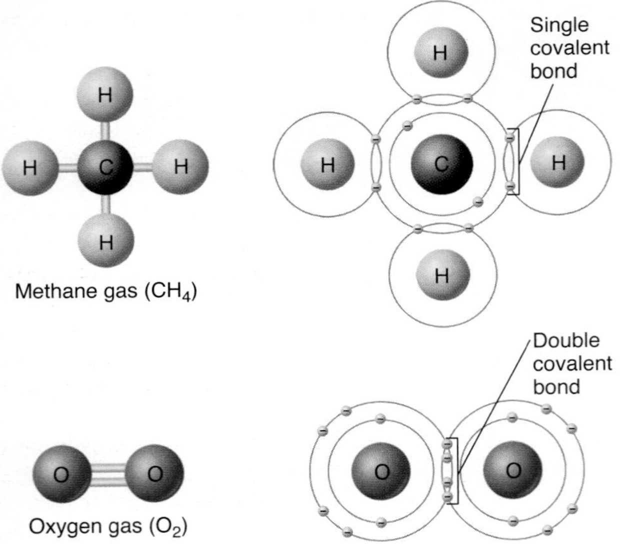

Figure 2.10 Single and double covalent bonds.

Single covalent bonds involve the sharing of one pair of electrons, as in methane (CH_4). In double covalent bonds, two pairs of electrons are shared, as in oxygen gas.

Covalent Bonds

LEARNING OBJECTIVE 2.3.3 Explain why most chemical bonds in organisms are covalent bonds, and distinguish between polar and nonpolar covalent bonds.

Strong chemical bonds called **covalent bonds** form between two atoms when they share electrons (figure 2.9). Most of the atoms in your body are linked to other atoms by covalent bonds. Why do atoms in molecules share electrons? Remember, all atoms seek to fill up their outermost shell of orbiting electrons, which in all atoms (except tiny hydrogen and helium) takes eight electrons. For example, an atom with six outer shell electrons seeks to share them with an atom that has two outer shell electrons or with two atoms that have single outer shell electrons. The carbon atom has four electrons in its outermost shell, and so carbon can form as many as four covalent bonds in its attempt to fully populate its outermost shell of electrons. Because there are many ways four covalent bonds can form, carbon atoms participate in many different kinds of molecules. The strength of covalent bonds increases as more electrons are shared. If only one pair of electrons is shared between two atoms, the covalent bond is called a *single covalent bond.* If two pairs of electrons are shared, it is a stronger bond, called a *double covalent bond;* and if three pairs of electrons are shared it is a very strong *triple covalent bond.*

The atoms in nitrogen gas (N_2) are held together by a very strong triple covalent bond. As described on page 412, only a few kinds of bacteria are able to break this bond and make the nitrogen available to other organisms.

The two key properties of covalent bonds that make them ideal for their molecule-building role in living systems are that (1) they are strong, involving the sharing of lots of energy; and (2) they are very directional—allowing bonds to form between two specific atoms, rather than creating a generalized attraction of one atom for its neighbors. For example, compare the covalent bonds of the methane molecule in figure 2.10 with the ionic bonds of the NaCl crystal in figure 2.8.

Both covalent and ionic bonds are relatively strong bonds, but for completely different reasons. A couple walking down the street moves as a unit, the two people bonded to each other whether they are holding hands or walking side by side. If the couple is holding hands, they are joined together physically, much like covalent bonds—electrons are shared and a physical bond forms between atoms. If the couple is not holding hands, they stay together, step for step, linked by their awareness of each other. This is much like ionic bonds—no physical connection forms between atoms, but they are strongly attracted to one another due to their opposite charges.

Polar Covalent Bonds. When a covalent bond forms between two atoms, one nucleus may be much better at attracting the shared electrons than the other. In water, for example, the shared electrons are much more strongly attracted to the oxygen atom than to the hydrogen atoms. When this happens, shared electrons spend more time in the vicinity of the oxygen atom, making it somewhat negative in charge; they spend less time in the vicinity of the hydrogens, and these become somewhat positive in charge. The charges are not full electrical charges, as in ions, but rather tiny *partial charges.* What you end up with is a sort of molecular magnet, with positive and negative ends, or "poles." Molecules like this are said to be **polar molecules** (see figure 2.11).

Putting the Concept to Work

Why don't covalent bonds promote crystal formation?

Ice, Carbon Dioxide, and Polar Bears

Simple molecules can play major roles in our lives. Take water, an oxygen atom covalently bonded to two hydrogen atoms, and carbon dioxide, a carbon atom covalently bonded to two oxygen atoms. The news this year is full of stories about water and carbon dioxide. The water stories feature melting ice and earth's disappearing polar ice cap. At the heart of many of these ice stories are polar bears. You know, the big white ones that live in the Arctic and at your favorite zoo.

As much as people are intrigued by polar bears and find them endearing, we prefer to admire them from a distance—through a telephoto camera lens or across a fence and waterless moat in a zoo. Why? Unlike other bears, polar bears eat people. Recent attacks on humans by polar bears remind us of how dangerous the largest land carnivores are, no matter how cute and cuddly they appear. Polar bear attacks on humans have been quite rare until recently, not because polar bears are particularly adverse to the taste of human flesh, but because the bears rarely come into contact with us.

Not so rare any more, however, for the native peoples that live near the Arctic Circle. There, encounters with polar bears are becoming more frequent, and these encounters are often deadly. Three years ago a polar bear entered the small village of Ivujivik in northern Canada. Three young boys were playing hockey outside of the youth center in town when the polar bear approached them. The mother of one of the youngsters was nearby and saw the approaching polar bear. She ran over screaming at the bear to distract it from the boys. The bear turned on the mother and started attacking. The boys alerted a neighbor who shot and killed the bear. Amazingly, the mother survived this hand-to-claw street fight, but many other victims of polar bear attacks aren't as lucky.

The authorities always pursue any bear involved in an attack and kill it, but it's hard for a biologist to blame the polar bears. They are just doing what is in their nature to do. Until now, nature hadn't been bringing them this close to humans. Why are the bears encroaching where they never did before? The answer—overlapping habitats. In the past, most bear attacks have occurred at camp sites or other areas where humans have come into the bear's habitat. What we are now seeing is something quite different and new: In Ivujivik and other arctic outposts, polar bears have traveled outside of their normal habitat and invaded a human community in search of food.

Polar bears are roamers. They travel up to 15 miles a day, covering over 100,000 square miles in their lifetime, some 2% of the five million square miles of the Arctic sea ice that makes up their entire range. What drives them to move is an endless search for food. They feed primarily on seals that spend most of their time in the water. In search of a meal, a polar bear will sit perched over a hole in the ice. When a seal surfaces to breathe, the polar bear will grab it and drag it out. Because of its limited diet and method of hunting, polar bears feed only during the winter when the ice pack is largest and thickest. The bears move on shore and fast during the ice-free summer months, and migrate back to the ice when it reforms.

The Arctic ice is the only place where polar bears can successfully hunt. Without these ice platforms, they cannot feed. Although they are strong swimmers and can travel long distances between large patches of ice, they don't have the speed and agility of a seal in water, and so have little hope of catching and killing a seal in open water. Without the Arctic sea ice, polar bears would starve. Sometimes, in desperation, they wander into human villages like Ivujivik and try to eat people.

And this is where water molecules come into the story. Distressingly, the ice so vital to polar bear survival is melting away as air and water temperatures rise at northern latitudes. Anyone who has read ahead to chapter 22 knows why—because of the other molecule we mentioned, carbon dioxide. Levels of CO_2 are rising in earth's atmosphere, leading to a process now universally dubbed global warming. Global warming is caused when so-called greenhouse gases like carbon dioxide are produced as by-products of the burning of fossil fuels like coal and gasoline. These gases accumulate in the atmosphere and trap heat from the sun.

Scientists have found that the outer edges of the Arctic ice cap are retreating earlier in the season each year as global warming proceeds, and reforming later. Wildlife census data indicate that this is causing polar bears to migrate to land earlier, and to remain there longer. The result is that the polar bears have a shorter hunting season and a longer fasting season.

In Washington D. C., our legislators continue to ponder the wisdom of global warming legislation. The economic consequences of legislation aimed at reducing carbon emissions are being considered carefully before any changes are instituted.

What do the polar bears do in the meantime? As the ice melts ever further each summer, the polar bear is trapped on land, not able to hunt. Every year it takes longer for the ice to reform, the polar bears inching closer to starvation as they wait out the delayed freezing. And as the border of the ice cap moves ever farther away from land, the starvation-weakened polar bears have to swim farther to get out to it. This is a game of "chase the carrot" the bears cannot win. Eventually they will drown. All of them.

The only way the bears can win is if we do. The challenge they face is to survive until the human lawmakers act, and then to keep struggling through the long years of climate recovery. If every time a Washington legislator votes on climate change issues in the coming months, he or she tries, just for a moment, to see the issue as a polar bear sees it, we all will have a better chance at a fruitful outcome. It isn't only polar bears that are threatened by global warming. We too are an endangered species. Their plight helps to focus our attention on the danger in the future we all face together.

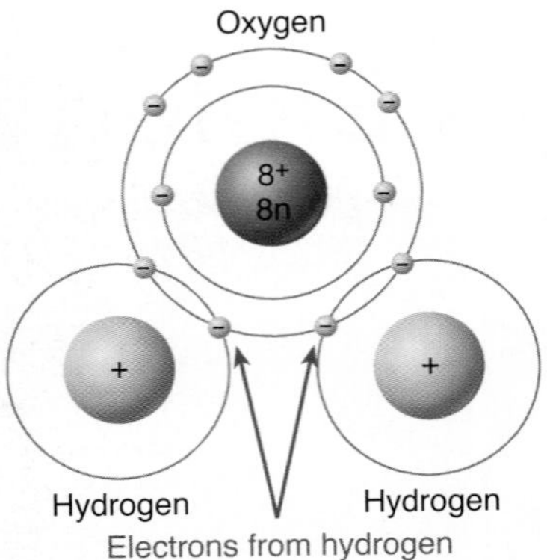

(a) Electron shells in a water molecule

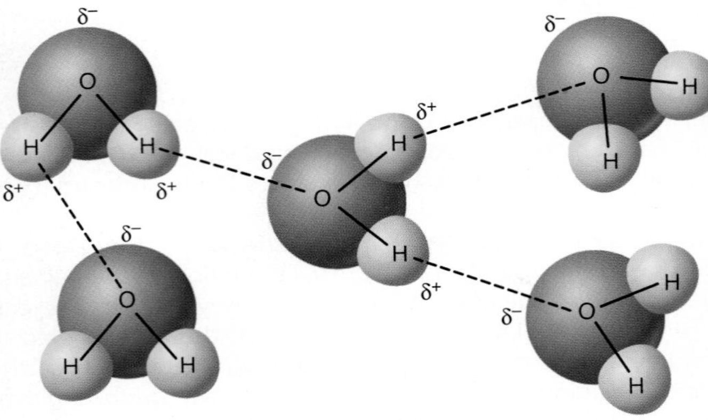

(b) Hydrogen bonding in water molecules

(c)

Figure 2.11 Hydrogen bonding in water molecules.

(a) A water molecule is composed of one oxygen atom (red) and two hydrogen atoms (blue). (b) Because electrons are more attracted to oxygen atoms than to hydrogen atoms, the shared electrons spend more time near the oxygen atom, making the water molecule polar. Each oxygen atom in a water molecule has a partial negative charge (δ−), and each hydrogen atom in a water molecule has a partial positive charge (δ+). Hydrogen bonds (dashed lines) form between the positive end of one water molecule and the negative end of another water molecule. (c) Water molecules form strong hydrogen bonds with each other, giving liquid water many unique properties.

Hydrogen Bonds

LEARNING OBJECTIVE 2.3.4 Predict which molecules will form hydrogen bonds with each other.

Polar molecules like water are attracted to one another through a special type of weak chemical bond called a **hydrogen bond.** Hydrogen bonds occur when the positive end of one polar molecule is attracted to the negative end of another, like two magnets drawn to each other. In a hydrogen bond, an electropositive hydrogen from one polar molecule is attracted to an electronegative atom, often oxygen (O) or nitrogen (N), from another polar molecule.

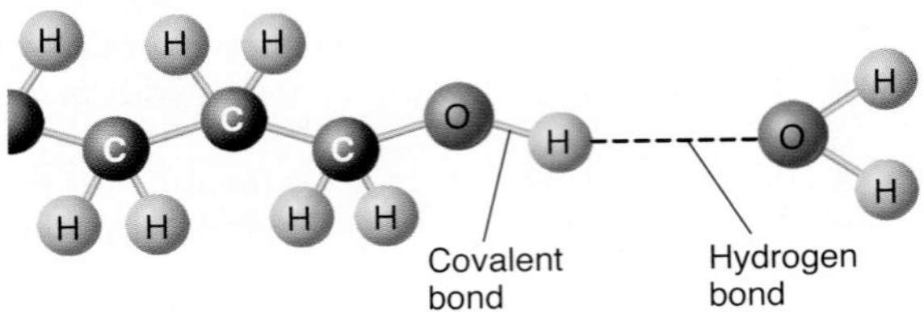

Water is very polar, because the oxygen atoms in water molecules are more electronegative (attract electrons more strongly) than the hydrogen atoms (figure 2.11). In a water molecule, each oxygen has a partial negative charge (δ−) and each hydrogen has a partial positive charge (δ+). Hydrogen bonds (shown as dashed lines in figure 2.11) form between the positive end of one polar water molecule and the negative end of another polar water molecule.

Two key properties of hydrogen bonds cause them to play an important role in the molecules found in organisms. First, hydrogen bonds are highly directional. Second, they are weak and so are not effective over long distances like more powerful covalent and ionic bonds. Too weak to actually form stable molecules, they act more like Velcro, forming a tight bond by the additive effects of many weak interactions.

Putting the Concept to Work

Would you expect a sodium ion to form hydrogen bonds with surrounding water molecules?

Van der Waals Forces

LEARNING OBJECTIVE 2.3.5 Distinguish between a chemical bond and van der Waals interactions.

Another important kind of chemical attraction, too weak to be considered a chemical bond, is a nondirectional attractive force called **van der Waals forces.** These chemical forces come into play only when two atoms are very close to one another. The attraction is very weak, and disappears if the atoms move even a little apart. It becomes significant when numerous atoms in one molecule simultaneously come close to numerous atoms of another molecule—that is, when their shapes match precisely. For example, this interaction is important when antibodies in your blood recognize the shape of an invading virus as foreign (see chapter 28).

Putting the Concept to Work

Can you think of any other biological processes where van der Waals forces might play an important role? What do all these processes have in common?

Author's Corner

How Tropical Lizards Climb Vertical Walls

Science is most fun when it tickles your imagination. This is particularly true when you see something you know just can't be true. A few years ago, my wife, Barbara, and I were on a tropical vacation, and I was lying on the bed when a little lizard walked up the wall beside me and across the ceiling, stopping right over my head, and looked down at me.

This was no special effect, no trick with mirrors. I was seeing it with my own eyes, real as day, right there above me. The lizard, a green gecko about the size of a toothbrush, stood upside down on the ceiling and seemed to laugh at me for several minutes before trotting over to the far wall and down.

How did my gecko friend perform this gripping feat? Investigators have puzzled over the adhesive properties of geckos for decades. What force prevented gravity from dropping the gecko on my nose?

The most reasonable hypothesis seemed suction—salamanders' feet form suction cups that let them climb walls, so maybe geckos' do too. The way to test this is to see if the feet adhere in a vacuum, with no air to create suction. Salamander feet don't adhere, but gecko feet do. It's not suction.

How about friction? Cockroaches climb using tiny hooks that grapple onto irregularities in the surface, much as rock climbers use crampons. Geckos, however, happily run up walls of smooth polished glass that no cockroach can climb. It's not friction.

Electrostatic attraction? Clothes in a dryer stick together because of electrical charges created by their rubbing together. You can stop this by adding a "static remover" that is itself heavily ionized. But a gecko's feet still adhere in ionized air. It's not electrostatic attraction.

Could it be glue? Many insects use adhesive secretions from glands in their feet to aid climbing. But there are no gland cells in gecko feet, no secreted chemical. It's not glue.

There was one tantalizing clue, however, the kind that experimenters love. Gecko feet seem to get stickier on surfaces with highly ordered molecules. This suggests that geckos are tapping directly into the molecular structure of the surfaces they walk on!

Tracking down this clue, Robert Full of the University of California, Berkeley, and his research team took a closer look at gecko feet. Geckos have rows of tiny hairs on the bottoms of their feet, like the bristles of a toothbrush. There are about half a million of these hairs on each foot, pointed toward the heel.

When you look at these hairs under a microscope, the end of each hair is divided into between 400 and 1,000 fine projections, the projections sticking out from the tip like tiny stiff brushes.

When a gecko takes a step, it drives the sole of its foot onto the surface and pushes it backward. This shoves the forest of tips directly against the surface. The atoms of each gecko tip become closely engaged with the atoms of the surface, and *that* is the force that defies gravity. When two atoms approach each other very closely—closer than the diameter of an atom—a subtle nuclear attraction called "van der Waals forces" comes into play. These forces are individually very weak, but when lots of atoms add their little bits, the sum can add up to quite a lot.

Full and his team used microelectrical mechanical sensors, originally designed to be used with atomic force microscopes that map a surface by "feeling" it with a mechanical probe. Using the sensors, they were able to measure the force exerted by a single hair removed from a gecko's foot. It was 200 micronewtons, a tiny force but stupendous for a single hair. Enough to hold up an ant. A million hairs could support a small child. My little gecko, ceiling-walking with 2 million of them, could have carried an 80-pound backpack—talk about being overengineered!

If they stick that well, how do geckos ever become unstuck? For a gecko's foot to stick, each hair projection must butt up squarely against the surface, so the hair's individual atoms can come into play. Tipped past a critical angle—30 degrees—the attractive forces between hair and surface atoms weaken to nothing. The trick is to tip the foot hairs until the projections let go. Geckos release their feet by curling up each toe and peeling it off, sort of like undoing Velcro.

Now I can laugh with my little gecko friend, should I see it again, for I know its secret.

Water: Cradle of Life

TABLE 2.2 The Properties of Water

Property	Explanation
Heat storage	Hydrogen bonds require considerable heat before they break, minimizing temperature changes.
Ice formation	Water molecules in an ice crystal are spaced relatively far apart because of hydrogen bonding.
High heat of vaporization	Many hydrogen bonds must be broken for water to evaporate, which requires considerable heat.
Cohesion	Hydrogen bonds hold molecules of water together.
High polarity	Water molecules are attracted to ions and other polar compounds.

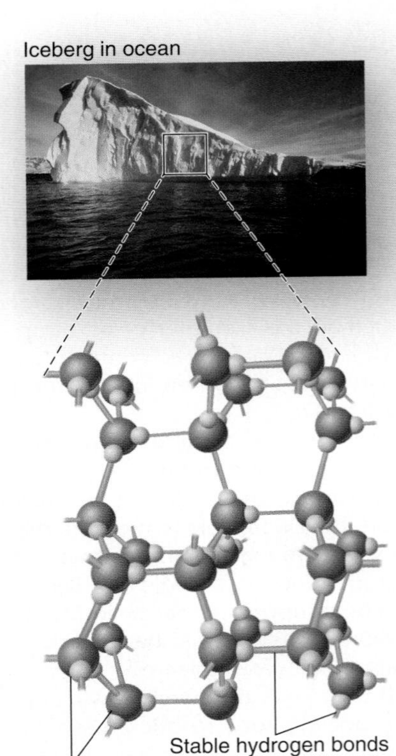

Figure 2.12 Ice formation.

When water (a) cools below 0°C, it forms a regular crystal structure (b) that floats. The individual water molecules are spaced apart and held in position by hydrogen bonds.

IMPLICATION FOR YOU Will the melting of the polar ice cap (ice floating in the ocean) due to global warming raise sea level? [Hint: If you leave a glass of ice water on the table, does the level of water in the glass change as the ice melts?]

2.4 Unique Properties of Water

Three-fourths of the earth's surface is covered by liquid water. About two-thirds of your body is water, and you cannot exist long without it. All other organisms also require water. The chemistry of life, then, is water chemistry.

Water's ability to form hydrogen bonds is responsible for much of the organization of living chemistry, from the structure of membranes that encase every cell to how large molecules fold. The weak hydrogen bonds that form between a hydrogen atom of one water molecule and the oxygen atom of another produce a lattice of hydrogen bonds within liquid water. Each of these bonds is individually very weak and short-lived—a single bond lasts only 1/100,000,000,000 of a second. However, the cumulative effect of large numbers of these bonds is enormous and is responsible for many of the important physical properties of water (**table 2.2**).

Heat Storage

LEARNING OBJECTIVE 2.4.1 Explain why water heats up so slowly.

The temperature of any substance is a measure of how rapidly its individual molecules are moving. Due to the many hydrogen bonds that water molecules form with one another, a large input of thermal energy is required to disrupt the organization of liquid water and raise its temperature. Because of this, water heats up more slowly than almost any other compound and holds its temperature longer. That is a major reason why your body, which is mostly water, is able to maintain a relatively constant internal temperature.

Putting the Concept to Work

Would adding table salt to a pan of water cause the water to come to a boil faster on a stove?

Ice Formation

LEARNING OBJECTIVE 2.4.2 Explain why ice floats.

If the temperature is low enough, very few hydrogen bonds between water molecules will break. Instead, the lattice of these bonds assumes a crystal-like structure, forming a solid we call ice. Interestingly, ice is less dense than water—that is why icebergs and ice cubes float. Why is ice less dense? This is best understood by comparing the molecular structures of liquid water and ice that you see in **figure 2.12**. At temperatures above freezing (0°C or 32°F), water molecules in **figure 2.12*a*** move around each other with hydrogen bonds breaking and forming. As temperatures drop, the movement of water molecules decreases, allowing hydrogen bonds to stabilize and hold individual molecules farther apart, as in **figure 2.12*b***. This stabilized lattice makes the ice structure less dense.

Putting the Concept to Work

Would adding table salt to a bottle of water cause the water to freeze to ice faster when you place the bottle in the freezer?

High Heat of Vaporization

LEARNING OBJECTIVE 2.4.3 Explain why sweating cools you.

If the temperature is high enough, many hydrogen bonds between water molecules will break, with the result that the liquid is changed into vapor (a gas). A considerable amount of heat energy is required to do this—every gram of water that evaporates from your skin removes 2,452 joules of heat from your body, which is equal to the energy released by lowering the temperature of 586 grams of water 1°C (which is quite a lot of heat). That is why sweating cools you off; as the sweat evaporates (vaporizes) it takes energy with it, in the form of heat, cooling the body.

Putting the Concept to Work

Does an athlete wearing a sweat suit cool off as quickly as one wearing only shorts?

Cohesion

LEARNING OBJECTIVE 2.4.4 Distinguish cohesion from adhesion.

Because water molecules are very polar, they are attracted to other polar molecules—hydrogen bonds bind polar molecules to each other. When the other polar molecule is another water molecule, the attraction is called **cohesion.** The surface tension of water is created by cohesion. Surface tension is the force that causes water to bead or supports the weight of an insect (**figure 2.13**). When the other polar molecule is a different substance, the attraction is called **adhesion.** Water clings to any substance with which it can form hydrogen bonds. Adhesion is why things get "wet" when they are dipped in water and why waxy substances do not—they are composed of nonpolar molecules that don't form hydrogen bonds with water molecules.

Cohesion and adhesion are properties of water that are necessary for the movement of water in plants from the roots to the leaves, as described on page 629.

Putting the Concept to Work

Explain why an insect can walk on water, while you cannot.

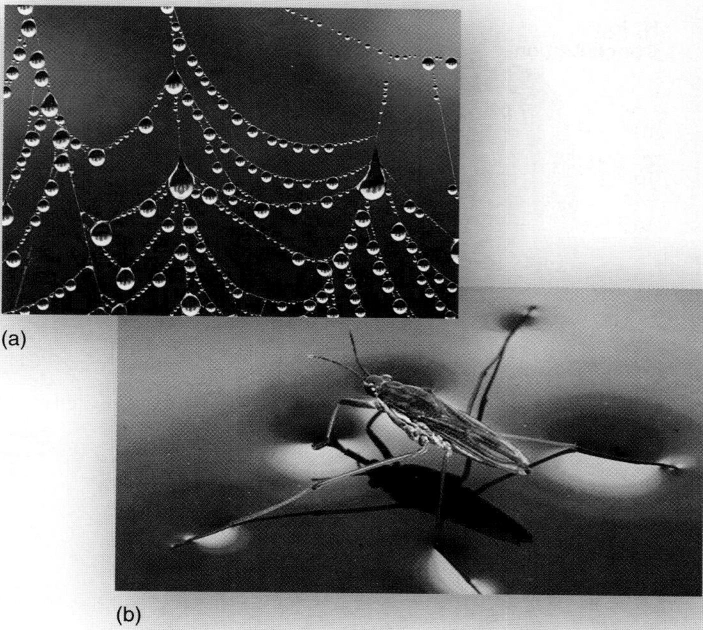

Figure 2.13 Cohesion.

(a) Cohesion allows water molecules to stick together and form droplets. (b) Surface tension is a property derived from cohesion—that is, water has a "strong" surface due to the force of its hydrogen bonds. Some insects, such as this water strider, literally walk on water.

IMPLICATION FOR YOU If you were to devise very large footpads made of lightweight film, would you be able to walk on water like this water strider? Why would you have to wear footpads and not just bare feet?

High Polarity

LEARNING OBJECTIVE 2.4.5 Explain why oil will not dissolve in water.

Water molecules in solution tend to form the maximum number of hydrogen bonds possible and gather around polar molecules or molecules with an electrical charge. For example, when a salt crystal dissolves in water, what really happens is that individual ions break off from the crystal and become surrounded by water molecules (**figure 2.14**). Water molecules orient around each ion and form a *hydration shell,* preventing the ions from reassociating with the crystal. Polar molecules that dissolve in water in this way are said to be **soluble** in water. In contrast, when nonpolar molecules are placed in water, water molecules shy away. The nonpolar molecules are forced into association with one another and are referred to as **hydrophobic** (Greek *hydros,* water, and *phobos,* fearing). Polar molecules, on the other hand, are called **hydrophilic** (Greek *hydros,* water, and *philic,* loving).

Putting the Concept to Work

What molecules would you expect to dissolve in vegetable oil?

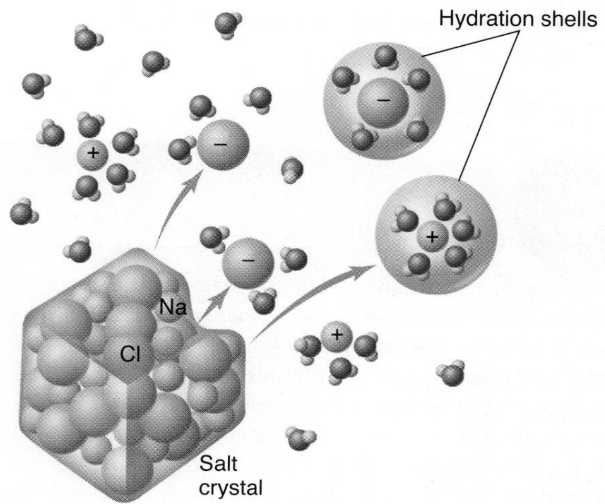

Figure 2.14 How salt dissolves in water.

Salt is soluble in water because the partial charges on water molecules are attracted to the charged sodium and chloride ions. The water molecules surround the ions, forming what are called hydration shells. When all of the ions have been separated from the crystal, the salt is said to be dissolved.

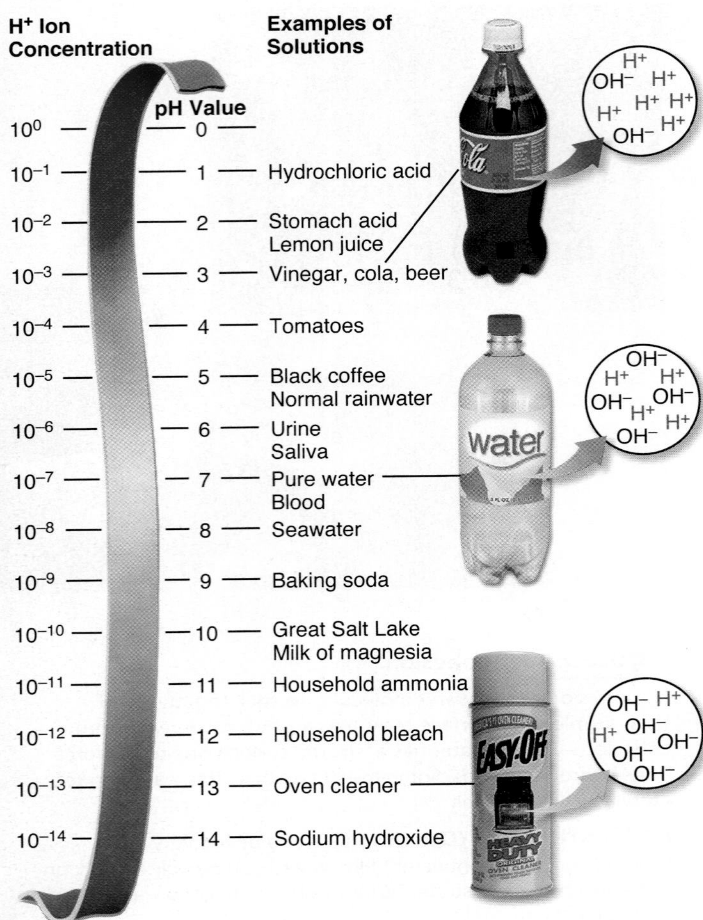

Figure 2.15 The pH scale.

A fluid is assigned a value according to the number of hydrogen ions present in a liter of that fluid. The scale is logarithmic, so that a change of only 1 means a 10-fold change in the concentration of hydrogen ions; thus lemon juice with a pH of 2 is 100 times more acidic than tomatoes with a pH of 4, and seawater is 10 times more basic than pure water.

BIOLOGY & YOU

Heartburn. Your stomach contains large amounts of hydrochloric acid, used to digest food. Sometimes this acid backs up from the stomach into the esophagus (the food pipe) stretching up from the stomach to the throat. This escape of acid from the stomach, called acid reflux, causes a painful burning sensation as the acid attacks the inner lining of the esophagus. Because the esophagus lies just behind the heart, the burning sensation is informally referred to as "heartburn." Nearly one-third of the adult population of the U.S. experiences acid reflux to some degree at least once a month. For minor heartburn you might take an antacid, such as Tums, which is a base that counteracts stomach acidity.

2.5 Water Ionizes

LEARNING OBJECTIVE 2.5.1 Define pH and predict the change in hydrogen ion concentration represented by a difference of 1 on the pH scale.

Ionization

The covalent bonds within a water molecule sometimes break spontaneously. When it happens, a proton (hydrogen atom nucleus) dissociates from the molecule as a positively charged ion, *hydrogen ion* (H^+). The rest of the dissociated water molecule, which has retained the shared electron from the covalent bond, is a negatively charged *hydroxide ion* (OH^-).

$$\underset{\text{water}}{H_2O} \longleftrightarrow \underset{\text{hydroxide ion}}{OH^-} + \underset{\text{hydrogen ion}}{H^+}$$

pH

A convenient way to express the hydrogen ion concentration of a solution is to use the **pH scale** (figure 2.15). This scale ranges from 0 (highest hydrogen ion concentration) to 14 (lowest hydrogen ion concentration). Pure water has a pH of 7. Each pH unit represents a 10-fold change in hydrogen ion concentration. This means that a solution with a pH of 4 has *10 times* the H^+ concentration of one with a pH of 5, and *100 times* the H^+ concentration of one with a pH of 6.

Acids. Any substance that dissociates in water to increase the concentration of H^+ is called an **acid.** Acidic solutions have pH values below 7. The stronger an acid, the more H^+ and so the lower its pH. For example, hydrochloric acid (HCl), which is abundant in your stomach, ionizes completely in water, giving the solution a pH of 1.

Bases. A substance that combines with H^+ when dissolved in water is called a **base.** By combining with H^+, a base lowers the H^+ concentration in the solution. Basic (or alkaline) solutions, therefore, have pH values above 7. Very strong bases, such as sodium hydroxide (NaOH), have pH values of 12 or more.

Buffers

The pH inside almost all living cells, and in the fluid surrounding cells in multicellular organisms, is fairly close to 7. The many proteins that govern metabolism are all extremely sensitive to pH, and slight alterations in pH can cause the molecules to take on different shapes that disrupt their activities. For this reason, it is important that a cell maintain a constant pH level. The pH of your blood, for example, is 7.4, and you would survive only a few minutes if it were to fall to 7.0 or rise to 7.8.

What keeps an organism's pH constant? Cells contain chemical substances called **buffers** that minimize changes in concentrations of H^+ and OH^- by taking up or releasing hydrogen ions into solution as the hydrogen ion concentration of the solution changes. As the "Today's Biology" feature on the facing page explains, when acid in rain or snow exceeds the buffering capacity of a tree or other organism, death may result.

Putting the Concept to Work

When you drink a cola, you are consuming an acid. Why doesn't your body's pH go down as a result?

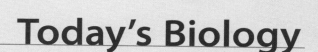

Acid Rain

As you study biology, you will learn that hydrogen ions play many roles in the chemistry of life. When conditions become overly acidic—too many hydrogen ions—serious damage to organisms often results. One important example of this is acid precipitation, more informally called **acid rain.** Acid precipitation is just what it sounds like, the presence of acid in rain or snow. Where does the acid come from? Coal-burning power plants send smoke high into the atmosphere through tall smokestacks, each of which is over 65 meters high. The smoke the stacks belch out contains high concentrations of sulfur dioxide (SO_2), because the coal that the plants burn is rich in sulfur. The sulfur-rich smoke is dispersed and diluted by winds and air currents. Since the 1950s, such tall stacks have become popular in the United States and Europe—there are now over 800 of them in the United States alone.

In the 1970s, 20 years after the stacks were introduced, ecologists began to report evidence that the tall stacks were not eliminating the problems associated with the sulfur, just exporting the ill effects elsewhere. The lakes and forests of the Northeast suffered drastic drops in biodiversity, with forests dying and lakes becoming devoid of life. It turned out that the SO_2 introduced into the upper atmosphere by high smokestacks combines with water vapor to produce sulfuric acid (H_2SO_4). When this water later falls back to earth as rain or snow, it carries the sulfuric acid with it. When schoolchildren measured the pH of natural rainwater as part of a nationwide project in 1989, rain and snow in the Northeast often had a pH as low as 2 or 3—more acidic than vinegar.

After accumulating in soils for over 50 years, the effects of acid rain are now only too evident. The impact of acid rain on forests first became apparent in the Northeast. Some 15% of the lakes in New England have become chronically acidic and are dying biologically as their pH levels fall to below 5.0. Many of the forests of the northeastern United States and Canada have also been seriously damaged. The trees in this photo show the ill effects of acid precipitation. In the last decades, acid added to forest soils has caused the loss from these soils of over half the essential plant nutrients calcium and magnesium. Researchers blame excess acids for dissolving Ca^{++} and Mg^{++} ions into drainage waters much faster than weathering rocks can replenish them. Without them, trees stop growing and die.

Now, some 30 years later, acid rain effects are becoming apparent in the Southeast as well. Researchers suggest the reason for the delay is that southern soils are generally thicker than northern ones and thus able to sponge up far more acid. But now that southern forest soils are becoming saturated, they too are beginning to die. In a third of the southeastern streams studied, fish are declining or already gone.

The solution is straightforward: capture and remove the emissions instead of releasing them into the atmosphere. Progressively tougher pollution laws over the past three decades have reduced U.S. emissions of sulfur dioxide by about 40% from its 1973 peak of 28.8 metric tons a year. Despite this significant progress, much remains to be done. Researchers predict that unless levels are cut further, forests may not recover for centuries.

An informed public will be essential. While textbook treatments have in the past tended to minimize the impact of this issue on students ("the vast majority of North American forests are not suffering substantially from acid precipitation"), it is important that we face the issue squarely and support continued efforts to address this serious problem.

Inquiry & Analysis

Using Radioactive Decay to Date the Iceman

In the fall of 1991, sticking out of the melting snow on the crest of a high pass near the mountainous border between Italy and Austria, two Austrian hikers found a corpse. Right away it was clear the body was very old, frozen in an icy trench where he had sought shelter long ago and only now released as the ice melted. In the years since this startling find, scientists have learned a great deal about the dead man, who they named Ötzi. They know his age, his health, the clothing he wore, what he ate, and that he died from an arrow that ripped through his back. Its tip is still embedded in the back of his left shoulder. From the distribution of chemicals in his teeth and bones, we know he lived his life within 60 kilometers of where he died.

When did this Iceman die? Scientists answered this key question by measuring the degree of decay of the short-lived carbon isotope ^{14}C in Ötzi's body. While most carbon atoms are the stable isotope ^{12}C, a tiny proportion are the unstable radioactive isotope ^{14}C, created by the bombardment of nitrogen-14 (^{14}N) atoms with cosmic rays. This proportion of ^{14}C is captured by plants in photosynthesis and is present in the carbon molecules of the animal's body that eats the plant. After the plant or animal dies, it no longer accumulates any more carbon, and the ^{14}C present at the time of death decays over time back to ^{14}N. Thus, over time the ratio of ^{14}C to ^{12}C decreases. It takes 5,730 years for half of the ^{14}C present to decay, a length of time called the **half-life** of the ^{14}C isotope. Because the half-life is a constant that never changes, the extent of radioactive decay allows you to date a sample. Thus a sample that had one quarter of its original proportion of ^{14}C remaining would be approximately 11,460 years old (two half-lives).

The graph to the right displays the radioactive decay curve of the carbon isotope ^{14}C. Scientists know it takes 5,730 years for half of the ^{14}C present in a sample to decay to nitrogen-14 (^{14}N). When Ötzi's carbon isotopes were analyzed, researchers determined that the ratio of ^{14}C to ^{12}C (a **ratio** is the size of one variable relative to another), also written as the fraction $^{14}C/^{12}C$, in Ötzi's body was 0.435 of the fraction found in tissues of a person who has recently died.

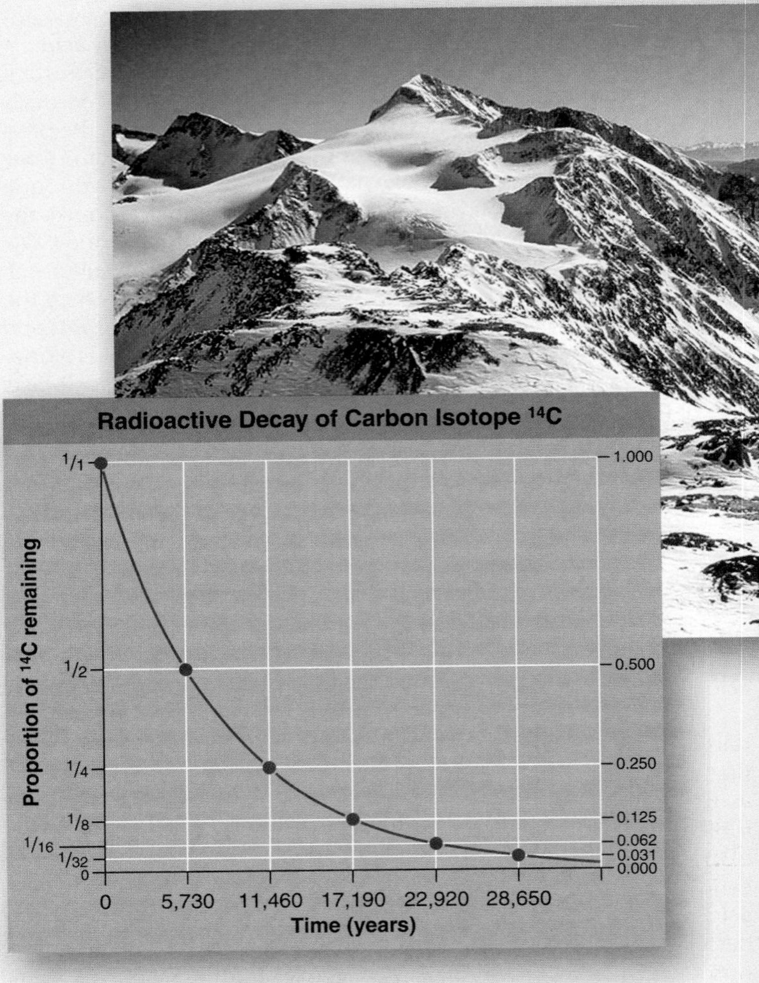

Analysis

1. **Applying Concepts** What proportion (a **proportion** is the size of a variable relative to the whole) of the ^{14}C present in Ötzi's body when he died is still there today? When he died, it would have been 1.0.
2. **Interpreting Data** Plot this proportion on the ^{14}C radioactive decay curve above. How many half-lives does this point represent?
3. **Making Inferences** If Ötzi were indeed a recent corpse, made to look old by the harsh weather conditions found on the high mountain pass, what would you expect the ratio of ^{14}C to ^{12}C to be, relative to that in your own body?
4. **Drawing Conclusions** When did Ötzi the Iceman die?

Summary of Learning Outcomes

Some Simple Chemistry

Atoms

2.1.1 An atom is the smallest particle that retains the chemical properties of its substance. Atoms contain a core nucleus of protons and neutrons; electrons spin around the nucleus. The number of electrons equals the number of protons in a typical atom.

- The number of protons in an atom is called its atomic number. The mass that is contributed by the protons and neutrons is called the atom's mass number. All atoms that have the same atomic number are said to be the same element.

2.1.2 Protons are positively charged particles, and neutron particles carry no charge. Electrons are negatively charged particles that orbit around the nucleus at different energy levels. Electrons determine the chemical behavior of an atom because they are the subatomic particles that interact with other atoms.

2.1.3 It takes energy to hold the electrons in their orbits; this energy of position is called potential energy. The amount of potential energy of an electron is based on its distance from the nucleus.

- Most electron shells hold up to eight electrons and atoms will undergo chemical reactions in order to fill the outermost electron shell, either by gaining, losing, or sharing electrons.

Ions and Isotopes

2.2.1 Ions are atoms that have either gained one or more electrons (negative ions called anions) or lost one or more electrons (positive ions called cations).

2.2.2 Isotopes are atoms that have the same number of protons but differing numbers of neutrons. Isotopes tend to be unstable and break up into other elements through a process called radioactive decay. All isotopes of an atom have the same chemical properties.

Molecules

2.3.1 Molecules are atoms linked together by chemical bonds. There are three main types of chemical bonds.

2.3.2 Ionic bonds form when ions of opposite electrical charge are attracted to each other. Table salt is formed by ionic bonds between positive sodium ions and negative chloride ions.

2.3.3 Most biological molecules are held together by covalent bonds. Covalent bonds form when two atoms share electrons, attempting to fill empty electron orbitals. Covalent bonds are stronger when more electrons are shared. The sharing of two pairs of electrons in a double covalent bond, shown here from **figure 2.10**, is stronger than a single covalent bond, and a triple bond is even stronger.

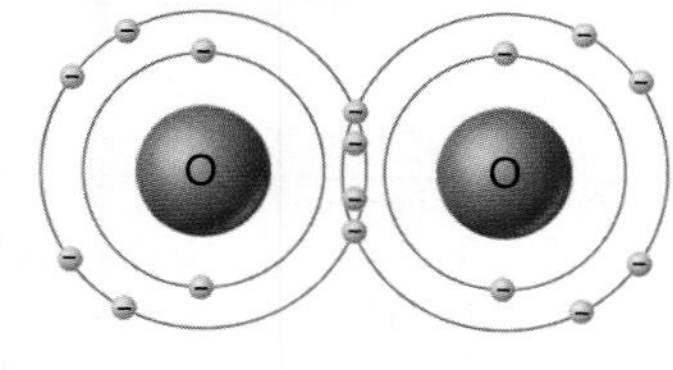

2.3.4 The atoms in a polar molecule are held together by covalent bonds in which the shared electrons are unevenly distributed around their nuclei, giving the molecule a slightly positive end and a slightly negative end. Hydrogen bonds form when the positive end of one molecule is attracted to the negative end of another.

- Hydrogen bonds form between polar molecules, typically between an electropositive hydrogen atom of one polar molecule and an electronegative oxygen or nitrogen atom of another polar molecule.

2.3.5 Weak chemical attractions, called van der Waals forces, can hold two atoms together temporarily when they come into contact. However, van der Waals forces are not considered chemical bonds.

Water: Cradle of Life

Unique Properties of Water

2.4.1 Water molecules form a network of hydrogen bonds with each other in liquid, and dissolve other polar molecules. Many of the key properties of water arise because it takes considerable energy to break liquid water's many hydrogen bonds.

- Because water molecules are attracted to each other by hydrogen bonds, a significant amount of heat energy is needed to pull the molecules apart. For this reason, water heats up slowly and holds its temperature longer.

2.4.2 The hydrogen bonds that hold water molecules together become more stable at lower temperatures and as a result they lock water molecules into place in solid crystal structures called ice, such as that shown here from **figure 2.12**. Individual water molecules maintain a set distance from neighboring molecules due to the stable formation of the hydrogen bonds. In liquid water, hydrogen bonds break and reform, allowing individual water molecules more movement, bringing them into closer proximity to each other. This results in a substance that is more dense than ice.

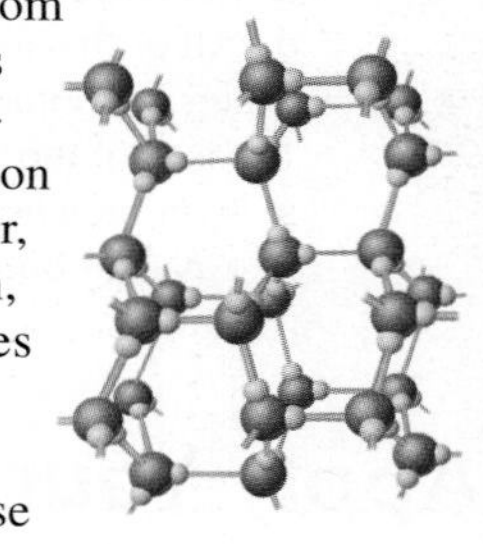

2.4.3 In order for water to vaporize into a gas, a significant input of heat energy is needed to break the hydrogen bonds. This high heat of vaporization is a property of water used by our bodies in regulating body temperature.

2.4.4 Because water molecules are polar molecules, they will form hydrogen bonds with other polar molecules. If the other polar molecules are water molecules, the process is called cohesion. If the other polar molecules are some other substance, the process is called adhesion.

2.4.5 When water molecules form hydrogen bonds with other polar molecules, water molecules will tend to surround other polar molecules, forming a barrier around them called a hydration shell. Polar molecules are said to be hydrophilic and are water-soluble. Nonpolar molecules do not form hydrogen bonds and will cluster together when placed in water. They are said to be hydrophobic and are water-insoluble.

Water Ionizes

2.5.1 A tiny fraction of water molecules spontaneously ionize at any moment, forming H^+ and OH^- ions. The pH of a solution is a measure of its H^+ concentration. Low pH values indicate high H^+ ion concentrations (acidic solutions), and high pH values indicate low H^+ ion concentrations (basic solutions).

- An acid has a pH below 7. A base has a pH above 7. A buffer is a chemical substance that minimizes changes in pH by taking up excess H^+ in acidic solution, or releasing H^+ in basic solutions.

Test Your Understanding

2.1.1 The smallest particle into which a substance can be divided and still retain all of its chemical properties is
a. matter. **c.** a molecule.
b. an atom. **d.** mass.

2.2.1 An atom that has gained or lost one or more electrons is
a. an isotope. **c.** an ion.
b. a neutron. **d.** radioactive.

2.3.1 Atoms are held together by a force called a chemical bond. The three types of chemical bond are
a. positive, negative, and neutral.
b. hydrophobic, hydrophilic, and van der Waals interactions.
c. magnetic, electric, and radioactive.
d. ionic, covalent, and hydrogen.

2.3.3 Carbon has four electrons in its outer electron shell, therefore
a. it has a completely filled outer electron shell.
b. it can form four single covalent bonds.
c. it does not react with any other atom.
d. it has a positive charge.

2.3.3 The partial separation of charge in the water molecule
a. results from the electrons' greater attraction to the oxygen atom.
b. means the molecule has a positive end and a negative end.
c. indicates that the water molecule is a polar molecule.
d. All of the above.

2.4.1 Water has some very unusual properties. These properties occur because of the
a. hydrogen bonds between the individual water molecules.
b. covalent bonds between the individual water molecules.
c. hydrogen bonds within each individual water molecule.
d. ionic bonds between the individual water molecules.

2.4.3 Which of the following properties are somehow related to the need for significant heat energy to break hydrogen bonds?
a. cohesion and adhesion
b. hydrophobic and hydrophilic
c. heat storage and heat of vaporization
d. ice formation and high polarity

2.4.4 The attraction of water molecules to other water molecules is called
a. cohesion. **c.** solubility.
b. capillary action. **d.** adhesion.

2.5.1 Water sometimes ionizes, a single molecule breaking apart into a hydrogen ion and a hydroxide ion. Other materials may dissociate in water, resulting in either (1) an increase of hydrogen ions or (2) decrease of hydrogen ions in the solution. We call the results
a. (1) acids and (2) bases.
b. (1) bases and (2) acids.
c. (1) neutral solutions and (2) neutronic solutions.
d. (1) hydrogen solutions and (2) hydroxide solutions.

2.5.1 Which of the following is *not* true about buffers?
a. A buffer takes up H^+ from the solution.
b. A buffer keeps the pH relatively constant.
c. A buffer stops water from ionizing.
d. A buffer releases H^+ into the solution.

Apply Your Understanding

2.3.3 This figure shows an oxygen atom forming covalent bonds with two hydrogen atoms. A carbon atom, like oxygen, has two electrons in its innermost shell, but only four electrons in its outermost shell. Using this water molecule and figure 2.10 as guides, draw a diagram showing how carbon forms covalent bonds with two oxygen atoms in a carbon dioxide (CO_2) molecule.

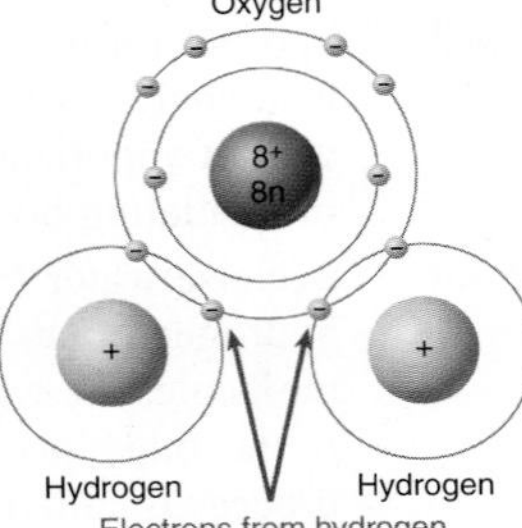

2.4.4 This insect is walking on water. Why doesn't it sink?

Synthesize What You Have Learned

2.1.3 Hydrogen forms a diatomic gas, H_2 (H-H). Oxygen does as well, O_2 (O=O). So does nitrogen, N_2 (N≡N). Carbon does not. Why do you suppose carbon does not form a C_2 diatomic gas?

2.3.3 Explain why it is possible for a bacterium to break the triple covalent bond of N_2 gas, whereas you and other animals cannot.

2.5.1 You are on a 10-day backpacking trip with a small group of friends. Yvonne has washed out a set of water bottles with bleach. Before she can rinse them, Carlos, hot and thirsty, picks one up and drinks it, drops it, and begins to choke. What is the problem, and what can you do for him?

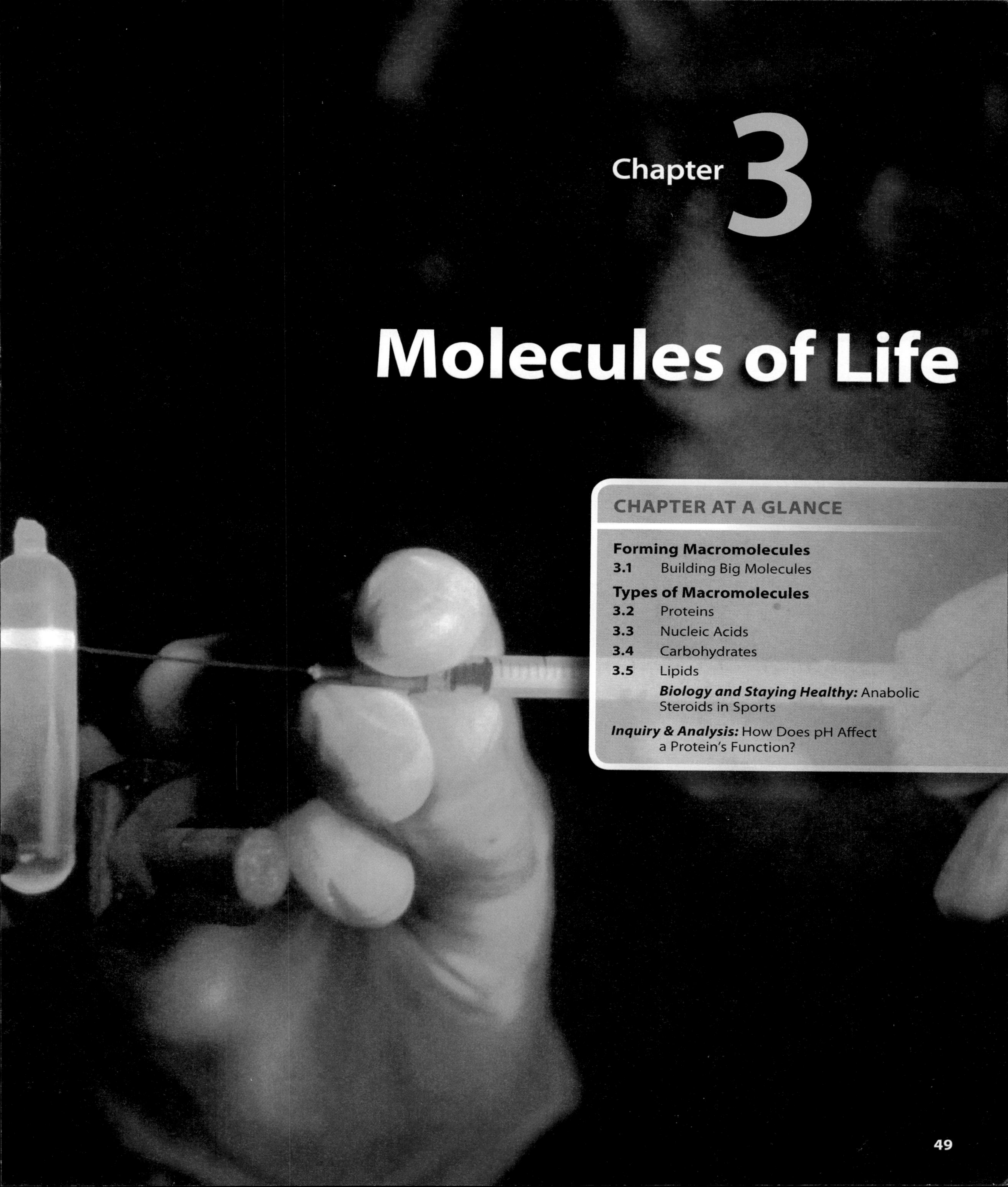

Chapter 3

Molecules of Life

CHAPTER AT A GLANCE

Forming Macromolecules

3.1 Building Big Molecules

Types of Macromolecules

3.2 Proteins

3.3 Nucleic Acids

3.4 Carbohydrates

3.5 Lipids

Biology and Staying Healthy: Anabolic Steroids in Sports

Inquiry & Analysis: How Does pH Affect a Protein's Function?

Forming Macromolecules

Nutrition Facts

Serving Size 2 tbsp (33g) (makes 3.5 cups popped)
Servings Per Bag about 3
Servings Per Box about 9

Amount Per Serving	2 tbsp (33g) Unpopped	Per 1 cup Popped
Calories	170	35
Calories from Fat	90	20
	% Daily Value**	
Total Fat 10g*	**15%**	**3%**
Saturated Fat 2g	**10%**	**0%**
Trans Fat 3.5g		
Cholesterol 0mg	**0%**	**0%**
Sodium 440mg	**18%**	**4%**
Total Carbohydrate 19g	**6%**	**1%**
Dietary Fiber 3g	**12%**	**4%**
Sugars 0g		
Protein 3g		
Iron	6%	0%

Figure 3.1 What's in a nutritional label?

Fats, cholesterol, carbohydrates, and proteins—just some of the molecules found in popcorn and in other foods—are discussed in this chapter.

Group	Structural Formula	Ball-and-Stick Model	Found In
Hydroxyl	—OH	O H	Carbohydrates
Carbonyl	>C=O	C O	Lipids
Carboxyl	—C(=O)OH	C O O H	Proteins
Amino	—N(H)H	H N H	Proteins
Phosphate	—O—P(O⁻)(=O)—O⁻	O⁻ O P O⁻ O	DNA, ATP

Figure 3.2 Five principal functional groups.

These functional groups can be transferred from one molecule to another and are common in organic molecules.

IMPLICATION FOR YOU The hydroxyl group present in carbohydrates like bread is also common in household bleach. Why do you think you can eat bread but not drink bleach?

3.1 Building Big Molecules

LEARNING OBJECTIVE 3.1.1 Distinguish between a polymer and a monomer.

The bodies of organisms contain thousands of different kinds of molecules and atoms. Organisms obtain many of these molecules from their surroundings and from what they consume. You might be familiar with some of the substances listed on nutritional labels, such as the one shown in figure 3.1. But what do the words on these labels mean? Some of them are names of minerals, such as calcium and iron (discussed in chapters 23, 25, 32, and others). Others are vitamins, which are discussed in chapter 26. Still others are the subject of this chapter: large molecules that are found in our food and that make up the bodies of organisms, such as proteins, carbohydrates (including sugars), and lipids (including fats, trans fats, saturated fats, and cholesterol). These molecules, called *organic molecules,* are formed by living organisms and consist of a carbon-based core with special groups attached. These groups of atoms have special chemical properties and are referred to as *functional groups.* Functional groups, like those listed in figure 3.2, tend to act as units during chemical reactions and confer specific chemical properties on the molecules that possess them.

The bodies of organisms contain thousands of different kinds of organic molecules, but much of the body is made of just four kinds: *proteins, nucleic acids, carbohydrates,* and *lipids.* Called **macromolecules** because they can be very large, these four are the building materials of cells, the "bricks and mortar" that make up the body of a cell and the machinery that runs within it.

Macromolecules are assembled by sticking smaller bits, called **monomers,** together much as a train is built by linking rail-cars together. A molecule built up of long chains of similar subunits is called a **polymer.**

Putting the Concept to Work

Which functional group is not present in either proteins or carbohydrates?

Making (and Breaking) Macromolecules

LEARNING OBJECTIVE 3.1.2 Contrast hydrolysis with dehydration synthesis.

The four different kinds of macromolecules (proteins, nucleic acids, carbohydrates, and lipids) are built from different monomers, as shown in figure 3.3, but all have their subunits put together in the same way. A covalent bond is formed between two subunits in which a hydroxyl group (OH) is removed from one subunit and a hydrogen (H) is removed from the other. This process, illustrated in figure 3.4*a*, is called *dehydration synthesis* because, in effect, the removal of the OH and H groups (highlighted by the blue oval) constitutes removal

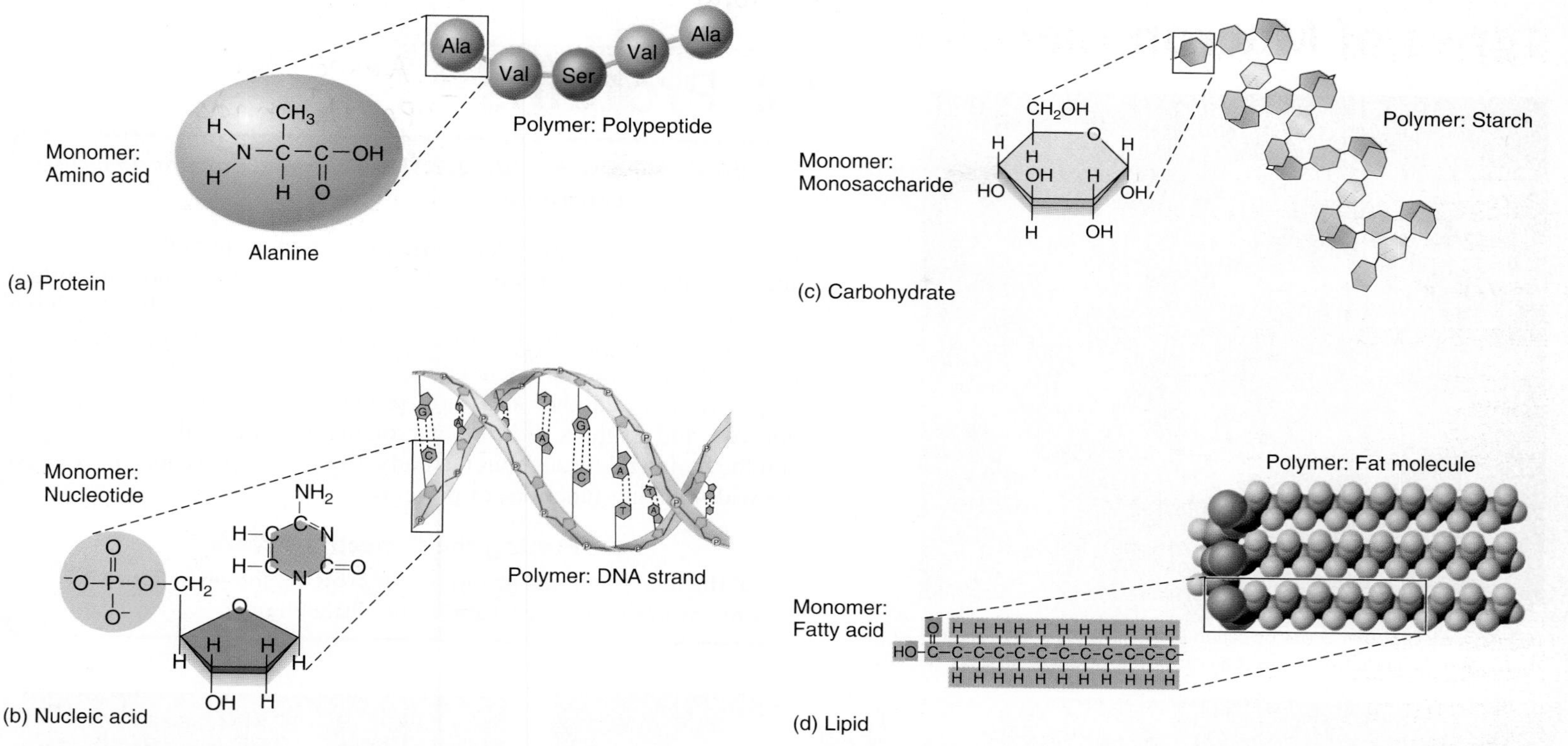

Monomer: Amino acid

Alanine

Polymer: Polypeptide

(a) Protein

Monomer: Monosaccharide

Polymer: Starch

(c) Carbohydrate

Monomer: Nucleotide

Polymer: DNA strand

(b) Nucleic acid

Monomer: Fatty acid

Polymer: Fat molecule

(d) Lipid

Figure 3.3 Polymers are built from monomers.

Each macromolecule polymer is built from different monomers. (a) A protein polymer, called a polypeptide, is built from amino acid monomers. (b) A nucleic acid polymer, such as a strand of DNA, is built from nucleotide monomers. (c) A carbohydrate polymer, such as a starch molecule, is built from monosaccharide monomers. (d) A lipid polymer, such as a fat molecule, is built from fatty acids.

of a molecule of water—the word *dehydration* means "taking away water." This process requires the help of a special class of proteins called **enzymes** to facilitate the positioning of the molecules so that the correct chemical bonds are stressed and broken. The process of tearing down a molecule such as the protein or fat contained in the food you eat is essentially the reverse of dehydration synthesis: instead of removing a water molecule, one is added. When a water molecule comes in, as shown in figure 3.4*b*, a hydrogen becomes attached to one subunit and a hydroxyl to another, and the covalent bond is broken. The breaking up of a polymer in this way is called **hydrolysis.**

Recall from page 44 that water molecules will undergo a process of ionization, where the molecule dissociates into H^+ and OH^- ions. Enzymes can help facilitate this process thereby facilitating dehydration and hydrolysis reactions in the cell.

Putting the Concept to Work

Do you think hydrolysis of a protein requires an enzyme like dehydration synthesis does? Explain.

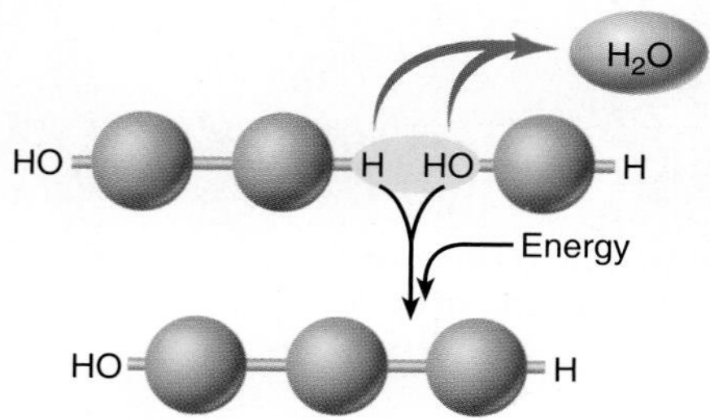

(a) Dehydration synthesis

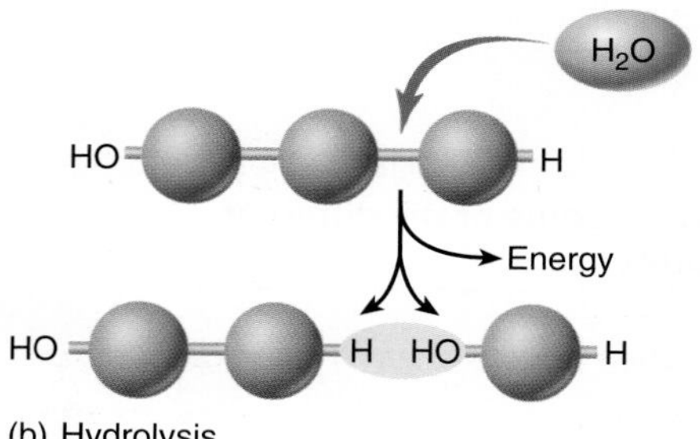

(b) Hydrolysis

Figure 3.4 Dehydration and hydrolysis.

(a) Biological molecules are formed by linking subunits with a covalent bond in a dehydration synthesis, during which a water molecule is released. (b) Breaking such a bond requires the addition of a water molecule, a reaction called hydrolysis.

Types of Macromolecules

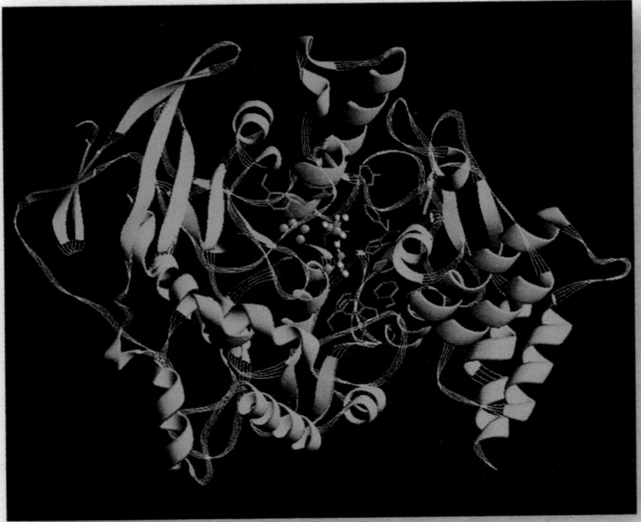

(a) **Enzymes:** Globular proteins called enzymes play a key role in many chemical reactions. This is a computer model of an enzyme.

3.2 Proteins

LEARNING OBJECTIVE 3.2.1 **Explain what proteins do by listing five functional groupings of proteins.**

Complex macromolecules called **proteins** are important biological macromolecules within the bodies of all organisms. One of the most important types of proteins are *enzymes,* which have the key role in cells of helping to carry out particular chemical reactions. Other proteins play structural roles. Cartilage, bones, and tendons all contain a structural protein called collagen. Keratin, another structural protein, forms hair, the horns of a rhinoceros, and feathers. Still other proteins act as chemical messengers within the brain and throughout the body. Figure 3.5 presents an overview of the wide-ranging functions of proteins.

Putting the Concept to Work

Of the five functional groupings of proteins shown in figure 3.5, are any of them not present in your little finger?

(b) **Structural proteins (keratin):** Keratin forms hair, nails, feathers, and components of horns.

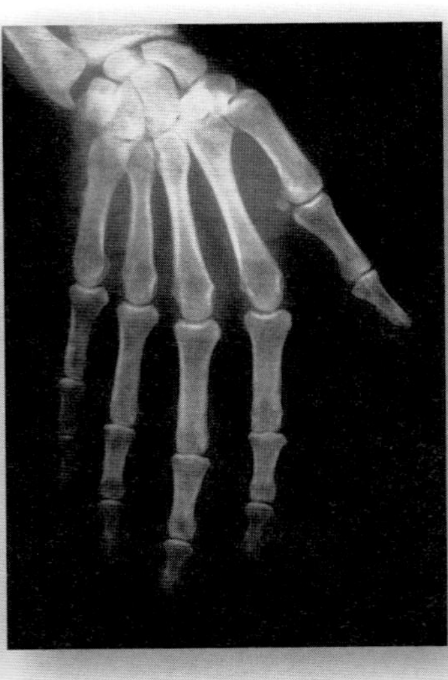

(c) **Structural proteins (collagen):** Collagen is present in bones, tendons, and cartilage.

(d) **Contractile proteins:** Proteins called actin and myosin are present in muscles.

Figure 3.5 **Some of the different types of proteins.**

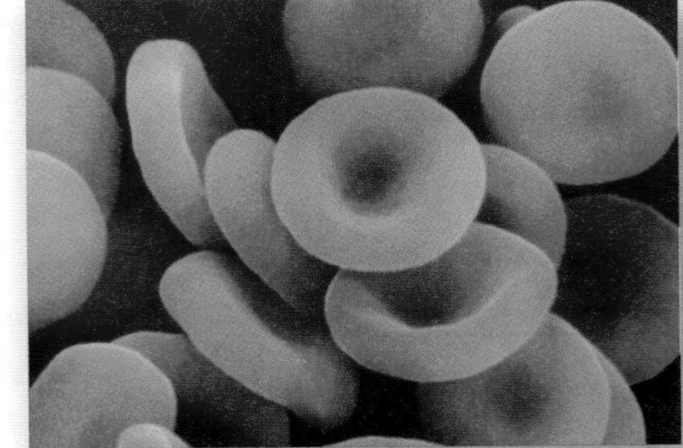

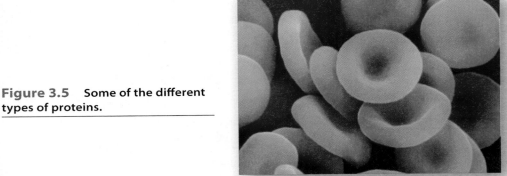

(e) **Transport proteins:** Red blood cells contain the protein hemoglobin, which transports oxygen in the body.

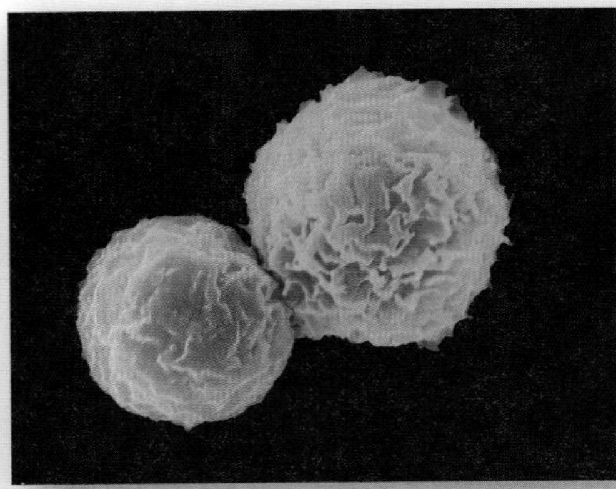

(f) **Defensive proteins:** White blood cells destroy foreign cells in the body and make antibody proteins that attack invaders.

Amino Acids

LEARNING OBJECTIVE 3.2.2 Diagram the structure of an amino acid, and the formation of a peptide bond.

Despite their diverse functions, all proteins have the same basic structure: a long polymer chain made of subunits called amino acids. **Amino acids** are small molecules with a simple basic structure: a central carbon atom attached to an amino group (—NH_2), a carboxyl group (—COOH), a hydrogen atom (H), and a functional group, designated "R."

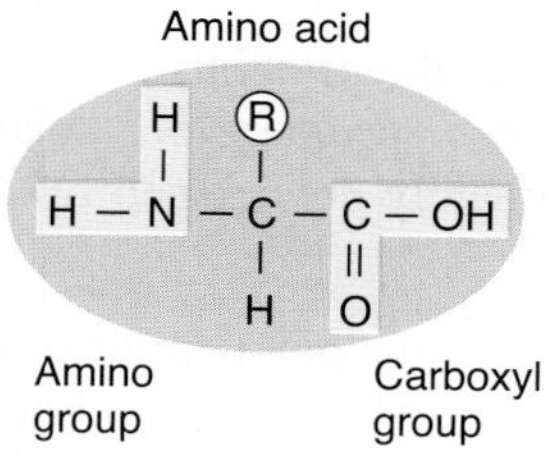

There are 20 common amino acids that differ from one another by the identity of their functional R group. The R group of an amino acid largely determines its chemical properties. Some amino acid R groups are polar, interacting with water; some are nonpolar, shying away from water; and others have special chemical groups that are important in forming links between protein chains or in forming kinks in their shapes.

Linking Amino Acids. An individual protein is made by linking specific amino acids together in a particular order, just as a word is made by putting letters of the alphabet together in a particular order. The covalent bond linking two amino acids together is called a **peptide bond** (figure 3.6). You can see in the figure below that a water molecule is released as the peptide bond forms. Long chains of amino acids linked by peptide bonds are called **polypeptides.**

Putting the Concept to Work

Why don't the amino groups of amino acids make all proteins polar?

IN THE NEWS

Deadly Baby Food. Babies the world over live on milk, rich in proteins, fats, and other nutrients. In China in 2008 thousands of babies became critically ill from the formula they were fed. Why did they get sick? The manufacturer of the baby formula purchased the milk used to make the formula from milk traders. The milk traders buy raw milk from small farmers and mix it together to resell. In order to maximize their profits, some traders were adding water to the milk to increase their volumes. Manufacturers in China routinely check the protein level of milk by measuring the amount of nitrogen the milk contains. Protein is the only significant source of nitrogen in milk and so nitrogen is an indicator of the levels of protein. Diluted milk would reveal lower than normal amounts of nitrogen and so would be rejected. To get around this, some traders added the chemical melamine to their diluted milk. Used in making plastics and fertilizers, melamine ($C_3H_6N_6$) is rich in nitrogen, allowing the diluted milk to fool the manufacturers' test. Tragically, melamine causes kidney failure in infants. In the United States commercial milk is checked more carefully. In the future it will be checked in China as well.

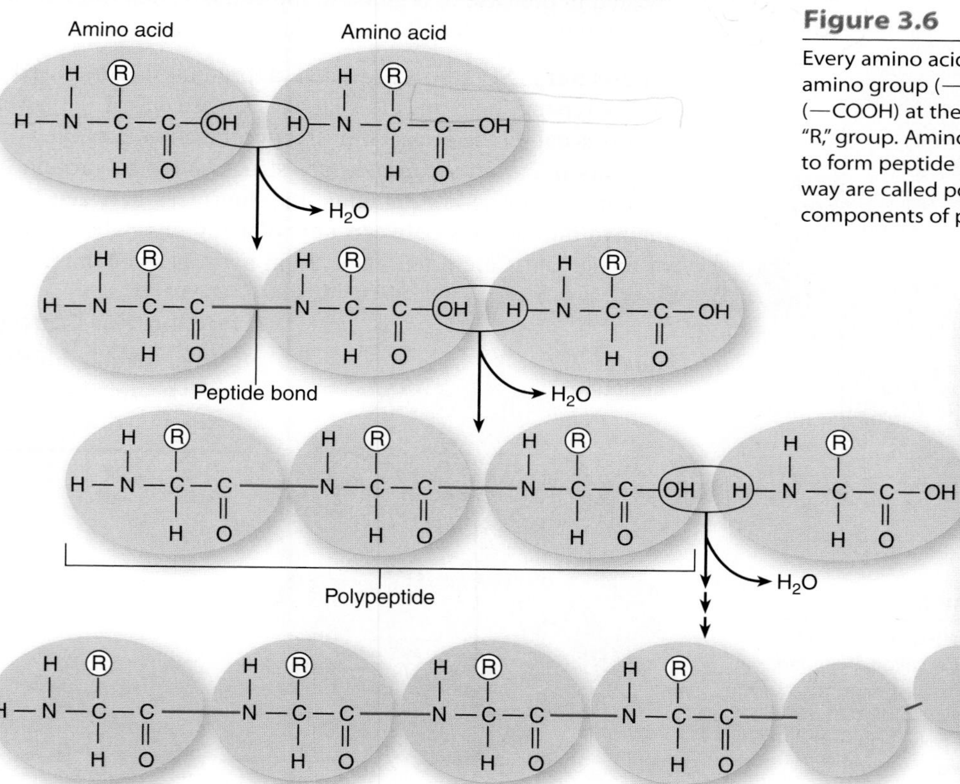

Figure 3.6 The formation of a peptide bond.

Every amino acid has the same basic structure, with an amino group (—NH_2) at one end and a carboxyl group (—COOH) at the other. The only variable is the functional, or "R," group. Amino acids are linked by dehydration synthesis to form peptide bonds. Chains of amino acids linked in this way are called polypeptides and are the basic structural components of proteins, such as keratin in human hair.

Protein Structure

LEARNING OBJECTIVE 3.2.3 Describe the four general levels of protein structure, and how the polar nature of water influences them.

Functional polypeptides are more commonly called proteins. Some proteins, like keratin in human hair, form long, thin fibers, whereas others are globular, their strands coiled up and folded back on themselves. The shape of a protein is very important because it determines the protein's function. There are four general levels of protein structure: primary, secondary, tertiary, and quaternary (figure 3.7); all are ultimately determined by the sequence of amino acids.

Primary Structure. The sequence of amino acids of a polypeptide chain is termed the polypeptide's **primary structure.** The amino acids are linked together by peptide bonds, forming long chains like a "beaded strand." The primary structure of a protein, the sequence of its amino acids, determines all other levels of protein structure. Because amino acids can be assembled in any sequence, a great diversity of proteins is possible.

Secondary Structure. Hydrogen bonds forming between different parts of the polypeptide chain stabilize the folding of the polypeptide. As you can see, these stabilizing hydrogen bonds, indicated by red dotted lines, do not involve the R groups themselves, but rather the polypeptide backbone. This initial folding is called the **secondary structure** of a protein. Hydrogen bonding within this secondary structure can fold the polypeptide into coils, called α-helices, and sheets, called β-pleated sheets.

Tertiary Structure. Because some of the amino acids are nonpolar, a polypeptide chain folds up in water, which is very polar, pushing nonpolar amino acid functional groups from the watery environment. The final three-dimensional shape, or **tertiary structure,** of the protein, folded and twisted in the case of a globular molecule, is determined by exactly where in a polypeptide chain the nonpolar amino acids occur.

Quaternary Structure. When a protein is composed of more than one polypeptide chain, the spatial arrangement of the several component chains is called the **quaternary structure** of the protein. For example, four subunits make up the quaternary structure of the protein hemoglobin. In proteins composed of subunits, the interfaces between the subunits often involve interactions between nonpolar regions, whereas the polar regions of the subunits are often involved in hydrogen bonding.

Putting the Concept to Work

What force holds the subunits of a protein like hemoglobin together?

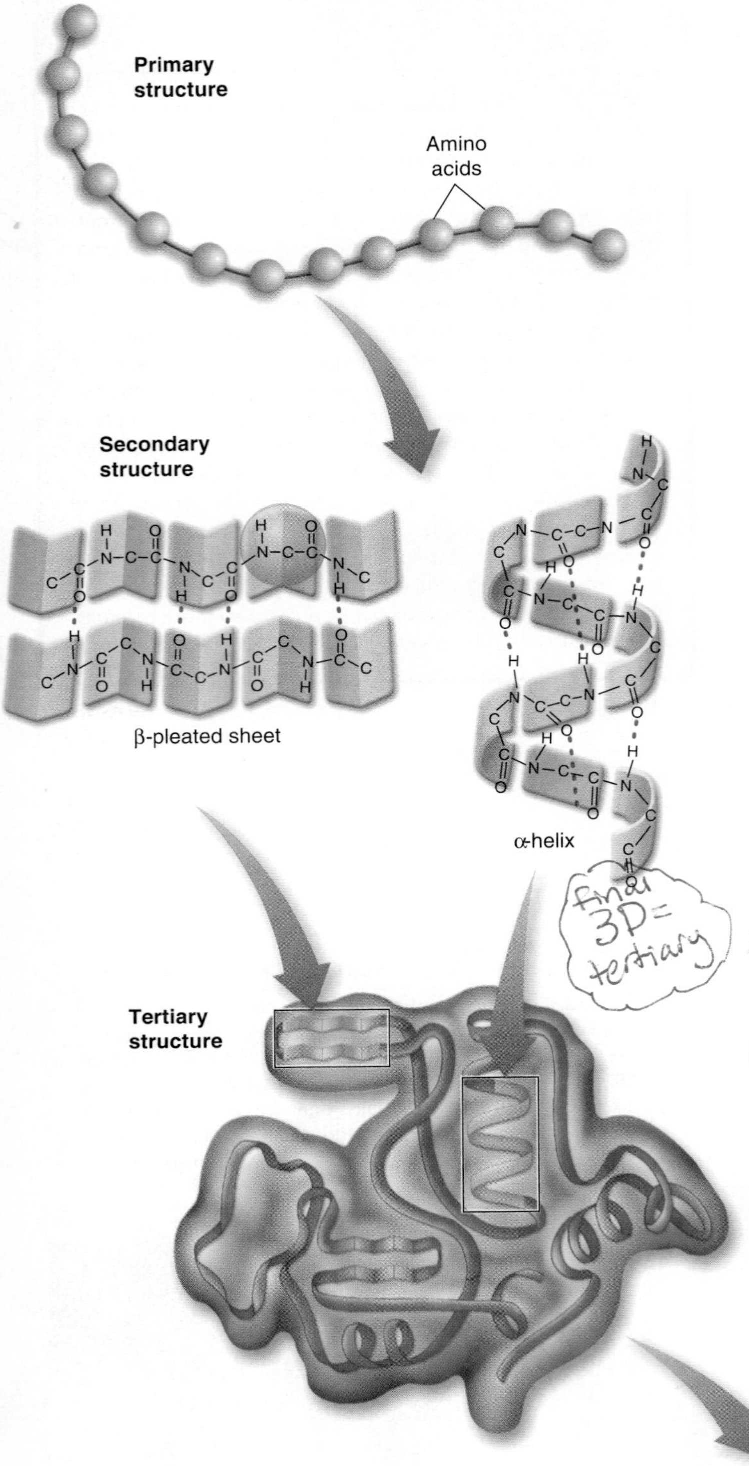

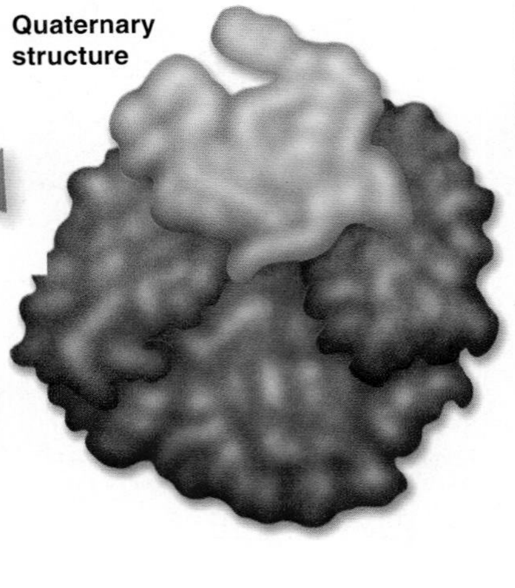

Figure 3.7 Levels of protein structure.

The *primary structure* of a protein is its sequence of amino acids. Twisting or pleating of the chain of amino acids, called *secondary structure,* is due to the formation of localized hydrogen bonds (the *red* dotted lines) within the chain. More-complex folding of the chain is referred to as *tertiary structure.* Two or more polypeptide chains associated together form a *quaternary structure.*

Protein Folding and Denaturation

LEARNING OBJECTIVE 3.2.4 Explain the forces that cause a protein to denature.

The polar nature of the watery environment in the cell influences how the polypeptide folds into the functional protein. The protein in figure 3.8 is folded in such a way that allows it to carry out its function. If the polar nature of the protein's environment changes by either increasing temperature or lowering pH, both of which alter hydrogen bonding, the protein may unfold, as in the lower right of the figure. When this happens the protein is said to be *denatured*. When proteins are denatured, they usually lose their ability to function properly. When the polar nature of the solvent is reestablished, some proteins may spontaneously refold, but most don't. Cooking an egg is an example of denaturing proteins that do not refold. The egg proteins denature as temperature increases, but do not refold as the egg cools down—they are permanently denatured. Protein denaturation is also the rationale behind traditional methods of preserving food. Prior to the ready availability of refrigerators and freezers, a practical way to keep microorganisms from growing in food was to keep the food in a solution containing a high concentration of vinegar, a treatment called pickling. The low pH of the vinegar denatures proteins in microorganisms and so keeps them from growing on the food.

You will discover on page 96 how enzyme function is affected by temperature and pH. Most enzymes have optimal ranges of temperature and pH. Conditions above or below their ranges can interfere with enzyme function.

Putting the Concept to Work

Why do you think most heat-denatured proteins don't spontaneously refold when they cool back to room temperature?

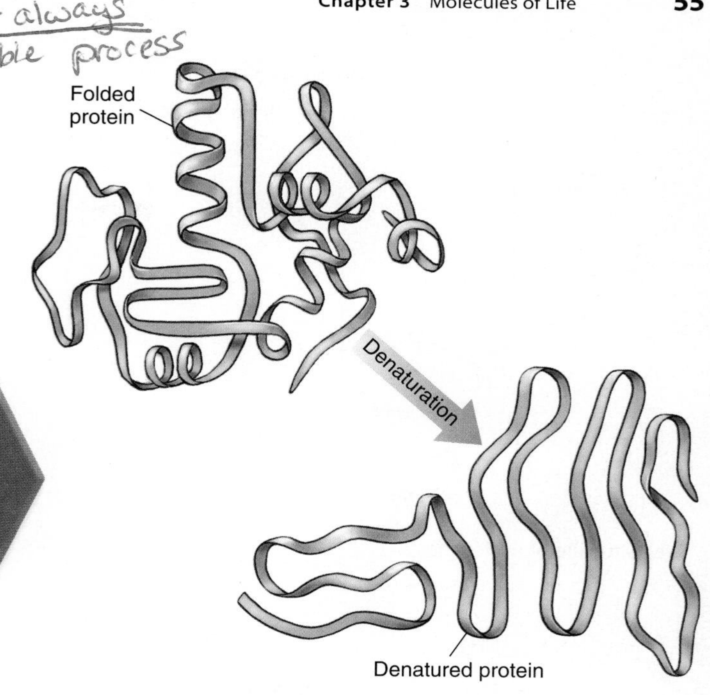

Figure 3.8 Protein denaturation.

Changes in a protein's environment, such as variations in temperature or pH, can cause a protein to unfold and lose its shape in a process called denaturation. In this denatured state, proteins are biologically inactive.

IMPLICATION FOR YOU A tiger can eat raw meat with relish, but most of us humans prefer our steak cooked. Is this just a matter of taste, or does cooking meat before eating it have any benefit?

Protein Structure Determines Function

LEARNING OBJECTIVE 3.2.5 Describe how the structure of an enzyme enables it to catalyze a chemical reaction.

The three-dimensional shape of a protein determines its function. For example, many structural proteins assume long cable-like shapes that let them play architectural roles within cells (figure 3.9*a*). *Enzymes* are globular proteins that help particular chemical reactions to occur in the cell. When the polypeptide folds correctly, the enzyme surface has a groove or depression that precisely fits a particular molecule. For example, the red molecule binding to the groove on the surface of the enzyme in figure 3.9*b* is a sugar. Once within the groove, the molecule is induced to undergo a chemical reaction, such as the formation or breaking of one of its covalent bonds. By bringing two atoms close together, an enzyme can make it easier for them to share electrons and form covalent bonds. Other enzymes function by positioning a molecule so that there is stress on a particular bond so that it breaks.

Because the primary structure of a protein (its sequence of amino acids) determines how the protein folds into its functional shape, a change in the identity of even one amino acid can have profound effects on a protein's shape, and so on its ability to function properly.

Putting the Concept to Work

What sorts of chemicals might act to block the action of a particular enzyme and not others?

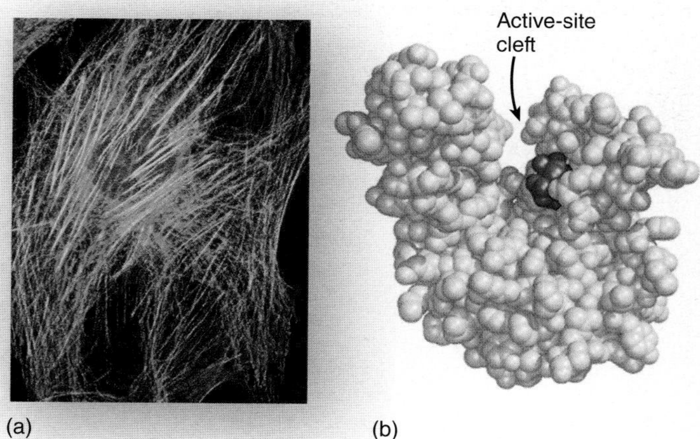

Figure 3.9 Protein structure determines function.

(a) Fluorescently labeled structural proteins within a cell.
(b) Enzymes are globular proteins that aid chemical reactions in the cell. This enzyme (*blue*) has a deep groove that binds a specific chemical (*red*) at a site on the enzyme called the active site.

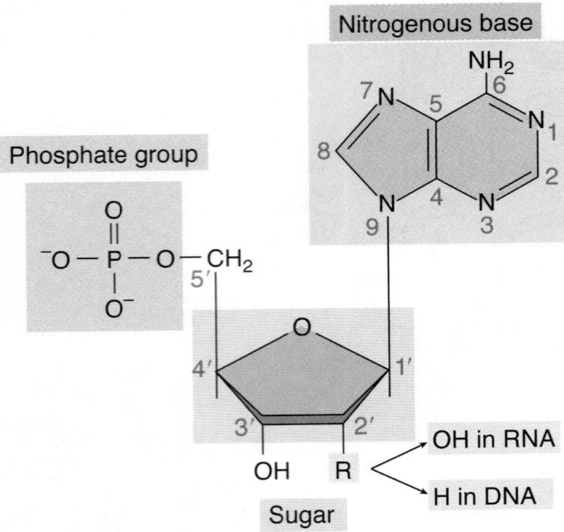

(a) Structure of nucleotide

Adenine

Guanine

Cytosine

Thymine (DNA only)

Uracil (RNA only)

(b) Nitrogenous bases

Figure 3.10 The structure of a nucleotide.

(a) Nucleotides are composed of three parts: a five-carbon sugar, a phosphate group, and an organic nitrogenous base. The nitrogenous base can be one of five, shown in (b).

3.3 Nucleic Acids

Nucleotides

LEARNING OBJECTIVE 3.3.1 Name the three parts of a nucleotide.

Very long polymers called **nucleic acids** serve as the genetic information storage devices of cells, just as DVDs or hard drives store the information that computers use. Nucleic acids are long polymers of repeating subunits called **nucleotides.** Each nucleotide is a complex organic molecule composed of three parts shown in figure 3.10*a:* a five-carbon sugar (in blue), a phosphate group (in yellow, PO_4), and an organic nitrogen-containing base (in orange). In the formation of a nucleic acid, the individual sugars with their attached nitrogenous bases are linked through dehydration reactions in a line by the phosphate groups in very long **polynucleotide chains** (shown to the right). The nitrogenous bases extend out from the backbone of the chain.

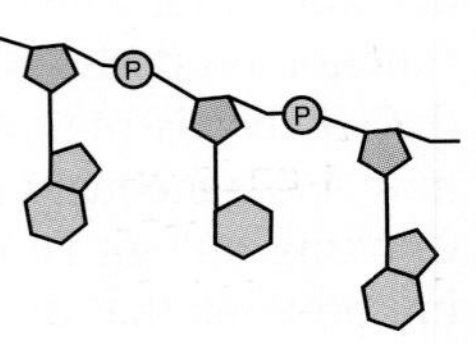

How does the long, chainlike structure of a nucleic acid permit it to store the information necessary to specify what an organism is like? If nucleic acids were simply monotonous repeating polymers, they could not encode the message of life. Imagine trying to write a story using only the letter *E* and no spaces or punctuation. All you could ever say is "EEEEEEE. . . ." You need more than one letter to communicate—the English alphabet uses 26 letters. Nucleic acids can encode information because they contain more than one kind of nucleotide. There are five different nucleotides found in nucleic acids: two larger ones that contain the nitrogenous bases adenine and guanine (shown in the top row of figure 3.10*b*), and three smaller ones that contain the nitrogenous bases cytosine, thymine, and uracil (in the bottom row). Nucleic acids encode information by varying the identity of the nucleotide at each position in the polymer.

Putting the Concept to Work

Try writing a ten-word sentence using only five letters.

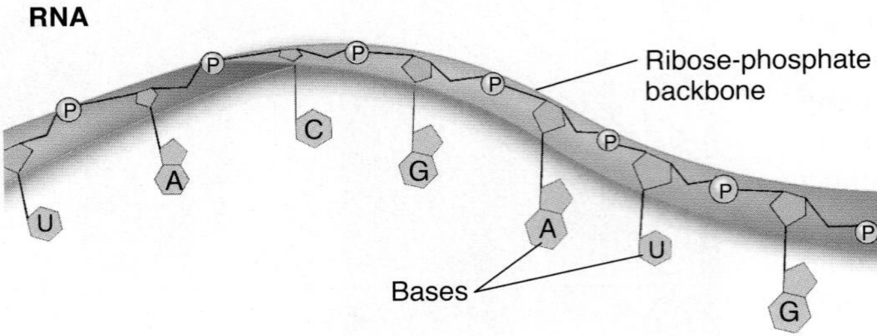

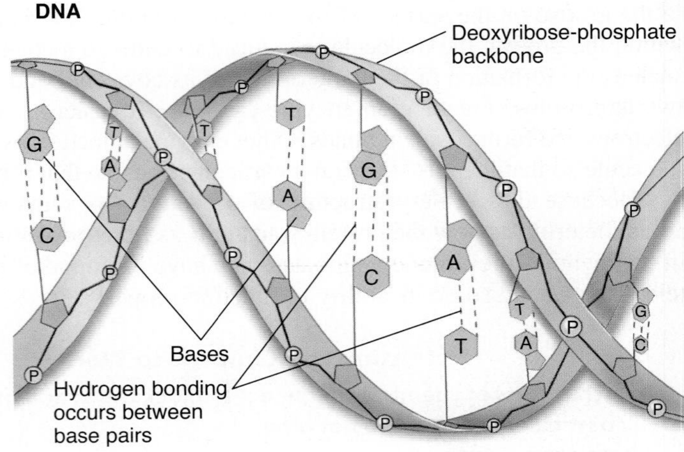

Figure 3.11 How DNA structure differs from RNA.

RNA is a single strand of ribose nucleotides containing uracil (*left*). DNA is a double strand of deoxyribose nucleotides that contain thymine and that are wrapped around each other, A pairing with T and G with C (*right*).

DNA and RNA

LEARNING OBJECTIVE 3.3.2 **State the two major chemical differences between DNA and RNA.**

Nucleic acids come in two varieties, **deoxyribonucleic acid (DNA)** and **ribonucleic acid (RNA).** Both are polymers of nucleotides but they have different functions in the cell and they differ in their structures. RNA is similar to DNA, but with two major chemical differences. First, RNA molecules contain the sugar ribose, in which the 2′ carbon (this is the carbon labeled 2′ in figure 3.10*a*) is bonded to a hydroxyl group (—OH). In DNA, this hydroxyl group is replaced with a hydrogen atom. Second, DNA contains the thymine nucleotide, RNA molecules do not; they contain the uracil nucleotide instead. Structurally, RNA is also different. RNA is a long, single strand of nucleotides (figure 3.11) while DNA consists of *two* polynucleotide chains wound around each other in a **double helix,** like strands of a pearl necklace twisted together (figures 3.11 and 3.12). RNA and DNA also have different roles to play in the cell. DNA stores the genetic information (figure 3.13). The sequence of nucleotides in DNA determines the order of amino acids in the primary structure of the protein. RNA regulates how the information in DNA is used, and carries this information from the DNA to the protein-making machinery in the cell.

Putting the Concept to Work

What prevents RNA from forming a double helix like DNA does?

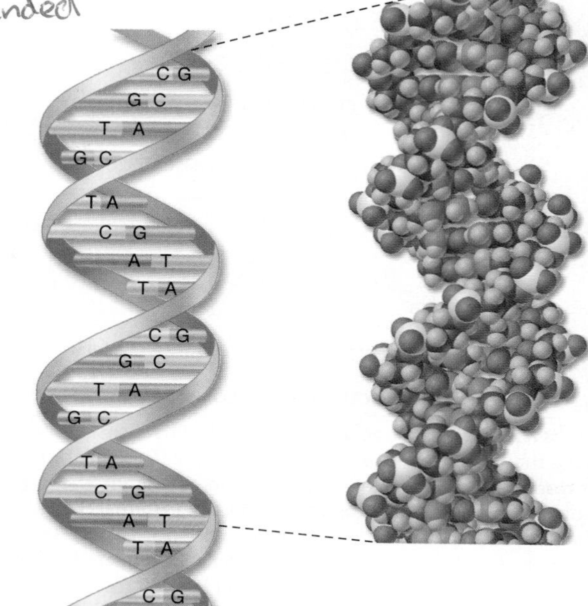

Figure 3.12 **The DNA double helix.**

The DNA molecule is composed of two polynucleotide chains twisted together to form a double helix. The two chains of the double helix are joined by hydrogen bonds between the A–T and G–C base pairs. The section of DNA on the right is a space-filling model of DNA, where atoms are indicated by colored balls.

The Double Helix

LEARNING OBJECTIVE 3.3.3 **Identify what two base pairings are possible in DNA, and explain why the other four potential base pairings do not occur.**

How does DNA form a double helix? Look carefully at the structure of DNA in figure 3.12: the bases of each chain point inward toward the other. The bases of the two chains are linked in the middle of the molecule by hydrogen bonds, like two columns of people holding hands across (see also figure 3.11). The key to understanding the double helix structure of DNA is revealed by looking at the nucleotide bases: *only two base pairs are possible.* Because the distance between the two strands is consistent, this suggests that two big bases cannot pair together—the combination is simply too bulky to fit; similarly, two little ones cannot pair, as they would pinch the helix inward too much. To form a double helix, it is necessary to pair a big base with a little one. *In every DNA double helix, adenine (A) pairs with thymine (T) and guanine (G) pairs with cytosine (C).* The reason A doesn't pair with C and G doesn't pair with T is that these base pairs cannot form proper hydrogen bonds—the electron-sharing atoms are not aligned with each other.

The simple A–T, G–C base pairs within the DNA double helix allow the cell to copy the information in a very simple way. It just unzips the helix and adds the nucleotides with complementary bases to each strand! That is the great advantage of a double helix—it actually contains two copies of the information, one the mirror image of the other. If the sequence of one chain is ATTGCAT, the sequence of its helix partner *must* be TAACGTA.

Putting the Concept to Work

If one chain of a DNA strand has the sequence ACCTGGAAT, what is the sequence of the other strand?

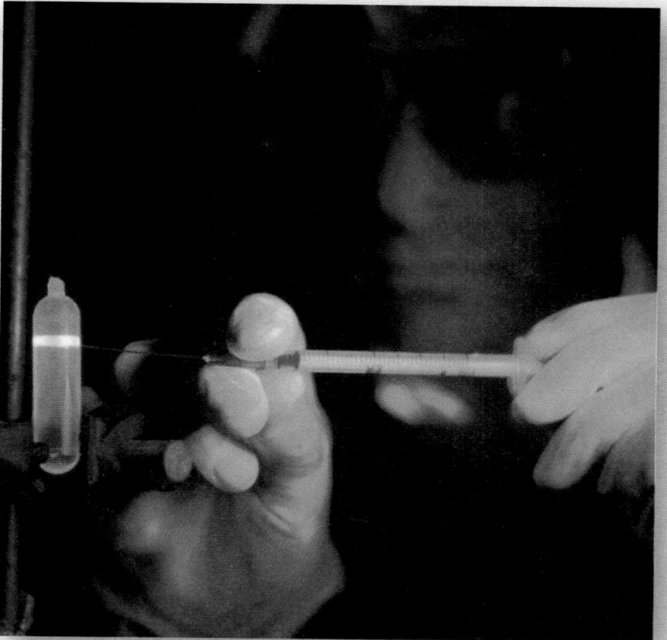

Figure 3.13 **Extracting DNA.**

Working under fluorescent light, this investigator is inserting a syringe into a glowing band of DNA, which can then be extracted and studied. The tube, containing DNA, has been spun by the investigator in a high-speed centrifuge to establish a density gradient. Within the tube, the DNA molecules have migrated to a position on the gradient corresponding to DNA's density. Because this DNA has been fluorescently labeled, its position appears as a glowing band in fluorescent light. Studying DNA helps scientists learn how genes determine what a cell is like.

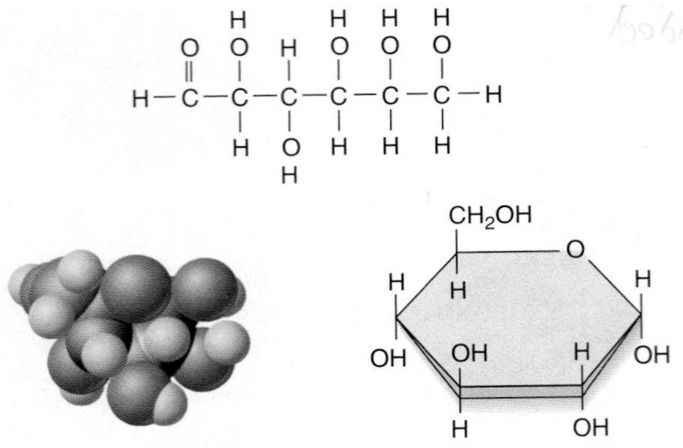

Figure 3.14 The structure of glucose.

Glucose is a monosaccharide and consists of a linear six-carbon molecule that forms a ring when placed in water. This illustration shows three ways glucose can be pictured in a diagram. The long chain of carbon atoms at the top of the figure is its formal chemical structure. When placed in water, the chain folds into the ring structure shown on the lower right. The individual atoms are depicted in the "3-D" space-filling model you see in the lower left.

IMPLICATION FOR YOU Many vitamin and fruit drinks are marketed as being healthier because they are "all natural," with "no refined sugars." Yet reading the nutrition facts label reveals that a single 12-ounce bottle typically contains 29 grams of sugar, often delivered as fructose corn syrup. In what way do you think "natural" sugar is different from "refined" sugar?

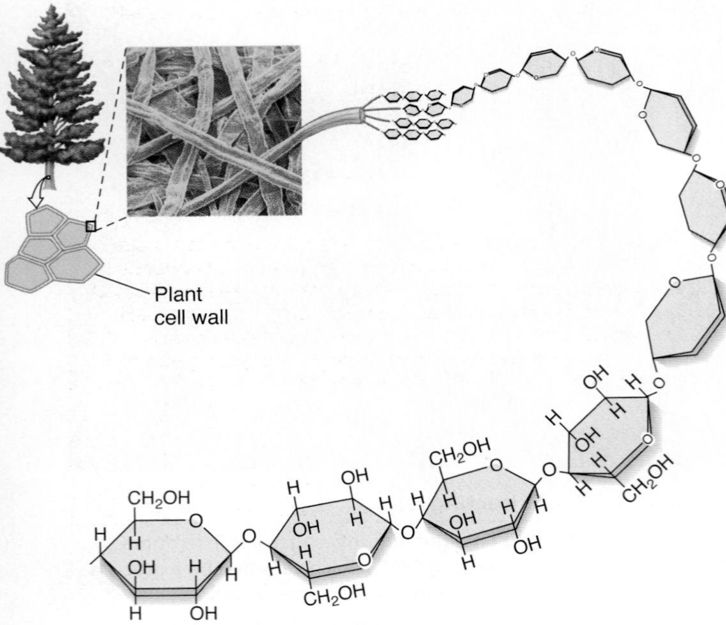

Figure 3.15 A polysaccharide: cellulose.

The polysaccharide cellulose is found in the cell walls of plant cells and is composed of glucose subunits.

3.4 Carbohydrates

LEARNING OBJECTIVE 3.4.1 Define carbohydrate. Distinguish between monosaccharides and polysaccharides.

Polymers called **carbohydrates** make up the structural framework of certain cells and play a critical role in energy storage. A carbohydrate is any molecule that contains carbon, hydrogen, and oxygen in the ratio 1:2:1. Some carbohydrates are small monomers or dimers and are called simple carbohydrates. Others are long polymers and are called complex carbohydrates. Because they contain many carbon-hydrogen (C—H) bonds, carbohydrates are well-suited for energy storage. Such C—H bonds are the ones most often broken by organisms to obtain energy. Table 3.1 on the facing page shows some examples of carbohydrates.

Simple Carbohydrates

The simplest carbohydrates are the *simple sugars* or **monosaccharides** (from the Greek *monos,* single, and *saccharon,* sweet). These molecules consist of one subunit. For example, glucose, the sugar that carries energy to the cells of your body, is made of six carbons and has the chemical formula $C_6H_{12}O_6$. A molecule of glucose is pictured in several ways in figure 3.14. Another type of simple carbohydrate is a **disaccharide,** which forms when two monosaccharides link together through a dehydration reaction. Table sugar is a disaccharide, sucrose, made by linking two six-carbon sugars together, a glucose and a fructose (see table 3.1).

Complex Carbohydrates

Organisms store their metabolic energy by converting sugars, which are water-soluble, into insoluble forms that can be deposited in specific storage areas in the body. This trick is achieved by linking the sugars together into long polymer chains called **polysaccharides.** Plants and animals store energy in polysaccharides formed from glucose. The glucose polysaccharide that plants use to store energy is called *starch*—that is why potatoes are referred to as "starchy" food. In animals, energy is stored in *glycogen,* a highly insoluble macromolecule formed of glucose polysaccharides that are very long and, unlike starch, highly branched.

Plants and animals also use glucose chains as building materials, linking the subunits together in different orientations not recognized by most enzymes. These structural polysaccharides are *chitin* in animals and *cellulose* in plants. The cellulose deposited in the cell walls of plant cells, like the cellulose strand shown in figure 3.15, cannot be digested by humans and makes up the fiber in our diets. Microbes in the digestive tracts of cows and horses, however, have the cellulose-digesting enzymes we humans lack. The microbial enzyme breaks the bonds holding the glucose molecules together so that they can be used by the animal cells for energy. These animals can thrive on a diet of grass, but you can't. Termites have these enzymes too, which is why a termite can eat wood while you would starve on a diet of tree limbs or lumber.

As discussed on page 317, fungi possess enzymes that can break down cellulose, which is why fungi often grow on dead trees. Some bacteria are also able to break down cellulose and live in the digestive system of certain animals as described on page 519.

Putting the Concept to Work

Why can you digest starch but not cellulose?

TABLE 3.1 Carbohydrates and Their Functions

Carbohydrate	Example	Description
Transport Disaccharides		
	Lactose 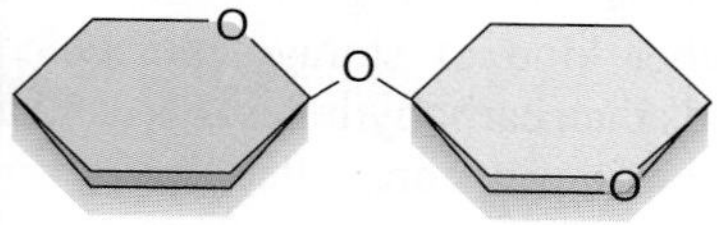	Glucose is transported within some organisms as a disaccharide. In this form, it is less readily metabolized because the normal glucose-utilizing enzymes of the organism cannot break the bond linking the two monosaccharide subunits. One type of disaccharide is called lactose. Many mammals supply energy to their young in the form of lactose, which is found in milk. Another transport disaccharide is sucrose. Many plants transport glucose throughout the plant in the form of sucrose, which is harvested from sugarcane to make granulated sugar.
	Sucrose 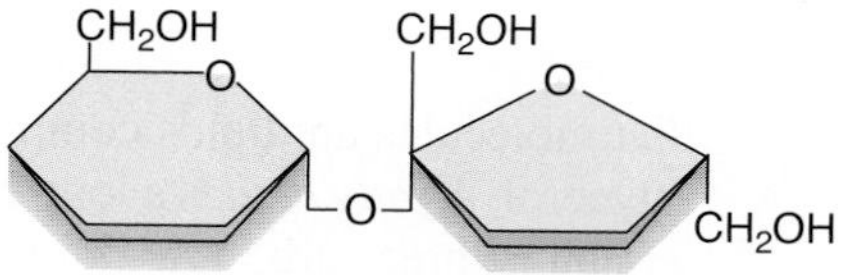 (CH_2OH, O, CH_2OH, O, O, CH_2OH)	
Storage Polysaccharides		
	Starch 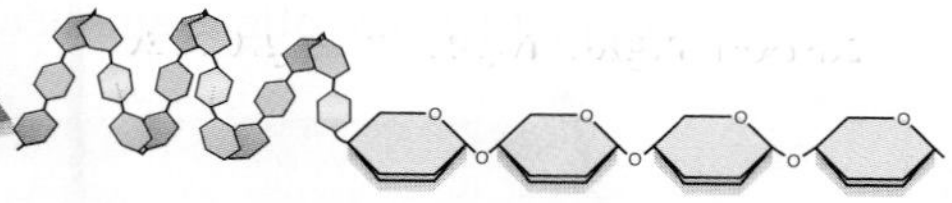	Organisms store energy in long chains of glucose molecules called polysaccharides. The chains tend to coil up in water, making them insoluble and ideal for storage. The storage polysaccharides found in plants are called starches, which can be branched or unbranched. Starch is found in potatoes and in grains, such as corn and wheat.
	Glycogen 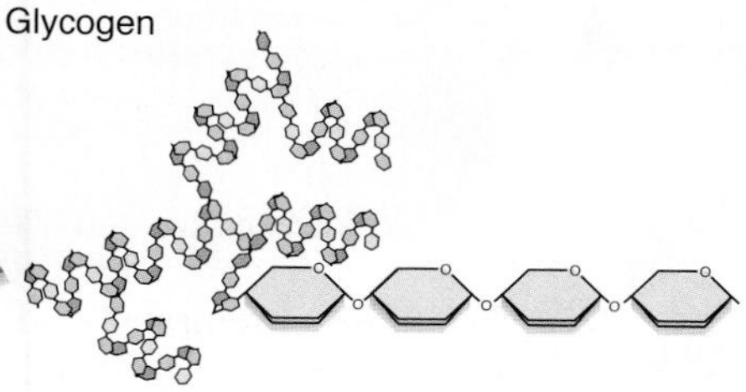	In animals, glucose is stored as glycogen. Glycogen is similar to starch in that it consists of long chains of glucose that coil up in water and are insoluble. But glycogen chains are much longer and highly branched. Glycogen can be stored in muscles and the liver.
Structural Polysaccharides		
	Cellulose 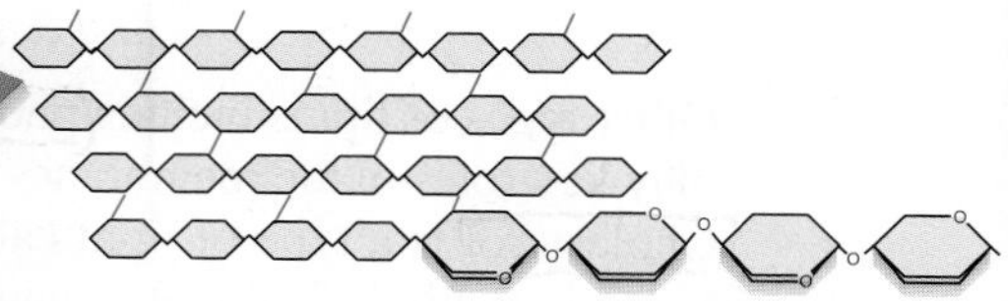	Cellulose is a structural polysaccharide found in the cell walls of plants; its glucose subunits are joined in a way that cannot be broken down readily. Cleavage of the links between the glucose subunits in cellulose requires an enzyme most organisms lack. Some animals, such as cows, are able to digest cellulose by means of bacteria and protists they harbor in their digestive tract, which provide the necessary enzymes.
	Chitin 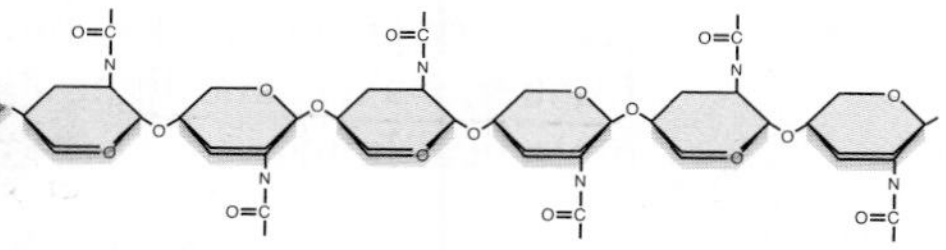	Chitin is a type of structural polysaccharide found in the external skeletons of many invertebrates, including insects and crustaceans, and in the cell walls of fungi. Chitin is a modified form of cellulose with a nitrogen group added to the glucose units. When cross-linked by proteins, it forms a tough, resistant surface material.

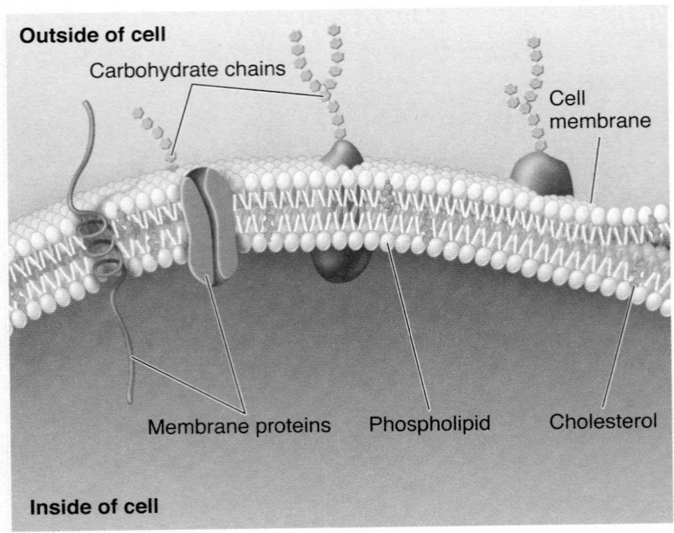

Figure 3.16 Lipids are a key component of biological membranes.

Lipids are one of the most common molecules in the human body, because the membranes of all cells are composed of phospholipids. Membranes also contain cholesterol, another type of lipid.

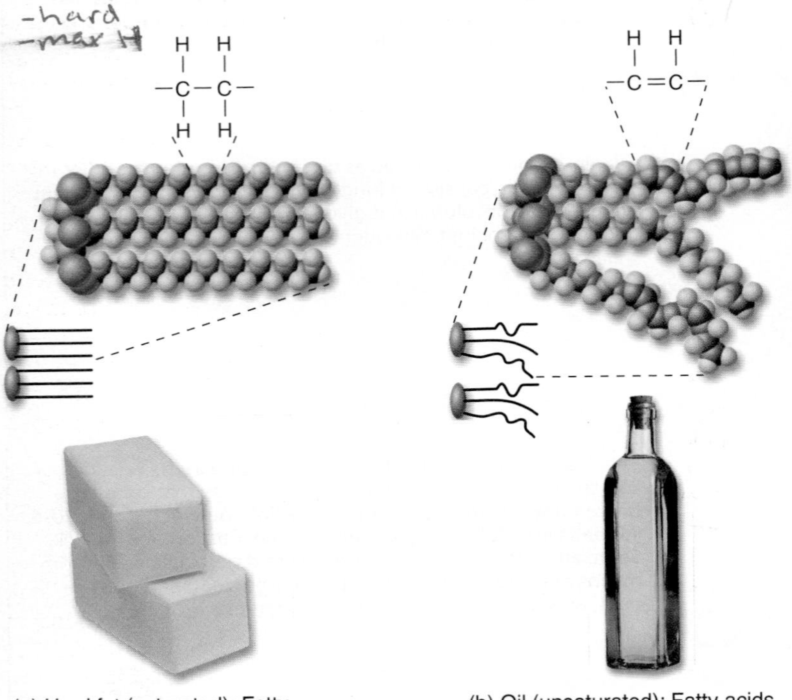

3.5 Lipids

LEARNING OBJECTIVE 3.5.1 Distinguish between saturated and unsaturated fats, and explain why one is a solid and the other a liquid at room temperature.

For long-term energy storage, organisms usually convert glucose into fats, another kind of storage molecule that contains more energy-rich C—H bonds than carbohydrates. Fats and all other biological molecules that are not soluble in water are called **lipids.** Lipids are nonpolar; in water, fat molecules cluster together because they cannot form hydrogen bonds with water molecules. This is why oil forms into a layer on top of water when the two substances are mixed. A special type of lipid called a phospholipid is important because it forms boundary layers in cells called membranes (figure 3.16).

Fats

Fat molecules are lipids composed of two kinds of subunits: fatty acids and glycerol. A *fatty acid* is a long chain of carbon and hydrogen atoms. Glycerol contains three carbons and forms the backbone to which three fatty acids are attached through dehydration reactions.

The chemical composition of the fatty acids that make up a fat molecule can affect its physical properties. Fats whose fatty acid chains are composed of the maximum number of hydrogen atoms are said to be *saturated* (figure 3.17*a*). Saturated fats are solid at room temperature. Animal fats are often saturated and occur as hard fats. On the other hand, fats composed of fatty acids with double bonds between one or more pairs of carbon atoms contain fewer than the maximum number of hydrogen atoms and are called *unsaturated* (figure 3.17*b*). Unsaturated fats are liquid at room temperature. Many plant fats are unsaturated and occur in oils. Unsaturated fats in food products may be artificially *hydrogenated* (industrial addition of hydrogens), extending the shelf life of products like peanut butter. In some cases, the hydrogenation creates *trans fats,* a type of unsaturated fat linked to heart disease.

Covalent bonds, as discussed on page 38, form when atoms share electrons. The single covalent bonds in saturated fats result when the carbons share one pair of electrons. The double covalent bonds in unsaturated fats result when two pairs of electrons are shared between carbon atoms.

H H
—C—C—
H H

(a) Hard fat (saturated): Fatty acids with single bonds between all carbon pairs

H H
—C=C—

(b) Oil (unsaturated): Fatty acids that contain double bonds between one or more pairs of carbon atoms

Figure 3.17 Saturated and unsaturated fats.

Fat molecules each contain a three-carbon glycerol to which is attached three fatty acid tails. (a) Most animal fats are "saturated" (every carbon atom carries the maximum load of hydrogens). Their fatty acid chains fit closely together and form immobile arrays called hard fats. (b) Most plant fats are unsaturated, which prevents close association between chains and so results in oils.

Other Types of Lipids

Other types of lipids include phospholipids and cholesterol, which play key roles in the membranes that encase all cells of your body. Cholesterol is a type of lipid called a *steroid.* Cholesterol plays a key role in biological membranes, helping them stay flexible. The male and female sex hormones testosterone and estradiol are also steroids. The chemical structure of steroids consists of multiple carbon rings and looks somewhat like a section of chicken wire. Rubber, waxes, and light-absorbing pigments are other important biological lipids.

Putting the Concept to Work

If you hydrogenate an unsaturated fat, does the treatment make the fat more solid? Explain.

Anabolic Steroids in Sports

Among the most notorious of lipids in recent years has been the class of synthetic hormones known as anabolic steroids. Since the 1950s some athletes have been taking these chemicals to build muscle and so boost athletic performance. Both because of the intrinsic unfairness of this and because of health risks, the use of anabolic steroids has been banned in sports for decades. Controversy over their use in professional baseball has recently returned anabolic steroids to the nation's front pages.

Anabolic steroids were developed in the 1930s to treat hypogonadism, a condition in which the male testes do not produce sufficient amounts of the hormone testosterone for normal growth and sexual development. Scientists soon discovered that by slightly altering the chemical structure of testosterone, they could produce synthetic versions that facilitated the growth of skeletal muscle in laboratory animals. The word "anabolic" means growing or building. Further tweaking reduced the added impact of these new chemicals on sexual development. More than 100 different anabolic steroids have been developed, most of which have to be injected to be effective. All require a prescription to be used legally in the United States, and all are banned in professional, college, and high school sports.

Another way to increase the body's level of testosterone is to use a chemical that is not itself anabolic but that the body converts to testosterone. One such chemical is 4-androstenedione, more commonly called "andro." It was first developed in the 1970s by East German scientists to try to enhance their athletes' Olympic performances. Because andro does not have the same side effects as anabolic steroids, it was legally available until 2004. It was used by Mark McGwire, but it is now banned in all sports, and possession of andro is a federal crime.

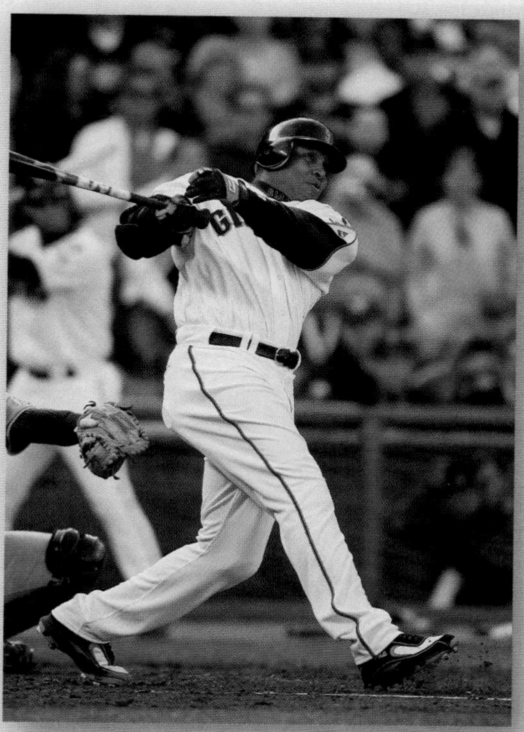

Home-run slugger Barry Bonds was involved in a steroid controversy in 2006.

Anabolic steroids work by signaling muscle cells to make more protein. They bind to special "androgenic receptor" proteins within the cells of muscle tissue. Like jabbing these proteins with a poker, the binding prods the receptors into action, causing them to activate genes on the cell's chromosomes that produce muscle tissue proteins, triggering an increase in protein synthesis. At the same time, the anabolic steroid molecules bind to so-called "cortisol receptor" proteins in the cell, preventing these receptors from doing their job of causing protein breakdown, the muscle cell's way of suppressing inflammation and promoting the use of proteins for fuel during exercise. By increasing protein production and inhibiting the breakdown of proteins in muscle cells after workouts, anabolic steroids significantly increase the mass of an athlete's muscle tissue.

If the only effect of anabolic steroids on your body were to enhance your athletic performance by increasing your muscle mass, using them would still be wrong, for one very simple and important reason: fairness. To gain advantage in competition by concealed use of anabolic steroids—"doping"—is simply cheating. That is why these drugs are banned in sports.

The use of anabolic steroids by athletes and others is not only wrong, but also illegal, because increased muscle mass is not the only effect of using these chemicals. Among adolescents, anabolic steroids can also lead to premature termination of the adolescent growth spurt, so that for the rest of their lives, users remain shorter than they would have been without the drugs. Adolescents and adults are also affected by steroids in the following ways. Anabolic steroids can lead to potentially fatal liver cysts and liver cancer (the liver is the organ of the body that attempts to detoxify the blood), cholesterol changes and hypertension (both of which can promote heart attack and stroke), and acne. Other signs of steroid use in men include reduced size of testicles, balding, and development of breasts. In women, signs include the growth of facial hair, lowering of the voice, and cessation of menstruation.

In the fall of 2003, athletic organizations learned that some athletes were using a new performance-enhancing anabolic steroid undetectable by standard antidoping tests, tetrahydrogestrinone (THG). The use of THG was discovered only because an anonymous coach sent a spent syringe to U.S. antidoping officials. THG's chemical structure is similar to gestrinone, a drug used to treat a form of pelvic inflammation, and can be made from it by simply adding four hydrogen atoms, an easy chemical task. THG tends to break down when prepared for analysis by standard means, which explains why antidoping tests had failed to detect it. New urine tests for THG that were developed in 2004 have been used to catch several well-known sports figures, including British athlete Dwain Chambers, baseball slugger Rafael Palmeiro, and several Tour de France cyclists.

Inquiry & Analysis

How Does pH Affect a Protein's Function?

The red blood cells you see to the lower right carry oxygen to all parts of your body. These cells are red because they are chock-full of a large iron-rich protein called *hemoglobin.* The iron atoms in each hemoglobin molecule provide a place for oxygen gas molecules to stick to the protein. When oxygen levels are highest (in the lungs), oxygen atoms bind to hemoglobin tightly, and a large percentage of the hemoglobin molecules in a cell possess bound oxygen atoms. When oxygen levels are lower (in the tissues of the body), hemoglobin doesn't bind oxygen atoms as tightly, and as a consequence hemoglobin releases its oxygen to the tissues. What causes this difference between lungs and tissues in how hemoglobin loads and unloads oxygen? Oxygen concentration is not the only factor that might be responsible. A protein's function can be affected by pH, and blood pH, for example, also differs between lungs and body tissues (**pH** is a measure of how many H^+ ions a solution contains). Tissues are slightly more acidic (that is, they have more H^+ ions and a lower pH). Their metabolic activities release CO_2 into the blood, which quickly becomes converted to carbonic acid and lowers the pH.

The graph to the right displays so-called "oxygen loading curves" that reveal the effectiveness with which hemoglobin binds oxygen. The more effective the binding, the less oxygen required before hemoglobin becomes fully loaded, and the further to the left a loading curve is shifted. To assess the impact of pH on this process, O_2 loading curves were carried out at three different blood pH values. In the graph, oxygen levels in the blood are presented on the *x* axis, and for each data point the corresponding % hemoglobin saturation (**%, or percent,** is the numerator [top part] of a fraction whose denominator [bottom part] is 100—in this case, a measure of the fraction of the hemoglobin that is bound to oxygen) is presented on the *y* axis. The oxygen-loading curve was repeated at pH values of 7.6, 7.4, and 7.2, corresponding to the blood pH that might be expected in resting, exercising, and very active muscle tissue, respectively.

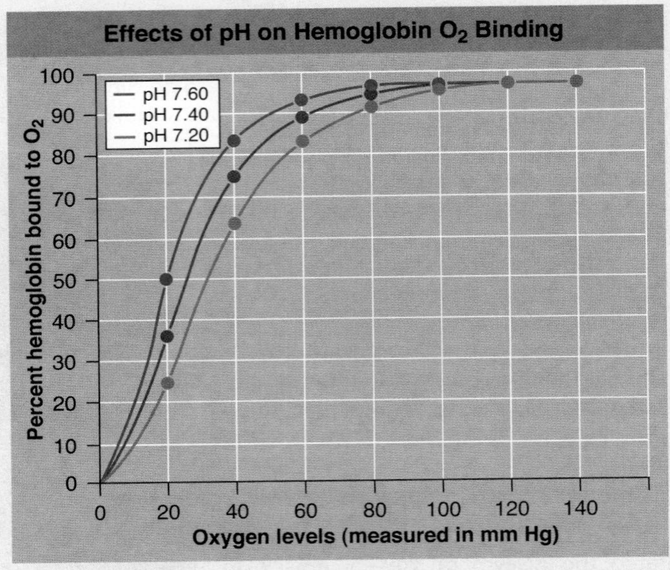

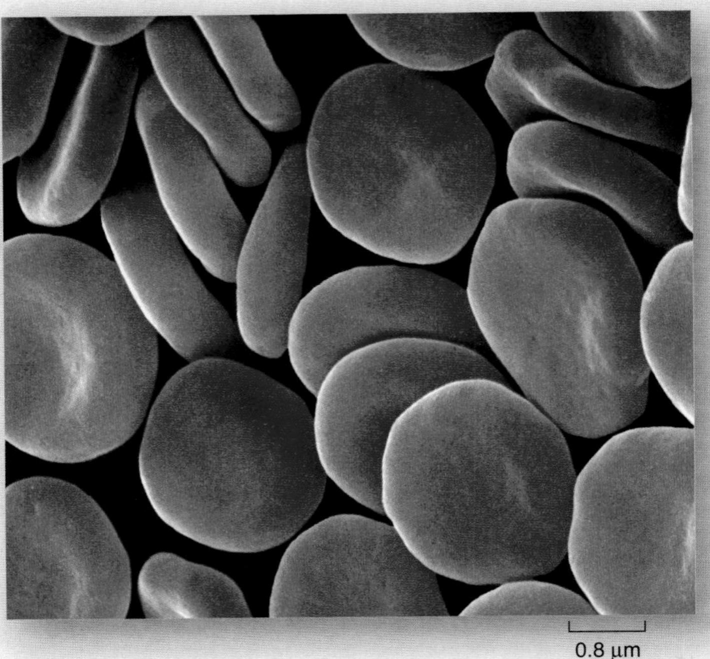

Analysis

1. **Applying Concepts** Which of the three pH values represents the highest concentration of hydrogen ions? (The **concentration** of a substance is the amount of that substance present in a given volume.) Is this value more acidic or more basic than the other two?
2. **Interpreting Data** What is the percent hemoglobin bound to O_2 for each of the three pH concentrations at saturation (where the lines flatten out)? at an oxygen level of 20 mm Hg? at 40 mm Hg? at 60 mm Hg?
3. **Making Inferences** At an oxygen level of 40 mm Hg, would hemoglobin bind oxygen more tightly at a pH of 7.8 or 7.0?
4. **Drawing Conclusions** How does pH affect the release of oxygen from hemoglobin?

Summary of Learning Outcomes

Forming Macromolecules

Building Big Molecules

3.1.1 Living organisms produce organic macromolecules, which are large carbon-based molecules. The chemical properties of these molecules are due to unique functional groups that are attached to the carbon core.

3.1.2 Macromolecules are formed by the linking together of subunits, called monomers, to form long chains called polymers. Amino acids are the subunits that link together to form polypeptides. Nucleotide monomers link together to form nucleic acids. Monosaccharide monomers link together to form carbohydrates. Fatty acids are the monomers that link together to form a type of lipid called fats.

- Polymers are formed by dehydration reactions, like the reaction shown here from **figure 3.4*a*.** Dehydration reactions produce covalent bonds that link monomers together. The reaction is called a dehydration reaction because a water molecule is removed as each link is formed.

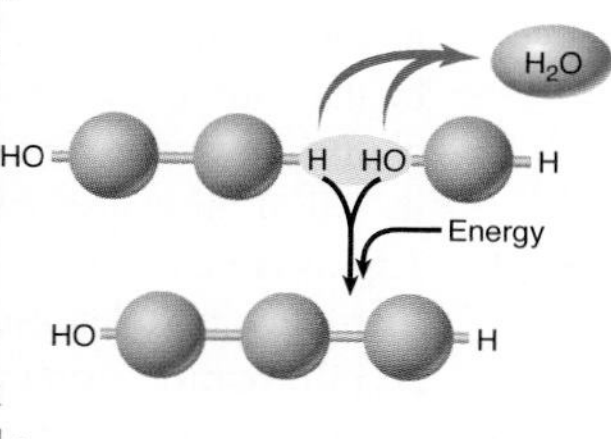

- The breakdown of macromolecules involves hydrolysis reactions, where a water molecule is added back, causing the bond to break.

Types of Macromolecules

Proteins

3.2.1 Proteins are long chains of amino acids that fold into complex shapes.

3.2.2 There are 20 different amino acids found in proteins. All amino acids have the same basic core structure. They differ in the type of functional group attached to the core. The functional groups are referred to as R groups. Some functional groups are polar, some are nonpolar, and still others give the amino acid unique chemical properties. Amino acids are linked together with covalent bonds referred to as peptide bonds.

3.2.3 The sequence of amino acids within the polypeptide is the primary structure of the protein. The chain of amino acids can twist into a secondary structure, where hydrogen bonding holds portions of the polypeptide in a coiled shape, called an α-helix, or in sheets called β-pleated sheets. Further bending and folding of the polypeptide results in its tertiary structure. When two or more polypeptides are present in a protein, the interaction of these polypeptide subunits is its quaternary structure.

3.2.4 Changes in environmental conditions that disrupt hydrogen bonding can cause a protein to unfold, a process called denaturation. Globular proteins, like the enzyme shown here from **figure 3.9,** cannot function if they are denatured. Some denatured proteins can refold back into their functional shapes.

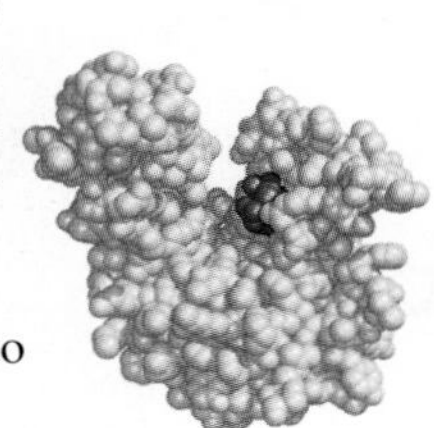

3.2.5 The sequence of a protein's amino acids determines how it folds into its three-dimensional shape, and thus determines its function in the cell.

Nucleic Acids

3.3.1 Nucleic acids, such as DNA and RNA, are long chains of nucleotides. Nucleotides contain three parts: a 5-carbon sugar, a phosphate group, and a nitrogenous base. DNA and RNA function in information storage and retrieval in the cell, carrying the information needed to build proteins. The information is stored as different sequences of nucleotides that determine the order of amino acids in proteins.

3.3.2 DNA and RNA differ chemically in that the sugar found in DNA is deoxyribose and in RNA it is ribose. The nitrogenous bases in DNA are cytosine, adenine, guanine, and thymine, and the same are found in RNA except for thymine, which is substituted in RNA with uracil.

- DNA and RNA also differ structurally. DNA contains two strands of nucleotides wound around each other, called a double helix. RNA, as shown here from **figure 3.11,** is a single strand of nucleotides.

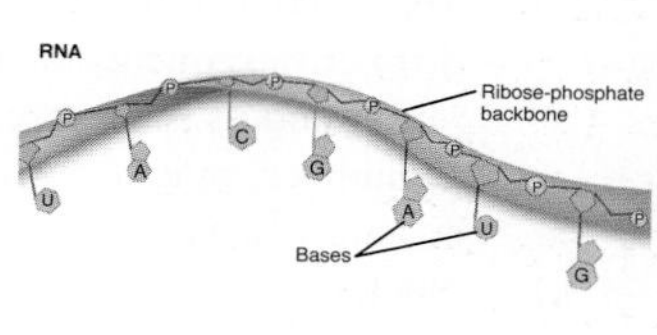

3.3.3 The two nucleotide strands of the DNA double helix are held together through hydrogen bonding between nitrogenous bases: adenine (A) pairs with thymine (T), and cytosine (C) pairs with guanine (G) .

Carbohydrates

3.4.1 Carbohydrates are macromolecules that contain C, H, and O atoms in the ratio 1:2:1. They serve two primary functions in the cell: structural framework and energy storage.

- Carbohydrates that consist of only one or two monomers are called simple carbohydrates, such as the glucose monosaccharide, shown here from **figure 3.14,** and disaccharides. Carbohydrates that consist of long chains of monomers are called complex carbohydrates or polysaccharides.

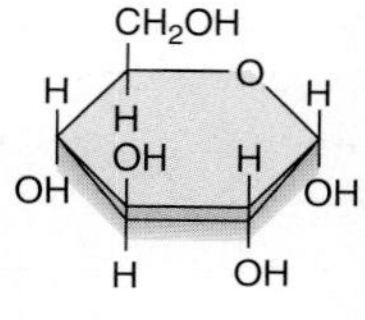

- Polysaccharides such as starch and glycogen provide a means of storing energy in the cell. They are broken down in the cells when energy is needed. Carbohydrates such as cellulose and chitin provide structural integrity and are not broken down by animals because they lack the enzyme necessary. Certain microbes in the guts of some animals are able to breakdown cellulose.

Lipids

3.5.1 Lipids are large nonpolar molecules that are insoluble in water. Lipids called phospholipids are components of biological membranes. Lipids called fats function in long-term energy storage. They include saturated fats, as shown here from **figure 3.17,** and unsaturated fats. Saturated fats are solid at room temperature and are found in animals, while unsaturated fats are liquid (oils) at room temperature and are found in plants.

- Other lipids include the steroids (including the sex steroids and cholesterol), rubber, and pigments.

Test Your Understanding

3.1.1 The four kinds of organic macromolecules are
- **a.** hydroxyls, carboxyls, aminos, and phosphates.
- **b.** proteins, carbohydrates, lipids, and nucleic acids.
- **c.** DNA, RNA, simple sugars, and amino acids.
- **d.** carbon, hydrogen, oxygen, and nitrogen.

3.1.2 Organic molecules are made up of monomers. Which of the following is *not* considered a monomer of organic molecules?
- **a.** amino acids
- **b.** monosaccharides
- **c.** polypeptides
- **d.** nucleotides

3.2.2 A peptide bond forms
- **a.** by the removal of a water molecule.
- **b.** by a dehydration reaction.
- **c.** between two amino acids.
- **d.** All of the above.

3.2.5 Your body is filled with many types of proteins. Each type has a distinctive sequence of amino acids that determines both its unique _____ and its specialized _____.
- **a.** number, weight
- **b.** length, mass
- **c.** structure, function
- **d.** charge, pH

3.3.1 Nucleic acids
- **a.** are the energy source for our bodies.
- **b.** act on other molecules, breaking them apart or building new ones to help us function.
- **c.** are only found in a few, specialized locations within the body.
- **d.** are information storage devices found in body cells.

3.3.3 The two strands of a DNA molecule are held together through hydrogen bonds between nucleotide bases. Which of the following best describes this base pairing in DNA?
- **a.** Adenine forms hydrogen bonds with thymine.
- **b.** Adenine forms hydrogen bonds with cytosine.
- **c.** Cytosine forms hydrogen bonds with thymine.
- **d.** Guanine forms hydrogen bonds with adenine.

3.4.1 Carbohydrates are used for
- **a.** structure and energy.
- **b.** information storage.
- **c.** fat storage and hair.
- **d.** hormones and enzymes.

3.4.1 Which of the following carbohydrates is *not* found in plants?
- **a.** glycogen
- **b.** cellulose
- **c.** starch
- **d.** All are found in plants.

3.5.1 A characteristic common to fat molecules is that
- **a.** they contain long chains of C—H bonds.
- **b.** they are insoluble in water.
- **c.** they have a glycerol backbone.
- **d.** All of these are characteristics of fat molecules.

3.5.1 Lipids are used for
- **a.** motion and defense.
- **b.** information storage.
- **c.** energy storage and some hormones.
- **d.** enzymes and some hormones.

Apply Your Understanding

3.2.2 The molecule below, on the left, is a peptide made from monomers of amino acids. The molecule below, on the right, is a disaccharide made from monomers of simple sugars. Both molecules were synthesized using a common chemical reaction. What is the chemical reaction that formed these molecules and what is the common by-product of both these reactions?

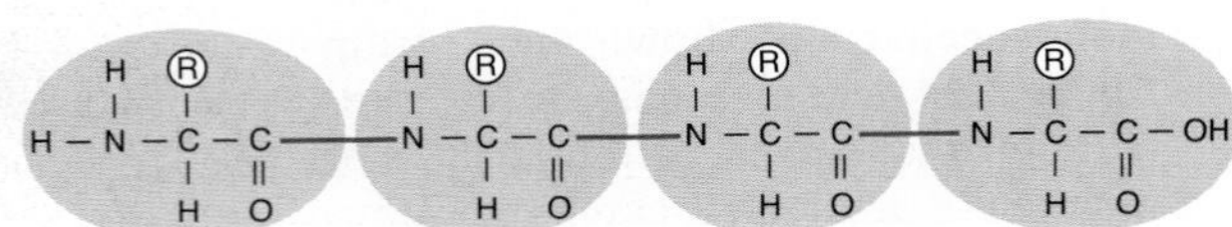

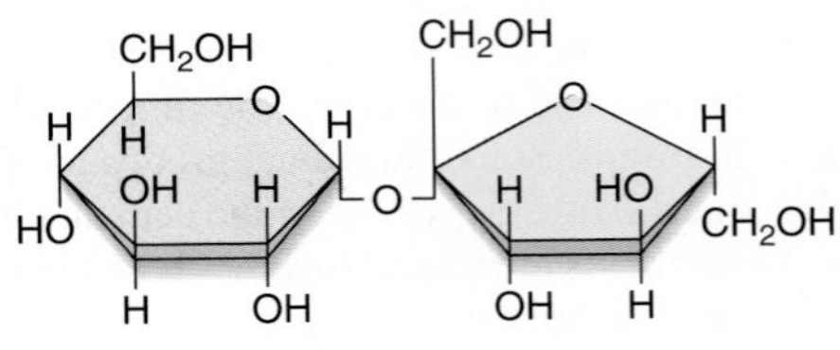

3.5.1 Below are two lipid molecules. The lipid on the left is a saturated fat and the one on the right is an unsaturated fat. What is the difference in the chemical structure of their fatty acid tails, and how does this affect their physical properties?

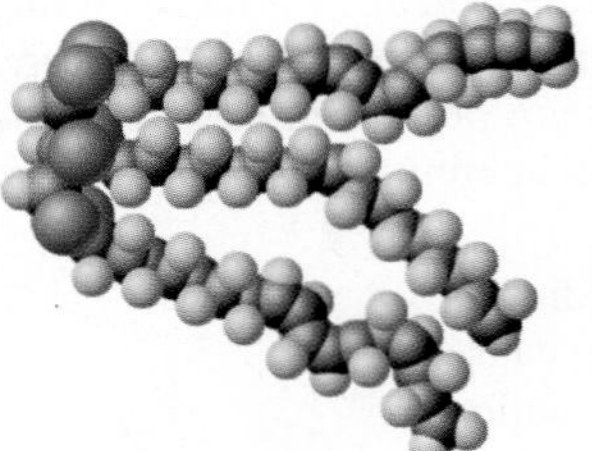

Synthesize What You Have Learned

3.2.2 How many molecules of water are used up in the breakdown of a polypeptide that is 15 amino acids in length?

3.4.1 The enzyme amylase present in the cells of your body can break the bonds between the glucose monomers in starch but it cannot break the bonds between the glucose monomers in cellulose. Enzymes are very specific in what molecules they bind to. After examining the chemical structures of starch and cellulose in table 3.1, explain why the same enzyme that breaks down starch cannot break down cellulose.

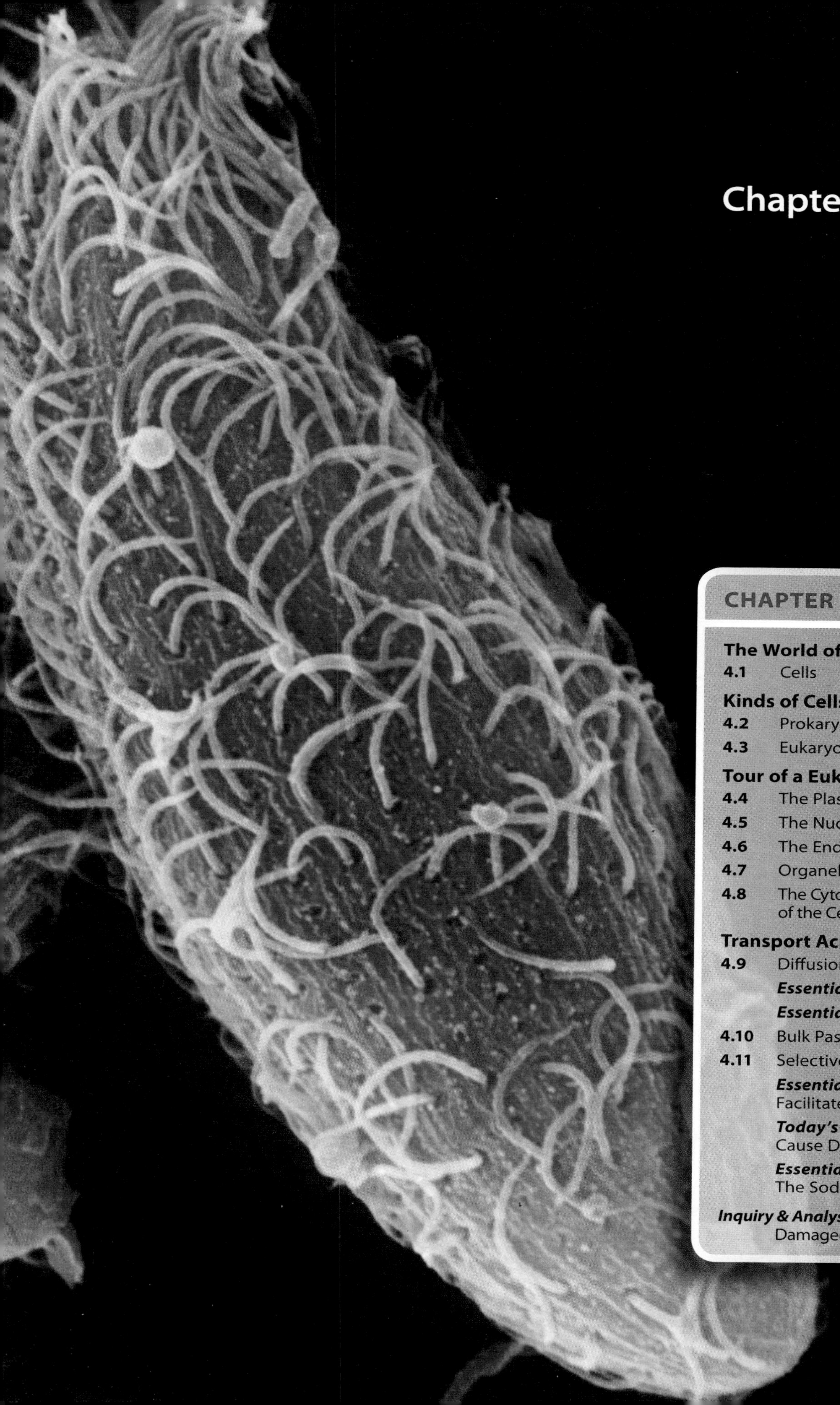

Chapter 4

Cells

CHAPTER AT A GLANCE

The World of Cells

4.1 Cells

Kinds of Cells

4.2 Prokaryotic Cells

4.3 Eukaryotic Cells

Tour of a Eukaryotic Cell

4.4 The Plasma Membrane

4.5 The Nucleus: The Cell's Control Center

4.6 The Endomembrane System

4.7 Organelles That Harvest Energy

4.8 The Cytoskeleton: Interior Framework of the Cell

Transport Across Plasma Membranes

4.9 Diffusion and Osmosis

Essential Biological Process 4A: Diffusion

Essential Biological Process 4B: Osmosis

4.10 Bulk Passage into and out of Cells

4.11 Selective Permeability

Essential Biological Process 4C: Facilitated Diffusion

Today's Biology: Membrane Defects Can Cause Disease

Essential Biological Process 4D: The Sodium-Potassium Pump

Inquiry & Analysis: Why Does a Cell's Disposal of Damaged Proteins Consume Energy?

The World of Cells

4.1 Cells

LEARNING OBJECTIVE 4.1.1 State the cell theory, and outline its three principles.

Hold your finger up and look at it closely. What do you see? Skin. It looks solid and smooth, creased with lines and flexible to the touch. But if you were able to remove a bit and examine it under a microscope, it would look very different. Figure 4.1 takes you on a journey into your fingertip. The crammed bodies you see in panels 3 and 4 are skin cells, laid out like a tiled floor. As your journey continues, you travel inside one of the cells and see organelles, structures in the cell that perform specific functions. Proceeding even further inward, you encounter the molecules of which the structures are made, and finally the atoms shown in panels 8 and 9. While some organisms are composed of a single cell, your body is composed of many cells. A human body has as many cells as there are stars in a galaxy, 10 trillion to 100 trillion, depending on your size. All of your body cells, however, are small. In this chapter we look more closely at cells and learn something of their internal structure and how they communicate with their environment.

The Cell Theory

Cells are small, so small that no one observed them until microscopes were invented in the mid-seventeenth century. Robert Hooke first described cells in 1665, when he used a microscope he had built to examine a thin slice of nonliving plant tissue called cork. Hooke observed a honeycomb of tiny, empty (because the cells were dead) compartments. He called the compartments in the cork *cellulae* (Latin, small rooms), and the term has come down to us as **cells.** For another century and a half, however, biologists failed to recognize the importance of cells. In 1838, botanist Matthias Schleiden made a careful study of plant tissues and developed the first statement of the cell theory. He stated that all plants "are aggregates of fully individualized, independent, separate beings, namely the cells themselves." In 1839, Theodor Schwann reported that all animal tissues also consist of individual cells.

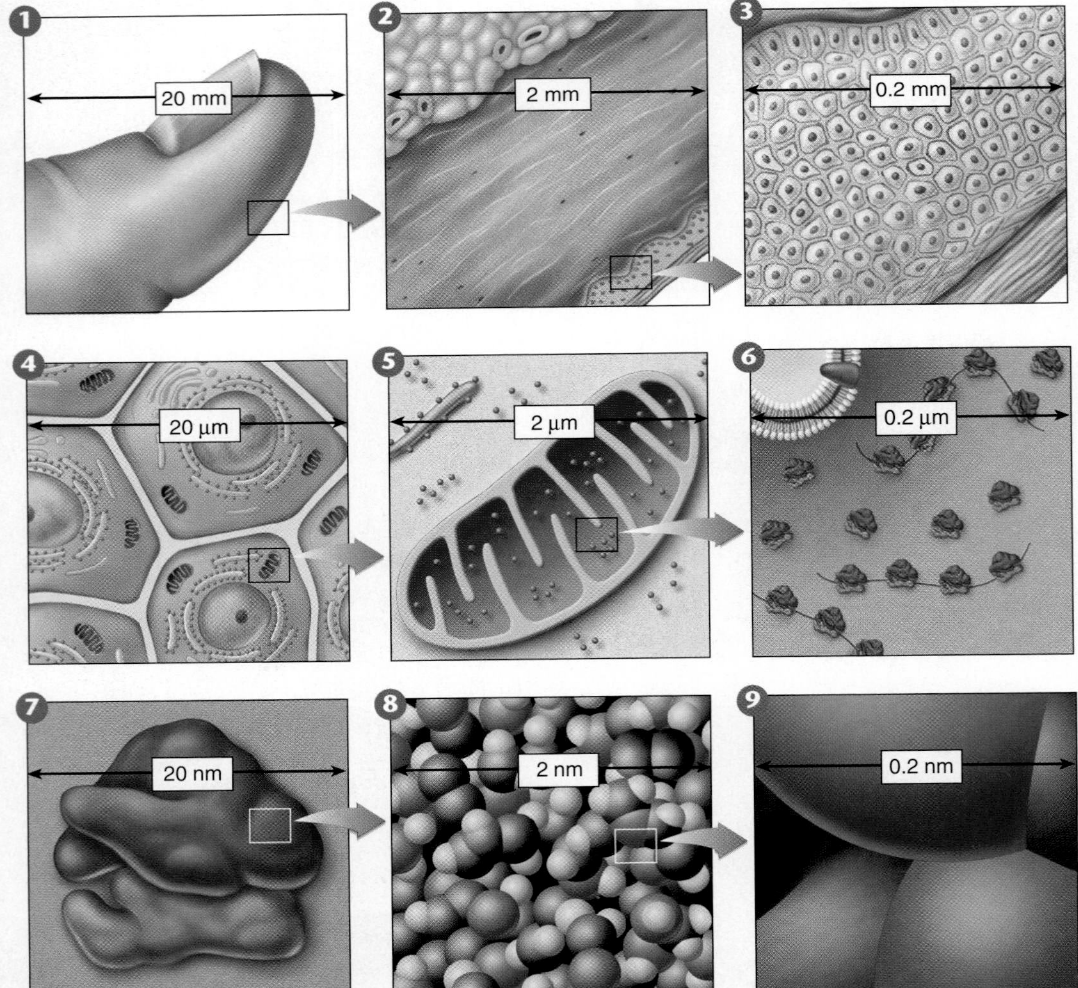

Figure 4.1 The size of cells and their contents.

This diagram shows the size of human skin cells, organelles, and molecules. In general, the diameter of a human skin cell is a little less than 20 micrometers (µm), of a mitochondrion is 2 µm, of a ribosome is 20 nanometers (nm), of a protein molecule is 2 nm, and of an atom is 0.2 nm.

The idea that all organisms are composed of cells is called the cell theory. In its modern form, the cell theory includes three principles:

1. All organisms are composed of one or more cells, within which the processes of life occur.
2. Cells are the smallest living things. Nothing smaller than a cell is considered alive.
3. Cells arise only by division of a previously existing cell. Although life likely evolved spontaneously in the environment of the early earth, biologists have concluded that no additional cells are originating spontaneously at present. Rather, life on earth represents a continuous line of descent from those early cells.

Putting the Concept to Work

Some viruses are larger than a small cell. Are they alive?

Most Cells Are Very Small

LEARNING OBJECTIVE 4.1.2 Explain why most cells are so small.

Cells are not all the same size. Individual marine alga cells, for example, can be up to 5 centimeters long—as long as your little finger. In contrast, the cells of your body are typically from 5 to 20 micrometers (μm) in diameter, too small to see with the naked eye. It would take anywhere from 100 to 400 human cells to span the diameter of the head of a pin. The cells of bacteria are even smaller than your cells, only a few micrometers thick (figure 4.2).

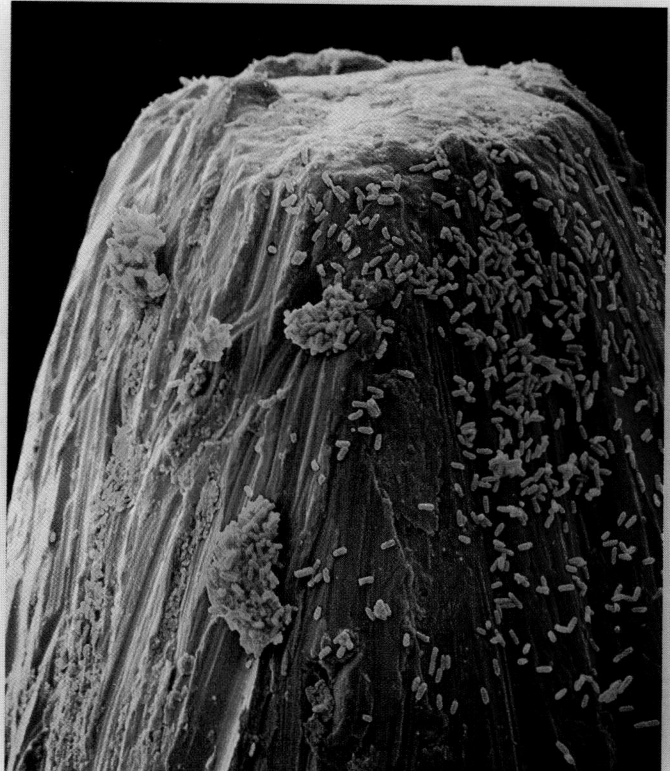

Figure 4.2 Bacteria on the point of a pin (175×).

Why are most cells so tiny? Most cells are small because larger cells do not function as efficiently. In the center of every cell is a command center that must issue orders to all parts of the cell, directing the synthesis of certain enzymes, the entry of ions and molecules from the exterior, and the assembly of new cell parts. These orders must pass from the core to all parts of the cell, and it takes them a very long time to reach the periphery of a large cell. For this reason, an organism composed of relatively small cells has an advantage over one made of large cells.

Another reason cells are not larger is the advantage of having a greater surface area. A cell's surface provides the interior's only opportunity to interact with the environment, as its surface provides the only way for substances to pass into and out of the cell. As cells grow larger, their interior volume increases much more than their surface area, and as a result there is far less surface available to service each unit of volume. In the same way, before airplanes and trains were invented the size of cities was limited because the surrounding countryside could not support all the people living in a big city—only so many roads could be built into the city, only so many farms were close enough to the city to use them.

Some larger cells still function quite efficiently because they have structural features that increase surface area. Cells of the nervous system have long thread-like extensions called axons extending more than a meter in length, so thin that their interior regions are not far from the surface at any point. For the same reason, many body cells are flat and plate-shaped. Another structural feature that increases surface area are small finger-like projections called microvilli that dramatically increase a cell's surface area.

Putting the Concept to Work

Why is it advantageous for your body to be made up of so many flat, plate-shaped cells?

IN THE NEWS

High Resolution TV. A new generation of "high definition" televisions is providing remarkable pictures of very high resolution. Computer and television engineers define resolution very simply as the number of individual points of color (or "pixels") you can see. A traditional 15-inch television displays 640 dots on each of 480 vertical lines, so-called 480 resolution. Until recently, DVD discs provided the best resolution for a TV picture. DVDs use red-laser light beams to read and project 720 vertical lines. This was as many dots per line as you could get without two dots being read by adjacent red-laser beams overlapping. With the invention of the much narrower blue laser, it became possible to squeeze dots much more closely together on a true high-resolution HD TV screen—1,080 vertical lines, yielding over 2 million dots of color. This produces an image of vivid clarity difficult to distinguish from what your eye would deliver.

Visualizing Cells

LEARNING OBJECTIVE 4.1.3 Explain visualizing cells.

The reason we can't see small objects like cells is the limited resolution of the human eye. *Resolution* is defined as the minimum distance two points can be apart and still be distinguished as two separated points. The limit of resolution of the human eye is about 100 micrometers. When two objects are closer together than about 100 micrometers, the light reflected from each strikes the same "detector" cell at the rear of the eye.

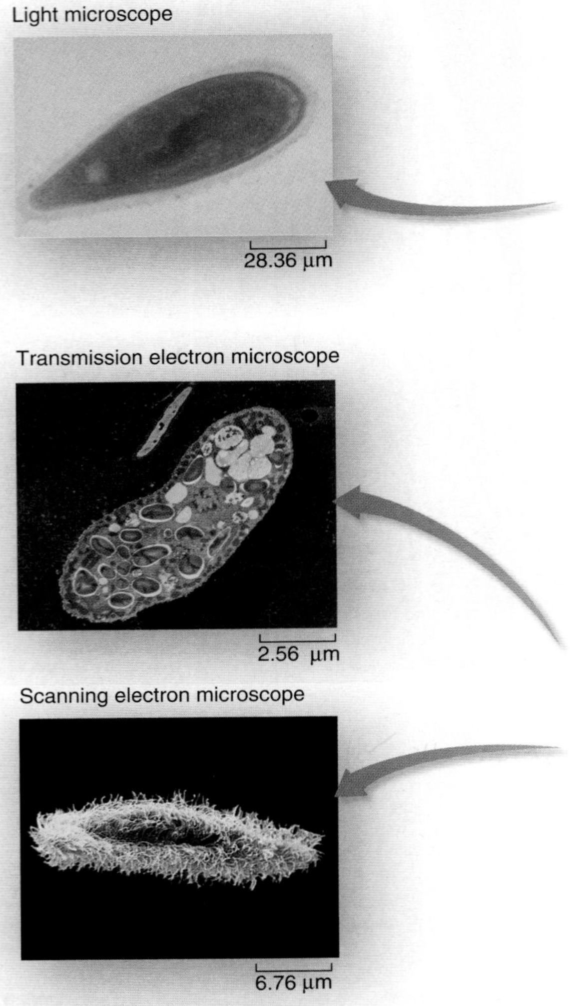

Microscopes. One way to increase resolution is to increase magnification, so that small objects appear larger. Modern *light microscopes* use two magnifying lenses (and a variety of correcting lenses) to achieve very high magnification and clarity by magnifying the image and focusing it on the receptor cells inside the back of the eye. Microscopes that magnify in stages using several lenses are called **compound microscopes.** They can resolve structures that are separated by as little as 200 nanometers (nm).

Increasing Resolution. Light microscopes, even compound ones, are not powerful enough to resolve many structures within cells. Why not just add another magnifying lens to the microscope and so increase its resolving power? Because when two objects are closer than a few hundred nanometers, the light beams reflecting from the two images start to overlap. One way to avoid overlap is by using a beam of electrons rather than a beam of light. Electrons have a much shorter wavelength, and a microscope employing electron beams has 1,000 times the resolving power of a light microscope. A **transmission electron microscope (TEM)** is capable of resolving objects only 0.2 nanometers apart—just twice the diameter of a hydrogen atom (figure 4.3)! A second kind of electron microscope, the **scanning electron microscope (SEM),** beams the electrons onto the surface of the specimen. The beam knocks electrons off of atoms on the surface, these electrons are amplified, and the image created is transmitted to a screen and photographed, producing an often striking three-dimensional picture.

Putting the Concept to Work

Why can't you see a ribosome with a light microscope?

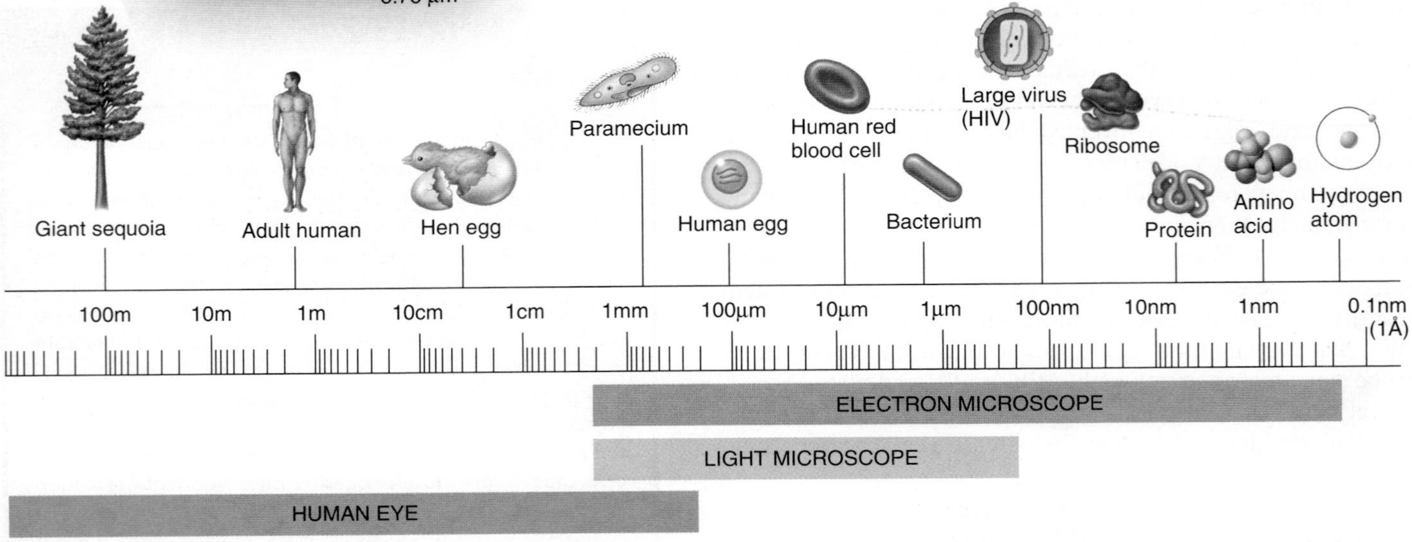

Figure 4.3 A scale of visibility.

Most cells are microscopic in size, although some vertebrate gametes can be seen with the unaided eye. Bacterial cells are generally 1 to 2 μm in diameter.

Kinds of Cells

4.2 Prokaryotic Cells

LEARNING OBJECTIVE 4.2.1 Describe the interior of a prokaryotic cell.

There are two major kinds of cells: prokaryotes and eukaryotes. **Prokaryotes** have a relatively uniform interior that is not subdivided by internal membranes into separate compartments. They do not, for example, have special membrane-bounded compartments, called *organelles,* or a *nucleus* (a membrane-bounded compartment that holds hereditary information). As discussed in chapter 1, figure 1.1, the two main groups of prokaryotes are *bacteria* and *archaea;* all other organisms are eukaryotes.

Prokaryotes are the simplest cellular organisms. Over 5,000 species are recognized, but doubtless many times that number actually exist and have not yet been described. Although these species are diverse in form, their organization is fundamentally similar: They are single-celled organisms; the cells are small (typically about 1 to 10 micrometers thick); the cells are enclosed by a plasma membrane; and there are no distinct interior compartments. Outside of almost all bacteria and archaea is a *cell wall,* composed of different molecules in different groups (see table 15.1 and section 16.2). In some bacteria, another layer called the *capsule* encloses the cell wall. Archaea are extremely diverse and inhabit diverse environments. Bacteria are abundant and play critical roles in many biological processes. Bacteria assume many shapes, like the sausage or spiral shapes shown in figure 4.4*a,b*. They can also adhere in masses or chains, as shown in figure 4.4*c,* but in these cases the individual cells remain functionally separate from one another.

The plasma membrane, as described on page 60, is composed of phospholipids that are arranged to form two layers, where the polar heads are oriented to the outside and the nonpolar tails extend in toward the interior of the membrane.

If you were able to peer into a prokaryotic cell, you would be struck by its simple organization. The entire interior of the cell is one unit, with no internal compartments bounded by membranes and little or no internal support structure (the rigid wall, the purple layer surrounding the cell in figure 4.5, supports the cell's shape). Scattered throughout the cytoplasm of prokaryotic cells are small structures called *ribosomes,* the small spherical structures you see inside the cell in figure 4.5. Ribosomes are the sites where proteins are made, but they are not considered organelles because they lack a membrane boundary. Prokaryotic DNA is found in a region of the cytoplasm called the *nucleoid region.* Although the DNA is localized in this region of the cytoplasm, it is not considered a nucleus because, as you can see in figure 4.5, the nucleoid region and its associated DNA are not enclosed within an internal membrane.

Some prokaryotes use a **flagellum** (plural, **flagella**) to move. Flagella are long, threadlike structures, made of protein fibers that project from the surface of a cell. They are used in locomotion and feeding. Bacteria can swim at speeds up to 20 cell diameters per second, rotating their flagella like screws.

Some prokaryotic cells contain **pili** (singular, **pilus**), which are short flagella (only several micrometers long, and about 7.5 to 10 nanometers thick). Pili help the prokaryotic cell attach to appropriate substrates and aid in the exchange of genetic information between cells.

Putting the Concept to Work

Are there membrane-bounded organelles within a bacterial cell?

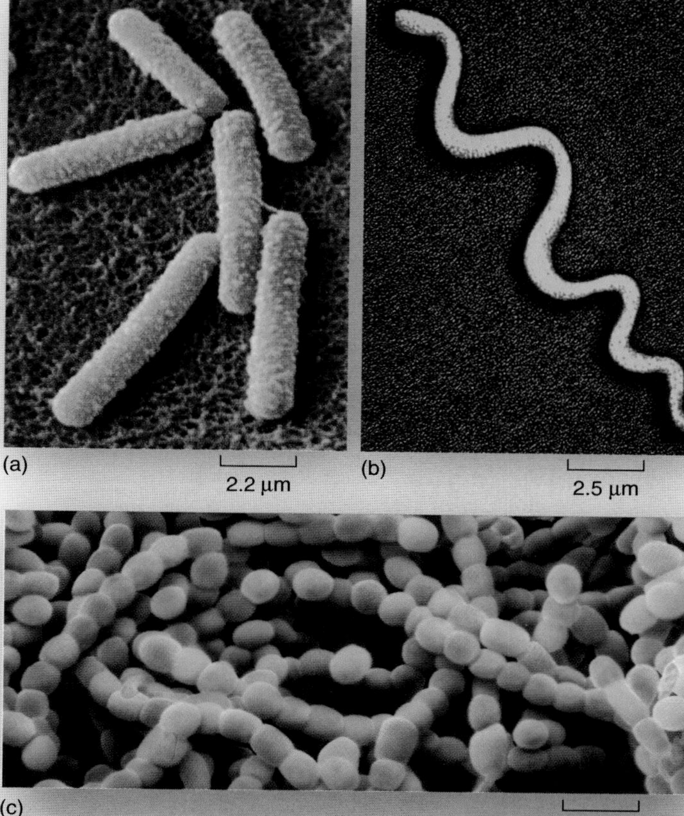

Figure 4.4 Bacterial cells have different shapes.

(a) *Bacillus* is a rod-shaped bacterium. (b) *Treponema* is a coil-shaped bacterium; rotation of internal filaments produces a corkscrew movement. (c) *Streptomyces* is a more or less spherical bacterium in which the individuals adhere in chains.

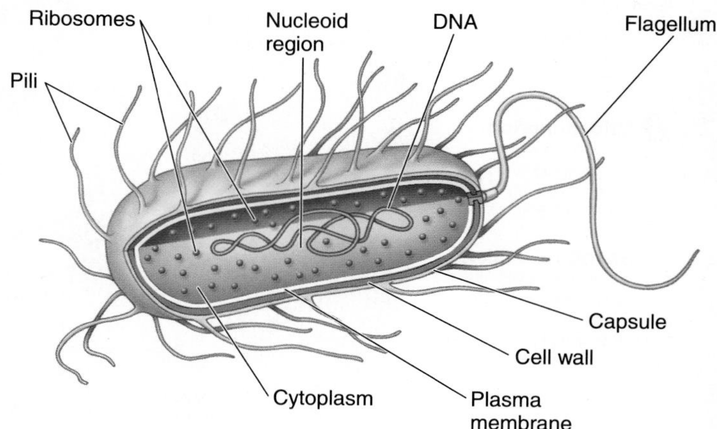

Figure 4.5 Organization of a prokaryotic cell.

Prokaryotic cells lack internal compartments. Not all prokaryotic cells have a flagellum or a capsule like the one illustrated here, but all have a nucleoid region, ribosomes, a plasma membrane, cytoplasm, and a cell wall.

4.3 Eukaryotic Cells

LEARNING OBJECTIVE 4.3.1 List the organelles unique to eukaryotic cells, and state which of them are not present in plant cells.

Eukaryotic cells are much larger and profoundly different from prokaryotic cells, with a complex interior organization. Figures 4.6 and 4.7 present cross-sectional diagrams of idealized animal and plant cells. As you can see, the interior of a eukaryotic cell is much more complex than the prokaryotic cell you encountered in figure 4.5. The **plasma membrane** ❶ encases a semifluid matrix called the **cytoplasm** ❷, which contains within it the nucleus and various cell structures called organelles. An **organelle** is a specialized structure within which particular cell processes occur. Each organelle, such as a **mitochondrion** ❸, has a specific function in the eukaryotic cell. The organelles are anchored at specific locations in the cytoplasm by an interior scaffold of protein fibers, the **cytoskeleton** ❹.

One of the organelles is very visible when these cells are examined with a microscope, filling the center of the cell like the pit of a peach, the **nucleus** ❺ (plural, *nuclei*), from the Latin word for "kernel." Inside the nucleus, the DNA is wound tightly around proteins and packaged into compact units called chromosomes. It is the nucleus that gives **eukaryotes** their name, from the Greek words *eu*, true, and *karyon*, nut; by way of contrast, the earlier-evolving bacteria and archaea are called prokaryotes ("before the nut").

Figure 4.6 **Structure of an animal cell.**

In this generalized diagram of an animal cell, the plasma membrane encases the cell, which contains the cytoskeleton and various cell organelles and interior structures suspended in a semifluid matrix called the cytoplasm. Some kinds of animal cells possess fingerlike projections called microvilli. Other types of eukaryotic cells—for example, many protist cells—may possess flagella, which aid in movement, or cilia, which can have many different functions.

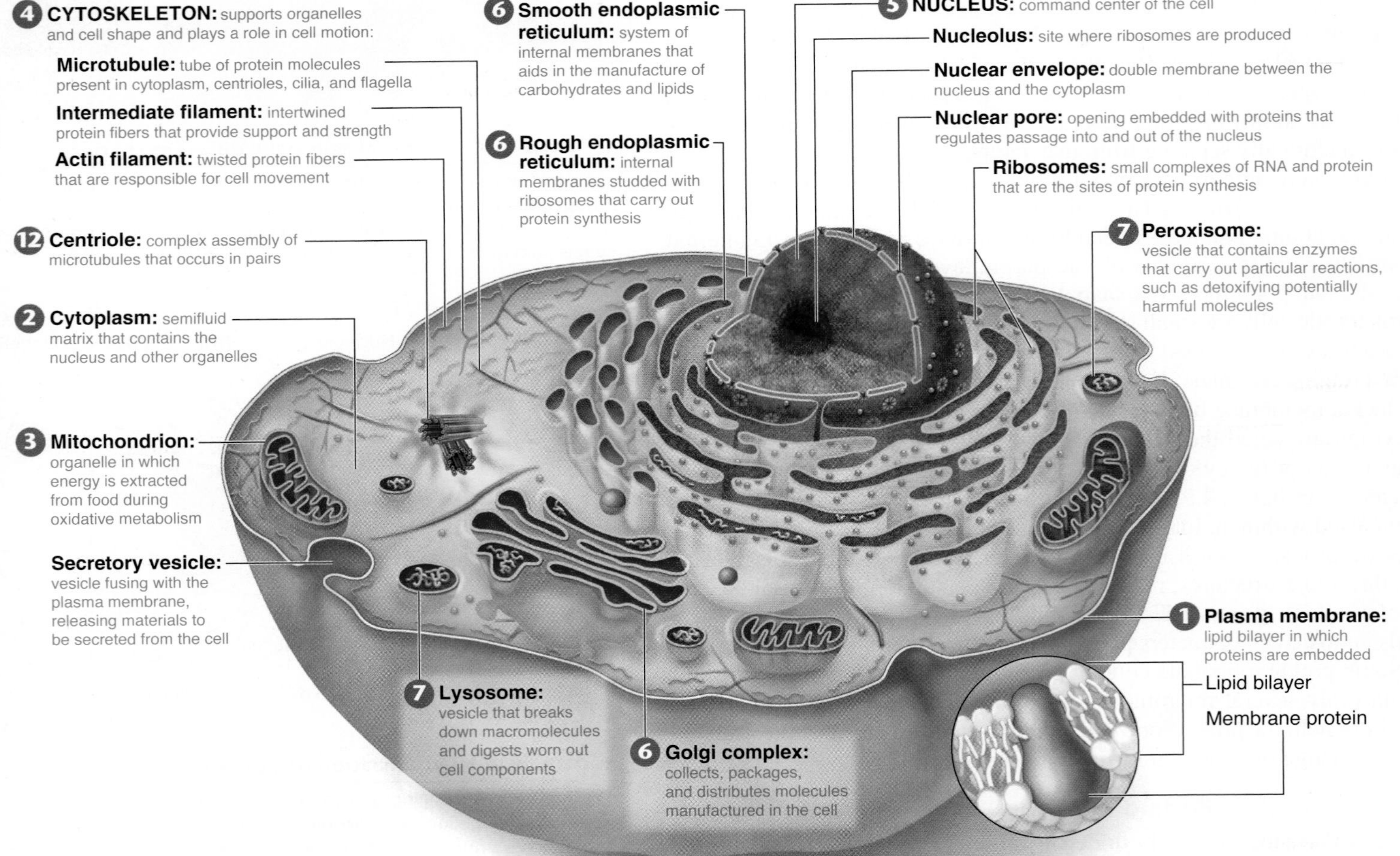
4 CYTOSKELETON: supports organelles and cell shape and plays a role in cell motion:
Microtubule: tube of protein molecules present in cytoplasm, centrioles, cilia, and flagella
Intermediate filament: intertwined protein fibers that provide support and strength
Actin filament: twisted protein fibers that are responsible for cell movement
12 Centriole: complex assembly of microtubules that occurs in pairs
2 Cytoplasm: semifluid matrix that contains the nucleus and other organelles
3 Mitochondrion: organelle in which energy is extracted from food during oxidative metabolism
Secretory vesicle: vesicle fusing with the plasma membrane, releasing materials to be secreted from the cell
6 Smooth endoplasmic reticulum: system of internal membranes that aids in the manufacture of carbohydrates and lipids
6 Rough endoplasmic reticulum: internal membranes studded with ribosomes that carry out protein synthesis
5 NUCLEUS: command center of the cell
Nucleolus: site where ribosomes are produced
Nuclear envelope: double membrane between the nucleus and the cytoplasm
Nuclear pore: opening embedded with proteins that regulates passage into and out of the nucleus
Ribosomes: small complexes of RNA and protein that are the sites of protein synthesis
7 Peroxisome: vesicle that contains enzymes that carry out particular reactions, such as detoxifying potentially harmful molecules
1 Plasma membrane: lipid bilayer in which proteins are embedded
Lipid bilayer
Membrane protein
7 Lysosome: vesicle that breaks down macromolecules and digests worn out cell components
6 Golgi complex: collects, packages, and distributes molecules manufactured in the cell

If you examine the organelles in figures 4.6 and 4.7, you can see that most of them form separate compartments within the cytoplasm, bounded by their own membranes. *The hallmark of the eukaryotic cell is this compartmentalization.* This internal compartmentalization is achieved by an extensive **endomembrane system** 6 that weaves through the cell interior.

Vesicles 7 (small membrane-bounded sacs that store and transport materials) form closed-off compartments in the cell, allowing different processes to proceed simultaneously without interfering with one another, just as rooms do in a house. For example, organelles called *lysosomes* are recycling centers that have acidic interiors in which old organelles are broken down and their component molecules recycled. This acid would be very destructive if released into the cytoplasm.

Comparing figure 4.6 with figure 4.7, you will see the same set of organelles, with a few interesting exceptions. For example, the cells of plants, fungi, and many protists have strong exterior **cell walls** 8 composed of cellulose or chitin fibers, while the cells of animals lack cell walls. All plants and many kinds of protists have **chloroplasts** 9, within which photosynthesis occurs. No animal or fungal cells contain chloroplasts. Plant cells also contain a large **central vacuole** 10 that stores water, and **plasmodesmata** 11, which are openings in the cell wall that create cytoplasmic connections between cells. **Centrioles** 12, which will be described later, are present in animal cells but absent in plant and fungal cells.

Putting the Concept to Work

If they work so well, why don't animal cells use central vacuoles?

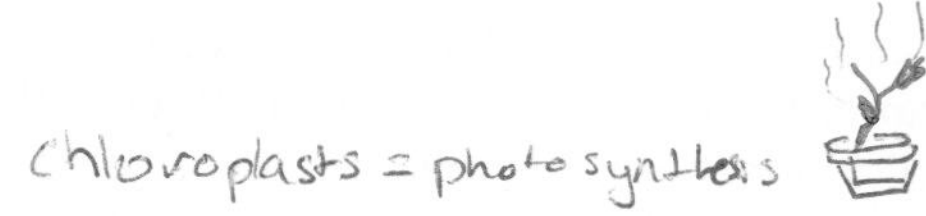

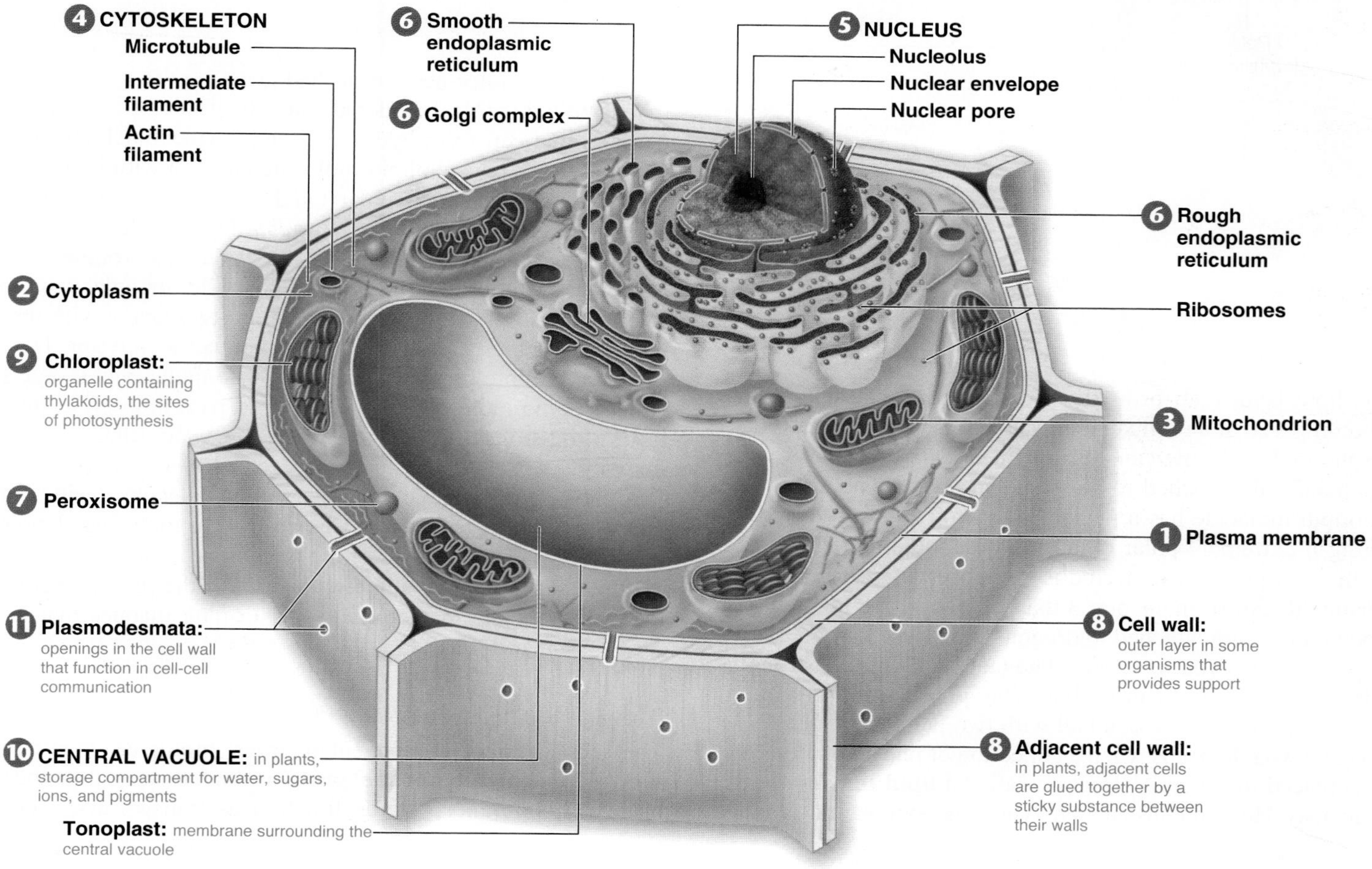

Figure 4.7 Structure of a plant cell.

Most mature plant cells contain large central vacuoles, which occupy a major portion of the internal volume of the cell, and organelles called chloroplasts, within which photosynthesis takes place. The cells of plants, fungi, and some protists have cell walls, although the composition of the walls varies among the groups. Plant cells have cytoplasmic connections through openings in the cell wall called plasmodesmata. Flagella occur in sperm of a few plant species, but are otherwise absent in plant and fungal cells. Centrioles are also absent in plant and fungal cells.

Tour of a Eukaryotic Cell

4.4 The Plasma Membrane

LEARNING OBJECTIVE 4.4.1 Explain why a lipid bilayer forms spontaneously, and how proteins are anchored within it.

Encasing all living cells is a delicate sheet of molecules called the **plasma membrane.** It would take more than 10,000 of these molecular sheets, which are about 5 nanometers thick, piled on top of one another to equal the thickness of this sheet of paper. However, the sheets are not simple in structure, like a soap bubble's skin. Rather, they are made up of a diverse collection of proteins floating within a lipid framework like small boats bobbing on the surface of a pond. Regardless of the kind of cell they enclose, all plasma membranes have the same basic structure of proteins embedded in a sheet of lipids, called the **fluid mosaic model.**

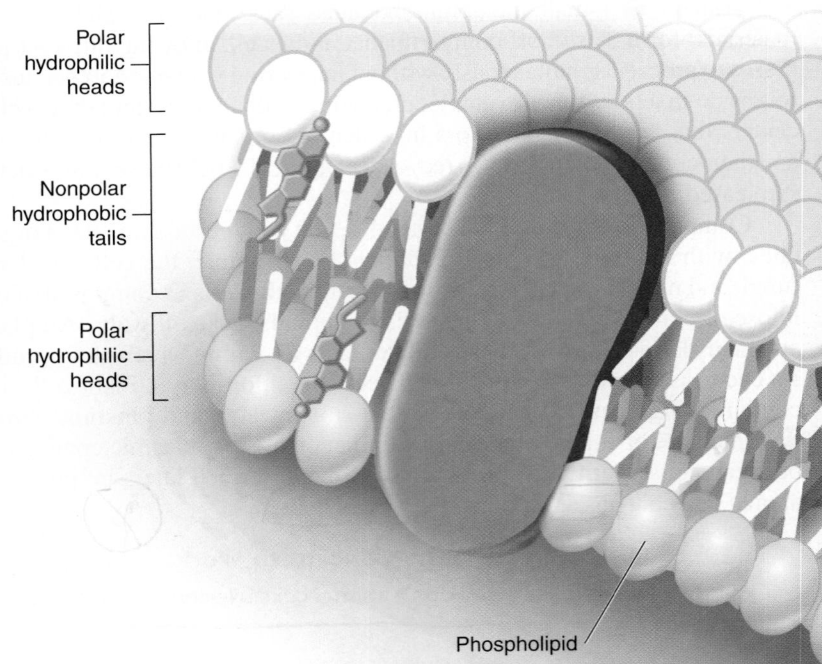

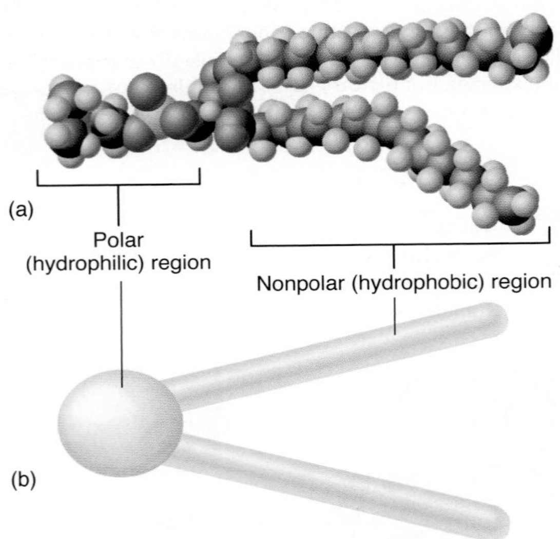

The lipid layer that forms the foundation of a plasma membrane is composed of modified fat molecules called **phospholipids.** A phospholipid molecule can be thought of as a polar head with two nonpolar tails attached to it, as shown above. The head of a phospholipid molecule has a phosphate chemical group linked to it, making it extremely polar (and thus water-soluble). The other end of the phospholipid molecule is composed of two long fatty acid chains. Recall from chapter 3 that fatty acids are long chains of carbon atoms with attached hydrogen atoms. The carbon atoms are the gray spheres you see above. The fatty acid tails are strongly nonpolar and thus water-insoluble. The phospholipid is often depicted diagrammatically as a ball with two tails.

Imagine what happens when a collection of phospholipid molecules is placed in water. A structure called a **lipid bilayer** forms spontaneously. How can this happen? The long nonpolar tails of the phospholipid molecules are pushed away by the water molecules that surround them, shouldered aside as the water molecules seek partners that can form hydrogen bonds. After much shoving and jostling, every phospholipid molecule ends up with its polar head facing water and its nonpolar tail facing away from water. The phospholipid molecules form a *double* layer, called a bilayer. As you can see in the figure above, the watery environments inside and outside the plasma membrane push the nonpolar tails to the interior of the bilayer. Because there are two layers with the tails facing each other, no tails are ever in contact with water. Thus, the interior of a lipid bilayer is completely nonpolar, and it repels any water-soluble molecules that attempt to pass through it, just as a layer of oil stops the passage of a drop of water (that's why ducks do not get wet).

Cholesterol, another nonpolar lipid molecule, resides in the interior portion of the bilayer. Cholesterol is a multiringed molecule that affects the fluid nature of the membrane. Although cholesterol is important in maintaining the integrity of the plasma membrane, it can accumulate in blood vessels, forming plaques that lead to cardiovascular disease.

Proteins Within the Membrane

The second major component of every biological membrane is a collection of **membrane proteins** that float within the lipid bilayer. Membrane proteins function as transporters, receptors, and cell surface markers. As you can see here in the figure, some proteins (the purple structures) pass through the lipid bilayer, providing channels through which molecules and information pass. While some membrane proteins are fixed into position, others move about freely.

Many membrane proteins project up from the surface of the plasma membrane like buoys, often with carbohydrate chains or lipids attached to their tips like flags. These *cell surface proteins* act as markers to identify particular types of cells, or as beacons to bind specific hormones or proteins to the cell.

Cell surface markers called MHC proteins discussed on page 549 identify a person's cells as "self" so the immune system won't attack them. Transmembrane proteins are present in nerve cells and function as ion transports, as discussed on page 564.

Proteins that extend all the way across the bilayer can provide passageways for ions and polar molecules like water so they can pass into and out of the cell. How do these *transmembrane proteins* manage to span the membrane, rather than just floating on the surface in the way that a drop of water floats on oil? The part of the protein that actually traverses the lipid bilayer is a specially constructed spiral helix of nonpolar amino acids—the red coiled areas of the transmembrane protein you see in the inset. Water responds to these nonpolar amino acids much as it does to nonpolar lipid chains, and as a result the helical spiral is held within the lipid interior of the bilayer, anchored there by the strong tendency of water to avoid contact with these nonpolar amino acids.

Phospholipids

Polar areas of protein

Cholesterol

Nonpolar areas of protein

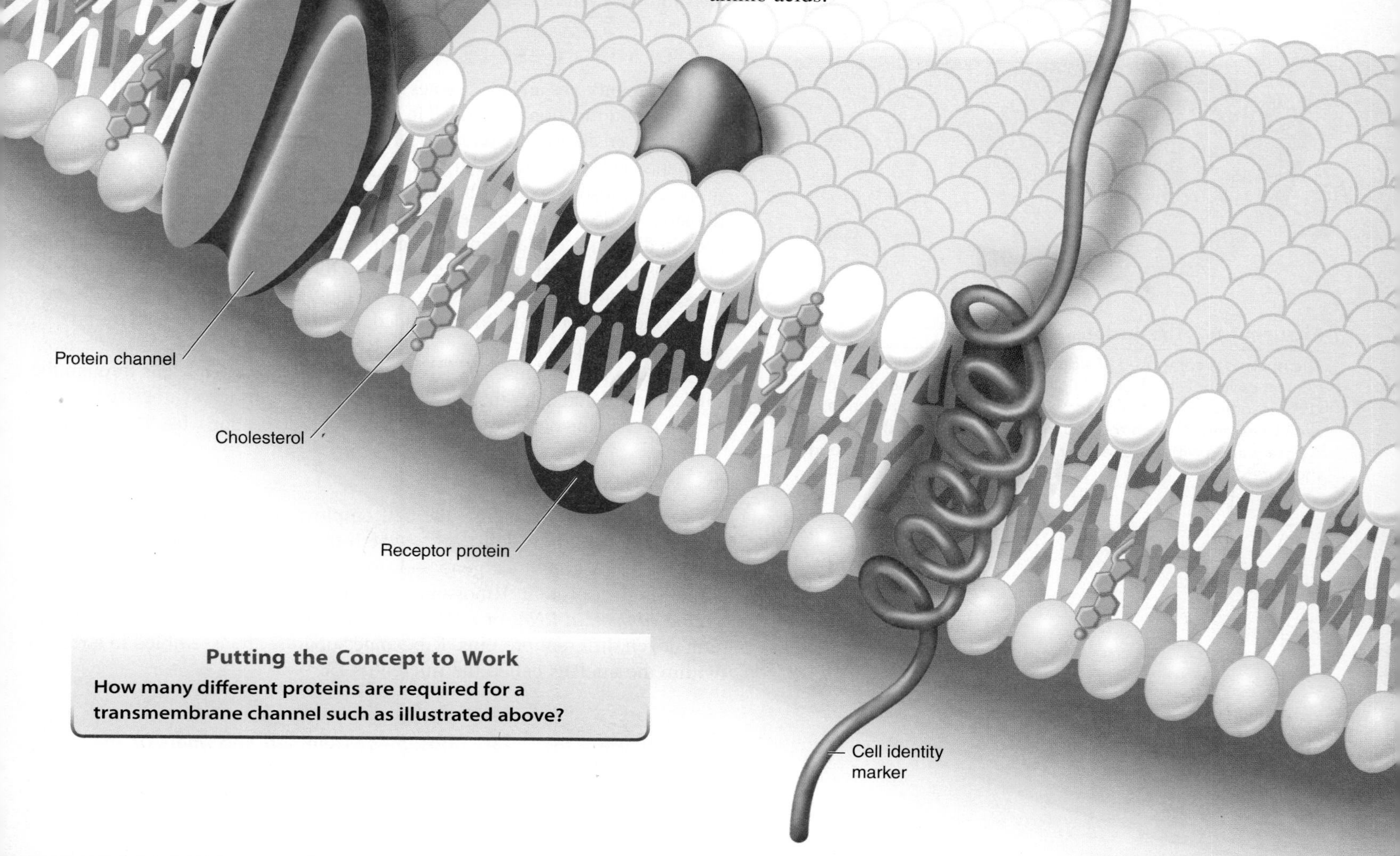

Protein channel

Cholesterol

Receptor protein

Cell identity marker

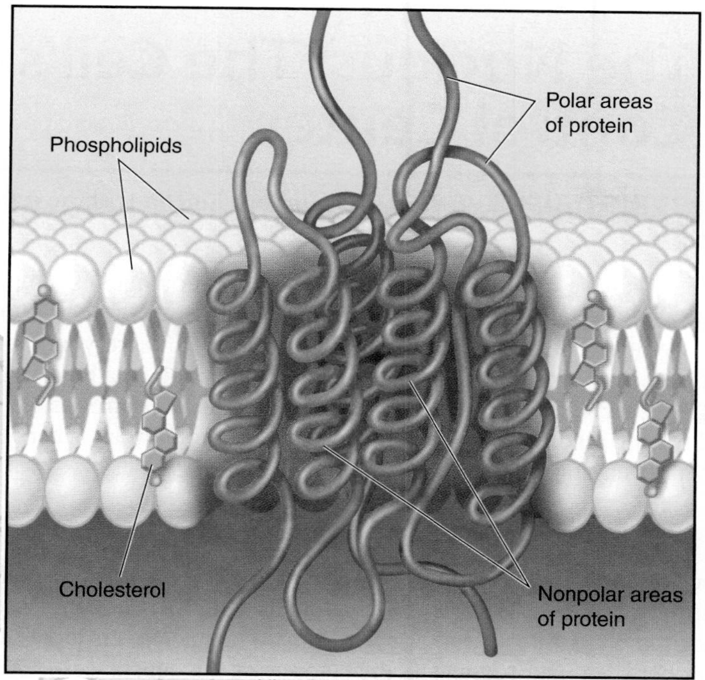

Putting the Concept to Work

How many different proteins are required for a transmembrane channel such as illustrated above?

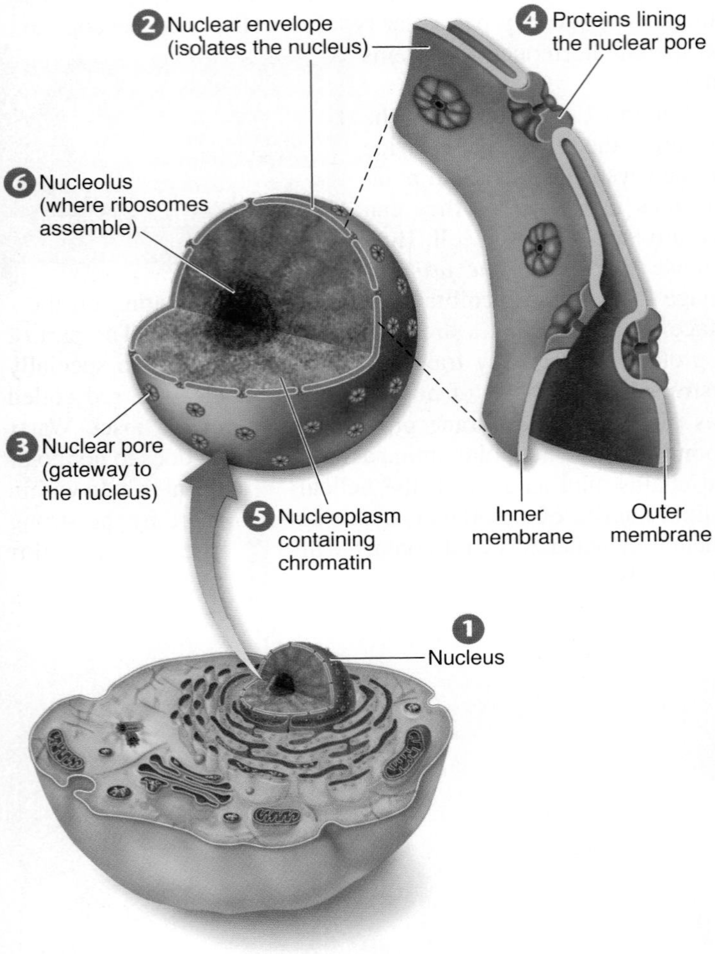

4.5 The Nucleus: The Cell's Control Center

LEARNING OBJECTIVE 4.5.1 Recount two functions of the cell nucleus.

Eukaryotic cells have many structural components and organelles in common (table 4.1). If you were to journey far into the interior of one of your cells, you would eventually reach the center of the cell. There you would find, cradled within a network of fine filaments like a ball in a basket, the **nucleus** ① (figure 4.8). The nucleus is the command and control center of the cell, directing all of its activities. It is also the genetic library where the hereditary information is stored.

Nuclear Membrane

The surface of the nucleus is bounded by a special kind of membrane called the **nuclear envelope** ②. The nuclear envelope is actually *two* membranes, one outside the other, like a sweater over a shirt. The nuclear envelope acts as a barrier between the nucleus and the cytoplasm, but substances need to pass through the envelope. The exchange of materials occurs through openings scattered over the surface of this envelope. Called **nuclear pores** ③, these openings form when the two membrane layers of the nuclear envelope pinch together. A nuclear pore is not an empty opening, however; rather, it has many proteins embedded within it that permit proteins and RNA to pass into and out of the nucleus ④.

Chromosomes

In both prokaryotes and eukaryotes, all hereditary information specifying cell structure and function is encoded in DNA. However, unlike prokaryotic DNA that forms an enclosed circle, the DNA of eukaryotes is divided into several segments and associated with protein, forming **chromosomes.** The proteins in the chromosome permit the DNA to wind tightly and condense during cell division. Under a light microscope, these condensed chromosomes are readily seen in dividing cells as densely staining rods. After cell division, eukaryotic chromosomes uncoil and fully extend into threadlike strands called **chromatin** ⑤ that can no longer be distinguished individually with a light microscope within the nucleoplasm. Once uncoiled, the chromatin is available for protein synthesis. The process begins when RNA copies of genes are made from the DNA in the nucleus. The RNA molecules leave the nucleus through the nuclear pores and enter the cytoplasm where proteins are synthesized. These proteins, carrying out many different functions, determine what the cell is like.

Ribosomes

To make its many proteins, the cell employs a special structure called a **ribosome,** a kind of platform on which the proteins are built. Ribosomes read the RNA copy of a gene and use that information to direct the construction of a protein. Ribosomes are made up of a special form of RNA called *ribosomal RNA*, or *rRNA*, that is bound up within a complex of several dozen different proteins. Ribosome subunits are assembled in a region within the nucleus called the **nucleolus** ⑥.

Putting the Concept to Work

Where in the cell are ribosomes assembled, and where do they function?

Figure 4.8 The nucleus.

The nucleus is composed of a double membrane, called a nuclear envelope, enclosing a fluid-filled interior containing the chromosomes. In cross section, the individual nuclear pores are seen to extend through the two membrane layers of the envelope. A pore is lined with protein, which acts to control access through the pore.

TABLE 4.1 Eukaryotic Cell Organelles and Their Functions

Structure	Description	Function
Structural Elements		
Cell wall	Outer layer of cellulose or chitin; absent in animal cells	Protection; support
Cytoskeleton	Network of protein filaments	Structural support; cell movement
Flagella and cilia	Cellular extensions with 9 + 2 arrangement of pairs of microtubules	Motility or moving fluids over surfaces
Plasma Membrane and Endomembrane System Organelles		
Plasma membrane	Lipid bilayer in which proteins are embedded	Regulates what passes into and out of cell; cell-to-cell recognition
Endoplasmic reticulum	Network of internal membranes	Forms compartments and vesicles; participates in protein and lipid synthesis
Nucleus	Structure (usually spherical) that contains chromosomes; surrounded by double membrane	Control center of cell; directs protein synthesis and cell reproduction
Golgi complex	Stacks of flattened vesicles	Packages proteins for export from the cell; forms secretory vesicles
Lysosomes	Vesicles derived from Golgi complex that contain hydrolytic digestive enzymes	Digest worn-out organelles and cell debris; play role in cell death
Energy-Producing Organelles		
Mitochondria	Bacteria-like elements with double membrane	Sites of oxidative metabolism; provide ATP for cellular energy
Chloroplasts	Bacteria-like organelles found in plants and algae; complex inner membrane consists of stacked vesicles	Sites of photosynthesis
Organelles of Gene Expression		
Chromosomes	Long threads of DNA that form a complex with protein	Contain hereditary information
Nucleolus	Site of genes for rRNA synthesis	Assembles ribosomes
Ribosomes	Small, complex assemblies of protein and RNA, often bound to endoplasmic reticulum	Sites of protein synthesis

4.6 The Endomembrane System

Surrounding the nucleus within the interior of the eukaryotic cell is a tightly packed mass of membranes. They fill the cell, dividing it into compartments, channeling the transport of molecules through the interior of the cell and providing the surfaces on which enzymes act. The system of internal compartments created by these membranes in eukaryotic cells constitutes the most fundamental distinction between the cells of eukaryotes and prokaryotes.

Endoplasmic Reticulum: Transportation System

LEARNING OBJECTIVE 4.6.1 **Distinguish between rough ER and smooth ER.**

The extensive system of internal membranes is called the **endoplasmic reticulum,** often abbreviated **ER.** The term *endoplasmic* means "within the cytoplasm," and the term *reticulum* is a Latin word meaning "little net." Looking at the sheets of membrane weaving through the interior of the cell in figure 4.9, you can see how the ER got its name. The ER creates a series of channels and interconnections, and it also isolates some spaces as membrane-enclosed sacs called **vesicles.**

The surface of the ER is the place where the cell makes proteins intended for export (such as enzymes secreted from the cell surface). The surface of those regions of the ER devoted to the synthesis of such transported proteins is heavily studded with ribosomes and appears pebbly, like the surface of sandpaper, when seen through an electron microscope. For this reason, these regions are called **rough ER.** Regions in which ER-bound ribosomes are relatively scarce are correspondingly called **smooth ER.** The surface of the smooth ER is embedded with enzymes that aid in the manufacture of carbohydrates and lipids.

Putting the Concept to Work

Explain why proteins intended for export are made at rough ER, while proteins intended for the cytoplasm are not.

Figure 4.9 The endoplasmic reticulum (ER).

The endoplasmic reticulum provides the cell with an extensive system of internal membranes for the synthesis and transport of materials. Ribosomes are associated with only one side of the rough ER; the other side is the boundary of a separate compartment within the cell into which the ribosomes extrude newly made proteins destined for secretion. Smooth endoplasmic reticulum has few to no bound ribosomes.

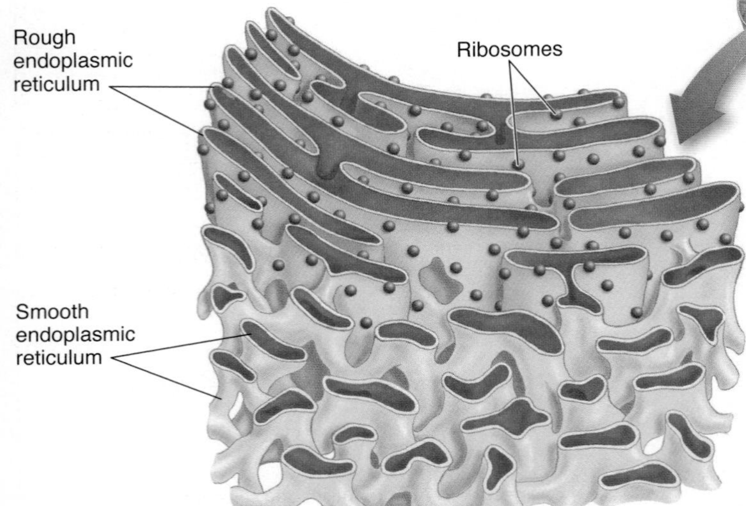

Figure 4.10 Golgi complex.

This vesicle-forming system, called the Golgi complex after its discoverer, is an integral part of the cell's internal membrane system. The Golgi complex processes and packages materials for transport to another region within the cell and/or for export from the cell. It receives material for processing in transport vesicles on one side and sends the material packaged in secretory vesicles off the other side. (a) Diagram of a Golgi complex. (b) Micrograph of a Golgi complex showing vesicles.

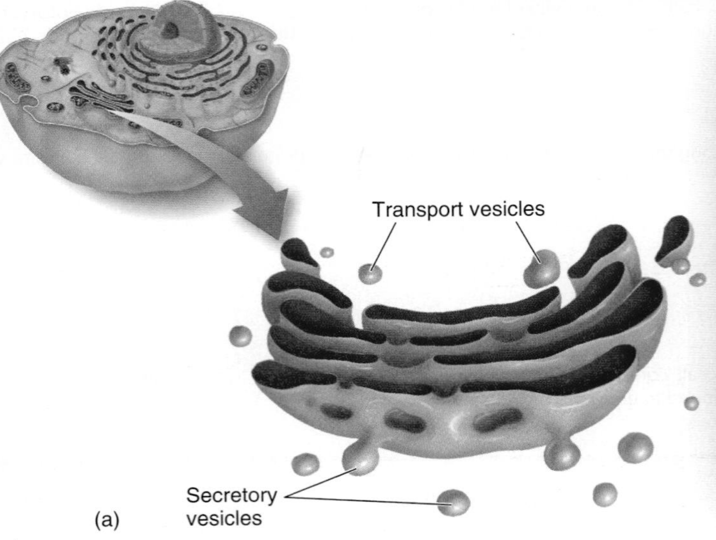

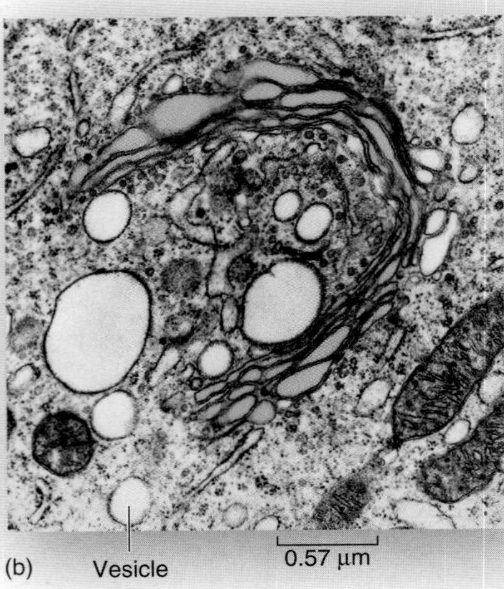

The Golgi Complex: Delivery System

LEARNING OBJECTIVE 4.6.2 Explain how Golgi bodies ensure the correct delivery of substances made in the ER.

As new molecules are made on the surface of the ER, they are passed from the ER to flattened stacks of membranes called **Golgi bodies** (figure 4.10), which look like pancakes stacked one on top of the other. The number of Golgi bodies a cell contains ranges from a few in protists, to 20 in animal cells and several hundred in certain plant cells. Golgi bodies function in the collection, packaging, and distribution of molecules manufactured in the cell. Scattered through the cytoplasm, Golgi bodies are collectively referred to as the **Golgi complex.**

The rough ER, smooth ER, and Golgi work together as an endomembrane transport system in the cell. Figure 4.11 walks you through the path that molecules take from the ER through the Golgi and out to their final destinations. Proteins and lipids that are manufactured on the ER membranes are transported through the channels of the ER and are packaged into transport vesicles that bud off from the ER ❶. The vesicles fuse with the membrane of the Golgi bodies, dumping their contents into the Golgi ❷. Within the Golgi bodies the molecules may take one of many paths, indicated by the branching arrows in figure 4.11. Many of these molecules become tagged with carbohydrates. The molecules collect at the ends of the membranous folds of the Golgi bodies; these folds are given the special name *cisternae* (Latin, collecting vessels). Vesicles that pinch off from the cisternae carry the molecules to the different compartments of the cell ❸ and ❹, or to the inner surface of the plasma membrane, where molecules to be secreted are released to the outside ❺.

Other organelles called **lysosomes** arise from the Golgi complex (the light orange vesicle budding at ❸) and contain a concentrated mix of the powerful enzymes manufactured in the rough ER that break down macromolecules. Lysosomes are the recycling centers of the cell, breaking down failing organelles and other structures within cells, digesting worn-out cell components, and recycling the proteins and other materials of the old parts.

Putting the Concept to Work

How do vesicles pinched off from the Golgi "know" where to go?

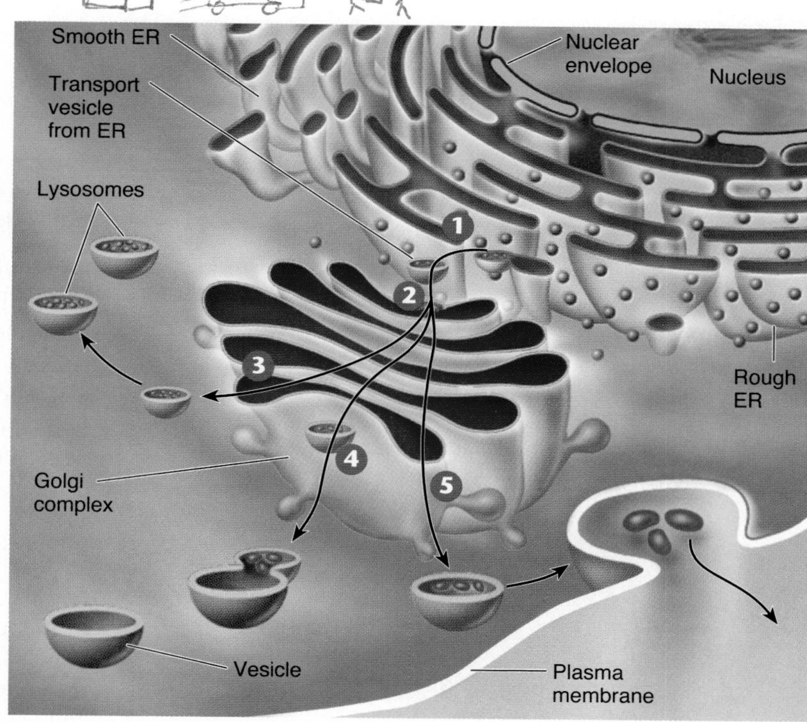

Figure 4.11 How the endomembrane system works.

A highly efficient highway system within the cell, the endomembrane system transports material from the ER to the Golgi and from there to other destinations.

Vacuoles: Storage Compartments

LEARNING OBJECTIVE 4.6.3 Describe the function of plant vacuoles.

The interiors of plant and many protist cells contain membrane-bounded storage compartments called **vacuoles.** The center of the plant cell shown in figure 4.12, as in all plant cells, contains a large, apparently empty space, called the *central vacuole*. This vacuole is not really empty; it contains large amounts of water and other materials, such as sugars, ions, and pigments. The central vacuole functions as a storage center for these important substances.

Putting the Concept to Work

Do you imagine the vacuole is bounded by a membrane? Explain.

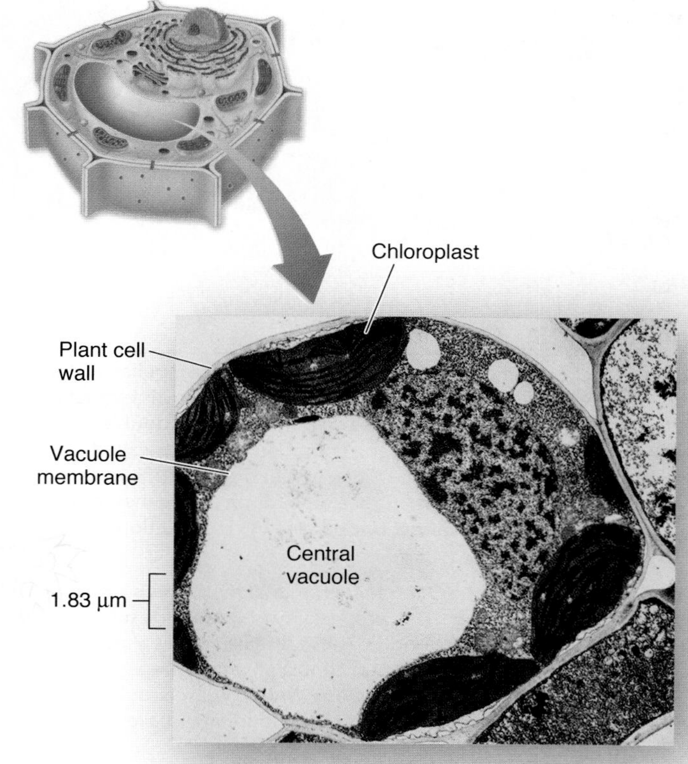

Figure 4.12 A plant central vacuole.

A plant's central vacuole stores dissolved substances and can increase in size to increase the surface area of a plant cell.

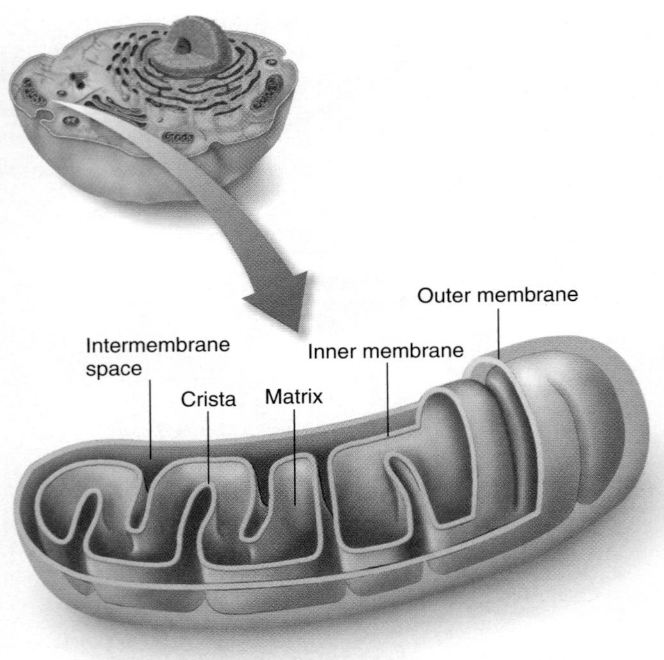

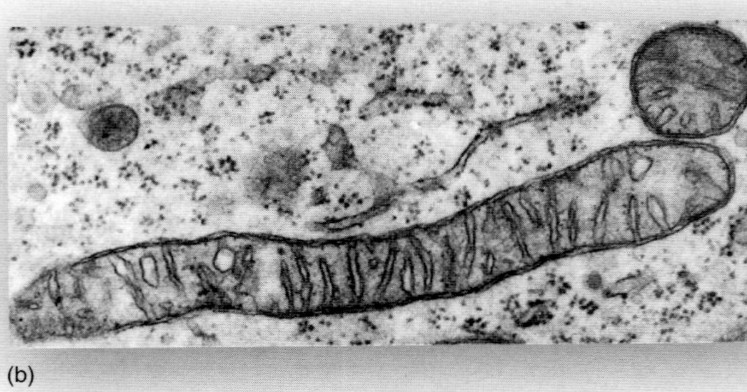

Figure 4.13 Mitochondria.

The mitochondria of a cell are sausage-shaped organelles within which oxidative metabolism takes place, and energy is extracted from food using oxygen. (a) A mitochondrion has a double membrane. The inner membrane is shaped into folds called cristae. The space within the cristae is called the matrix. The cristae greatly increase the surface area for oxidative metabolism. (b) Micrograph of two mitochondria, one in cross section, the other cut lengthwise.

IMPLICATION FOR YOU Mitochondrial medicine is a new and rapidly developing medical speciality of diseases resulting from failure of the mitochondria. These diseases affect almost all organs, for the simple reason that almost all organs depend on mitochondria for the energy they use. Which organs would you expect to exhibit the most serious mitochondrial diseases? Explain why you chose the organs you did.

4.7 Organelles That Harvest Energy

LEARNING OBJECTIVE 4.7.1 Differentiate between mitochondria and chloroplasts.

Eukaryotic cells contain several kinds of complex, energy-harvesting organelles that contain their own DNA and appear to have been derived from ancient bacteria. These bacteria were taken up by ancestral eukaryotic cells in the distant past and remained living inside the host cell, forming a relationship called symbiosis. These organelles include mitochondria (which occur in the cells of all but a very few eukaryotes) and chloroplasts (which occur only in algae and plant cells—they do not occur in animal or fungal cells).

Mitochondria: Powerhouses of the Cell

Eukaryotic organisms extract energy from organic molecules ("food") in a complex series of chemical reactions called **oxidative metabolism,** which takes place only in their mitochondria. **Mitochondria** (singular, **mitochondrion**) are sausage-shaped organelles about the size of a bacterial cell. Mitochondria are bounded by two membranes. The outer membrane, shown partially cut away in figure 4.13, is smooth and apparently derives from the plasma membrane of the host cell that first took up the bacterium long ago. The inner membrane, apparently the plasma membrane of the bacterium that gave rise to the mitochondrion, is bent into numerous folds called **cristae** (singular, **crista**) that resemble the folded plasma membranes in various groups of bacteria. The cutaway view of the figure shows how the cristae partition the mitochondrion into two compartments, an inner **matrix** and an outer compartment, called the **intermembrane space.** As you will learn in chapter 7, this architecture is critical to successfully carrying out oxidative metabolism.

During the 1.5 billion years in which mitochondria have existed in eukaryotic cells, most of their genes have been transferred to the chromosomes of the host cells. But mitochondria still have some of their original genes, contained in a circular, closed, naked molecule of DNA (called *mitochondrial DNA,* or *mtDNA*) that closely resembles the circular DNA molecule of a bacterium. On this mtDNA are several genes that produce some of the proteins essential for oxidative metabolism. In both mitochondria and bacteria, the circular DNA molecule is replicated during the process of division. When a mitochondrion divides, it copies its DNA located in the matrix and splits into two by simple fission, dividing much as bacteria do.

Chloroplasts: Energy-Capturing Centers

All photosynthesis in plants and algae takes place within another bacteria-like organelle, the **chloroplast** (figure 4.14). There is strong evidence that chloroplasts, like mitochondria, were derived from bacteria by symbiosis. A chloroplast is bounded, like a mitochondrion, by two membranes, the inner derived from the original bacterium and the outer resembling the host cell's ER. Chloroplasts are larger than mitochondria, and have a more complex organization. Inside the

The light-dependent reactions of photosynthesis are discussed on pages 108 to 111. Proteins embedded in the thylakoid membrane use energy from the sun to make two molecules, ATP and NADPH. These molecules are used to make sugar molecules.

chloroplast, another series of membranes are fused to form stacks of closed vesicles called **thylakoids.** The energy-harvesting reactions of photosynthesis take place within the thylakoids. The thylakoids are stacked on top of one another to form a column called a **granum** (plural, **grana**). The interior of a chloroplast is bathed with a semiliquid substance called the **stroma.**

Like mitochondria, chloroplasts have a circular DNA molecule. This DNA contains many of the genes coding for the proteins necessary to carry out photosynthesis. Plant cells can contain from one to several hundred chloroplasts, depending on the species. Neither mitochondria nor chloroplasts can be grown in a cell-free culture; they are totally dependent on the cells within which they occur.

Putting the Concept to Work

What exactly does a mitochondrion need to get from a living cell?

Endosymbiosis

LEARNING OBJECTIVE 4.7.2 Describe the evidence that mitochondria evolved from ancient bacteria.

Symbiosis is a close, integrated relationship between organisms of different species that live together. The theory of **endosymbiosis** proposes that some of today's eukaryotic organelles evolved by a symbiosis in which one cell of a prokaryotic species was engulfed by and lived inside the cell of another species of prokaryote that was a precursor to eukaryotes. Figure 4.15 shows how this is thought to have occurred. Many cells take up food or other substances through endocytosis, a process whereby the plasma membrane of a cell wraps around the substance, enclosing it within a vesicle inside the cell. According to the endosymbiont theory the engulfed prokaryotes provided their hosts with certain advantages associated with their special metabolic abilities. Two key eukaryotic organelles just described are believed to be the descendants of these endosymbiotic prokaryotes: mitochondria, which are thought to have originated as bacteria capable of carrying out oxidative metabolism; and chloroplasts, which apparently arose from photosynthetic bacteria.

The endosymbiont theory is supported by a wealth of evidence. Both mitochondria and chloroplasts are surrounded by two membranes; the inner membrane probably evolved from the plasma membrane of the engulfed bacterium, while the outer membrane is probably derived from the plasma membrane or endoplasmic reticulum of the host cell. Mitochondria are about the same size as most bacteria, and the cristae formed by their inner membranes resemble the folded membranes in various groups of bacteria. Mitochondrial ribosomes are also similar to bacterial ribosomes in size and structure. Both mitochondria and chloroplasts contain circular molecules of DNA similar to those in bacteria. Finally, mitochondria divide by simple fission, splitting in two just as bacterial cells do, and they apparently replicate and partition their DNA in much the same way as bacteria do.

Putting the Concept to Work

What is the principal difference between mitochondria and chloroplasts?

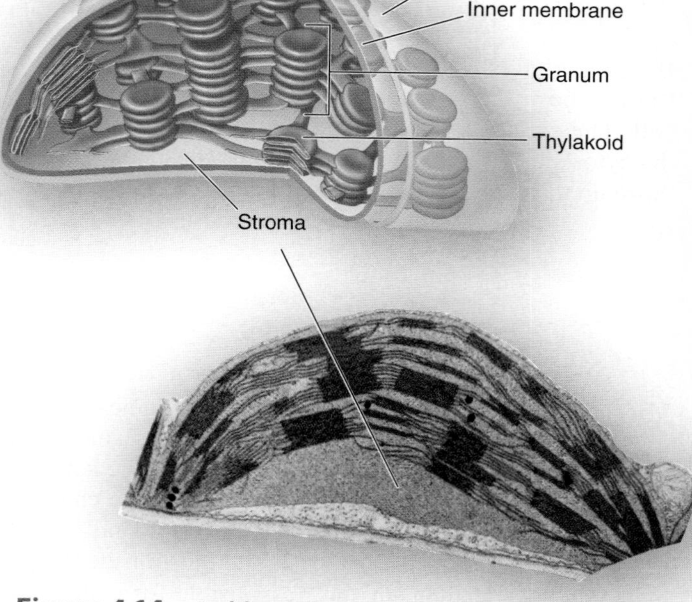

Figure 4.14 A chloroplast.

Bacteria-like organelles called chloroplasts are the sites of photosynthesis in photosynthetic eukaryotes. Like mitochondria, they have a complex system of internal membranes on which chemical reactions take place. The internal membranes of a chloroplast are fused to form stacks of closed vesicles called thylakoids. Photosynthesis occurs within these thylakoids. Thylakoids are stacked one on top of the other in columns called grana. The interior of the chloroplast is bathed in a semiliquid substance called the stroma.

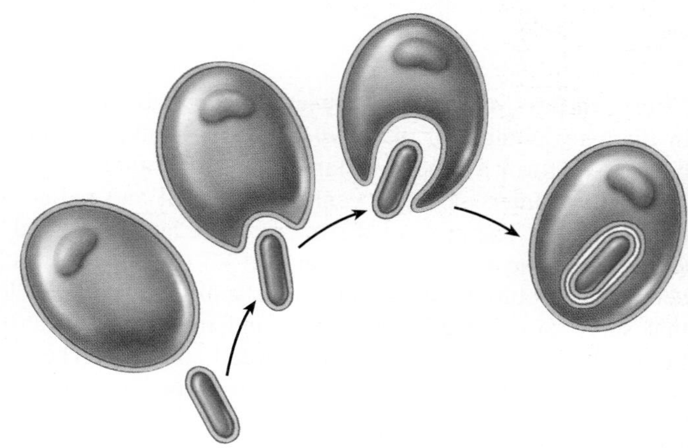

Figure 4.15 Endosymbiosis.

This figure shows how a double membrane may have been created during the symbiotic origin of mitochondria or chloroplasts.

IMPLICATION FOR YOU When first proposed by Professor Lynn Margulis of Amherst College, the endosymbiosis theory was widely ridiculed as absurd speculation, until molecular evidence was found to support it. Her more recent Gaia hypothesis that our planet is a super-organism is being similarly discounted. How do you feel about such an idea?

4.8 The Cytoskeleton: Interior Framework of the Cell

LEARNING OBJECTIVE 4.8.1 Describe the protein fibers of the cytoskeleton.

If you were to shrink down and enter into the interior of a eukaryotic cell, your view would be similar to what you see in the illustration shown here: a dense network of protein fibers called the **cytoskeleton** provides a framework that supports the shape of the cell. The cytoskeleton also anchors organelles like the mitochondria to fixed locations within the cell interior. The protein fibers of the cytoskeleton are a dynamic system, constantly being formed and disassembled. There are three different kinds of protein fibers that make up the cytoskeleton, shown as enlargements below.

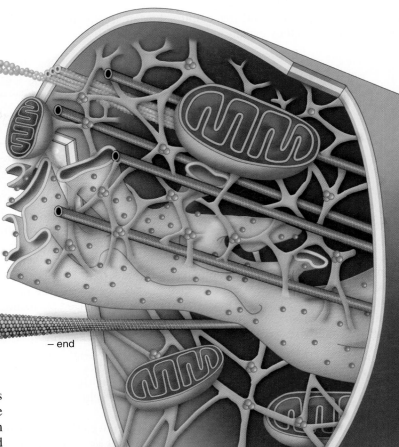

Actin filament
Actin subunit
7 nm

Microfilaments (actin filaments) Actin filaments are long fibers about 7 nanometers in diameter. Each filament is composed of two protein chains loosely twined together like two strands of pearls. Each "pearl," or subunit, on the chains is the globular protein **actin**. Actin filaments are found throughout the cell but are most highly concentrated just inside the plasma membrane. Actin filaments are responsible for cellular movements such as contraction, crawling, "pinching" during division, and formation of cellular extensions.

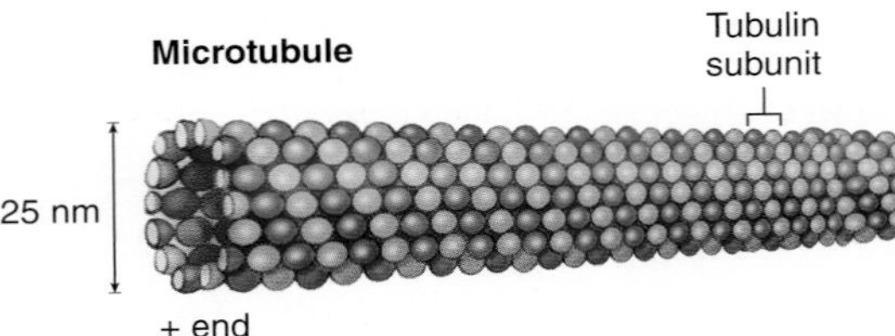

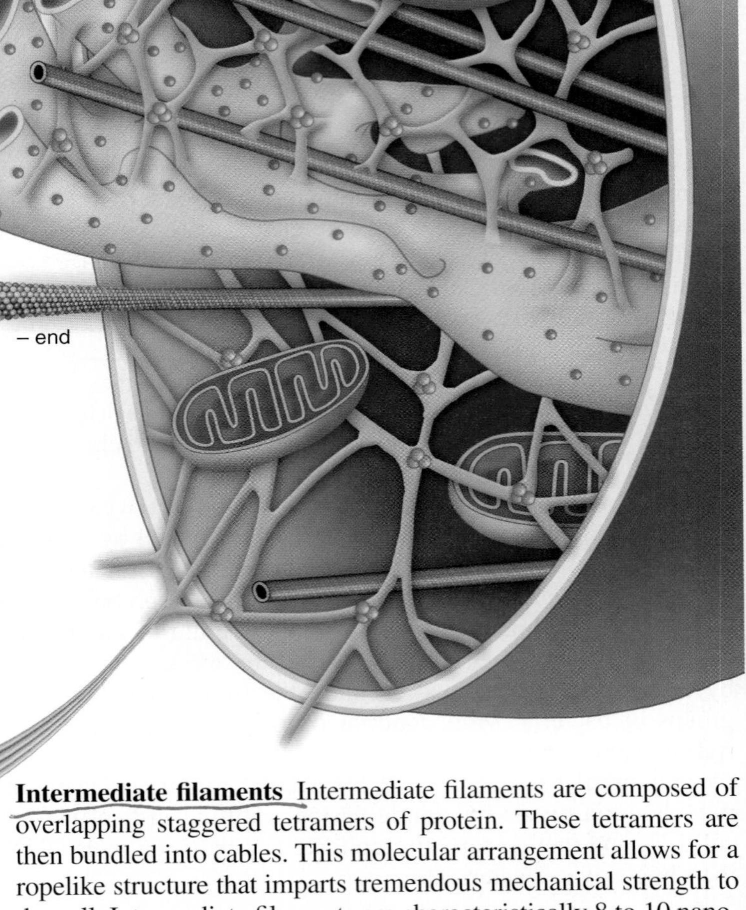

Microtubules Microtubules are hollow tubes about 25 nanometers in diameter composed of *tubulin* protein subunits arranged side by side to form a tube. In many cells, microtubules form from nucleation centers near the center of the cell and radiate toward the periphery. The ends of the microtubule are designated as "+" (away from the nucleation center) or "-" (toward the nucleation center). Microtubules are comparatively stiff cytoskeletal elements that serve to organize metabolism and intracellular transport in the nondividing cell and to stabilize cell structure. They are also responsible for the movement of chromosomes in mitosis.

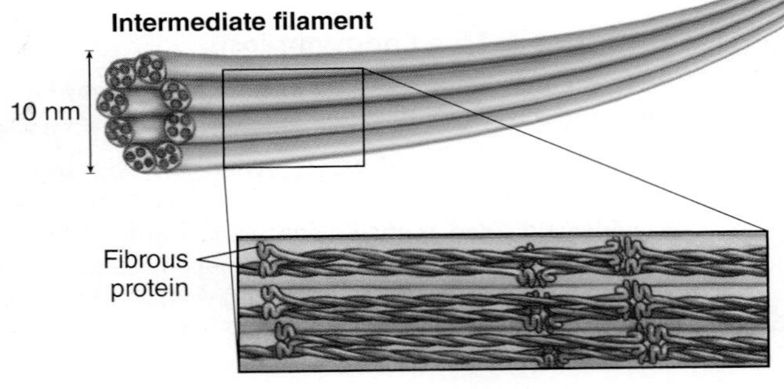

Intermediate filaments Intermediate filaments are composed of overlapping staggered tetramers of protein. These tetramers are then bundled into cables. This molecular arrangement allows for a ropelike structure that imparts tremendous mechanical strength to the cell. Intermediate filaments are characteristically 8 to 10 nanometers in diameter, intermediate in size between actin filaments and microtubules. Once formed, intermediate filaments are stable and usually do not break down. They provide structural reinforcement to the cell and organelles.

Centrioles

Complex structures called **centrioles** assemble microtubules from tubulin subunits in the cells of animals and most protists. Centrioles occur in pairs within the cytoplasm, usually located at right angles to one another as you can see in figure 4.16. They are usually found near the nuclear envelope and are among the most structurally complex microtubular assemblies of the cell.

> **Centrioles are involved in assembling a network of microtubules that attach to and separate the chromosomes during cell division. This network of microtubules, called the spindle, is discussed in more detail in chapters 8 and 9.**

Putting the Concept to Work

Which of the three fibers of the cytoskeleton is the thickest?

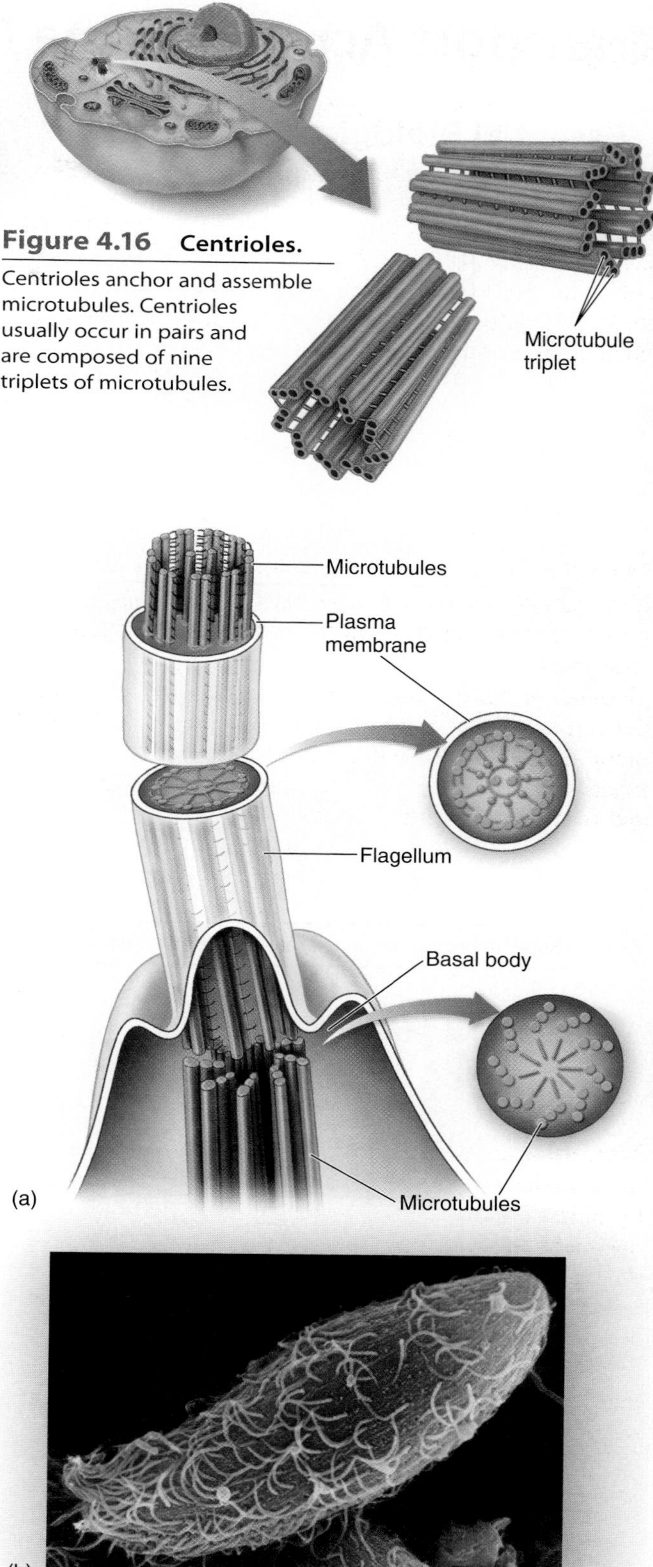

Figure 4.16 Centrioles.

Centrioles anchor and assemble microtubules. Centrioles usually occur in pairs and are composed of nine triplets of microtubules.

Figure 4.17 Flagella and cilia.

(a) A eukaryotic flagellum springs directly from a basal body and is composed of a ring of nine pairs of microtubules with two microtubules in its core. (b) The surface of this *Dileptus* is covered with a dense forest of cilia, which it uses to propel itself.

Cell Movement

LEARNING OBJECTIVE 4.8.2 Explain how animal cells move.

Like a tendon that anchors a muscle to a bone, intermediate filaments act as intracellular tendons, preventing excessive stretching of cells. Actin microfilaments play a major role in determining the shape of cells. Essentially, all cell motion is tied to the movement of actin microfilaments, microtubules, or both. Because actin microfilaments can form and dissolve so readily, they enable some cells to change shape quickly and move from place to place.

Some Cells Crawl. It is the arrangement of actin microfilaments within the cell cytoplasm that allows cells to "crawl," literally! Crawling is a significant cellular phenomenon, essential to inflammation, clotting, wound healing, and the spread of cancer. White blood cells in particular exhibit this ability. Produced in the bone marrow, these cells are released into the circulatory system and eventually crawl out of capillaries and into the tissues to destroy potential pathogens. The crawling mechanism is an exquisite example of cellular coordination.

Swimming with Flagella and Cilia. Some eukaryotic cells contain **flagella** (singular, **flagellum**), fine, long, threadlike organelles protruding from the cell surface. Figure 4.17*a* shows how a flagellum arises from a microtubular structure called a **basal body,** with groups of microtubules arranged in rows of three, shown in the cross-sectional view. Some of these microtubules extend up into the flagellum, which consists of a circle of nine microtubule pairs surrounding two central microtubules. This **9 + 2 arrangement** is a fundamental feature of eukaryotes and apparently evolved early in their history. In humans, we find a single long flagellum on each sperm cell that propels the cell in a swimming motion. If flagella are numerous and organized in dense rows, they are called **cilia** (figure 4.17*b*). Cilia do not differ from flagella in their structure, but cilia are usually shorter. In humans, dense mats of cilia project from cells that line our breathing tube, the trachea, to move mucus and dust particles out of the respiratory tract into the throat (where we can expel these contaminants by spitting or swallowing). Eukaryotic flagella serve a similar function as the bacterial flagella discussed in section 4.2, but are very different structurally.

Putting the Concept to Work

Which element of the cytoskeleton is active in the crawling of white blood cells?

Transport Across Plasma Membranes

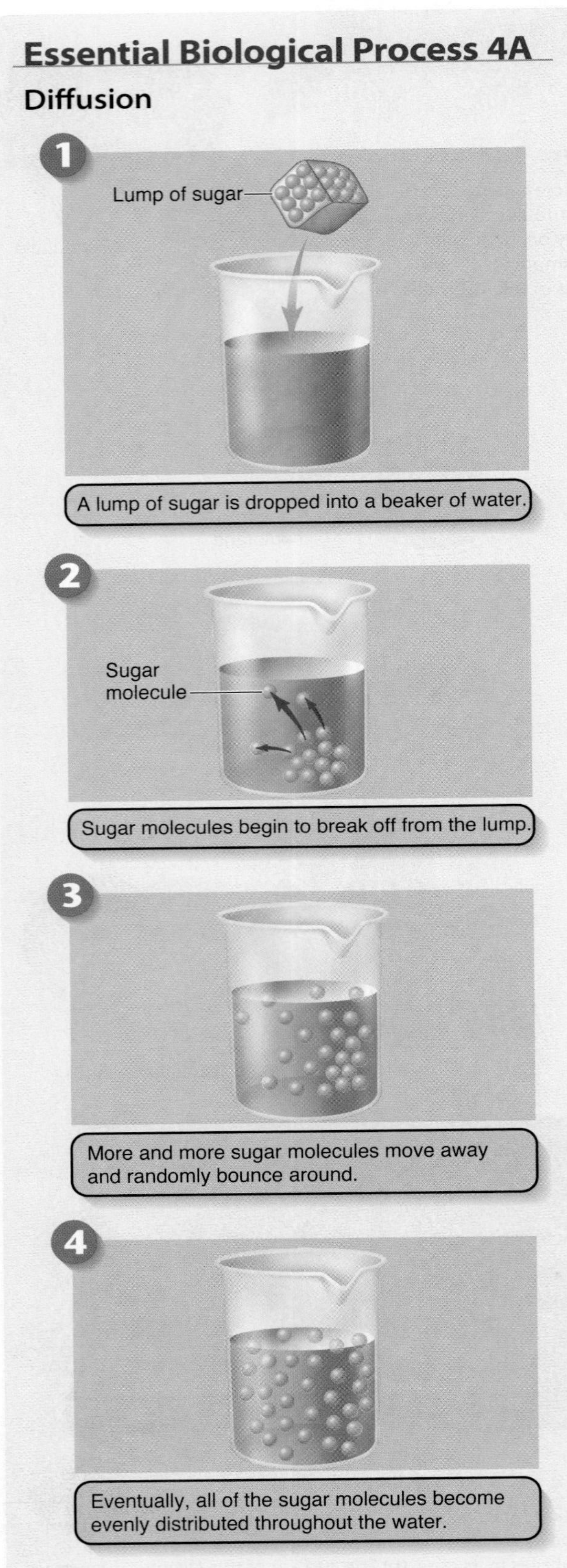

Essential Biological Process 4A
Diffusion
1
Lump of sugar
A lump of sugar is dropped into a beaker of water.
2
Sugar molecule
Sugar molecules begin to break off from the lump.
3
More and more sugar molecules move away and randomly bounce around.
4
Eventually, all of the sugar molecules become evenly distributed throughout the water.

4.9 Diffusion and Osmosis

For cells to survive, nutrients, water, and other materials must pass into the cell, and waste materials must be eliminated. All of this moving back and forth across the cell's plasma membrane occurs in one of three ways: (1) water and other substances diffuse through the membrane, (2) food particles are engulfed by the plasma membrane folding around them, or (3) proteins in the membrane act as doors that admit certain molecules only.

Diffusion

LEARNING OBJECTIVE 4.9.1 Define diffusion and explain why diffusion occurs down a concentration gradient, rather than up.

How a molecule moves—just where it goes—is totally random, like shaking marbles in a cup, so if two kinds of molecules are added together, they soon mix. The random motion of molecules always tends to produce uniform mixtures because a substance moves from regions where its concentration is high to regions where its concentration is lower (that is, *down* the **concentration gradient**). How does a molecule "know" in what direction to move? It doesn't—molecules don't "know" anything. A molecule is equally likely to move in any direction and is constantly changing course in random ways. There are simply more molecules able to move from where they are common than from where they are scarce. This mixing process is called **diffusion.** Diffusion (*Essential Biological Process 4A*) is the net movement of molecules down a concentration gradient toward regions of lower concentration (that is, where there are relatively fewer of them) as a result of random motion. For example, a lump of sugar dropped into a beaker of water will break apart into individual sugar molecules that will move about randomly. However, they will tend to travel away from the area of high concentration (the sugar cube) to an area of lower concentration (the rest of the beaker). Eventually, the substance will achieve a state of *equilibrium,* where there is no net movement toward any particular direction (as shown in panel 4). The individual molecules of the substance are still in motion, but there is no net change in direction.

Putting the Concept to Work

Would you expect polar molecules to diffuse into water more completely than nonpolar ones? Explain.

Osmosis

LEARNING OBJECTIVE 4.9.2 Define osmosis and discuss three ways organisms maintain osmotic balance.

Ions and polar molecules cannot cross the very nonpolar environment found in the lipid core of the membrane bilayer. However, the movement of water molecules, which are very polar, is not blocked—water diffuses freely across the plasma membrane. How is this possible? Water molecules pass through small channels, called **aquaporins,** that traverse the membrane. These water channels are very selective, even blocking the passage of protons (hydrogen ions), which are smaller than water molecules—a cluster of positively charged amino acids that line the pore repel protons, which are also positively charged.

As in diffusion, water passes across a cell membrane down its concentration gradient, a process called **osmosis** (*Essential Biological Process 4B*). To understand how water moves into and out of a cell, let's first focus on the water molecules already present inside a cell. What are they doing? Many of them are interacting with the sugars, proteins, and other polar molecules inside. Remember, water is very polar itself and readily interacts with other polar molecules. Instead of freely moving about, a shell of water molecules remains clustered around each polar molecule inside the cell. As a result, a water molecule coming into the cell by random motion may not be free to come out again. For example, in *Essential Biological Process 4B,* the addition of a polar solute reduces the number of free water molecules on the right side of the beaker, which can be thought of as the inside of a cell. Because the "outside" of the cell (on the left) has more unbound water molecules, water moves by diffusion into the cell (to the right).

The concentration of *all* molecules dissolved in a solution (the **solutes**) is called the osmotic concentration of the solution. If the osmotic concentrations of two solutions are equal, the solutions are **isotonic** (Greek *iso,* the same). If two solutions have unequal osmotic concentrations, the solution with the higher solute concentration is said to be **hypertonic** (Greek *hyper,* more than), and the solution with the lower one is **hypotonic** (Greek *hypo,* less than).

Movement of water into a cell by osmosis creates pressure, called osmotic pressure, which can cause a cell to swell and burst (figure 4.18). Most animal cells cannot withstand osmotic pressure unless their plasma membranes are braced to resist the swelling. If placed in pure water, they soon burst like overinflated balloons. That is why the cells of so many kinds of organisms have cell walls to stiffen their exteriors. In fact, this osmotic pressure, called turgor pressure in plants, is important for plant cells to maintain their shape. Without adequate water inside the cells, the plants wilt. In animals, the fluids bathing the cells have as many polar molecules dissolved in them as the cells do, making them isotonic, so the problem doesn't arise.

Putting the Concept to Work

Explain how water diffuses across the plasma membrane.

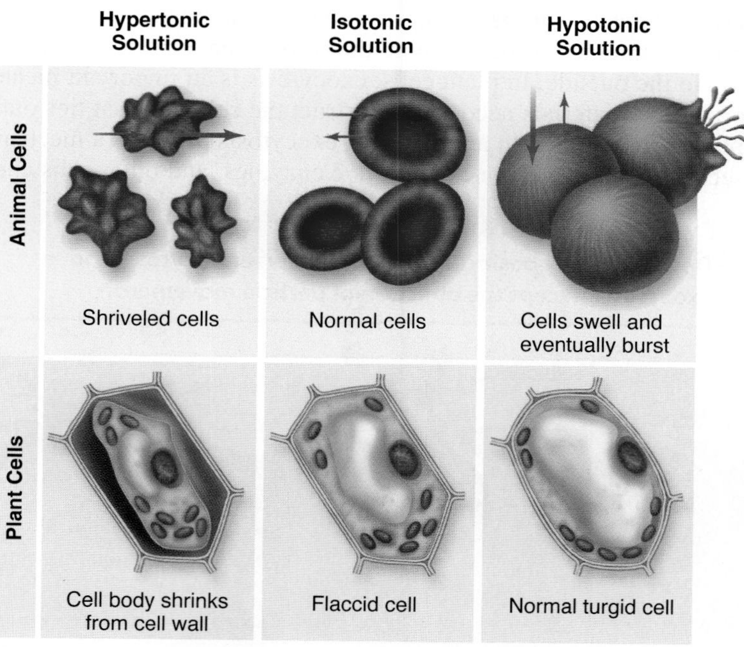

Figure 4.18 Osmotic pressure in animal and plant cells.

Essential Biological Process 4B

Osmosis

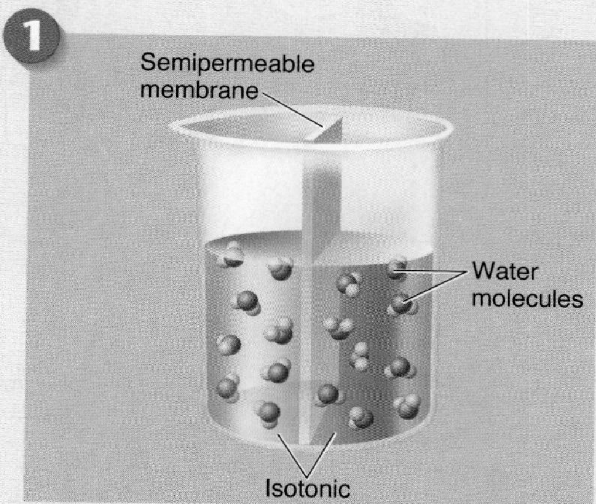

Diffusion causes water molecules to distribute themselves equally on both sides of a semipermeable membrane.

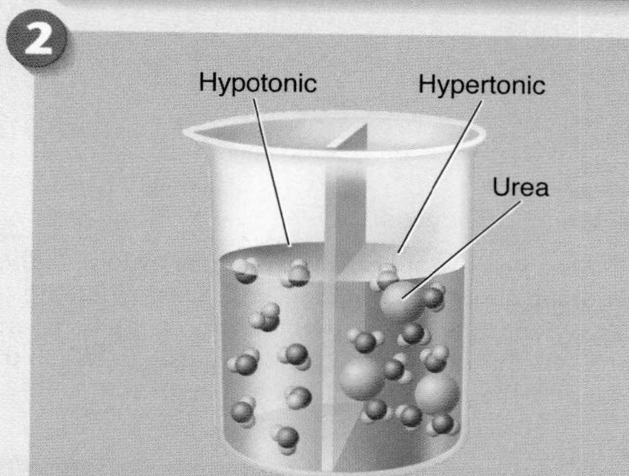

Addition of solute molecules that cannot cross the membrane reduces the number of free water molecules on that side, as they bind to the solute.

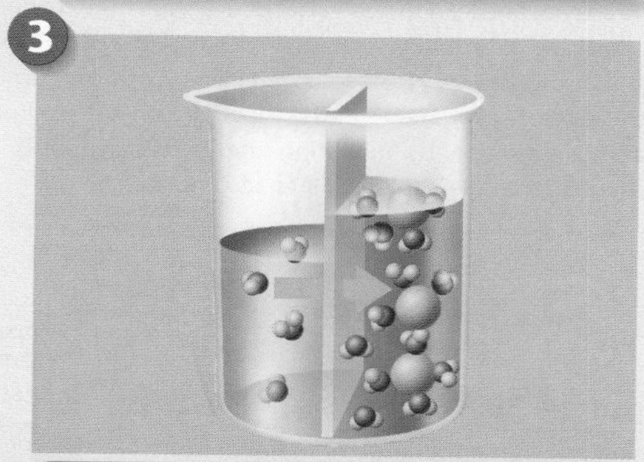

Diffusion then causes free water molecules to move from the side where their concentration is higher to the solute side, where their concentration is lower.

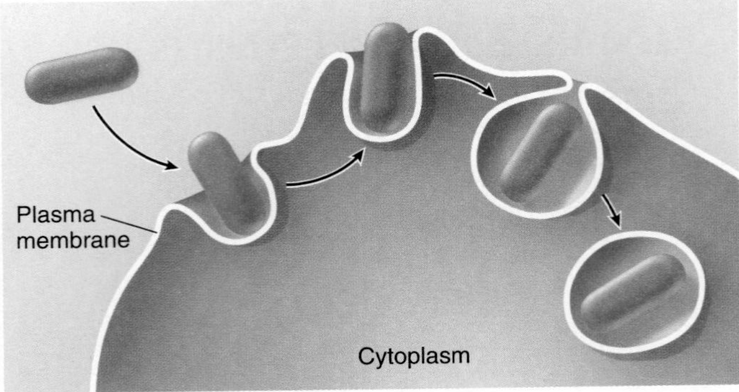

(a) Phagocytosis

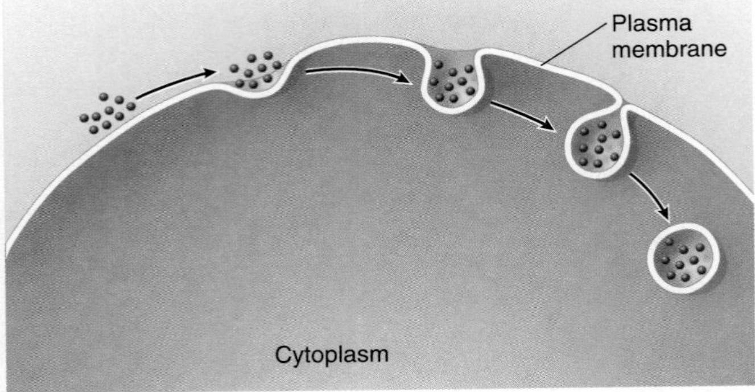

(b) Pinocytosis

Figure 4.19 Endocytosis.

Endocytosis is the process of engulfing material by folding the plasma membrane around it, forming a vesicle. (a) When the material is an organism or some other relatively large fragment of organic matter, the process is called phagocytosis. (b) When the material is a liquid, the process is called pinocytosis.

4.10 Bulk Passage into and out of Cells

LEARNING OBJECTIVE 4.10.1 Distinguish phagocytosis from pinocytosis.

Endocytosis

The cells of many eukaryotes take in food and liquids by extending their plasma membranes outward toward food particles. The membrane engulfs the particle and forms a vesicle—a membrane-bounded sac—around it. This process is called **endocytosis** (figure 4.19).

If the material the cell takes in is particulate (made up of discrete particles), such as an organism, like the red bacterium in figure 4.19*a*, or some other fragment of organic matter, the process is called **phagocytosis** (Greek *phagein,* to eat, and *cytos,* cell). If the material the cell takes in is liquid or substances dissolved in a liquid, like the small particles in figure 4.19*b*, it is called **pinocytosis** (Greek *pinein,* to drink). Pinocytosis is common among animal cells. Mammalian egg cells, for example, "nurse" from surrounding cells; the nearby cells secrete nutrients that the maturing egg cell takes up by pinocytosis. Virtually all eukaryotic cells constantly carry out these kinds of endocytosis, trapping particles and extracellular fluid in vesicles and ingesting them. Endocytosis rates vary from one cell type to another. They can be surprisingly high: Some types of white blood cells ingest 25% of their cell volume each hour!

Exocytosis

The reverse of endocytosis is **exocytosis,** the discharge of material from vesicles at the cell surface. The vesicle in figure 4.20 contains a substance to be discharged, or released, from the cell. The purple particles remain suspended in the vesicle as it fuses with the plasma membrane. The membrane that forms the vesicle is made of phospholipids, and as it comes in contact with the plasma membrane, the phospholipids of both membranes interact, forming a pore through which the contents leave the vesicle to the outside. In plant cells, exocytosis is an important means of exporting the materials needed to construct the cell wall that lies outside the plasma membrane. In animal cells, exocytosis provides a mechanism for secreting many hormones, digestive enzymes, and other substances.

Putting the Concept to Work

Do you see any basic difference between endocytosis and exocytosis, except the direction of particle movement?

BIOLOGY & YOU

Statins. High levels of cholesterol, which can coat the arteries and lead to heart attacks, are often due to a gene defect that blocks the endocytosis of cholesterol (the membrane protein that triggers endocytosis is defective). Not taken up by cells, cholesterol accumulates in the bloodstream. Statin drugs combat this situation by inhibiting the body's synthesis of cholesterol, so that there is less of it to accumulate.

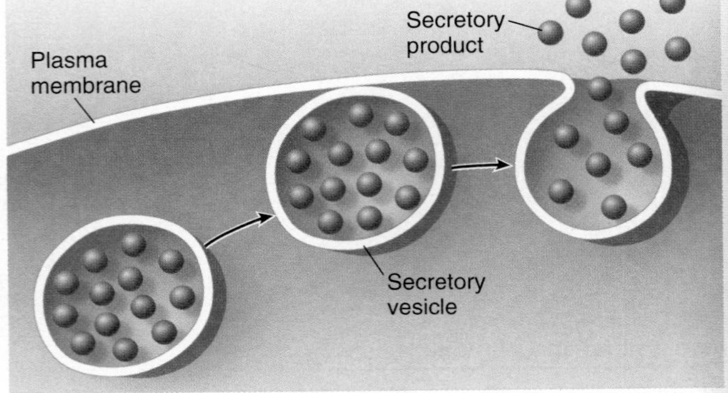

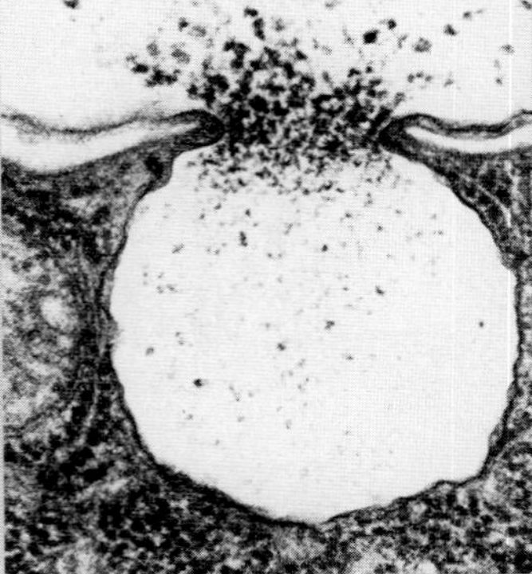

Figure 4.20 Exocytosis.

Exocytosis is the discharge of material from vesicles at the cell surface. Proteins and other molecules are secreted from cells in small pockets called secretory vesicles, whose membranes fuse with the plasma membrane, thereby allowing the secretory vesicles to release their contents to the cell surface. In the photomicrograph, you can see exocytosis taking place somewhat explosively.

4.11 Selective Permeability

LEARNING OBJECTIVE 4.11.1 Distinguish between selective diffusion and facilitated diffusion.

From the point of view of efficiency, the problem with endocytosis is that it is expensive to carry out—the cell must make and move a lot of membrane. Also, endocytosis is not picky—in pinocytosis particularly, engulfing liquid does not allow the cell to choose which molecules come in. Cells solve this problem by using proteins in the plasma membrane as channels to pass molecules into and out of the cell. Because each kind of channel allows passage of only a certain kind of molecule, the cell can control what enters and leaves, an ability called **selective permeability.**

Selective Diffusion

Some channels act like open doors. As long as a molecule fits the channel, it is free to pass through in either direction. Diffusion tends to equalize the concentration of such molecules on both sides of the membrane, with the molecules moving toward the side where they are scarcest. This mechanism of transport is called **selective diffusion.** One class of selectively open channels consists of ion channels, which are pores that span the membrane. Ions that fit the pore can diffuse through it in either direction. Such ion channels play an essential role in signaling by the nervous system.

Facilitated Diffusion

Most diffusion occurs through use of special carrier proteins. These proteins bind only certain kinds of molecules, such as a particular sugar, amino acid, or ion. The molecule physically binds to the carrier on one side of the membrane and is released to the other side. The direction of the molecule's net movement depends on its concentration gradient across the membrane. If the concentration is greater outside the cell, the molecule is more likely to bind to the carrier on the extracellular side of the membrane, as shown in panel 1 of *Essential Biological Process 4C*, and be released on the cytoplasmic side, as in panel 3. If the concentration of the molecule is greater inside the cell, the net movement will be from inside to outside. Thus the net movement always occurs from high concentration to low, just as it does in simple diffusion, but the process is facilitated by the carriers. For this reason, this mechanism of transport is given a special name, **facilitated diffusion.**

A characteristic feature of transport by carrier proteins is that its rate can be saturated. If the concentration of a substance is progressively increased, the rate of transport of the substance increases up to a certain point and then levels off. There are a limited number of carrier proteins in the membrane, and when the concentration of the transported substance is raised high enough, all the carriers will be in use. The transport system is then said to be "saturated." When an investigator wishes to know if a particular substance is being transported across a membrane by a carrier protein, or is diffusing across, he or she conducts experiments to see if the transport system can be saturated. If it can be saturated, it is carrier-mediated; if it cannot be saturated, it is not.

Putting the Concept to Work

Explain why saturation indicates the action of a carrier protein.

Essential Biological Process 4C

Facilitated Diffusion

1

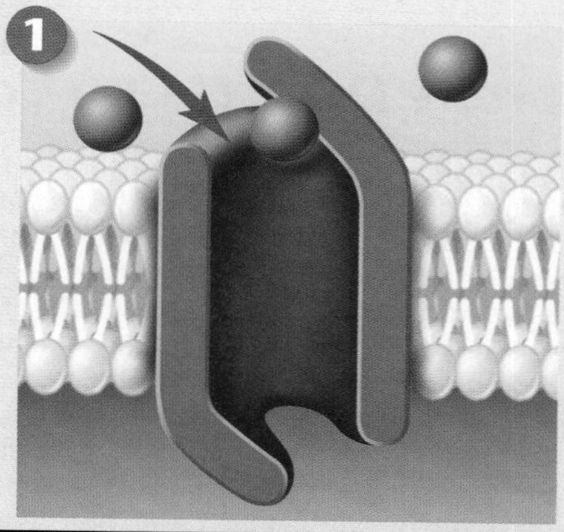

Particular molecules can bind to special protein carriers in the plasma membrane.

2

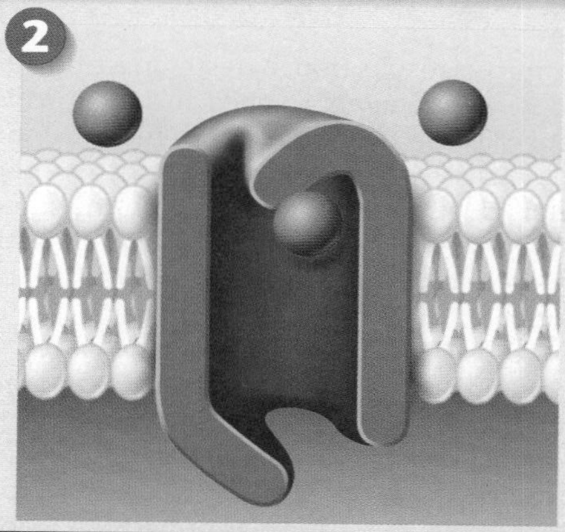

The protein carrier helps (facilitates) the diffusion process and does not require energy.

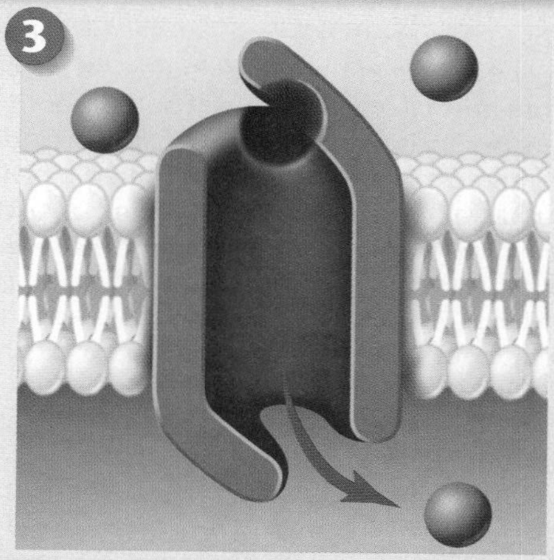

3

The molecule is released on the far side of the membrane. Protein carriers transport only certain molecules across the membrane but will take them in either direction down their concentration gradients.

Membrane Defects Can Cause Disease

The year 1993 marked an important milestone in the treatment of human disease. That year the first attempt was made to cure **cystic fibrosis** (**CF**), a deadly genetic disorder, by transferring healthy genes into sick individuals. Cystic fibrosis is a fatal disease in which the body cells of affected individuals secrete a thick mucus that clogs the airways of the lungs. The cystic fibrosis patient in the photograph is breathing into a Vitalograph, a device that measures lung function. These same secretions block the ducts of the pancreas and liver so that the few patients who do not die of lung disease die of liver failure. Cystic fibrosis is usually thought of as a children's disease because until recently few affected individuals lived long enough to become adults. Even today half die before their mid-twenties. There is no known cure.

Cystic fibrosis results from a defect in a single gene that is passed down from parent to child. It is the most common fatal genetic disease of Caucasians. One in 20 individuals possesses at least one copy of the defective gene. Most of these individuals are not afflicted with the disease; only those children who inherit a copy of the defective gene from each parent succumb to cystic fibrosis—about 1 in 2,500 infants.

Cystic fibrosis has proven difficult to study. Many organs are affected, and until recently it was impossible to identify the nature of the defective gene responsible for the disease. In 1985 the first clear clue was obtained. An investigator, Paul Quinton, seized on a commonly observed characteristic of cystic fibrosis patients, that their sweat is abnormally salty, and performed the following experiment. He isolated a sweat duct from a small piece of skin and placed it in a solution of salt (NaCl) that was three times as concentrated as the NaCl inside the duct. He then monitored the movement of ions. Diffusion tends to drive both the sodium (Na^+) and the chloride (Cl^-) ions into the duct because of the higher outer ion concentrations. In skin isolated from normal individuals, Na^+ and Cl^- both entered the duct, as expected. In skin isolated from cystic fibrosis individuals, however, only Na^+ entered the duct—no Cl^- entered. For the first time, the molecular nature of cystic fibrosis became clear. Water accompanies chloride, and was not entering the ducts because chloride was not, creating thick mucus. Cystic fibrosis is a defect in a plasma membrane protein called CFTR (*c*ystic *f*ibrosis *t*ransmembrane conductance *r*egulator) that normally regulates passage of Cl^- into and out of the body's cells.

The defective *cf* gene was isolated in 1987, and its position on a particular human chromosome (chromosome 7) was pinpointed in 1989. Interestingly, many cystic fibrosis patients produce a CFTR protein with a normal amino acid sequence. The *cf* mutation in these cases appears to interfere with how the CFTR protein folds, preventing it from folding into a functional shape.

Soon after the *cf* gene was isolated, experiments were begun to see if it would be possible to cure cystic fibrosis by gene therapy—that is, by transferring healthy *cf* genes into the cells with defective ones. In 1990 a working *cf* gene was successfully transferred into human lung cells growing in tissue culture, using adenovirus, a cold virus, to carry the gene into the cells. The CFTR-defective cells were "cured," becoming able to transport chloride ions across their plasma membranes. Then in 1991 a team of researchers successfully transferred a normal human *cf* gene into the lung cells of a living animal—a rat. The *cf* gene was first inserted into the adenovirus genome because adenovirus is a cold virus and easily infects lung cells. The treated virus was then inhaled by the rat. Carried piggyback, the *cf* gene entered the rat lung cells and began producing the normal human CFTR protein within these cells!

These results were very encouraging, and at first the future for all cystic fibrosis patients seemed bright. Clinical tests using adenovirus to introduce healthy *cf* genes into cystic fibrosis patients were begun with much fanfare in 1993.

They were not successful. As described in detail in chapter 13, there were insurmountable problems with the adenovirus being used to transport the *cf* gene into cystic fibrosis patients. The difficult and frustrating challenge that cystic fibrosis researchers had faced was not over. Research into clinical problems is often a time-consuming and frustrating enterprise, never more so than in this case. Recently, new ways of introducing the healthy *cf* gene have been tried with better results. The long, slow journey toward a cure has taught us not to leap to the assumption that a cure is now at hand, but the steady persistence of researchers has taken us a long way, and again the future for cystic fibrosis patients seems bright.

Active Transport

LEARNING OBJECTIVE 4.11.2 Define active transport, and describe the operation of the sodium-potassium pump, including the role of ATP.

Other carrier proteins through the plasma membrane are closed doors. These proteins open only when energy is provided. They are designed to enable the cell to maintain high or low concentrations of certain molecules, much more or less than exists outside the cell. Like motor-driven turnstiles, these transport proteins operate to move a certain substance *up* its concentration gradient. The operation of these one-way, energy-requiring proteins results in **active transport,** the movement of molecules across a membrane to a region of higher concentration by the expenditure of energy.

You might think that the plasma membrane possesses all sorts of active transport proteins for the transport of sugars, amino acids, and other molecules, but in fact, most of the active transport in cells is carried out by one kind of transporter, the sodium-potassium pump.

The Sodium-Potassium Pump. The most important active transport protein is the *sodium-potassium (Na^+-K^+) pump,* which expends metabolic energy to actively pump sodium ions (Na^+) out of cells, and potassium ions (K^+) into cells (*Essential Biological Process 4D*). More than one-third of all the energy expended by your body's cells is spent driving Na^+-K^+ pump carrier proteins. This energy is derived from *adenosine triphosphate (ATP),* a molecule we will learn more about in chapter 5. The transportation of two different ions in opposite directions happens because energy causes a change in the shape of the protein carrier. The panels to the right walk you through one cycle of the pump. Each transport protein can move over 300 sodium ions per second when working full tilt. As a result of all this pumping, there are far fewer sodium ions in the cell. This concentration gradient, paid for by the expenditure of considerable metabolic energy in the form of ATP molecules, is exploited by your cells in many ways. Two of the most important are (1) the conduction of signals along nerve cells (discussed in detail in chapter 29) and (2) the pulling of valuable molecules such as sugars and amino acids into the cell *against* their concentration gradient!

We will focus for a moment on this second process. The plasma membranes of many cells are studded with facilitated diffusion transport proteins, which offer a path for sodium ions that have been pumped out by the Na^+-K^+ pump to diffuse back in. There is a catch, however; these transport proteins require that the sodium ions have a partner in order to pass through—like a dancing party where only couples are admitted through the door—which is why these are called *coupled* transport proteins. Coupled transport proteins won't let sodium ions across unless another molecule tags along, crossing hand in hand with the sodium ion. In some cases the partner molecule is a sugar, in others an amino acid or other molecule. Because the concentration gradient for sodium is so large, many sodium ions are trying to get back in, and this diffusion pressure drags in the partner molecules as well, even if they are already in high concentration within the cell. In this way, sugars and other actively transported molecules enter the cell—via special coupled transport protein channels.

Putting the Concept to Work

Explain how cells are able to take up sugar even when they already have a high concentration of that molecule in their cytoplasm.

Essential Biological Process 4D

The Sodium-Potassium Pump

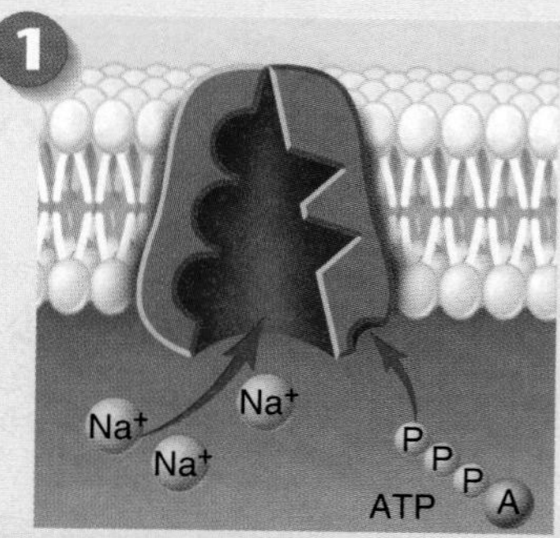

The sodium-potassium pump utilizes a transport protein that binds three sodium ions and a molecule of ATP.

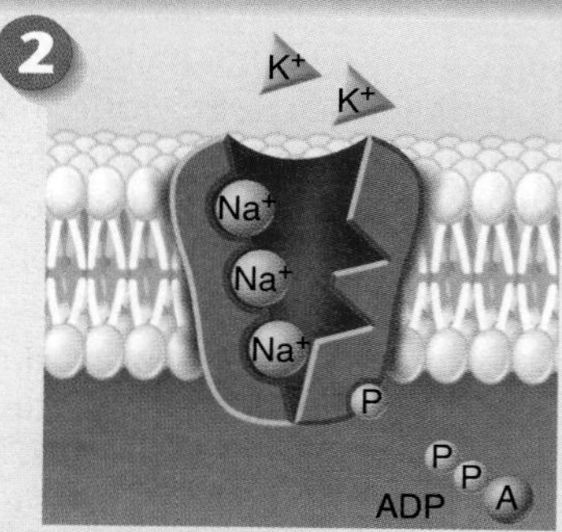

The splitting of ATP provides energy to change the shape of the transport protein. The sodium ions are driven through the pump.

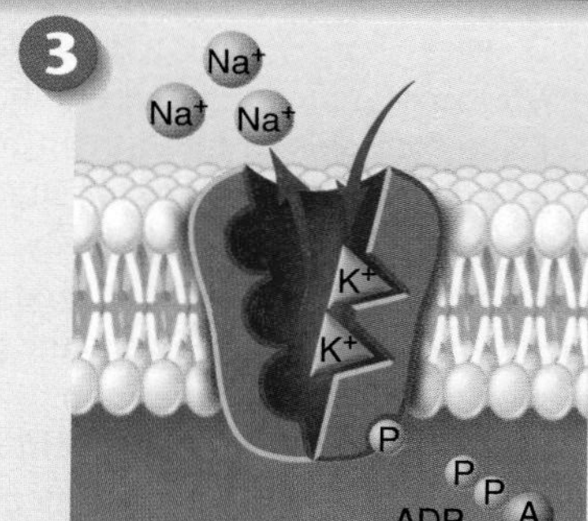

The sodium ions are released to the outside of the membrane, and the new shape of the pump allows two potassium ions to bind.

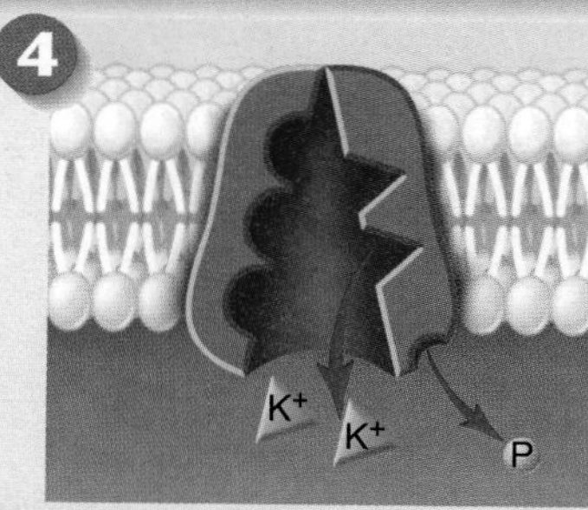

Release of the phosphate allows the sodium-potassium pump's transport protein to revert to its original form, releasing the potassium ions on the inside of the membrane.

Why Does a Cell's Disposal of Damaged Proteins Consume Energy?

Much of modern biology is devoted to learning how cells build things—how the information encoded in DNA is used by cells to manufacture the proteins that make us what we are. The Nobel Prize in Chemistry was awarded in 2004 to researchers for their discovery of how the opposite, less glamorous process works: How cells break down and recycle proteins that are damaged or have outlived their usefulness.

It turns out that a cell's recycling of proteins is much more than just "taking out the trash." Particular proteins are removed, often quite quickly, and cells use such targeted removals to control a lot of their activities, timing when a cell carries out particular functions, when it divides, and even when it dies. Of the 25,000 genes in your DNA, about 1,000 take part in this protein recycling system.

Our understanding of how this system works begins with a puzzle first noted in the 1950s. Most enzymes that break down proteins, including those that digest food, do not need energy to work. But a cell's recycling of its own proteins does consume energy. Researchers had no idea why energy was needed.

The answer to this puzzle came from an unexpected direction. In 1975 scientists discovered a small protein in calves' brains consisting of just 76 amino acids. Soon they realized that exactly the same protein is found in all eukaryotes, from yeasts to humans. They called this ubiquitous ("found everywhere") protein *ubiquitin.*

In the early 1980s researchers figured out that ubiquitin is a label that the cell attaches to proteins to mark them for destruction, a sort of molecular "kiss of death." The process of attaching ubiquitin takes energy, solving the puzzle of why protein recycling requires energy. The tagged proteins are taken to a barrel-shaped chamber in the cell's cytoplasm called a *proteasome,* which slices the proteins into bits that are then recycled by the cell into new protein.

The graph above displays the sort of protein-recycling experiment that revealed ubiquitin's key role. The experiment monitors levels of a particular protein involved in cell division (the "target" protein) within human cells growing in culture in a laboratory flask. Two cultures are monitored in side-by-side experiments: In the culture indicated by red dots, cells contain functional copies of the ubiquitin gene (*ubi*$^+$); in the culture indicated by blue dots the ubiquitin gene has been deleted from the DNA (*ubi*$^-$). After 20 minutes, energy in the form of ATP is made available to the growing cells, which until then had been energy-starved.

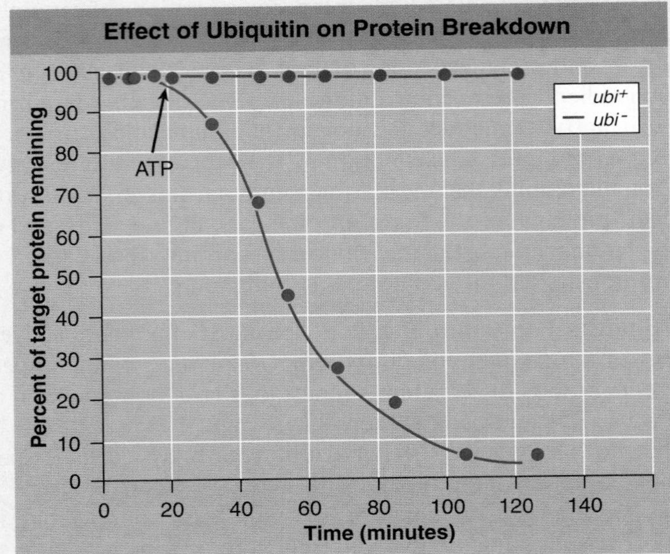

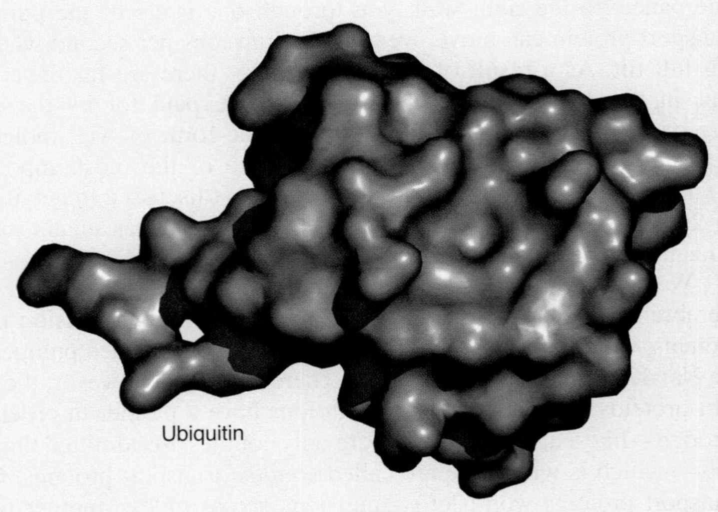
Ubiquitin

1. **Applying Concepts**
   a. **Variable.** In the graph, what is the dependent variable?
   b. **Concentration.** After 100 minutes, which of the two cultures represents the higher concentration of target protein?
2. **Interpreting Data** Does the addition of ATP affect the level of target protein in either culture? Which one?
3. **Making Inferences** How does this culture differ from the other? Why might ATP stimulate removal of target protein from this culture, but not the other?
4. **Drawing Conclusions** Using the information in the graph, suggest why the functioning of ubiquitin requires ATP energy for the effective removal of the target protein.

Summary of Learning Outcomes

The World of Cells

Cells

4.1.1 Cells are the smallest living structure. They consist of cytoplasm enclosed in a plasma membrane. All living things are composed of one or more cells.

4.1.2 A smaller cell can function more efficiently, from transporting materials throughout the cell to transporting materials across the plasma membrane. A smaller cell has a larger surface-to-volume ratio, which increases the area through which materials may pass.

4.1.3 Most cells and their components are so small they can only be seen using microscopes. There are many different types of microscopes, each providing a slightly different view. Light microscopes magnify and enhance resolution. Transmission and scanning electron microscopes increase resolution.

Kinds of Cells

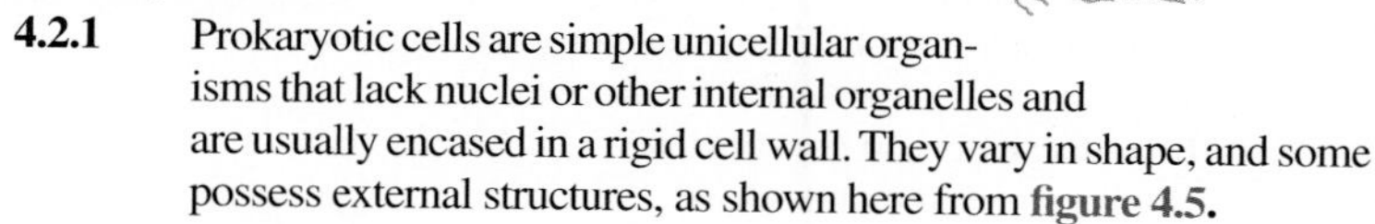

Prokaryotic Cells

4.2.1 Prokaryotic cells are simple unicellular organisms that lack nuclei or other internal organelles and are usually encased in a rigid cell wall. They vary in shape, and some possess external structures, as shown here from **figure 4.5.**

Eukaryotic Cells

4.3.1 Eukaryotic cells are larger and more structurally complex compared with prokaryotic cells. Eukaryotic cells have a system of internal membranes and membrane-bounded organelles like the nucleus that subdivide the cell interior into functional compartments.

Tour of a Eukaryotic Cell

The Plasma Membrane

4.4.1 All cells are encased within a delicate double layer of lipids, called the plasma membrane, in which proteins are embedded that act as cell markers or transports through the membrane. The proposal describing this structure of the plasma membrane is called the fluid mosaic model.

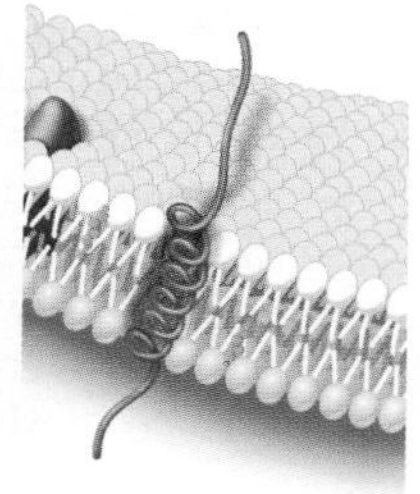

- The lipid bilayer of the plasma membrane is made up of special lipid molecules called phospholipids, which have a polar (water-soluble) end and a nonpolar (water-insoluble) end. The bilayer forms because the nonpolar ends move away from the watery surroundings, forming the two layers. Membrane proteins are typically embedded within the membrane. Transmembrane proteins are held in place by the interaction of nonpolar sections of amino acids with the interior lipid portion of the bilayer.

The Nucleus: The Cell's Control Center

4.5.1 The nucleus is the command and control center of the cell. It contains the cell's DNA, which encodes the hereditary information that runs the cell. An RNA copy of the DNA guides the production of the proteins that carry out cell activities.

The Endomembrane System

4.6.1 The endomembrane system is an extensive system of interior membranes that organize and divide the cell's interior into functional compartments: The endoplasmic reticulum (ER) is a transport system that modifies and moves proteins and other molecules produced in the ER to the Golgi complex.

4.6.2 The Golgi complex is a delivery system that carries molecules to the surface of the cell where they are released to the outside.

4.6.3 Lysosomes and vacuoles are other compartments in the cell. Lysosomes contain enzymes that digest worn out organelles. Vacuoles are storage compartments.

Organelles That Harvest Energy

4.7.1 The mitochondrion, shown here from **figure 4.13,** is called the powerhouse of the cell because it is the site of oxidative metabolism, an energy-extracting process. Chloroplasts are the site of photosynthesis and are present in plant and algal cells.

4.7.2 Mitochondria and chloroplasts are cell-like organelles that have their own DNA and appear to be ancient bacteria that formed endosymbiotic relationships with early eukaryotic cells.

The Cytoskeleton: Interior Framework of the Cell

4.8.1 The interior of the cell contains a latticework of protein fibers, called the cytoskeleton, that determines the shape of the cell and anchors organelles to particular locations within the cytoplasm. Centrioles are paired structures that assemble microtubules in the cell.

4.8.2 Cilia and flagella propel the cell through its environment.

Transport Across Plasma Membranes

Diffusion and Osmosis

4.9.1 Random movements of molecules cause them to move to areas of lower concentration, a process called diffusion.

4.9.2 Water molecules associated with polar solutes are not free to diffuse, causing a net movement of water across a membrane toward the side with less "free" water, a process called osmosis.

Bulk Passage into and out of Cells

4.10.1 The plasma membrane can engulf materials by endocytosis, folding the membrane around the material to encase it within a vesicle. Exocytosis is essentially this process in reverse, using vesicles to expel substances from the cell.

Selective Permeability

4.11.1 Selective transport of materials across the membrane is accomplished by facilitated diffusion and active transport.

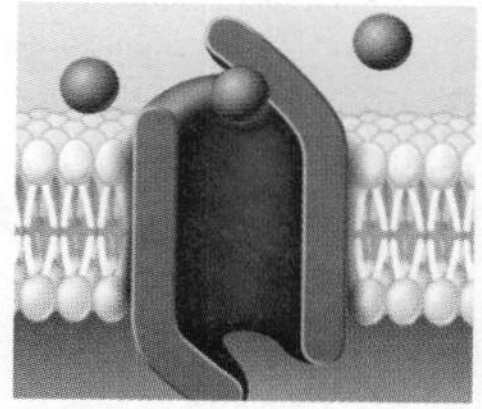

- Facilitated diffusion is driven by the concentration gradient, transporting substances down their concentration gradient, but substances must bind to a membrane transporter, called a carrier, in order to pass across the membrane.

4.11.2 Active transport involves the input of energy to transport substances against (or up) their concentration gradients. Examples include the sodium-potassium pump, which pumps sodium ions out of the cell and potassium ions into the cell. Coupled transport proteins are powered by the large sodium concentration gradient created by the actions of the sodium-potassium pump.

Test Your Understanding

4.1.1 Cell theory includes the principle that
a. cells are the smallest living things; nothing smaller than a cell is considered alive.
b. all cells are surrounded by cell walls that protect them.
c. all organisms are made up of many cells arranged in specialized, functional groups.
d. all cells contain membrane-bounded structures called organelles.

4.2.1 Organisms that have cells with a relatively uniform cytoplasm and no nucleus are called ______, and organisms whose cells have organelles and a nucleus are called ______.
a. cellulose, nuclear **c.** flagellated, streptococcal
b. eukaryotes, prokaryotes **d.** prokaryotes, eukaryotes

4.4.1 The plasma membrane is
a. a carbohydrate layer that surrounds groups of cells to protect them.
b. a double lipid layer with proteins inserted in it, which surrounds every cell individually.
c. a thin sheet of structural proteins that encloses cytoplasm.
d. composed of proteins that form a protective barrier.

4.5.1 Within the nucleus of a cell you can find
a. a nucleolus. **c.** mitochondria.
b. a cytoskeleton. **d.** All of these.

4.6.1 The endomembrane system within a cell includes the
a. cytoskeleton and the ribosomes.
b. prokaryotes and the eukaryotes.
c. endoplasmic reticulum and the Golgi complex.
d. mitochondria and the chloroplasts.

4.7.1 It was once thought that only the nucleus of each cell contained DNA. We now know that DNA is also found in the
a. cytoskeleton and the ribosomes.
b. prokaryotes and the eukaryotes.
c. endoplasmic reticulum and the Golgi bodies.
d. mitochondria and the chloroplasts.

4.8.1 Which of the following structures is not a component of the cytoskeleton?
a. microtubules **c.** intermediate filaments
b. cristae **d.** actin

4.9.1 If you put a drop of food coloring into a glass of water, the drop of color will
a. fall to the bottom of the glass and sit there unless you stir the water; this is because of hydrogen bonding.
b. float on the top of the water, like oil, unless you stir the water; this is because of surface tension.
c. instantly disperse throughout the water; this is because of osmosis.
d. slowly disperse throughout the water; this is because of diffusion.

4.10.1 When large molecules, such as food particles, need to get into a cell, they cannot easily pass through the plasma membrane, and so they move across the membrane through the processes of
a. diffusion and osmosis.
b. endocytosis and phagocytosis.
c. exocytosis and pinocytosis.
d. facilitated diffusion and active transport.

4.11.2 Active transport of specific molecules involves
a. facilitated diffusion.
b. endocytosis and pinocytosis.
c. energy and specialized pumps or carrier proteins.
d. permeability and a concentration gradient.

Apply Your Understanding

4.1.3 The first microscope was used in about 1590. Electron microscopes came into common use about 70 years ago. Just over 100 years ago most physicians did not wash up between patients, even when someone had just died, or was very sick. Explain why early physicians didn't think it important to wash their hands.

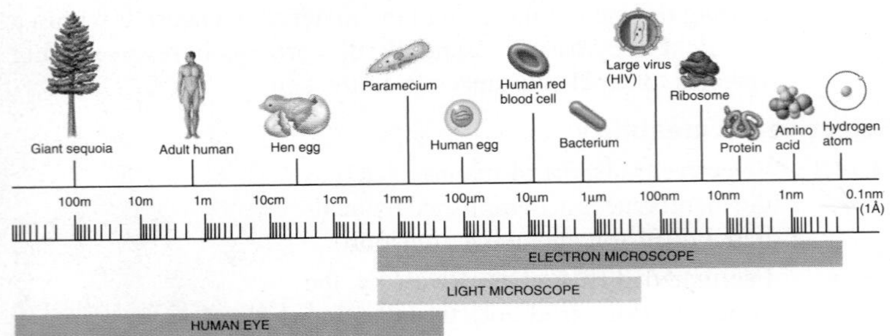

4.11.1 In the lungs, there are steep concentration gradients for oxygen and carbon dioxide molecules such that large numbers of these molecules move across the plasma membrane of the cells that line the lungs. These molecules pass through the plasma membranes by simple diffusion. This process is fast and efficient. Would this process be just as efficient if the oxygen and carbon dioxide molecules passed through the membranes by facilitated diffusion? Why or why not?

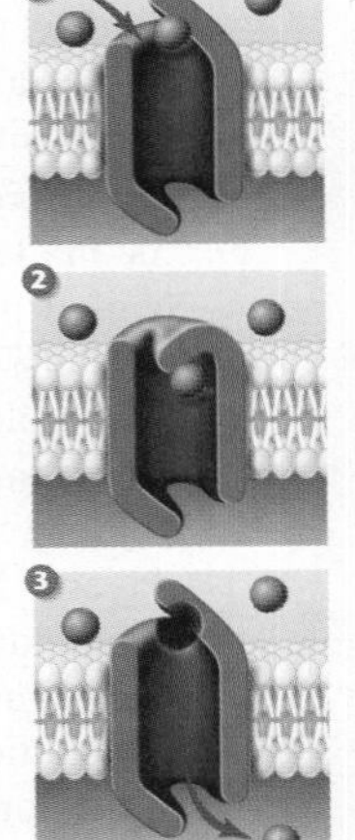

Synthesize What You Have Learned

4.1.2 You are using a computer program to design a new single-celled organism. Discuss why a smaller cell will be more efficient in transporting materials than a larger cell.

4.2.1 Antibiotics are medicines that target bacterial infections in vertebrates. How can an antibiotic kill all the bacterial cells and not harm vertebrate cells? Hint: what part of the bacterial cell must antibiotics be targeting?

4.3.1 Compare the cellular organelles and other structures to the parts of a city—for example, the nucleus is city hall and the DNA is all the city's laws and instructions.

4.5.1 A ribosome contains two subunits. The ribosome subunits are assembled within the nucleus, but ribosomes act in the cytoplasm. How do you imagine the subunits get out of the nucleus and into the cytoplasm?

Chapter 5

Energy and Life

CHAPTER AT A GLANCE

Cells and Energy
5.1 The Flow of Energy in Living Things
5.2 The Laws of Thermodynamics
Cell Chemistry
5.3 Chemical Reactions
Enzymes
5.4 How Enzymes Work
Essential Biological Process 5A: How Enzymes Work
5.5 How Cells Regulate Enzymes
Essential Biological Process 5B: Regulating Enzyme Activity
How Cells Use Energy
5.6 ATP: The Energy Currency of the Cell
Inquiry & Analysis: Do Enzymes Physically Attach to Their Substrates?

Cells and Energy

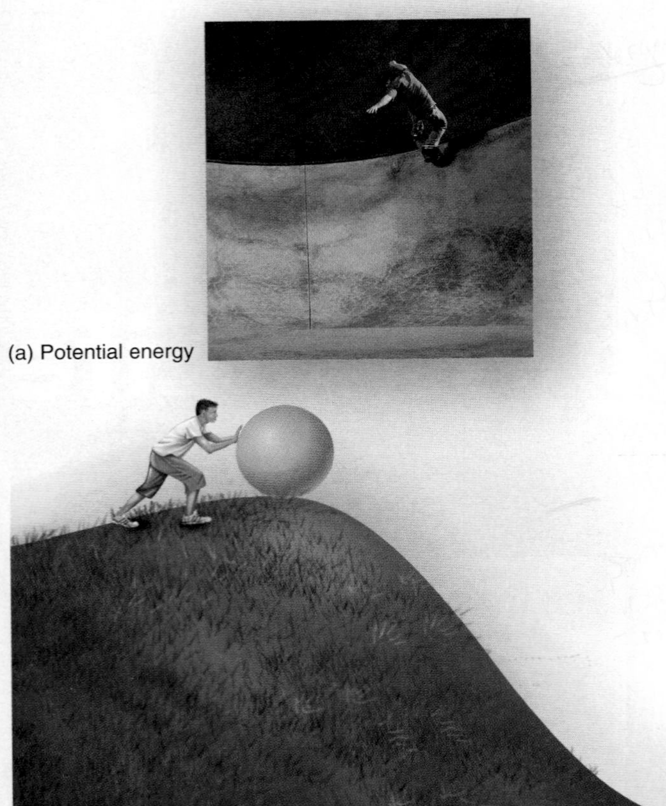

(a) Potential energy

(b) Potential energy

(c) Kinetic energy

Figure 5.1 Potential and kinetic energy.

Objects that have the capacity to move but are not moving have potential energy, while objects that are in motion have kinetic energy. (a) The kinetic energy of this skateboarder becomes potential energy at the peak of this slope. (b) The energy required to move the ball up the hill is stored as potential energy. (c) This stored energy is released as kinetic energy as the ball rolls down the hill.

5.1 The Flow of Energy in Living Things

LEARNING OBJECTIVE 5.1.1 Define energy and differentiate between kinetic and potential energy.

All life is driven by energy. The concepts and processes discussed in the next three chapters are key to life. We are chemical machines, powered by chemical energy, and for the same reason that a successful race car driver must learn how the engine of a car works, we must look at cell chemistry. Indeed, if we are to understand ourselves, we must "look under the hood" at the chemical machinery of our cells and see how it operates.

As described in chapter 2, **energy** is defined as the ability to do work. It can be considered to exist in two states: kinetic energy and potential energy. **Kinetic energy** is the energy of motion. Objects that are not in the process of moving but have the capacity to move are said to possess **potential energy,** or stored energy (**figure 5.1*a***). A boulder perched on a hilltop (**figure 5.1*b***) has potential energy; after the man pushes the boulder and it begins to roll downhill (**figure 5.1*c***), some of the boulder's potential energy is converted into kinetic energy. All of the work carried out by organisms also involves the transformation of potential energy to kinetic energy.

Energy exists in many forms: mechanical energy, heat, sound, electric current, light, or radiation. Because it can exist in so many forms, there are many ways to measure energy. The most convenient is in terms of heat, because all other forms of energy can be converted to heat. Thus the study of energy is called *thermodynamics,* meaning "heat changes."

Energy flows into the biological world from the sun, which shines a constant beam of light on the earth. It is estimated that the sun provides the earth with more than 13 × 10^{23} calories per year, or 40 million billion calories per second! Plants, algae, and certain kinds of bacteria capture a fraction of this energy through photosynthesis. In photosynthesis, energy garnered from sunlight is used to combine small molecules (water and carbon dioxide) into more complex molecules (sugars). These complex sugar molecules have potential energy due to the arrangement of their atoms. This potential energy, in the form of chemical energy, will eventually be used by the cell to do its work. Recall from chapter 2 that a covalent bond forms when two atomic nuclei share electrons. Breaking such a bond requires energy to pull the nuclei apart. Indeed, the strength of a covalent bond is measured by the amount of energy required to break it. For example, it takes 98.8 kcal to break 1 mole (6.023 × 10^{23}) of carbon–hydrogen (C—H) bonds.

You will see in chapter 6 how plants use the sun's energy to build carbohydrates, storing this energy as potential energy. Chapter 7 explains how this potential energy is used by the plants and other organisms to fuel the functions of living.

All the chemical activities within cells can be viewed as a series of chemical reactions between molecules. A **chemical reaction** is the making or breaking of chemical bonds—gluing atoms together to form new molecules, or tearing molecules apart and sometimes sticking the pieces onto other molecules.

Putting the Concept to Work

Is the energy in a "high-energy" food bar kinetic or potential?

5.2 The Laws of Thermodynamics

Running, thinking, singing, reading these words—all activities of living organisms involve changes in energy. A set of universal laws we call the laws of thermodynamics govern these and all other energy changes in the universe.

The First Law of Thermodynamics

LEARNING OBJECTIVE 5.2.1 State the first law of thermodynamics.

The first of these universal laws, the **first law of thermodynamics,** concerns the amount of energy in the universe. It states that energy can change from one state to another (from potential to kinetic, for example) but it can never be destroyed, nor can new energy be made. The total amount of energy in the universe remains constant.

The field mouse eating a kernel of wheat in figure 5.2 is in the process of acquiring energy. The mouse isn't creating new energy; rather it is merely transferring some of the potential energy stored in the tissues of the kernel to its own body. Within any living organism, this chemical potential energy can be shifted to other molecules and stored in chemical bonds, or it can be converted into kinetic energy, or into other forms of energy. During each conversion, some of the energy dissipates into the environment as heat energy, a measure of the random motions of molecules (and, hence, a measure of one form of kinetic energy). Energy continuously flows through the biological world in one direction, with new energy from the sun constantly entering the system to replace the energy dissipated as heat.

Putting the Concept to Work

When Albert Pujols's bat strikes a baseball, is what happens to the baseball a chemical reaction?

Figure 5.2 Acquiring energy.

EVOLUTION

Creationists and the Law. One objection often made by creationists to the theory of evolution is that it violates the second law of thermodynamics. If disorder is continually increasing in the universe, making disorder more likely than order, then they assert that a more ordered system (cells) could not arise spontaneously without direction. Evolutionary biologists respond to this criticism by pointing out that this creationist objection misstates the second law of thermodynamics by omitting a key provision: *"in a closed system."* The living world is by no means a closed system, as energy is continually being supplied to it by the sun. It is this energy, captured in photosynthesis, that powers the organized system we call life. In no sense does this in any way violate the second law.

The Second Law of Thermodynamics

LEARNING OBJECTIVE 5.2.2 State the second law of thermodynamics.

The **second law of thermodynamics** concerns this transformation of potential energy into heat, or random molecular motion. It states that the disorder in a closed system like the universe is continuously increasing. Put simply, disorder is more likely than order. For example, it is much more likely that a column of bricks will tumble over than that a pile of bricks will arrange themselves spontaneously to form a column. Also, without an input of energy from the teenager (or a parent), the ordered room in figure 5.3 falls into disorder. When the input of energy is localized, one area can become far more organized than its disordered surroundings, like cleaning one room of a messy house. It is in just this way that a cell uses energy to keep more organized than its surroundings.

Entropy is a measure of the degree of disorder of a system, so the second law of thermodynamics can also be stated simply as "entropy increases."

Putting the Concept to Work

When an organism dies, what happens to its entropy?

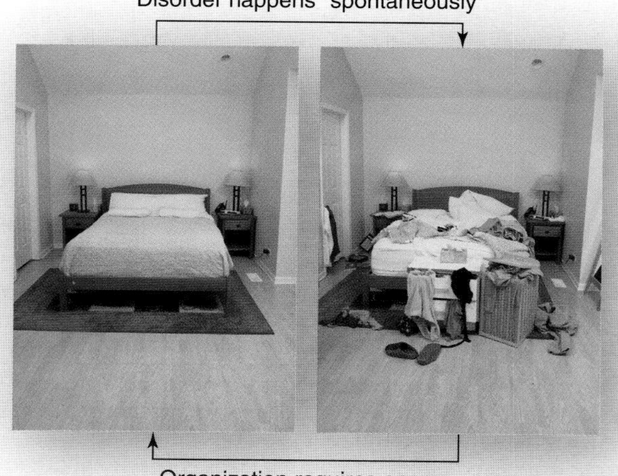
Disorder happens "spontaneously"
Organization requires energy

Figure 5.3 Entropy in action.

As time elapses, a teenager's room becomes more disorganized. It takes energy to clean it up.

Cell Chemistry

5.3 Chemical Reactions

LEARNING OBJECTIVE 5.3.1 Differentiate between endergonic and exergonic reactions.

In a chemical reaction, the original molecules before the chemical reaction occurs are called **reactants,** or sometimes **substrates,** whereas the molecules that result after the reaction has taken place are called the **products.** Not all chemical reactions are equally likely to occur. Just as a boulder is more likely to roll downhill than uphill, so a reaction is more likely to occur if it releases energy than if it needs to have energy supplied. Consider how the chemical reaction proceeds in figure 5.4 ❶. Like rolling a boulder uphill, energy needs to be supplied because the product of the reaction contains more energy than the reactant. This type of chemical reaction, called **endergonic,** does not occur spontaneously. By contrast, an **exergonic** reaction, shown in ❷, tends to occur spontaneously because the product has less energy than the reactant, like a boulder that has rolled downhill.

Putting the Concept to Work

If exergonic reactions tend to occur spontaneously, why haven't they all done so? What stops the world's gasoline from burning?

Activation Energy

LEARNING OBJECTIVE 5.3.2 Define activation energy and catalysis.

If all chemical reactions that release energy tend to occur spontaneously, it is fair to ask, "Why haven't all exergonic reactions occurred already?" They haven't because almost all chemical reactions require an input of energy to get started—it is first necessary to break existing chemical bonds in the reactants, and this takes energy. The extra energy required to destabilize existing chemical bonds and so initiate a chemical reaction is called **activation energy,** indicated by brackets in figure 5.4 ❷ and ❸. You must first nudge a boulder out of the hole it sits in before it can roll downhill. Activation energy is simply a chemical nudge.

Catalysis

One way to make a reaction more likely to happen is to lower the necessary activation energy. Like digging away the ground below your boulder, lowering activation energy reduces the nudge needed to get things started. The process of lowering the activation energy of a reaction is called **catalysis.** Catalysis cannot make an endergonic reaction occur spontaneously—you cannot avoid the need to supply energy—but it can make a reaction, endergonic or exergonic, proceed much faster. Compare the activation energy levels (the red arched arrows) in the second and third panels to the left: The catalyzed reaction ❸ has a lower barrier to overcome.

Putting the Concept to Work

Why is the speed of a chemical reaction affected by the amount of activation energy required to initiate it?

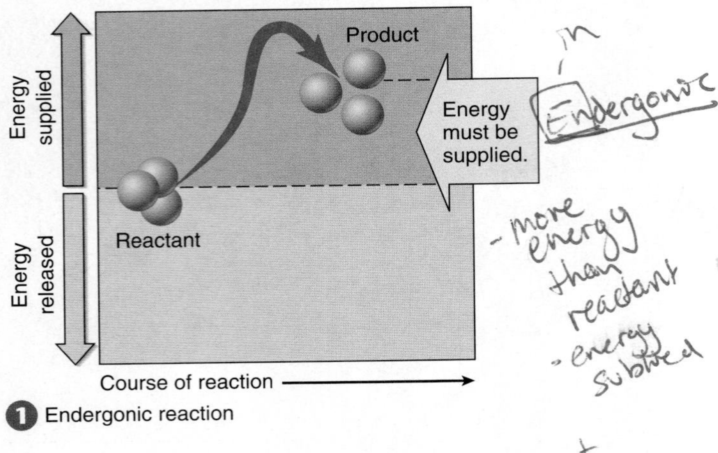

❶ Endergonic reaction

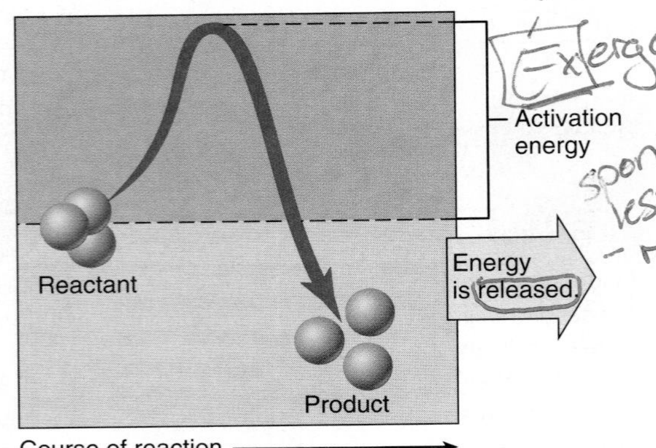

❷ Exergonic reaction

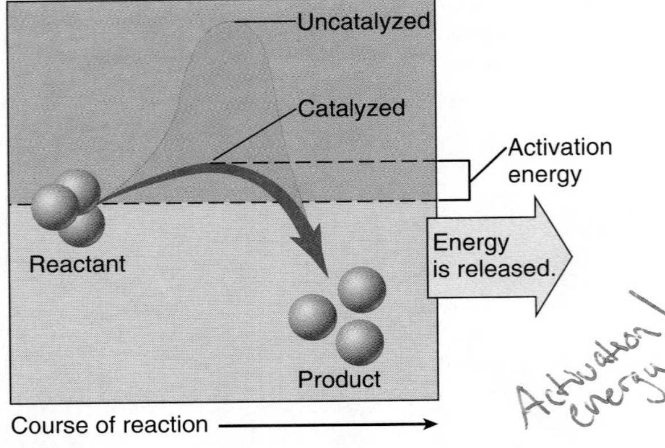

❸ Catalyzed reaction

Figure 5.4 Chemical reactions and catalysis.

❶ The products of endergonic reactions contain more energy than the reactants. ❷ The products of exergonic reactions contain less energy than the reactants, but exergonic reactions do not necessarily proceed rapidly, because it takes energy to get them going. The "hill" in this energy diagram represents energy that must be supplied to destabilize existing chemical bonds. ❸ Catalyzed reactions occur faster because the amount of activation energy required to initiate the reaction—the height of the energy hill that must be overcome—is lowered.

Enzymes

5.4 How Enzymes Work

LEARNING OBJECTIVE 5.4.1 **Differentiate between active site and substrate binding site.**

Macromolecules called **enzymes** are the protein catalysts used by cells to touch off particular chemical reactions. By controlling which enzymes are present, and when they are active, cells are able to control what happens within themselves, just as a conductor controls the music an orchestra produces by dictating which instruments play when.

An enzyme works by binding to a specific molecule in such a way as to make a particular reaction more likely (*Essential Biological Process 5A*). The key to this activity is the shape of the enzyme. An enzyme is specific for a particular reactant, or substrate, because the enzyme surface provides a mold that very closely fits the shape of the desired reactant. For example, the blue-colored lysozyme enzyme in **figure 5.5** is contoured to fit a specific sugar molecule (the yellow reactant). Other molecules that fit less perfectly simply don't adhere to the enzyme's surface. The site on the enzyme surface where the reactant fits is called the **active site.** The site on the reactant that binds to an enzyme is called its **binding site.** In **figure 5.5*b*,** the edges of the lysozyme hug the sugar molecule, leading to an "induced fit" between the enzyme and its reactant, like a hand wrapping around a baseball. The enzyme is not affected by the chemical reaction and is available to be used again.

An enzyme lowers the activation energy of a particular reaction. In the case of lysozyme, an enzyme found in human tears, the enzyme has an antibacterial function, encouraging the breaking of a particular chemical bond in molecules that make up the cell wall of bacteria. The enzyme weakens this bond by drawing away some of its electrons.

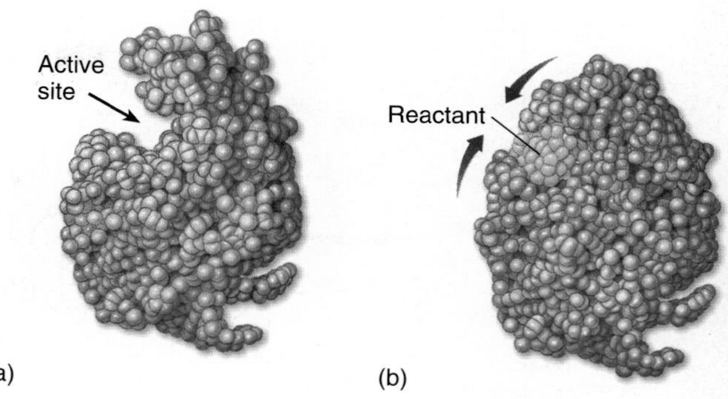

Figure 5.5 **An enzyme's shape determines its activity.**

(a) A groove runs through the lysozyme enzyme that fits the shape of the reactant—in this case, a chain of sugars. (b) When such a chain of sugars slides into the groove, it induces the protein to change its shape slightly and embrace the substrate more intimately. This induced fit causes a chemical bond between two sugar molecules within the chain to break.

IMPLICATION FOR YOU University of Chicago researchers have found the activity levels of protein kinase C (an enzyme linked to depression) to be much lower in the brains of teenage suicides. What sort of investigations would you propose to look into the link between this enzyme and teen suicide?

Essential Biological Process 5A

How Enzymes Work

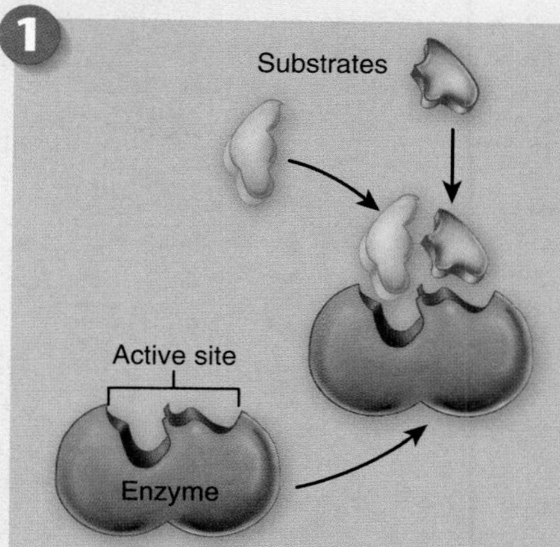

Enzymes have a complex three-dimensional surface to which particular reactants (called substrates of that enzyme) fit, like a hand in a glove.

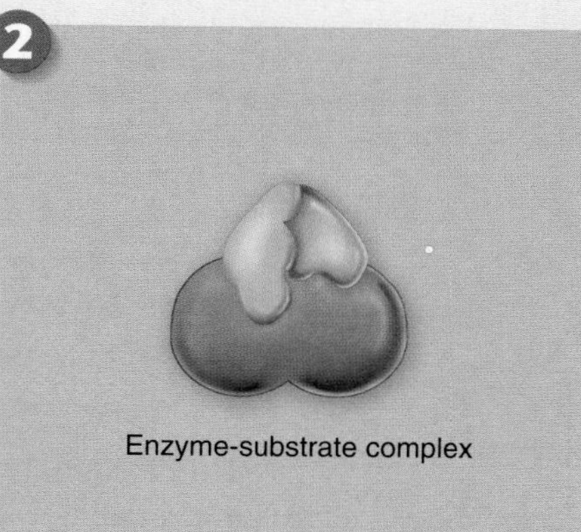

An enzyme and its substrate(s) bind tightly together, forming an enzyme-substrate complex. The binding brings key atoms near each other and stresses key covalent bonds.

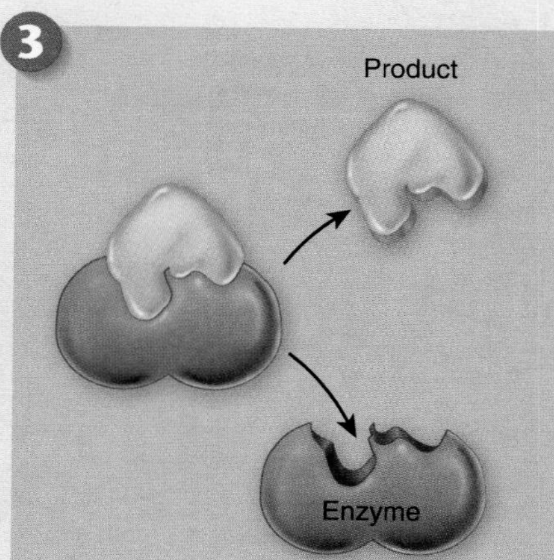

As a result, a chemical reaction occurs within the active site, forming the product. The product then diffuses away, freeing the enzyme to work again.

membrane

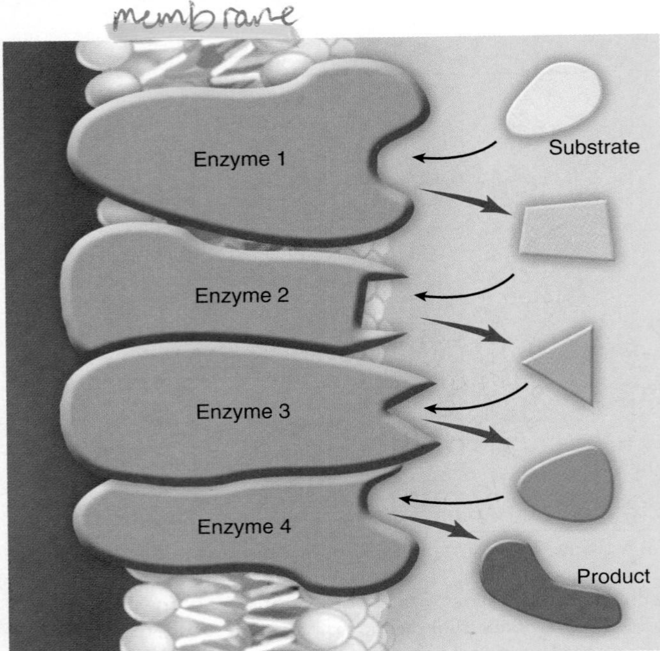

Figure 5.6 A biochemical pathway.

The original substrate is acted on by enzyme 1, changing the substrate to a new form recognized by enzyme 2. Each enzyme in the pathway acts on the product of the previous stage.

Biochemical Pathways

Every organism contains thousands of different kinds of enzymes that together catalyze a bewildering variety of reactions. Often several of these reactions occur in a fixed sequence called a **biochemical pathway,** the product of one reaction becoming the substrate for the next. You can see in figure 5.6 how the initial substrate is altered by enzyme 1 so that it now fits into the active site of another enzyme, becoming the substrate for enzyme 2, and so on until the final product is produced. Because these reactions occur in sequence, the enzymes involved are often positioned near each other in the cell. For example, the enzymes involved in this biochemical pathway are all embedded in a membrane near each other. The close proximity of the enzymes allows the reactions of a biochemical pathway to proceed faster. Biochemical pathways are the organizational units of metabolism.

The Calvin cycle on page 112 is a biochemical pathway in photosynthesis where the product of one reaction is the substrate for the next reaction. Similarly, glycolysis on page 120 and the Krebs cycle on page 122 are biochemical pathways.

Putting the Concept to Work

Describe how an enzyme lowers the activation energy of a chemical reaction.

Factors Affecting Enzyme Activity

LEARNING OBJECTIVE 5.4.2 Explain the effects of temperature and pH on enzyme-catalyzed reactions.

Enzyme activity is affected by any change in condition that alters the enzyme's three-dimensional shape. For this reason, temperature and pH can have a major influence on the action of enzymes.

Temperature. When the temperature increases, the bonds that determine enzyme shape are too weak to hold it in the proper position, and the enzyme denatures. As a result, enzymes function best within an optimum temperature range, which is relatively narrow for most human enzymes. In the human body, enzymes work best at temperatures near the normal body temperature of 37°C, as shown by the brown curve in figure 5.7*a*. Also notice that the rates of enzyme reactions tend to drop quickly at higher temperatures, when the enzyme begins to unfold. This is why an extremely high fever in humans can be fatal. However, the shapes of the enzymes found in hotsprings bacteria (the red curve) are more stable, allowing the enzymes to function at much higher temperatures. This allows the bacteria to live in water that is near 70°C.

pH. In addition, most enzymes also function within an optimal pH range, because the shape-determining polar interactions of enzymes are quite sensitive to hydrogen ion (H^+) concentration. Most human enzymes, such as the protein-degrading enzyme trypsin (the dark blue curve in figure 5.7*b*) work best within the range of pH 6 to 8. Blood has a pH of 7.4. However, some enzymes, such as the digestive enzyme pepsin (the light blue curve) are able to function in very acidic environments such as the stomach, but can't function at the higher pH where trypsin works best.

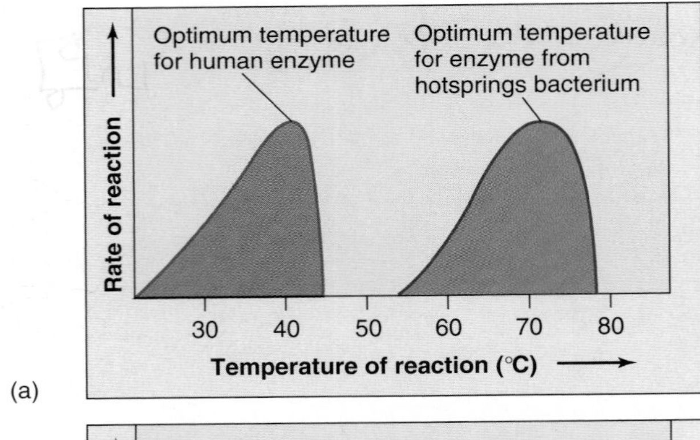

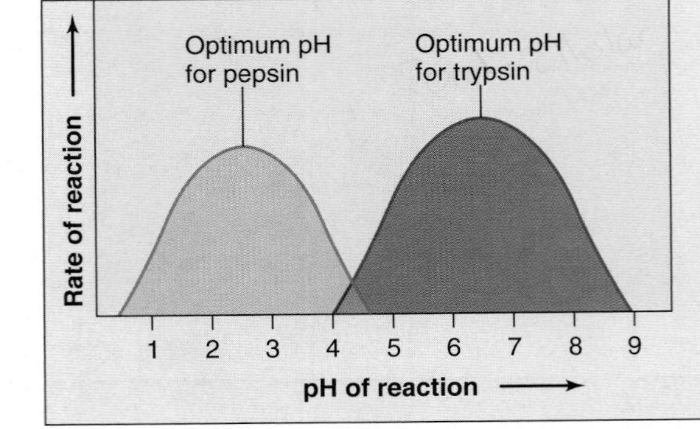

Figure 5.7 Enzymes are sensitive to their environment.

The activity of an enzyme is influenced by both (a) temperature and (b) pH. Most human enzymes work best at temperatures near 37°C and within a pH range of 6 to 8.

Putting the Concept to Work

Explain how hotsprings bacteria can live in near-boiling water (70° C = 158° F) that would kill a human bather.

Essential Biological Process 5B

Regulating Enzyme Activity

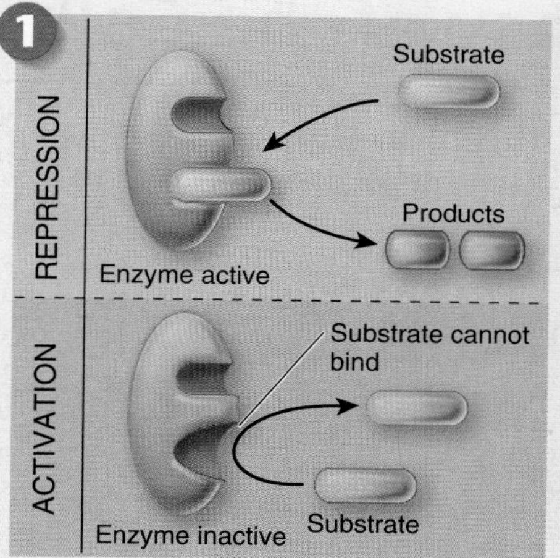

Allosteric enzymes subject to repression are active in the absence of signal molecules, while allosteric enzymes that rely on activation are not active in the absence of signal molecules.

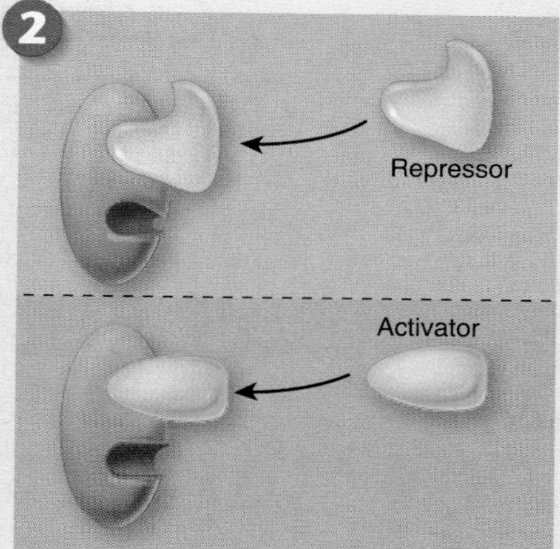

When signal molecules bind allosteric enzymes, they change the shape of the active site. Repressors disrupt the active site, while activators restore it.

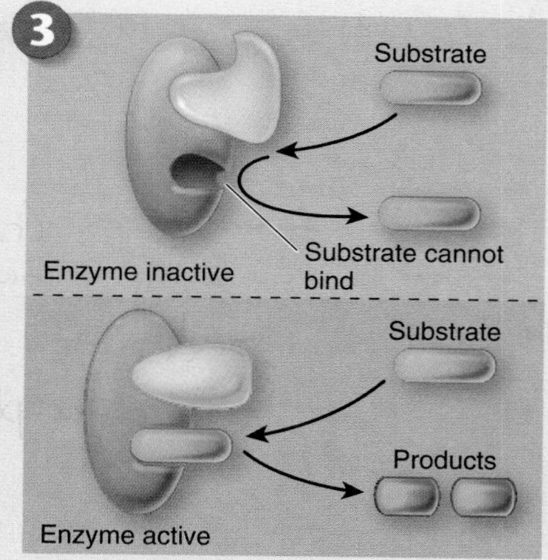

Allosteric enzymes subject to repression are not active in the presence of signal molecules, while allosteric enzymes that rely on activation require signal molecules to be active.

5.5 How Cells Regulate Enzymes

LEARNING OBJECTIVE 5.5.1 Describe how repressors interact with allosteric sites of enzymes and the results of this interaction.

Because an enzyme must have a precise shape to work correctly, it is possible for the cell to control when an enzyme is active by altering its shape. Many enzymes have shapes that can be altered by the binding of "signal" molecules to their surfaces, making them work better (activation) or worse (inhibition). These are called *allosteric enzymes.* For example, the upper panels of *Essential Biological Process 5B* show an enzyme that is inhibited. The binding of a signal molecule called a **repressor** (panel 2) alters the shape of the enzyme's active site such that it cannot bind the substrate. In other cases, the enzyme may not be able to bind the reactants *unless* the signal molecule is bound to the enzyme. The lower set of panels shows a signal molecule serving as an **activator.** The substrate cannot bind to the enzyme's active site unless the activator is first in place.

Enzymes are often regulated by a mechanism called **feedback inhibition,** where the product of the reaction acts as a repressor. Feedback inhibition can occur in two ways: *competitive* and, much more commonly, *noncompetitive.* The blue molecule in figure 5.8*a* functions as a competitive inhibitor, blocking the active site so that the substrate cannot bind. The yellow molecule in figure 5.8*b* functions as a noncompetitive inhibitor. It binds to an allosteric site, changing the shape of the enzyme such that it is unable to bind to the substrate.

Putting the Concept to Work

Can a single type of signal molecule activate one enzyme and repress another?

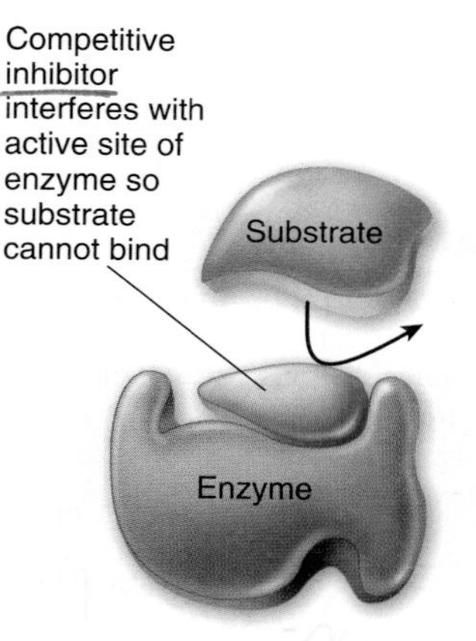

(a) Competitive inhibition

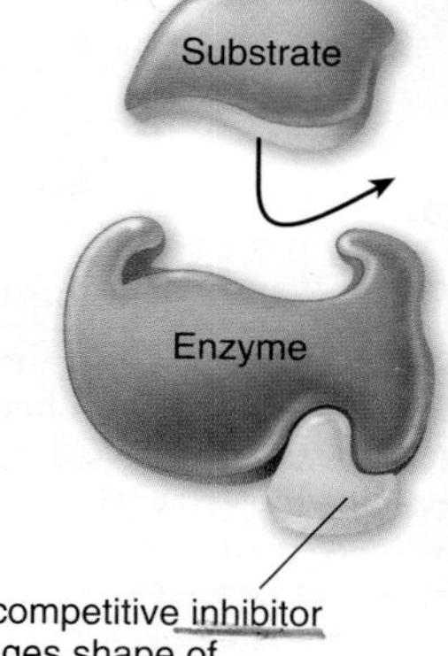

(b) Noncompetitive inhibition

Figure 5.8 How enzymes can be inhibited.

(a) In competitive inhibition, the inhibitor interferes with the active site of the enzyme. (b) In noncompetitive inhibition, the inhibitor binds to the enzyme at a place away from the active site, effecting a conformational change in the enzyme so that it can no longer bind to its substrate.

IMPLICATION FOR YOU Many antibiotics work by inhibiting enzymes. The antibiotic penicillin inhibits an enzyme bacteria use in making cell walls. Imagine that as a confused patient you mistakenly took two to three times the number of prescribed penicillin pills at one time. Is it likely that you would be seriously harmed? Explain.

How Cells Use Energy

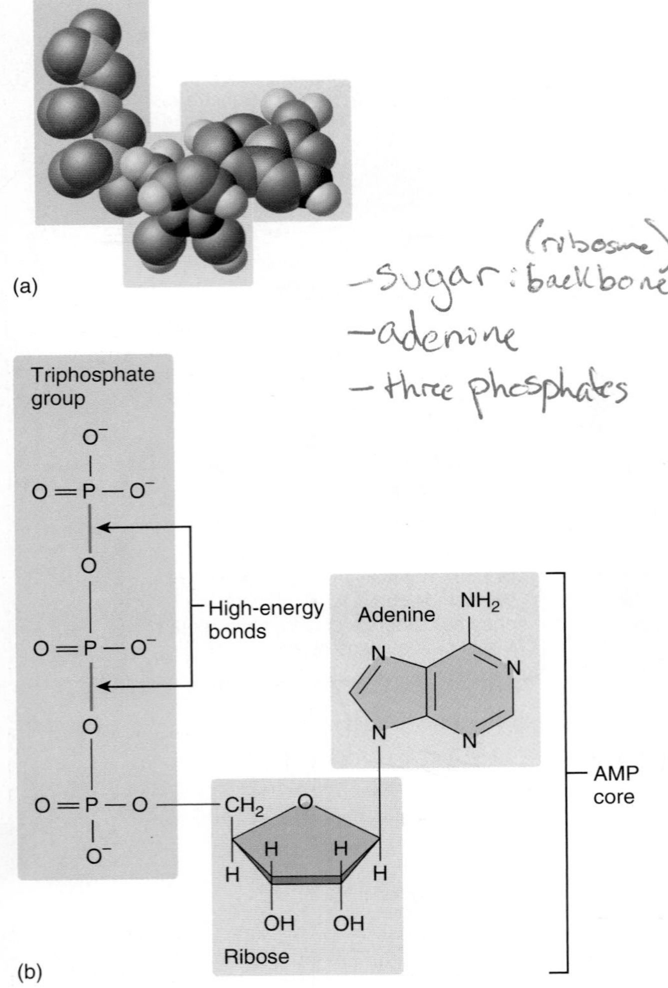

Figure 5.9 The parts of an ATP molecule.

The model (a) and structural diagram (b) both show that ATP consists of three phosphate groups attached to a ribose (five-carbon sugar) molecule. The ribose molecule is also attached to an adenine molecule (also one of the nitrogenous bases of DNA and RNA). When the endmost phosphate group is split off from the ATP molecule, considerable energy is released.

5.6 ATP: The Energy Currency of the Cell

LEARNING OBJECTIVE 5.6.1 Explain how the phosphate groups of ATP store potential energy, and how organisms use this energy to power endergonic reactions.

Cells use energy to do all those things that require work, but how does the cell use energy from the sun or the potential energy stored in molecules to power its activities? The sun's radiant energy and the energy stored in molecules are energy sources, but like money that is invested in stocks and bonds or real estate, these energy sources cannot be used directly to run a cell, any more than money invested in stocks can be used to buy a candy bar at the store. To be useful, the energy from the sun or food molecules must first be converted to a source of energy that a cell can use, like someone converting stocks and bonds to ready cash. The "cash" molecule in the body is **adenosine triphosphate (ATP).**

Structure of the ATP Molecule

Each ATP molecule is composed of three parts (figure 5.9): (1) a sugar (colored blue) that serves as the backbone to which the other two parts are attached, (2) adenine (colored peach), which is also one of the four nitrogenous bases in DNA and RNA, and (3) a chain of three phosphates (colored yellow) that contain high-energy bonds. As you can see in the figure, the phosphates carry negative electrical charges, and so it takes considerable chemical energy to hold the line of three phosphates next to one another at the end of ATP. Like a compressed spring, the phosphates are poised to push apart. It is for this reason that the chemical bonds linking the phosphates are such chemically reactive bonds. When the endmost phosphate is broken off an ATP molecule, a sizable packet of energy is released. The reaction converts ATP to adenosine diphosphate, ADP, and P_i, inorganic phosphate:

$$\text{ATP} \longleftrightarrow \text{ADP} + \text{P}_i + \text{energy}$$

Chemical reactions require activation energy, and endergonic reactions require the input of even more energy, and so these reactions in the cell are usually coupled with the breaking of the phosphate bond in ATP, called *coupled reactions*. Because almost all chemical reactions in cells require less energy than is released by this reaction, ATP is able to power many of the cell's activities. Table 5.1 introduces you to some of the key cell activities powered by the breakdown of ATP. ATP is continually recycled from ADP and P_i via the ATP-ADP cycle (figure 5.10).

Cells use two different but complementary processes to convert energy from the sun and food molecules into potential energy stored in the chemical bonds of ATP. Some cells convert energy from the sun into molecules of ATP through the process of **photosynthesis,** the subject of chapter 6. This ATP is then used to manufacture sugar molecules, converting the energy from ATP into potential energy stored in the bonds that hold the atoms in the sugar molecule together. All cells convert the potential energy found in food molecules like sugar into ATP through **cellular respiration,** the subject of chapter 7.

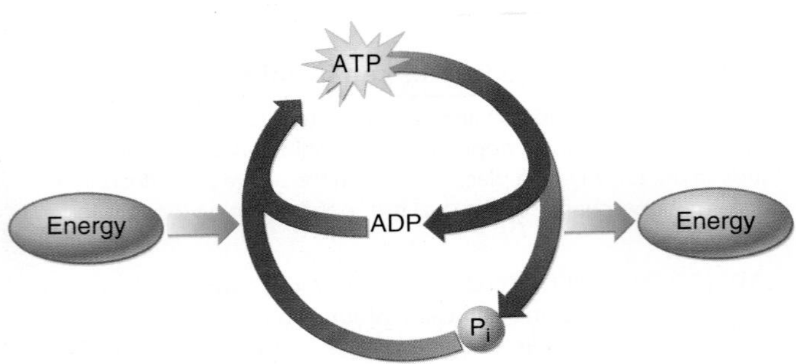

Figure 5.10 The ATP-ADP cycle.

Putting the Concept to Work

Compare and contrast ATP with the nucleotides found in DNA and RNA. [Hint: see figure 3.10.]

TABLE 5.1 How Cells Use ATP Energy to Power Cellular Work

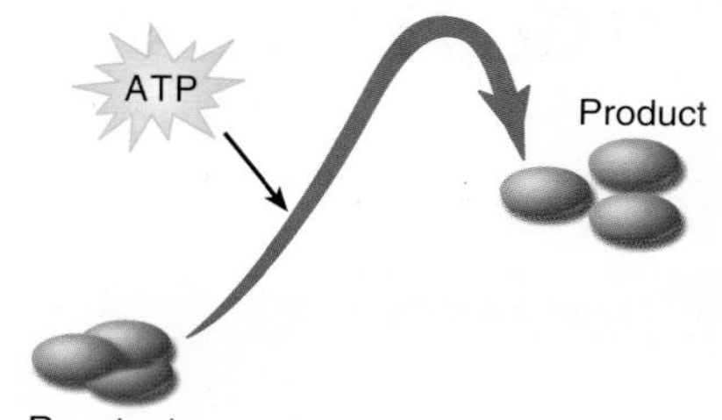

Biosynthesis

Cells use the energy released from the exergonic hydrolysis of ATP to drive endergonic reactions like those of protein synthesis, an approach called energy coupling.

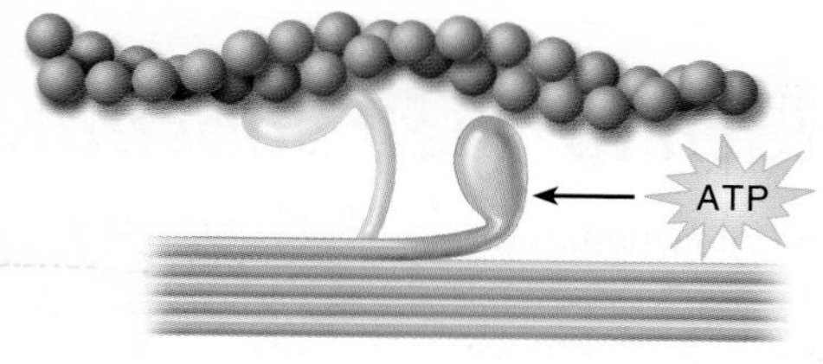

Contraction

In muscle cells, filaments of protein repeatedly slide past each other to achieve contraction of the cell. An input of ATP is required for the filaments to reset and slide again.

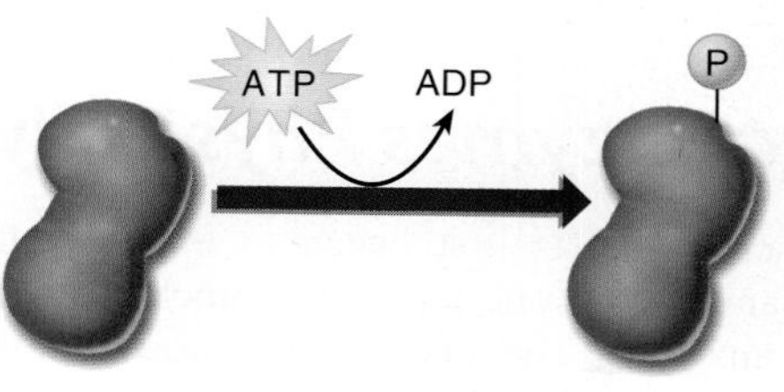

Chemical Activation

Proteins can become activated when a high-energy phosphate from ATP attaches to the protein, activating it. Other types of molecules can also become phosphorylated by transfer of a phosphate from ATP.

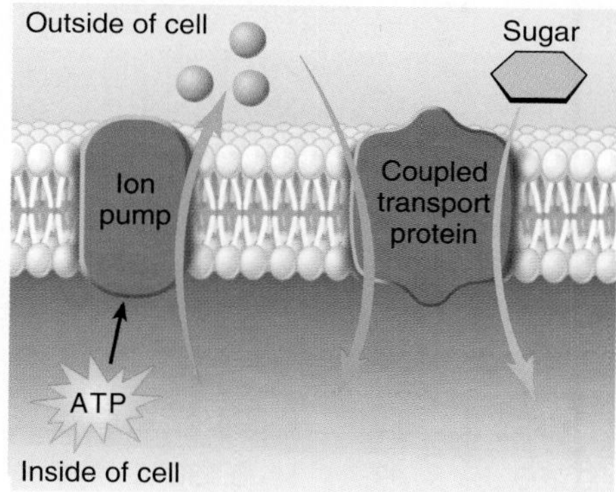

Importing Metabolites

Metabolite molecules such as amino acids and sugars can be transported into cells against their concentration gradients by coupling the intake of the metabolite to the inward movement of an ion moving down its concentration gradient, this ion gradient being established using ATP.

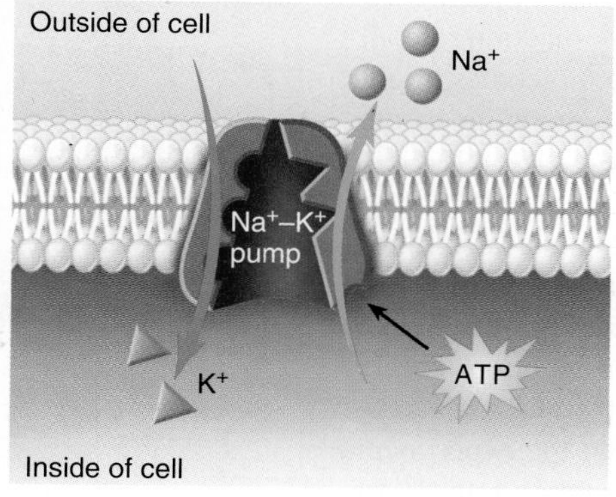

Active Transport: Na^+–K^+ Pump

Most animal cells maintain a low internal concentration of Na^+ relative to their surroundings, and a high internal concentration of K^+. This is achieved using a protein called the sodium-potassium pump, which actively pumps Na^+ out of the cell and K^+ in, using energy from ATP.

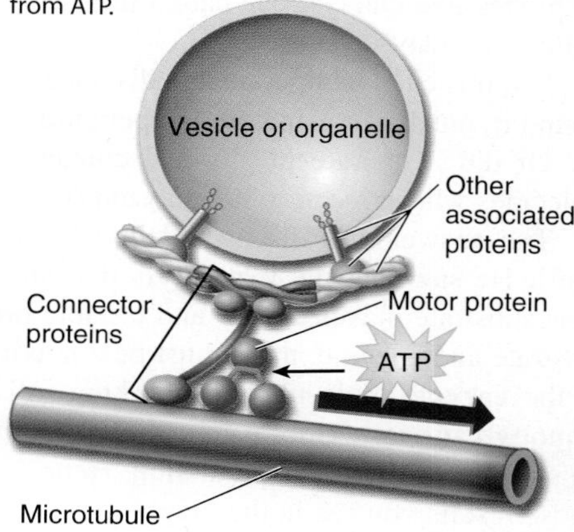

Cytoplasmic Transport

Within a cell's cytoplasm, vesicles or organelles can be dragged along microtubular tracks using molecular motor proteins, which are attached to the vesicle or organelle with connector proteins. The motor proteins use ATP to power their movement.

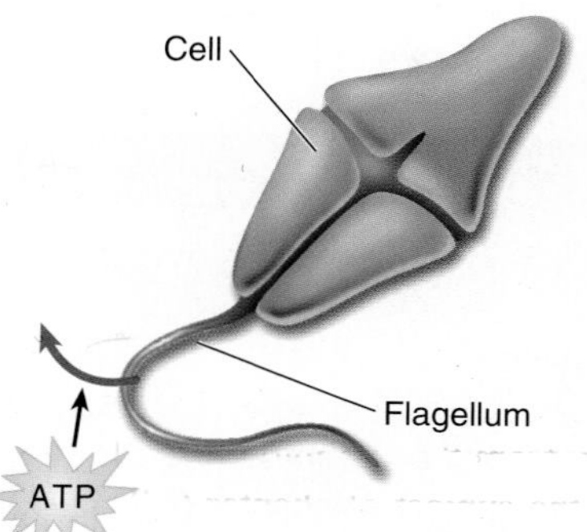

Flagellar Movements

Microtubules within flagella slide past each other to produce flagellar movements. ATP powers the sliding of the microtubules.

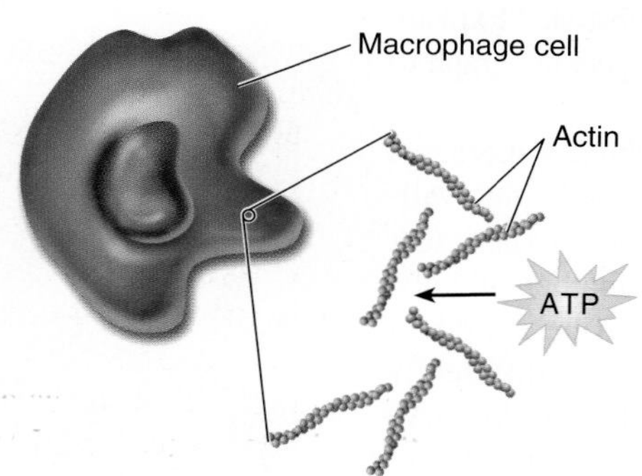

Cell Crawling

Actin filaments in a cell's cytoskeleton continually assemble and disassemble to achieve changes in cell shape and to allow cells to crawl over substrates or engulf materials. The dynamic character of actin is controlled by ATP molecules bound to actin filaments.

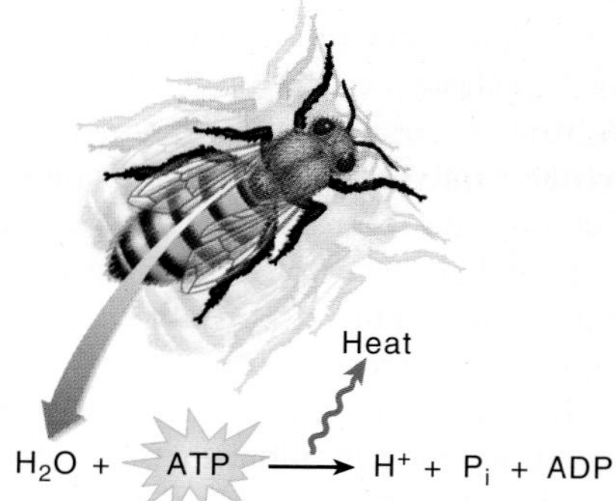

Heat Production

The hydrolysis of the ATP molecule releases heat. Reactions that hydrolyze ATP often take place in mitochondria or in contracting muscle cells and may be coupled to other reactions. The heat generated by these reactions can be used to maintain an organism's temperature.

Inquiry & Analysis

Do Enzymes Physically Attach to Their Substrates?

When scientists first began to examine the chemical activities of organisms, no one knew that biochemical reactions were catalyzed by enzymes. The first enzyme was discovered in 1833 by French chemist Anselme Payen. He was studying how beer is made from barley: First barley is pressed and gently heated so its starches break down into simple two-sugar units; then yeasts convert these units into ethanol. Payen found that the initial breakdown requires a chemical factor that is not alive, and which does not seem to be used up during the process—a catalyst. He called this first enzyme *diastase* (we call it amylase today).

Did this catalyst operate at a distance, increasing reaction rate all around it, much as raising the temperature of nearby molecules might do? Or did it operate in physical contact, actually attaching to the molecules whose reaction it catalyzed (its "substrate")?

The answer was discovered in 1903 by French chemist Victor Henri. He saw that the hypothesis that an enzyme physically binds to its substrate makes a clear and testable prediction: In a solution of substrate and enzyme, there must be a maximum reaction rate. When all the enzyme molecules are working full tilt, the reaction simply cannot go any faster, no matter how much more substrate you add to the solution. To test this prediction, Henri carried out the experiment whose results you see in the graph, measuring the reaction rate (V) of diastase at different substrate concentrations (S).

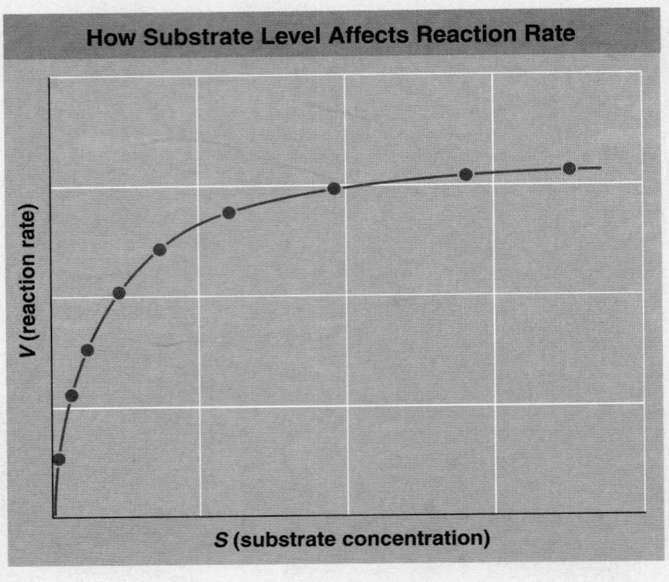

Trial	S	1/S	V	1/V
1	5	0.200	7.7	0.130
2	10	____	15.4	____
3	25	____	23.1	____
4	50	____	30.8	____
5	75	____	38.5	____
6	125	____	40.7	____
7	200	____	46.2	____
8	275	____	47.7	____
9	350	____	48.5	____

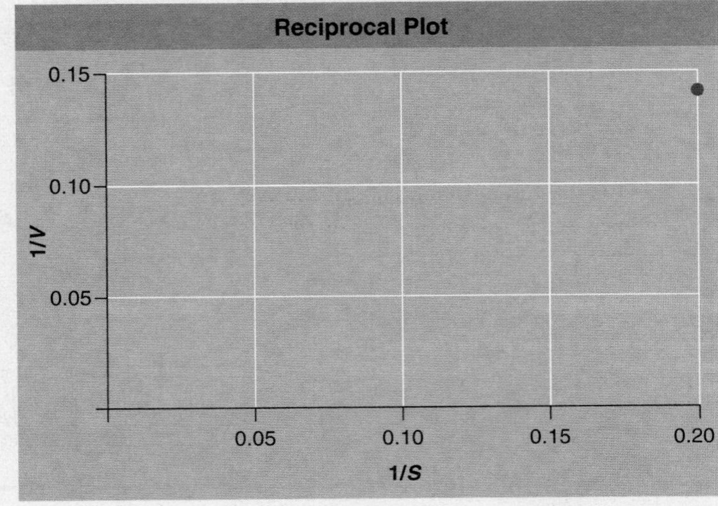

Analysis

1. **Making Inferences** As S increases, does V increase? If so, in what manner—steadily, or by smaller and smaller amounts? Is there a maximum reaction rate?
2. **Drawing Conclusions** Does this result provide support for the hypothesis that an enzyme binds physically to its substrate? Explain. If the hypothesis were incorrect, what would you expect the graph to look like?
3. **Further Analysis** If the smaller amounts by which V increases are strictly the result of fewer unoccupied enzymes being available at higher values of S, then the curve in Henri's experiment should show a pure exponential decline in V—mathematically, meaning a reciprocal plot ($1/V$ versus $1/S$) should be a straight line. If some other factor is also at work that reacts differently to substrate concentration, then the reciprocal plot would curve upward or downward. Fill in the reciprocal values in the table to the right, and then plot the values on the lower graph ($1/S$ on the x axis and $1/V$ on the y axis). Is a reciprocal plot of Henri's data a straight line?

Summary of Learning Outcomes

Cells and Energy

The Flow of Energy in Living Things

5.1.1 Energy is the ability to do work, either actively (kinetic energy) or stored for later possible use (potential energy).

- Kinetic energy is the energy of motion. Potential energy is stored energy, which exists in objects that aren't in motion but have the capacity to move, like a ball poised at the top of a hill shown here from **figure 5.1.** Work carried out by living organisms involves the transformation of potential energy into kinetic energy. Energy also exists in different forms in the universe, such as light, electrical, or heat energy.

- Energy flows from the sun to the earth, where it is trapped by photosynthetic organisms and stored in carbohydrates as potential energy. This energy is transferred during chemical reactions, when the covalent bonds linking atoms together are formed or broken.

The Laws of Thermodynamics

5.2.1 The laws of thermodynamics describe changes in energy in our universe. The first law of thermodynamics explains that energy cannot be created or destroyed, only changed from one form to another. The total amount of energy in the universe remains constant.

5.2.2 The second law of thermodynamics states that disorder in the universe tends to increase—that is, that the conversion of potential energy into random molecular motion is constantly increasing. This conversion of energy progresses from an ordered but less stable form to a disordered but stable form. Entropy, which is a measure of disorder in a system, is constantly increasing. Energy must be used to oppose this tendency and maintain order.

Cell Chemistry

Chemical Reactions

5.3.1 Chemical reactions involve the breaking or formation of covalent bonds. The starting molecules are called the reactants, and the molecules produced by the reaction are called the products. Chemical reactions in which the products contain more potential energy than the reactants are called endergonic reactions. Chemical reactions that release energy are called exergonic reactions and are more likely to occur.

5.3.2 All chemical reactions require an input of energy. The energy required to start a reaction is called activation energy and is indicated by the red arrow in the chemical reaction shown here from **figure 5.4.**

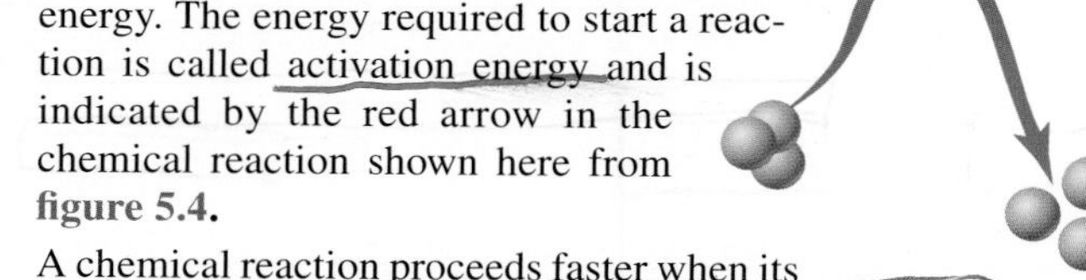

- A chemical reaction proceeds faster when its activation energy is lowered, a process called catalysis.

Enzymes

How Enzymes Work

5.4.1 Enzymes are molecules that act as cellular catalysts by lowering the activation energy of chemical reactions in the cell.

- An enzyme, like the lysozyme shown here from **figure 5.5,** binds the reactant, or substrate. The substrate binds to the enzyme's active site. The enzyme molds around the reactant and acts to stress covalent bonds or bring atoms into closer proximity. The actions of the enzyme increase the likelihood that chemical bonds will break or form. An enzyme lowers the activation energy of the reaction. The enzyme is not affected by the reaction and can be used over and over again.
- Sometimes enzymes work in a series of reactions called a biochemical pathway. The product of one reaction becomes the substrate for the next reaction. The enzymes that are involved are usually located near each other in the cell.

5.4.2 In the cell, chemical reactions are regulated by controlling which enzymes are active. Other factors, such as temperature and pH, also affect enzyme shape and activity. Most enzymes have an optimal temperature and pH range.

- Higher temperatures can disrupt the bonds that hold the enzyme in its proper shape, decreasing its ability to catalyze a chemical reaction. The bonds that hold the enzyme's shape are also affected by hydrogen ion concentrations, and so increasing or decreasing the pH can disrupt the enzyme's function.

How Cells Regulate Enzymes

5.5.1 An enzyme can be inhibited or activated in the cell as a means of regulation by temporarily altering the enzyme's shape. An enzyme can be inhibited when a molecule called a repressor binds to the enzyme and alters the shape of the active site so that it cannot bind the substrate. Some enzymes need to be activated, or turned on, in order to bind to their substrate. A molecule called an activator binds to the enzyme and changes the shape of the active site so that it is able to bind the substrate. Enzymes that are controlled in this way are allosteric enzymes.

- A repressor molecule can bind to the active site of the enzyme, blocking it. This is called competitive inhibition. In noncompetitive inhibition, the repressor binds to a different site on the enzyme, altering the shape of the active site so it cannot bind its substrate.

How Cells Use Energy

ATP: The Energy Currency of the Cell

5.6.1 Cells store chemical energy in ATP molecules. ATP contains a sugar, an adenine, and a chain of three phosphates, as shown here from **figure 5.9.** The three phosphates are held together with high-energy bonds. When the endmost phosphate bond breaks, considerable energy is released. A cell uses this energy to drive reactions in the cell by coupling the breakdown of ATP with other chemical reactions in the cell.

Test Your Understanding

5.1.1 The ability to do work is the definition for
a. thermodynamics. **c.** energy.
b. radiation. **d.** entropy.

5.2.1 The first law of thermodynamics
a. says that energy recycles constantly, as organisms use and reuse it.
b. says that entropy, or disorder, continually increases in a closed system.
c. is a formula for measuring entropy.
d. says that energy can change forms, but cannot be created or destroyed.

5.2.2 The second law of thermodynamics
a. says that energy recycles constantly, as organisms use and reuse it.
b. says that entropy, or disorder, continually increases in a closed system.
c. is a formula for measuring entropy.
d. says that energy can change forms, but cannot be made nor destroyed.

5.3.1 Chemical reactions that occur spontaneously are called
a. exergonic and release energy.
b. exergonic and their products contain more energy.
c. endergonic and release energy.
d. endergonic and their products contain more energy.

5.4.1 The catalysts that help an organism carry out needed chemical reactions are called
a. hormones. **c.** reactants.
b. enzymes. **d.** substrates.

5.4.2 Factors that affect the activity of an enzyme molecule include
a. peptides and energy.
b. activation energy.
c. temperature and pH.
d. entropy and thermodynamics.

5.5.1 In order for an enzyme to work properly,
a. it must have a particular shape.
b. the temperature must be within certain limits.
c. the pH must be within certain limits.
d. All of the above.

5.5.1 In competitive inhibition
a. an enzyme molecule has to compete with other enzyme molecules for the necessary substrate.
b. an enzyme molecule has to compete with other enzyme molecules for the necessary energy.
c. an inhibitor molecule competes with the substrate for the active site on the enzyme.
d. two different products compete for the same active site on the enzyme.

5.6.1 Which of the following is not a component of ATP?
a. active site **c.** adenine
b. ribose **d.** phosphate groups

5.6.1 Endergonic reactions can occur in the cell because they are coupled with
a. the breaking of phosphate bonds in ATP.
b. uncatalyzed reactions.
c. activators.
d. All of the above.

Apply Your Understanding

5.4.2 Examine the graphs shown here. Describe what happens to a human enzyme at a temperature of 50°C. Looking at part (b), what happens to trypsin's ability to function as the surrounding concentration of H^+ ions increases? How would the enzyme pepsin respond to a change in pH from 4 to 3?

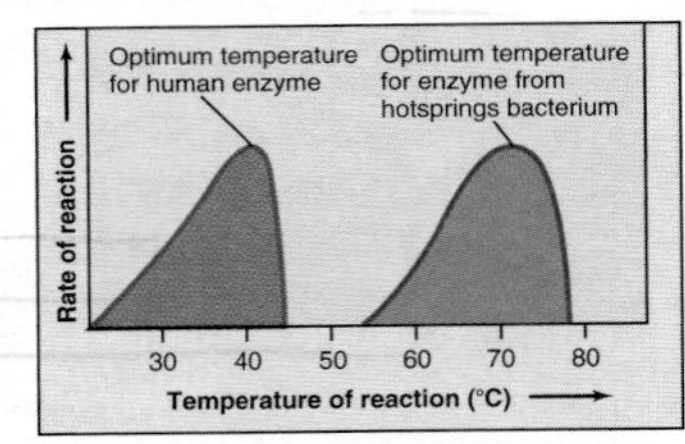

(a)

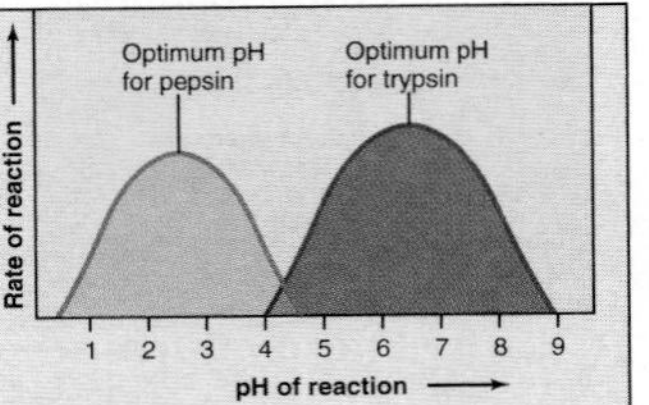

(b)

5.6.1 ATP forms primarily from the breakdown of glucose. If your blood glucose level drops, what sorts of problems can that cause in your body?

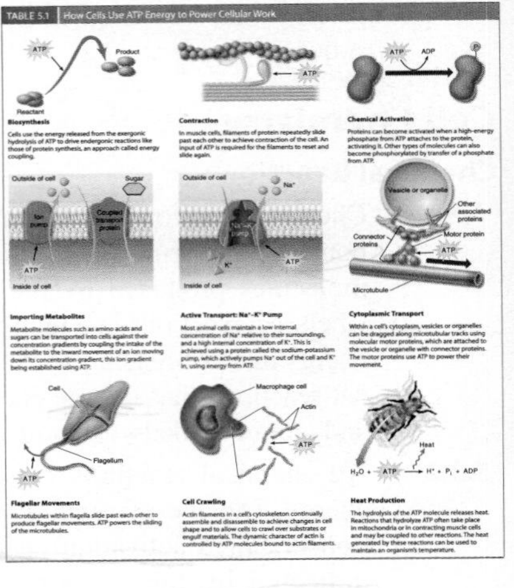

Synthesize What You Have Learned

5.1.1 Photosynthetic organisms, such as plants, algae, and bacteria, capture the sun's energy and use it to build sugar molecules that other organisms can use. The formation of these molecules involves endergonic reactions. Explain what this means and where the sun's energy is stored in these sugar molecules.

5.2.1 When a baseball thrown by a pitcher encounters the swinging bat of a slugger, what happens to the ball's kinetic energy? What happens to the bat's kinetic energy?

5.4.1 A restriction endonuclease is an enzyme that cuts DNA at a specific, unique sequence, like GATTC. How does a particular restriction enzyme "know" when it has found its target sequence?

Chapter 6

Photosynthesis: Acquiring Energy from the Sun

CHAPTER AT A GLANCE

Photosynthesis

6.1 An Overview of Photosynthesis

6.2 How Plants Capture Energy from Sunlight

6.3 How Photosystems Convert Light to Chemical Energy

6.4 Building New Molecules

Essential Biological Process 6A: The Calvin Cycle

Photorespiration

6.5 Photorespiration: Putting the Brakes on Photosynthesis

Inquiry & Analysis: Does Iron Limit the Growth of Ocean Phytoplankton?

Photosynthesis

6.1 An Overview of Photosynthesis

LEARNING OBJECTIVE 6.1.1 Define photosynthesis and name the three layers of a leaf through which light must pass to reach chloroplasts.

Life is powered by sunshine. All of the energy used by almost all living cells comes ultimately from the sun, captured by plants, algae, and some bacteria through the process of **photosynthesis.** Every oxygen atom in the air we breathe was once part of a water molecule, liberated by photosynthesis, as you will discover in this chapter. Life as we know it is possible only because our earth is awash in energy streaming inward from the sun. Each day, the radiant energy that reaches the earth is equal to that of about 1 million Hiroshima-sized atomic bombs. About 1% of it is captured by photosynthesis and provides the energy needed to synthesize carbohydrates that drives almost all life on earth. Use the arrows on this page and the next three pages to follow the path of energy from the sun through photosynthesis.

Trees. Many kinds of organisms carry out photosynthesis, not only the diversity of plants that make our world green, but also bacteria and algae. Photosynthesis is somewhat different in bacteria, but we will focus our attention on photosynthesis in plants, starting with this maple tree crowned with green leaves. Later we will look at the grass growing beneath the maple tree—it turns out that grasses and other related plants sometimes take a different approach to photosynthesis, depending on the conditions.

Leaves. To learn how this maple tree captures energy from sunlight, follow the light. It comes beaming in from the sun, down through earth's atmosphere, bathing the top of the tree in light. What part of the maple tree is actually being struck by this light? The green leaves are. Each branch at the top of the tree ends in a spread of these leaves, each leaf flat and thin like the page of a book. Within these green leaves is where photosynthesis occurs. No photosynthesis occurs within this tree's stem, covered with bark, and none in the roots, buried within the soil—little to no light reaches these parts of the plant. The tree has a very efficient internal plumbing system that transports the products of photosynthesis to the stem, roots, and other parts of the plant so that they too may benefit from the capture of the sun's energy.

The Leaf Surface. Now follow the light as it passes into a leaf. The beam of light first encounters a waxy protective layer called the cuticle. The cuticle acts a bit like a layer of clear fingernail polish, providing a thin, watertight, and surprisingly strong layer of protection. Light passes right through this transparent wax, and then proceeds to pass right on through a layer of cells immediately beneath the cuticle called the epidermis. Only one cell layer thick, this epidermis acts as the "skin" of the leaf, providing more protection from damage and, very importantly, controlling how gases and water enter and leave the leaf. Very little of the light is absorbed by the cuticle or the epidermis.

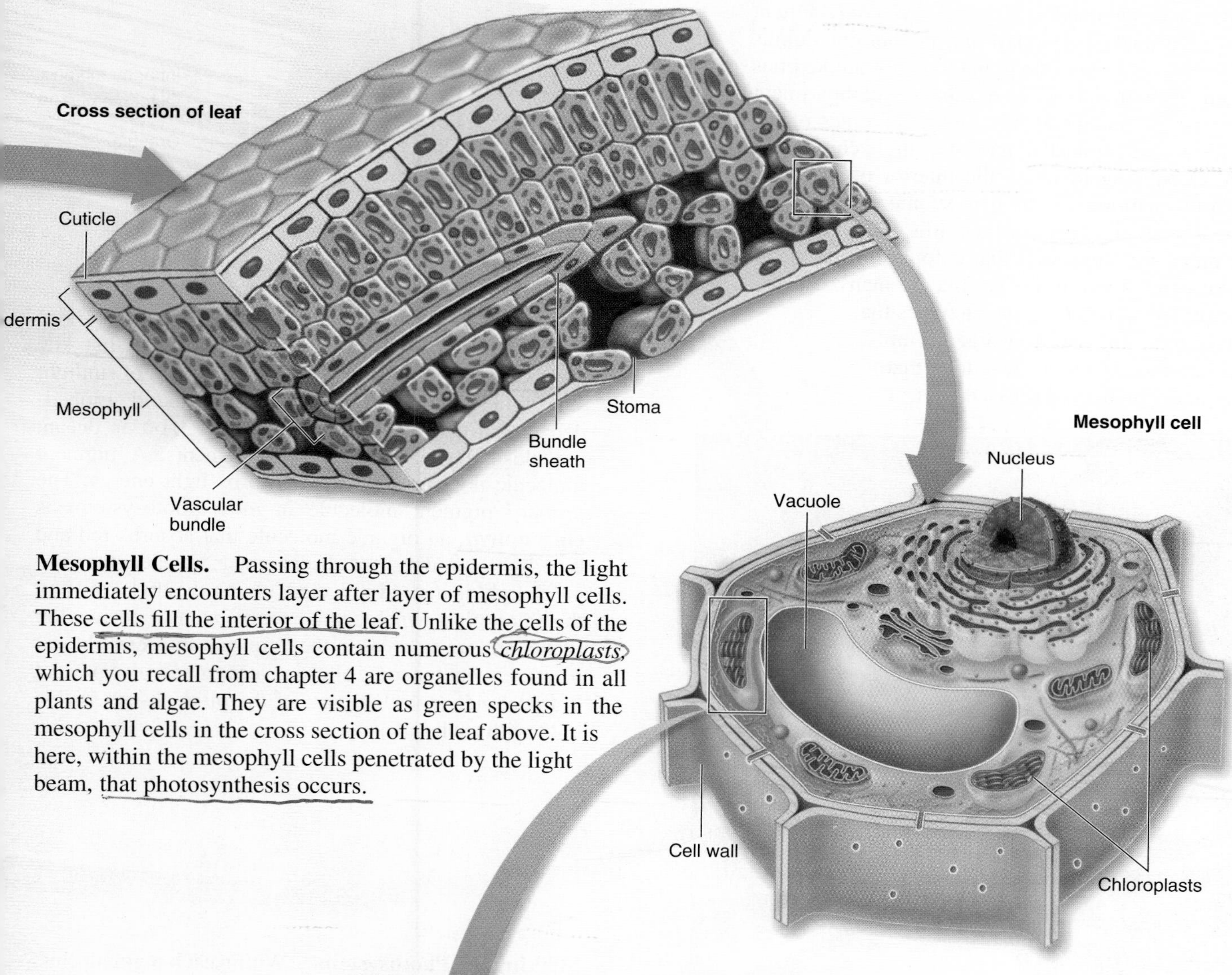

Mesophyll Cells. Passing through the epidermis, the light immediately encounters layer after layer of mesophyll cells. These cells fill the interior of the leaf. Unlike the cells of the epidermis, mesophyll cells contain numerous *chloroplasts*, which you recall from chapter 4 are organelles found in all plants and algae. They are visible as green specks in the mesophyll cells in the cross section of the leaf above. It is here, within the mesophyll cells penetrated by the light beam, that photosynthesis occurs.

Chloroplasts. The cell walls of the mesophyll cells don't absorb light. Why not? Because the cell walls contain few, if any, molecules that absorb visible light. If chloroplasts were not also present in these cells, most of this light would pass right through, just as it passed through the epidermis. But chloroplasts are present, lots of them. One chloroplast is highlighted by a box in the mesophyll cell above. Light passes into the cell and when it reaches the chloroplast, it passes through the outer and inner membranes to reach the thylakoid structures within the chloroplast, clearly seen as the green disks in the cutaway chloroplast shown here.

Putting the Concept to Work

Why is there no photosynthesis within an oak tree's stem?

Inside the Chloroplast

LEARNING OBJECTIVE 6.1.2 Diagram the structure of a chloroplast, and contrast the light-dependent and light-independent reactions that occur there.

All the important events of photosynthesis happen inside the chloroplast. The journey of light into the chloroplasts ends when the light beam encounters a series of internal membranes within the chloroplast organized into flattened sacs called *thylakoids.* Often, numerous thylakoids are stacked on top of one another in columns called *grana*. In the drawing below, the grana look not unlike piles of dishes. Although each thylakoid is a separate compartment that functions more or less independently, the membranes of the individual thylakoids are all connected, part of a single continuous membrane system. Occupying much of the interior of the chloroplast, this thylakoid membrane system is submerged within a semi-liquid substance called *stroma,* which fills the interior of the chloroplast in much the same way that cytoplasm fills the interior of a cell. Suspended within the stroma are many enzymes and other proteins, including the enzymes that act later in photosynthesis to assemble organic molecules from carbon dioxide (CO_2) in reactions that do not require light and which are discussed later.

Thylakoid
Inner membrane
Outer membrane
Granum
Stroma
Chloroplast

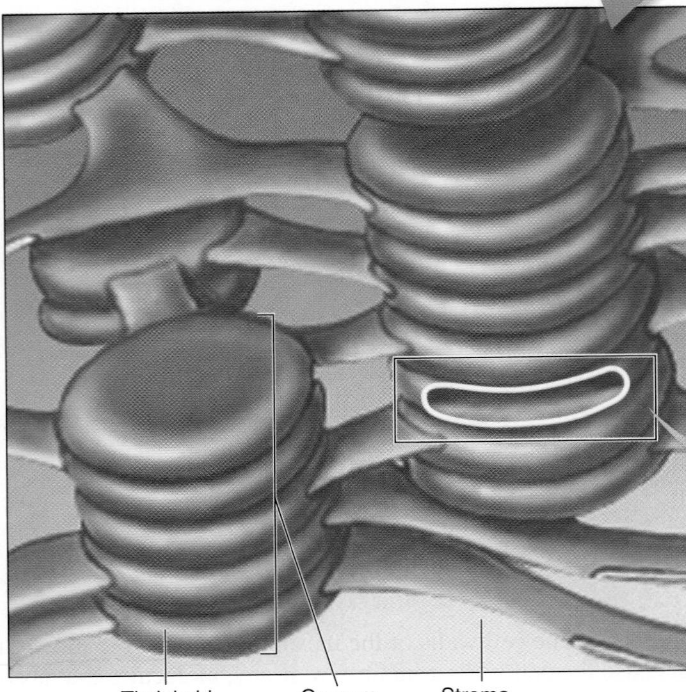

Penetrating the Thylakoid Surface. The first key event of photosynthesis occurs when a beam of sunlight strikes the surface membrane of a thylakoid. Embedded within this membrane, like icebergs on an ocean, are clusters of light-absorbing pigments. A pigment molecule is a molecule that absorbs light energy. The primary pigment molecule in most photosystems is **chlorophyll,** an organic molecule that absorbs red and blue light, but does not absorb green wavelengths. The green light is instead reflected, giving the thylakoid and the chloroplast which contains it an intense green color. Plants are green because they are rich in green chloroplasts. Except for some alternative pigments also present in thylakoids, no other parts of the plant absorb visible light with such intensity.

Striking the Photosystem. Within each pigment cluster, the chlorophyll molecules are arranged in a network called a *photosystem.* The light-absorbing chlorophyll molecules of a photosystem act together as an antenna to capture photons (units of light energy). A lattice of structural proteins, indicated by the purple element inserted into the thylakoid membrane in the diagram on the facing page, anchors each of the chlorophyll molecules of a photosystem into a precise position, such that every chlorophyll molecule is touching several others. Wherever light strikes the photosystem, some chlorophyll molecule will be in position to receive it.

Energy Absorption. When sunlight strikes any chlorophyll molecule in the photosystem, the chlorophyll molecule absorbs energy. The energy becomes part of the chlorophyll molecule, boosting some of its electrons to higher energy levels. Possessing these more energetic electrons, the chlorophyll molecule is said to now be "excited." With this key event, the biological world has captured energy from the sun.

Excitation of the Photosystem. The excitation that the absorption of light creates is then passed from the chlorophyll molecule that was hit to another, and then to another, like a hot potato being passed down a line of people. This shuttling of excitation is not a chemical reaction, in which an electron physically passes between atoms. Rather, it is energy that passes from one chlorophyll molecule to its neighbor. A crude analogy to this form of energy transfer is the initial "break" in a game of pool. If the cue ball squarely hits the point of the triangular array of 15 billiard balls, the two balls at the far corners of the triangle fly off, and none of the central balls move at all. The kinetic energy is transferred through the central balls to the most distant ones. In much the same way, the sun's excitation energy moves through the photosystem from one chlorophyll to the next.

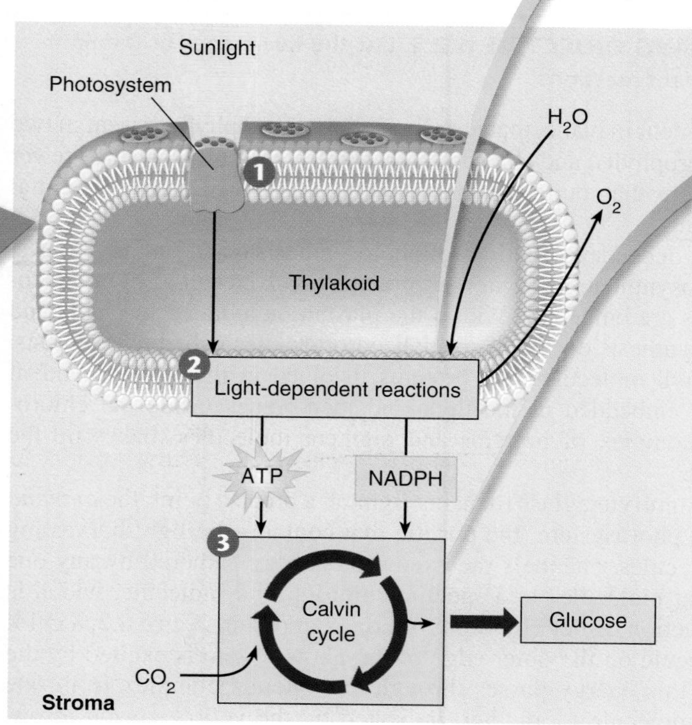

Energy Capture. As the energy shuttles from one chlorophyll molecule to another within the photosystem network, it eventually arrives at a key chlorophyll molecule, the only one that is touching a membrane-bound protein. Like shaking a marble in a box with a walnut-sized hole in it, the excitation energy will find its way to this special chlorophyll just as sure as the marble will eventually find its way to and through the hole in the box. The special chlorophyll then transfers an excited (high-energy) electron to the acceptor molecule it is touching.

The Light-Dependent Reactions. Like a baton being passed from one runner to another in a relay race, the electron is then passed from that acceptor protein to a series of other proteins in the membrane that put the energy of the electron to work making ATP and NADPH. In a way you will explore later in this chapter, the energy is used to power the movement of protons across the thylakoid membrane to make ATP and another key molecule, NADPH. So far, photosynthesis has consisted of two stages, indicated by numbers in the diagram to the lower left: 1 capturing energy from sunlight—accomplished by the photosystem; and 2 using the energy to make ATP and NADPH. These first two stages of photosynthesis take place only in the presence of light, and together are traditionally called the **light-dependent reactions.** ATP and NADPH are important energy-rich chemicals, and after this, the rest of photosynthesis becomes a chemical process.

The Light-Independent Reactions. The ATP and NADPH molecules generated by the light-dependent reactions are then used to power a series of chemical reactions in the stroma of the chloroplast, each catalyzed by an enzyme present there. Acting together like the many stages of a manufacturing assembly line, these reactions accomplish the synthesis of carbohydrates from CO_2 in the air 3. This third stage of photosynthesis, the formation of organic molecules like glucose from atmospheric CO_2, is called the **Calvin cycle,** but is also referred to as the **light-independent reactions** because it doesn't require light directly. We will examine the Calvin cycle in detail later in this chapter.

This completes our brief overview of photosynthesis. In the rest of the chapter we will revisit each stage and consider its elements in more detail. For now, the overall process may be summarized by the following simple equation:

$$6\,CO_2 + 12\,H_2O + \text{light energy} \longrightarrow C_6H_{12}O_6 + 6\,H_2O + 6\,O_2$$

carbon dioxide + water + light energy → glucose + water + oxygen

Putting the Concept to Work

Why does a photosystem capture photons better than a random mixture of chlorophyll molecules?

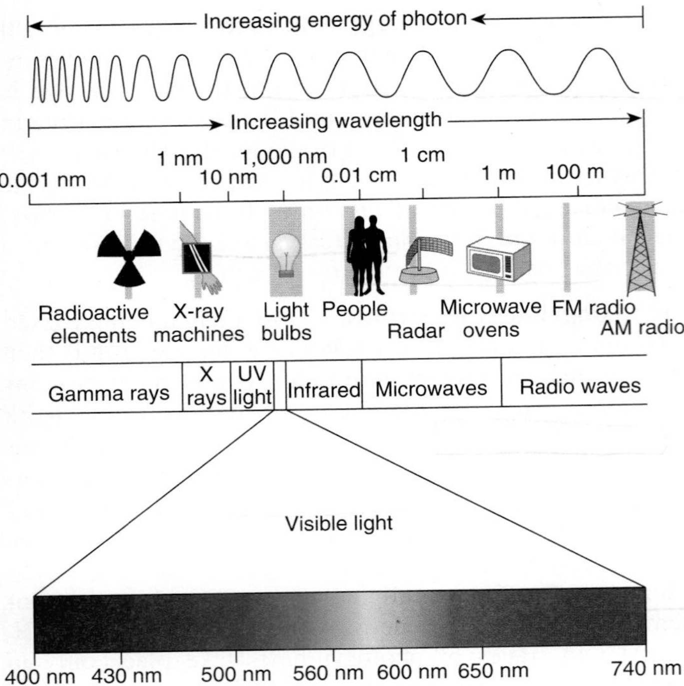

Figure 6.1 Photons of different energy: the electromagnetic spectrum.

Light is composed of packets of energy called photons. Some of the photons in light carry more energy than others. The shorter the wavelength of light, the greater the energy of its photons. Visible light represents only a small part of the electromagnetic spectrum, that with wavelengths between about 400 and 740 nanometers.

6.2 How Plants Capture Energy from Sunlight

LEARNING OBJECTIVE 6.2.1 Describe what a photon is made of, and state in what way its energy is related to its wavelength.

Where is the energy in light? Light actually consists of tiny packets of energy called **photons,** which have properties both of particles and of waves. When light shines on your hand, your skin is being bombarded by a stream of these photons.

Sunlight contains photons of many energy levels, only some of which we "see." We call the full range of these photons the **electromagnetic spectrum.** As you can see in figure 6.1, some of the photons in sunlight have shorter wavelengths (toward the left side of the spectrum) and carry a great deal of energy—for example, gamma rays and ultraviolet (UV) light. Others, such as radio waves, have longer wavelengths (hundreds to thousands of meters long) and carry very little energy. Molecules that absorb light energy are called **pigments.** When we speak of visible light, we refer to those wavelengths that the pigment within human eyes, called *retinal,* can absorb—roughly with wavelengths from 400 nanometers (violet) to 740 nanometers (red). Plants are even more picky, absorbing mainly blue and red light and reflecting back what is left of the visible light. Plants are perceived by our eyes as green simply because only the green wavelengths of light are reflected off the plant leaves.

Putting the Concept to Work

What color would your body be if you reflected all wavelengths of visible light? if you absorbed only green light?

Pigments and Photosystems

LEARNING OBJECTIVE 6.2.2 List the five stages of the light-dependent reactions.

The main pigment in plants that absorbs light is chlorophyll, present in two versions: chlorophyll *a* and chlorophyll *b*. While chlorophyll absorbs fewer kinds of photons than our eye pigment retinal, it is much more efficient at capturing them.

The light-dependent reactions of photosynthesis occur on membranes. In most photosynthetic bacteria, the proteins involved in the light-dependent reactions are embedded within the plasma membrane. In plants and algae, photosynthesis occurs in specialized organelles called chloroplasts. The chlorophyll molecules and proteins involved in the light-dependent reactions are embedded in the thylakoid membranes inside the chloroplasts. This complex of proteins and pigment molecules makes up the **photosystem.**

Like a magnifying glass focusing light on a precise point, the *antenna complex* of a photosystem, the portion that contains the light-harvesting pigment molecules, channels the excitation energy gathered by any one of its pigment molecules to a specific chlorophyll *a* molecule, which is called the reaction center chlorophyll. For example, in figure 6.2, a chlorophyll molecule on the outer edge of the photosystem is excited by the photon, and this energy passes through the antenna complex from one chlorophyll molecule to another, indicated by the yellow zigzag arrow, until it reaches the reaction center molecule. This molecule then passes

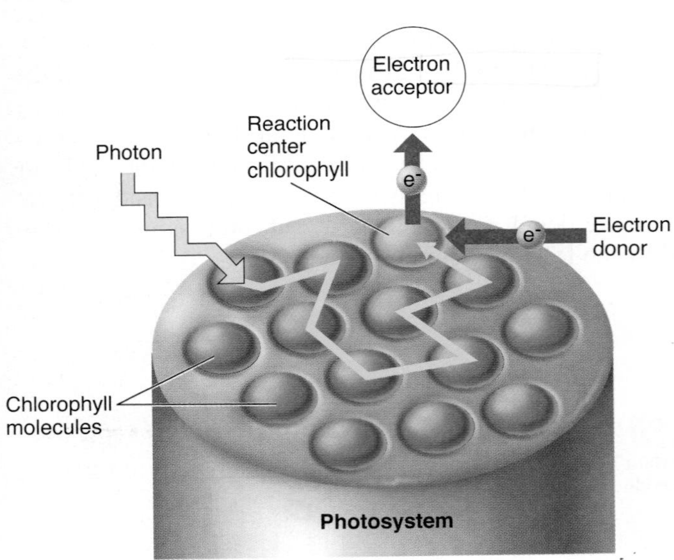

Figure 6.2 How a photosystem works.

When light of the proper wavelength strikes any pigment molecule within a photosystem, the light is absorbed and its excitation energy is then transferred from one molecule to another within the cluster of pigment molecules (the antenna complex) until it encounters the reaction center, which exports the energy as high-energy electrons to an acceptor molecule.

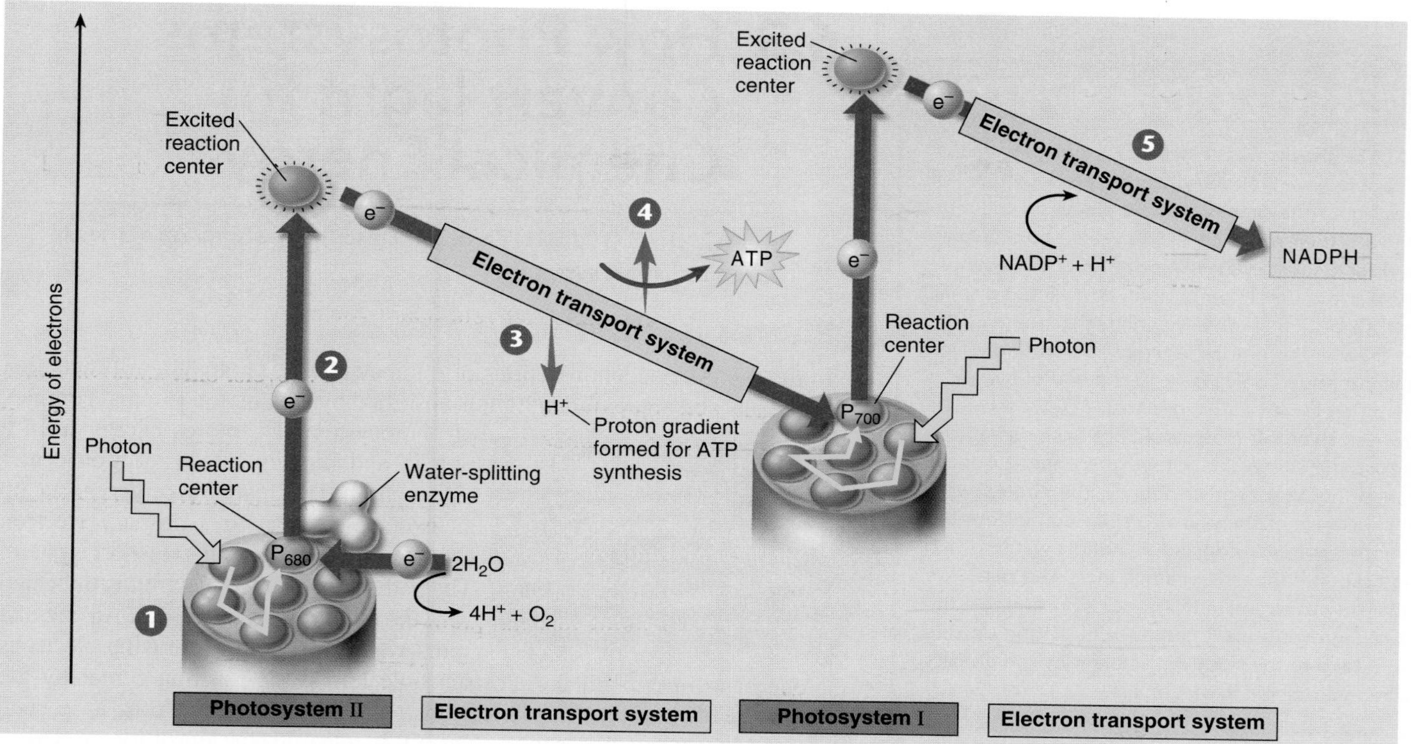

Figure 6.3 Plants use two photosystems in the light-dependent reactions.

In stage ❶, a photon excites pigment molecules in photosystem II. In stage ❷, a high-energy electron is transferred to the electron transport system. In stage ❸, the excited electron is used to pump a proton across the membrane. In stage ❹, the concentration gradient of protons is used to produce a molecule of ATP. In stage ❺, the ejected electron then passes to photosystem I to power the forming of NADPH.

the energy, in the form of an excited electron, out of the photosystem to drive the synthesis of ATP and organic molecules.

Using Two Photosystems

In the light-dependent reactions, plants and algae use two photosystems, photosystems I and II (**figures 6.3** and **6.4**). Photosystem II captures the energy that is used to produce the ATP needed to build sugar molecules. The light energy that it captures is used to transfer the energy of a photon of light ❶ to an excited electron ❷, which is then shuttled along a series of electron-carrier molecules embedded in the membrane called the **electron transport system** ❸. The energy of this electron is then used to produce ATP ❹, which will be used in the Calvin cycle.

The electron then enters photosystem I, where it is "re-energized" by the absorption of another photon of light. Photosystem I passes this energized electron to a second electron transport system, where the electron, carried by a hydrogen ion (a proton), is used to form NADPH from $NADP^+$ ❺. NADPH shuttles hydrogens to the Calvin cycle where sugars are made.

Photosystem I thus powers the production of the hydrogen atoms needed to build sugars and other organic molecules from CO_2, which has no hydrogen atoms, while photosystem II powers the production of ATP. These reactions are discussed in more detail in the next section.

Putting the Concept to Work

How is bacterial photosynthesis different from that in an oak leaf?

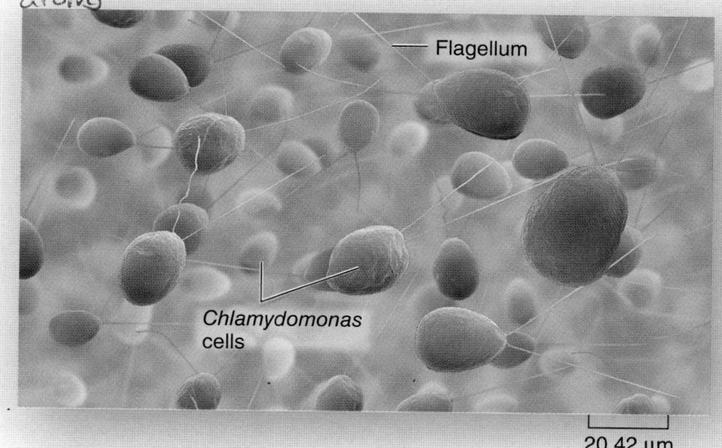

Figure 6.4 Plants aren't the only ones that carry out photosynthesis.

Each of these green balls is a single-celled photosynthetic organism, a green alga called *Chlamydomonas* that is common in pond water.

IMPLICATION FOR YOU Photosynthetic algae and bacteria in the oceans, called phytoplankton, carry out much of the earth's photosynthesis, removing far more CO_2 from the atmosphere than their cellular respiration adds to it. However, increases in ocean temperatures speed up cellular respiration much faster than photosynthesis. What would you expect the effect of global warming to be on the ocean's influence on atmospheric CO_2? Why is this consequence important to you, or is it?

6.3 How Photosystems Convert Light to Chemical Energy

LEARNING OBJECTIVE 6.3.1 Describe the function of the electron transport system.

Photosystem II

In the light-dependent reactions of photosynthesis, photosystem II acts first in plants and algae. When light is absorbed by a plant, the antenna complex of photosystem II captures energy from a photon and funnels it to a reaction center chlorophyll. The reaction center gives up an excited electron to a primary electron acceptor in the electron transport system. The path of the excited electron is indicated with the red arrow in **figure 6.5**. An enzyme splits water molecules, removing electrons one at a time to fill the electron hole left in the reaction center by the departure of light-energized electrons. As soon as four electrons have been removed from two water molecules, O_2 is released (far left of **figure 6.5**).

To better understand how energy from the sun is captured by the plant, look back to figure 2.3 on page 35. An electron in the reaction center absorbs energy from the sun and is moved to a higher energy level. This energized electron is now carrying energy from the sun.

Electron Transport System

The light-energized electrons leaving photosystem II are passed to the electron-carrier molecules of the electron transport system. One of the molecules is a "proton pump" protein. The energy of the electron is used by this protein to pump a proton from the stroma into the thylakoid space (indicated by the blue arrow through the electron transport system). A nearby protein in the membrane then carries the now energy-depleted electron on to photosystem I.

Putting the Concept to Work

Which photosystem powers the production of ATP, I or II?

BIOLOGY & YOU

The Greeks Get It Wrong. From the time of the Greeks, people have wondered where the body mass of a plant comes from—the Greeks thought plants sucked it up from the soil with their roots. Over 300 years ago a Belgian doctor named Jan Baptista van Helmont thought of a simple way to find out if the Greeks were right. He planted a small willow tree in a pot of soil after weighing the tree and the soil. The tree grew in the pot for several years, during which time van Helmont added only water. At the end of five years the tree was much larger: its weight had increased by 164 pounds. However, all of this mass could not have come from the soil, because the soil in the pot weighed only 2 ounces less than it had five years earlier! Clearly, the Greeks were wrong—the substance of the plant had not come from the soil. van Helmont incorrectly concluded that the water he had been adding accounted for the willow's increased mass. We now know that he was wrong in this conclusion, and that the added mass of a growing plant comes from carbon dioxide gas in the air, added to the body of the plant by the process of carbon fixation discussed in section 6.4.

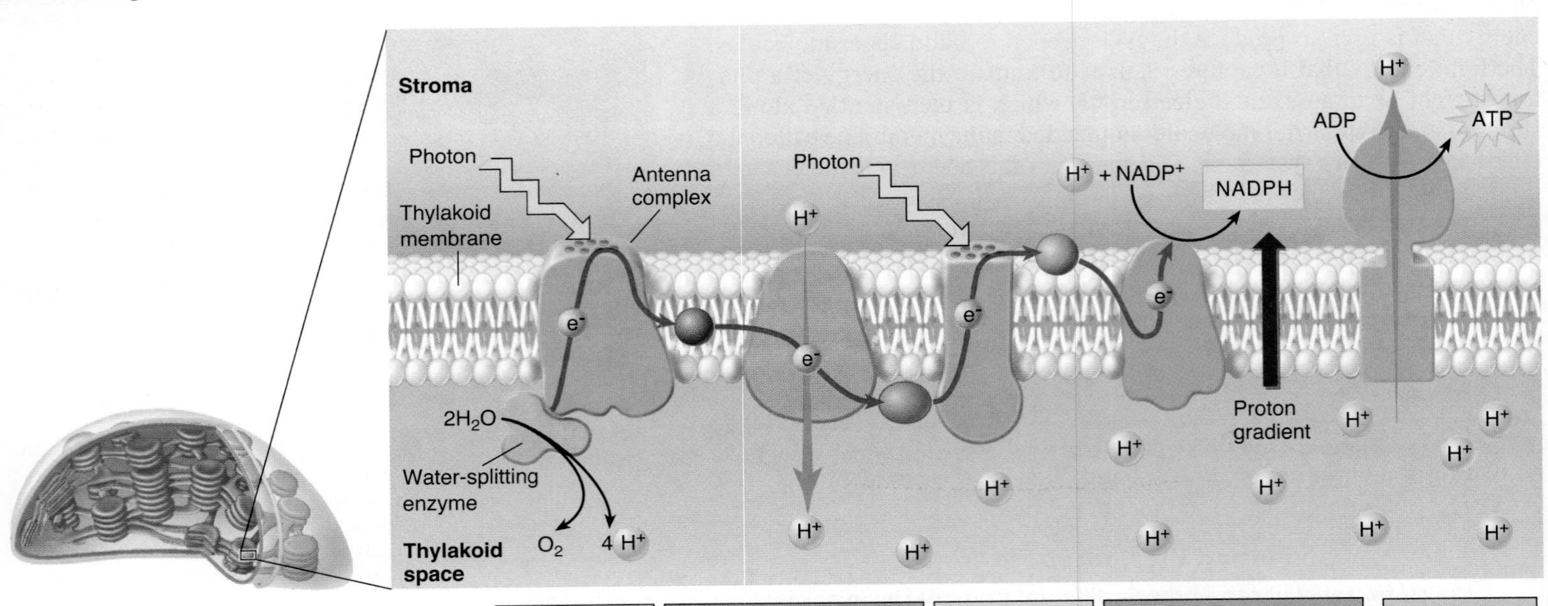

Figure 6.5 The photosynthetic electrons are used to produce ATP and NADPH.

The energy of the electron absorbed by photosystem II powers the pumping of protons into the thylakoid space. These protons then pass back out through ATP synthase channels, their movement powering the production of ATP. The energy of the electron absorbed by photosystem I powers the attachment of a proton to $NADP^+$, forming NADPH.

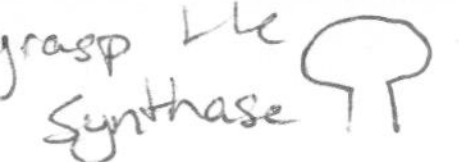

Making ATP: Chemiosmosis

LEARNING OBJECTIVE 6.3.2 Define chemiosmosis, and state the function of ATP synthase.

Before progressing onto photosystem I, let's see what happens with the protons that were pumped into the thylakoid by the electron transport system. The thylakoid membrane you see in figure 6.5 is impermeable to protons, so protons that have been pumped across the membrane by the first electron transport system build up inside the thylakoid space, creating a very large concentration gradient. These protons now diffuse back out of the thylakoid space, down their concentration gradient, passing through a special channel protein called *ATP synthase.* The ATP synthase is the membrane protein on the far right side of figure 6.5, protruding like a knob out of the external surface of the thylakoid membrane. As protons pass out of the thylakoid through the ATP synthase channels, a phosphate group is added onto ADP to form ATP in a process called phosphorylation. ATP is released into the stroma (the fluid matrix inside the chloroplast). Because the chemical formation of ATP is driven by a diffusion process similar to osmosis, this type of ATP formation is called **chemiosmosis.**

Putting the Concept to Work

What would happen to photosynthesis if you were to puncture the thylakoid membrane?

Figure 6.6 Capturing energy from sunlight.

Sunlight beams down in this forest glade. Although only a few of the plants you see are bathed in direct sunlight, all of the trees and shrubs and grasses are receiving an ample amount of sunlight, their photosystems running full bore in even dim light.

Photosystem I: Making NADPH

LEARNING OBJECTIVE 6.3.3 Differentiate between photosystems I and II.

Now, with ATP formed, let's return to the middle of figure 6.5 where photosystem I accepts an electron from the electron transport system. Energy is fed to photosystem I by an antenna complex of chlorophyll molecules. The electron arriving from the first electron transport system has by no means lost all of its light-excited energy; almost half remains. Thus, the absorption of another photon of light energy by photosystem I boosts the electron leaving its reaction center to a very high energy level (figure 6.6 and see figure 6.3).

Like photosystem II, photosystem I passes electrons to an electron transport system. When two of these electrons reach the end of this electron transport system, they are then donated to a molecule of $NADP^+$ along with a proton (a hydrogen ion) to form NADPH. Because the reaction occurs on the stromal side of the membrane and involves the uptake of a proton, it contributes further to the proton concentration gradient established during photosynthetic electron transport.

Products of the Light-Dependent Reactions

The ATP and NADPH produced in the light-dependent reactions end up being passed on to the Calvin cycle in the stroma of the chloroplast. The stroma contains the enzymes that catalyze the light-independent reactions. There, ATP is used to power chemical reactions that build carbohydrates, with NADPH providing the necessary hydrogens and electrons.

Putting the Concept to Work

Is the electron passing through photosystem I the same electron that passed through photosystem II?

IN THE NEWS

Using Algae to Fix Global Warming. Engineers at Ohio University have come up with a novel solution to the problem of what to do with the massive amounts of CO_2 that are generated by burning coal. They have created a photo bioreactor that passes streams of CO_2 over sheets of a woven material made of living algae. The algae use photosynthesis to remove CO_2 from the air stream! When an algal sheet has grown substantially, it is removed and the algae dried and used as feed for farm animals. Test facilities are already up and running. A full-scale reactor that produces 1.25 million square meters of algae sheets is under development.

EVOLUTION

Global Warming and the Calvin Cycle. Photosynthesis removes CO_2 from air by binding it to the compound RuBP in the first step of the Calvin cycle. The enzyme that catalyzes this reaction, with a long chemical name usually shortened to RuBisCO, is the most abundant enzyme in the world, and also one of the least efficient. It is a thousand times slower than most other enzymes. Its inefficiency limits the amount of CO_2 plants can remove from the atmosphere. For years scientists have tried to engineer a speedier variant of the RuBisCO enzyme by altering specific sites on the enzyme and then looking to see if the change improved the enzyme. Nothing they tried has worked—there are just too many possible changes to test. However, scientists at Emory University have found a way through the thicket of possibilities. With a nod to Darwin, they have used a process called "directed evolution." They added the gene for RuBisCO to a bacterium in such a way that the bacterium could not survive unless the enzyme functioned; then they randomly altered the gene. The fastest growing bacteria were those with the most efficient RuBisCO! The best experimental results exhibited a 500% increase in enzyme speed. The next step . . . to get this engineered enzyme into plants.

6.4 Building New Molecules

The Calvin Cycle

LEARNING OBJECTIVE 6.4.1 Describe the function of the Calvin cycle, and explain why it requires NADPH as well as ATP.

Stated very simply, photosynthesis is a way of making organic molecules from carbon dioxide (CO_2). The actual assembly of new molecules employs a complex battery of enzymes in what is called the **Calvin cycle,** or **C_3 photosynthesis** (C_3 because the first molecule produced in the process is a three-carbon molecule). The process takes place in three stages, indicated by the three panels in *Essential Biological Process 6A*. Three turns of the cycle are needed to produce one molecule of glyceraldehyde 3-phosphate. In any *one* turn of the cycle, a carbon atom from a carbon dioxide molecule is first added to a five-carbon sugar, producing two three-carbon sugars. This process is called **carbon fixation** because it attaches a carbon atom that was in a gas to an organic molecule. The cycle has to "turn" six times in order to form a new glucose molecule. The cycle is driven by energy from ATP and hydrogen atoms are supplied by NADPH, both produced in the light-dependent reactions.

Putting the Concept to Work

What three substances are needed by the Calvin cycle to produce a molecule of glucose?

Essential Biological Process 6A

The Calvin Cycle

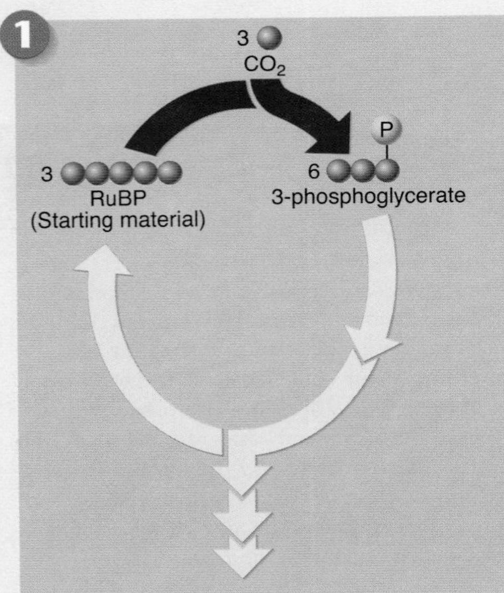

The Calvin cycle begins when a carbon atom from a CO_2 molecule is added to a five-carbon molecule (the starting material). The resulting six-carbon molecule is unstable and immediately splits into three-carbon molecules. (Three "turns" of the cycle are indicated here with three molecules of CO_2 entering the cycle.)

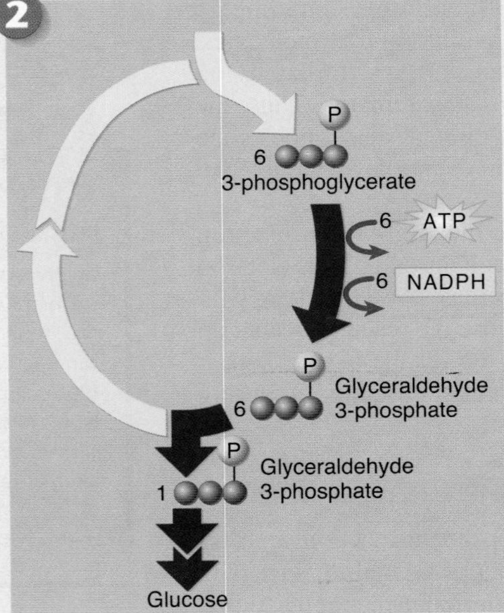

Then, through a series of reactions, energy from ATP and hydrogens from NADPH (the products of the light-dependent reactions) are added to the three-carbon molecules. The now-reduced three-carbon molecules either combine to make glucose or are used to make other molecules.

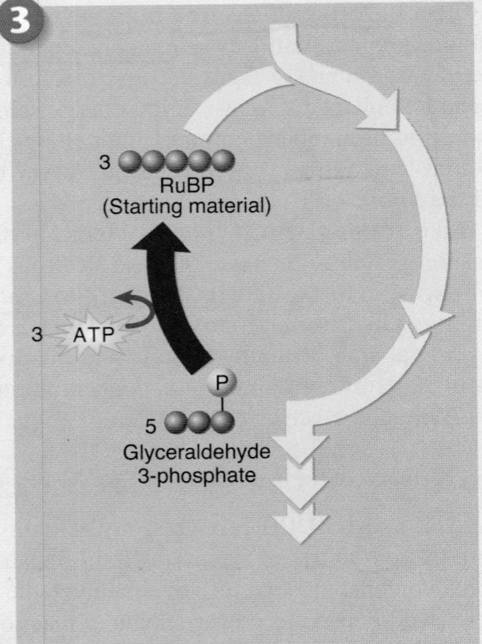

Most of the reduced three-carbon molecules are used to regenerate the five-carbon starting material, thus completing the cycle.

Photorespiration

6.5 Photorespiration: Putting the Brakes on Photosynthesis

LEARNING OBJECTIVE 6.5.1 Contrast C_3, C_4, and CAM photosynthesis.

Many plants have trouble carrying out C_3 photosynthesis when the weather is hot. As temperatures increase in hot, arid weather, plants partially close their **stomata** (singular, **stoma**) to conserve water. The stomata are openings in the epidermis through which water vapor and O_2 pass out of the leaf and CO_2 passes in. As a result, when stomata close, CO_2 and O_2 are not able to enter and exit the leaves (**figure 6.7**). The concentration of CO_2 in the leaves falls, while the concentration of O_2 in the leaves rises. Under these conditions the active site of the enzyme that carries out the first step of the Calvin cycle (called rubisco) binds O_2 instead of CO_2. When this occurs, CO_2 is ultimately released as a by-product of an alternate reaction, effectively short-circuiting the Calvin cycle. This failure of photosynthesis is called **photorespiration.**

Oxygen and carbon dioxide both bind to rubisco at the same active site. In this way, oxygen is a competitive inhibitor of the enzyme, a topic discussed on page 97.

Leaf epidermis

Heat

Under hot, arid conditions, the stomata close to conserve water. But as a result, O_2 builds up inside leaves, and CO_2 cannot enter the leaves. This leads to photorespiration.

O_2

O_2

CO_2

Stoma

CO_2

Figure 6.7 Plant response in hot weather.

C_4 Photosynthesis

Some plants are able to adapt to climates with higher temperatures by performing **C_4 photosynthesis.** In this process, plants such as sugarcane, corn, and many grasses are able to fix carbon using different types of cells and chemical reactions within their leaves, thereby avoiding a reduction in photosynthesis due to higher temperatures.

A cross section of a leaf from a C_4 plant is shown in **figure 6.8**. Examining it, you can see how these plants solve the problem of photorespiration. In the enlargement, you see two cell types: The green cell is a mesophyll cell and the tan cell is a bundle-sheath cell. In the mesophyll cell, CO_2 combines with a three-carbon molecule instead of RuBP (the five-carbon starting molecule in the Calvin cycle). This reaction produces a four-carbon molecule, oxaloacetate (hence the name, C_4 photosynthesis), rather than the three-carbon molecule, phosphoglycerate, shown in **panel 1** of *Essential Biological Process 6A*. C_4 plants carry out this process using a different enzyme. The oxaloacetate is then converted to malate, which is transferred to the bundle-sheath cells of the leaf. In the tan bundle-sheath cell, malate is broken down to regenerate CO_2, which enters the Calvin cycle and sugars are synthesized. Why go to all this trouble? Because the bundle-sheath cells are impermeable to CO_2 and so the concentration of CO_2 increases within them, which substantially lowers the rate of photorespiration.

A second strategy to decrease photorespiration is used by many succulent (water-storing) plants such as cacti and pineapples. Called **crassulacean acid metabolism (CAM)** plants after the plant family Crassulaceae in which it was first discovered, these plants open their stomata and fix CO_2 into organic compounds during the night when it's cooler, and then close the stomata during the day.

Putting the Concept to Work

Are C_4 plants more likely to be common in Arizona or Maine? Why?

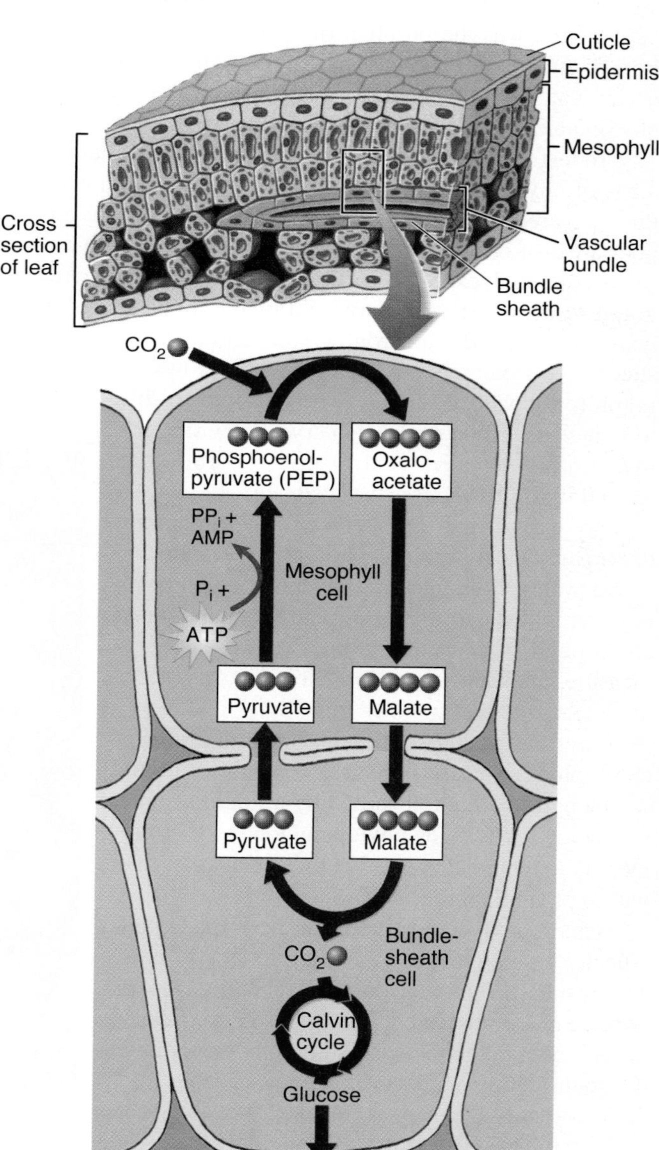

Figure 6.8 Carbon fixation in C_4 plants.

In mesophyll cells, oxaloacetate is converted into malate that is transported into bundle-sheath cells. Once there, malate undergoes a chemical reaction producing carbon dioxide. The carbon dioxide is trapped in the bundle-sheath cell, where it enters the Calvin cycle.

Inquiry & Analysis

Does Iron Limit the Growth of Ocean Phytoplankton?

Phytoplankton are microscopic organisms that live in the oceans, carrying out much of the earth's photosynthesis. The photo below is of *Chaetoceros,* a phytoplankton. Decades ago, scientists noticed "dead zones" in the ocean where little photosynthesis occurred. Looking more closely, they found that phytoplankton collected from these waters are not able to efficiently fix CO_2 into carbohydrates. In an attempt to understand why not, the scientists hypothesized that lack of iron was the problem (the electron transport system requires iron to function properly), and they predicted that fertilizing these ocean waters with iron could trigger an explosively rapid growth of phytoplankton.

To test this idea, they carried out a field experiment, seeding large areas of phytoplankton-poor ocean waters with iron crystals to see if this triggered phytoplankton growth. Other similarly phytoplankton-poor areas of ocean were not seeded with iron and served as controls.

In one such experiment, the results of which are presented in the graph to the right, a 72-km^2 grid of phytoplankton-deficient ocean water was seeded with iron crystals and a tracer substance in three successive treatments, indicated with arrows on the *x* axis of the graph (on days 0, 3, and 7). The multiple seedings were carried out to reduce the effect of the iron crystals dissipating over time. A smaller control grid, 24 km^2, was seeded with just the tracer substance.

To assess the numbers of phytoplankton organisms carrying out photosynthesis in the ocean water, investigators did not actually count organisms. Instead, they estimated the amount of chlorophyll *a* in water samples as an easier-to-measure index. An **index** is a parameter that accurately reflects the quantity of another less easily measured parameter. In this instance, the level of chlorophyll *a*, easily measured by monitoring the wavelengths of light absorbed by a liquid sample, is a suitable index of phytoplankton, as this pigment is found nowhere else in the ocean other than within phytoplankton.

Chlorophyll *a* measurements were made periodically on both test and control grids for 14 days. The results are plotted on the graph. Red points indicate chlorophyll *a* concentrations in iron-seeded waters; blue points indicate chlorophyll *a* levels in the control grid waters that were not seeded.

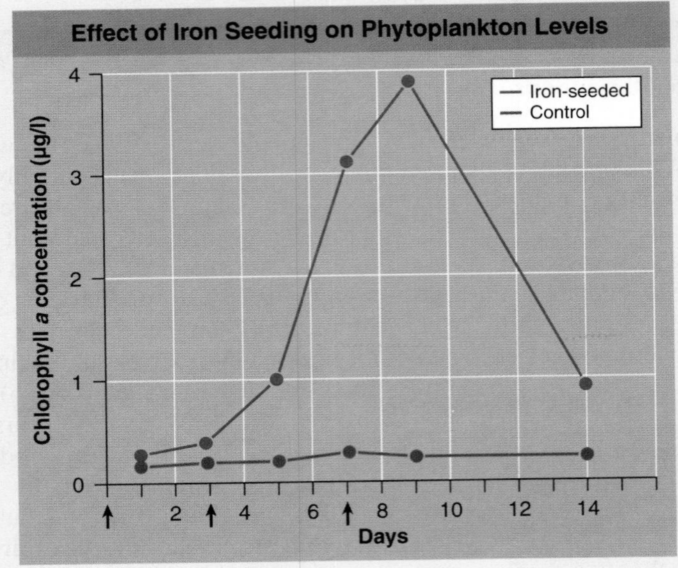

Analysis

1. **Applying Concepts** What substance is lacking in the waters sampled in the blue-dot plots?
2. **Interpreting Data** Comparing the red line to the blue line, about how many times more numerous are phytoplankton in iron-seeded waters on each of the three days of seeding?
3. **Making Inferences**
   a. What general statement can be made regarding the effect of seeding phytoplankton-poor regions of the ocean with iron?
   b. Why did chlorophyll *a* levels drop by day 14?
4. **Drawing Conclusions** Do these results support the claim that lack of iron is limiting the growth of phytoplankton, and thus of photosynthesis, in certain areas of the oceans?

Summary of Learning Outcomes

Photosynthesis

An Overview of Photosynthesis

6.1.1 Photosynthesis uses energy from sunlight to power the synthesis of organic molecules from CO_2 in the air.

6.1.2 Photosynthesis consists of a series of chemical reactions that occurs in two stages: the light-dependent reactions that produce ATP and NADPH occur on the thylakoid membranes of chloroplasts in plants, and the light-independent reactions (the Calvin cycle) that synthesize carbohydrates occur in the stroma of the chloroplasts.

How Plants Capture Energy from Sunlight

6.2.1 Sunlight contains packets of energy called photons, which contain varying amounts of energy. As light wavelengths increase in size, the amount of energy in the photons decreases. Visible light consists of wavelengths absorbed by pigments in the human eye (between 400 and 740 nanometers). Pigments are molecules that capture light energy. Plants use the pigment chlorophyll to absorb light energy.

6.2.2 Plants appear green because of their chlorophyll pigments. Chlorophyll absorbs wavelengths in the far ends of the visual spectrum (the blue and red wavelengths) and reflects the green wavelengths, which is why leaves appear green.

- The light-dependent reactions occur on the thylakoid membranes of chloroplasts in plants. The chlorophyll molecules and other pigments involved in photosynthesis are embedded in a complex of proteins within the membrane called a photosystem.
- The energy from a photon of light is absorbed by a chlorophyll molecule and is transferred between chlorophyll molecules in the photosystem, as shown here from **figure 6.2.** Once the energy is passed to the reaction center, it excites an electron, which is transferred to the electron transport system.
- The energized electron is used to generate ATP and NADPH. ATP powers the Calvin cycle, and NADPH donates hydrogen atoms toward the building of carbohydrate molecules. Plants utilize two photosystems that occur in series. Photosystem II leads to the formation of ATP, and photosystem I leads to the formation of NADPH.

How Photosystems Convert Light to Chemical Energy

6.3.1 The excited electron that leaves the reaction center of photosystem II is replenished with an electron captured from the breakdown of a water molecule. Oxygen gas is released as a by-product of this reaction.

- The excited electron is passed from one protein to another in the electron transport system, where energy from the electron is used to operate a proton pump that pumps hydrogen ions across the membrane against a concentration gradient.

6.3.2 The hydrogen ion concentration gradient is used as a source of energy to generate molecules of ATP. As the concentration of H^+ ions inside the thylakoid increases, H^+ ions diffuse back across the membrane through a specialized channel protein called ATP synthase, which catalyzes the formation of ATP, a process called chemiosmosis shown here from **figure 6.5.**

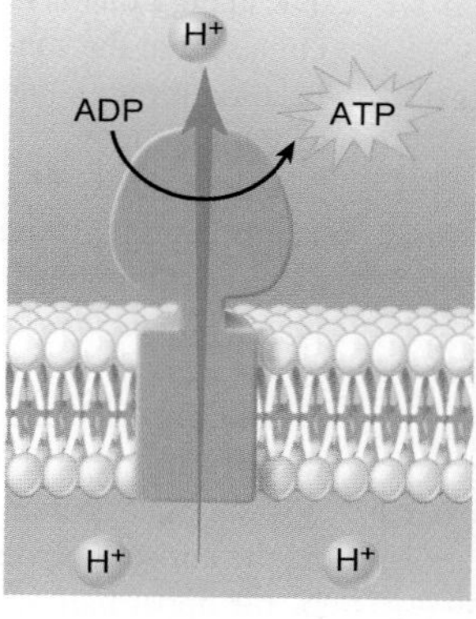

6.3.3 After the electron passes along the first electron transport system, it is then transferred to a second photosystem, photosystem I, where it gets an energy boost from the capture of another photon of light. This reenergized electron is passed along another electron transport system to an ultimate electron acceptor, $NADP^+$. $NADP^+$ binds electrons and an H^+ ion to produce NADPH, which is shuttled to the Calvin cycle.

Building New Molecules

6.4.1 ATP and NADPH from the light-dependent reactions are shuttled to the stroma, where they are used in the Calvin cycle.

- The Calvin cycle is carried out by a series of enzymes that use the energy from ATP and electrons and hydrogen ions from NADPH to build molecules of carbohydrates by reducing CO_2 from the air.

Photorespiration

Photorespiration: Putting the Brakes on Photosynthesis

6.5.1 Photorespiration occurs as a response to the buildup of oxygen within photosynthetic cells: a product of photosynthesis, oxygen tends to push photosynthesis backward. In hot dry weather, plants will close the stomata in their leaves to conserve water. As a result, the levels of O_2 increase in the leaves, and CO_2 levels drop, as shown here from **figure 6.7.** Under these conditions, the Calvin cycle, also called C_3 photosynthesis, is disrupted. When there is a higher internal concentration of oxygen, O_2 rather than CO_2 enters the Calvin cycle, a process called photorespiration. In this case, the first enzyme in the Calvin cycle, rubisco, binds oxygen instead of carbon dioxide.

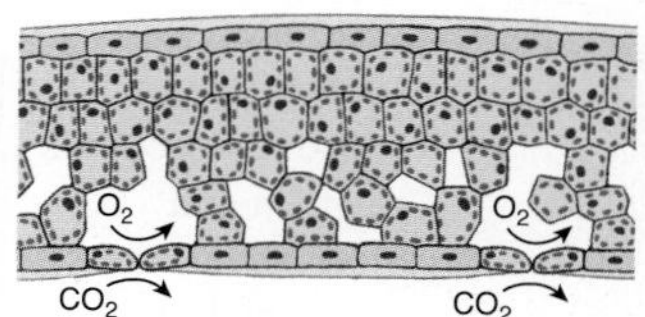

- C_4 plants reduce the effects of photorespiration by modifying the carbon-fixation step, splitting it into two steps that take place in different cells. The C_4 pathway produces malate in mesophyll cells. Malate is then transferred to bundle-sheath cells, where it breaks down to produce carbon dioxide. This CO_2 then enters the Calvin cycle in the bundle-sheath cells.
- In CAM plants, carbon dioxide is processed into organic molecules during the night when stomata are open.

Test Your Understanding

6.1.1 The energy that is used by almost all living things on our planet comes from the sun. It is captured by plants, algae, and some bacteria through the process of
a. thylakoid.
b. chloroplasts.
c. photosynthesis.
d. the Calvin cycle.

6.1.2 Plants capture the energy from sunlight
a. through photorespiration.
b. with molecules called pigments that absorb photons and use their energy.
c. with the light-independent reactions.
d. with the electron transport system.

6.2.1 Visible light occupies what part of the electromagnetic spectrum?
a. the entire spectrum
b. the upper half of the spectrum (with longer wavelengths)
c. a small portion in the middle of the spectrum
d. the lower half of the spectrum (with shorter wavelengths)

6.2.1 The colors of light that are absorbed by chlorophyll are
a. red and blue.
b. green and yellow.
c. infrared and ultraviolet.
d. All colors are equally absorbed.

6.2.2 Once a plant has initially captured the energy of a photon,
a. a series of reactions occurs in thylakoid membranes of the cell.
b. the energy drives the synthesis of ATP.
c. a water molecule is broken down, releasing oxygen.
d. All of the above.

6.3.1 Plants use two photosystems to capture energy used to produce ATP and NADPH. The electrons used in these photosystems
a. recycle through the system, with energy added from the photons.
b. recycle through the system several times and then are lost due to entropy.
c. go through the system only once; they are obtained by splitting a water molecule.
d. go through the system only once; they are obtained from the photon.

6.3.2 During photosynthesis, ATP molecules are generated by
a. the Calvin cycle.
b. chemiosmosis.
c. the splitting of a water molecule.
d. photons of light being absorbed by chlorophyll molecules.

6.3.3 NADPH is recycled during photosynthesis. It is produced during the ________ and used in the__________.
a. electron transport system of photosystem I, Calvin cycle
b. process of chemiosmosis, Calvin cycle
c. electron transport system of photosystem II, electron transport system of photosystem I
d. light-independent reactions, light-dependent reactions

6.4.1 The overall purpose of the Calvin cycle is to
a. generate molecules of ATP.
b. generate NADPH.
c. build sugar molecules.
d. produce oxygen.

6.5.1 Many plants cannot carry out the typical C_3 photosynthesis in hot weather, so some plants
a. use the ATP cycle.
b. use C_4 photosynthesis or CAM.
c. shut down photosynthesis completely.
d. All of these are true for different plants.

Apply Your Understanding

6.2.2 This figure shows the areas of the visible spectrum that are absorbed by two forms of chlorophyll. The green and yellow wavelengths are reflected back and so plants appear green. The red skin of an apple contains different pigments. What areas of the spectrum do you think are absorbed and reflected by these pigments?

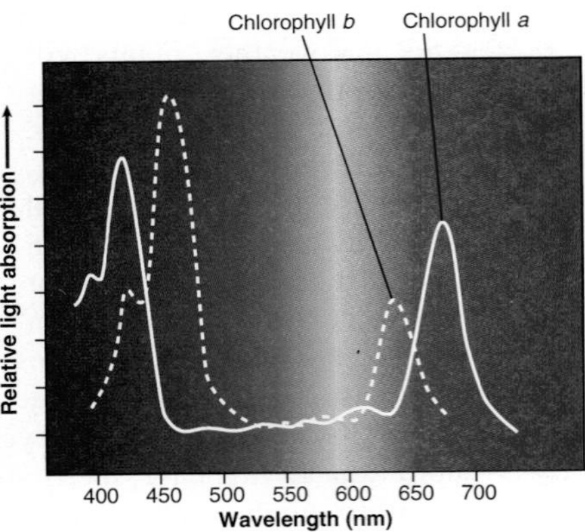

6.3.2 Could a plant cell produce ATP through chemiosmosis if the thylakoid membrane was "leaky" with regard to protons? Explain.

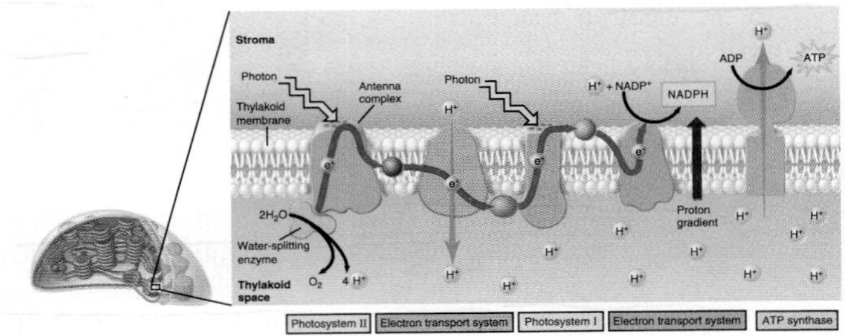

Synthesize What You Have Learned

6.4.1 To reduce six molecules of carbon dioxide to glucose via photosynthesis, how many molecules of NADPH and ATP are required?

6.4.1 In theory, a plant kept in total darkness could still manufacture glucose if it were supplied with which molecules?

6.5.1 If you were going to design a plant that would survive in the deserts of Arizona and New Mexico, how would you balance its need for CO_2 with its need to avoid water loss in the hot summer temperatures?

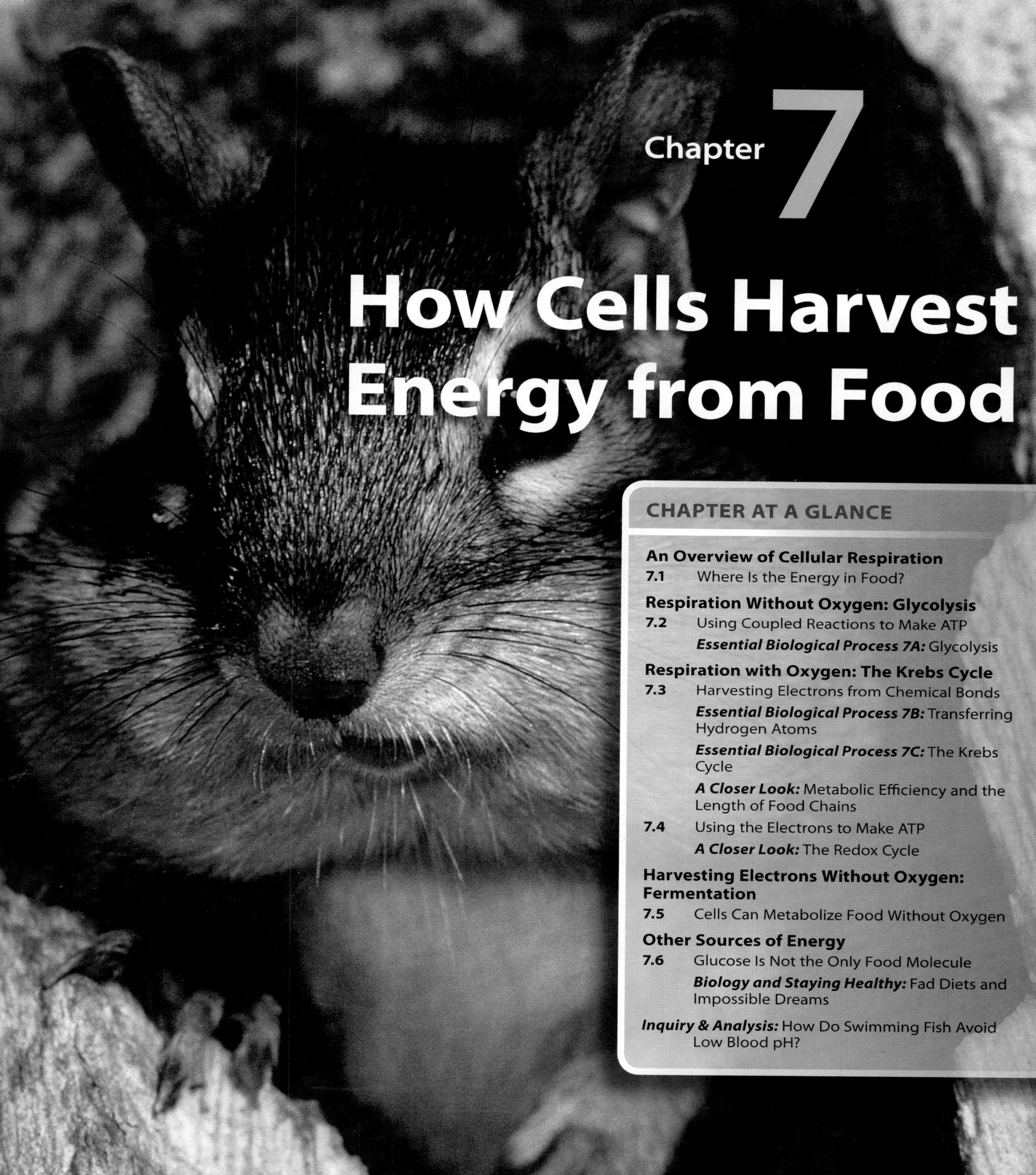

Chapter 7

How Cells Harvest Energy from Food

CHAPTER AT A GLANCE

An Overview of Cellular Respiration
7.1 Where Is the Energy in Food?

Respiration Without Oxygen: Glycolysis
7.2 Using Coupled Reactions to Make ATP
Essential Biological Process 7A: Glycolysis

Respiration with Oxygen: The Krebs Cycle
7.3 Harvesting Electrons from Chemical Bonds
Essential Biological Process 7B: Transferring Hydrogen Atoms
Essential Biological Process 7C: The Krebs Cycle
A Closer Look: Metabolic Efficiency and the Length of Food Chains
7.4 Using the Electrons to Make ATP
A Closer Look: The Redox Cycle

Harvesting Electrons Without Oxygen: Fermentation
7.5 Cells Can Metabolize Food Without Oxygen

Other Sources of Energy
7.6 Glucose Is Not the Only Food Molecule
Biology and Staying Healthy: Fad Diets and Impossible Dreams

Inquiry & Analysis: How Do Swimming Fish Avoid Low Blood pH?

An Overview of Cellular Respiration

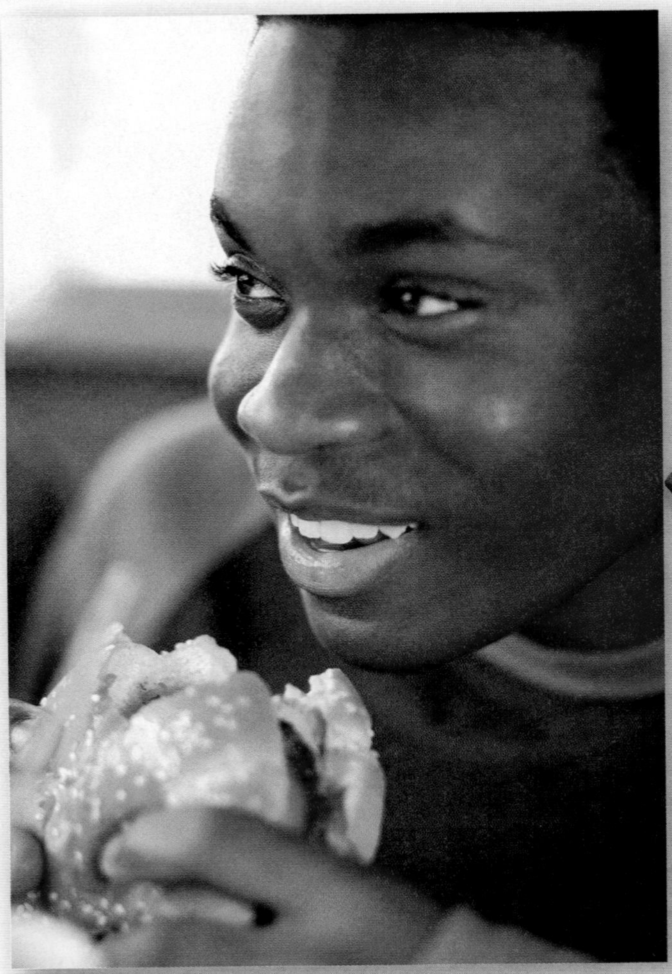

Figure 7.1 A human acquiring energy.

Energy that this teen extracts from the hamburger he is eating will be used to power his thinking, fuel his running, and build a bigger teenager.

7.1 Where Is the Energy in Food?

LEARNING OBJECTIVE 7.1.1 Distinguish between oxidation and reduction, and write a chemical equation for the oxidation of glucose.

In plants and animals, and in fact in almost all organisms, the energy for living is obtained by breaking down the organic molecules originally produced by photosynthetic organisms, such as plants, algae, and certain bacteria. The energy invested in building the organic molecules is retrieved by stripping away the energetic electrons and using them to make ATP, a process called **cellular respiration.** Do not confuse the term cellular respiration with the breathing of oxygen gas that your lungs carry out, which is called simply respiration.

All cells use ATP to power biological functions. The depth and breadth of some of these functions were illustrated in table 5.1, page 99.

The cells of plants fuel their activities with sugars and other molecules that they produce through photosynthesis and break down in cellular respiration. Nonphotosynthetic organisms eat plants, extracting energy from plant tissue using cellular respiration. Other animals, like the teenager gobbling up the hamburger in **figure 7.1**, eat these animals.

Eukaryotes produce the majority of their ATP by harvesting electrons from chemical bonds of the food molecule glucose. The electrons are transferred along an electron transport chain (similar to the electron transport system in photosynthesis), and eventually donated to oxygen gas. Chemically, there is little difference between this process in a cell and the burning of wood in a fireplace. In both instances, the reactants are carbohydrates and oxygen, and the products are carbon dioxide, water, and energy:

$$C_6H_{12}O_6 + 6\ O_2 \longrightarrow 6\ CO_2 + 6\ H_2O + \textbf{energy (heat or ATP)}$$

In a chemical reaction, when an atom or molecule loses an electron, it is said to be *oxidized,* and the process by which this occurs is called **oxidation.** The name reflects the fact that in biological systems, oxygen, which attracts electrons strongly, is the most common electron acceptor. This is certainly the case in cellular respiration, where oxygen is the final electron acceptor. Conversely, when an atom or molecule gains an electron, it is said to be *reduced,* and the process is called **reduction.** Oxidation and reduction always take place together, because every electron that is lost by an atom through oxidation is gained by some other atom through reduction. Therefore, chemical reactions of this sort are called **oxidation-reduction (redox) reactions.** In redox reactions, energy follows the electron, as shown in **figure 7.2**.

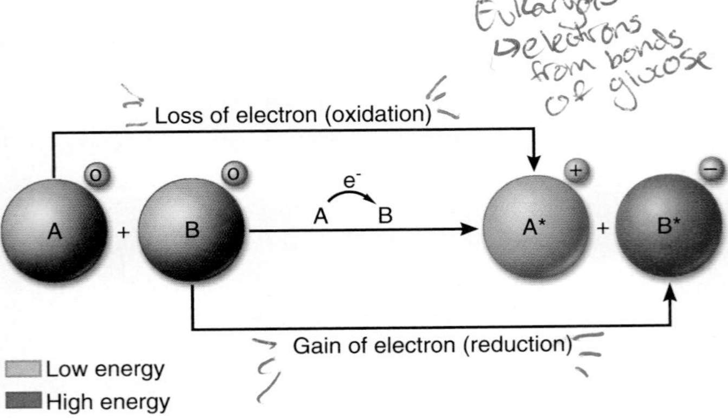

Figure 7.2 Redox reactions.

Oxidation is the loss of an electron; reduction is the gain of an electron. Here the charges of molecules A and B are shown in small circles to the upper right of each molecule. Molecule A loses energy as it loses an electron, while molecule B gains energy as it gains an electron.

Cellular respiration is carried out in two stages, illustrated in **figure 7.3**. The first stage uses coupled reactions to make ATP. This stage, *glycolysis,* takes place in the cell's cytoplasm (the blue area in **figure 7.3**). Importantly, it is anaerobic (that is, it does not require oxygen). This ancient energy-extracting process is thought to have evolved over 2 billion years ago, when there was no oxygen in the earth's atmosphere.

The second stage is aerobic (requires oxygen) and takes place within the mitochondrion (the tan sausage-shaped structure in **figure 7.3**). The focal point of this stage is the *Krebs cycle,* a cycle of chemical reactions that harvests electrons from C—H chemical bonds and passes the energy-rich electrons to carrier molecules, NADH and $FADH_2$. These molecules deliver the electrons to an electron transport chain, which uses their energy to power the production of ATP. The harvesting of electrons, a form of *oxidation*, is far more powerful than glycolysis at recovering energy from food molecules, and is how the bulk of the energy used by eukaryotic cells is extracted from food molecules.

Putting the Concept to Work

The Krebs cycle harvests electrons from what kind of chemical bond? Are the carbon atoms of the bond being oxidized or reduced?

Figure 7.3 An overview of cellular respiration.

Electrons harvested from C—H chemical bonds are first transferred to NADH and $FADH_2$; these then carry the electrons to the electron transport chain, as indicated by the long red arrow on the left. The energy-depleted electron is finally donated with a proton to oxygen, forming a molecule of water.

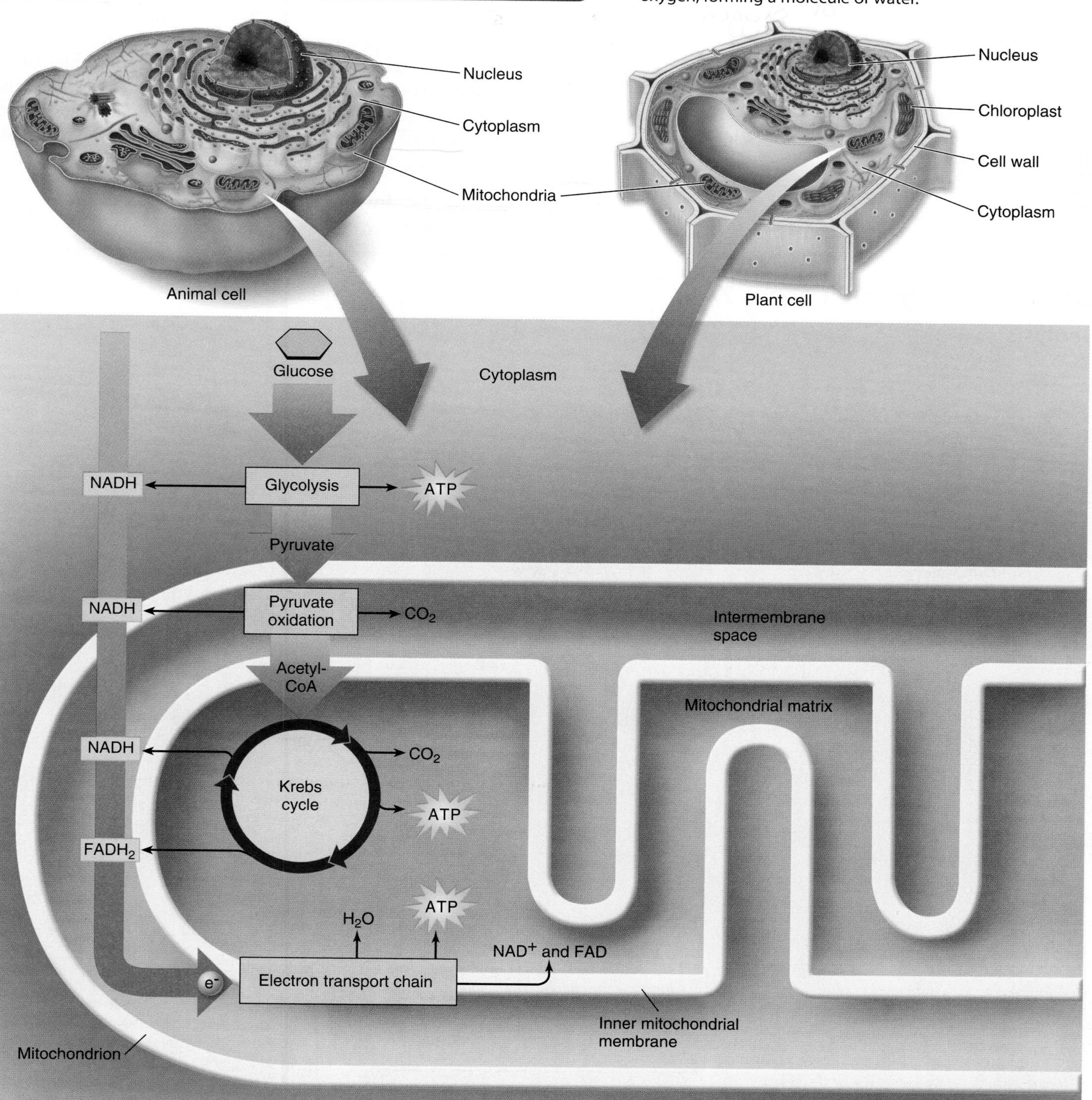

Respiration Without Oxygen: Glycolysis

7.2 Using Coupled Reactions to Make ATP

LEARNING OBJECTIVE 7.2.1 Define coupled reactions and explain how glycolysis uses them to produce ATP from glucose.

The first stage in cellular respiration is a series of 10 reactions called **glycolysis** (*Essential Biological Process 7A*) in which the six-carbon sugar glucose is cleaved into two three-carbon molecules of pyruvate. Where is the energy extracted? In each of two "coupled" reactions, the breaking of a chemical bond releases enough energy to drive the formation of an ATP molecule from ADP (an endergonic reaction). This transfer of a high-energy phosphate group from a substrate to ADP is called **substrate-level phosphorylation.** In the absence of oxygen, this is the only way organisms can get energy from food.

Putting the Concept to Work

How many ATPs are made from glucose in the absence of oxygen?

Essential Biological Process 7A

Glycolysis

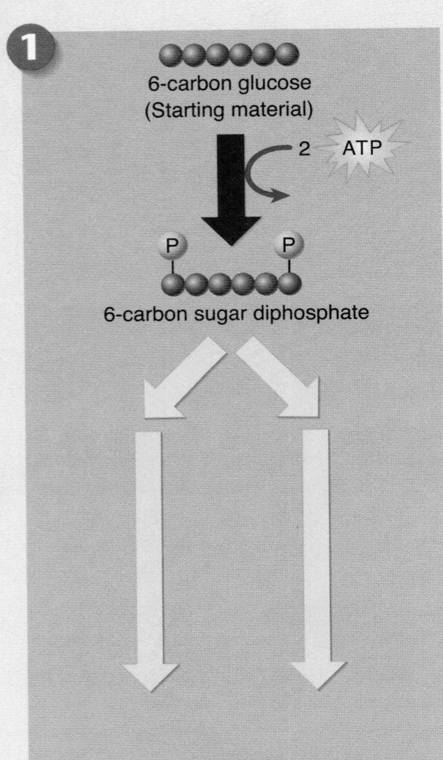

Priming reactions. Glycolysis begins with the addition of energy. Two high-energy phosphates from two molecules of ATP are added to the six-carbon molecule glucose, producing a six-carbon molecule with two phosphates.

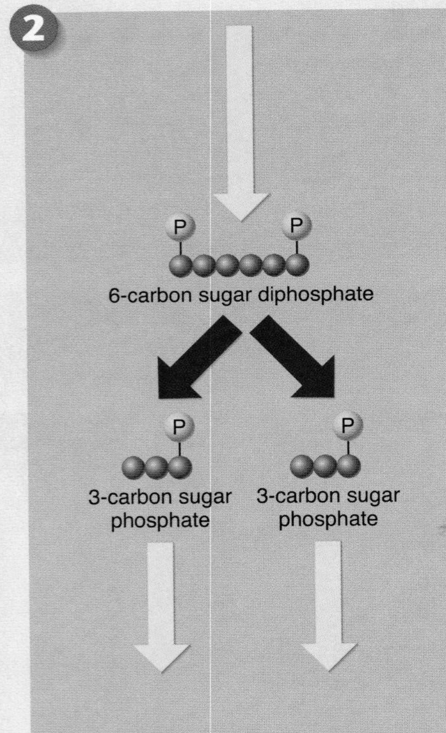

Cleavage reactions. Then, the phosphorylated six-carbon molecule is split in two, forming two three-carbon sugar phosphates.

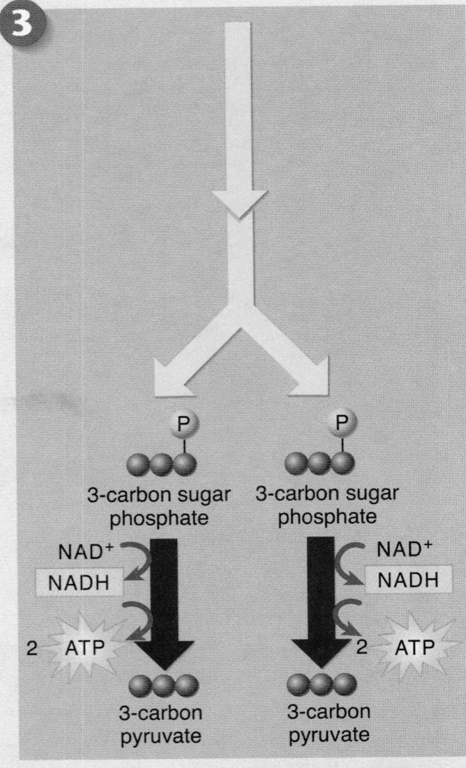

Energy-harvesting reactions. Finally, in a series of reactions, each of the two three-carbon sugar phosphates is converted to pyruvate. In the process, an energy-rich hydrogen is harvested as NADH, and two ATP molecules are formed for each pyruvate.

Respiration with Oxygen: The Krebs Cycle

7.3 Harvesting Electrons from Chemical Bonds

LEARNING OBJECTIVE 7.3.1 Name and describe the enzyme that removes CO_2 from pyruvate.

The first step of oxidative respiration in the mitochondrion is the oxidation of the three-carbon molecule called pyruvate, which is the end product of glycolysis. The cell harvests electrons from pyruvate in two steps: first, by oxidizing pyruvate to form acetyl-CoA, and then by oxidizing acetyl-CoA in the Krebs cycle.

Step One: Producing Acetyl-CoA

Pyruvate is oxidized in a single reaction that cleaves off one of pyruvate's three carbons. Pyruvate dehydrogenase, the complex of enzymes that removes CO_2 from pyruvate, is one of the largest enzymes known. It contains 60 subunits! In the course of the reaction, a hydrogen and electrons are removed from pyruvate and donated to NAD^+ to form NADH. *Essential Biological Process 7B* shows how an enzyme catalyzes this redox reaction. As with all redox reactions, the oxidation and reduction reactions are coupled—pyruvate is oxidized when an electron (with its energy) is transferred along with a hydrogen atom to NAD^+, reducing it to NADH. Now focus on figure 7.4. The two-carbon fragment (called an acetyl group) that remains after removing CO_2 from pyruvate is joined to a cofactor called coenzyme A (CoA) by pyruvate dehydrogenase, forming a compound known as **acetyl-CoA.** If the cell has a plentiful supply of ATP, acetyl-CoA is funneled into fat synthesis, with its energetic electrons preserved for later needs. If the cell needs ATP, the fragment is directed instead into the Krebs cycle.

Carbon dioxide, a by-product of cellular respiration, is released from organisms as waste. As you will see on page 508, vertebrates expel this waste as carbon dioxide gas from the lungs.

Putting the Concept to Work

Does the oxidation of pyruvate harvest any energy? If so, how?

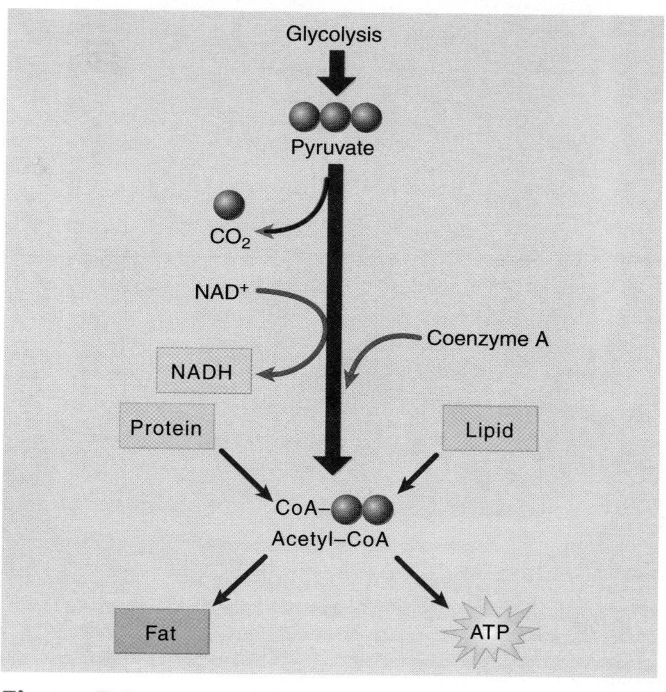

Figure 7.4 Producing acetyl-CoA.

Pyruvate, the three-carbon product of glycolysis, is oxidized to the two-carbon molecule acetyl-CoA, and in the process loses one carbon atom as CO_2 and an electron (donated to NAD^+ to form NADH). Almost all the molecules you use as foodstuffs are converted to acetyl-CoA; the acetyl-CoA is then channeled into fat synthesis or into ATP production, depending on your body's needs.

IMPLICATION FOR YOU What do you think might determine how much of your acetyl-CoA is channeled into fat?

Essential Biological Process 7B

Transferring Hydrogen Atoms

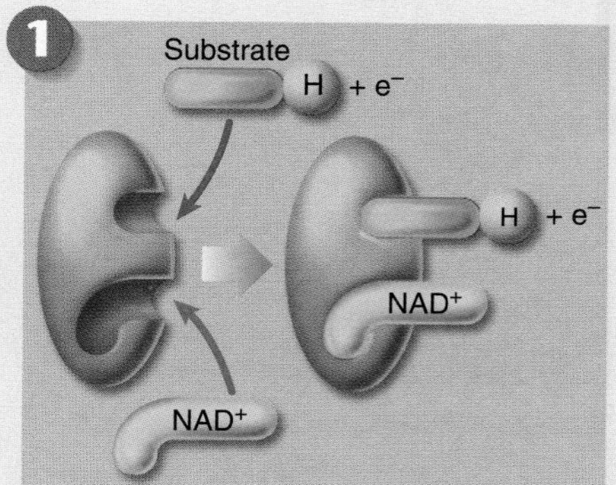

Enzymes that harvest hydrogen atoms have a binding site for NAD^+ located near the substrate binding site.

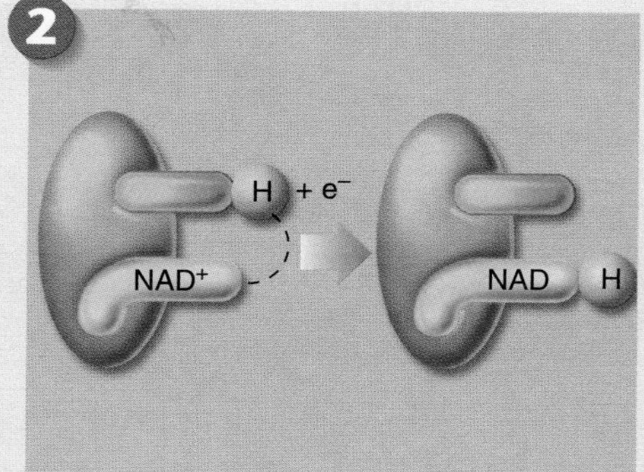

In an oxidation-reduction reaction, the hydrogen atom and an electron are transferred to NAD^+, forming NADH.

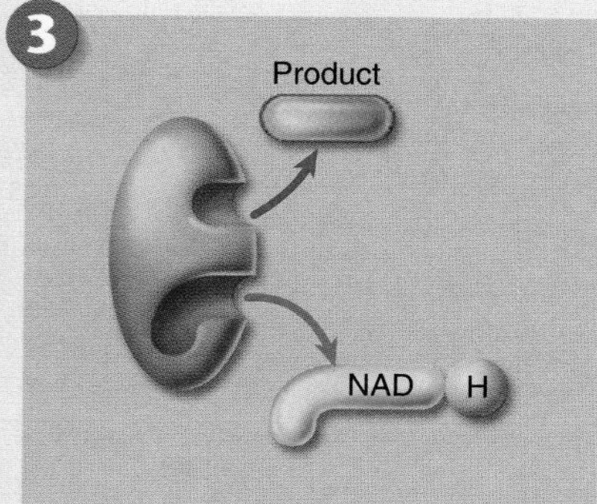

NADH then diffuses away and is available to donate the hydrogen to other molecules.

Figure 7.5 Putting food to work.

This chipmunk has a cheek full of acorns. Recently part of an oak tree, the acorns are soon destined to become part of this chipmunk's life. Climbing trees, chewing on acorns, seeing and smelling and hearing its surroundings, thinking the thoughts that chipmunks think—all are powered by ATP made from its food.

Step Two: The Krebs Cycle

LEARNING OBJECTIVE 7.3.2 Identify the overall substrates for the nine-reaction Krebs cycle, and the overall products.

The next stage in oxidative respiration is called the **Krebs cycle,** named after the man who discovered it. The Krebs cycle takes place within the mitochondrion.

Stage 1. The cycle starts when the two-carbon acetyl-CoA fragment produced from pyruvate is stuck onto a four-carbon sugar, producing a six-carbon molecule (*Essential Biological Process 7C*).

Stage 2. Then, in rapid-fire order, two carbons are removed as CO_2, their electrons donated to NAD^+, and a four-carbon molecule is left. A molecule of ATP is also produced.

Stage 3. When it is all over, two carbon atoms have been expelled as CO_2, more energetic electrons are extracted and taken away as NADH or $FADH_2$, and we are left with the same four-carbon sugar we started with.

The process is a cycle—a circle of nine reactions. In each turn of the cycle, a new acetyl group replaces the two CO_2 molecules lost, and more electrons are extracted. In the process of cellular respiration, glucose is entirely consumed. All that is left to mark the passing of the glucose molecule into six CO_2 molecules is its energy (figure 7.5), preserved in four ATP molecules (two from glycolysis and two from the Krebs cycle) and electrons carried by 10 NADH and two $FADH_2$ carriers.

Putting the Concept to Work

Why can't the Krebs cycle function in the absence of oxygen?

Essential Biological Process 7C

The Krebs Cycle

1

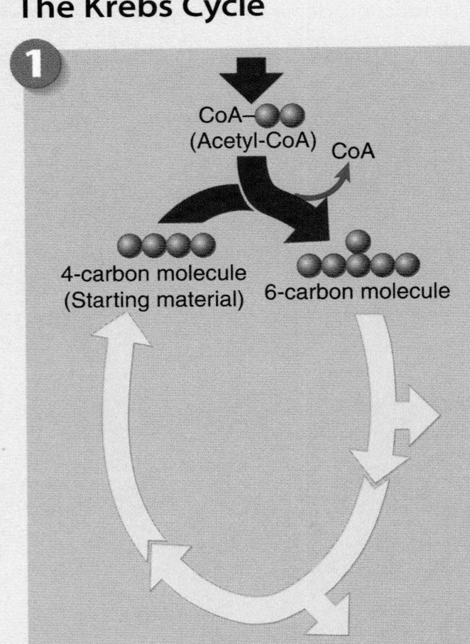

The Krebs cycle begins when a two-carbon fragment is transferred from acetyl-CoA to a four-carbon molecule (the starting material).

2

6-carbon molecule

NADH

CO_2

4-carbon molecule

5-carbon molecule

NADH

ATP

CO_2

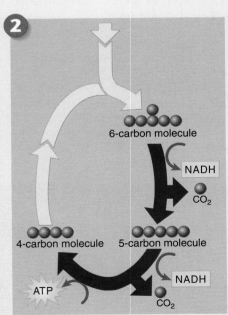

Then, the resulting six-carbon molecule is oxidized (a hydrogen removed to form NADH) and decarboxylated (a carbon removed to form CO_2). Next, the five-carbon molecule is oxidized and decarboxylated again, and a coupled reaction generates ATP.

3

4-carbon molecule (Starting material)

NADH

$FADH_2$

4-carbon molecule

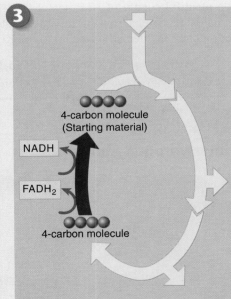

Finally, the resulting four-carbon molecule is further oxidized (hydrogens removed to form $FADH_2$ and NADH). This regenerates the four-carbon starting material, completing the cycle.

A Closer Look

Metabolic Efficiency and the Length of Food Chains

In the earth's ecosystems, the organisms that carry out photosynthesis are often consumed as food by other organisms. We call these "organism-eaters" *heterotrophs.* Humans are heterotrophs, as no human photosynthesizes.

It is thought that the first heterotrophs were ancient bacteria living in a world where photosynthesis had not yet introduced much oxygen into the oceans or atmosphere. The only mechanism they possessed to harvest chemical energy from their food was glycolysis. Neither oxygen-generating photosynthesis nor the oxidative stage of cellular respiration had evolved yet. It has been estimated that a heterotroph limited to glycolysis, as these ancient bacteria were, captures only 3.5% of the energy in the food it consumes. Hence, if such a heterotroph preserves 3.5% of the energy in the photosynthesizers it consumes, then any other heterotrophs that consume the first heterotroph will capture through glycolysis 3.5% of the energy in it, or 0.12% of the energy available in the original photosynthetic organisms. A very large base of photosynthesizers would thus be needed to support a small number of heterotrophs.

When organisms became able to extract energy from organic molecules by oxidative cellular respiration, which we discuss on the next page, this constraint became far less severe, because the efficiency of oxidative respiration is estimated to be about 32%. This increased efficiency results in the transmission of much more energy from one trophic level to another than does glycolysis. (A *trophic level* is a step in the movement of energy through an ecosystem.) The efficiency of oxidative cellular respiration has made possible the evolution of food chains, in which photosynthesizers are consumed by heterotrophs, which are consumed by other heterotrophs, and so on. You will read more about food chains in chapter 20.

Even with this very efficient oxidative metabolism, approximately two-thirds of the available energy is lost at each trophic level, and that puts a limit on how long a food chain can be. Most food chains, like the East African grassland ecosystem illustrated here, involve only three or rarely four trophic levels. Too much energy is lost at each transfer to allow chains to be much longer than that. For example, it would be impossible for a large human population to subsist by eating lions captured from the grasslands of East Africa; the amount of grass available there would not support enough zebras and other herbivores to maintain the number of lions needed to feed the human population. Thus, the ecological complexity of our world is fixed in a fundamental way by the chemistry of oxidative cellular respiration.

Photosynthesizers. The grass under this yellow fever tree grows actively during the hot, rainy season, capturing the energy of the sun and storing it in molecules of glucose, which are then converted into starch and stored in the grass.

Herbivores. These zebras consume the grass and transfer some of its stored energy into their own bodies.

Carnivores. The lion feeds on zebras and other animals, capturing part of their stored energy and storing it in its own body.

Scavengers. This hyena and the vultures occupy the same stage in the food chain as the lion. They also consume the body of the dead zebra, after it has been abandoned by the lion.

Refuse utilizers. These butterflies, mostly *Precis octavia,* are feeding on the material left in the hyena's dung after the food the hyena consumed had passed through its digestive tract.

A food chain in the savannas, or open grasslands, of East Africa.

At each of these levels in the food chain, only about a third or less of the energy present is used by the recipient.

7.4 Using the Electrons to Make ATP

Moving Electrons Through the Electron Transport Chain

LEARNING OBJECTIVE 7.4.1 Describe the components of the electron transport chain.

In eukaryotes, aerobic respiration takes place within the mitochondria present in virtually all cells. The internal compartment, or **matrix,** of a mitochondrion contains the enzymes that carry out the reactions of the Krebs cycle. As described earlier, the electrons harvested by oxidative respiration are passed along the electron transport chain, and the energy they release transports protons out of the matrix and into the **intermembrane space.**

The NADH and $FADH_2$ molecules formed during the first stages of aerobic respiration each contain electrons and hydrogens that were gained when NAD^+ and FAD were reduced (refer back to figure 7.3). The NADH and $FADH_2$ molecules carry their electrons to the inner mitochondrial membrane (an enlarged area of the membrane is shown below), where they transfer the electrons to a series of membrane-associated molecules collectively called the **electron transport chain.** The electron transport chain works much like the electron transport system you encountered in studying photosynthesis.

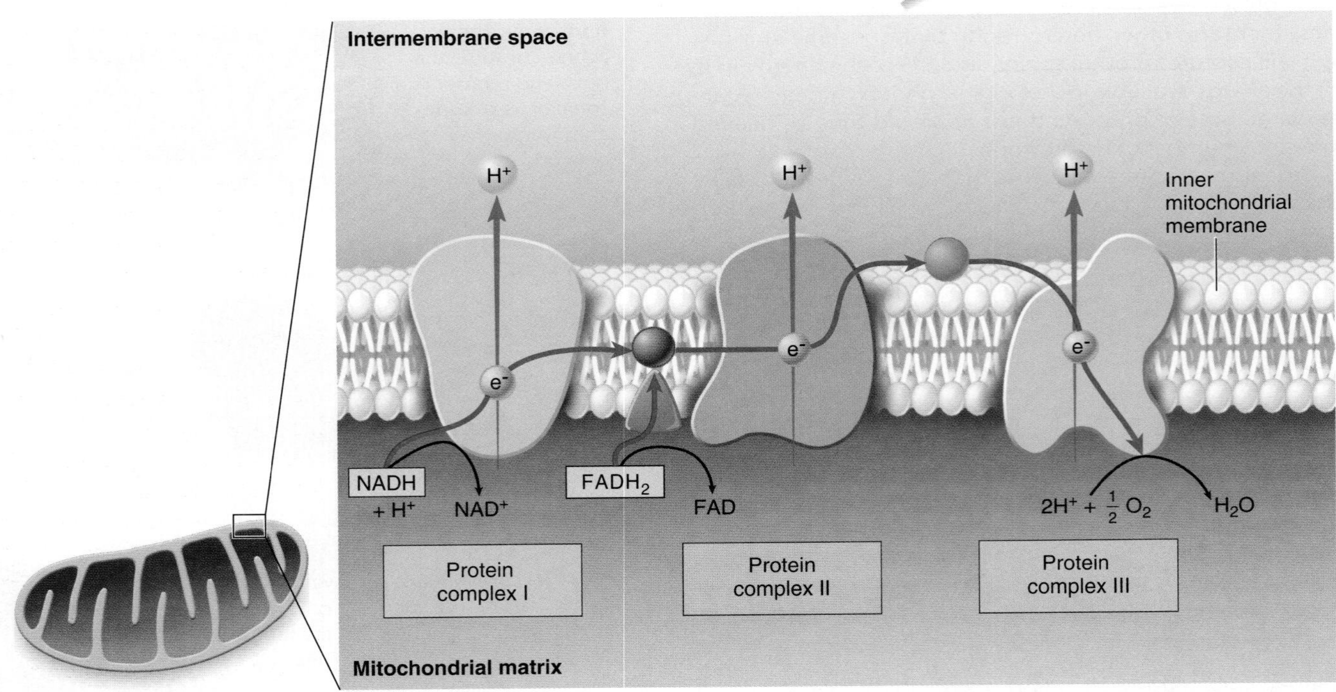

A protein complex (the light pink structure above) receives the electrons and, using a mobile carrier, passes these electrons to a second protein complex (the purple structure). This protein complex, along with others in the chain, operates as a proton pump, using the energy of the electrons to drive a proton out across the membrane into the intermembrane space. The arrows indicate the transport of the protons into the top half of the figure, which represents the intermembrane space. The electron is then shuttled by another carrier to a third protein complex (the light blue structure). This complex uses electrons such as this one to link oxygen atoms with hydrogen ions to form molecules of water. It is the availability of a plentiful supply of electron acceptor molecules like oxygen that makes oxidative respiration possible.

The electron transport chain used in aerobic respiration is similar to, and may well have evolved from, the electron transport system employed in photosynthesis. Photosynthesis is thought to have preceded cellular respiration in the evolution of biochemical pathways, generating the oxygen that is necessary as the electron acceptor in cellular respiration. Natural selection didn't start from scratch and design a new biochemical pathway for cellular respiration; instead, it built on the photosynthetic pathway that already existed, which uses many of the same reactions.

Putting the Concept to Work

What does NADH do that $FADH_2$ cannot? Why can't $FADH_2$ do this?

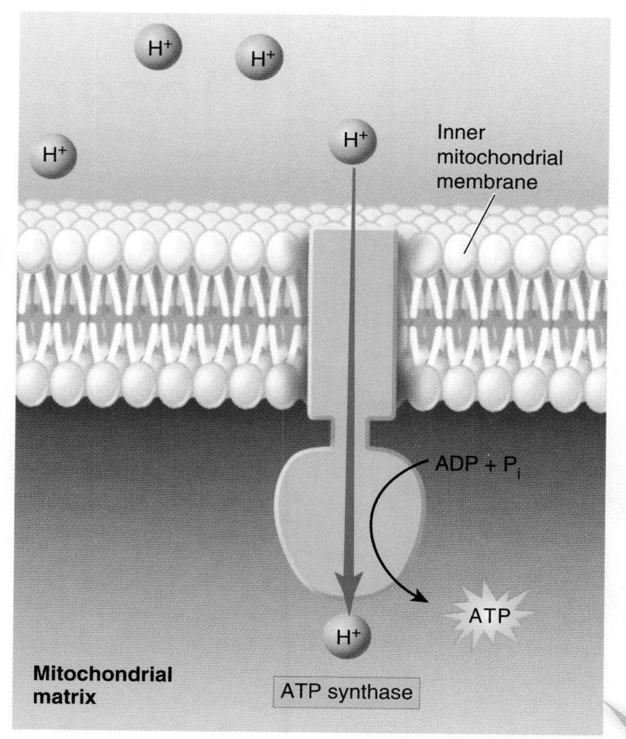

Producing ATP: Chemiosmosis

LEARNING OBJECTIVE 7.4.2 Calculate how many ATP molecules a cell can harvest from a glucose molecule in the presence of oxygen and in its absence.

As the proton concentration in the intermembrane space rises above that in the matrix, the concentration gradient induces the protons to reenter the matrix by diffusion through a special proton channel called **ATP synthase.** ATP synthase channels are embedded in the inner mitochondrial membrane, as shown in the illustration. As the protons pass through, these channels synthesize ATP from ADP and P_i within the matrix. The ATP is then transported by facilitated diffusion out of the mitochondrion and into the cell's cytoplasm. This ATP synthesizing process is the same chemiosmosis process that you encountered in studying photosynthesis in chapter 6.

Although we have discussed electron transport and chemiosmosis as separate processes, in a cell they are integrated as shown below, left. The electron transport chain uses two electrons harvested in glycolysis, two harvested in pyruvate oxidation, and eight harvested in aerobic respiration (red arrows) to pump a large number of protons out across the inner mitochondrial membrane (shown in the upper right of the panel below). Their subsequent reentry back into the mitochondrial matrix drives the synthesis of 34 ATP molecules by chemiosmosis (shown in the lower right). Two additional ATPs were harvested by a coupled reaction in glycolysis, and two more in the Krebs cycle. As two ATPs must be expended to transport NADH into the mitochondria by active transport, the grand total of ATPs harvested is thus 36 molecules.

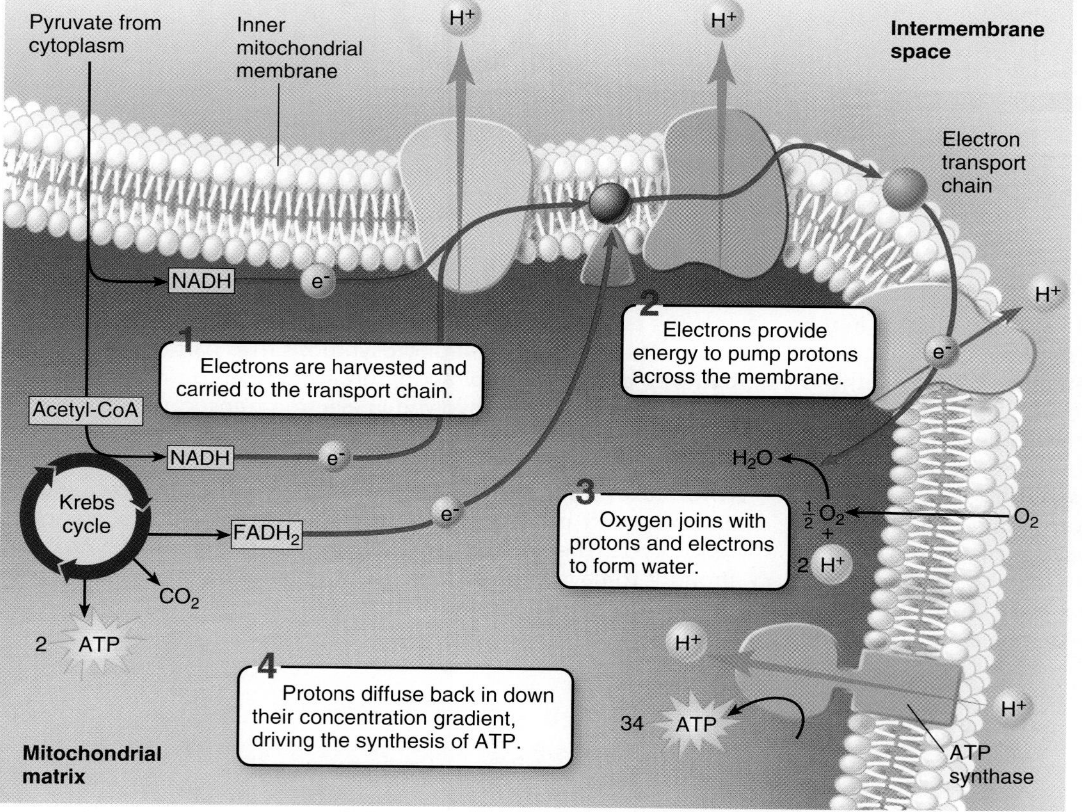

Putting the Concept to Work

If the electron transport chain uses the energy harvested from C–H bonds to drive protons out of the matrix, how is it that the ATP molecules formed as a consequence are *within* the matrix?

A Closer Look

The Redox Cycle

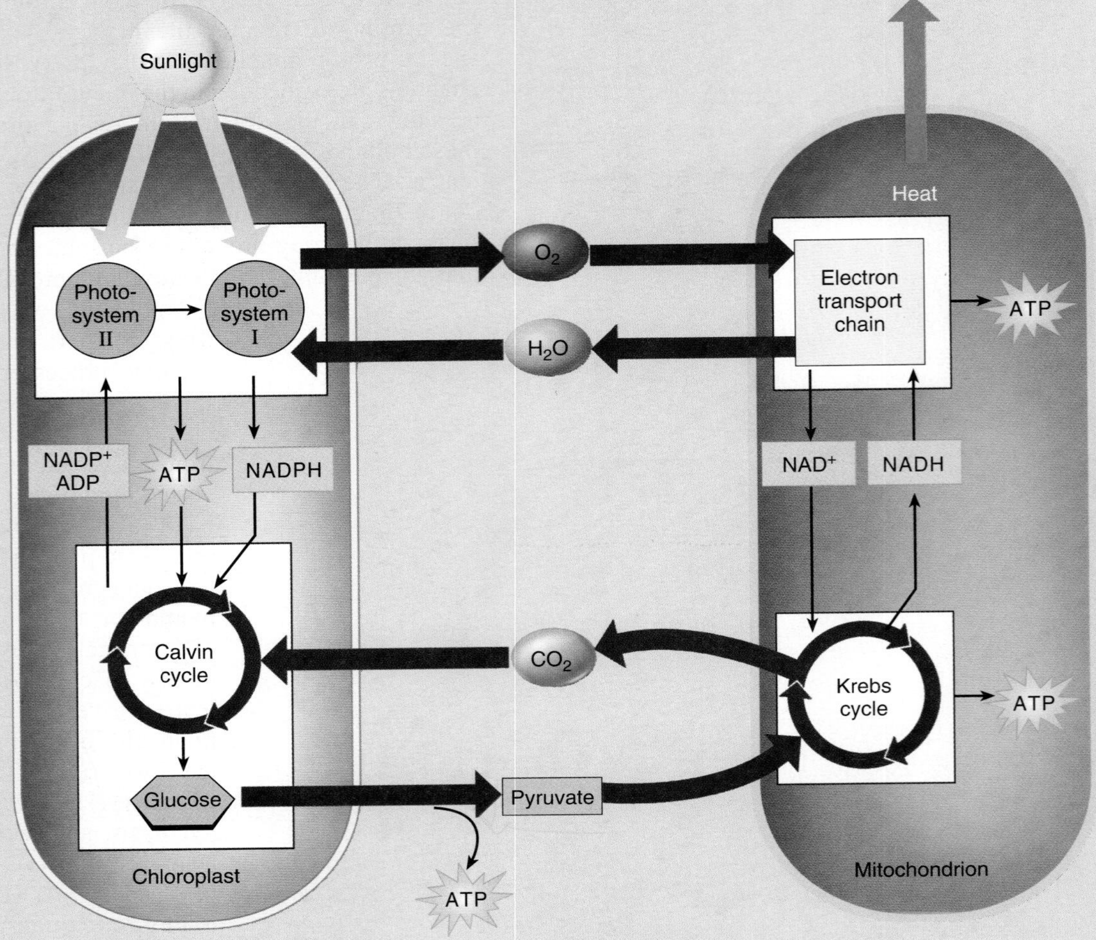

The energy-capturing metabolism of the chloroplasts studied in the previous chapter and the energy-utilizing metabolism of the mitochondria studied in this chapter are intimately related. Photosynthesis carried out by chloroplasts uses the products of cellular respiration as starting substrates and reduces carbon by adding hydrogen atoms. Cellular respiration carried out by mitochondria uses the products of photosynthesis as its starting substrates and oxidizes carbon by removing hydrogen atoms. Together, photosynthesis and cellular respiration form an oxidation-reduction cycle, as diagrammed here. Note that it is electrons that cycle between chloroplasts and mitochondria. Energy passes through the redox cycle, flowing into the cycle from the sun, passing through newly assembled molecules, and eventually flowing out of the cycle as heat.

The evolutionary history of the redox cycle can be seen in its elements. The Calvin cycle of photosynthesis uses part of the glycolytic pathway of cellular respiration, run in reverse, to produce glucose. The principal proteins involved in electron transport in chloroplasts are related to those in mitochondria, and in many cases are actually the same. Biologists believe the glycolysis stage of cellular respiration, which takes place in the cytoplasm, converting glucose to pyruvate and requiring no oxygen, to be the most ancient process in the redox cycle. The chloroplast's oxygen-generating photosynthesis is thought to have evolved next, followed later by the oxidative reactions of the mitochondria's cellular respiration.

Harvesting Electrons Without Oxygen: Fermentation

7.5 Cells Can Metabolize Food Without Oxygen

LEARNING OBJECTIVE 7.5.1 Define fermentation, and distinguish between ethanol fermentation and lactic acid fermentation.

Fermentation

In the absence of oxygen, aerobic metabolism (the Krebs cycle and electron transport chain) cannot occur, and cells must rely exclusively on glycolysis to produce ATP. Under these conditions, the hydrogen atoms and electrons that were involved in the oxidation of NAD^+ to NADH in glycolysis are donated to organic molecules instead of the electron transport chain, in a process called **fermentation.** Fermentation recycles NAD^+ so that glycolysis can continue.

Ethanol Fermentation. Bacteria carry out more than a dozen kinds of fermentations, all using some form of organic molecule to accept the hydrogen atom from NADH. By contrast, eukaryotic cells are capable of only a few types of fermentation. In one type, which occurs in single-celled fungi called yeast, the molecule that accepts hydrogen from NADH is derived from pyruvate, the end product of glycolysis itself. Yeast enzymes remove a CO_2 group from pyruvate through decarboxylation, producing a two-carbon molecule called acetaldehyde. The CO_2 released causes bread made with yeast to rise, while bread made without yeast (unleavened bread) does not. The acetaldehyde accepts a hydrogen atom from NADH, producing NAD^+ and ethanol (**figure 7.6**, *upper panel*). This particular type of fermentation is of great interest to humans, because it is the source of the ethanol in wine and beer. Ethanol is a by-product of fermentation that is actually toxic to yeast; as it approaches a concentration of about 12%, it begins to kill the yeast. That is why naturally fermented wine contains only about 12% ethanol.

Humans have been using yeast for thousands of years to produce bread and alcohol, but yeast has many other commercial uses. The manufacturing potential of yeast will be discussed in more detail on page 319.

Lactic Acid Fermentation. Most animal cells regenerate NAD^+ by a second type of fermentation, using an enzyme called lactate dehydrogenase to transfer a hydrogen atom from NADH back to the pyruvate that is produced by glycolysis. This reaction converts pyruvate into lactic acid and regenerates NAD^+ from NADH (**figure 7.6**, *lower panel*). It therefore closes the metabolic circle, allowing glycolysis to continue as long as glucose is available. Circulating blood removes excess lactate (the ionized form of lactic acid) from muscles. It was once thought that during strenuous exercise, when the removal of lactic acid cannot keep pace with its production, the accumulation induces muscle fatigue. However, scientists now believe that lactic acid is actually used by muscles as another source of fuel.

Putting the Concept to Work

What would happen to glycolysis if NAD^+ wasn't recycled?

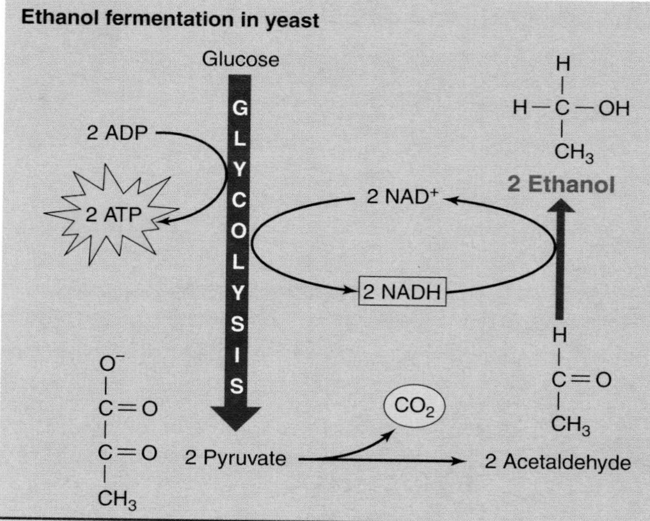

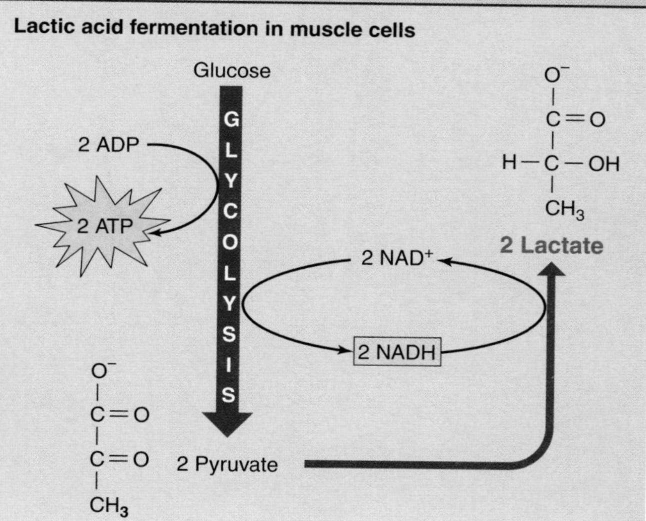

Figure 7.6 Fermentation.

Yeasts carry out the conversion of pyruvate to ethanol. Muscle cells convert pyruvate into lactate, which is less toxic than ethanol. In both cases, NAD^+ is regenerated to allow glycolysis to continue.

IMPLICATION FOR YOU Despite our best intentions, once in a while most of us consume a little more alcohol than we should and wake up the next morning with a "hangover"—a pounding headache, nausea, shakiness, and often a very dry mouth. Many of these symptoms are those of dehydration. What sort of hangover prevention does this "dehydration" hypothesis suggest?

Other Sources of Energy

7.6 Glucose Is Not the Only Food Molecule

LEARNING OBJECTIVE 7.6.1 Describe how cells garner energy from proteins and from fats.

We have considered in detail the fate of a molecule of glucose, a simple sugar, in cellular respiration. But how much of what you eat is sugar? As a more realistic example of the food you eat, consider the fate of a fast-food hamburger. The hamburger is composed primarily of carbohydrates, fats, and proteins. This diverse collection of complex molecules is broken down by the process of digestion in your stomach and intestines into simpler molecules. Carbohydrates are broken down into simple sugars, fats into fatty acids, and proteins into amino acids. Nucleic acids are also present in the food you eat, but these macromolecules store little energy that the body actually uses.

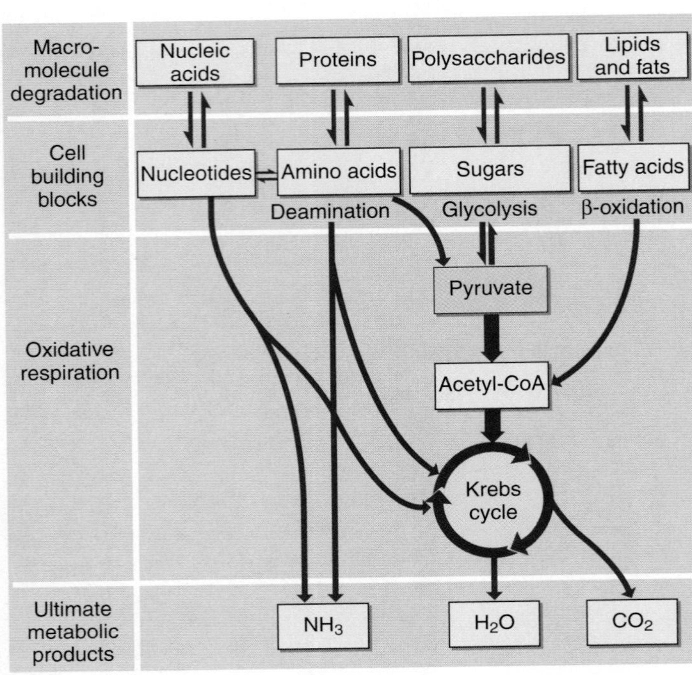

Figure 7.7 How cells obtain energy from foods.

Most organisms extract energy from organic molecules by oxidizing them. The first stage of this process, breaking down macromolecules into their subunits, yields little energy. The second stage, cellular respiration, extracts energy, primarily in the form of high-energy electrons. The subunit of many carbohydrates, glucose, readily enters glycolysis and passes through the biochemical pathways of oxidative respiration. However, the subunits of other macromolecules must be converted into products that can enter the biochemical pathways found in oxidative respiration.

IMPLICATION FOR YOU Many fad diets assert that weight loss will result from a high-protein, low-carb diet such as the ones discussed on the facing page. Have you ever tried this sort of diet? Did you lose weight? For how long?

Cellular Respiration of Protein

Proteins (the second category in **figure 7.7**) are first broken down into their individual amino acids. A series of *deamination* reactions removes the nitrogen side groups (called amino groups) and converts the rest of the amino acid into a molecule that takes part in the Krebs cycle. For example, alanine is converted into pyruvate, glutamate into α-ketoglutarate, and aspartate into oxaloacetate. The reactions of the Krebs cycle then extract the high-energy electrons from these molecules and put them to work making ATP.

Cellular Respiration of Fat

Lipids and fats (the fourth category in **figure 7.7**) are first broken down into fatty acids. A fatty acid typically has a long tail of sixteen or more $—CH_2$ links, and the many C—H bonds in these long tails provide a rich harvest of energy. Enzymes in the matrix of the mitochondrion first remove one two-carbon acetyl group from the end of a fatty acid tail, and then another, and then another, in effect chewing down the length of the tail in two-carbon bites. Eventually the entire fatty acid tail is converted into acetyl groups. Each acetyl group then combines with coenzyme A to form acetyl-CoA, which feeds into the Krebs cycle. This process is known as *β-oxidation.*

Recall from the discussion of lipids on page 60 that fats are composed of a three-carbon glycerol backbone attached to three fatty acid tails. The breakdown of fats, as described here, occurs with the removal of two carbons at a time from the fatty acid tails.

Putting the Concept to Work

What part of a hamburger would yield energy in the absence of oxygen?

Fad Diets and Impossible Dreams

Most Americans put on weight in middle age, slowly adding 30 or more pounds. They did not ask for that weight, do not want it, and are constantly looking for a way to get rid of it. It is not a lonely search—it seems like everyone past the flush of youth is trying to lose weight. Many have been seduced by fad diets, investing hope only to harvest frustration. The much discussed Atkins' diet is the fad diet most have tried—*Dr. Atkins' Diet Revolution* is one of the 10 best-selling books in history, prominently displayed in bookstores. The reason this diet doesn't deliver on its promise of pain-free weight loss is well understood by science, but not by the general public. Only hope and hype make it a perpetual best seller.

The secret of the Atkins' diet, stated simply, is to avoid carbohydrates. Atkins' basic proposition is that your body, if it does not detect blood glucose (from metabolizing carbohydrates), will think it is starving and start to burn body fat, even if there is lots of fat already circulating in your bloodstream. You may eat all the fat and protein you want, all the steak and eggs and butter and cheese, and you will still burn fat and lose weight—just don't eat any carbohydrates, any bread or pasta or potatoes or fruit or candy. Despite the title of Atkins' book, this diet is hardly revolutionary. A basic low-carbohydrate diet was first promoted over a century ago in the 1860s by William Banting, an English casket maker, in his best-selling book *Letter on Corpulence*. Books promoting low-carbohydrate diets have continued to be best sellers ever since.

Those who try the Atkins' diet often lose 10 pounds in two to three weeks. In three months it is all back, and then some. So what happened? Where did the pounds go, and why did they come back? The temporary weight loss turns out to have a simple explanation. Carbohydrates act as water sponges in your body, and so forcing your body to become depleted of carbohydrates causes your body to lose water. The 10 pounds lost on this diet was not fat weight but water weight, quickly regained with the first starchy foods eaten.

The Atkins' diet is the sort of diet the American Heart Association tells us to avoid (all those saturated fats and cholesterol), and it is difficult to stay on. If you do hang in there, you will lose weight, simply because you eat less. Other popular diets these days, *The Zone* diet of Dr. Barry Sears and *The South Beach Diet* of Dr. Arthur Agatston, are also low-carbohydrate diets, although not as extreme as the Atkins' diet. Like the Atkins' diet, they work not for the bizarre reasons claimed by their promoters, but simply because they are low-calorie diets.

There are two basic laws that no diet can successfully violate:

1. All calories are equal.
2. (calories in) – (calories out) = fat.

The fundamental fallacy of the Atkins' diet, the Zone diet, the South Beach diet, and indeed of all fad diets, is the idea that somehow carbohydrate calories are different from fat and protein calories. This is scientific foolishness. Every calorie you eat contributes equally to your eventual weight, whether it comes from carbohydrate, fat, or protein.

To the extent these diets work at all, they do so because they obey the second law. By reducing calories in, they reduce fat. If that were all there was to it, we should all go out and buy a diet book. Unfortunately, losing weight isn't that simple, as anyone who has seriously tried already knows. The problem is that your body will not cooperate.

If you try to lose weight by exercising and eating less, your body will attempt to compensate by metabolizing more efficiently. It has a fixed weight, what obesity researchers call a "set point," a weight to which it will keep trying to return. A few years ago, a group of researchers at Rockefeller University in New York, in a landmark study, found that if you lose weight, your metabolism slows down and becomes more efficient, burning fewer calories to do the same work—your body will do everything it can to gain the weight back! Similarly, if you gain weight, your metabolism speeds up. In this way your body uses its own natural weight control system to keep your weight at its set point. No wonder it's so hard to lose weight!

Clearly our bodies don't keep us at one weight all our adult lives. It turns out your body adjusts its fat thermostat—its set point—depending on your age, food intake, and amount of physical activity. Adjustments are slow, however, and it seems to be a great deal easier to move the body's set point up than to move it down. Apparently higher levels of fat reduce the body's sensitivity to the leptin hormone that governs how efficiently we burn fat. That is why you can gain weight, despite your set point resisting the gain—your body still issues leptin alarm calls to speed metabolism, but your brain doesn't respond with as much sensitivity as it used to. Thus the fatter you get, the less effective your weight control system becomes.

This doesn't mean that we should give up and learn to love our fat. Rather, now that we are beginning to understand the biology of weight gain, we must accept the hard fact that we cannot beat the requirements of the two diet laws. The real trick is not to give up. Eat less and exercise more, and keep at it. In one year, or two, or three, your body will readjust its set point to reflect the new reality you have imposed by constant struggle. There simply isn't any easy way to lose weight.

How Do Swimming Fish Avoid Low Blood pH?

Animals that live in oxygen-poor environments, like worms living in the oxygen-free mud at the bottom of lakes, are not able to obtain the energy required for muscle movement from the Krebs cycle. Their cells lack the oxygen needed to accept the electrons stripped from food molecules. Instead, these animals rely on glycolysis to obtain ATP, donating the electron to pyruvate, forming lactic acid. While much less efficient than the Krebs cycle, glycolysis does not require oxygen. Even when oxygen is plentiful, the muscles of an active animal may use up oxygen more quickly than it can be supplied by the bloodstream and so be forced to temporarily rely on glycolysis to generate the ATP for continued contraction.

This presents a particular problem for fish. Fish blood is much lower in carbon dioxide than yours is, and as a consequence, the amount of sodium bicarbonate acting as a buffer in fish blood is also quite low. Now imagine you are a trout, and need to suddenly swim very fast to catch a mayfly for dinner. The vigorous swimming will cause your muscles to release large amounts of lactic acid into your poorly buffered blood; this could severely disturb the blood's acid-base balance and so impede contraction of your swimming muscles before the prey is captured.

The graph to the right presents the results of an experiment designed to explore how a trout solves this dilemma. In the experiment, the trout was made to swim vigorously for 15 minutes in a laboratory tank, and then allowed a day's recovery. The lactic acid concentration in its blood was monitored periodically during swimming and recovery phases.

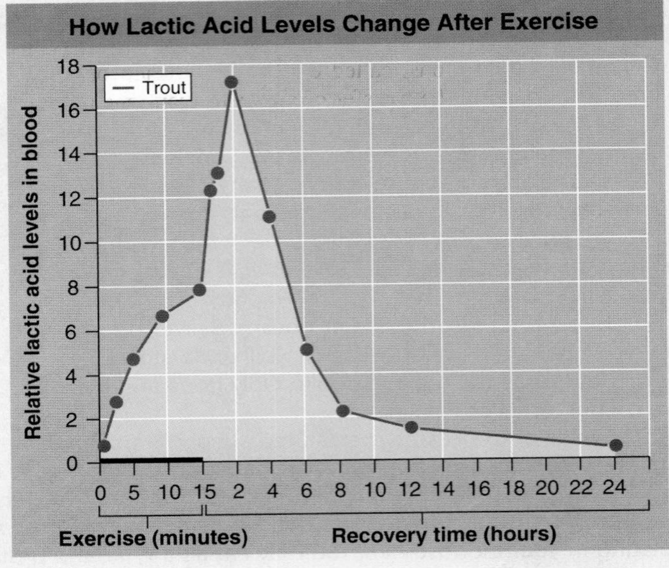

Analysis

1. **Applying Concepts** Lactic acid levels are presented for both swimming and recovery periods. In what time units are the swimming data presented? The recovery data?
2. **Interpreting Data** What is the effect of exercise on the level of lactic acid in the trout's blood? How does the level of lactic acid change after exercise stops?
3. **Making Inferences** About how much of the total lactic acid created by vigorous swimming is released after this exercise stops? [Hint: Notice that the *x* axis scale changes from minutes to hours.]
4. **Drawing Conclusions** Is this result consistent with the hypothesis that fish maintain blood pH levels by delaying the release of lactic acid from muscles? Why might this be beneficial to the fish?

Summary of Learning Outcomes

An Overview of Cellular Respiration

Where Is the Energy in Food?

7.1.1 Nonphotosynthetic organisms acquire energy from the breakdown of food, either by eating plants that store the food or by eating animals that have eaten plants. Energy stored in carbohydrate molecules is extracted through the process of cellular respiration and is stored in the cell as ATP.

- Coupled reactions, called oxidation-reduction or redox reactions, involve the transfer of electrons from one atom or molecule to another. The atom or molecule that loses an electron is said to be oxidized and loses energy. The atom or molecule that gains the electron is said to be reduced and gains energy.
- Cellular respiration is carried out in two stages: glycolysis occurring in the cytoplasm and oxidation occurring in the mitochondria.

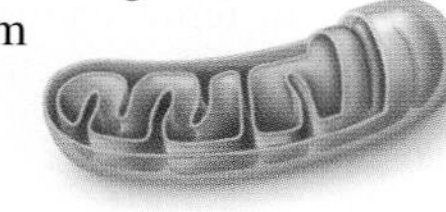

Respiration Without Oxygen: Glycolysis

Using Coupled Reactions to Make ATP

7.2.1 Glycolysis is an energy-extracting series of 10 chemical reactions that shuffle around the chemical bonds of glucose to produce two net molecules of ATP by substrate-level phosphorylation, as shown in *Essential Biological Process 7A*.

- Electrons extracted from glucose are donated to a carrier molecule, NAD^+, which becomes NADH. NADH carries electrons and hydrogen atoms to be used in a later stage of oxidative respiration.

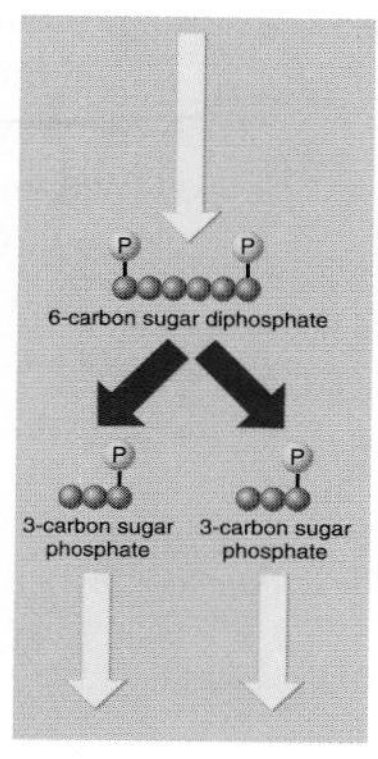

Respiration With Oxygen: The Krebs Cycle

Harvesting Electrons from Chemical Bonds

7.3.1 The two molecules of pyruvate formed in glycolysis are passed into the mitochondrion, where they are converted into two molecules of acetyl-coenzyme A. In the process, another molecule of NADH is formed. What the cell does with acetyl-CoA depends on the needs of the cell. If the cell has enough ATP, acetyl-CoA is used in synthesizing fat molecules. If the cell needs energy, acetyl-CoA is directed to the Krebs cycle.

- The formation of NADH is an enzyme-catalyzed reaction, as shown here from *Essential Biological Process 7B*. The enzyme brings the substrate and NAD^+ into close proximity. Through a redox reaction, a hydrogen atom and an electron are transferred to NAD^+, reducing it to NADH. NADH then carries the electrons and hydrogen to a later step in oxidative respiration.

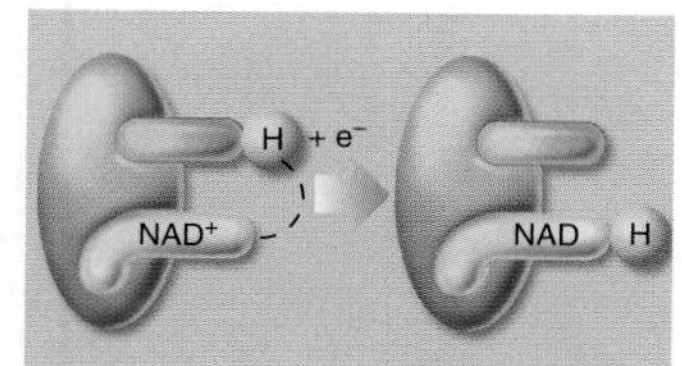

7.3.2 Acetyl-CoA enters a series of chemical reactions called the Krebs cycle, where one molecule of ATP is produced in a coupled reaction. Energy is also harvested in the form of electrons that are transferred to molecules of NAD^+ and FAD to produce NADH and $FADH_2$, respectively.

- The Krebs cycle makes two turns for every molecule of glucose that is oxidized.

Using the Electrons to Make ATP

7.4.1 The electrons harvested by oxidizing food molecules are used to power proton pumps that chemiosmotically drive the production of ATP. The molecules of NADH and $FADH_2$ that were produced during glycolysis and the Krebs cycle carry electrons to the inner mitochondrial membrane. Here they give up electrons to the electron transport chain. The electrons, along with their energy, are passed along the electron transport chain. The energy from the electrons drives proton pumps that pump H^+ across the inner membrane from the matrix to the intermembrane space, creating an H^+ concentration gradient.

- When the electrons reach the end of the electron transport chain, they bind with oxygen and hydrogen to form water molecules.

7.4.2 ATP is produced in the mitochondrion through chemiosmosis. The H^+ concentration gradient in the intermembrane space drives H^+ back across the membrane through ATP synthase channels, as shown here from **page 125**. The energy from the movement of H^+ through the channel is transferred to the chemical bonds in ATP.

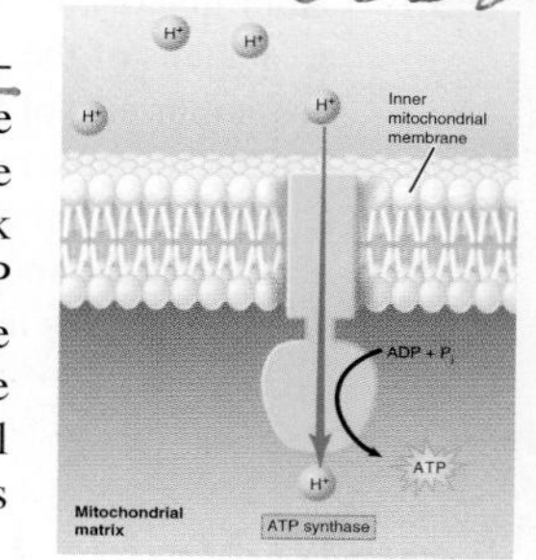

Harvesting Electrons Without Oxygen: Fermentation

Cells Can Metabolize Food Without Oxygen

7.5.1 In the absence of oxygen, other molecules can be used as electron acceptors. When the electron acceptor is an organic molecule, the process is called fermentation. Depending on what type of organic molecule accepts the electrons, either ethanol or lactic acid, in the form of lactate, is formed.

Other Sources of Energy

Glucose Is Not the Only Food Molecule

7.6.1 Food sources other than glucose are also used in oxidative respiration. Macromolecules, such as proteins, lipids, and nucleic acids, are broken down into intermediate products that feed into cellular respiration in different reaction steps, as shown here from **figure 7.7**.

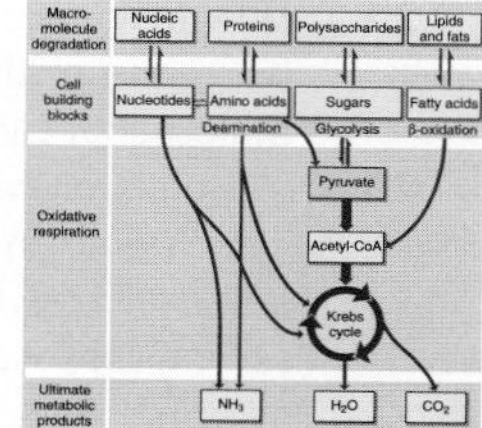

Test Your Understanding

7.1.1 In animals, the energy for life is obtained by cellular respiration. This involves
a. breaking down the organic molecules that were consumed.
b. capturing photons from plants.
c. obtaining ATP from plants.
d. breaking down CO_2 that was produced by plants.

7.2.1 During glycolysis, ATP forms by
a. the breakdown of pyruvate.
b. chemiosmosis.
c. substrate-level phosphorylation.
d. NAD^+.

7.2.1 Which of the following processes can occur in the absence of oxygen?
a. the Krebs cycle
b. glycolysis
c. chemiosmosis
d. All of the above

7.2.1 Every living creature on this planet is capable of carrying out the rather inefficient biochemical process of glycolysis, which
a. makes glucose, using the energy from ATP.
b. makes ATP by splitting a molecule of glucose in half and capturing the energy.
c. phosphorylates ATP to make ADP.
d. makes glucose, using oxygen and carbon dioxide and water.

7.3.1 After glycolysis, the pyruvate molecules go to the
a. nucleus of the cell and provide energy.
b. membranes of the cell and are broken down in the presence of CO_2 to make more ATP.
c. mitochondria of the cell and are broken down in the presence of O_2 to make more ATP.
d. Golgi bodies and are packaged and stored until needed.

7.3.2 The electrons generated from the Krebs cycle are transferred to ____________ which then carries them to ______________.
a. NAD^+, oxygen
b. NAD^+, the electron transport chain
c. NADH, oxygen
d. NADH, the electron transport chain

7.4.2 The vast majority of the ATP molecules produced within a cell are produced
a. during pyruvate oxidation.
b. during glycolysis.
c. during the Krebs cycle.
d. during the electron transport chain.

7.5.1 NAD^+ is recycled during
a. glycolysis.
b. fermentation.
c. the Krebs cycle.
d. the formation of acetyl-CoA.

7.5.1 The final electron acceptor in lactic acid fermentation is
a. pyruvate.
b. NAD^+.
c. lactic acid.
d. O_2.

7.6.1 Cells can extract energy from foodstuffs other than glucose because
a. proteins, fatty acids, and nucleic acids get converted to glucose and then enter oxidative respiration.
b. each type of macromolecule has its own oxidative respiration pathway.
c. each type of macromolecule is broken down into its subunits, which enter the oxidative respiration pathway.
d. they can all enter the glycolytic pathway.

Apply Your Understanding

7.4.2 Consider the structure of a mitochondrion, as shown here in a cutaway view. If you poke a hole in a mitochondrion, can it still perform oxidative respiration? Explain. Can fragments of a mitochondrion perform oxidative respiration? Explain.

7.6.1 Your friend wants to go on a low-carbohydrate diet so that he can lose some of the "baby fat" he's still carrying. He asks your advice; what do you tell him?

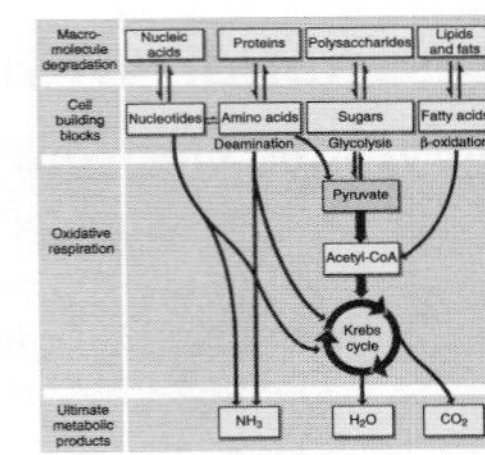

Synthesize What You Have Learned

7.3.1 How much less ATP would be generated in the cells of a person who consumed a diet of pyruvate instead of glucose (use one molecule of each for your calculation)?

7.4.1 The electron carrier cytochrome *c* is one of many different cytochrome proteins, but unlike the others, the amino acid sequence of cytochrome *c* is nearly identical in all species. Why do you suppose this is so? Among humans, no genetic disorder affecting cytochrome *c* has ever been reported. Why do you suppose this is so?

7.5.1 Soft drinks are artificially carbonated, which is what causes them to fizz. Beer and sparkling wines are naturally carbonated. How does this natural carbonation occur?

7.6.1 Which of the following food molecules would generate the most ATP molecules, assuming that glycolysis, the Krebs cycle, and the electron transport chain were all functioning and that the foods were consumed in equal amounts: carbohydrates, proteins, or fats? Explain your answer.

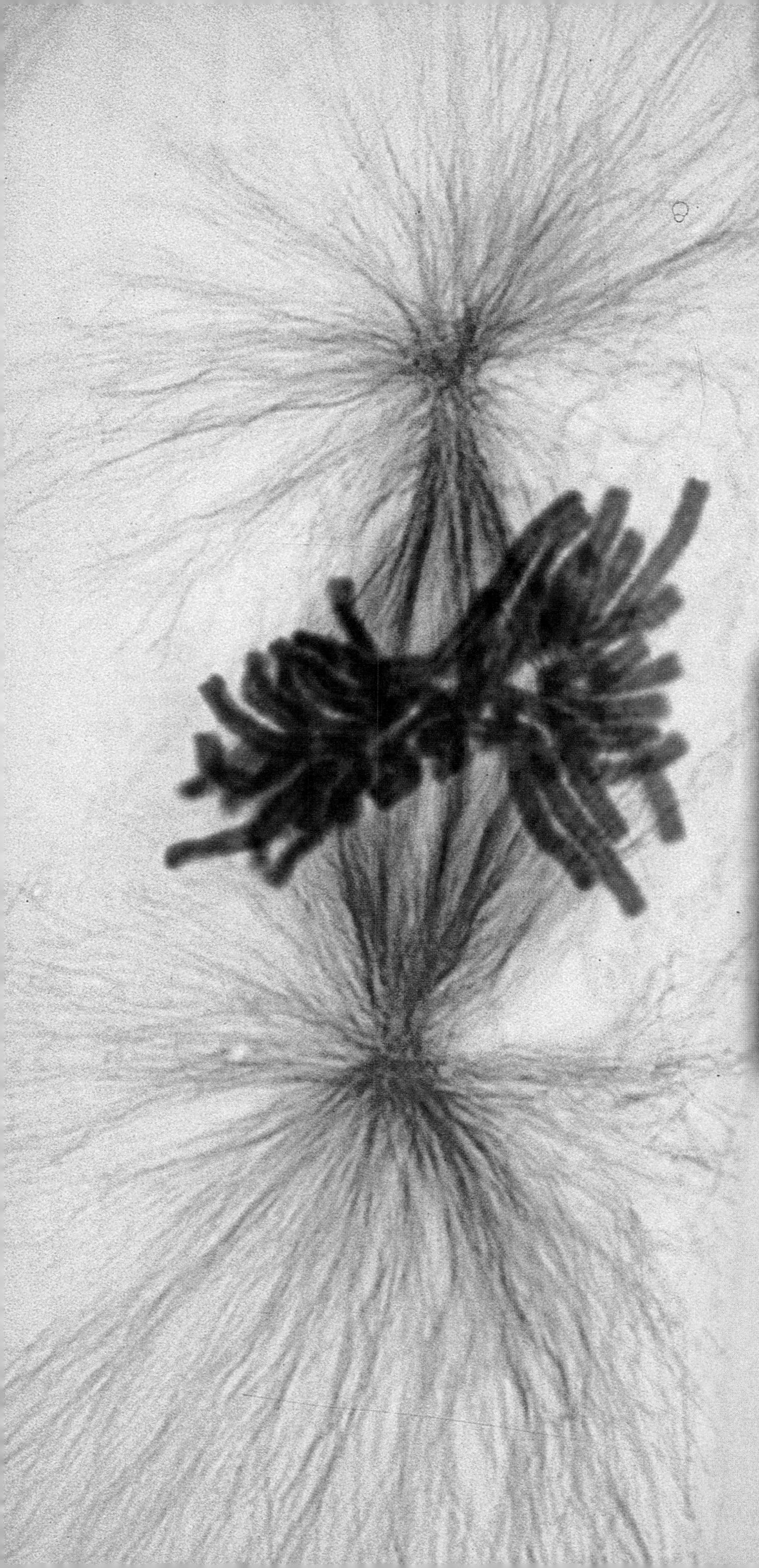

Chapter 8

Mitosis

CHAPTER AT A GLANCE

Cell Division
8.1 Prokaryotes Have a Simple Cell Cycle
8.2 Eukaryotic Cell Cycle
Essential Biological Process 8A: The Cell Cycle
8.3 Chromosomes
8.4 Cell Division
Essential Biological Process 8B: Cell Division
Cancer and the Cell Cycle
8.5 What Is Cancer?
Biology and Staying Healthy: Curing Cancer
Inquiry & Analysis: Why Do Human Cells Age?

Cell Division

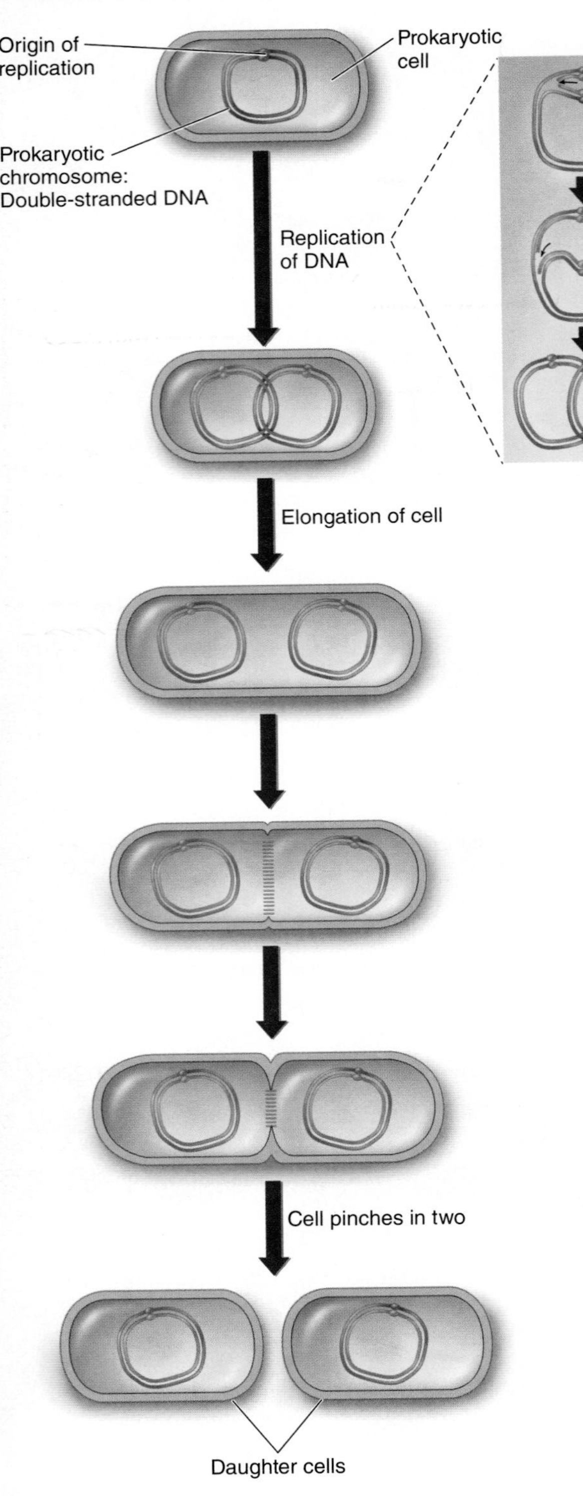

8.1 Prokaryotes Have a Simple Cell Cycle

LEARNING OBJECTIVE 8.1.1 Diagram the prokaryotic cell cycle, identifying DNA replication, DNA partitioning, and cell fission.

All species reproduce, passing their hereditary information on to their offspring. In prokaryotes, the hereditary information—that is, the genes that specify the prokaryote—is encoded in a single circle of DNA, called a prokaryotic chromosome. Before a prokaryotic cell divides to reproduce, the DNA circle makes a copy of itself, a process called *replication.* Starting at one point, the origin of replication, the double helix of DNA begins to unzip, exposing the two strands. The enlargement on the right of figure 8.1*a* shows how the DNA replicates. The new double helix is formed from each naked strand by placing on each exposed nucleotide its complementary nucleotide (that is, A with T, G with C, as discussed in chapter 3). DNA replication is discussed in more detail in chapter 11. When the unzipping has gone all the way around the circle, the cell possesses two copies of its hereditary information.

As described on pages 56 and 57, DNA is a type of nucleic acid. The hereditary information is encoded in the DNA molecule through the order of the nucleotides that make up the long double-stranded DNA molecule.

When the DNA has been copied, the cell grows, resulting in elongation. The newly replicated DNA molecules are partitioned toward each end of the cell. This partitioning process involves DNA sequences near the origin of replication, and results in these sequences being attached to the membrane. When the cell reaches an appropriate size, the prokaryotic cell begins to split into two equal halves, a process called **binary fission.** New plasma membrane and cell wall are added at a point between where the two DNA copies are partitioned, indicated by the green divider in figure 8.1*a*. As the growing plasma membrane pushes inward, the cell is constricted in two, eventually forming two *daughter cells.* Each contains one prokaryotic chromosome that is genetically identical to the parent cell's and each is a complete living cell in its own right.

Putting the Concept to Work

How does a dividing bacterial cell ensure that one copy of its chromosome goes to each daughter cell?

(b)

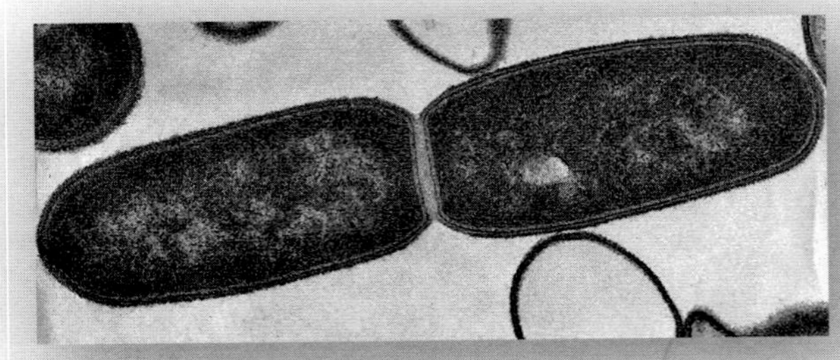

Figure 8.1 The prokaryotic cell cycle.

Prokaryotic cells divide by a process of binary fission. (a) Before the cell splits, the circular DNA molecule of a prokaryote initiates replication at a single site, called the origin of replication, moving out in both directions. When the two moving replication points meet on the far side of the molecule, its replication is complete. The cell then undergoes binary fission, where the cell divides into two daughter cells. (b) Here, a prokaryotic cell has divided in two and is about to be pinched apart by the growing plasma membrane.

8.2 Eukaryotic Cell Cycle

LEARNING OBJECTIVE 8.2.1 List and describe the phases of the eukaryotic cell cycle, including the three phases of interphase.

Cell division in eukaryotes is more complex than in prokaryotes. Eukaryotes contain far more DNA than prokaryotes, and eukaryotic DNA is wound tightly around proteins that condense into a compact shape, the eukaryotic **chromosome.** The cells of eukaryotic organisms either undergo mitosis or meiosis to divide up their DNA. **Mitosis** is the mechanism of cell division that occurs in an organism's nonreproductive cells, called *somatic cells*. **Meiosis** divides the DNA in sexually reproductive *germ-line cells*.

Essential Biological Process 8A outlines the eukaryotic cell cycle:

Interphase. Interphase is composed of three phases:

G_1 phase. This "first gap" phase is the cell's primary growth phase. For most organisms, this phase occupies much of the cell's life span.

S phase. In this "synthesis" phase, the DNA replicates, producing two copies of each chromosome.

G_2 phase. Cell division preparation begins in the "second gap" phase with the replication of mitochondria, chromosome condensation, and the synthesis of microtubules.

M phase. In mitosis, which is continuous but can be thought of as occurring in four phases, a microtubular apparatus binds to the chromosomes and moves them apart.

C phase. In cytokinesis, the cytoplasm divides, creating two daughter cells.

Putting the Concept to Work

Do eukaryotic chromosomes condense before they replicate?

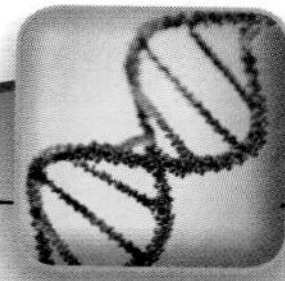

IN THE NEWS

Alzheimer's Disease Linked to Cell Cycle. Alzheimer's disease, common among the elderly, involves the degeneration of brain nerve cells. The dying cells become clogged with masses of protein called amyloid plaques, but why the plaques appear is not known. Recently several research laboratories have reported findings that shed light on this critical point. What they report is that the nerve cell degeneration of Alzheimer's appears to be a disease of inappropriate cell cycle control. Six months or more before the first amyloid deposits appear, proteins associated with the cell cycle, such as proteins called cyclins, are seen within affected nerve cells in the frontal cortex of the brain. What is important to note is that normally adult brain cells don't divide; after development they go into a resting state. Apparently, this initiation of the cell cycle leads to amyloid deposits and cell death because nerve cells that reenter the cell cycle die rather than divide. These findings suggest that therapies targeted toward preventing mitotic changes may have a profound and positive impact on Alzheimer's disease progression.

Essential Biological Process 8A

The Cell Cycle

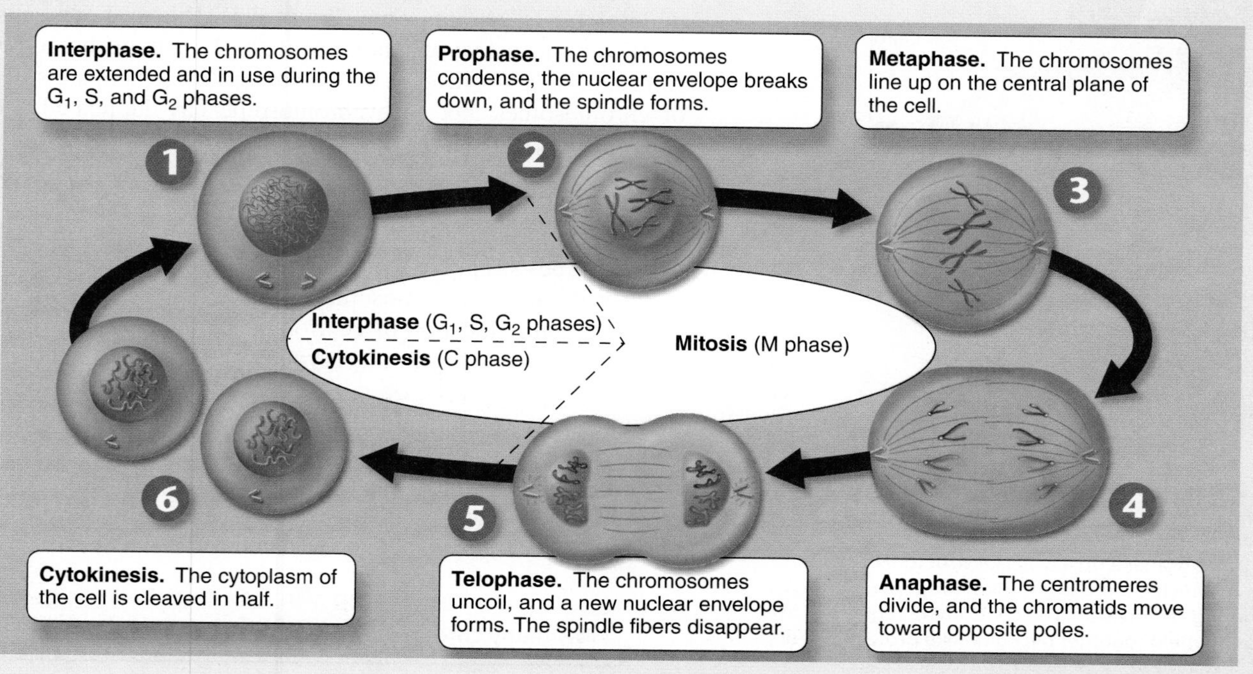

Interphase. The chromosomes are extended and in use during the G1, S, and G2 phases.
Prophase. The chromosomes condense, the nuclear envelope breaks down, and the spindle forms.
Metaphase. The chromosomes line up on the central plane of the cell.
1
2
3
Interphase (G1, S, G2 phases)
Cytokinesis (C phase)
Mitosis (M phase)
6
5
4
Cytokinesis. The cytoplasm of the cell is cleaved in half.
Telophase. The chromosomes uncoil, and a new nuclear envelope forms. The spindle fibers disappear.
Anaphase. The centromeres divide, and the chromatids move toward opposite poles.

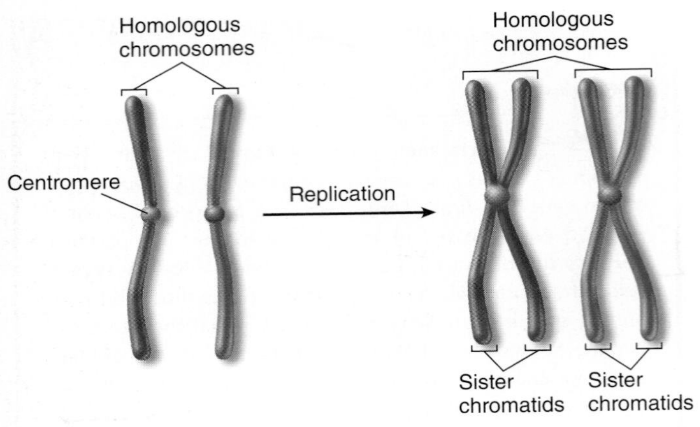

Figure 8.2 The difference between homologous chromosomes and sister chromatids.

Homologous chromosomes are a pair of the same chromosome—say, chromosome number 16. Sister chromatids are the two replicas of a single chromosome held together by the centromere after DNA replication. A duplicated chromosome looks somewhat like an X.

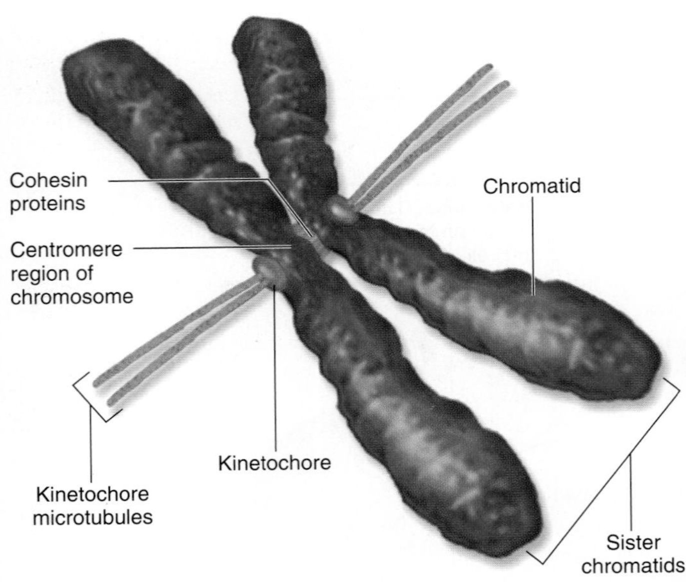

Figure 8.3 A closer look at the centromere.

The centromere is a point of constriction on a chromosome containing certain repeated DNA sequences that bind specific proteins. These proteins make up a disc-like structure called the kinetochore to which microtubules bind and separate the chromosomes during cell division. The centromere regions of two sister chromatids are held together by a glue-like protein called cohesin.

8.3 Chromosomes

LEARNING OBJECTIVE 8.3.1 Distinguish between a homologue and a sister chromatid.

Chromosomes were first observed by the German embryologist Walther Flemming in 1879, while he was examining the rapidly dividing cells of salamander larvae. When Flemming looked at the cells through what would now be a rather primitive light microscope, he saw minute threads within their nuclei that appeared to be dividing lengthwise. Flemming called their division *mitosis,* based on the Greek word *mitos,* meaning "thread."

Chromosome Number

Since their initial discovery, chromosomes have been found in the cells of all eukaryotes examined. Their number may vary enormously from one species to another. A few kinds of organisms—such as the Australian ant *Myrmecia* spp.; the plant *Haplopappus gracilis,* a relative of the sunflower that grows in North American deserts; and the fungus *Penicillium*—have only 1 pair of chromosomes, while some ferns have more than 500 pairs. Most eukaryotes have between 10 and 50 chromosomes in their body cells.

Homologous Chromosomes

Chromosomes exist in somatic cells as pairs, called **homologous chromosomes,** or **homologues.** Homologues carry information about the same traits at the same locations on each chromosome but the information can vary between homologues, which will be discussed in chapter 10. Cells that have two of each type of chromosome are called **diploid cells.** One chromosome of each pair is inherited from the mother (colored green in figure 8.2) and the other from the father (colored purple). Before cell division, each homologous chromosome replicates, resulting in two identical copies, called **sister chromatids.** The sister chromatids remain joined together after replication at a special linkage site called the **centromere,** the knoblike structure in the middle of each chromosome (figure 8.3). Human body cells have a total of 46 chromosomes, which are actually 23 pairs of homologous chromosomes. In their duplicated state, before mitosis, there are still only 23 pairs of chromosomes, but each chromosome has duplicated and consists of two sister chromatids, for a total of 92 chromatids. The duplicated sister chromatids can make it confusing to count the number of chromosomes in an organism, but keep in mind that the number of centromeres doesn't increase with replication, and so you can always determine the number of chromosomes simply by counting the centromeres.

The 46 human chromosomes can be paired as homologues by comparing size, shape, location of centromeres, and so on. This arrangement of chromosomes is called a **karyotype.** An example of a human karyotype is shown in figure 8.4. Possession of all 46 of the chromosomes is essential to human survival. Individuals missing even one chromosome, a condition called monosomy, do not usually survive embryonic development. Nor does the human embryo develop properly with an extra copy of any one chromosome, a condition called trisomy. For all but a few of the smallest chromosomes, trisomy is fatal; even in those cases, serious problems result.

Putting the Concept to Work

How many chromosomes does a cell of your finger possess?

Chromosome Structure

LEARNING OBJECTIVE 8.3.2 Diagram a nucleosome and discuss its function.

Chromosomes are composed of **chromatin,** a complex of DNA and protein; most are about 40% DNA and 60% protein. A significant amount of RNA is also associated with chromosomes because chromosomes are the sites of RNA synthesis. The DNA of a chromosome is one very long, double-stranded fiber that extends unbroken through the entire length of the chromosome. A typical human chromosome contains about 140 million (1.4×10^8) nucleotides in its DNA. Furthermore, if the strand of DNA from a single chromosome were laid out in a straight line, it would be about 5 centimeters (2 inches) long. The amount of information in one human chromosome would fill about 2,000 printed books of 1,000 pages each! Fitting such a strand into a nucleus is like cramming a string the length of a football field into a baseball—and that's only 1 of 46 chromosomes! In the cell, however, the DNA is coiled, allowing it to fit into a much smaller space than would otherwise be possible.

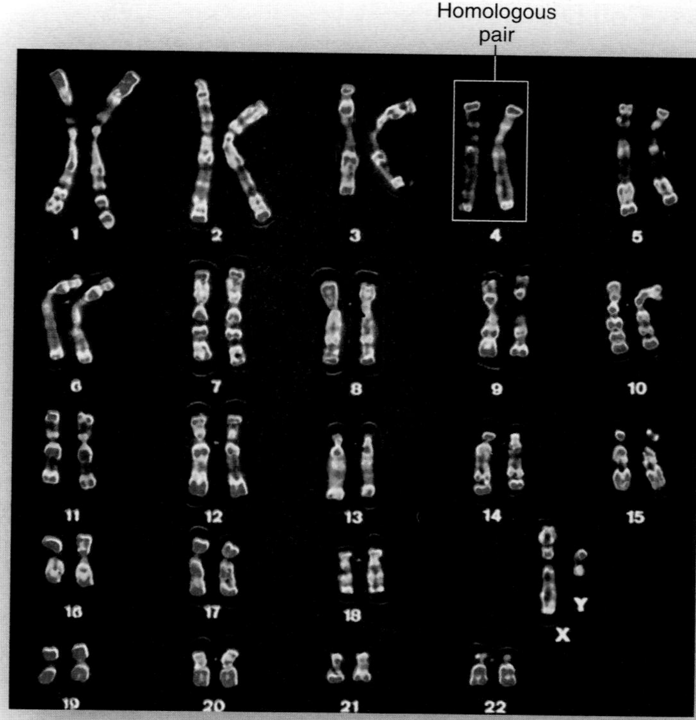

Figure 8.4 The 46 chromosomes of a human.

In this presentation, photographs of the individual chromosomes of a human male have been cut out and paired with their homologues, creating an organized display called a karyotype. The chromosomes are in a duplicated state, and the sister chromatids can actually be seen in many of the homologous pairs. The different sizes and shapes of chromosomes allow scientists to pair together the ones that are homologous. For example, chromosome 1 is much larger than chromosome 14, and its centromere is more centrally located on the chromosome.

Chromosome Coiling

Eukaryotic DNA is formed into chromosomes, such as the duplicated sister chromatids seen in **figure 8.4**, by winding and twisting the long DNA strands into much more compact forms. Winding up DNA presents an interesting challenge. Because the phosphate groups of DNA molecules have negative charges, it is impossible to just tightly wind up DNA—all the negative charges would simply repel one another. As you can see in **figure 8.5**, the DNA helix wraps around proteins with positive charges called **histones.** The positive charges of the histones counteract the negative charges of the DNA, so that the complex has no net charge. Every 200 nucleotides, the DNA duplex is coiled around a core of eight histone proteins, forming a complex known as a **nucleosome.** The nucleosomes are further coiled into a solenoid. This solenoid is then organized into looped domains. The final organization of the chromosome is not known, but it appears to involve further radial looping into rosettes around a preexisting scaffolding of protein. This complex of DNA and histone proteins, coiled tightly, forms a compact chromosome.

Putting the Concept to Work

Why does DNA coiling require positively charged histone proteins?

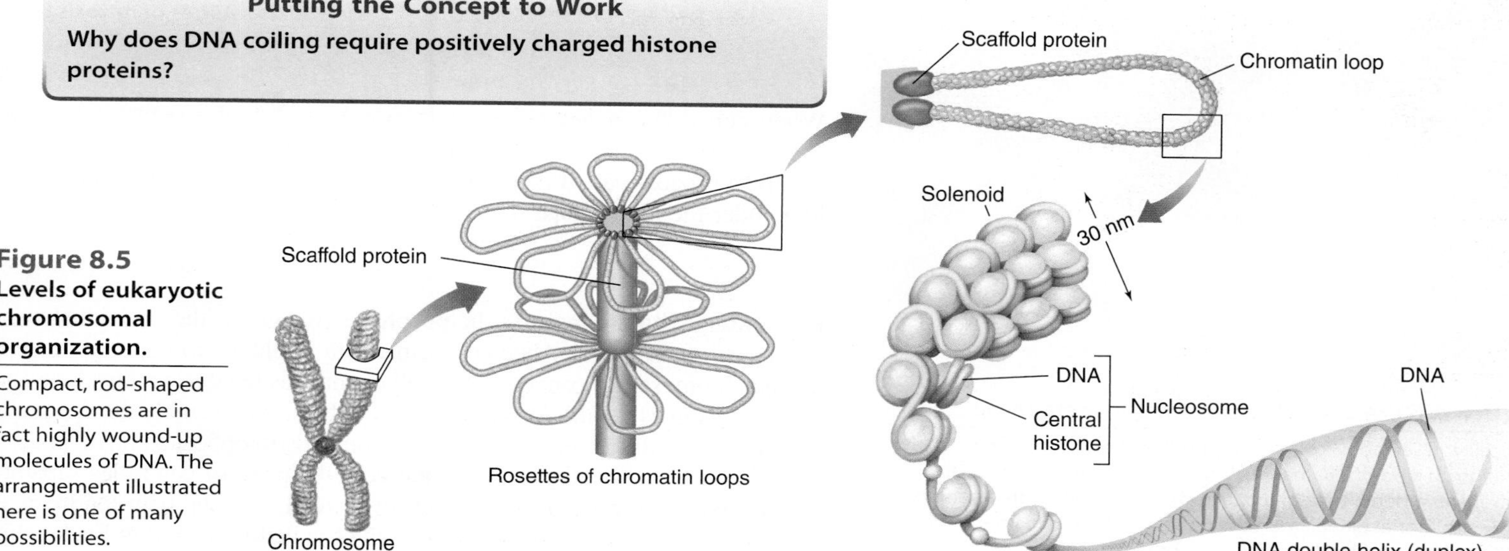

Figure 8.5 Levels of eukaryotic chromosomal organization.

Compact, rod-shaped chromosomes are in fact highly wound-up molecules of DNA. The arrangement illustrated here is one of many possibilities.

Essential Biological Process 8B

Cell Division

1 **Interphase**

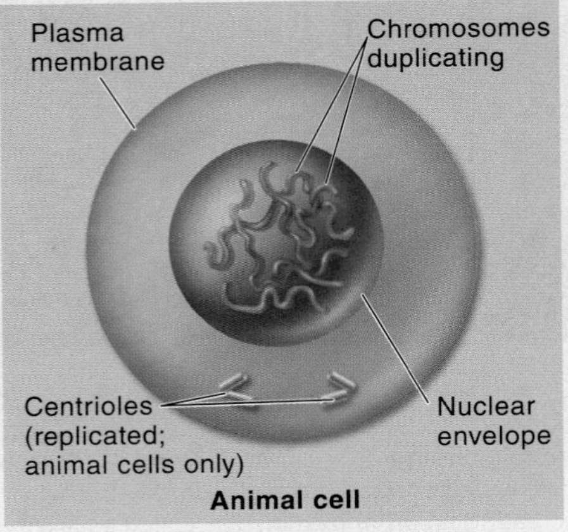

DNA replicates and begins to condense. Centrioles, if present, also replicate, and the cell prepares for division.

2 **Mitosis**

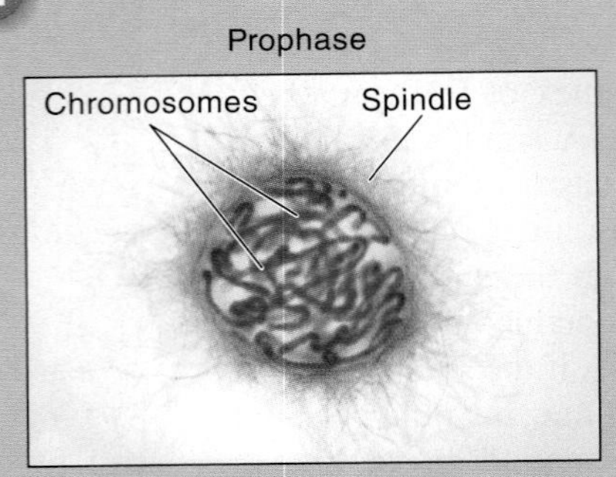

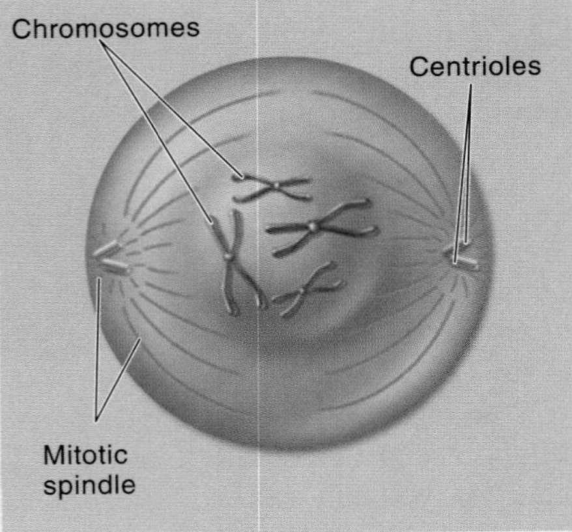

The nuclear envelope begins to break down. DNA further condenses into chromosomes. The mitotic spindle begins to form; it is complete at the end of prophase.

3

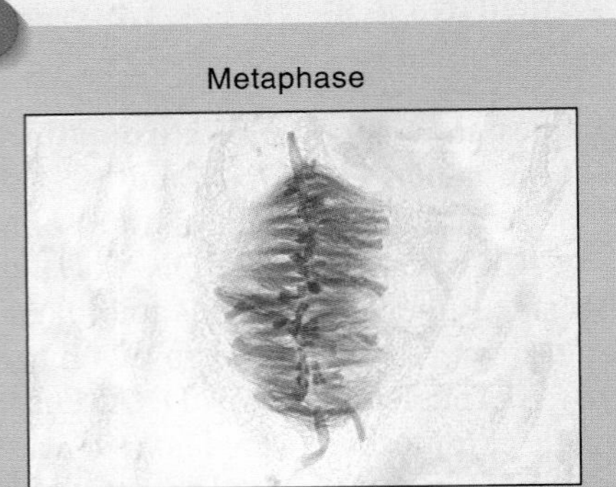

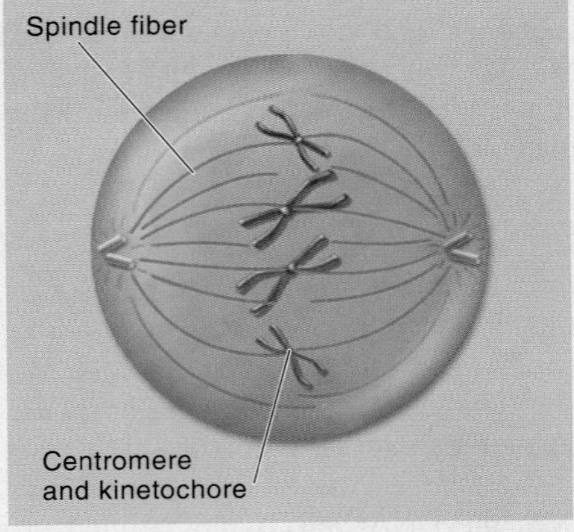

The chromosomes align on a plane in the center of the cell. The spindle fibers attach to the kinetochores on opposite sides of the centromeres.

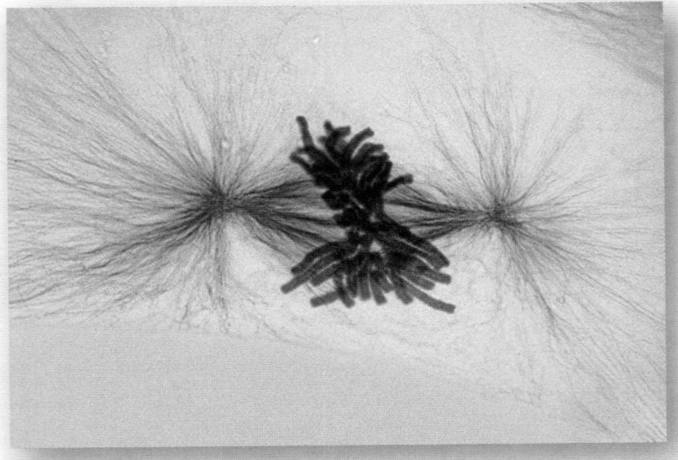

Figure 8.6 A cell's chromosomes in metaphase.

The cell you see above is a dividing cell of the Oregon newt *Taricha granulosa*, a kind of salamander. The image captures the cell in metaphase, when all the blue-stained chromosomes are lined up on the equatorial plane. Soon the red-stained spindle fibers will draw duplicates of the homologous chromosomes to opposite poles of the cell.

8.4 Cell Division

LEARNING OBJECTIVE 8.4.1 Describe the stages of mitosis.

Interphase

When cell division begins in interphase (panel 1 of *Essential Biological Process 8B*), chromosomes first replicate, and then begin to wind up tightly, a process called **condensation.** Chromosomes are not usually visible under the microscope during interphase.

Mitosis

Prophase: Mitosis Begins. In **prophase** (panel 2), the individual condensed chromosomes first become visible with a light microscope. As the replicated chromosomes condense, the cell dismantles the nuclear envelope and two centrosomes (centrioles in animal cells) begin to assemble the apparatus it will use to pull the replicated sister chromatids to opposite ends ("poles") of the cell. In the center of an animal cell, the pairs of centrioles separate and move apart toward opposite poles of the cell, forming between them as they move apart a network of protein cables called the **spindle.** Each cable is called a *spindle fiber* and is made of microtubules, which are long, hollow

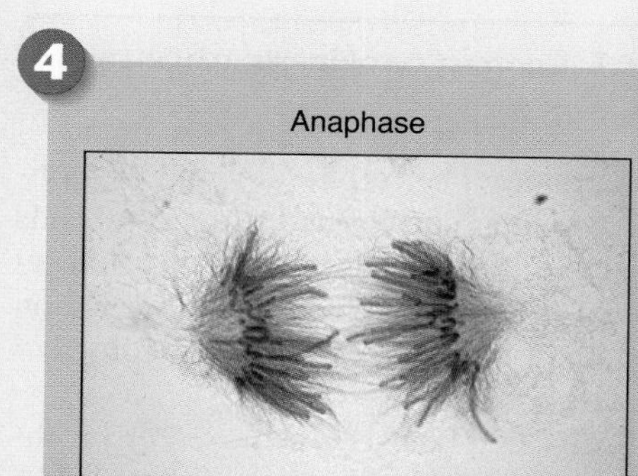

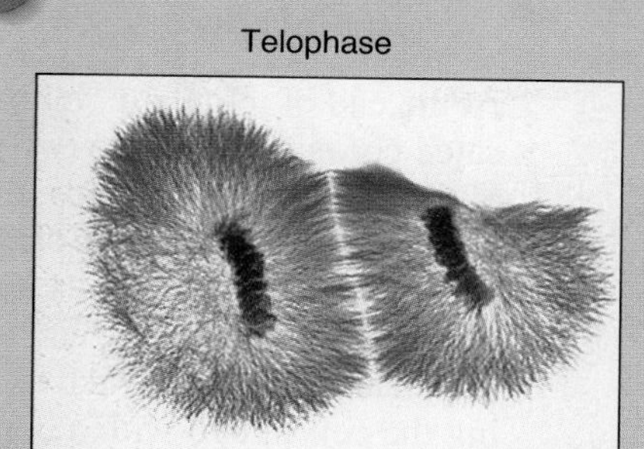

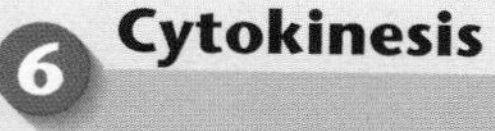

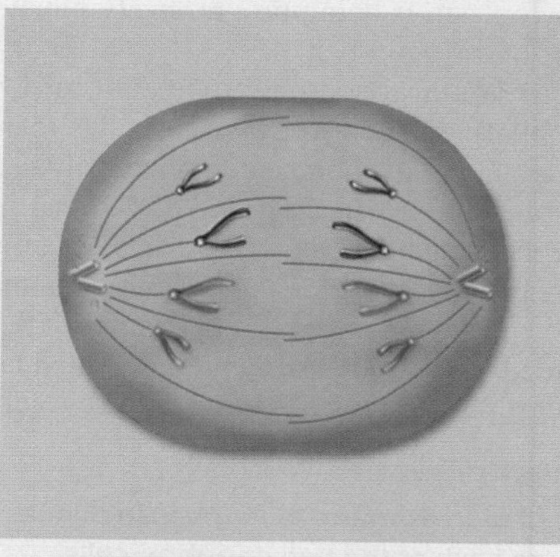

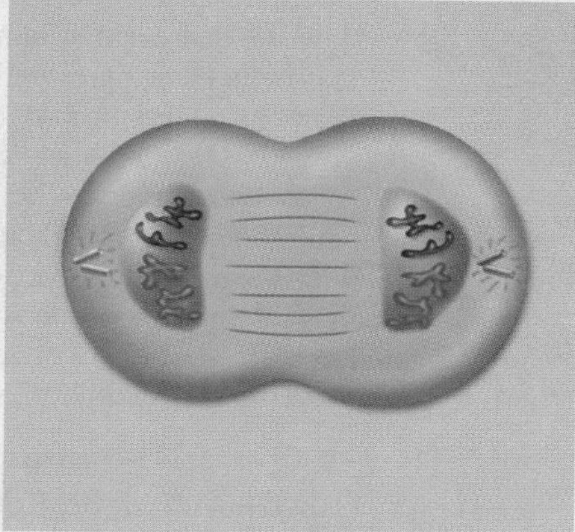

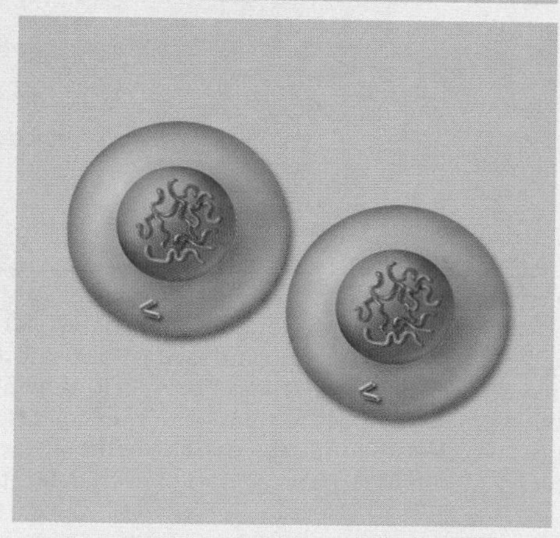

The centromeres replicate. The sister chromatids separate and move to opposite poles.

The nuclear envelope reappears. The chromosomes decondense. As telophase progresses, cytokinesis also occurs.

In cytokinesis two daughter cells form. Each cell is a replicate of the parent cell and is diploid.

tubes of protein. Plant cells lack centrioles and instead brace the ends of the spindle toward the poles. The spindle fibers attach to the chromosomes, and when the process is complete, one sister chromatid of each pair is attached by microtubules to one pole and the other sister chromatid to the other pole.

Metaphase: Alignment of the Chromosomes. The second phase of mitosis, **metaphase,** begins when the chromosomes, each consisting of a pair of sister chromatids, align in the center of the cell along an imaginary plane that divides the cell in half, referred to as the equatorial plane. Microtubules attached to the centromeres extend back toward the opposite poles of the cell (figure 8.6).

Anaphase: Separation of the Chromatids. In **anaphase,** the centromeres split, and the sister chromatids are freed from each other. Cell division is now simply a matter of reeling in the microtubules, dragging the sister chromatids (now referred to as daughter chromosomes) to the poles.

Telophase: Re-formation of the Nuclei. In **telophase,** the mitotic spindle disassembles, and a nuclear envelope forms around each set of chromosomes while they begin to uncoil. The nucleolus also reappears.

Putting the Concept to Work

After interphase, how many chromatids does a cell contain?

EVOLUTION

Nanobees Attack Dividing Cells. Cancer occurs when the genes that regulate the cell cycle are damaged, releasing the brakes that normally restrain cell division. In 2011, Washington University researchers announced a powerful new treatment for cancer that directly targets rapidly dividing cancer cells. It takes advantage of a particularly potent venom, the protein melittin that bees inject into their sting victims. In high enough concentration, melittin can destroy any cell. The researchers attached it to nano-sized particles (lipid-coated perfluorocarbon beads). When the toxin-loaded nanoparticles are injected into tumors, cancer cells take up the particles. Once inside cells, the melittin pokes holes in their internal membranes, progressively chewing away at the cell's interior until the cell dies. While cancer cells can develop resistance to many anticancer agents, it is hard for them to find a way around the mechanism that melittin uses to kill them. Using these nanobees, researchers have already succeeded in reducing the size of melanoma tumors 88 percent.

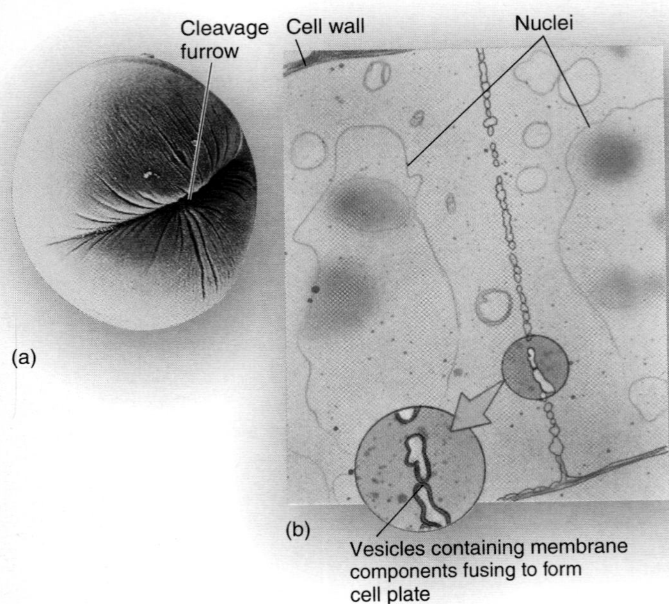

Figure 8.7 Cytokinesis.

The division of cytoplasm that occurs after mitosis is called cytokinesis and cleaves the cell into roughly equal halves. (a) In an animal cell, such as this sea urchin egg, a cleavage furrow forms around the dividing cell. (b) In this dividing plant cell, a cell plate is forming between the two newly forming daughter cells. Note that the flattened vesicles are forming a double membrane, one element of which is destined to become part of each daughter cell.

Cytokinesis

LEARNING OBJECTIVE 8.4.2 Contrast cytokinesis in plant and animal cells.

At the end of telophase, mitosis is complete. The cell has divided its replicated chromosomes into two nuclei, which are positioned at opposite ends of the cell. As mitosis ends, the division of the cytoplasm, called **cytokinesis,** occurs, and the cell is cleaved into roughly equal halves. The formation of these two daughter cells, shown in the last panel of *Essential Biological Process 8B,* signals the end of cell division.

In animal cells, which lack cell walls, cytokinesis is achieved by pinching the cell in two with a contracting belt of actin filaments (**figure 8.7*a***). As contraction proceeds, a *cleavage furrow* becomes evident around the cell's circumference, where the cytoplasm is being progressively pinched inward by the decreasing diameter of the actin belt.

Plant cells have rigid walls that are far too strong to be deformed by actin filament contraction. A different approach to cytokinesis has therefore evolved in plants. Plant cells assemble membrane components in their interior, at right angles to the mitotic spindle. In **figure 8.7*b*,** you can see how membrane is deposited between the daughter cells by vesicles that fuse together. This expanding partition, called a *cell plate*, grows outward until it reaches the interior surface of the plasma membrane and fuses with it, at which point it has effectively divided the cell in two. Cellulose is then laid down over the new membranes, forming the cell walls of the two new cells.

Putting the Concept to Work

How do you suppose the cell plate forming in figure 8.7*b* divides to form *two* cell walls, one for each of the two daughter cells?

Cell Death

LEARNING OBJECTIVE 8.4.3 Describe the role that programmed cell death plays in the life of a human individual.

Despite the ability to divide, no cell lives forever. The ravages of living slowly tear away at a cell's machinery. To some degree damaged parts can be replaced, but no replacement process is perfect. If food supplies are cut off, animal cells cannot obtain the energy necessary to maintain their lysosome membranes and die, digested from within by their own enzymes.

During fetal development, many cells are programmed to die. In human embryos, hands and feet appear first as "paddles" (**figure 8.8**), but the skin cells between bones die as programmed to form the separated toes and fingers. In ducks, this cell death is not part of the developmental program, which is why ducks have webbed feet.

Human cells appear to be programmed to undergo only so many cell divisions and then die, following a plan written into the genes. In tissue culture, cell lines divide about 50 times, and then the entire population of cells dies off. Even if some of the cells are frozen for years, when they are thawed they simply resume where they left off and die on schedule. Only cancer cells appear to thwart these instructions, dividing endlessly. All other cells in your body contain a hidden clock that keeps time by counting cell divisions, and when the alarm goes off, the cells die.

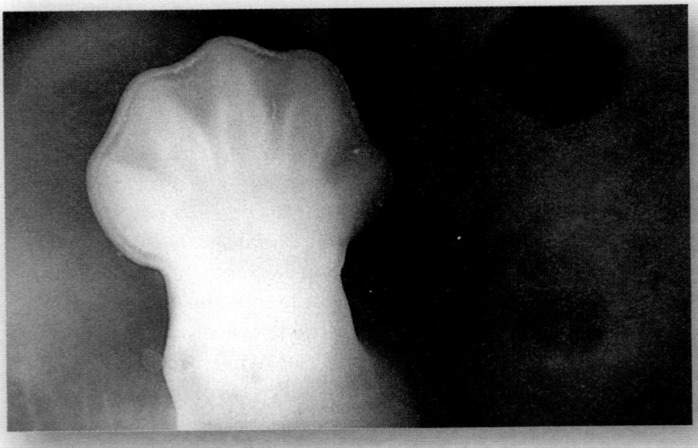

Figure 8.8 Programmed cell death.

In the human embryo, programmed cell death results in the formation of fingers and toes from paddlelike hands and feet.

Putting the Concept to Work

If human cells divide only 50 times, is that enough to generate the 100 trillion cells of an adult human from an initial single cell?

Cancer and the Cell Cycle

8.5 What Is Cancer?

LEARNING OBJECTIVE 8.5.1 Explain how mutation is linked to cancer, and describe the genes most often involved.

Cancer is a growth disorder of cells. It starts when an apparently normal cell begins to divide in an uncontrolled way. The result is a cluster of cells, called a **tumor,** that constantly expands in size. The cluster of pink lung cells in the photo in figure 8.9 have begun to form a malignant tumor called a *carcinoma*. Malignant tumors are invasive, their cells able to break away from the tumor, enter the bloodstream, and spread to other areas of the body (figure 8.10), forming new tumors at distant sites called **metastases.**

Cancer is perhaps the most devastating and deadly disease. Most of us have had family or friends affected by the disease. In 2010, 1.5 million American men and women were diagnosed with cancer; in that same year, over half a million Americans died of cancer. One in every two Americans born will be diagnosed with some form of cancer during their lifetime. In the U.S., the three deadliest human cancers are lung cancer, cancer of the colon and rectum, and breast cancer. Lung cancer, responsible for the most cancer deaths, is largely preventable; most cases result from smoking cigarettes. Colorectal cancers appear to be fostered by the high-meat diets so favored in the United States. The cause of breast cancer is still a mystery.

Not surprisingly, researchers are expending a great deal of effort to learn the cause of cancer. Scientists have made considerable progress in the last 30 years using molecular biological techniques, and the rough outlines of understanding are now emerging. We now know that cancer is a gene disorder of somatic tissue, in which damaged genes fail to properly control cell growth and division. The cell division cycle is regulated by a sophisticated group of proteins called growth factors. Cancer results from damage to the genes encoding these proteins. Damage to DNA, such as damage to these genes, is called **mutation.** Cancer can be caused by chemicals that alter DNA like the tars in cigarette smoke (we will examine the link between smoking and lung cancer in considerable detail in chapter 25), by environmental factors such as UV rays that damage DNA (discussed in chapter 11), or in some instances by viruses that circumvent the cell's normal growth and division controls (viruses are discussed in chapter 16).

Mutations are errors in DNA and are discussed in detail in chapter 11, pages 198–199. Damage to DNA often involves an incorrect nucleotide being inserted during DNA replication, which changes the information encoded in the DNA.

There are two general classes of growth factor genes that are usually involved in cancer: proto-oncogenes and tumor-suppressor genes. Genes known as **proto-oncogenes** encode proteins that stimulate cell division. Mutations that activate or improve the functioning of these genes "step on the accelerator" of cell division, causing mutated cells to divide excessively. Mutated proto-oncogenes become cancer-causing genes called **oncogenes.**

The second class of cancer-causing genes are called **tumor-suppressor genes.** Cell division is normally turned off in healthy cells by proteins encoded by tumor-suppressor genes. Mutations to these genes essentially "release the brakes" of cell division, allowing the cell containing the mutated gene to divide uncontrolled. The cell cycle never stops in a cancerous line of cells.

Putting the Concept to Work

What things might lead to the DNA damage that initiates cancer?

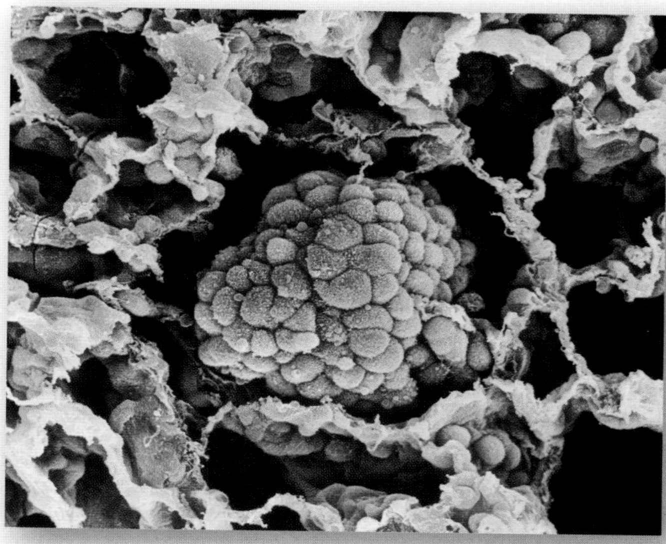

Figure 8.9 Lung cancer cells (300×).

These cells are from a tumor located in the alveolus (air sac) of a human lung.

IMPLICATION FOR YOU 157,300 people died of lung cancer in the United States in 2010, almost all of them cigarette smokers. Fully 7.5% of pack-a-day smokers will die of lung cancer within 30 years of their first cigarette. That's 1 in 13. Do you smoke? Do any of your friends? Can you think of a reason that would justify the risk?

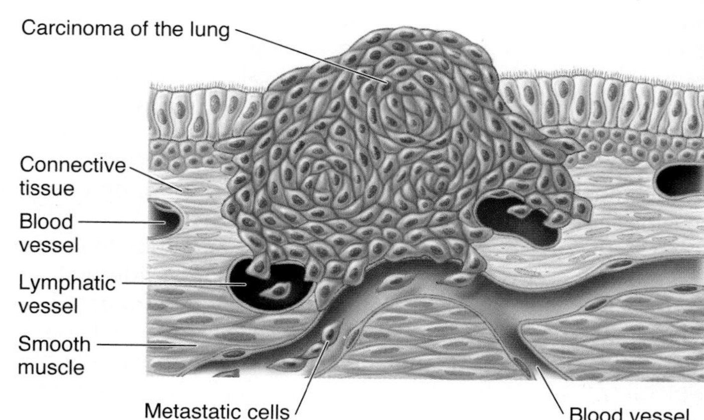

Figure 8.10 Portrait of a tumor.

This ball of cells is a carcinoma (cancer tumor) developing from epithelial cells that line the interior surface of a human lung. As the mass of cells grows, it invades surrounding tissues, eventually penetrating lymphatic and blood vessels, both of which are plentiful within the lung. These vessels carry metastatic cancer cells throughout the body, where they lodge and grow, forming new masses of cancerous tissue.

Curing Cancer

Half of all Americans will face cancer at some point in their lives. Potential cancer therapies are being developed on many fronts. Some act to prevent the start of cancer within cells. Others act outside cancer cells, preventing tumors from growing and spreading. The figure on the right indicates targeted areas for the development of cancer treatments. The following discussion will examine each of these areas.

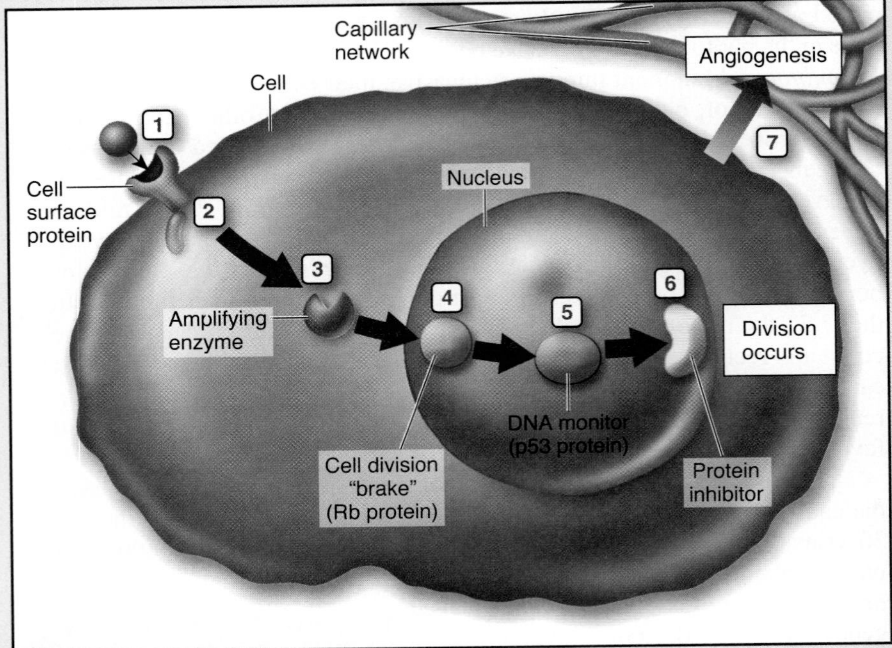

Seven different stages in the cancer process.

(1) On the cell surface, a growth factor's signal to divide is increased. (2) Just inside the cell, a protein relay switch that passes on the divide signal gets stuck in the "ON" position. (3) In the cytoplasm, enzymes that amplify the signal are amplified even more. In the nucleus, (4) a "brake" preventing DNA replication is inoperable, (5) proteins that check for damage in the DNA are inactivated, and (6) other proteins that inhibit the elongation of chromosome tips are destroyed. (7) The new tumor promotes angiogenesis, the formation of new blood vessels that promote growth.

Preventing the Start of Cancer

Many promising cancer therapies act within potential cancer cells, focusing on different stages of the cell's "Shall I divide?" decision-making process.

1 **Receiving the Signal to Divide.** The first step in the decision process is receiving a "divide" signal, usually a small protein called a growth factor released from a neighboring cell. The growth factor, the red ball at #1 in the figure, is received by a protein receptor on the cell surface. Like banging on a door, its arrival signals that it's time to divide. Mutations that increase the number of receptors on the cell surface amplify the division signal and so lead to cancer. Over 20% of breast cancer tumors prove to overproduce a protein called HER2 associated with the receptor for epidermal growth factor (EGF).

Therapies directed at this stage of the decision process utilize the human immune system to attack cancer cells. Special protein molecules called *monoclonal antibodies,* created by genetic engineering, are the therapeutic agents. These monoclonal antibodies are designed to seek out and stick to HER2. Like waving a red flag, the presence of the monoclonal antibody calls down attack by the immune system on the HER2 cell. Because breast cancer cells overproduce HER2, they are killed preferentially. The biotechnology research company Genentech's recently approved monoclonal antibody, called herceptin, has given promising results in clinical tests.

Up to 70% of colon, prostate, lung, and head/neck cancers have excess copies of a related receptor, epidermal growth factor 1 (HER1). The monoclonal antibody C225, directed against HER1, has succeeded in shrinking 22% of advanced, previously incurable colon cancers in early clinical trials. Apparently blocking HER1 interferes with the ability of tumor cells to recover from chemotherapy or radiation.

2 **Passing the Signal via a Relay Switch.** The second step in the decision process is the passage of the signal into the cell's interior, the cytoplasm. This is carried out in normal cells by a protein called Ras that acts as a relay switch, #2 in the figure. When growth factor binds to a receptor like EGF, the adjacent Ras protein acts like it has been "goosed," contorting into a new shape. This new shape is chemically active, and initiates a chain of reactions that passes the "divide" signal inward toward the nucleus. Mutated forms of the Ras protein behave like a relay switch stuck in the "ON" position, continually instructing the cell to divide when it should not. Thirty percent of all cancers have a mutant form of Ras. So far, no effective therapies have been developed targeting this step.

3 **Amplifying the Signal.** The third step in the decision process is the amplification of the signal within the cytoplasm. Just as a TV signal needs to be amplified in order to be received at a distance, so

a "divide" signal must be amplified if it is to reach the nucleus at the interior of the cell, a very long journey at a molecular scale. To get a signal all the way into the nucleus, the cell employs a sort of pony express. The "ponies" in this case are enzymes called *tyrosine kinases*, #3 in the figure. These enzymes add phosphate groups to proteins, but only at a particular amino acid, tyrosine. No other enzymes in the cell do this, so the tyrosine kinases form an elite corps of signal carriers not confused by the myriad of other molecular activities going on around them.

Cells use an ingenious trick to amplify the signal as it moves toward the nucleus. Ras, when "ON," activates the initial protein kinase. This protein kinase activates other protein kinases that in their turn activate still others. The trick is that once a protein kinase enzyme is activated, it goes to work like a demon, activating hoards of others every second! And each and every one it activates behaves the same way too, activating still more, in a cascade of ever-widening effect. At each stage of the relay, the signal is amplified a thousandfold.

Mutations stimulating any of the protein kinases can dangerously increase the already amplified signal and lead to cancer. Some 15 of the cell's 32 internal tyrosine kinases have been implicated in cancer. Five percent of all cancers, for example, have a mutant hyperactive form of the protein kinase Src. The trouble begins when a mutation causes one of the tyrosine kinases to become locked into the "ON" position, sort of like a stuck doorbell that keeps ringing and ringing.

To cure the cancer, you have to find a way to shut the bell off. Each of the signal carriers presents a different problem, as you must quiet it without knocking out all the other signal pathways the cell needs. The cancer therapy drug Gleevec, a monoclonal antibody, has just the right shape to fit into a groove on the surface of the tyrosine kinase called "abl." Mutations locking abl "ON" are responsible for chronic myelogenous leukemia, a lethal form of white blood cell cancer. Gleevec totally disables abl. In clinical trials, blood counts revert to normal in more than 90% of cases.

4 Releasing the Brake. The fourth step in the decision process is the removal of the "brake" the cell uses to restrain cell division. In healthy cells this brake, a tumor-suppressor protein called Rb, blocks the activity of a protein called E2F, #4 in the figure. When free, E2F enables the cell to copy its DNA. Normal cell division is triggered to begin when Rb is inhibited, unleashing E2F. Mutations that destroy Rb release E2F from its control completely, leading to ceaseless cell division. Forty percent of all cancers have a defective form of Rb.

Therapies directed at this stage of the decision process are only now being attempted. They focus on drugs able to inhibit E2F, which should halt the growth of tumors arising from inactive Rb. Experiments in mice in which the *E2F* genes have been destroyed provide a model system to study such drugs, which are being actively investigated.

5 Checking That Everything Is Ready. The fifth step in the decision process is the mechanism used by the cell to ensure that its DNA is undamaged and ready to divide. This job is carried out in healthy cells by the tumor-suppressor protein p53, which inspects the integrity of the DNA, #5 in the figure. When it detects damaged or foreign DNA, p53 stops cell division and activates the cell's DNA repair systems. If the damage doesn't get repaired in a reasonable time, p53 pulls the plug, triggering events that kill the cell. In this way, mutations such as those that cause cancer are either repaired or the cells containing them eliminated. If p53 is itself destroyed by mutation, future damage accumulates unrepaired. Among this damage are mutations that lead to cancer. Fifty percent of all cancers have a disabled p53. Fully 70% to 80% of lung cancers have a mutant inactive p53—the chemical benzo[*a*]pyrene in cigarette smoke is a potent mutagen of p53.

6 Stepping on the Gas. Cell division starts with replication of the DNA. In healthy cells, another tumor suppressor "keeps the gas tank nearly empty" for the DNA replication process by inhibiting production of an enzyme called *telomerase*. Without this enzyme, a cell's chromosomes lose material from their tips, called *telomeres*. Every time a chromosome is copied, more tip material is lost. After some 30 divisions, so much is lost that copying is no longer possible. Cells in the tissues of an adult human have typically undergone 25 or more divisions. Cancer can't get very far with only the five remaining cell divisions, so inhibiting telomerase is a very effective natural brake on the cancer process, #6 in the figure. It is thought that almost all cancers involve a mutation that destroys the telomerase inhibitor, releasing this brake and making cancer possible. It should be possible to block cancer by reapplying this inhibition. Cancer therapies that inhibit telomerase are just beginning clinical trials.

Preventing the Spread of Cancer

7 Stopping Tumor Growth. Once a cell begins cancerous growth, it forms an expanding tumor. As the tumor grows ever-larger, it requires an increasing supply of food and nutrients, obtained from the body's blood supply. To facilitate this necessary grocery shopping, tumors leak out substances into the surrounding tissues that encourage the formation of small blood vessels, a process called angiogenesis, #7 in the figure. Chemicals that inhibit this process are called *angiogenesis inhibitors*. Two such natural angiogenesis inhibitors, angiostatin and endostatin, caused tumors to regress to microscopic size in mice, but initial human trials were disappointing.

Laboratory drugs are more promising. A monoclonal antibody drug called Avastin, targeted against a blood vessel growth promoting substance called vascular endothelial growth factor (VEGF), destroys the ability of VEGF to carry out its blood-vessel-forming job. Given to hundreds of advanced colon cancer patients as part of a large clinical trial, Avastin improved colon cancer patients' chance of survival by 50% over chemotherapy.

Inquiry & Analysis

Why Do Human Cells Age?

Human cells appear to have built-in life spans. In 1961 cell biologist Leonard Hayflick reported the startling result that skin cells growing in tissue culture, such as those growing in culture flasks in the photo below, will divide only a certain number of times. After about 50 population doublings cell division stops (a **doubling** is a round of cell division producing two daughter cells for each dividing cell, for example going from a population of 30 cells to 60 cells). If a cell sample is taken after 20 doublings and frozen, when thawed it resumes growth for 30 more doublings, and then stops. An explanation of the "Hayflick limit" was suggested in 1986 when researchers first glimpsed an extra length of DNA at the end of chromosomes. Dubbed *telomeres*, these lengths proved to be composed of the simple DNA sequence TTAGGG, repeated nearly a thousand times. Importantly, telomeres were found to be substantially shorter in the cells of older body tissues. This led to the hypothesis that a run of some 16 TTAGGGs was where the DNA replicating enzyme, called polymerase, first sat down on the DNA (16 TTAGGGs being the size of the enzyme's "footprint"), and because of being its docking spot, the polymerase was unable to copy that bit. Thus a 100-base portion of the telomere was lost by a chromosome during each doubling as DNA replicated. Eventually, after some 50 doubling cycles, each with a round of DNA replication, the telomere would be used up and there would be no place for the DNA replication enzyme to sit. The cell line would then enter senescence, no longer able to proliferate.

This hypothesis was tested in 1998. Using genetic engineering, researchers transferred into newly established human cell cultures a gene that leads to expression of an enzyme called *telomerase* that all cells possess but no body cell uses. This enzyme adds TTAGGG sequences back to the end of telomeres, in effect rebuilding the lost portions of the telomere. Laboratory cultures of cell lines with (telomerase plus) and without (normal) this gene were then monitored for many generations. The graph above displays the results.

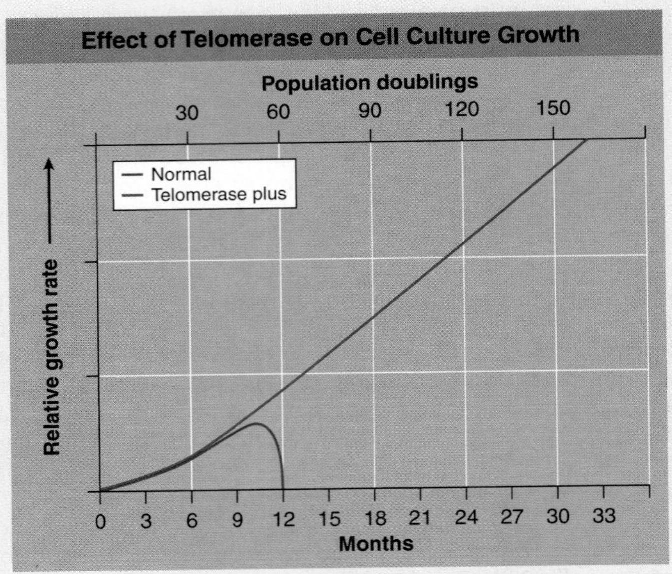

TTAGGG TTAGGG TTAGGG TTAGGG TTAGGG--------

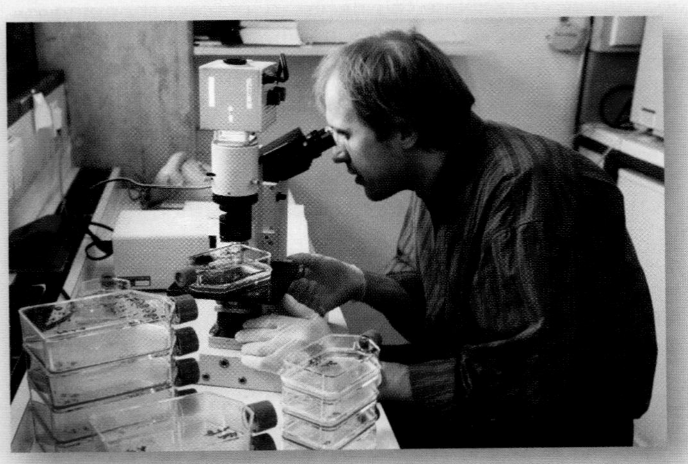

Analysis

1. **Applying Concepts** Comparing continuous processes, how do normal skin cells (blue line) differ in their growth history from telomerase plus cells with the telomerase gene (red line)?
2. **Interpreting Data** After how many doublings do the normal cells cease to divide? the telomerase plus cells?
3. **Making Inferences** After 9 population doublings, would the rate of cell division be different between the two cultures? after 15? Why?
4. **Drawing Conclusions** How does the addition of the telomerase gene affect the senescence (death by old age) of skin cells growing in culture? Does this result confirm the telomerase hypothesis this experiment had set out to test?

Summary of Learning Outcomes

Cell Division

Prokaryotes Have a Simple Cell Cycle

8.1.1 Prokaryotic cells divide in a two-step process: DNA replication followed by binary fission. The genetic information in a prokaryotic cell is present as a single loop of DNA. The DNA begins replication at a site called the origin of replication. The DNA double strand unzips, and new strands form along the original strands, producing two circular prokaryotic chromosomes that separate to the ends of the cell. New plasma membrane and cell wall are added down the middle of the cell, as shown here from **figure 8.1**, splitting the cell in two. This cell division, called binary fission, produces two daughter cells that are genetically identical to the parent cell.

Eukaryotic Cell Cycle

8.2.1 Cell division in eukaryotes is more complex than in prokaryotes because eukaryotic cells contain more DNA and their DNA is packaged into linear chromosomes.

- Eukaryotic cells divide by one of two methods, mitosis or meiosis. Mitosis occurs in nonreproductive cells, called somatic cells. Meiosis occurs in cells that are involved in sexual reproduction, forming germ-line cells, such as sperm and eggs.
- The complex cell cycle in eukaryotic cells can be subdivided into several phases: interphase, M phase, and C phase. Interphase is the first portion of the cell cycle. Interphase is also broken down into phases. The G_1 phase is the growing phase and takes up the major portion of the cell's life cycle. The S phase is the synthesis phase and is when the DNA is replicated. The G_2 phase involves the final preparations for cell division with the replication of mitochondria, chromosome condensation, and synthesis of microtubules.
- During the M phase the chromosomes are distributed into opposite sides of the cell. During the C phase the cell divides its cytoplasm into two separate daughter cells.

Chromosomes

8.3.1 All eukaryotic cells store their hereditary information in chromosomes. Coiling of the DNA into chromosomes allows it to fit into the nucleus. The number of chromosomes varies greatly between species. Most eukaryotes have between 10 and 50 chromosomes.

- Chromosomes exist in cells as pairs called homologous chromosomes. Two chromosomes that carry copies of the same genes, like the two shown here from **figure 8.2**, are homologous chromosomes.
- Before cells divide, the DNA replicates, forming two identical copies of each chromosome, called sister chromatids. Sister chromatids stay connected at an area called the centromere. Human somatic cells have 46 chromosomes, and after DNA replication, there are 92 sister chromatids.
- Chromosomes are not uniform; they vary in size, shape, and placement of centromeres. These variations allow researchers to match up homologues making an array, called a karyotype, where homologues are positioned next to each other.

8.3.2 The DNA in a chromosome is one long double-stranded fiber. After the DNA is replicated, it associates with proteins, forming chromatin. Chromatin begins to coil up in a process called condensation. The negatively charged DNA can coil up tightly because it wraps around positively charged histone proteins. There are several levels of chromosomal organization. The DNA wraps around a histone complex forming a nucleosome and then further folds and loops on itself forming a compact chromosome.

Cell Division

8.4.1 In interphase, the chromosomes replicate and then begin to condense. In the mitosis that follows, they will be drawn by microtubules to opposite ends of the cell.

- Prophase signals the beginning of mitosis. The DNA that was replicated during interphase condenses into chromosomes. The sister chromatids stay attached at the centromeres. The nuclear envelope disappears. Centrioles, when present, migrate to opposite sides of the cell, called the poles, and begin forming the spindle. Microtubules that form the spindle extend from the poles and attach to the chromosomes at the centromeres, anchoring sister chromatids to opposite poles.
- Metaphase involves the alignment of sister chromatids along the equatorial plane.
- During anaphase, the centromeres split, freeing the sister chromatids. The microtubules shorten, pulling the sister chromatids apart and toward opposite poles.
- Telophase signals the completion of nuclear division. The microtubule spindle is dismantled, the chromosomes begin to uncoil; nuclear envelopes form.

8.4.2 Following mitosis, the cell separates into two daughter cells in a process called cytokinesis. Cytokinesis in animal cells involves a pinching in of the cell around its equatorial plane until the cell eventually splits into two cells. Cytokinesis in plant cells involves the assembly of plasma membranes and cell walls between the two poles, eventually, forming two separate cells.

8.4.3 Many cells are programmed to die, either as part of development or after a set number of cell divisions (usually about 50 divisions). Only cancer cells appear to divide endlessly.

Cancer and the Cell Cycle

What Is Cancer?

8.5.1 Cancer is a growth disorder of cells. The unrestrained cell growth and division of a cancer is caused by damage to one or more of the genes that regulate the cell cycle. Cells with this sort of DNA mutation begin to divide in an uncontrolled way, forming a mass of cells called a tumor, shown here from **figure 8.10**. Metastases occur when cells from a tumor break away from the mass and spread to other tissues.

Test Your Understanding

8.1.1 Prokaryotes reproduce by
a. copying DNA, then undergoing binary fission.
b. splitting in half.
c. undergoing mitosis.
d. copying DNA, then undergoing the M phase.

8.2.1 The eukaryotic cell cycle is different from prokaryotic cell division in all the following ways *except*
a. the amount of DNA present in the cells.
b. how the DNA is packaged.
c. the production of genetically identical daughter cells.
d. the involvement of microtubules.

8.3.1 In eukaryotes, the genetic material is found in chromosomes, and
a. the more complex the organism, the more pairs of chromosomes it has.
b. many organisms have only one chromosome.
c. most eukaryotes have between 10 and 50 pairs of chromosomes.
d. most eukaryotes have between 2 and 10 pairs of chromosomes.

8.3.1 Homologous chromosomes
a. are also referred to as sister chromatids.
b. are genetically identical.
c. carry information about the same traits located in the same places on the chromosomes.
d. are connected to each other at their centromeres.

8.3.2 Chromosomes are composed of
a. DNA. **c.** chromatin.
b. proteins. **d.** All of the above.

8.4.1 In mitosis, when the duplicated chromosomes line up in the center of the cell, that stage is called
a. prophase. **c.** anaphase.
b. metaphase. **d.** telophase.

8.4.2 The division of the cytoplasm in the eukaryotic cell cycle is called
a. interphase. **c.** cytokinesis.
b. mitosis. **d.** binary fission.

8.4.3 Which of the following pairings is correct?
a. cell death/cytokinesis
b. animal cells/cell plate
c. plant cells/cleavage furrow
d. interphase/DNA replication

8.5.1 The cell cycle is controlled by
a. growth factors. **c.** centromeres.
b. histones. **d.** All of the above.

8.5.1 When cell division becomes unregulated, and a cluster of cells begins to grow without regard for the normal controls, that is called
a. a mutation. **c.** metastases.
b. cancer. **d.** oncogenes.

Apply Your Understanding

8.3.1 This karyotype shows a complete set of human chromosomes of an individual. At what stage of the cell cycle are such photos taken? Explain.

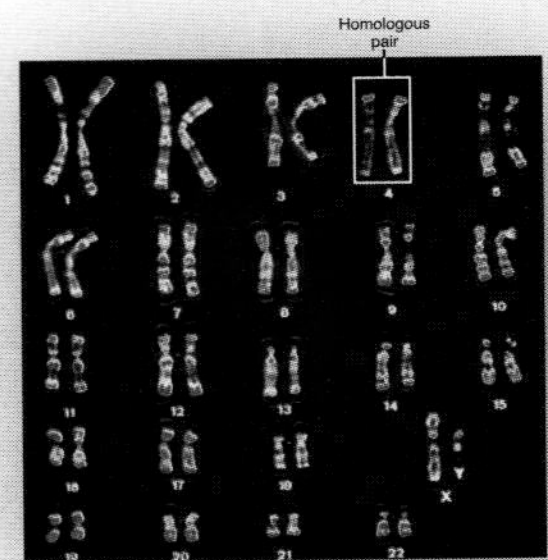

8.3.2 During interphase, the DNA is not visible through a microscope. Why isn't it visible, and why would you expect this to be the case?

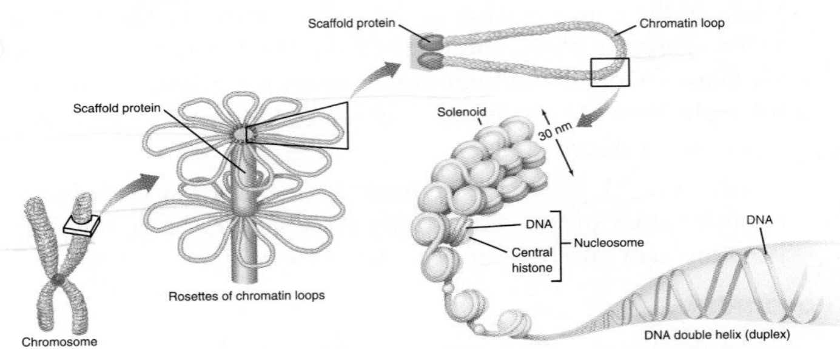

Synthesize What You Have Learned

8.4.1 Why does the DNA in a cell need to change periodically from a long, double-helix chromatin molecule into a tightly wound-up chromosome? What does it do in one configuration that it cannot do in the other?

8.5.1 Despite all we know about cancer today, some types of cancers are still increasing in frequency. Lung cancer in women is one of those. What reason(s) might there be for this increasing problem? Can you suggest a solution?

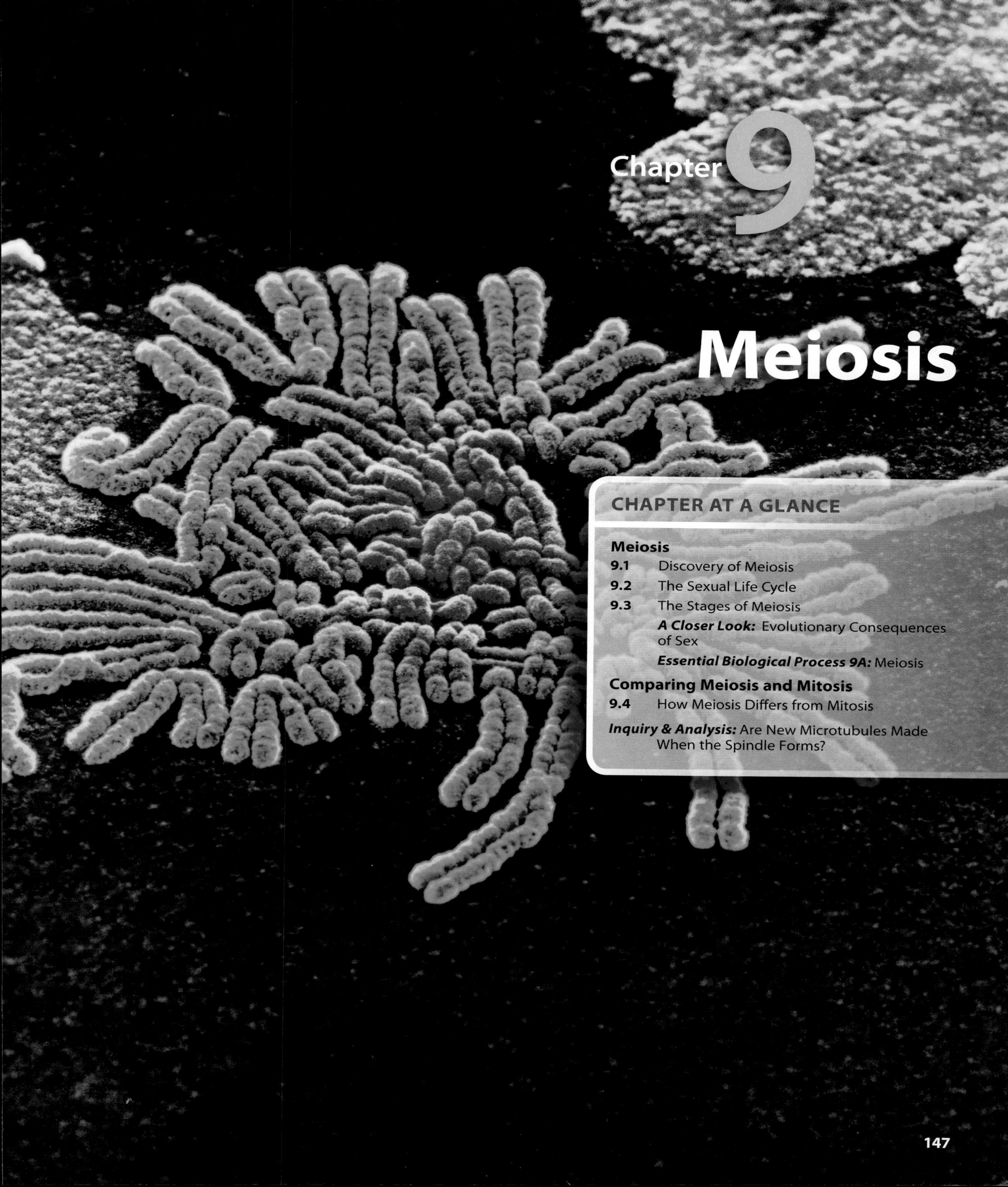

Chapter 9 Meiosis

CHAPTER AT A GLANCE

Meiosis

9.1 Discovery of Meiosis

9.2 The Sexual Life Cycle

9.3 The Stages of Meiosis

A Closer Look: Evolutionary Consequences of Sex

Essential Biological Process 9A: Meiosis

Comparing Meiosis and Mitosis

9.4 How Meiosis Differs from Mitosis

Inquiry & Analysis: Are New Microtubules Made When the Spindle Forms?

Meiosis

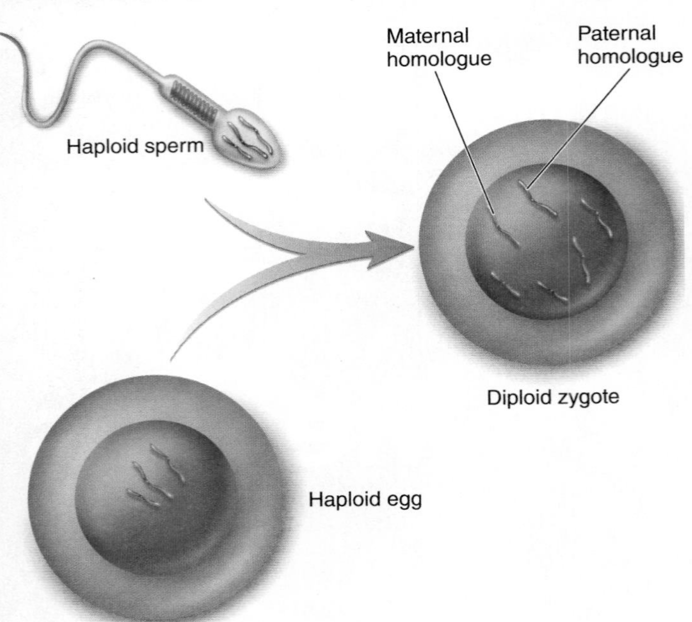

Figure 9.1 Diploid cells carry chromosomes from two parents.

A diploid cell contains two versions of each chromosome, a maternal homologue contributed by the haploid egg of the mother, and a paternal homologue contributed by the haploid sperm of the father.

IMPLICATION FOR YOU Many male veterans of the Vietnam War claim that their children born years later have birth defects caused by the herbicide Agent Orange used as a defoliant in the war. What types of cells would the chemical have to have affected in these men to cause the birth defects? How might these cells have become exposed to the chemical?

9.1 Discovery of Meiosis

LEARNING OBJECTIVE 9.1.1 Distinguish sexual from asexual reproduction, haploid from diploid, gamete from zygote, and meiosis from mitosis.

Only a few years after Walther Flemming's discovery of chromosomes in 1879, Belgian cytologist Pierre-Joseph van Beneden was surprised to find different numbers of chromosomes in different types of cells in the roundworm *Ascaris.* Specifically, he observed that the **gametes** (eggs and sperm) each contained two chromosomes, whereas the somatic (nonreproductive) cells of embryos and mature individuals each contained four. From his observations, van Beneden proposed in 1887 that an egg and a sperm, each containing half the complement of chromosomes found in other cells, fuse to produce a single cell called a **zygote.** The zygote, like all of the somatic cells ultimately derived from it, contains two copies of each chromosome. The fusion of gametes to form a new cell is called **fertilization,** or **syngamy.**

The Problem Solved by Meiosis

It was clear even to early investigators that gamete formation must involve some mechanism that reduces the number of chromosomes to half the number found in other cells. If it did not, the chromosome number would double with each fertilization, and after only a few generations, the number of chromosomes in each cell would become impossibly large. For example, after one generation the 46 chromosomes present in human cells would increase to 92 (46×2^1) chromosomes, after two generations it would increase to 184, and by 10 generations, the 46 chromosomes present in human cells would increase to over 47,000 (46×2^{10}) chromosomes.

The number of chromosomes does not explode in this way because of a special reduction division that occurs during gamete formation, producing cells with half the normal number of chromosomes. The subsequent fusion of two of these cells ensures a consistent chromosome number from one generation to the next. This reduction division process is known as **meiosis.**

Sexual Reproduction

Meiosis and fertilization together constitute a cycle of reproduction. Two sets of chromosomes are present in the somatic cells of adult individuals, making them **diploid** cells (Greek, *di,* two and often indicated by $2n$, where "n" is the number of sets of chromosomes), but only one set is present in the gametes, which are thus **haploid** (Greek, *haploos,* one and often indicated by $1n$). For example, if a sperm cell containing three chromosomes from the father fused with an egg cell containing three chromosomes from the mother, a diploid zygote with six chromosomes would result (figure 9.1). Reproduction that involves this alternation of meiosis and fertilization is called **sexual reproduction.** Some organisms however, reproduce by mitotic division and don't involve the fusion of gametes. Reproduction in these organisms is referred to as **asexual reproduction.** Some organisms are able to reproduce both asexually and sexually (figure 9.2).

Figure 9.2 Sexual and asexual reproduction.

Reproduction in an organism is not always either sexual or asexual. The strawberry reproduces both asexually (runners) and sexually (flowers).

Putting the Concept to Work

How many chromatids are present in a human gamete?

9.2 The Sexual Life Cycle

LEARNING OBJECTIVE 9.2.1 Compare the life cycles of protists, plants, and animals, distinguishing between somatic and germ-line cells.

Alternation of Generations

The life cycles of all sexually reproducing organisms follow the same basic pattern of alternation between diploid chromosome numbers and haploid ones (**figure 9.3**). In unicellular eukaryotic organisms like the protist shown in **figure 9.4*a***, individuals are haploid for most of their lives. When they encounter environmental stress, haploid cells sometimes fuse with other haploid cells to form a diploid cell. Later, this cell undergoes meiosis to reform the haploid phase.

In most animals, like the frog you see in **figure 9.4*b***, fertilization results in the formation of a diploid zygote. This single diploid cell divides by mitosis, eventually giving rise to the adult frog shown in the photo. Almost all animals are diploid for the multicellular stage of their life cycle.

In plants like the fern you see in **figure 9.4*c***, haploid and diploid individuals alternate. Certain cells of a diploid individual undergo meiosis making haploid gametes that divide repeatedly by mitosis to form a multicellular haploid individual. Some cells of this haploid individual eventually differentiate into eggs or sperm, which fuse to form a diploid zygote. Dividing by mitosis, the zygote forms a diploid individual.

Germ-Line Tissues

In animals, the cells that will eventually undergo meiosis to produce gametes are set aside from other cells early in the course of development. The cells of the body are called **somatic** cells, from the Latin word for "body," while gamete-forming cells, located in the reproductive organs of males and females, are referred to as **germ-line** cells. Both the somatic cells and the gamete-producing germ-line cells are diploid. Somatic cells undergo mitosis to form genetically identical, diploid daughter cells. The germ-line cells undergo meiosis, producing haploid gametes.

Putting the Concept to Work

How is the plant sexual life cycle different from the animal sexual life cycle?

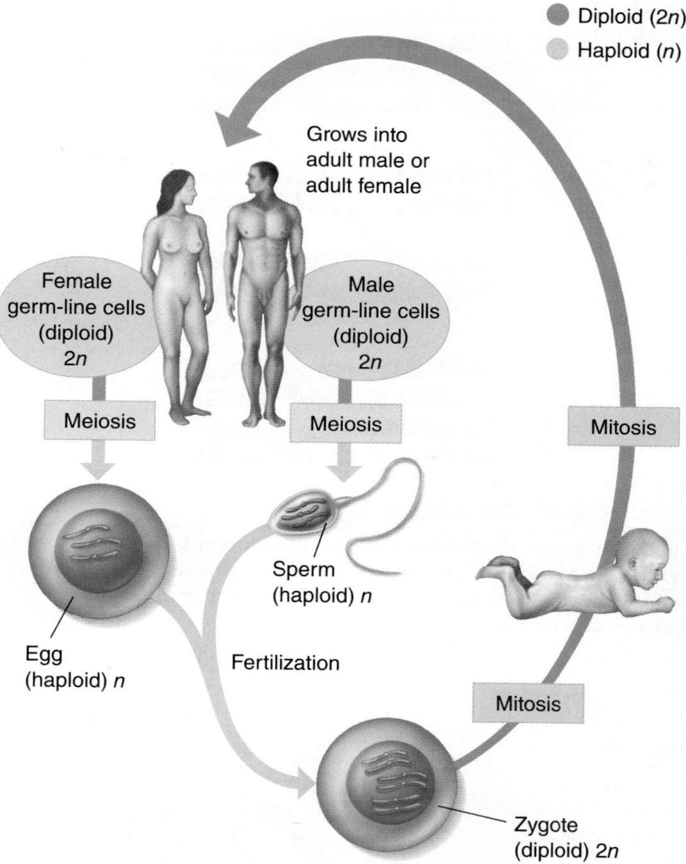

Figure 9.3 The sexual life cycle in animals.

In animals, the completion of meiosis is followed soon by fertilization. Thus, the vast majority of the life cycle is spent in the diploid stage. In this text, *n* stands for haploid and 2*n* stands for diploid. Germ-line cells are set aside early in development and undergo meiosis to form haploid gametes (eggs or sperm). The rest of the body cells are called somatic cells.

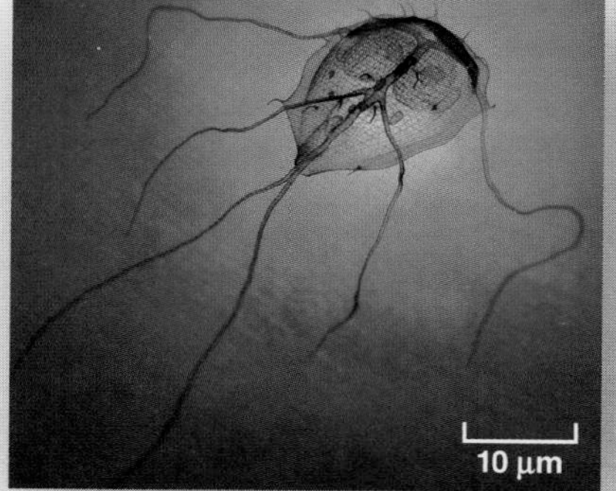

(a) Protist: spends most of its life cycle as a haploid individual

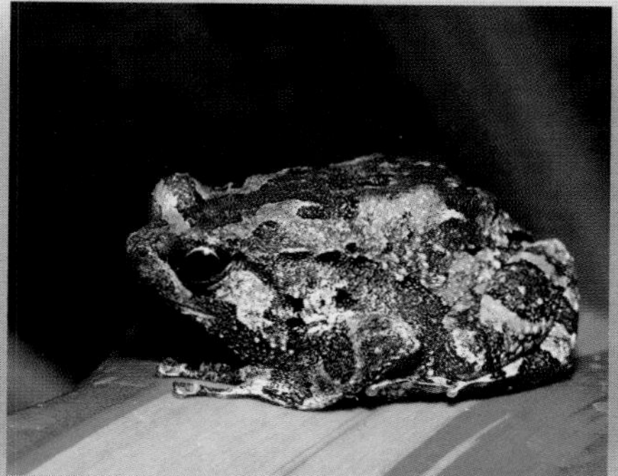

(b) Animal: spends most of its life cycle as a diploid individual

(c) Plant: spends significant portions of its life cycle as haploid and diploid individuals

Figure 9.4 Three types of sexual life cycles.

In sexual reproduction, haploid cells or organisms alternate with diploid cells or organisms.

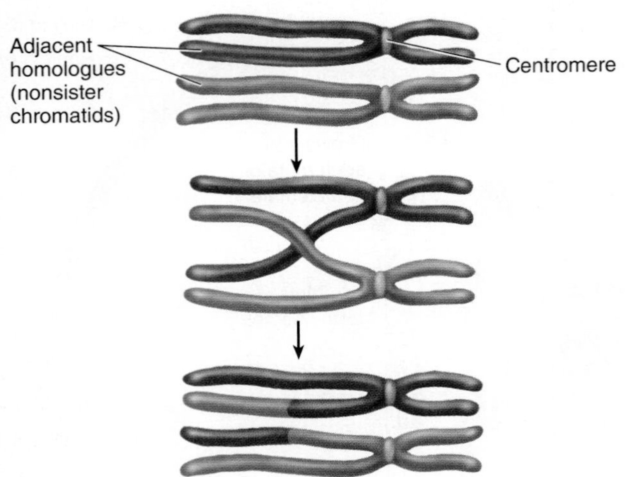

Figure 9.5 Crossing over.

In crossing over, the two homologues of a chromosome exchange portions. During the crossing over process, nonsister chromatids that are next to each other exchange chromosome arms or segments.

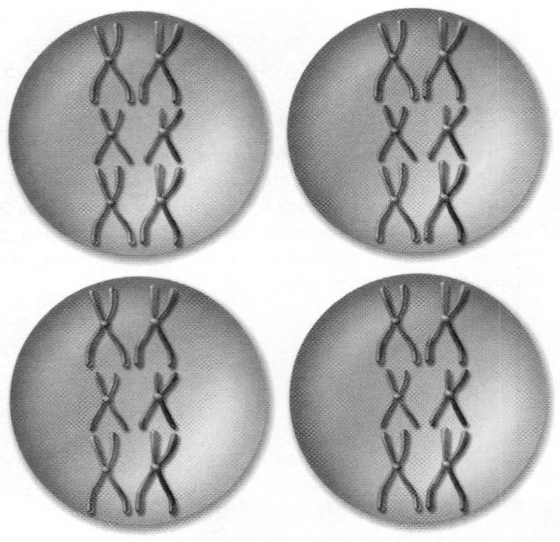

Figure 9.6 Independent assortment.

Independent assortment occurs because the orientation of chromosomes on the metaphase plate is random. Shown here are four possible orientations of chromosomes in a hypothetical cell. Each of the many possible orientations results in gametes with different combinations of parental chromosomes.

IMPLICATION FOR YOU The number of different combinations of gametes can be calculated using 2^n, where "n" is the number of pairs of chromosomes. Your family dog has 39 pairs of chromosomes, while you have 23 pairs. Considering only the independent assortment of homologous chromosomes to the gametes, how many more genetically different gametes are possible for your dog than for you?

9.3 The Stages of Meiosis

Now, let's look more closely at the process of meiosis. Just as in mitosis, the chromosomes have replicated before meiosis begins, during a period called interphase. The first of the two divisions of meiosis, called **meiosis I,** serves to separate the homologous chromosomes (or homologues); the second division, **meiosis II,** serves to separate the *sister chromatids.* Thus when meiosis is complete, what started out as one diploid cell ends up as four haploid cells. Because there was one replication of DNA but *two* cell divisions, the process reduces the number of chromosomes by half.

Meiosis I

LEARNING OBJECTIVE 9.3.1 Outline what happens in the four stages of meiosis I, describing the process of crossing over.

Meiosis I is traditionally divided into four stages (see the left side of *Essential Biological Process 9A* on page 152):

1. **Prophase I.** The two versions of each chromosome (the two homologues) pair up and exchange segments.
2. **Metaphase I.** The chromosomes align on a central plane.
3. **Anaphase I.** One homologue with its two sister chromatids still attached moves to a pole of the cell, and the other homologue moves to the opposite pole.
4. **Telophase I.** Individual chromosomes gather together at the two poles.

In **prophase I,** individual chromosomes first become visible, when viewed with a light microscope, as their DNA coils more and more tightly. Because the DNA replicates before the onset of meiosis, each of the thread-like chromosomes actually consists of two sister chromatids associated along their lengths and joined at their centromeres, just as in mitosis. However, now meiosis begins to differ from mitosis. During prophase I, the two homologous chromosomes line up side by side, physically touching one another, as you see in figure 9.5. It is at this point that a process called **crossing over** is initiated, in which the chromosomes actually break in the same place on both nonsister chromatids and sections of chromosomes are swapped between the homologous chromosomes, producing a hybrid chromosome that is part maternal chromosome (the green sections) and part paternal chromosome (the purple sections).

Crossing over between homologous chromosomes can occur because, as discussed in chapter 8 on page 136, homologues carry information about the same traits at the same locations on the chromosomes, although details of the information may vary between the homologues.

In **metaphase I,** the spindle apparatus forms, but because homologues are held close together by crossovers, spindle fibers can attach to only the outward-facing portion of each centromere. For each pair of homologues, the orientation on the metaphase plate is random. Each orientation of homologues results in gametes with different combinations of parental chromosomes. This process is called **independent assortment** (figure 9.6).

In **anaphase I,** the spindle attachment is complete, and homologues are pulled apart and move toward opposite poles. At the end of anaphase I, each pole has half as many chromosomes as were present in the cell when meiosis began. Remember that the chromosomes replicated and thus contained two sister chromatids before the start of meiosis, but sister chromatids are not counted as separate chromosomes. As in mitosis, count the number of centromeres to determine the number of chromosomes.

Evolutionary Consequences of Sex

Meiosis is a lot more complicated than mitosis. Why has evolution gone to so much trouble? While our knowledge of how meiosis and sex evolved is sketchy, it is abundantly clear that meiosis and sexual reproduction have an enormous impact on how species continue to evolve today, because of their ability to rapidly generate new genetic combinations. Three mechanisms each make key contributions: independent assortment, crossing over, and random fertilization.

Independent Assortment

The reassortment of genetic material that takes place during meiosis is the principal factor that has made possible the evolution of eukaryotic organisms, in all their bewildering diversity, over the past 1.5 billion years. Sexual reproduction represents an enormous advance in the ability of organisms to generate genetic variability. To understand, recall that most organisms have more than one pair of chromosomes. For example, the organism represented in the figure below has three pairs of chromosomes, each offspring receiving three homologues from each parent, purple from the father and green from the mother. The offspring in turn produces gametes, but the distribution of homologues into the gametes is completely random. A gamete could receive all homologues that are paternal in origin, as on the far left; or it could receive all maternal homologues, as on the far right, or any combination. Independent assortment alone leads to eight possible gamete combinations in this example. In humans, each gamete receives one homologue of each of the 23 chromosomes, but which homologue of a particular chromosome it receives is determined randomly. Each of the 23 pairs of chromosomes migrates independently, so there are 2^{23} (more than 8 million) different possible kinds of gametes that can be produced.

To make this point to his class, one professor offers an "A" course grade to any student who can write down all the possible combinations of heads and tails (an "either/or" choice, like that of a chromosome migrating to one pole or the other) with flipping a coin 23 times (like 23 chromosomes moving independently). No student has ever won an "A"; there are over 8 million possibilities.

Crossing Over

The DNA exchange that occurs when the arms of nonsister chromatids cross over adds even more recombination to the independent assortment of chromosomes that occurs later in meiosis. Thus, the number of possible genetic combinations that can occur among gametes is virtually unlimited.

Random Fertilization

Also, the zygote that forms a new individual is created by the fusion of two gametes, each produced independently, so fertilization squares the number of possible outcomes ($2^{23} \times 2^{23} = 70$ trillion).

Importance of Generating Diversity

Paradoxically, the evolutionary process is both revolutionary and conservative. It is revolutionary in that the pace of evolutionary change is quickened by genetic recombination, much of which results from sexual reproduction. It is conservative in that change is not always favored by selection, which may instead preserve existing combinations of genes. These conservative pressures appear to be greatest in some asexually reproducing organisms that do not move around freely and that live in especially demanding habitats. In vertebrates, on the other hand, the evolutionary premium appears to have been on versatility, and sexual reproduction is the predominant mode of reproduction.

Whatever the forces that led to sexual reproduction, its evolutionary consequences have been profound. No genetic process generates diversity more quickly; and as you will see in chapter 10, genetic diversity is the raw material of evolution, the fuel that drives it and determines its potential directions.

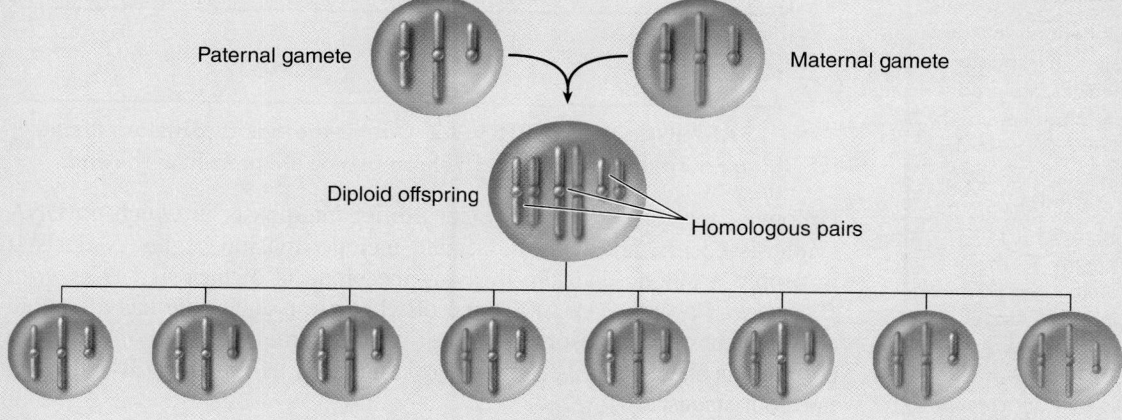

Independent assortment increases genetic variability.

Independent assortment contributes new gene combinations to the next generation because the orientation of chromosomes on the metaphase plate is random. In the cell shown here with three chromosome pairs, there are eight different gametes that can result, each with different combinations of parental chromosomes.

Essential Biological Process 9A

Meiosis

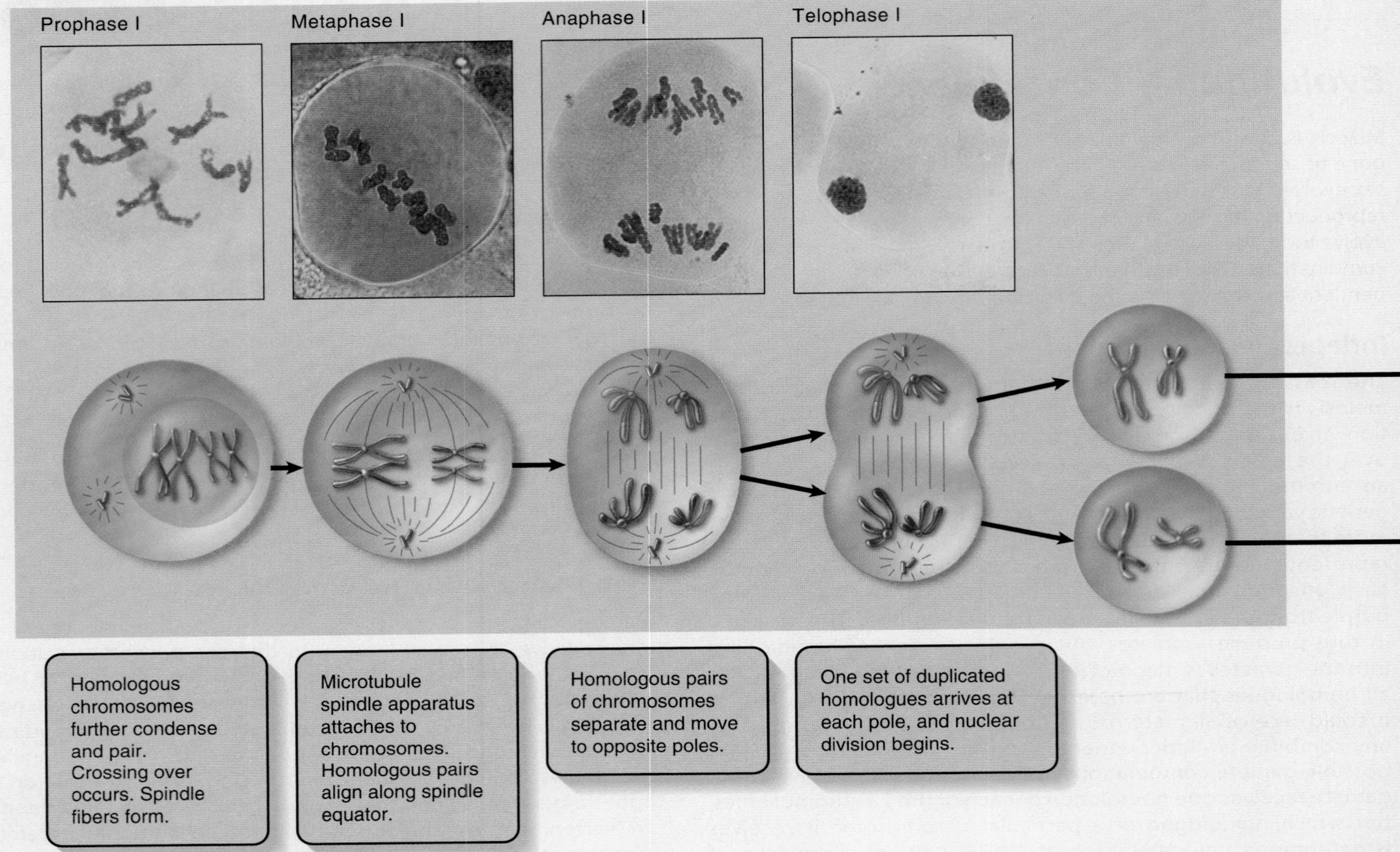

Homologous chromosomes further condense and pair. Crossing over occurs. Spindle fibers form.

Microtubule spindle apparatus attaches to chromosomes. Homologous pairs align along spindle equator.

Homologous pairs of chromosomes separate and move to opposite poles.

One set of duplicated homologues arrives at each pole, and nuclear division begins.

In **telophase I,** the chromosomes gather at their respective poles to form two chromosome clusters. After an interval, meiosis II occurs, in which the sister chromatids are separated as in mitosis.

Putting the Concept to Work

At the end of meiosis I, are sister chromatids still attached?

IN THE NEWS

Bloom's Syndrome. A rare inherited disorder called Bloom's syndrome has long puzzled investigators. Affected people have severe growth deficiencies, are predisposed to a wide variety of cancers, and are often sterile—a very unhappy state of affairs. What sort of gene disorder could lead to such a broad array of defects? Recent reports implicate events early in meiosis. It turns out that the gene defective in Bloom's syndrome patients encodes a protein dubbed BLM that binds to homologues early in meiotic prophase I. A properly functioning BLM protein is required to release homologues that are interlocked during crossover, in preparation for homologous chromosome separation during anaphase I. In Bloom's syndrome individuals, the BLM protein is defective and cannot remove cross-links that are created during crossover, resulting in a high incidence of gaps and breaks in homologous chromosomes as they separate.

Meiosis II

LEARNING OBJECTIVE 9.3.2 Outline the events of meiosis II, stating how many copies of each chromosome are present at the end.

Following meiosis I, the cells enter a brief interphase, in which no DNA synthesis occurs, and then the second meiotic division begins. Meiosis II is simply a mitotic division involving the products of meiosis I (*Essential Biological Process 9A*). At the end of telophase I, each pole has a haploid complement of chromosomes, each of which is still composed of two sister chromatids attached at the centromere. Like meiosis I, meiosis II is divided into four stages:

1. **Prophase II.** At the two poles of the cell, the clusters of chromosomes enter a brief prophase II, where a new spindle forms.

Meiosis II

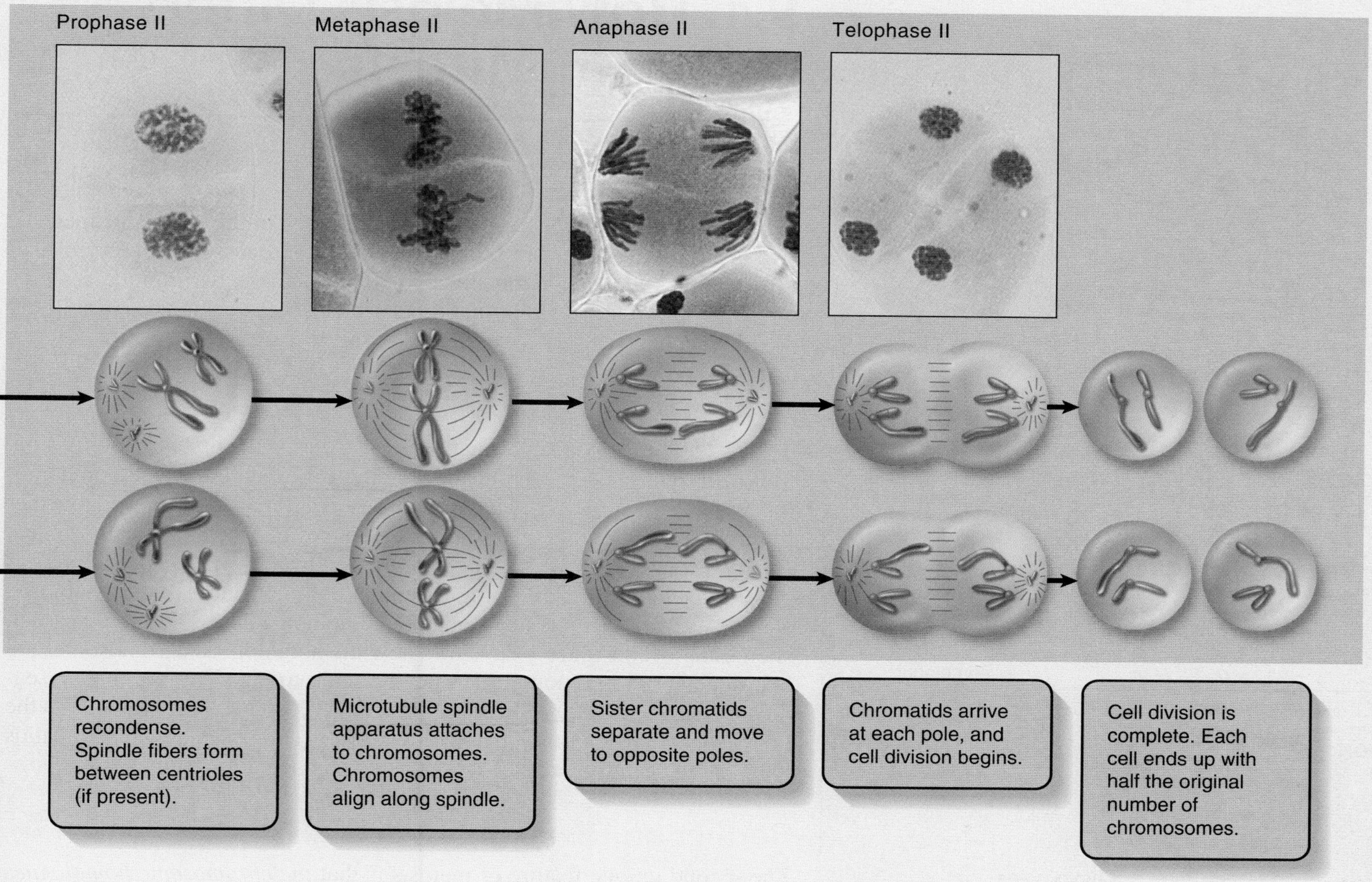

Prophase II

Metaphase II

Anaphase II

Telophase II

Chromosomes recondense. Spindle fibers form between centrioles (if present).

Microtubule spindle apparatus attaches to chromosomes. Chromosomes align along spindle.

Sister chromatids separate and move to opposite poles.

Chromatids arrive at each pole, and cell division begins.

Cell division is complete. Each cell ends up with half the original number of chromosomes.

2. **Metaphase II.** Spindle fibers bind to both sides of the centromeres, and the chromosomes line up along a central plane (figure 9.7).
3. **Anaphase II.** The spindle fibers shorten, splitting the centromeres and moving the sister chromatids to opposite poles.
4. **Telophase II.** Finally, the nuclear envelope re-forms around the four sets of daughter chromosomes.

The main outcome of the four stages of meiosis II is to separate the sister chromatids. The final result of this division is four cells containing haploid sets of chromosomes. No two are alike because of the crossing over in prophase I.

If you think about it, the key to meiosis is that the sister chromatids of each chromosome do not separate from each other in the first division, prevented by the crossing over that occurred in prophase I. Imagine two people dancing closely—you can tie a rope to the back of each person's belt, but you cannot tie a second rope to their belt buckles in front because the two dancers are facing each other and are very close. In just the same way, microtubules cannot attach to the inner sides of the centromeres to pull the two sister chromatids apart because crossing over holds the homologous chromosomes together like dancing partners.

Putting the Concept to Work

Do sister chromatids separate in meiosis I or II?

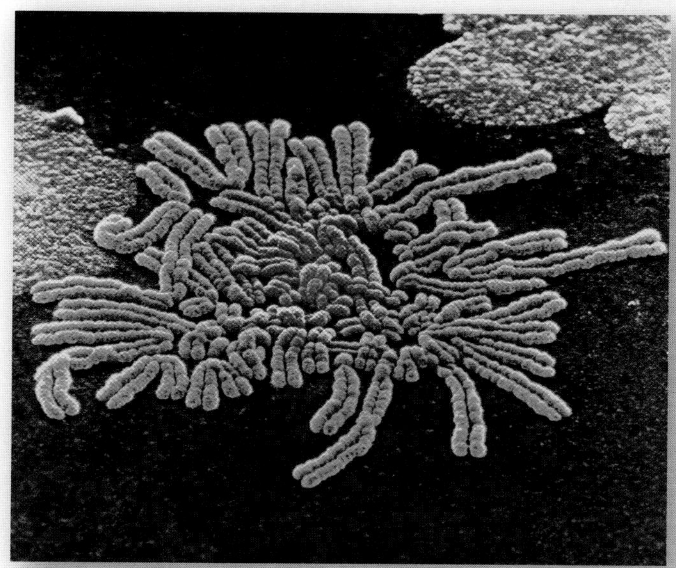

Figure 9.7 Getting ready to divide.

These human metaphase chromosomes are lining up to divide. Note that the sister chromatids have not yet been pulled apart.

Comparing Meiosis and Mitosis

9.4 How Meiosis Differs from Mitosis

LEARNING OBJECTIVE 9.4.1 **Explain the two unique features that distinguish meiosis from mitosis.**

While there are differences between eukaryotes in the details of meiosis, two consistent features are seen in the meiotic processes of every eukaryote: synapsis and reduction division. Indeed, these two unique features are the key differences that distinguish meiosis from mitosis, which you studied in chapter 8.

Synapsis

The first of these two features happens early during the first nuclear division. Following chromosome replication, homologous chromosomes or homologues *pair all along their lengths,* with sister chromatids being held together by proteins called cohesin. While homologues are thus physically joined, *genetic exchange occurs at one or more points between them.* The process of forming these complexes of homologous chromosomes is called **synapsis,** and the exchange process between paired homologues, as described earlier, is crossing over. Figure 9.8*a* shows how the homologous chromosomes are held together close enough that they are able to physically exchange segments of their DNA. Sister chromatids do not separate from each other in the first nuclear division, so each homologue is still composed of two chromatids joined at the centromere, and still considered one chromosome.

Reduction Division

The second unique feature of meiosis is that *the chromosome homologues do not replicate between the two nuclear divisions,* so that chromosome assortment in the second division separates sister chromatids of each chromosome into different daughter cells.

In most respects, the second meiotic division is identical to a normal mitotic division. However, because of the crossing over that occurred during the first division, the sister chromatids in meiosis II are not identical to each other. Also, there are only half the number of chromosomes in each cell at the beginning of meiosis II because only one of the homologues is present. Figure 9.8*b* shows how reduction division occurs. The diploid cell in the figure contains four chromosomes (two homologous pairs). After meiosis I, the cells contain just two chromosomes (remember to count the number of *centromeres*, because sister chromatids are not considered separate chromosomes). During meiosis II, the sister chromatids separate, but each gamete still only contains two chromosomes, half as many of the germ-line cell.

Because mitosis and meiosis use similar terminology, it is easy to confuse the two processes. Figure 9.9 compares the two processes side-by-side. Both processes start with a diploid cell, but you can see that early during meiosis I crossing over occurs, and that as a consequence homologous *pairs*, not individual centromeres, line up along the meiosis I metaphase plate. These two differences result in haploid cells in meiosis and diploid cells in mitosis.

Putting the Concept to Work

How do two sister chromatids entering meiosis II differ?

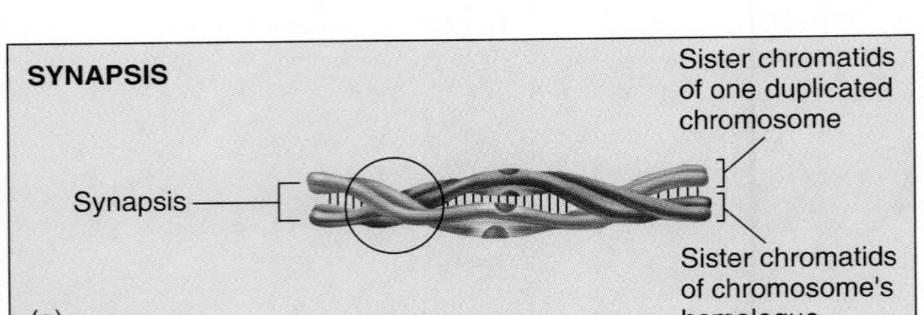

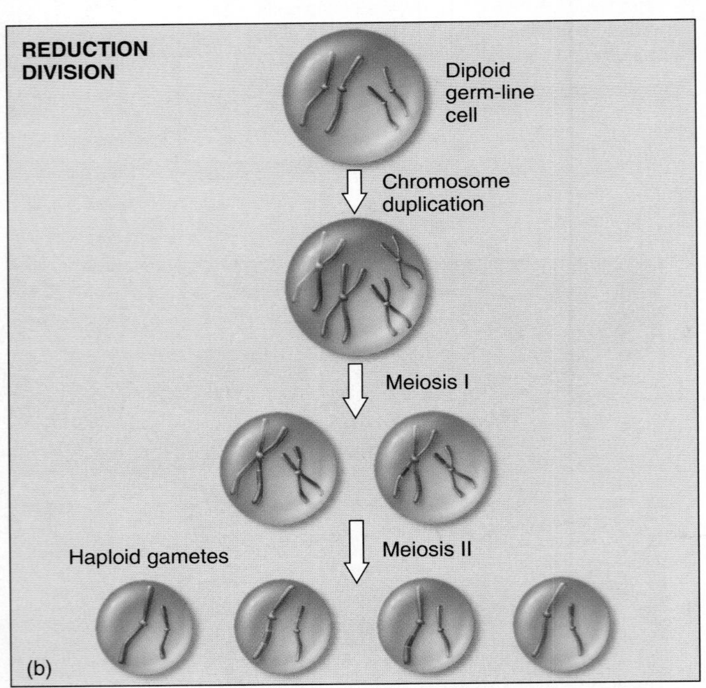

Figure 9.8 **Unique features of meiosis.**

(a) Synapsis draws homologous chromosomes together, all along their lengths, creating a situation (indicated by the circle) where two homologues can physically exchange portions of arms, a process called crossing over. (b) Reduction division, omitting a chromosome duplication before meiosis II, produces haploid gametes, thus ensuring that the chromosome number remains the same as that of the parents, following fertilization.

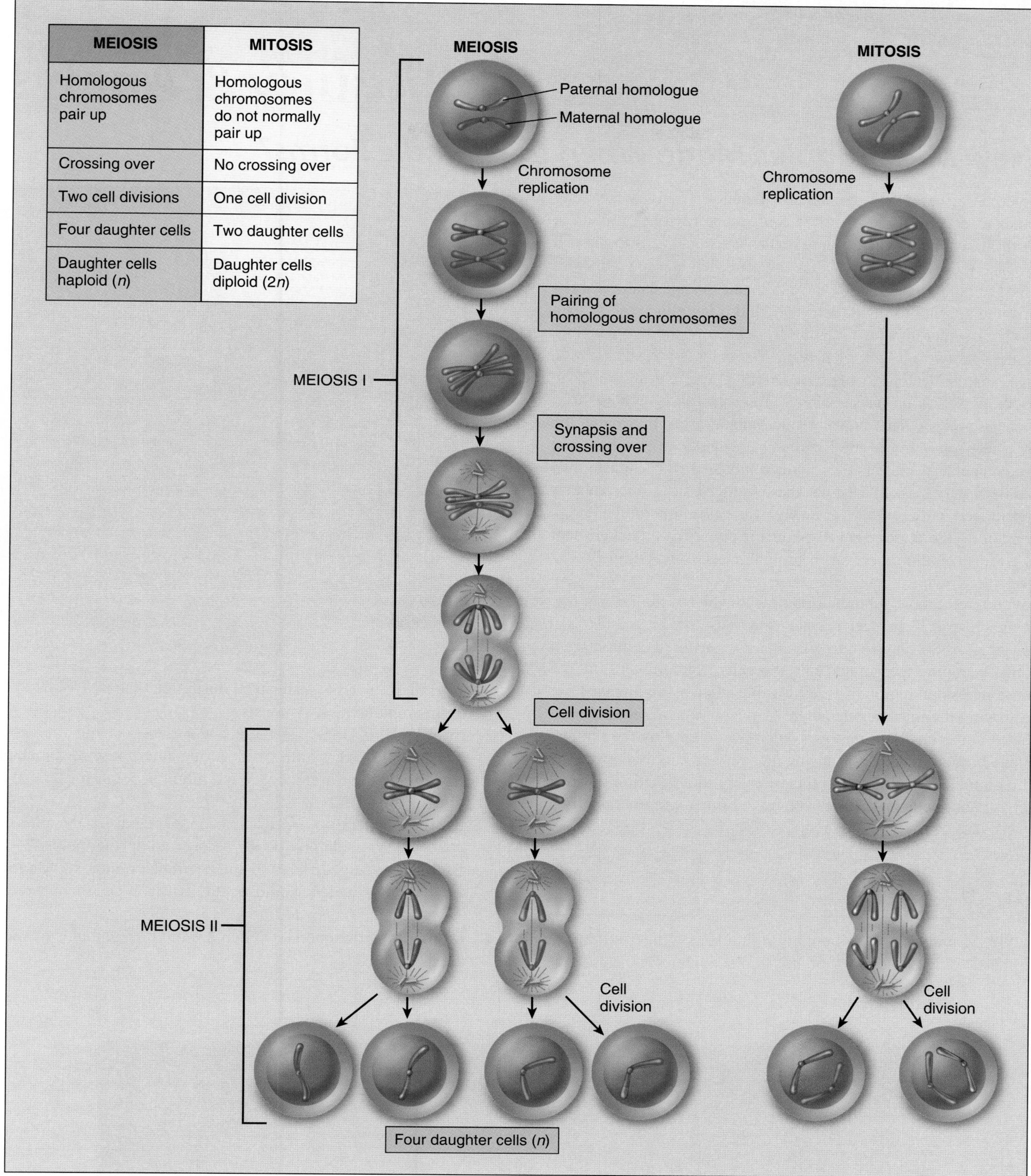

Figure 9.9 A comparison of meiosis and mitosis.

Meiosis differs from mitosis in several key ways, highlighted by the orange boxes. Meiosis involves two nuclear divisions with no DNA replication between them. It thus produces four daughter cells, each with half the original number of chromosomes. Also, crossing over occurs in prophase I of meiosis. Mitosis involves a single nuclear division after DNA replication. Thus, it produces two daughter cells, each containing the original number of chromosomes, which are genetically identical to those in the parent cell.

Inquiry & Analysis

Are New Microtubules Made When the Spindle Forms?

During interphase, before the beginning of meiosis, only a few long microtubules extend from the so-called *centrosome* (a zone around the centrioles of animal cells where microtubules are organized) to the cell periphery. Like most microtubules, they are refreshed at a low rate with resynthesis. Late in prophase, however, a dramatic change can be seen—the centrosome appears to divide into two, and a large increase is seen in the number of microtubules radiating from each of the two daughter centrosomes. The two clusters of new microtubules are easily seen as the green fibers connecting to the two sets of purple chromosomes in the micrograph of early prophase below (a **micrograph** is a photo taken through a microscope). This burst of microtubule assembly marks the beginning of the formation of the spindle characteristic of prophase and metaphase. When these clusters of new microtubules first became known to cell biologists, they asked whether these were existing microtubules being repositioned in the spindle, or newly synthesized microtubules.

The graph to the upper right displays the results of an experiment designed to answer this question. Mammalian cells in culture (cells **in culture** are growing in the laboratory on artificial medium) were injected with microtubule subunits (tubulin) to which a fluorescent dye had been attached (a **fluorescent dye** is one that glows when exposed to ultraviolet or short-wavelength visual light). After the fluorescent subunits had become incorporated into the cells' microtubules, all the fluorescence in a small region of a cell was bleached by an intense laser beam, destroying the microtubules there. Any subsequent rebuilding of microtubules in the bleached region would have to employ the fluorescent subunits present in the cell, causing recovery of fluorescence in the bleached region. The graph reports this recovery as a function of time, for interphase and metaphase cells. The dotted line represents the time for 50% recovery of fluorescence ($t_{1/2}$) (that is, $t_{1/2}$ is the time required for half of the microtubules in the region to be resynthesized).

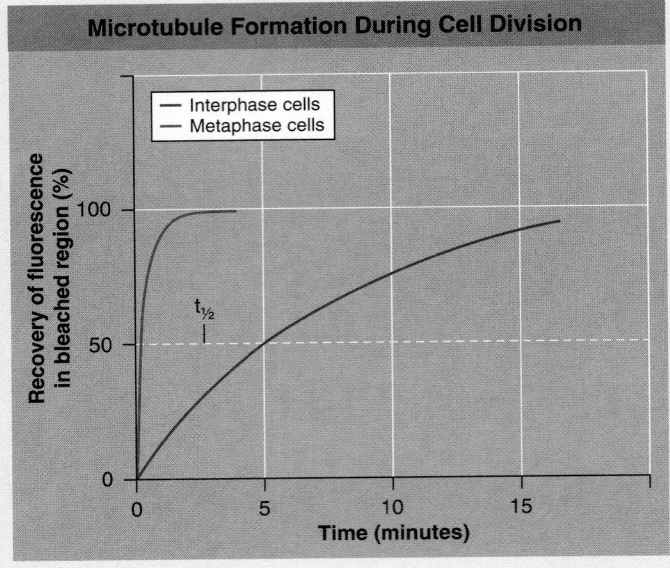

Analysis

1. **Applying Concepts** Are new microtubules synthesized during interphase? What is the $t_{1/2}$ of this replacement synthesis? Are new microtubules synthesized during metaphase? What is the $t_{1/2}$ of this replacement synthesis?
2. **Interpreting Data** Is there a difference in the rate at which microtubules are synthesized during interphase and metaphase? How big is the difference? What might account for it?
3. **Making Inferences**
   a. What general statement can be made regarding the relative rates of microtubule production before and during meiosis?
   b. Is there any difference in the final amount of microtubule synthesis which would occur if this experiment were to be continued for an additional 15 minutes?
4. **Drawing Conclusions** When are the microtubules of the spindle assembled?

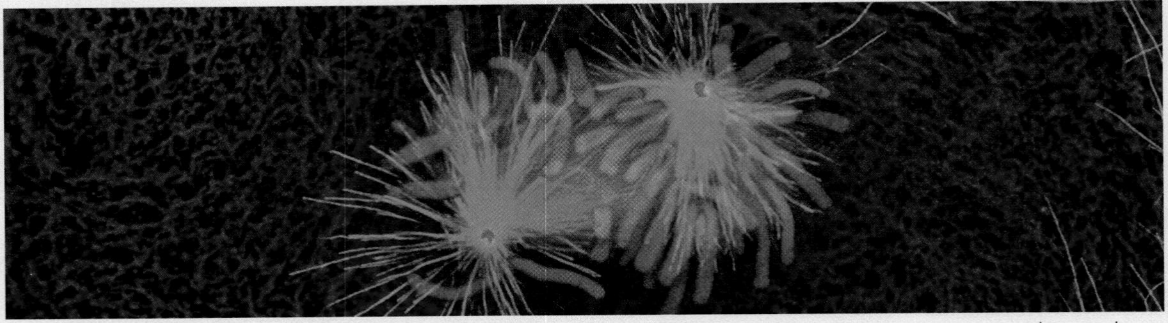

10 μm

Summary of Learning Outcomes

Meiosis

Discovery of Meiosis

9.1.1 Meiosis is a form of cell division in which the number of chromosomes is halved during gamete formation. In sexually reproducing organisms, a gamete from the male fuses with a gamete from the female to form a cell called the zygote. This process is called fertilization or syngamy, as shown here from **figure 9.1**. The number of chromosomes in gametes must be halved to maintain the correct number of chromosomes in offspring.

- A cell that contains a full set of chromosomes, two copies of each chromosome, is called a diploid cell. Cells, such as gametes, that contain only one copy of each chromosome are haploid cells.
- Sexual reproduction involves meiosis, but some organisms also undergo asexual reproduction, which is reproducing by mitosis or binary fission.

The Sexual Life Cycle

9.2.1 In the sexual life cycle, there is an alternation between diploid and haploid stages, with variation in the amount of time devoted to each stage. Three types of sexual life cycles exist: In many protists the majority of the life cycle is devoted to the haploid stage; in most animals the majority of the life cycle is devoted to the diploid stage; and in plants the life cycle is split more equally between a haploid stage and a diploid stage.

- Germ-line cells of an organism are diploid but produce haploid gametes through meiosis.

The Stages of Meiosis

9.3.1 Meiosis involves two nuclear divisions, meiosis I and meiosis II, each containing a prophase, metaphase, anaphase, and telophase. Like mitosis, the DNA replicates during interphase, before meiosis begins. Because there are two nuclear divisions but only one round of DNA replication, the four daughter cells contain half the number of chromosomes as the parent cell.

- During meiosis I, homologous chromosomes move to opposite poles of the cell. Meiosis I is divided into four stages: prophase I, metaphase I, anaphase I, and telophase I. Prophase I is distinguished by the exchange of genetic material between homologous chromosomes, a process called crossing over. In this process, homologous chromosomes align with each other along their lengths, and sections of non-sister chromatids are physically exchanged, as shown here from **figure 9.5**. This recombines the genetic information contained in the chromosomes.

- During metaphase I, microtubules in the spindle apparatus attach to homologous chromosomes, and chromosome pairs align along the metaphase plate. The alignment of the chromosomes is random: there is shuffling in the arrangement of paternal and maternal chromosomes along the metaphase plate, leading to the independent assortment of chromosomes into the gametes.
- The homologous chromosomes separate during anaphase I, being pulled apart by the spindle apparatus toward their respective poles. This differs from mitosis and later in meiosis II, where sister chromatids separate in anaphase.
- In telophase I, the chromosomes cluster at the poles. This leads to the next phase of meiosis, called meiosis II.

9.3.2 Meiosis II mirrors mitosis in that it involves the separation of sister chromatids through the phases of prophase II, metaphase II, anaphase II, and telophase II. Meiosis II differs from mitosis in that there is no DNA replication before meiosis II. Because homologous pairs were separated during meiosis I, each daughter cell, shown forming here in telophase II from ***Essential Biological Process 9A***, has only one-half the number of chromosomes. Also, the chromosomes in the daughter cells at the end of meiosis II are not genetically identical because of crossing over.

Comparing Meiosis and Mitosis

How Meiosis Differs from Mitosis

9.4.1 Two processes that distinguish meiosis from mitosis are crossing over through synapsis and reduction division.

- When homologous chromosomes come together during prophase I, they associate with each other along their lengths, a process called synapsis. Synapsis does not occur in mitosis. During synapsis, sections of homologous chromosomes are physically exchanged in crossing over. Crossing over results in daughter cells that are not genetically identical to the parent cell or to each other. In contrast, mitosis results in daughter cells that are genetically identical to the parent cell and to each other.
- Meiosis also differs from mitosis in reduction division, where the daughter cells contain half the number of chromosomes as the parent cell. As shown here from **figure 9.8*b***, reduction division occurs because meiosis contains two nuclear divisions (the first in meiosis I where the parent cell divides in two and the second in meiosis II, where the cells produced in meiosis I divide producing four daughter cells) but only one round of DNA replication during interphase.

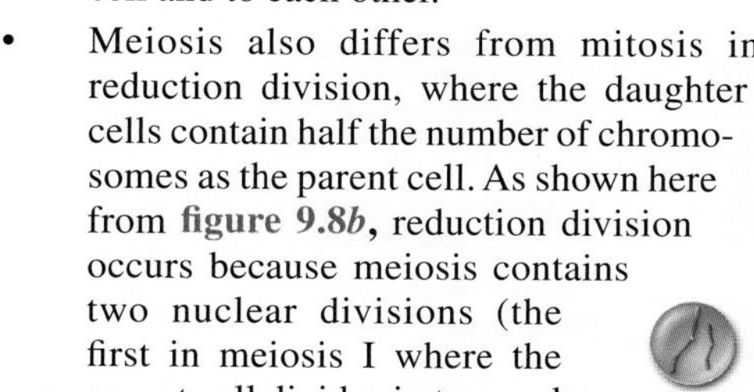

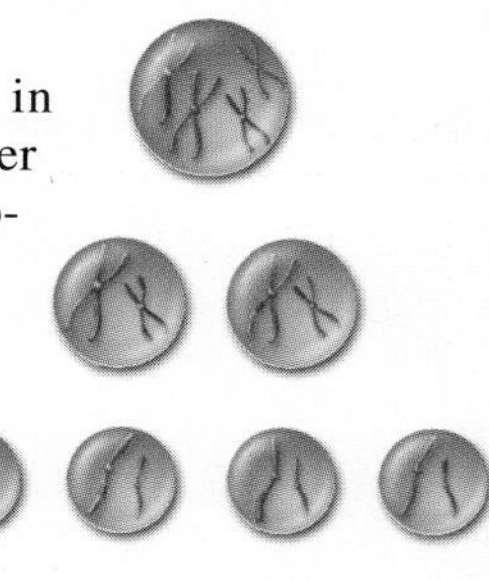

- The primary reasons for the differences in meiosis and mitosis stem from the synapsis of homologous chromosomes in prophase I. Because of synapsis, the arms of homologous chromosomes are close enough to undergo crossing over. Also, the close association of the homologous chromosomes in synapsis blocks the inner centromeres from attaching to the spindle. As a result, sister chromatids do not separate during meiosis I, resulting in reduction division.

Test Your Understanding

9.1.1 An egg and a sperm unite to form a new organism. To prevent the new organism from having twice as many chromosomes as its parents,
- **a.** half of the chromosomes in the new organism quickly disassemble, leaving the correct number.
- **b.** half of the chromosomes from the egg, and half from the sperm, are ejected from the new cell.
- **c.** the large egg contains all the chromosomes, the tiny sperm only contributes some DNA.
- **d.** the egg and sperm have only half the number of chromosomes found in the parents because of meiosis.

9.1.1 The diploid number of chromosomes in humans is 46. The haploid number is
- **a.** 138.
- **b.** 92.
- **c.** 46.
- **d.** 23.

9.2.1 In organisms that have sexual life cycles, there is a time when there are
- **a.** $1n$ gametes (haploid), followed by $2n$ zygotes (diploid).
- **b.** $2n$ gametes (haploid), followed by $1n$ zygotes (diploid).
- **c.** $2n$ gametes (diploid), followed by $1n$ zygotes (haploid).
- **d.** $1n$ gametes (diploid), followed by $2n$ zygotes (haploid).

9.3.1 Crossing over occurs during prophase I and is when
- **a.** homologous chromosomes exchange sections of chromosomes.
- **b.** homologous chromosomes cross over to opposite sides of the cell.
- **c.** sister chromatids exchange genetic information.
- **d.** the DNA replicates forming two sister chromatids that are attached at the centromere.

9.3.1 Which of the following occurs in meiosis I?
- **a.** All chromosomes duplicate.
- **b.** Homologous chromosomes randomly orient themselves on the metaphase plate, called independent assortment.
- **c.** The duplicated sister chromatids separate.
- **d.** The original cell divides into four diploid cells.

9.3.1 During which stage of meiosis does synapsis occur?
- **a.** prophase I
- **b.** anaphase I
- **c.** metaphase II
- **d.** interphase

9.3.2 Which of the following occurs in meiosis II?
- **a.** All chromosomes duplicate.
- **b.** Homologous chromosomes randomly separate, called independent assortment.
- **c.** The duplicated sister chromatids separate.
- **d.** Genetically identical daughter cells are produced.

9.4.1 Synapsis is the process whereby
- **a.** homologous pairs of chromosomes separate and migrate toward a pole.
- **b.** homologous chromosomes exchange chromosomal material.
- **c.** homologous chromosomes become closely associated.
- **d.** the daughter cells contain half of the number of chromosomes of the parent cell.

9.4.1 Mitosis results in ____, while meiosis results in _____.
- **a.** cells that are genetically identical to the parent cell/haploid cells
- **b.** haploid cells/diploid cells
- **c.** four daughter cells/two daughter cells
- **d.** cells with half the number of chromosomes as the parent cell/ cells which vary in chromosome number

9.4.1 Sister chromatids don't separate during meiosis I because
- **a.** they are held together through synapsis.
- **b.** of crossing over.
- **c.** the spindle fibers can only attach to the outward-facing side of the centromeres.
- **d.** All of the above.

Apply Your Understanding

9.3.1 How is it that, in meiosis, you can end up with four "daughter cells" that are all genetically different from one another?

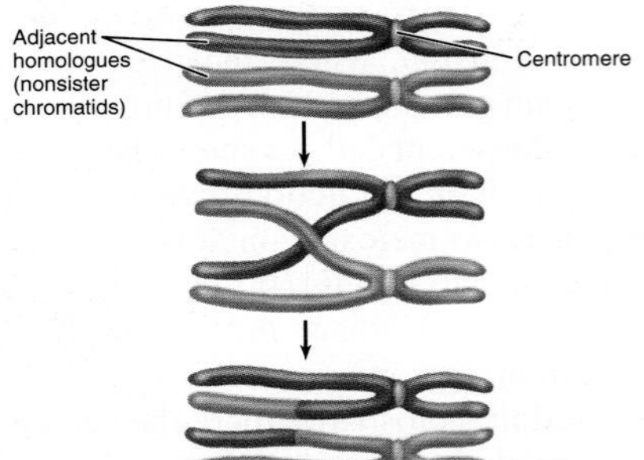

9.4.1 Referring to the homologous chromosomes shown here during prophase I, and knowing that they stay in synapsis during metaphase I, explain why it is that the sister chromatids don't separate in meiosis I as they do in mitosis.

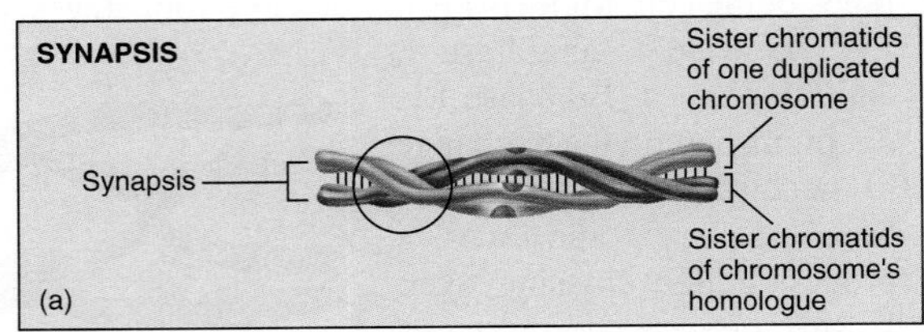

Synthesize What You Have Learned

9.1.1 It would seem that you only need one set of instructions for your body to do all the jobs it needs to carry out. So why aren't organisms simply haploid all their lives?

9.2.1 Are the gamete cells of your body haploid or diploid? Why not the alternative?

9.4.1 An organism has 56 chromosomes in its diploid stage. Indicate how many chromosomes are present in the following, and explain your reasoning:
- **a.** somatic cells
- **b.** metaphase I
- **c.** metaphase II
- **d.** gametes

Chapter 10

Foundations of Genetics

CHAPTER AT A GLANCE

Mendel

10.1 Mendel and the Garden Pea

10.2 What Mendel Observed

10.3 Mendel Proposes a Theory

10.4 Mendel's Laws

From Genotype to Phenotype

10.5 How Genes Influence Traits

10.6 Why Some Traits Don't Show Mendelian Inheritance

Today's Biology: Does Environment Affect I.Q.?

Chromosomes and Heredity

10.7 Chromosomes Are the Vehicles of Mendelian Inheritance

10.8 Human Chromosomes

Human Hereditary Disorders

10.9 Studying Pedigrees

10.10 The Role of Mutations in Human Heredity

10.11 Genetic Counseling and Therapy

Inquiry & Analysis: Why Woolly Hair Runs in Families

Mendel

10.1 Mendel and the Garden Pea

LEARNING OBJECTIVE 10.1.1 Contrast the experiments of T. A. Knight and Gregor Mendel.

When you were born, many things about you resembled your mother or father (**figure 10.1**). This tendency for traits to be passed from parent to offspring is called **heredity.** *Traits* are the expressions of a character, or a heritable feature. How does heredity happen? Before DNA and chromosomes were discovered, this puzzle was one of the greatest mysteries of science. The key to understanding the puzzle of heredity was found in the garden of an Austrian monastery over a century ago by a monk named Gregor Mendel. Mendel's solution to the puzzle of heredity was the first step on our journey to understanding heredity and one of the greatest intellectual accomplishments in the history of science.

Figure 10.1 Families look alike.

These two young women are mother and daughter. It is no accident that they look so much alike, as the daughter shares half her mother's genes.

IMPLICATION FOR YOU Not all members of families look as much alike as this. In your family, do your brothers and sisters resemble you a lot? See if you can learn in this chapter why all the children in your family might not look alike.

Early Ideas About Heredity

Mendel was not the first person to try to understand heredity by crossing pea plants (**figure 10.2**). Over 200 years earlier British farmers had performed similar crosses and obtained results similar to Mendel's. They observed that in crosses between two types—tall and short plants, for example—one type would disappear in one generation, only to reappear in the next. In the 1790s, for example, the British farmer T. A. Knight crossed a variety of the garden pea that had purple flowers with one that had white flowers. All the offspring of the cross had purple flowers. If two of these offspring were crossed, however, some of *their* offspring were white! Knight noted that the purple had a "stronger tendency" to appear than white, but he did not count the numbers of each kind of offspring.

Petals
Anther ♂
Carpel ♀

Gregor Mendel

Figure 10.2 The garden pea flower.

Because it is easy to cultivate and because there are many distinctive varieties, the garden pea, *Pisum sativum,* was a popular choice as an experimental subject in investigations of heredity for as long as a century before Mendel's studies. The flower shown here is partially cut away to show internal structures.

Mendel's Experiments

Gregor Mendel was born in 1822 to peasant parents and was educated in a monastery. He became a monk and was sent to the University of Vienna to study science and mathematics. Although he aspired to become a scientist and teacher, he failed his university exams and returned to the monastery, where he spent the rest of his life, eventually becoming abbot. Upon his return, Mendel joined an informal neighborhood science club. Under the patronage of a local nobleman, each member set out to undertake scientific investigations, which were then discussed at meetings and published in the club's own journal. Mendel undertook to repeat the classic crosses with pea plants done by Knight, but this time he intended to count the numbers of each kind of offspring in the hope that the numbers would give some hint of what was going on. Quantitative approaches to science—measuring and counting—were just becoming fashionable in Europe.

Putting the Concept to Work

Do you think it fair that Knight is not mentioned alongside Mendel today? Explain your response.

Mendel's Experimental System: The Garden Pea

LEARNING OBJECTIVE 10.1.2 List four characteristics that made the garden pea easy for Mendel to study, and describe Mendel's experimental design.

Mendel chose to study the garden pea because several of its characteristics made it easy to work with:

1. Many varieties were available. Mendel selected seven pairs of lines that differed in easily distinguished traits (including the white versus purple flowers that Knight had studied 60 years earlier).
2. Mendel knew from the work of Knight and others that he could expect the infrequent version of a character to disappear in one generation and reappear in the next. He knew, in other words, that he would have something to count.
3. Pea plants are small, easy to grow, produce large numbers of offspring, and mature quickly.
4. The reproductive organs of peas are enclosed within their flowers (see figure 10.2). Left alone, the flowers do not open. They simply fertilize themselves with their own pollen (male gametes). To carry out a cross, Mendel had only to pry the petals apart, reach in with a pair of scissors, and snip off the male organs (anthers); he could then dust the female organs (the tip of the carpel) with pollen from another plant to make the cross.

Flowers are the reproductive structures in a group of plants called angiosperms. Angiosperm reproduction, through the pollination and fertilization of flowers, is discussed in more detail on pages 636 through 639.

Mendel's Experimental Design

Mendel's experimental design was the same as Knight's, only Mendel counted his plants. The crosses were carried out in three steps that are presented in figure 10.3:

1. Mendel began by letting each variety self-fertilize for several generations. This ensured that each variety was true-breeding, meaning that it contained no other varieties of the trait, and so would produce only offspring of the same variety when it self-pollinated. The white flower variety, for example, produced only white flowers and no purple ones in each generation. Mendel called these lines the P generation (P for parental).
2. Mendel then conducted his experiment: He crossed two pea varieties exhibiting alternative traits, such as white versus purple flowers. The offspring that resulted he called the F_1 generation (F_1 for "first filial" generation, from the Latin word for "son" or "daughter").
3. Finally, Mendel allowed the plants produced in the crosses of step 2 to self-fertilize, and he counted the numbers of each kind of offspring that resulted in this F_2 ("second filial") generation. As reported by Knight and shown in step 3, the white flower trait reappeared in the F_2 generation, although not as frequently as the purple flower trait.

Putting the Concept to Work

In Mendel's crosses, the offspring of the F_1 generation self-fertilized to produce the F_2 generation. Why didn't Mendel allow the parent plants to self-fertilize like this in making the F_1 generation?

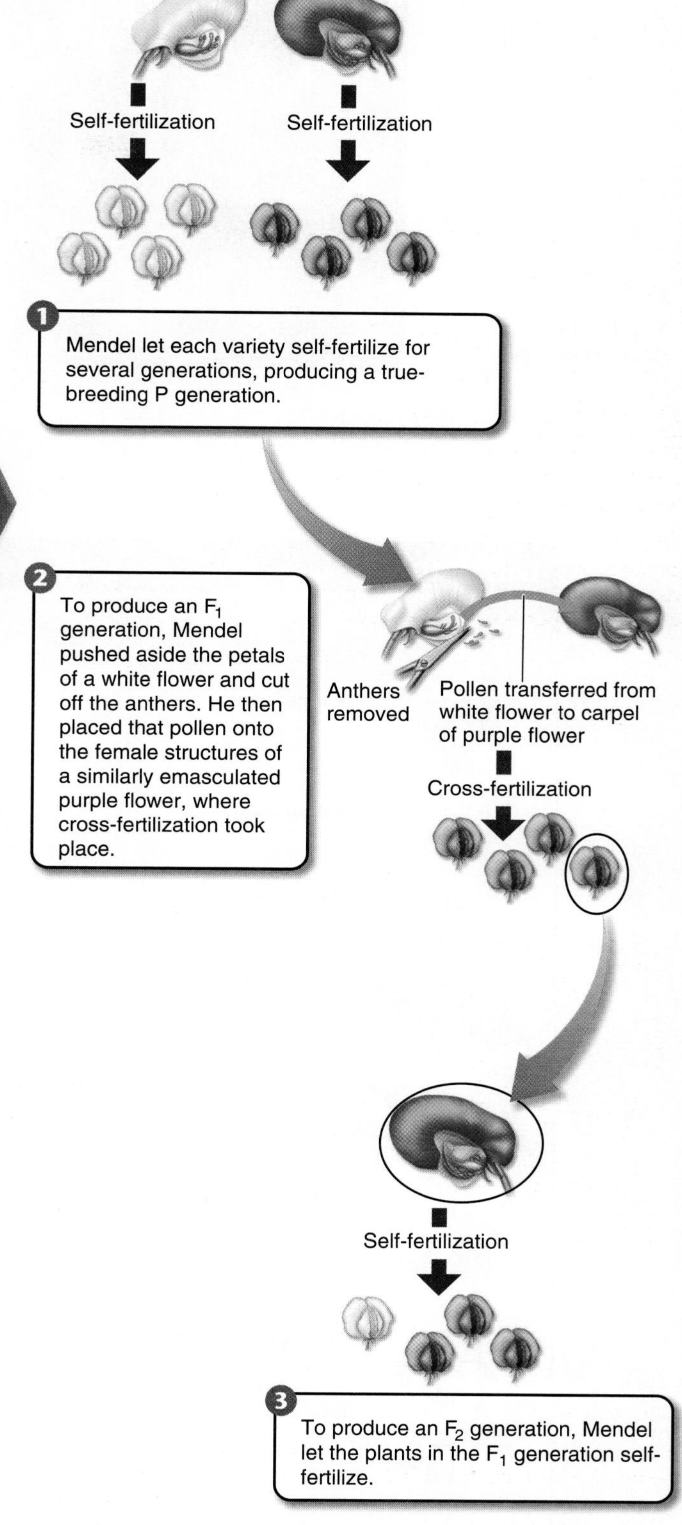

Self-fertilization
Self-fertilization
1 Mendel let each variety self-fertilize for several generations, producing a true-breeding P generation.
2 To produce an F_1 generation, Mendel pushed aside the petals of a white flower and cut off the anthers. He then placed that pollen onto the female structures of a similarly emasculated purple flower, where cross-fertilization took place.
Anthers removed
Pollen transferred from white flower to carpel of purple flower
Cross-fertilization
Self-fertilization
3 To produce an F_2 generation, Mendel let the plants in the F_1 generation self-fertilize.

Figure 10.3 How Mendel conducted his experiments.

Figure 10.4
The pod of a garden pea plant.

10.2 What Mendel Observed

LEARNING OBJECTIVE 10.2.1 Describe what Mendel observed when crossing two contrasting traits.

Mendel experimented with a variety of traits in the garden pea (**figure 10.4**) and repeatedly made similar observations. In all, Mendel examined seven pairs of contrasting traits, as shown in **table 10.1**. For each pair of contrasting traits that Mendel crossed, he observed the same result, shown in **figure 10.3**, where a trait disappeared in the F_1 generation only to reappear in the F_2 generation. We will examine in detail Mendel's crosses with flower color.

The F_1 Generation

In the case of flower color, when Mendel crossed purple and white flowers, all the F_1 generation plants he observed were purple; he did not see the contrasting trait, white flowers. Mendel called the trait expressed in the F_1 plants **dominant** and the trait not expressed **recessive.** In this case,

TABLE 10.1 Seven Characters Mendel Studied in His Experiments

Dominant Form	Character ×	Recessive Form	F_2 Generation Dominant: Recessive	Ratio
Purple flowers	×	White flowers	705:224	3.15:1 (3/4:1/4)
Yellow seeds	×	Green seeds	6022:2001	3.01:1 (3/4:1/4)
Round seeds	×	Wrinkled seeds	5474:1850	2.96:1 (3/4:1/4)
Green pods	×	Yellow pods	428:152	2.82:1 (3/4:1/4)
Inflated pods	×	Constricted pods	882:299	2.95:1 (3/4:1/4)
Axial flowers	×	Terminal flowers	651:207	3.14:1 (3/4:1/4)
Tall plants	×	Dwarf plants	787:277	2.84:1 (3/4:1/4)

purple flower color was dominant and white flower color recessive. Mendel studied several other characters in addition to flower color, and for every pair of contrasting traits Mendel examined, one proved to be dominant and the other recessive. The dominant and recessive traits for each character he studied are indicated in table 10.1.

Figure 10.5 Round versus wrinkled seeds.

One of the differences among varieties of pea plants that Mendel studied was the shape of the seed. In some varieties the seeds were round, whereas in others they were wrinkled.

The F_2 Generation

After allowing individual F_1 plants to mature and self-fertilize, Mendel collected and planted the seeds from each plant to see what the offspring in the F_2 generation would look like. Mendel found (as Knight had earlier) that some F_2 plants exhibited white flowers, the recessive trait. The recessive trait had disappeared in the F_1 generation, only to reappear in the F_2 generation. It must somehow have been present in the F_1 individuals but unexpressed!

At this stage Mendel instituted his radical change in experimental design. He *counted* the number of each type among the F_2 offspring. He believed the proportions of the F_2 types would provide some clue about the mechanism of heredity. In the cross between the purple-flowered F_1 plants, he counted a total of 929 F_2 individuals (see table 10.1). Of these, 705 (75.9%) had purple flowers and 224 (24.1%) had white flowers. Approximately one-fourth of the F_2 individuals exhibited the recessive form of the trait. Mendel carried out similar experiments with other traits, such as round versus wrinkled seeds (figure 10.5) and obtained the same result: Three-fourths of the F_2 individuals exhibited the dominant form of the character, and one-fourth displayed the recessive form. In other words, the dominant:recessive ratio among the F_2 plants was always approximately 3:1.

A Disguised 1:2:1 Ratio

Mendel let the F_2 plants self-fertilize for another generation and found that the one-fourth that were recessive were true-breeding—future generations showed nothing but the recessive trait. Thus, the white F_2 individuals described previously showed only white flowers in the F_3 generation (as shown on the right in figure 10.6). Among the three-fourths of the plants that had shown the dominant trait in the F_2 generation, only one-third of the individuals were true-breeding in the F_3 generation (as shown on the left in figure 10.6). The others showed both traits in the F_3 generation (as shown in the center)—and when Mendel counted their numbers, he found the ratio of dominant to recessive to again be 3:1! From these results Mendel concluded that the 3:1 ratio he had observed in the F_2 generation was in fact a disguised 1:2:1 ratio:

1	2	1
true-breeding :	not-true-breeding :	true-breeding
dominant	dominant	recessive

Putting the Concept to Work

If you were to pick an F_2 individual at random, what is the probability that the individual you pick will be not-true-breeding?

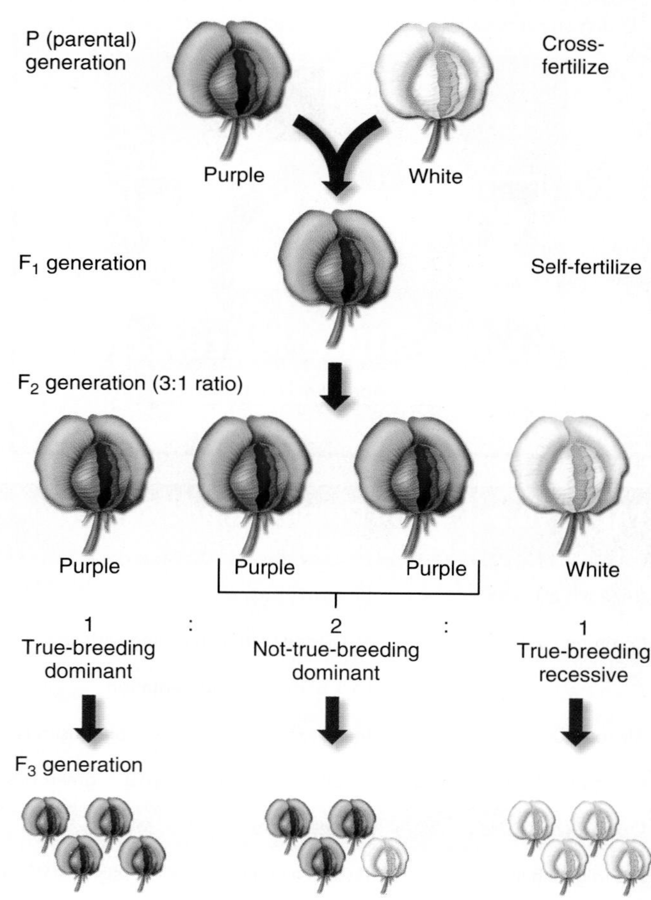

Figure 10.6 The F_2 generation is a disguised 1:2:1 ratio.

By allowing the F_2 generation to self-fertilize, Mendel found from the offspring (F_3) that the ratio of F_2 plants was one true-breeding dominant, two not-true-breeding dominant, and one true-breeding recessive.

BIOLOGY & YOU

Look-alike Meter. Have you ever wondered who you resemble more, your mother or your father? Using state-of-the-art face recognition technology, Internet services now allow you to answer this question in a very objective way. You upload a photo of your face, looking straight into the camera, and similar photos of your mom and dad, and the service analyzes them to provide you with your own personal "look-alike meter." Typically your mother's photo is shown on the left end of the meter scale, your father's on the right. If you resemble both parents equally, the meter's needle points to the middle (straight up). If, on the other hand, you look more like one parent than the other, then the needle will swing over toward the side of that parent. The more you resemble her or him, the closer to that side of the meter the needle points. When the baby girl of Tom Cruise and Katie Holmes was analyzed in this way with the look-alike meter shown below, Suri proved to look more like Tom, by 15%. Why do you think it is possible for Suri to look more like her father than her mother? Didn't she get half her genes from each parent?

TABLE 10.2	Some Dominant and Recessive Traits in Humans
Recessive Traits	**Phenotypes**
Common baldness	M-shaped hairline receding with age
Albinism	Lack of melanin pigmentation
Alkaptonuria	Inability to metabolize homogentisic acid
Red-green color blindness	Inability to distinguish red and green wavelengths of light
Dominant Traits	**Phenotypes**
Mid-digital hair	Presence of hair on middle segment of finger
Brachydactyly	Short fingers
Phenylthiocarbamide (PTC) sensitivity	Ability to taste PTC as bitter
Camptodactyly	Inability to straighten the little finger
Polydactyly	Extra fingers and toes

10.3 Mendel Proposes a Theory

LEARNING OBJECTIVE 10.3.1 State the five hypotheses of Mendel's theory, distinguishing between gene and allele, and between genotype and phenotype.

To explain his results, Mendel proposed a simple set of five hypotheses that would faithfully predict the results he had observed. Now called Mendel's theory of heredity, it has become one of the most famous theories in the history of science.

Hypothesis 1: *Parents do not transmit traits directly to their offspring.* Rather, they transmit information about the traits, what Mendel called *merkmal* (the German word for "factor"). These factors act later, in the offspring, to produce the trait. In modern terminology, we call Mendel's factors **genes.**

Hypothesis 2: *Each parent contains two copies of the factor governing each trait.* The two copies may or may not be the same. If the two copies of the factor are the same (both encoding purple or both white flowers, for example) the individual is said to be **homozygous.** If the two copies of the factor are different (one encoding purple, the other white, for example), the individual is said to be **heterozygous.**

Hypothesis 3: *Alternative forms of a factor lead to alternative traits.* Alternative forms of a factor are called **alleles.** Mendel used lowercase letters to represent recessive alleles and uppercase letters to represent dominant ones. In modern terms, we call the appearance of an individual its **phenotype.** Appearance is determined by which alleles of a gene an individual receives from its parents, and we call those particular alleles the individual's **genotype.** Thus a pea plant might have the phenotype "white flower" and the genotype *pp*.

Hypothesis 4: *The two alleles that an individual possesses do not affect each other,* any more than two letters in a mailbox alter each other's contents. Each allele is passed on unchanged when the individual matures and produces its own gametes (egg and sperm). At the time, Mendel did not know that his factors were carried from parent to offspring on chromosomes.

Hypothesis 5: *The presence of an allele does not ensure that a trait will be expressed in the individual that carries it.* In heterozygous individuals, only the dominant allele achieves expression; the recessive allele is present but unexpressed.

These five hypotheses, taken together, constitute Mendel's model of the hereditary process. Many traits in humans exhibit dominant or recessive inheritance similar to the traits Mendel studied in peas (table 10.2).

Putting the Concept to Work

Can you name a recessive allele displayed by a member of your family?

Analyzing Mendel's Results

LEARNING OBJECTIVE 10.3.2 Using a Punnett square analysis, explain the basis of the 3:1 Mendelian ratio.

To analyze Mendel's results, it is important to remember that each trait is determined by the inheritance of alleles from the parents, one allele from the mother and the other from the father. These alleles, present on chromosomes, are distributed to gametes during meiosis. Each gamete receives one copy of each chromosome, and therefore one copy of an allele.

During sexual reproduction, discussed on page 148, haploid gametes, that contain one allele for each trait, combine to form a diploid offspring. The genetic make up of the offspring is thus half maternal and half paternal.

Consider again Mendel's cross of purple-flowered with white-flowered plants. Like Mendel, we will assign the symbol *P*, written in uppercase, to the dominant allele associated with the production of purple flowers, and the symbol *p*, written in lowercase, to the recessive allele associated with the production of white flowers.

In this system, the genotype of an individual true-breeding for the recessive white-flowered trait would be designated *pp*, as both copies of the allele specify the white phenotype. Similarly, the genotype of a true-breeding purple-flowered individual would be designated *PP*, and a heterozygote would be designated *Pp* (dominant allele first). Using these conventions, and denoting a cross between two strains with ×, we can symbolize Mendel's original cross as *pp* × *PP*.

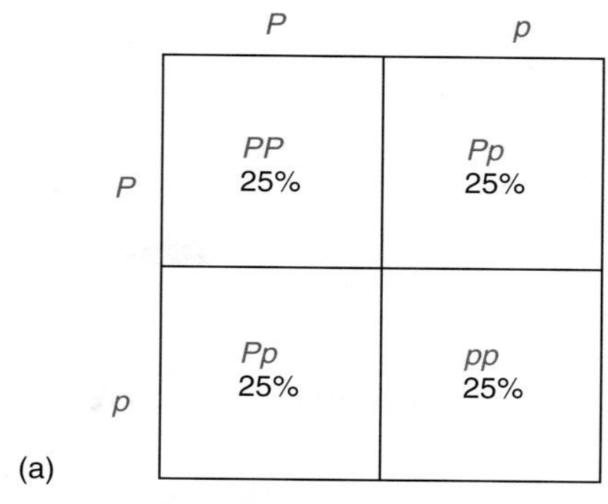

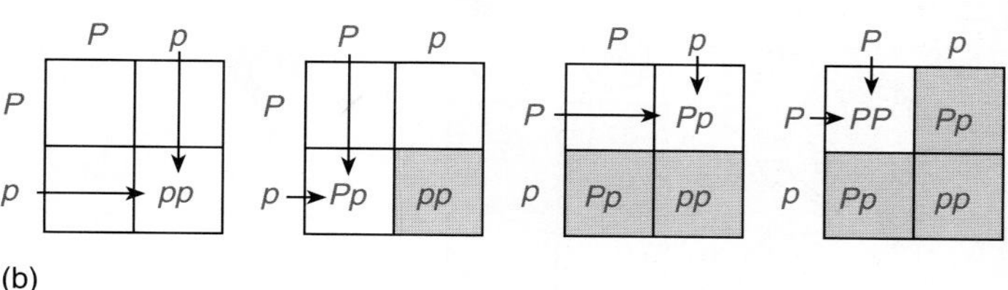

Figure 10.7 A Punnett square analysis.

(a) Each square represents 1/4 or 25% of the offspring from the cross. The squares in (b) show how the square is used to predict the genotypes of all potential offspring.

Punnett Squares

The possible results from a cross between a true-breeding, white-flowered plant (*pp*) and a true-breeding, purple-flowered plant (*PP*) can be visualized with a **Punnett square.** In a Punnett square, the possible gametes of one individual are listed along the horizontal side of the square, while the possible gametes of the other individual are listed along the vertical side. The genotypes of potential offspring are represented by the cells within the square. Figure 10.7 walks you through the set-up of a Punnett square crossing two plants that are heterozygous for flower color (*Pp* × *Pp*).

The frequency that these genotypes occur in the offspring is usually expressed by a **probability.** For example, in a cross between a homozygous white-flowered plant (*pp*) and a homozygous purple-flowered plant (*PP*), *Pp* is the only possible genotype for all individuals in the F_1 generation, as shown by the Punnett square on the left of figure 10.8. Because *P* is dominant to *p*, all individuals in the F_1 generation have purple flowers. When individuals from the F_1 generation are crossed, as shown by the Punnett square on the right, the probability of obtaining a homozygous dominant (*PP*) individual in the F_2 is 25% because one-fourth of the possible genotypes are *PP*. Similarly, the probability of an individual in the F_2 generation being homozygous recessive (*pp*) is 25%. Because the heterozygous genotype has two possible ways of occurring (*Pp* and *pP*, but both written as *Pp*), it occurs in half of the cells within the square; the probability of obtaining a heterozygous (*Pp*) individual is 50% (25% + 25%).

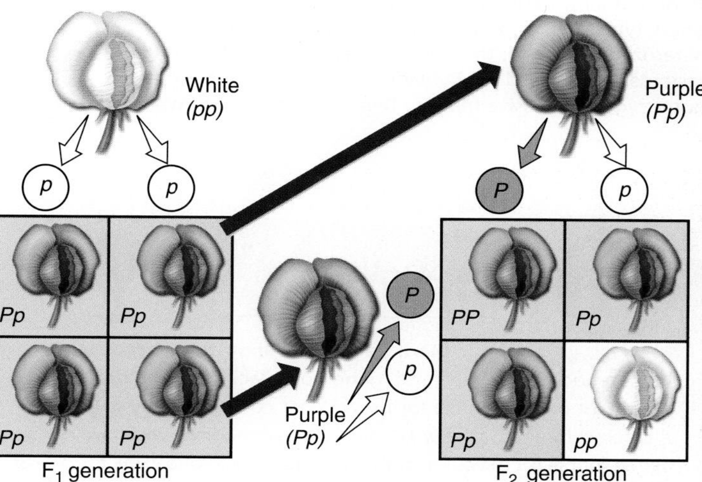

Figure 10.8 How Mendel analyzed flower color.

The only possible offspring of the first cross are *Pp* heterozygotes, purple in color. These individuals are known as the F_1 generation. When two heterozygous F_1 individuals cross, three kinds of offspring are possible: *PP* homozygotes (purple flowers); *Pp* heterozygotes (also purple flowers), which may form two ways; and *pp* homozygotes (white flowers). Among these individuals, known as the F_2 generation, the ratio of dominant phenotype to recessive phenotype is 3:1.

Putting the Concept to Work

What is the probability of NOT obtaining a heterozygous F_2 individual?

The Testcross

LEARNING OBJECTIVE 10.3.3 Diagram how a testcross reveals the genotype of an individual exhibiting a dominant phenotype.

How did Mendel know which of the purple-flowered individuals in the F_2 generation (or the F_1 generation) were homozygous (*PP*) and which were heterozygous (*Pp*)? It is not possible to tell simply by looking at them. For this reason, Mendel devised a simple and powerful procedure called the **testcross** to determine an individual's actual genetic composition. Consider a purple-flowered plant. It is impossible to determine such a plant's genotype simply by looking at its phenotype. To learn its genotype, you must cross it with some other plant. What kind of cross would provide the answer? If you cross it with a homozygous dominant individual, all of the progeny will show the dominant phenotype whether the test plant is homozygous or heterozygous. It is also difficult (but not impossible) to distinguish between the two possible test plant genotypes by crossing with a heterozygous individual. However, if you cross the test plant with a homozygous recessive individual, the two possible test plant genotypes will give totally different results. To see how this works, step through a testcross of a purple-flowered plant with a white-flowered plant. Figure 10.9 shows you the two possible alternatives:

Alternative 1 (on left): unknown plant is homozygous (*PP*). *PP* × *pp*: all offspring have purple flowers (*Pp*) as shown by the four purple squares.

Alternative 2 (on right): unknown plant is heterozygous (*Pp*). *Pp* × *pp*: one-half of offspring have white flowers (*pp*) and one-half have purple flowers (*Pp*) as shown by the two white and two purple squares.

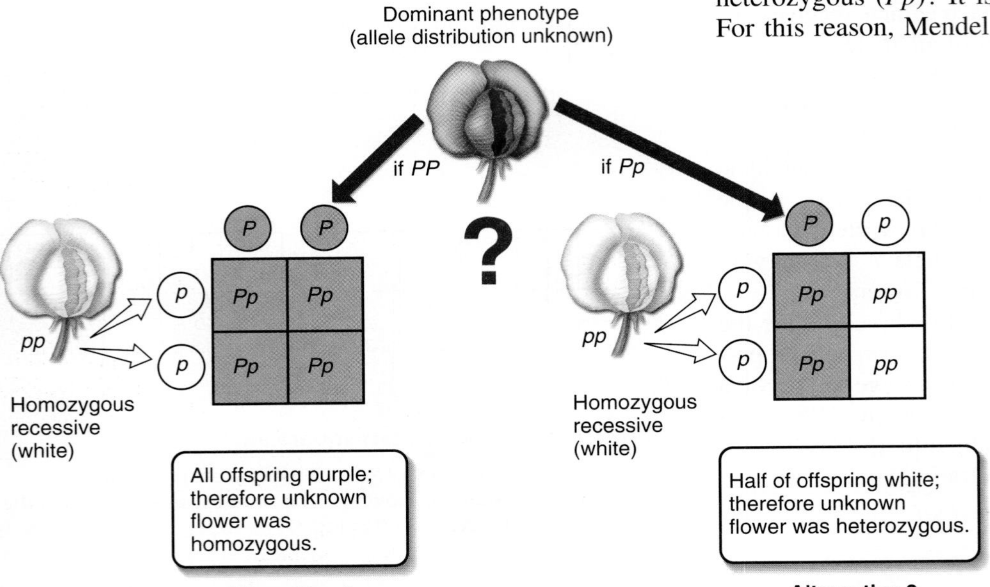

Figure 10.9 How Mendel used the testcross to detect heterozygotes.

To determine whether an individual exhibiting a dominant phenotype, such as purple flowers, was homozygous (*PP*) or heterozygous (*Pp*) for the dominant allele, Mendel devised the testcross. He crossed the individual in question with a known homozygous recessive (*pp*)—in this case, a plant with white flowers.

In one of his testcrosses, Mendel crossed F_1 individuals exhibiting the dominant trait back to the parent homozygous for the recessive trait. He predicted that the dominant and recessive traits would appear in a 1:1 ratio, and that is what he observed, as you can see illustrated in alternative 2 above.

Testcrosses can also be used to determine the genotype of an individual when two genes are involved. Mendel carried out many two-gene crosses, some of which we will soon discuss. He often used testcrosses to verify the genotypes of particular dominant-appearing F_2 individuals. Thus an F_2 individual showing both dominant traits (*A_ B_*) might have any of the following genotypes: *AABB*, *AaBB*, *AABb*, or *AaBb*. By crossing dominant-appearing F_2 individuals with homozygous recessive individuals (that is, *A_ B_* × *aabb*), Mendel was able to determine if either or both of the traits bred true among the progeny—any that did could not be heterozygous—and so determine the genotype of the F_2 parent.

Putting the Concept to Work

How did Mendel know which F_2-generation peas were heterozygous?

BIOLOGY & YOU

Is Your Black Labrador Puppy Homozygous?
In Labrador retrievers, the gene for black coat color is dominant over the gene for brown coat color. A puppy with a black-colored coat may be either true-breeding, with two alleles for black coat color, or heterozygous, with one allele for black coat color and one for brown coat color. To determine which genetic endowment your black lab puppy has, you can mate it (when it grows up) to a so-called chocolate lab, which has brown fur and two alleles for brown coat color. If all the offspring of this mating are black, your dog must be true-breeding and have both alleles for black coat color. If some of the young are chocolate brown, your dog must be heterozygous and have one allele for black coat color and one for brown coat color. Yellow labs, on the other hand, lack the allele for pigmentation, so they have light-colored coats.

10.4 Mendel's Laws

LEARNING OBJECTIVE 10.4.1 State Mendel's first and second laws, and show how they account for his experimental results. Describe a dihybrid cross.

Mendel's First Law: Segregation

Mendel's model brilliantly predicts the results of his crosses, accounting in a neat and satisfying way for the ratios he observed. Similar patterns of heredity have since been observed in countless other organisms. Traits exhibiting this pattern of heredity are called *Mendelian traits.* Because of its overwhelming importance, Mendel's theory is often referred to as Mendel's first law, or the **law of segregation.** In modern terms, Mendel's first law states that *the two alleles of a trait separate during the formation of gametes, so that half of the gametes will carry one copy and half will carry the other copy.*

Mendel's Second Law: Independent Assortment

Mendel went on to ask if the inheritance of one factor, such as flower color, influences the inheritance of other factors, such as plant height. To investigate this question, he followed the inheritance of two separate traits, called a **dihybrid** cross (*di* meaning two; a *monohybrid* cross examines one trait). He first established a series of true-breeding lines of peas that differed from one another with respect to two of the seven pairs of characteristics, and then crossed them. Figure 10.10 shows an experiment in which the P generation consists of homozygous individuals with round, yellow seeds (*RRYY* in the figure) that are crossed with individuals that are homozygous for wrinkled, green seeds (*rryy*). This cross produces F_1 individuals that have round, yellow seeds and are heterozygous for both of these traits (*RrYy*). The chromosomes then are allocated to the gametes during meiosis such that there are four types of gametes for these two traits.

Mendel then allowed the dihybrid individuals to self-fertilize. If the segregation of alleles affecting seed shape and alleles affecting seed color were independent, the probability that a particular pair of seed-shape alleles would occur together with a particular pair of seed-color alleles would simply be a product of the two individual probabilities that each pair would occur separately. For example, the probability of an individual with wrinkled, green seeds appearing in the F_2 generation would be equal to the probability of an individual with wrinkled seeds (1 in 4) multiplied by the probability of an individual with green seeds (1 in 4), or 1 in 16.

In his dihybrid crosses, Mendel found that the frequency of phenotypes in the F_2 offspring closely matched the 9:3:3:1 ratio predicted by the Punnett square analysis shown in figure 10.10. He concluded that for the pairs of traits he studied, the inheritance of one trait does not influence the inheritance of the other trait, a result often referred to as Mendel's second law, or the **law of independent assortment.** We now know that this result is valid only for genes not located near one another on the same chromosome. Thus in modern terms, Mendel's second law is often stated as follows: *genes located on different chromosomes are inherited independently of one another.*

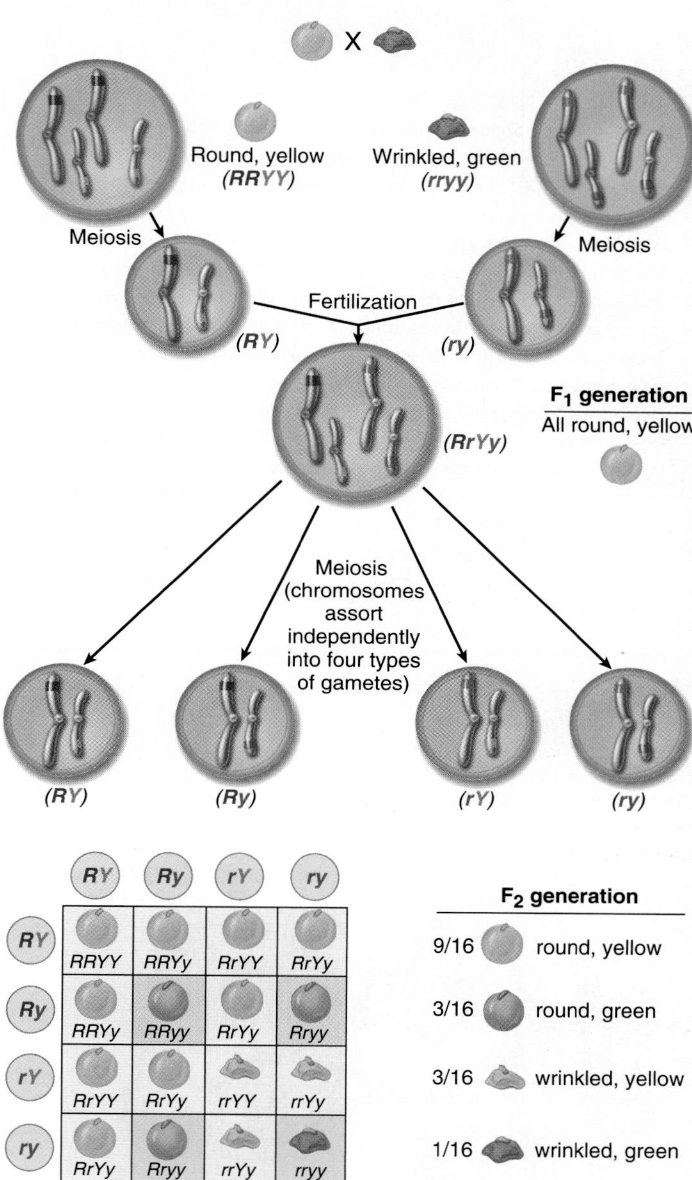

Figure 10.10 Analysis of a dihybrid cross.

This dihybrid cross shows round (*R*) versus wrinkled (*r*) seeds and yellow (*Y*) versus green (*y*) seeds. The ratio of the four possible phenotypes in the F_2 generation is predicted to be 9:3:3:1.

Putting the Concept to Work

If two genes *are* located near each other on a chromosome, would recessive alleles of each of these genes still exhibit 3:1 Mendelian ratios in the F_2 generation of a dihybrid cross?

From Genotype to Phenotype

10.5 How Genes Influence Traits

BIOLOGY & YOU

Sickle-Cell Disease. The inherited blood disorder sickle-cell disease occurs among African Americans in 3 of every 1,000 (or about 1 in 375) live births. In its severe form it affects more than 50,000 people. The first account of what was then called "sickle-cell anemia" was in 1910 when James Herrick, a Chicago physician, described the symptoms of a 20-year-old black male student from the West Indies. The man reported shortness of breath and had severe anemia (low red blood cell count). In a 1904 examination of the patient's blood cells under a microscope, Dr. Ernest Iron, Herrick's intern, described "elongated and irregular, sickle-shaped red blood cells." Because these deformed sickle cells can clog blood vessels, organ damage often eventually results. One of the most affected organs is the spleen (an organ of the immune system), and so affected individuals are more likely to get serious infections. The single nucleotide change responsible for sickle-cell disease thus has widespread effects on the health of the whole body.

LEARNING OBJECTIVE 10.5.1 Describe how genotype determines phenotype.

It is useful, before considering Mendelian genetics further, to gain a brief understanding of how genes work. With this in mind, we will sketch, in broad strokes, a picture of how a Mendelian trait is influenced by a particular gene. We will use the protein hemoglobin as our example—you can follow along on **figure 10.11**.

From DNA to Protein

Each body cell of an individual contains the same set of DNA molecules, called the genome of that individual. The human genome contains about 20,000 to 25,000 genes, parcelled out into 23 pairs of chromosomes. You can see in **figure 10.11** that the hemoglobin gene (*Hb*) is located on chromosome 11.

Individual genes are "read" from the chromosomal DNA by enzymes that create an RNA transcript of the gene sequence. After editing out unnecessary bits, this RNA transcript of the hemoglobin gene leaves the nucleus as messenger RNA (mRNA) and is delivered to ribosomes in the cytoplasm. Each ribosome is a tiny protein-assembly plant, and uses the nucleotide sequence of the mRNA to determine the amino acid sequence of a particular polypeptide. In the case of beta-hemoglobin, the mRNA encodes a strand of 146 amino acids.

How Proteins Determine the Phenotype

The beta-hemoglobin amino acid chain, which resembles beads on a string in the figure, spontaneously folds into a complex three-dimensional shape. This beta-hemoglobin associates with another beta chain and two alpha chains to form the active four-subunit hemoglobin protein (shown to the left) that binds oxygen in red blood cells. As a general rule, genes influence the phenotype by specifying the kind of proteins present in the body, which determines in large measure how that body looks and functions.

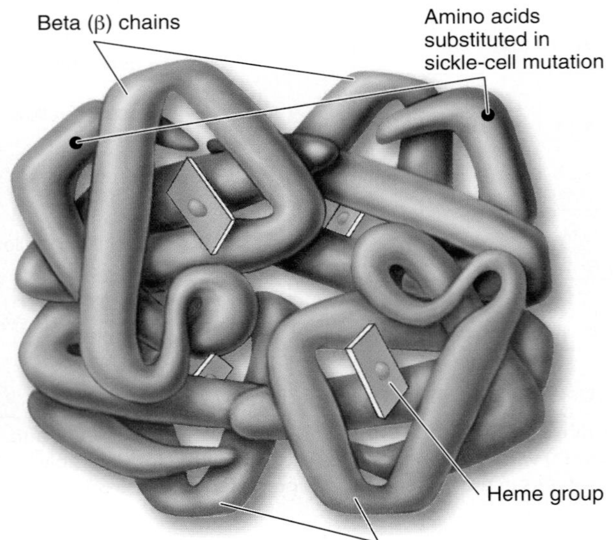

How Mutation Alters Phenotype

A change in the identity of a single nucleotide within a gene, called a mutation, can have a profound effect if the new version of the protein folds differently, as this may alter or destroy its function. For example, how well hemoglobin performs its oxygen transport duties depends on the precise shape that the protein subunits assume when they fold. A change in the sixth amino acid of beta-hemoglobin from glutamic acid to valine causes the hemoglobin molecules to aggregate into long chains that cause the blood cells to deform into a sickle shape that can no longer carry oxygen efficiently. The resulting sickle-cell disease can be fatal, as discussed further on page 182.

Putting the Concept to Work

Explain how a single nucleotide change in the gene for beta-hemoglobin can lead to organ damage and death.

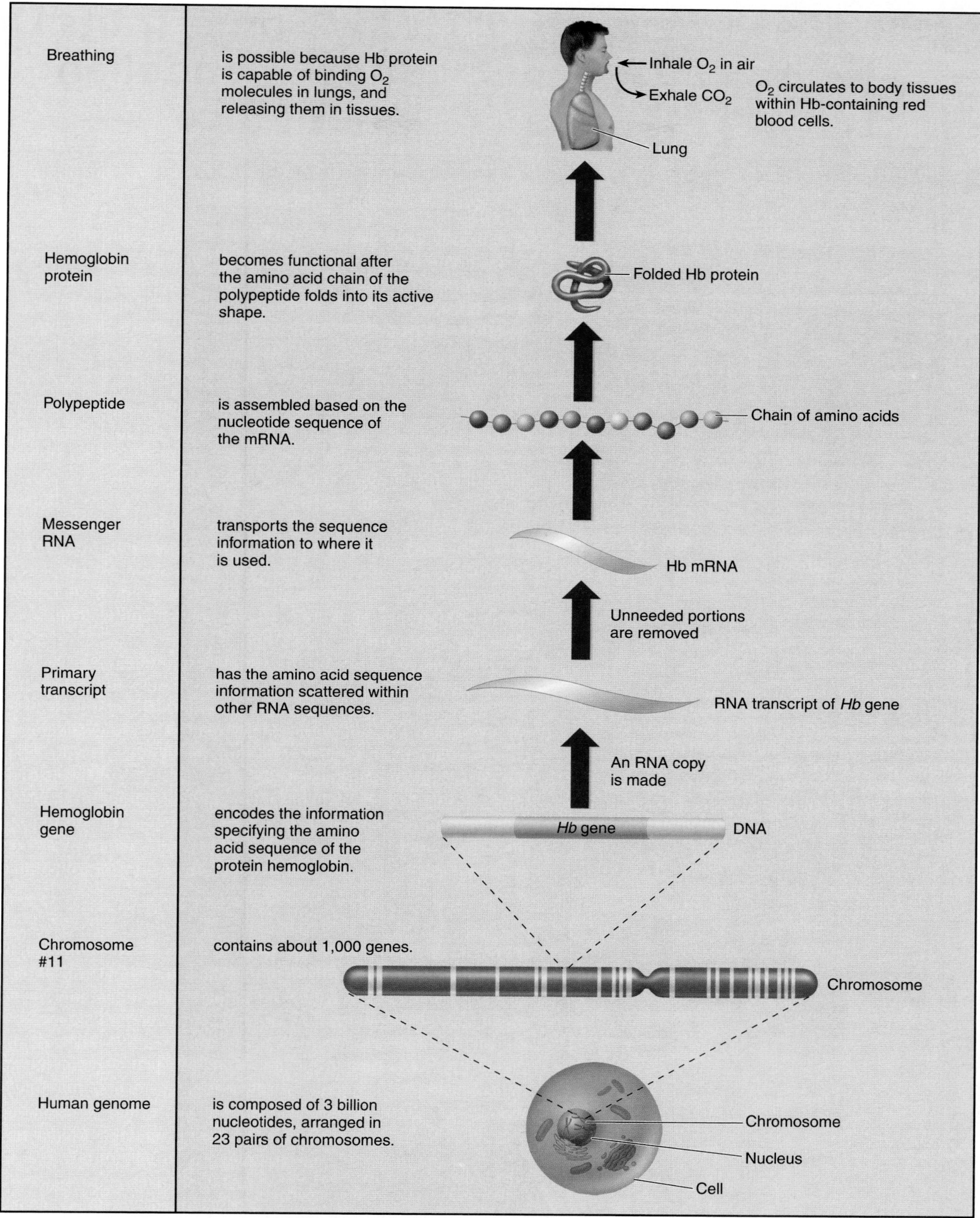
Breathing
is possible because Hb protein is capable of binding O_2 molecules in lungs, and releasing them in tissues.
Inhale O_2 in air
Exhale CO_2
O_2 circulates to body tissues within Hb-containing red blood cells.
Lung
Hemoglobin protein
becomes functional after the amino acid chain of the polypeptide folds into its active shape.
Folded Hb protein
Polypeptide
is assembled based on the nucleotide sequence of the mRNA.
Chain of amino acids
Messenger RNA
transports the sequence information to where it is used.
Hb mRNA
Unneeded portions are removed
Primary transcript
has the amino acid sequence information scattered within other RNA sequences.
RNA transcript of *Hb* gene
An RNA copy is made
Hemoglobin gene
encodes the information specifying the amino acid sequence of the protein hemoglobin.
Hb gene
DNA
Chromosome #11
contains about 1,000 genes.
Chromosome
Human genome
is composed of 3 billion nucleotides, arranged in 23 pairs of chromosomes.
Chromosome
Nucleus
Cell

Figure 10.11 The journey from DNA to phenotype.

What an organism is like is determined in large measure by its genes. Here you see how one gene of the 20,000 to 25,000 in the human genome plays a key role in allowing oxygen to be carried throughout your body. The many steps on the journey from gene to trait are the subject of chapters 11 and 12.

(a)

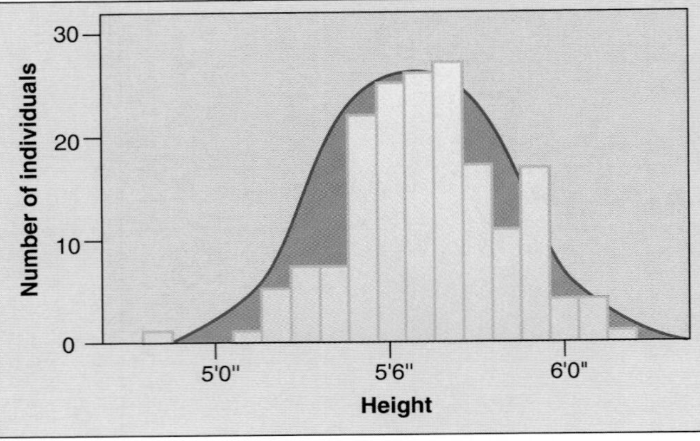

(b)

Figure 10.12 Height is a continuously varying character in humans.

(a) This photograph shows the variation in height among students of the 1914 class of the Connecticut Agricultural College. Because many genes contribute to height and tend to segregate independently of each other, there are many possible combinations of those genes. (b) The cumulative contribution of different combinations of alleles for height forms a continuous spectrum of possible heights, in which the extremes are much rarer than the intermediate values. This is quite different from the 3:1 ratio seen in Mendel's F_2 peas.

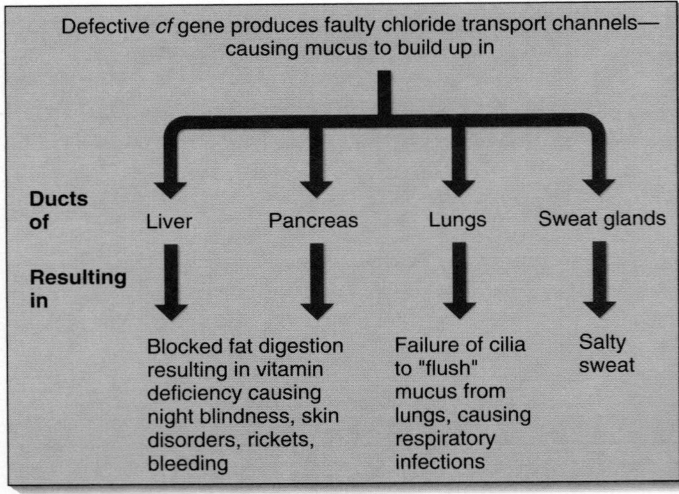

Figure 10.13 Pleiotropic effects of the cystic fibrosis gene, *cf*.

10.6 Why Some Traits Don't Show Mendelian Inheritance

LEARNING OBJECTIVE 10.6.1 List five factors that can disguise the Mendelian segregation of alleles.

Scientists attempting to confirm Mendel's theory often had trouble obtaining the same simple ratios he had reported. Often the expression of the genotype is not straightforward. Most phenotypes reflect the action of many genes. Some phenotypes can be affected by alleles that lack complete dominance, are affected by environmental conditions, or are expressed together.

Continuous Variation

When multiple genes act jointly to influence a character such as height or weight, the character often shows a range of small differences. Because all of the genes that play a role in determining these phenotypes segregate independently of each other, we see a gradation in the degree of difference when many individuals are examined. A classic illustration of this sort of variation is seen in figure 10.12, a photograph of a 1914 college class. The students were placed in rows according to their heights, under 5 feet toward the left and over 6 feet to the right. You can see that there is considerable variation in height in this population of students. We call this type of inheritance **polygenic** (many genes), and we call this gradation in phenotypes **continuous variation.**

How can we describe the variation in a character such as the height of the individuals in figure 10.12*a*? Individuals range from quite short to very tall, with average heights more common than either extreme. What we often do is to group the variation into categories. Each height, in inches, is a separate phenotypic category. Plotting the numbers in each height category produces a histogram, such as that in figure 10.12*b*. The histogram approximates an idealized bell-shaped curve, and the variation can be characterized by the mean and spread of that curve. Compare this to the inheritance of plant height in Mendel's peas; they were either tall or dwarf, no intermediate height plants existed because only one gene controlled that trait.

Pleiotropic Effects

Often, an individual allele has more than one effect on the phenotype. Such an allele is said to be **pleiotropic.** When the pioneering French geneticist Lucien Cuenot studied yellow fur in mice, a dominant trait, he was unable to obtain a true-breeding yellow strain by crossing individual yellow mice with one another. Individuals homozygous for the yellow allele died, because the yellow allele was pleiotropic: one effect was yellow color, but another was a lethal developmental defect. A pleiotropic gene alteration may be dominant with respect to one phenotypic consequence (yellow fur) and recessive with respect to another (lethal developmental defect). In pleiotropy, one gene affects many characters, in marked contrast to polygeny, where many genes affect one character. Pleiotropic effects are difficult to predict, because the genes that affect a character often perform other functions we may know nothing about.

Cystic fibrosis, discussed on page 86, is caused by a mutation in a single gene that disrupts the functions of a chloride channel in the plasma membrane. This allele has pleiotropic effects because the chloride channel is found in many different types of cells in the body.

Figure 10.14 Incomplete dominance.

In a cross between a red-flowered Japanese four o'clock, genotype C^RC^R, and a white-flowered one (C^WC^W), neither allele is dominant. The heterozygous progeny have pink flowers and the genotype C^RC^W. If two of these heterozygotes are crossed, the phenotypes of their progeny occur in a ratio of 1:2:1 (red:pink:white).

IMPLICATION FOR YOU Palomino is a golden coat color in horses. The color is created by the action of one allele of a gene called "cream" working on a red (chestnut) base coat. Two cream alleles create an almost white horse called "cremello." Imagine you were a horse breeder. Would it be possible for you to establish a true-breeding line of palomino horses? Explain.

Pleiotropic effects are characteristic of many inherited disorders, such as cystic fibrosis and sickle-cell disease, discussed later in this chapter. In these disorders, multiple symptoms can be traced back to a single gene defect. As shown in figure 10.13, cystic fibrosis patients exhibit overly sticky mucus, salty sweat, liver and pancreas failure, and a battery of other symptoms. All are pleiotropic effects of a single defect, a mutation in a gene that encodes a chloride ion transmembrane channel. In sickle-cell disease, a defect in the oxygen-carrying hemoglobin molecule causes anemia, heart failure, kidney failure, enlargement of the spleen, and many other symptoms.

Incomplete Dominance

Not all alternative alleles are fully dominant or fully recessive in heterozygotes. Some pairs of alleles exhibit **incomplete dominance** and produce a heterozygous phenotype that is intermediate between those of the parents. For example, the cross of red- and white-flowered Japanese four o'clocks described in figure 10.14 produced red-, pink-, and white-flowered F_2 plants in a 1:2:1 ratio—heterozygotes are intermediate in color. This is different than in Mendel's pea plants that didn't exhibit incomplete dominance; the heterozygotes expressed the dominant phenotype.

Environmental Effects

The degree to which many alleles are expressed depends on the environment. Some alleles are heat-sensitive, for example. Traits influenced by such alleles are more sensitive to temperature or light than are the products of other alleles. The arctic foxes in figure 10.15, for example, make fur pigment only when the weather is warm. Can you see why this trait would be an advantage for the fox? Imagine a fox that didn't possess this trait and was white all year round. It would be very visible to predators in the summer, standing out against its darker surroundings. Similarly, the *ch* allele in Himalayan rabbits and Siamese cats encodes a heat-sensitive version of tyrosinase, one of the enzymes mediating the production of melanin, a dark pigment. The ch version of the enzyme is inactivated at temperatures above about 33°C. At the surface of the main body and head, the temperature is above 33°C and the tyrosinase enzyme is inactive, while it is more active at body extremities such as the tips of the ears and tail, where the temperature is below 33°C. The dark melanin pigment this enzyme produces causes the ears, snout, feet, and tail to be black.

(a)

(b)

Figure 10.15 Environmental effects on an allele.

(a) An arctic fox in winter has a coat that is almost white, so it is difficult to see the fox against a snowy background. (b) In summer, the same fox's fur darkens to a reddish brown, so that it resembles the color of the surrounding tundra.

Does Environment Affect I.Q.?

Nowhere has the influence of environment on the expression of genetic traits led to more controversy than in studies of I.Q. scores. I.Q. is a controversial measure of general intelligence based on a written test that many feel to be biased toward white middle-class America. However well or poorly I.Q. scores measure intelligence, a person's I.Q. score has been believed for some time to be determined largely by his or her genes.

How did science come to that conclusion? Scientists measure the degree to which genes influence a multigene trait by using an off-putting statistical measure called the *variance*. Variance is defined as the square of the standard deviation (a measure of the degree-of-scatter of a group of numbers around their mean value), and has the very desirable property of being additive—that is, the total variance is equal to the sum of the variances of the factors influencing it.

What factors can contribute to the total variance of I.Q. scores? There are three: 1. The first factor is variation at the gene level, some gene combinations leading to higher I.Q. scores than others. 2. The second factor is variation at the environmental level, some environments leading to higher I.Q. scores than others. 3. The third factor is what a statistician calls the *covariance,* the degree to which environment affects genes.

The degree to which genes influence a trait like I.Q., the *heritability* of I.Q., is given the symbol H and is defined simply as the fraction of the total variance that is genetic.

So how heritable is I.Q.? Geneticists estimate the heritability of I.Q. by measuring the environmental and genetic contributions to the total variance of I.Q. scores. The environmental contributions to variance in I.Q. can be measured by comparing the I.Q. scores of identical twins reared together with those reared apart (any differences should reflect environmental influences). The genetic contributions can be measured by comparing identical twins reared together (which are 100% genetically identical) with fraternal twins reared together (which are 50% genetically identical). Any differences should reflect genes, as twins share identical prenatal conditions in the womb and are raised in virtually identical environmental circumstances. So, when traits are more commonly shared between identical twins than fraternal twins, the difference is likely genetic.

When these sorts of "twin studies" have been done in the past, researchers have uniformly reported that I.Q. is highly heritable, with values of H typically reported as being around 0.7 (a very high value). While it didn't seem significant at the time, almost all the twins available for study over the years have come from middle-class or wealthy families.

The study of I.Q. has proven controversial, because I.Q. scores are often different when social and racial groups are compared. What is one to make of the observation that I.Q. scores of poor children measure lower as a group than do scores of children of middle-class and wealthy families? This difference has led to the controversial suggestion by some that the poor are genetically inferior.

What should we make of such a harsh conclusion? To make a judgment, we need to focus for a moment on the fact that these measures of the heritability of I.Q. have all made a critical assumption, one to which population geneticists, who specialize in these sorts of things, object strongly. The assumption is that environment does not affect gene expression, so that covariance makes no contribution to the total variance in I.Q. scores—that is, that the covariance contribution to H is zero.

Studies have allowed a direct assessment of this assumption. Importantly, it proves to be flat wrong.

In November of 2003, researchers reported an analysis of twin data from a study carried out in the late 1960s. The National Collaborative Prenatal Project, funded by the National Institutes of Health, enrolled nearly 50,000 pregnant women, most of them black and quite poor, in several major U.S. cities. Researchers collected abundant data, and gave the children I.Q. tests seven years later. Although not designed to study twins, this study was so big that many twins were born, 623 births. Seven years later, 320 of these pairs were located and given I.Q. tests. This thus constitutes a huge "twin study," the first ever conducted of I.Q. among the poor.

When the data were analyzed, the results were unlike any ever reported. The heritability of I.Q. was different in different environments! Most notably, the influence of genes on I.Q. was far less in conditions of poverty, where environmental limitations seem to block the expression of genetic potential. Specifically, for families of high socioeconomic status, H = 0.72, much as reported in previous studies, but for families raised in poverty, H = 0.10, a very low value, indicating genes were making little contribution to observed I.Q. scores. The lower a child's socioeconomic status, the less impact genes had on I.Q.

These data say, with crystal clarity, that the genetic contributions to I.Q. don't mean much in an impoverished environment.

How does poverty in early childhood affect the brain? Neuroscientists reported in 2008 that many children growing up in very poor families experience poor nutrition and unhealthy levels of stress hormones, both of which impair their neural development. This affects language development and memory for the rest of their lives.

Clearly, improvements in the growing and learning environments of poor children can be expected to have a major impact on their I.Q. scores. Additionally, these data argue that the controversial differences reported in mean I.Q. scores between racial groups may well reflect no more than poverty, and are no more inevitable.

Codominance

A gene may have more than two alleles in a population, and in fact most genes possess several different alleles. Often in heterozygotes there isn't a dominant allele; instead, the effects of both alleles are expressed. In these cases, the alleles are said to be **codominant.** Codominance is seen in the color patterning of some animals, such as the "roan" pattern exhibited by some varieties of horses and cattle. A roan animal expresses both white and colored hairs because both alleles are being expressed. The gray horse in figure 10.16 is exhibiting the roan pattern. It looks like it has gray hairs, but if you were able to examine its coat closely, you would see both white hairs and black hairs.

A human gene that exhibits more than one dominant allele is the gene that determines ABO blood type. This gene encodes an enzyme that adds sugar molecules to lipids on the surface of red blood cells. These sugars act as recognition markers for cells in the immune system and are called cell surface antigens. The gene that encodes the enzyme, designated *I*, has three common alleles: I^B, whose product adds galactose; I^A, whose product adds galactosamine; and *i*, whose product does not add a sugar.

Different combinations of the three *I* gene alleles occur in different individuals because each person may be homozygous for any allele or heterozygous for any two. An individual heterozygous for the I^A and I^B alleles produces both forms of the enzyme and adds both galactose and galactosamine to the surfaces of red blood cells. Because both alleles are expressed simultaneously in heterozygotes, the I^A and I^B alleles are codominant. Both I^A and I^B are dominant over the *i* allele because both I^A or I^B alleles lead to sugar addition and the *i* allele does not. The different combinations of the three alleles produce four different phenotypes (figure 10.17):

1. Type A individuals add only galactosamine. They are either I^AI^A homozygotes or I^Ai heterozygotes (the three darkest boxes).
2. Type B individuals add only galactose. They are either I^BI^B homozygotes or I^Bi heterozygotes (the three lightest-colored boxes).
3. Type AB individuals add both sugars and are I^AI^B heterozygotes (the two intermediate-colored boxes).
4. Type O individuals add neither sugar and are *ii* homozygotes (the one white box).

These four different cell surface phenotypes are called the **ABO blood groups.** A person's immune system can distinguish between these four phenotypes. If a type A individual receives a transfusion of type B blood, the recipient's immune system recognizes that the type B blood cells possess a "foreign" antigen (galactose) and attacks the donated blood cells, causing the cells to clump or agglutinate. This also happens if the donated blood is type AB. However, if the donated blood is type O, it contains no galactose or galactosamine antigens on the surfaces of its blood cells, and so elicits no immune response to these antigens. For this reason, the type O individual is often referred to as a "universal donor." Because neither galactose nor galactosamine is foreign to type AB individuals (whose red blood cells have both sugars), those individuals ("universal recipients") may receive any type of blood.

Putting the Concept to Work

Is human blood type A dominant over blood type B? Explain.

Figure 10.16 Codominance in color patterning.

This roan horse is heterozygous for coat color. The offspring of a cross between a white homozygote and a black homozygote, it expresses both phenotypes. Some of the hairs on its body are white and some are black.

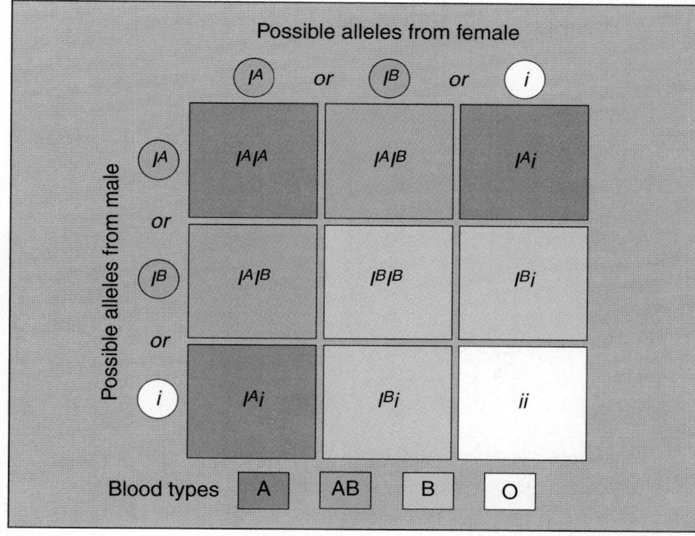

Figure 10.17 Multiple alleles controlling the ABO blood groups.

Three common alleles control the ABO blood groups. The different combinations of the three alleles result in four different blood type phenotypes: type A (either I^AI^A homozygotes or I^Ai heterozygotes), type B (either I^BI^B homozygotes or I^Bi heterozygotes), type AB (I^AI^B heterozygotes), and type O (*ii* homozygotes).

Chromosomes and Heredity

IN THE NEWS

Adding an Artificial Chromosome to Treat Disease. Attempts to treat inherited disorders with gene therapy (that is, adding a healthy copy of the defective gene, discussed in chapter 13) have been largely unsuccessful. One of the problems is that the virus used to carry the gene into the cells of the patient can insert the gene into the wrong place on a human chromosome, which can cause cancer. In a new approach, researchers are creating artificial chromosomes to deliver the therapeutic genes. Because this method avoids using viruses, the genes are not inserted into a patient's chromosomes, and so do not cause cancer. Scientists in British Columbia have built up an artificial chromosome from the key elements of a normal mouse chromosome, and added the gene for the human hormone erythropoietin (a blood hormone which triggers red blood cell production). When they injected cells that carry the artificial chromosome into mice, the mice produced the human hormone, leading to elevated levels of red blood cells. The artificial chromosome behaves like a normal one: It is duplicated when cells divide and is passed from generation to generation. Trials of this approach in humans are planned.

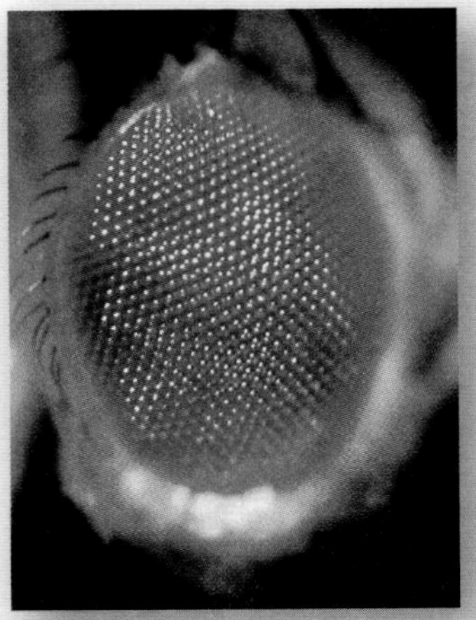
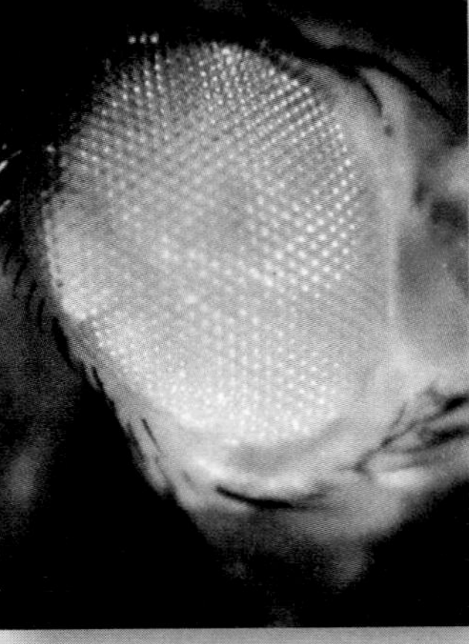

Figure 10.18 Red-eyed (wild type) and white-eyed (mutant) *Drosophila*.

The white-eye defect (shown on the *right*) is hereditary, the result of a mutation in a gene located on the X chromosome. By studying this mutation, Morgan first demonstrated that genes are on chromosomes.

10.7 Chromosomes Are the Vehicles of Mendelian Inheritance

LEARNING OBJECTIVE 10.7.1 Describe Morgan's surprising observation about white-eyed fruit flies and explain how it proved the chromosomal theory of inheritance.

The Chromosomal Theory of Inheritance

A central role for chromosomes in heredity was first suggested in 1900 by the German geneticist Karl Correns, in one of the papers announcing the rediscovery of Mendel's work. Soon observations that similar chromosomes paired with one another during meiosis led to the *chromosomal theory of inheritance,* first formulated by American Walter Sutton in 1902.

Several pieces of evidence supported Sutton's theory. One was that reproduction involves the initial union of only two cells, egg and sperm. While diploid individuals have two copies of each pair of homologous chromosomes, gametes have only one. This observation was consistent with Mendel's model, in which diploid individuals have two copies of each heritable gene and gametes have one. Even more compelling, chromosomes segregate during meiosis, and each pair of homologues orients on the metaphase plate independently of every other pair. Segregation and independent assortment were the two central characteristics of genes in Mendel's model.

Problems with the Chromosomal Theory

Investigators soon pointed out one problem with this theory, however. If Mendelian traits are determined by genes located on the chromosomes, and if the independent assortment of Mendelian traits reflects the independent assortment of chromosomes in meiosis, why does the number of traits that assort independently in a given kind of organism often greatly exceed the number of chromosome pairs the organism possesses? This seemed a fatal objection, and it led many early researchers to have serious reservations about Sutton's theory.

Morgan's White-Eyed Fly

The essential correctness of the chromosomal theory of heredity was demonstrated by a single small fly. In 1910 Thomas Hunt Morgan, studying the fruit fly *Drosophila melanogaster,* detected a mutant male fly that differed strikingly from normal fruit flies: Its eyes were white instead of red (figure 10.18).

Morgan immediately set out to determine if this new trait would be inherited in a Mendelian fashion. He first crossed the mutant male with a normal female to see if red or white eyes were dominant. All of the F_1 progeny had red eyes, so Morgan concluded that red eye color was dominant over white. Following the experimental procedure that Mendel had established long ago, Morgan then crossed the red-eyed flies from the F_1 generation with each other. Of the 4,252 F_2 progeny Morgan examined, 782 (18%) had white eyes. Although the ratio of red eyes to white eyes in the F_2 progeny was greater than 3:1, the results of the cross nevertheless provided clear evidence that eye color segregates. However, there was something about the outcome that was strange and totally unpredicted by Mendel's theory—*all of the white-eyed F_2 flies were males!*

How could this result be explained? Perhaps it was impossible for a white-eyed female fly to exist; such individuals might not be viable for some unknown reason. To test this idea, Morgan testcrossed the female F_1 progeny with the original white-eyed male. He obtained white-eyed and red-eyed males and females in a 1:1:1:1 ratio, just as Mendelian theory predicted. Hence, a female *could* have white eyes. Why, then, were there no white-eyed females among the progeny of the original cross?

Sex Linkage Confirms the Chromosomal Theory

The solution to this puzzle involved sex. In *Drosophila,* the sex of an individual is determined by the number of copies of a particular chromosome, the X chromosome, that an individual possesses. A fly with two X chromosomes is a female, and a fly with only one X chromosome is a male. In males, the single X chromosome pairs in meiosis with a large, dissimilar partner called the Y chromosome. The female thus produces only X gametes, while the male produces both X and Y gametes. When fertilization involves an X sperm, the result is an XX zygote, which develops into a female; when fertilization involves a Y sperm, the result is an XY zygote, which develops into a male.

The solution to Morgan's puzzle is that the gene causing the white-eye trait in *Drosophila* resides only on the X chromosome—it is absent from the Y chromosome. (We now know that the Y chromosome in flies carries almost no functional genes.) A trait determined by a gene on the sex chromosome is said to be **sex-linked.** Knowing the white-eye trait is recessive to the red-eye trait, we can now see that Morgan's result was a natural consequence of the Mendelian assortment of chromosomes (figure 10.19). In this experiment, the F_1 generation all had red eyes, while the F_2 generation contained flies with white eyes—but they were all males. This at-first-surprising result happens because the segregation of the white-eye trait has a one-to-one correspondence with the segregation of the X chromosome. In other words, the white-eye gene is on the X chromosome.

Morgan's experiment presented the first clear evidence that the genes determining Mendelian traits reside on chromosomes, just as Sutton had proposed. When Mendel observed the segregation of alternative traits in pea plants, he was observing a reflection of the meiotic segregation of the chromosomes, which contained the characters he was observing.

If genes are located on chromosomes, you might expect that two genes on the same chromosome would segregate together. However, if the two genes are located far from each other on the chromosome, like genes *A* and *I* in figure 10.20, the likelihood of crossing over occurring between them is very high, leading to independent assortment. Conversely, the closer two genes are to each other on a chromosome, like genes *I* and *T*, the less likely it is that a cross over event will occur between them. Genes that are located quite close to each other almost always segregate together, and so are inherited together. The tendency of close-together genes to segregate together is called **linkage.**

Crossing over, discussed on page 150, occurs during meiosis when homologous chromosomes physically exchange segments. As a result, an allele located on one chromosome may be transferred to its homologue, causing the alleles to segregate independently.

Putting the Concept to Work

What would Morgan have seen if the white-eye gene was also present on the Y chromosome?

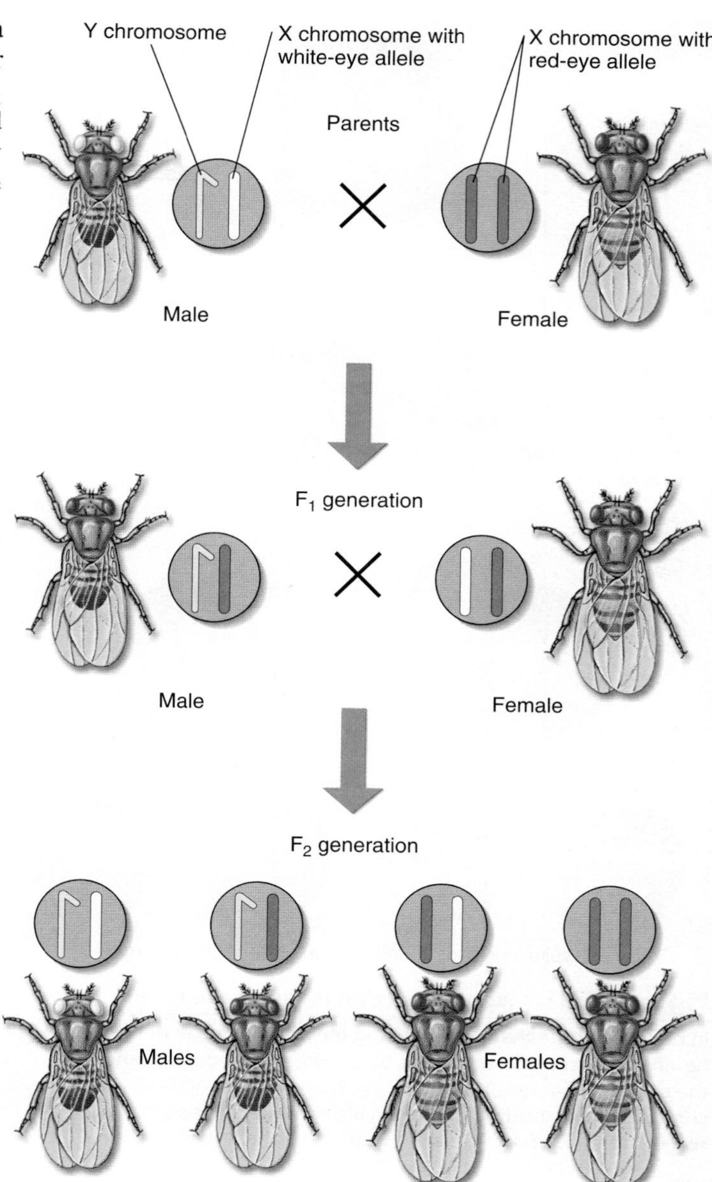

Figure 10.19 Morgan's experiment demonstrating the chromosomal basis of sex linkage.

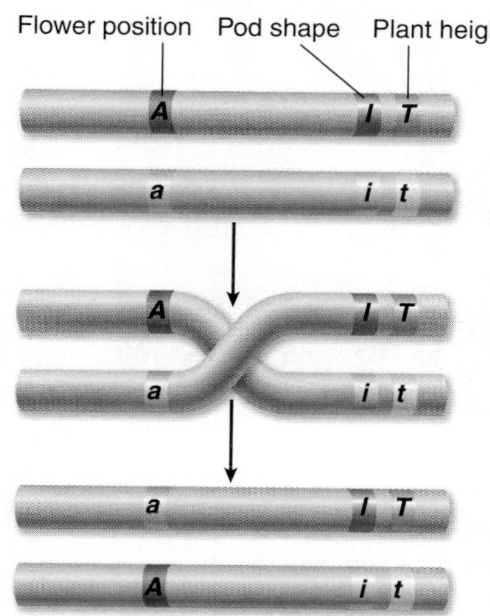

Figure 10.20 Linkage.

Genes that are located farther apart on a chromosome, like the genes for flower position (*A*) and pod shape (*I*) in Mendel's peas, will assort independently because crossing over results in recombination of these alleles. Pod shape (*I*) and plant height (*T*), however, are positioned very near each other, such that crossing over usually would not occur. These genes are said to be linked and do not undergo independent assortment.

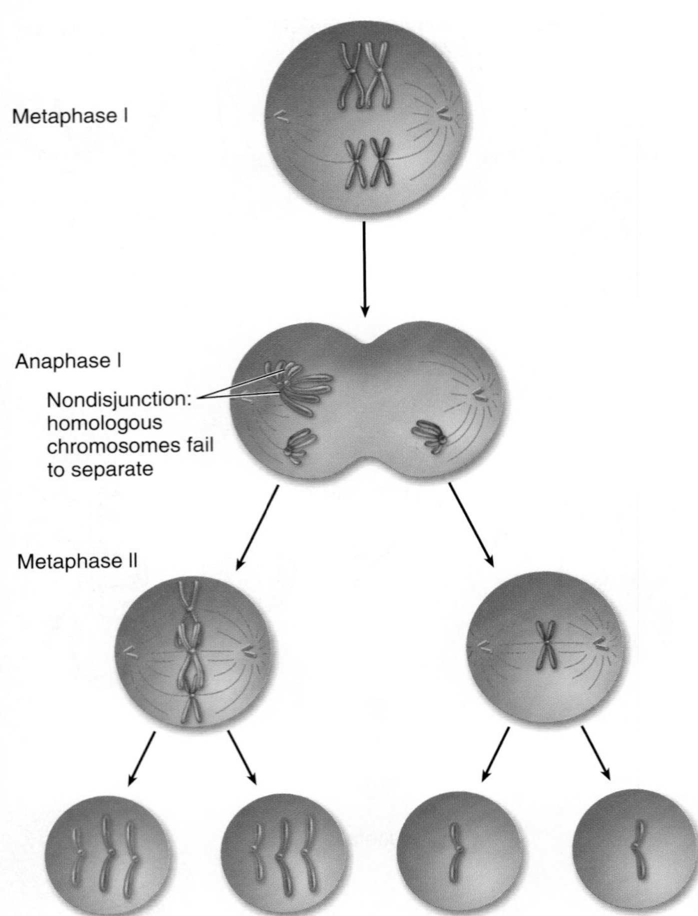

Figure 10.21 Nondisjunction in anaphase I.

In nondisjunction that occurs during meiosis I, one pair of homologous chromosomes fails to separate in anaphase I, and the gametes that result have one too many or one too few chromosomes. Nondisjunction can also occur in meiosis II, when sister chromatids fail to separate during anaphase II.

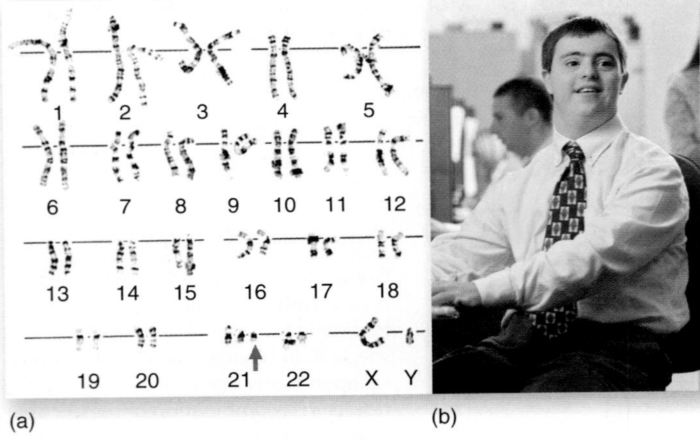

Figure 10.22 Down syndrome.

(a) In this karyotype of a male individual with Down syndrome, the trisomy at position 21 can be clearly seen. (b) A young man with Down syndrome.

10.8 Human Chromosomes

LEARNING OBJECTIVE 10.8.1 Contrast aneuploidy with nondisjunction, monosomic with trisomic, and Klinefelter syndrome with Turner syndrome.

Each human somatic cell normally has 46 chromosomes, which in meiosis form 23 pairs. Homologous chromosomes can be identified, according to size, shape, and appearance. Of the 23 pairs of human chromosomes, 22 are perfectly matched in both males and females and are called **autosomes.** The remaining pair, the **sex chromosomes,** consist of two similar chromosomes in females and two dissimilar chromosomes in males. In humans, females are designated XX and males are XY. The genes present on the Y chromosome determine "maleness" and therefore humans who inherit the Y chromosome develop into males.

Recent evidence suggests that a gene called *SRY* for "Sex-determining Region of the *Y* chromosome" may be responsible for the development of "maleness." This is discussed in more detail on page 599.

Nondisjunction

Sometimes during meiosis, homologous chromosomes or sister chromatids that paired up during metaphase remain stuck together instead of separating. The failure of chromosomes to separate correctly during either meiosis I or II is called **nondisjunction.** Nondisjunction leads to **aneuploidy,** an abnormal number of chromosomes. The nondisjunction you see in figure 10.21 occurs because the homologous pair of larger chromosomes failed to separate in anaphase I. The gametes that result from this division have unequal numbers of chromosomes. Under normal meiosis (refer back to *Essential Biological Process 9A*), all gametes in figure 10.21 would be expected to have two chromosomes, but as you can see, two of these gametes have three chromosomes, and the others have just one.

Almost all humans of the same sex have the same karyotype (refer back to figure 8.4) simply because other arrangements don't work well. Humans who have lost even one copy of an autosome (called **monosomics**) do not survive development. In all but a few cases, humans who have gained an extra autosome (called **trisomics**) also do not survive. However, five of the smallest chromosomes—those numbered 13, 15, 18, 21, and 22—can be present in humans as three copies and still allow the individual to survive for a time. The presence of an extra chromosome 13, 15, or 18 causes severe developmental defects, and infants with such a genetic makeup die within a few months. In contrast, individuals who have an extra copy of chromosome 21 or, more rarely, chromosome 22, usually survive to adulthood. In such individuals, the maturation of the skeletal system is delayed, so they generally are short and have poor muscle tone. Their mental development is also affected, and children with trisomy 21 or trisomy 22 are always mentally impaired.

Down Syndrome. The developmental defect produced by trisomy 21, an extra copy of chromosome 21 seen in the karyotype in figure 10.22, was first described in 1866 by J. Langdon Down; for this reason, it is called Down syndrome. About 1 in every 750 children exhibits Down syndrome, and the frequency is similar in all racial groups. It is much more common in children of older mothers. The graph in figure 10.23 shows the increasing incidence in older mothers. In mothers under 30 years old, the incidence is only about 0.6 per 1,000 (or 1 in 1,500 births), while in mothers 30 to 35 years old, the incidence doubles to about 1.3 per 1,000 births (or 1 in 750 births). In mothers over 45, the risk is as high as 63 per 1,000 births (or 1 in 16 births). The reason that older mothers are more prone to Down syndrome babies is that all the eggs that a woman will ever produce are present in her ovaries by the time she is born, and as she gets older they may accumulate damage that can result in nondisjunction.

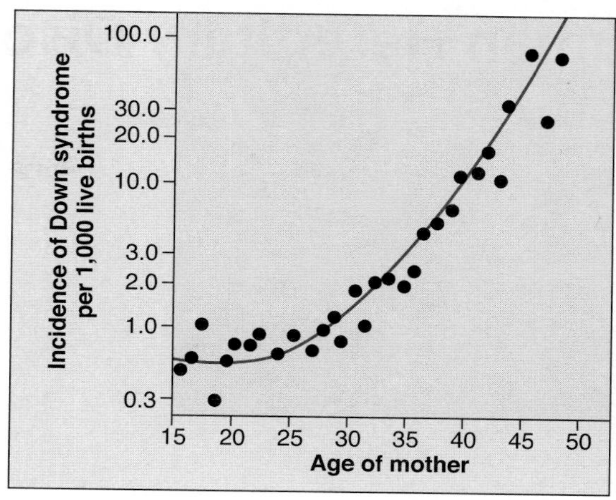

Figure 10.23 Correlation between maternal age and the incidence of Down syndrome.

As women age, the chances they will bear a child with Down syndrome increase. After a woman reaches age 35, the frequency of Down syndrome increases rapidly.

Nondisjunction Involving the Sex Chromosomes

As noted, 22 of the 23 pairs of human chromosomes are perfectly matched in both males and females and are called autosomes. The remaining pair are the sex chromosomes, X and Y. In humans, as in *Drosophila* (but by no means in all diploid species), females are XX and males XY; any individual with at least one Y chromosome is male. The Y chromosome is highly condensed and bears few functional genes in most organisms. Some of the active genes the Y chromosome does possess are responsible for the features associated with "maleness." Individuals who gain or lose a sex chromosome do not generally experience the severe developmental abnormalities caused by changes in autosomes. Such individuals may reach maturity, but with somewhat abnormal features.

Nondisjunction of the X Chromosome. When X chromosomes fail to separate during meiosis, some of the gametes that are produced possess both X chromosomes and so are XX gametes; the other gametes that result from such an event have no sex chromosome and are designated "O."

Figure 10.24 shows what happens if gametes from X chromosome nondisjunction combine with sperm. If an XX egg combines with an X sperm, the resulting XXX zygote develops into a female who is taller than average but other symptoms can vary greatly. Some are normal in most respects, others may have lower reading and verbal skills, and still others are mentally retarded. If an XX egg combines with a Y sperm, the XXY zygote develops into a sterile male who has many female body characteristics and, in some cases, diminished mental capacity. This condition, called *Klinefelter syndrome,* occurs in about 1 in 500 male births.

If an O egg fuses with a Y sperm, the OY zygote is nonviable and fails to develop further because humans cannot survive when they lack the genes on the X chromosome. If an O egg fuses with an X sperm, the XO zygote develops into a sterile female of short stature, with a webbed neck and immature sex organs that do not undergo changes during puberty. The mental abilities of XO individuals are normal in verbal learning but lower in nonverbal/math-based problem solving. This condition, called *Turner syndrome,* occurs roughly once in every 5,000 female births.

Nondisjunction of the Y Chromosome. The Y chromosome can also fail to separate in meiosis, leading to the formation of YY sperm. When these sperm combine with X eggs, the XYY zygotes develop into fertile males of normal appearance. The frequency of the XYY genotype is about 1 per 1,000 newborn males.

Putting the Concept to Work

Is it possible for a female to have Klinefelter syndrome? Explain.

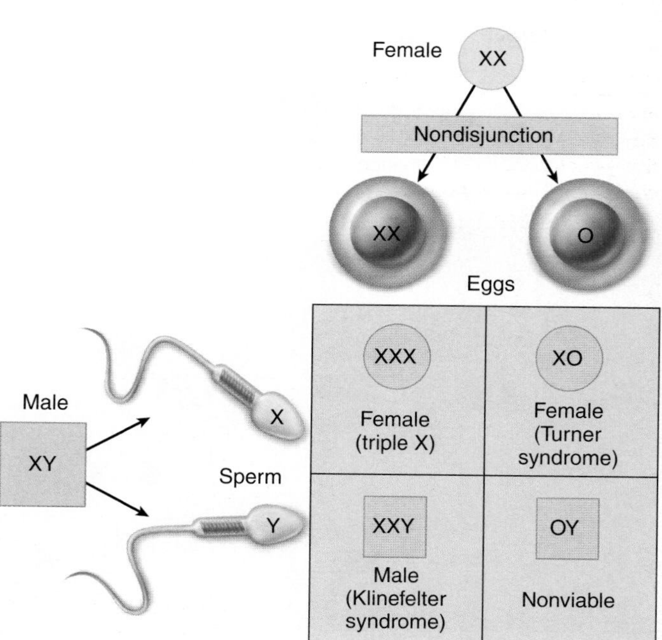

Figure 10.24 Nondisjunction of the X chromosome.

Nondisjunction of the X chromosome can produce sex chromosome aneuploidy—that is, abnormalities in the number of sex chromosomes.

Human Hereditary Disorders

10.9 Studying Pedigrees

LEARNING OBJECTIVE 10.9.1 List the three questions asked to analyze a human pedigree.

To study human heredity, scientists look at the results of crosses that have already been made. They study family trees, or **pedigrees,** to identify which relatives exhibit a trait. Then they can often determine whether the gene producing the trait is sex-linked (that is, located on the X chromosome) or autosomal, and whether the expression of the trait is dominant or recessive. Frequently the pedigree will also help an investigator infer which individuals in a family are homozygous and which are heterozygous for the allele specifying the trait.

Analyzing a Pedigree for Albinism

Albino individuals lack all pigmentation; their hair and skin are completely white. In the United States about 1 in 38,000 Caucasians and 1 in 22,000 African-Americans are albino. In the pedigree of albinism among a family of Hopi Indians presented in figure 10.25, each symbol represents one individual in the family history, with the circles representing females and the squares, males. In this pedigree, individuals that exhibit a trait being studied—in this case, albinism—are indicated by solid symbols; heterozygote "carriers" exhibiting normal phenotypes are indicated by half-filled symbols. Marriages are represented by horizontal lines connecting a circle and a square, from which a cluster of vertical lines descend indicating the children, arranged from left to right in order of their birth.

To analyze this pedigree of albinism, a geneticist traditionally asks three questions:

1. *Is albinism sex-linked or autosomal?* If the trait is sex-linked, it is usually seen only in males; if it is autosomal, it appears in both sexes fairly equally. In the pedigree below, the proportion of affected males (4 of 12, or 33%) is reasonably similar to the proportion of affected females (8 of 19, or 42%). (When counting numbers of affected individuals in a pedigree, exclude the parents in generation I, as well as any "outsiders" who marry into the family.) From this result, it is reasonable to conclude the trait is autosomal.
2. *Is albinism dominant or recessive?* If the trait is dominant, every albino child will have an albino parent. If recessive, however, an albino child's parents can appear normal, since both parents may be heterozygous "carriers". In the pedigree below, parents of most of the albino children do not exhibit the trait, which indicates that albinism is recessive. Four children in one family *do* have albino parents. The allele is very common among the Hopi Indians, from which this pedigree was derived, and thus homozygous individuals such as these albino parents are present in the Hopis in sufficient numbers that they sometimes marry. In this family, *both* parents are albino and all four children are albino, which is consistent with the finding that the trait albinism is recessive, with both parents homozygous for the allele.

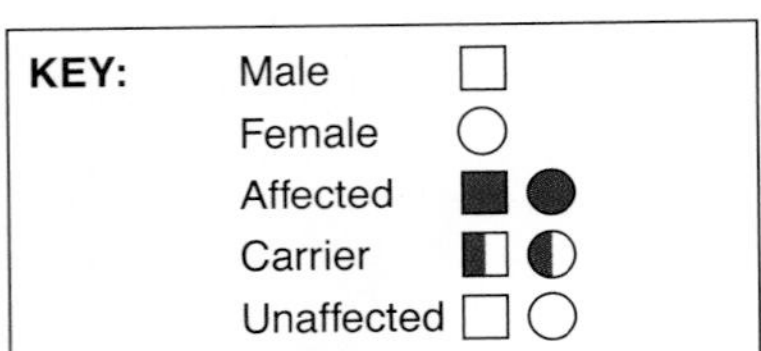

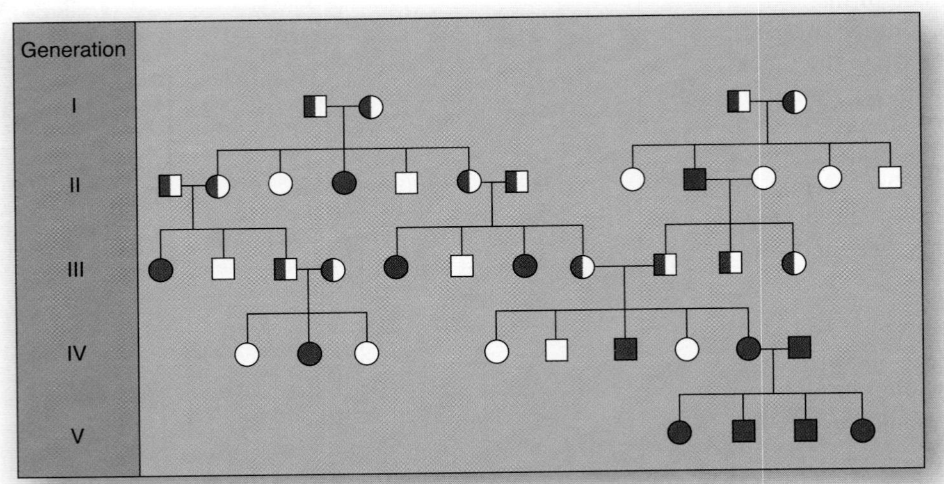

Figure 10.25 A pedigree of albinism.

In the photo, one of three girls from a Hopi Indian family (the left-most family in generation IV of the pedigree) is albino. The pedigree shows the inheritance of the gene causing albinism in this family, with the solid blue symbols indicating persons who are albino.

3. *Is the albinism trait determined by a single gene, or by several?* If the trait is determined by a single gene, then a ratio of 3:1 (normal to albino) offspring should be born to heterozygous parents (indicated by half-filled symbols), reflecting Mendelian segregation in a cross. Thus about 25% of these children should be albino. But if the trait is determined by several genes, albinism would be present only in a small percent. In this pedigree, 8 of 24 children born to heterozygotes, or 33%, exhibit albinism, strongly suggesting that only one gene is segregating in these crosses.

Analyzing a Pedigree for Color Blindness

The albinism pedigree analysis you have just examined indicates that albinism is an autosomal recessive trait controlled by a single gene. Now let us analyze a different trait. Red-green color blindness is an infrequent, although not rare, inherited trait in humans, affecting 5% to 9% of males. Color blindness is a group of eye disorders in which a person is not able to distinguish certain colors or shades of colors. It doesn't mean that they see only in black and white, but rather that they see colors but some different colors look the same to them. Special types of cells in the retina of the eye detect different colors of light and different shades.

Like albinism, a pedigree can be used to reveal the pattern of inheritance of color blindness. In the pedigree shown below (**figure 10.26**), a red-green color blind man has five children with a woman who is heterozygous for the allele. Again, the solid-color symbols indicate an affected individual, in this case red-green color blind. Half-filled symbols indicate a heterozygous individual who carries the trait but does not express it.

To analyze this pedigree, you ask the same three questions as before:

1. *Is red-green color blindness sex-linked or autosomal?* Of the five affected individuals, all are male. The trait is clearly sex-linked.
2. *Is red-green color blindness dominant or recessive?* If the trait is dominant, then every color-blind child should have a color-blind parent. In this pedigree, however, that is not true in any family after that of the original male. The trait is clearly recessive.
3. *Is the red-green color blindness trait determined by a single gene?* If it is, then children born to heterozygous parents should be color-blind in about 25% of cases, reflecting a 3:1 Mendelian segregation of the trait. In this pedigree, 4 of 14, or 28%, of the children of heterozygous parents are color blind, indicating that a single gene is segregating (do not count the five children of the generation I parents because the father in this case is homozygous for the trait).

The results of this pedigree indicate that color blindness is caused by a single sex-linked, recessive gene. This doesn't mean that females can't be color blind, but in order for a female to be color blind, both X chromosomes would have to carry the color blind gene, and this occurs in only 0.5% of females.

Putting the Concept to Work

When counting affected individuals in a pedigree, why don't you count the parents of generation I?

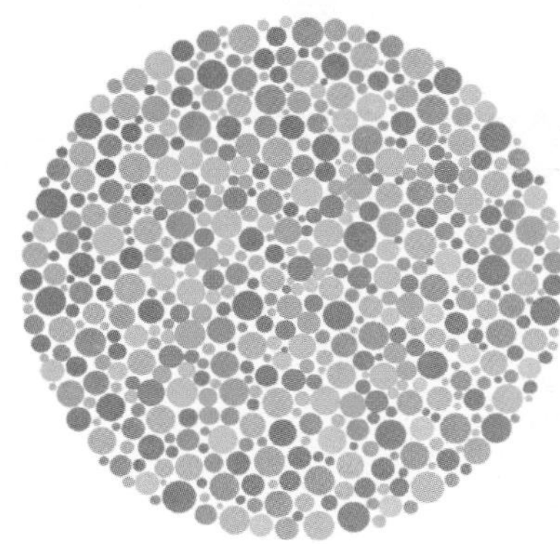

Source: This image has been reproduced from Ishihara's Tests for Color Deficiency published by KANEHARA TRADING INC., located in Tokyo, Japan. But tests for color deficiency cannot be conducted with this material. For accurate testing, the original plates should be used.

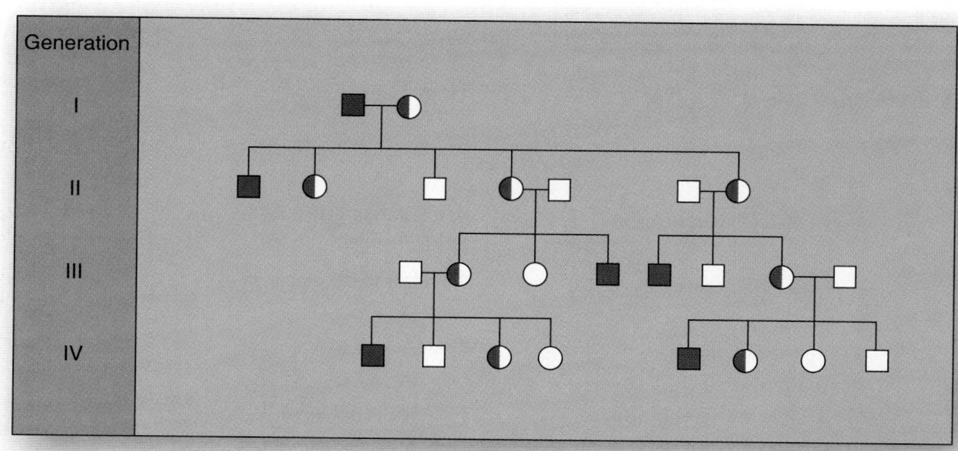

Figure 10.26 Pedigree of color blindness.

Test samples called Ishihara plates are used to determine if a person is color blind. The test plates contain different colored dots arranged to reveal a shape, often a number. Individuals who are red-green color blind cannot see the number in the test plate shown above, as all the dots appear the same color. The pedigree in this figure traces red-green color blindness through four generations of a family.

KEY:
Affected
Carrier
Unaffected
Female
Male

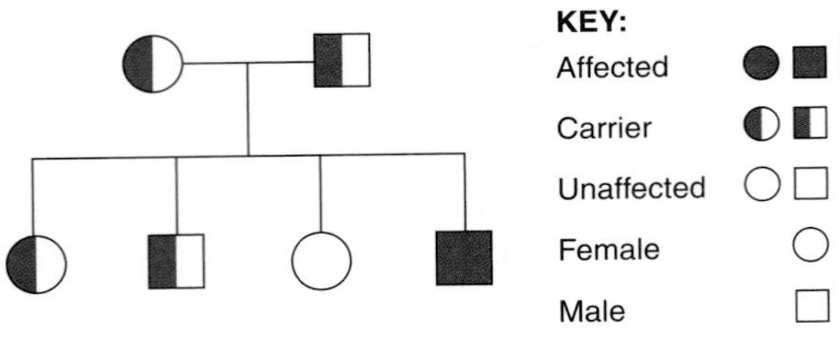

Figure 10.27 A general pedigree.
This pedigree is consistent with the inheritance of a recessive trait.

10.10 The Role of Mutations in Human Heredity

LEARNING OBJECTIVE 10.10.1 Contrast the inheritance of hemophilia, sickle-cell disease, Tay-Sachs disease, and Huntington's disease.

The proteins encoded by most of your genes must function in a very precise fashion for you to develop properly and for the many complex processes of your body to function correctly. Unfortunately, genes sometimes sustain damage or are copied incorrectly. We call these accidental changes in genes **mutations.** Mutations occur only rarely, because your cells police your genes and attempt to correct any damage they encounter. Still, some mutations get through. Many of them are bad for you in one way or another. It is easy to see why. Mutations hit genes at random—imagine that you randomly changed the number of a part on the design of a jet fighter. Sometimes it won't matter critically—a seat belt becomes a radio, say. But what if a key rivet in the wing becomes a roll of toilet paper? The chance of a random mutation in a gene improving the performance of its protein is about the same as that of a randomly selected part making the jet fly faster.

Mutations can occur in somatic cells or in germ-line cells. Both can have dramatic effects, but as discussed on page 199, only mutations in germ-line tissues are passed on to offspring and affect future generations.

Most mutations are rare in human populations. Almost all result in recessive alleles, and so they are not eliminated from the population by evolutionary forces—because they are not expressed in most individuals (heterozygotes) in which they occur. Do you see why they occur mostly in heterozygotes? Because mutant alleles are rare, it is unlikely that a person carrying a copy of the mutant allele will marry someone who also carries

TABLE 10.3 Some Important Genetic Disorders

Disorder	Symptom	Defect	Dominant/ Recessive	Frequency Among Human Births
Cystic fibrosis	Mucus clogs lungs, liver, and pancreas	Failure of chloride ion transport mechanism	Recessive	1/2,500 (Caucasians)
Sickle-cell disease	Poor blood circulation	Abnormal hemoglobin molecules	Recessive	1/625 (African Americans)
Tay-Sachs disease	Deterioration of central nervous system in infancy	Defective enzyme (hexosaminidase A)	Recessive	1/3,500 (Ashkenazi Jews)
Phenylketonuria (PKU)	Brain fails to develop in infancy	Defective enzyme (phenylalanine hydroxylase)	Recessive	1/12,000
Hemophilia	Blood fails to clot	Defective blood-clotting factor VIII	Sex-linked recessive	1/10,000 (Caucasian males)
Huntington's disease	Brain tissue gradually deteriorates in middle age	Production of an inhibitor of brain cell metabolism	Dominant	1/24,000
Muscular dystrophy (Duchenne)	Muscles waste away	Degradation of myelin coating of nerves stimulating muscles	Sex-linked recessive	1/3,700 (males)
Congenital hypothyroidism	Increased birth weight, puffy face, constipation, lethargy	Failure of proper thyroid development	Recessive	1/1,000 (Hispanics) 1/700 (Native Americans)
Hypercholesterolemia	Excessive cholesterol levels in blood, leading to heart disease	Abnormal form of cholesterol cell surface receptor	Dominant	1/500

it. Instead, he or she will typically marry someone homozygous dominant, and so none of their children would be homozygous for the mutant allele. While most mutations are harmful to normal functions and are usually recessive, that is not to say all mutations are undesirable; some mutations can lead to enhanced function. Nor are all mutations recessive; rarely they can occur as dominant alleles.

In some cases, particular mutant alleles have become more common in human populations. In these cases, the harmful effects that they produce are called *genetic disorders*. Some of the most common genetic disorders are listed in **table 10.3**. As mentioned in the previous section, scientists can study family pedigrees to determine whether the gene producing a certain genetic disorder is sex-linked or autosomal and whether the disorder is dominant or recessive. **Figure 10.27** shows a general pedigree for a recessive trait. As mentioned previously, females are indicated with circles and males with squares in most pedigrees. The lines connect the parents and display the offspring. Solid shapes indicate an individual affected by a disorder; half-filled shapes indicate a carrier (someone who is heterozygous); open shapes indicate an individual not affected.

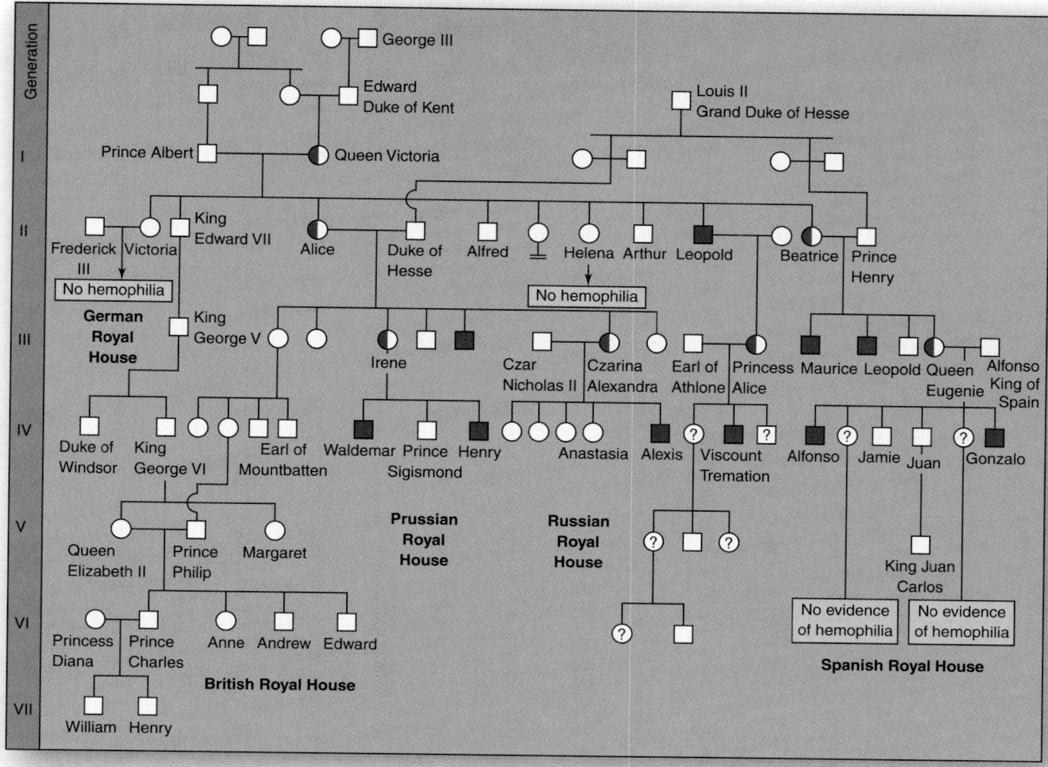

Hemophilia: A Sex-Linked Trait

Blood in a cut clots as a result of the polymerization of protein fibers circulating in the blood. A dozen proteins are involved in this process, and all must function properly for a blood clot to form. A mutation causing any of these proteins to lose their activity leads to a form of **hemophilia,** a hereditary condition in which the blood clots slowly or not at all.

Hemophilias are recessive disorders, expressed only when an individual does not possess any copy of the normal allele and so cannot produce one of the proteins necessary for clotting. Most of the genes that encode the blood-clotting proteins are on autosomes, but two (designated *VIII* and *IX*) are on the X chromosome. These two genes are sex-linked (see section 10.7). Any male who inherits a mutant allele will develop hemophilia, because his other sex chromosome is a Y chromosome that lacks any alleles of those genes.

The most famous instance of hemophilia, often called the Royal hemophilia, is a sex-linked form that arose in the royal family of England. This hemophilia was caused by a mutation in gene *IX* that occurred in one of the parents of Queen Victoria of England (1819–1901). The pedigree in **figure 10.28** shows that in the six generations since Queen Victoria, 10 of her male descendants have had hemophilia (the solid squares). The present British royal family has escaped the disorder because Queen Victoria's son, King Edward VII, did not inherit the defective allele, and all the subsequent rulers of England are his descendants. Three of Victoria's nine children did receive the defective allele, however, and they carried it by marriage into many of the other royal families of Europe. As you will learn in chapter 13, this type of hemophilia has been successfully treated using gene therapy.

Figure 10.28 The Royal hemophilia pedigree.

Queen Victoria's daughter Alice introduced hemophilia into the Russian and Prussian royal houses, and her daughter Beatrice introduced it into the Spanish royal house. Victoria's son Leopold, himself a victim, also transmitted the disorder in a third line of descent. Half-shaded symbols represent carriers with one normal allele and one defective allele; fully shaded symbols represent affected individuals. Squares represent males; circles represent females. In this photo, Queen Victoria of England is surrounded by some of her descendants in 1894. Standing behind Victoria and wearing feathered boas are two of Victoria's granddaughters, Alice's daughter's: Princess Irene of Prussia *(right)*, and Alexandra *(left)*, who would soon become Czarina of Russia. Both Irene and Alexandra were also carriers of hemophilia.

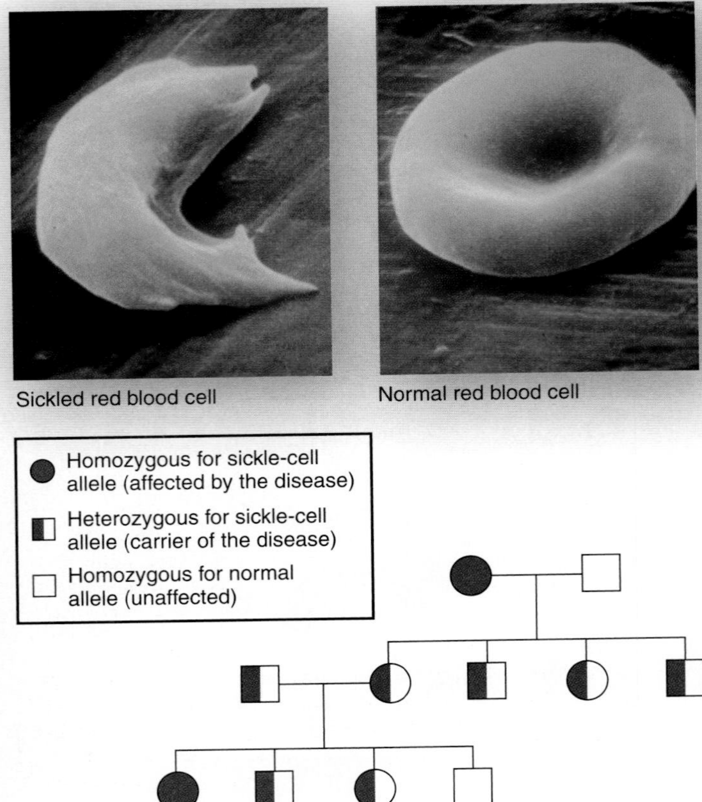

Figure 10.29 Inheritance of sickle-cell disease.

Sickle-cell disease is a recessive autosomal disorder. If one parent is homozygous for the recessive trait, all of the offspring will be carriers (heterozygotes) like the F_1 generation of Mendel's testcross. A normal red blood cell is shaped like a flattened sphere. In individuals homozygous for the sickle-cell trait, many of the red blood cells have sickle shapes.

Sickle-Cell Disease: Recessive Trait

Sickle-cell disease is a recessive hereditary disorder. Its inheritance is shown in the pedigree in figure 10.29, where affected individuals are homozygous, carrying two copies of the mutated gene. Affected individuals have defective molecules of hemoglobin, the protein within red blood cells that carries oxygen. Consequently, these individuals are unable to properly transport oxygen to their tissues.

The hemoglobin in the defective red blood cells differs from that in normal red blood cells in only one of beta-hemoglobin's 146 amino acid subunits. In the defective hemoglobin, the amino acid valine replaces a glutamic acid at a single position in each of the two beta-subunit proteins. Interestingly, the position of the change is far from the active site of hemoglobin where the iron-bearing heme group binds oxygen. Instead, the change occurs on the outer corners of the 4-subunit hemoglobin molecule. Why then is the result so catastrophic? The sickle-cell mutation puts a very nonpolar amino acid (valine) on the surface of the hemoglobin protein, creating a "sticky patch" that sticks to other such patches—nonpolar amino acids tend to associate with one another in polar environments like water. The defective hemoglobin molecules adhere to one another in chains. These hemoglobin chains form stiff, rodlike structures that result in sickle-shaped red blood cells (see figure 10.29). As a result of their stiffness and irregular shape, these cells have difficulty moving through the smallest blood vessels; they tend to accumulate in those vessels and form clots. People who have large proportions of sickle-shaped red blood cells tend to have intermittent illness and a shortened life span.

Individuals heterozygous for the sickle-cell allele are generally indistinguishable from normal persons. However, some of their red blood cells show the sickling characteristic when they are exposed to low levels of oxygen. The allele responsible for sickle-cell disease is particularly common among people of African descent because the sickle-cell allele is more common in Africa. About 9% of African Americans are heterozygous for this allele, and about 0.2% are homozygous and therefore have the disorder. In some groups of people in Africa, up to 45% of all individuals are heterozygous for this allele, and fully 6% are homozygous and express the disorder. What factors determine the high frequency of sickle-cell disease in Africa? It turns out that heterozygosity for the sickle-cell allele increases resistance to malaria, a common and serious disease in Central Africa. Comparing the two maps shown in figure 10.30, you can see that the area of the sickle-cell trait matches well with the incidence of malaria. The interactions of sickle-cell disease and malaria are discussed further in chapter 14.

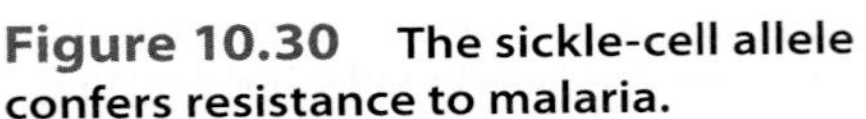

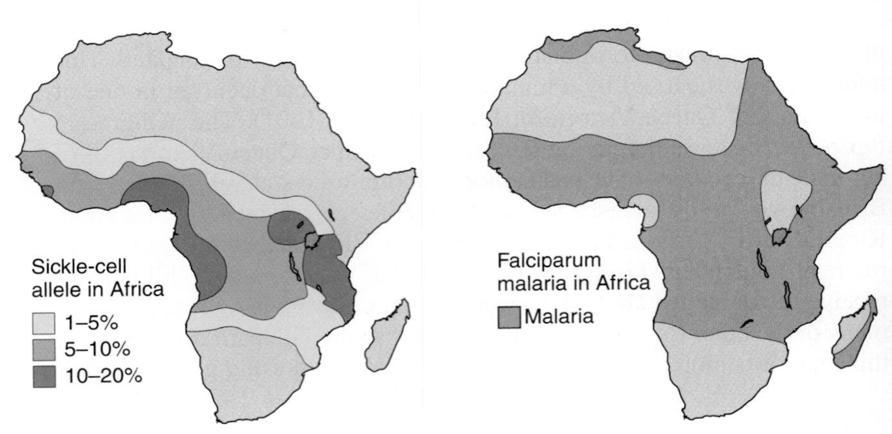

Figure 10.30 The sickle-cell allele confers resistance to malaria.

The distribution of sickle-cell disease closely matches the occurrence of malaria in central Africa. This is not a coincidence. The sickle-cell allele, when heterozygous, confers resistance to malaria, a very serious disease.

Tay-Sachs Disease: Recessive Trait

Tay-Sachs disease is an incurable hereditary disorder in which the brain deteriorates. Affected children appear normal at birth and usually do not develop symptoms until about the eighth month, when signs of mental deterioration appear. The children are blind within a year after birth, and they rarely live past five years of age.

The Tay-Sachs allele produces the disease by encoding a nonfunctional form of the enzyme hexosaminidase A. This enzyme breaks down *gangliosides,* a class of lipids occurring within the lysosomes of brain cells. As a result, the lysosomes fill with gangliosides, swell, and eventually burst, releasing oxidative enzymes that kill the cells. There is no known cure for this disorder.

Lysosomes are a component of the endomembrane system, as discussed on page 77. They are membrane-bounded vesicles that contain powerful enzymes that break down cellular debris. If the lysosome enzymes leak out, they will kill the cell from within.

Tay-Sachs disease is rare in most human populations, occurring in only 1 in 300,000 births in the United States. However, the disease has a high incidence among Jews of Eastern and Central Europe (Ashkenazi) and among American Jews, 90% of whom trace their ancestry to Eastern and Central Europe. In these populations, it is estimated that 1 in 28 individuals is a heterozygous carrier of the disease, and approximately 1 in 3,500 infants has the disease. Because the disease is caused by a recessive allele, most of the people who carry the defective allele do not themselves develop symptoms of the disease because, as shown by the middle bar in figure 10.31, their one normal gene produces enough enzyme activity (50%) to keep the body functioning normally.

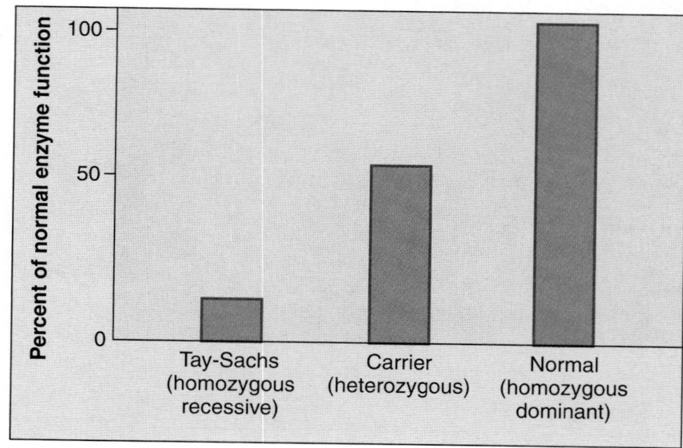

Figure 10.31 Tay-Sachs disease.

Homozygous individuals (*left bar*) typically have less than 10% of the normal level of hexosaminidase A (*right bar*), while heterozygous individuals (*middle bar*) have about 50% of the normal level—enough to prevent deterioration of the central nervous system.

IMPLICATION FOR YOU Tay-Sachs disease is named for Warren Tay, an eye doctor who first described the cherry-red spot on the retina that is now the marker for the disease, and Bernard Sachs, a neurologist who first described the changes in the brain and the prevalence among Ashkenazi Jews. Can you think of another disease, much in the news in recent years, named for its discoverer?

Huntington's Disease: Dominant Trait

Not all hereditary disorders are recessive. **Huntington's disease** is a hereditary condition caused by a dominant allele that causes the progressive deterioration of brain cells. Perhaps 1 in 24,000 individuals develops the disorder. Because the allele is dominant, every individual who carries the allele expresses the disorder. Nevertheless, the disorder persists in human populations because its symptoms usually do not develop until the affected individuals are more than 30 years old, and by that time most of those individuals have already had children. Consequently, as illustrated by the pedigree in figure 10.32, the allele is often transmitted before the lethal condition develops.

Putting the Concept to Work

If Huntington's disease is caused by a dominant allele and is lethal, why doesn't the disease disappear from the human population?

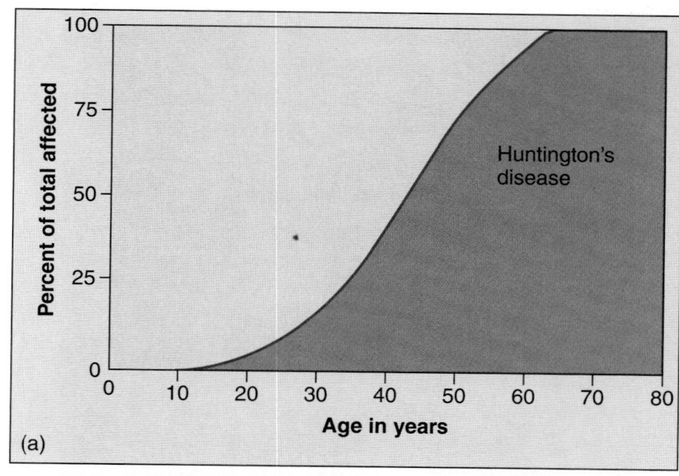

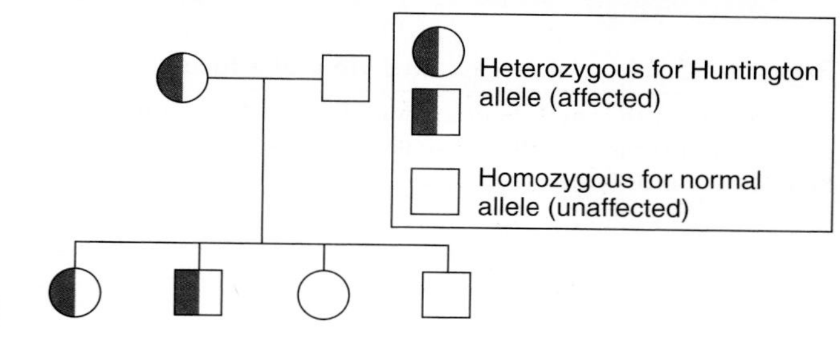

Figure 10.32 Huntington's disease is a dominant genetic disorder.

(a) Because of the late age of onset of Huntington's disease, the allele causing it persists despite being both dominant and fatal. (b) The pedigree illustrates how a dominant lethal allele can be passed from one generation to the next. Although the mother was affected, we can tell that she was heterozygous because if she were homozygous dominant, all of her children would have been affected. However, by the time she found out that she had the disease, she had probably already given birth to her children. In this way the trait passes on to the next generation even though it is fatal.

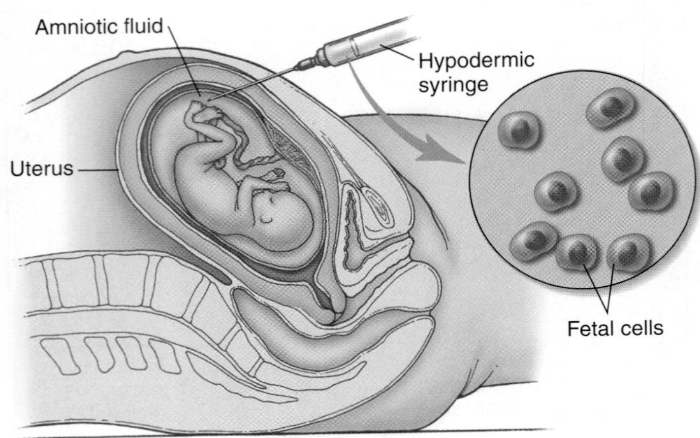

Figure 10.33 Amniocentesis.

A needle is inserted into the amniotic cavity, and a sample of amniotic fluid, containing some free cells derived from the fetus, is withdrawn into a syringe. The fetal cells are then grown in culture and their karyotype and many of their metabolic functions are examined.

IMPLICATION FOR YOU The risk of amniocentesis-related miscarriage due to infection, puncture leakage, or other complications is estimated to be as low as 1 in 600. In contrast, the risk of miscarriage for chorionic villus sampling is approximately 1 in 100, although the sampling may be done up to four weeks earlier. If you have a child, would you expect that you and your spouse would choose to carry out genetic screening? If so, which procedure would you wish to see used? Why?

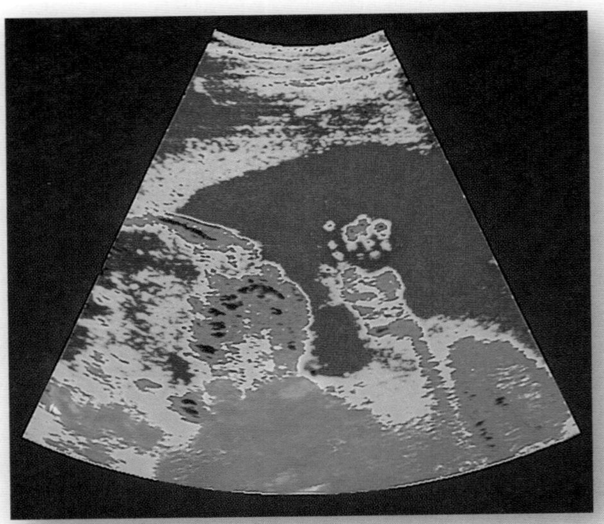

Figure 10.34 An ultrasound view of a fetus.

During the fourth month of pregnancy, when amniocentesis is normally performed, the fetus usually moves about actively. The head of the fetus (visualized in *green*) is to the *left*.

10.11 Genetic Counseling and Therapy

LEARNING OBJECTIVE 10.11.1 Describe three things geneticists examine in cells obtained by amniocentesis.

The process of identifying parents at risk of producing children with genetic defects and of assessing the genetic state of early embryos is called **genetic counseling.** Genetic counseling can help prospective parents determine their risk of having a child with a genetic disorder, and advise them on medical treatments or options if a genetic disorder is determined to exist in an unborn child.

Genetic Screening

When a pregnancy is diagnosed as being high risk, many women elect to undergo **amniocentesis,** a procedure that permits the prenatal diagnosis of many genetic disorders. Figure 10.33 shows how an amniocentesis is performed. In the fourth month of pregnancy, a sterile hypodermic needle is inserted into the expanded uterus of the mother, and a small sample of the amniotic fluid bathing the fetus is removed. Within the fluid are free-floating cells derived from the fetus; once removed, these cells can be grown in cultures in the laboratory. During amniocentesis, the position of the needle and that of the fetus are usually observed by means of **ultrasound.** The ultrasound image in figure 10.34 clearly reveals the fetus's position in the uterus.

In recent years, physicians have increasingly turned to another invasive procedure for genetic screening called **chorionic villus sampling.** In this procedure, the physician removes cells from the chorion, a membranous part of the placenta that nourishes the fetus. This procedure can be used earlier in pregnancy (by the eighth week) and yields results much more rapidly than does amniocentesis, but can increase the risk of miscarriage.

Genetic counselors look at three things in the cultures of cells obtained from amniocentesis or chorionic villus sampling:

1. **Chromosomal karyotype.** Analysis of the karyotype can reveal aneuploidy (extra or missing chromosomes) and gross alterations.
2. **Enzyme activity.** In many cases, it is possible to test directly for the proper functioning of enzymes involved in genetic disorders. The lack of normal enzymatic activity signals the presence of the disorder.
3. **Genetic markers.** Genetic counselors can look for an association with known genetic markers. For sickle-cell disease, Huntington's disease, and one form of muscular dystrophy (a genetic disorder characterized by weakened muscles), investigators have found other mutations on the same chromosomes that, by chance, occur at about the same place as the mutations that cause those disorders. By testing for the presence of these other mutations, a genetic counselor can identify individuals with a high probability of possessing the disorder-causing mutations.

Putting the Concept to Work

Why not use ultrasound instead of amniocentesis for prenatal diagnosis? Isn't it safer?

Inquiry & Analysis

Why Woolly Hair Runs in Families

The woman in the photo on the right does not cut her hair. Her hair breaks off naturally as it grows, keeping it from getting long. Other members of her family have the same sort of hair, suggesting it is a hereditary trait. Because of its curly, fuzzy texture, this trait has been given the name "woolly hair."

While the woolly hair trait is rare, it flares up in certain families. The extensive pedigree below (drawn curved to fit the large families produced by the second and subsequent generations) records the incidence of woolly hair in five generations (indicated by the Roman numerals on the left) of a Norwegian family. As is the convention, affected individuals are indicated by solid symbols, with circles indicating females and squares indicating males. The pedigree will provide you with all the information you need to discover how this trait is inherited within human families.

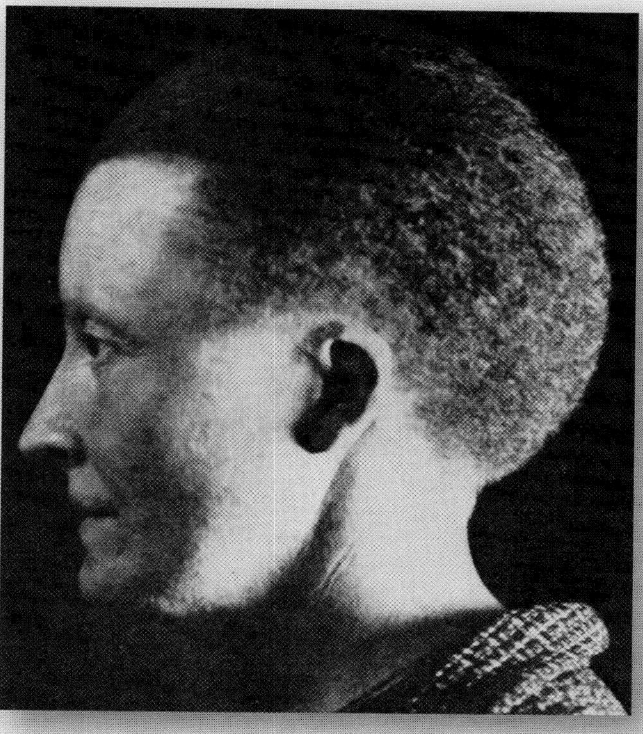

Analysis

1. **Applying Concepts** In the diagram below, how many individuals are documented? Are all of them related?
2. **Interpreting Data**
   a. Does the woolly hair trait appear in both sexes equally?
   b. Does every woolly hair child have a woolly hair parent?
   c. What percentage of the offspring born to a woolly haired parent are also woolly haired?
3. **Making Inferences**
   a. Is woolly hair sex-linked or autosomal?
   b. Is woolly hair dominant or recessive?
   c. Is the woolly hair trait determined by a single gene, or by several?
4. **Drawing Conclusions**
   a. How many copies of the woolly hair allele are necessary to produce a detectable change in a person's hair?
   b. Are there any woolly hair homozygous individuals in the pedigree? Explain.

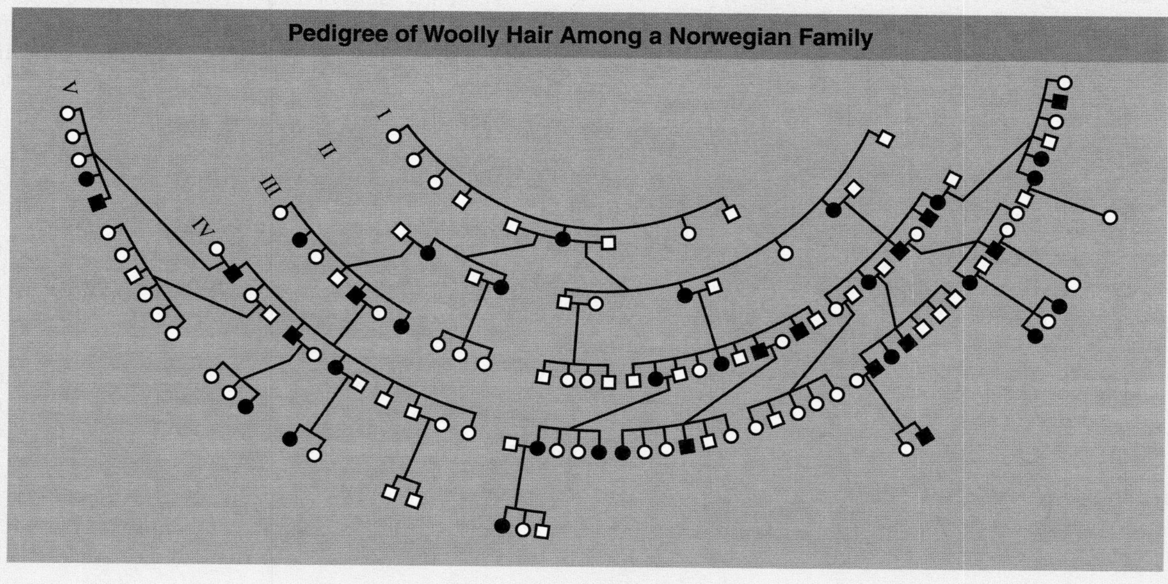

Summary of Learning Outcomes

Mendel

Mendel and the Garden Pea

10.1.1 Mendel studied heredity using the garden pea and an experimental system that included counting his results.

10.1.2 Mendel crossed plants that were true-breeding for easily scored alternative traits and then allowed the offspring of these crosses to self-fertilize and counted the numbers of each type of offspring.

What Mendel Observed

10.2.1 In Mendel's experiments, the first (F_1) generation plants all expressed the same alternative form, called the dominant trait. In the second (F_2) generation, 3/4 of the offspring expressed the dominant trait and 1/4 expressed the other form, called the recessive trait. Mendel found this 3:1 ratio in the F_2 generation in all the seven traits he studied. Mendel then found that this 3:1 ratio was actually a 1:2:1 ratio—1 true-breeding dominant: 2 not-true-breeding dominant: 1 true-breeding recessive.

Mendel Proposes a Theory

10.3.1 Mendel's theory of heredity proposes that characteristics are passed from parent to offspring, one version (called an allele) inherited from each parent. If both of the alleles are the same, the individual is homozygous for the trait. If the individual has one dominant and one recessive allele, it is heterozygous for the trait. An individual's alleles are its genotype, and the expression of those alleles is its phenotype.

10.3.2 A Punnett square can be used to predict the probabilities of inheriting certain genotypes and phenotypes in the offspring of a cross. The alleles are assigned letters: an uppercase letter for the dominant allele and a lowercase letter for the recessive allele.

10.3.3 A testcross determines the genotype of an individual exhibiting the phenotype of a dominant trait by mating the individual of unknown genotype with an individual that is homozygous recessive, and seeing if there are any offspring that do not exhibit the dominant trait.

Mendel's Laws

10.4.1 Mendel's law of segregation states that alleles are distributed into gametes so that half of the gametes will carry one copy of a trait and the remaining gametes carry the other copy of the trait. Mendel's law of independent assortment states that the inheritance of one trait does not influence the inheritance of other traits. Genes located on different chromosomes are inherited independent of each other, as exhibited in a dihybrid cross, like the one shown here from **figure 10.10.**

From Genotype to Phenotype

How Genes Influence Traits

10.5.1 Genes determine phenotype because DNA encodes the amino acid sequences of proteins, and proteins are the outward expression of genes.

Why Some Traits Don't Show Mendelian Inheritance

10.6.1 Not all traits exhibit the inheritance patterns outlined by Mendel. Continuous variation results when more than one gene contributes in a cumulative way to a phenotype, resulting in a continuous array of phenotypes. This pattern of inheritance is called polygenic. Pleiotropic effects result when one gene influences more than one trait. Incomplete dominance results when alternative alleles are not fully dominant or fully recessive such that heterozygous individuals express a phenotype that is intermediate between the dominant and recessive phenotypes. An example is the Japanese four o'clock flowers shown here from **figure 10.14.** The expression of some genes is influenced by environmental factors, such as the changing of fur color triggered by heat-sensitive alleles. Codominance occurs when there isn't a dominant allele—two alleles are expressed resulting in phenotypic expression of both alleles.

Chromosomes and Heredity

Chromosomes Are the Vehicles of Mendelian Inheritance

10.7.1 Genes segregate because they are located on chromosomes that segregate among the gametes during meiosis. Morgan demonstrated this using an X-linked gene in fruit flies. However, the farther apart two genes are on a chromosome, the more likely they are to assort independently because of crossing over.

Human Chromosomes

10.8.1 Humans have 23 pairs of homologous chromosomes, for a total of 46 chromosomes. They have 22 pairs of autosomes and one pair of sex chromosomes. Nondisjunction occurs when sister chromatids or homologous pairs fail to separate during meiosis, resulting in gametes with too many or too few chromosomes. Nondisjunction of autosomes is usually fatal, Down syndrome being an exception, but the effects of nondisjunction of sex chromosomes are less severe.

Human Hereditary Disorders

Studying Pedigrees

10.9.1 Study of family trees can reveal if an inherited trait is caused by a single gene, if that gene is located on the X chromosome, and if its mutant alleles are recessive.

The Role of Mutations in Human Heredity

10.10.1 Mutations can lead to genetic disorders such as hemophilia, sickle-cell disease, Tay-Sachs, and Huntington's disease.

Genetic Counseling and Therapy

10.11.1 Some genetic disorders can be detected during pregnancy using amniocentesis and chorionic villus sampling.

Test Your Understanding

10.1.2 Gregor Mendel studied the garden pea plants because
- **a.** pea plants are small, easy to grow, grow quickly, and produce lots of flowers and seeds.
- **b.** he knew about studies with the garden pea that had been done for hundreds of years, and wanted to continue them, using math—counting and recording differences.
- **c.** he knew that there were many varieties available with distinctive characteristics.
- **d.** All of the above.

10.2.1 Mendel examined seven characteristics, such as flower color. He crossed plants with two different forms of a character (purple flowers and white flowers). In crosses with flower color, the first generation of offspring (F_1) were
- **a.** all purple flowers.
- **b.** half purple flowers and half white flowers.
- **c.** 3/4 purple and 1/4 white flowers.
- **d.** all white flowers.

10.2.1 Following the question above, when Mendel allowed the F_1 generation to self-fertilize, the offspring in the F_2 generation were
- **a.** all purple flowers.
- **b.** half purple flowers and half white flowers.
- **c.** 3/4 purple and 1/4 white flowers.
- **d.** all white flowers.

10.3.1 Mendel then studied his results, and proposed a set of hypotheses to explain them. The basis of these hypotheses is that parents transmit
- **a.** traits directly to their offspring, and they are expressed.
- **b.** some factor, or information, about traits to their offspring, and it may or may not be expressed.
- **c.** some factor, or information, about traits to their offspring, and it will always be expressed.
- **d.** some factor, or information, about traits to their offspring, and both traits expressed in every generation, perhaps in a "blended" form with information from the other parent.

10.4.1 A cross between two individuals results in a ratio of 9:3:3:1 for four possible phenotype combinations. This is an example of a
- **a.** dihybrid cross.
- **b.** monohybrid cross.
- **c.** testcross.
- **d.** None of these are correct.

10.6.1 Human height shows a continuous variation from the very short to the very tall. Height is most likely controlled by
- **a.** a single gene.
- **b.** environmental factors.
- **c.** sex-linked genes.
- **d.** multiple genes.

10.6.1 In the human ABO blood grouping, the four basic blood types are type A, type B, type AB, and type O. The enzymes that produce types A and B are
- **a.** simple dominant and recessive traits.
- **b.** incomplete dominant traits.
- **c.** codominant traits.
- **d.** sex-linked traits.

10.7.1 What finding finally determined that genes were carried on chromosomes?
- **a.** heat sensitivity of certain enzymes that determined coat color
- **b.** sex-linked eye color in fruit flies
- **c.** the finding of complete dominance
- **d.** establishing pedigrees

10.8.1 Nondisjunction
- **a.** occurs when homologous chromosomes or sister chromatids fail to separate during meiosis.
- **b.** may lead to Down syndrome.
- **c.** results in aneuploidy.
- **d.** All of the above.

10.11.1 Which of the following analyses can detect aneuploidy?
- **a.** enzyme activity
- **b.** chromosomal karyotyping
- **c.** pedigrees
- **d.** genetic markers

Apply Your Understanding

10.4.1 Using the four gametes shown from the F_1 generation, how many possible crosses are there? Remember that a gamete type could cross with another of the same type (such as $RY \times RY$). Draw a Punnett square for each cross, and list the ratios of genotypes and phenotypes for the F_2 generation of that cross.

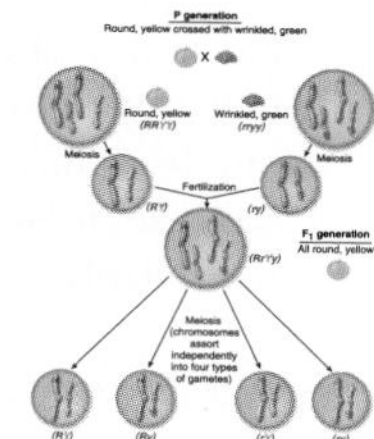

10.6.1 Referring to this figure, use Punnett squares to illustrate whether a type A female and a type B male can have a child with type O blood.

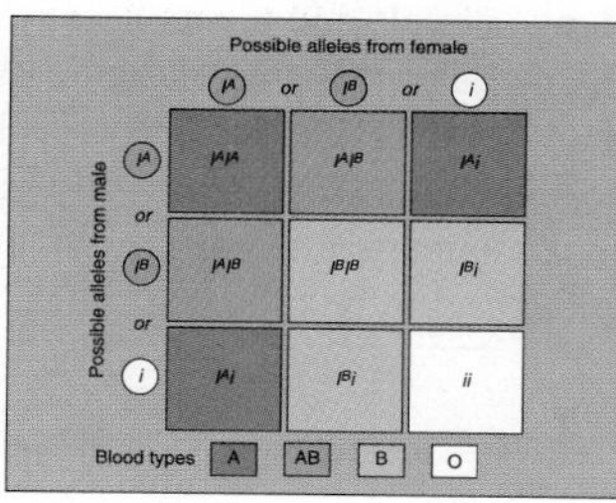

Synthesize What You Have Learned

10.4.1 As Mendel struggled with understanding inheritance and formed his laws, how would the outcome have been different if he had chosen two traits that are carried on the same chromosome, with loci that are in close proximity to each other?

10.7.1 Kim and Su-Ling are doing fruit fly crosses in their biology class. Kim wants to test whether the female they have is homozygous or heterozygous for red eyes by mating with a red-eyed male. How should Su-Ling explain the difficulty to him?

10.9.1 Your biology class is collecting information on heredity. Michael realizes that he, along with three of his four brothers, are color blind, but his four sisters are not, and neither are his parents nor his grandparents. Can you help Michael understand what happened?

10.11.1 Kuzungu is a child orphaned by civil war in her country and raised in a group home. She has sickle-cell disease, and type AB blood. Two couples who believe they are her grandparents ask you, a genetic counselor, to help them determine who her real grandparents are. What do you suggest?

Additional Genetics Problems

These genetics problems will help you see the far-reaching effects of Mendel's experiments. If you need help, the answers appear at www.mhhe.com/tlwessentials4.

1. Silky feathers in chickens is a single-gene recessive trait whose effect is to produce shiny plumage.
   a. If 108 birds were raised from a cross between individuals heterozygous for this gene, how many would be expected to be silky and how many normal?
   b. If you had a normal-feathered bird, what would be the easiest cross to perform in order to determine if the bird is homozygous or heterozygous for the silky allele?

2. Among Hereford cattle there is a dominant allele called *polled;* the individuals that have this allele lack horns. Suppose you acquire a herd consisting entirely of polled cattle, and you carefully determine that no cow in the herd has horns. Some of the calves born that year, however, grow horns. You remove them from the herd and make certain that no horned adult has gotten into your pasture. Despite your efforts, more horned calves are born the next year. What is the reason for the appearance of the horned calves? If your goal is to maintain a herd consisting entirely of polled cattle, what should you do?

3. An inherited trait among humans in Norway causes affected individuals to have very curly hair, not unlike that of a sheep. The trait, called *woolly,* is very evident when it occurs in families (see *Inquiry & Analysis*); no child possesses woolly hair unless at least one parent does. Imagine you are a Norwegian judge, and you have before you a woolly haired man suing his normal-haired wife for divorce because their first child has woolly hair but their second child has normal hair. The husband claims this constitutes evidence of his wife's infidelity. Do you accept his claim? Justify your decision.

4. Brachydactyly is a rare human trait that causes a shortening of the length of the fingers by a third. A review of medical records reveals that the progeny of marriages between a brachydactyl person and a normal person are approximately half brachydactylous. What proportion of offspring in matings between two brachydactylous individuals would be expected to be brachydactylous?

5. Many animals and plants bear recessive alleles for *albinism,* a condition in which homozygous individuals lack certain pigments. An albino plant, for example, lacks chlorophyll and is white, and an albino human lacks melanin. If two normally pigmented persons heterozygous for the same albinism allele marry, what proportion of their children would you expect to be albino?

6. You inherit a racehorse and decide to put him out to stud. In looking over the stud book, however, you discover that the horse's grandfather exhibited a rare disorder that causes brittle bones. The disorder is hereditary and results from homozygosity for a recessive allele. If your horse is heterozygous for the allele, it will not be possible to use him for stud because the genetic defect may be passed on. How would you determine whether your horse carries this allele?

7. Your instructor presents you with a *Drosophila* (fruit fly) with red eyes, as well as a stock of white-eyed flies and another stock of flies homozygous for the red-eye allele. You know that the presence of white eyes in *Drosophila* is caused by homozygosity for a recessive allele. How would you determine whether the single red-eyed fly was heterozygous for the white-eye allele?

8. Hemophilia is a recessive sex-linked human blood disease that leads to failure of blood to clot normally. One form of hemophilia has been traced to the royal family of England, from which it spread throughout the royal families of Europe. For the purposes of this problem, assume that it originated as a mutation either in Prince Albert or in his wife, Queen Victoria.
   a. Prince Albert did not have hemophilia. If the disease is a sex-linked recessive abnormality, how could it have originated in Prince Albert, a male, who would have been expected to exhibit sex-linked recessive traits?
   b. Alexis, the son of Czar Nicholas II of Russia and Empress Alexandra (a granddaughter of Victoria), had hemophilia, but their daughter Anastasia did not. Anastasia died, a victim of the Russian revolution, before she had any children. Can we assume that Anastasia would have been a carrier of the disease? Would your answer be different if the disease had been present in Nicholas II or in Alexandra?

9. A normally pigmented man marries an albino woman. They have three children, one of whom is an albino. What is the genotype of the father?

10. A man works in an atomic energy plant, and he is exposed daily to low-level background radiation. After several years, he has a child who has Duchenne muscular dystrophy, a recessive genetic defect caused by a mutation on the X chromosome. Neither the parents nor the grandparents have the disease. The man sues the plant, claiming that the abnormality in their child is the direct result of radiation-induced mutation of his gametes, and that the company should have protected him from this radiation. Before reaching a decision, the judge hearing the case insists on knowing the sex of the child. Which sex would be more likely to result in an award of damages, and why?

Chapter 11

DNA: The Genetic Material

CHAPTER AT A GLANCE

Genes Are Made of DNA

11.1 The Griffith Experiment

11.2 The Hereditary Material

11.3 Discovering the Structure of DNA

DNA Replication

11.4 How DNA Copies Itself

Essential Biological Process 11A: DNA Replication

Altering the Genetic Message

11.5 Mutation

Biology and Staying Healthy: Protecting Your Genes

Inquiry & Analysis: Are Mutations Random or Directed by the Environment?

Genes Are Made of DNA

Protiens and DNA

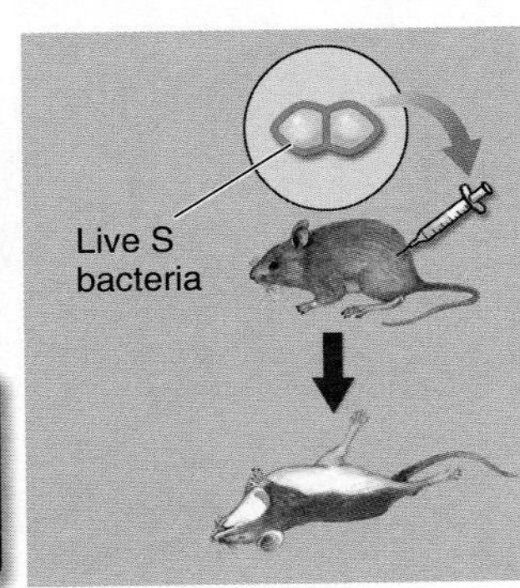

1 S bacteria have a polysaccharide capsule and are pathogenic. When they are injected into mice, the mice die.

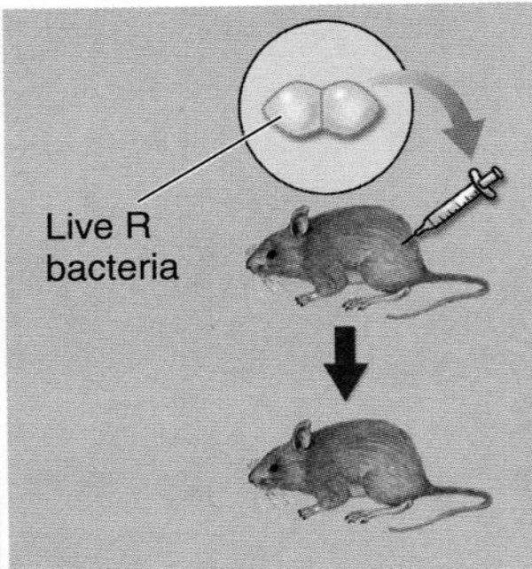

2 R bacteria do not have the capsule and do not kill mice.

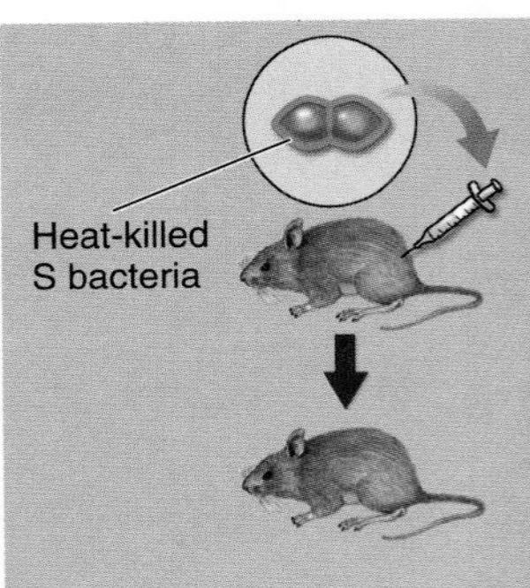

3 Heat-killed bacteria are dead but still have the capsule. They do not kill mice.

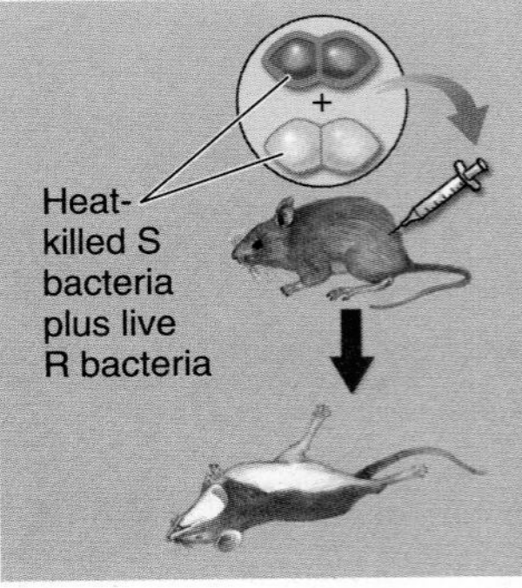

4 A mixture of live R bacteria and heat-killed S bacteria does cause mice to die.

Figure 11.1 How Griffith discovered transformation.

Griffith found that extracts of dead pathogenic strains of the bacterium *Streptococcus pneumoniae* can "transform" live harmless strains into live pathogenic strains.

11.1 The Griffith Experiment

LEARNING OBJECTIVE 11.1.1 Describe Griffith's experiment demonstrating transformation.

As we learned in chapters 8, 9, and 10, chromosomes contain genes, which, in turn, contain hereditary information. However, Mendel's work left a key question unanswered: What *is* a gene?

When biologists began to examine chromosomes in their search for genes, they soon learned that chromosomes are made of two kinds of macromolecules, both of which you encountered in chapter 3: **proteins** (long chains of *amino acid subunits* linked together in a string) and **DNA** (deoxyribonucleic acid—long chains of *nucleotide* subunits linked together in a string). It was possible to imagine that either of the two was the stuff that genes are made of—information might be stored in a sequence of different amino acids, or in a sequence of different nucleotides. But which one is the stuff of genes, protein or DNA? This question was answered clearly in a variety of different experiments, all of which shared the same basic design: If you separate the DNA in an individual's chromosomes from the protein, which of the two materials is able to change another individual's genes?

The Griffith Experiment

In a key experiment in 1928, British microbiologist Frederick Griffith made a series of unexpected observations while experimenting with pathogenic (disease-causing) bacteria. **Figure 11.1** takes you stepwise through his discoveries. When he infected mice with a virulent strain of *Streptococcus pneumoniae* bacteria (then known as *Pneumococcus*), the mice died of blood poisoning ❶. However, when he infected similar mice with a mutant strain of *S. pneumoniae* that lacked the virulent strain's polysaccharide capsule, the mice showed no ill effects ❷. The capsule was apparently necessary for infection. The normal pathogenic form of this bacterium is referred to as the S form because it forms smooth colonies in a culture dish. The mutant form, which lacks an enzyme needed to manufacture the polysaccharide capsule, is called the R form because it forms rough colonies.

To determine whether the polysaccharide capsule itself had a toxic effect, Griffith injected dead bacteria of the virulent S strain into mice, and the mice remained perfectly healthy ❸. Finally, he injected mice with a mixture containing dead S bacteria (the virulent strain) and live, capsuleless R bacteria, each of which by itself did not harm the mice. Unexpectedly, the mice developed disease symptoms and many of them died ❹. The blood of the dead mice was found to contain high levels of live, virulent *Streptococcus* type S bacteria, which had surface proteins characteristic of the live (previously R) strain. Somehow, the information specifying the polysaccharide capsule had passed from the dead, virulent S bacteria to the live, capsuleless R bacteria in the mixture, permanently transforming the capsuleless R bacteria into the virulent S variety. Griffith called this process **transformation.**

Putting the Concept to Work

Why is a mixture of two harmless things (dead bacteria with capsules and harmless live bacteria without capsules) deadly?

11.2 The Hereditary Material

The Avery Experiments

LEARNING OBJECTIVE 11.2.1 List the ways in which Avery's transforming principle resembled DNA.

The agent responsible for transforming *Streptococcus* went undiscovered until 1944. In a classic series of experiments, Oswald Avery and his coworkers Colin MacLeod and Maclyn McCarty characterized what they referred to as the "transforming principle." They prepared the same mixture of dead S *Streptococcus* and live R *Streptococcus* that Griffith had used, but first they removed as much of the protein as they could from their preparation of dead S *Streptococcus,* eventually achieving 99.98% purity. Despite the removal of protein from the dead S *Streptococcus,* the transforming activity was not reduced. Moreover, the chemical properties of the transforming principle resembled those of DNA, and protein-digesting enzymes did not affect the principle's activity, while a DNA-digesting enzyme destroyed all transforming activity. They concluded that "a nucleic acid of the deoxyribose type is the fundamental unit of the transforming principle of *Pneumococcus* Type III"—in essence, that DNA is the hereditary material.

Putting the Concept to Work

If protein had been the hereditary material, as most people then thought, what would have been different about Avery's results?

The Hershey-Chase Experiment

LEARNING OBJECTIVE 11.2.2 Describe how Hershey and Chase demonstrated that DNA was the hereditary material.

Avery's result was not widely appreciated at first, because most biologists still preferred to think that genes were made of proteins. In 1952, however, a simple experiment carried out by Alfred Hershey and Martha Chase was impossible to ignore. The team studied the genes of viruses that infect bacteria. These viruses attach themselves to the surface of bacterial cells and inject their genes into the interior; once inside, the genes take over the genetic machinery of the cell and conduct the manufacturing of hundreds of new viruses. These bacteria-infecting viruses have a very simple structure: a core of DNA surrounded by a coat of protein.

In their experiment (figure 11.2), Hershey and Chase used radioactive isotopes to "label" the DNA and protein of the viruses. DNA was labeled with radioactive phosphorus (^{32}P), and proteins were labeled with radioactive sulfur (^{35}S). After the labeled viruses were allowed to infect bacteria, Hershey and Chase shook the suspensions forcefully to dislodge attacking viruses from the surface of bacteria. They then used a rapidly spinning centrifuge to isolate the bacteria, and asked a very simple question: What did the viruses inject into the bacterial cells, protein or DNA? They found that the bacterial cells infected by viruses containing the ^{32}P label had labeled tracer in their interiors; cells infected by viruses containing the ^{35}S labeled tracer did not. The genes to specify new viruses are made of DNA and not protein.

Putting the Concept to Work

If Hershey and Chase had waited longer before shaking the bacteria-virus mixture, would this have altered their results?

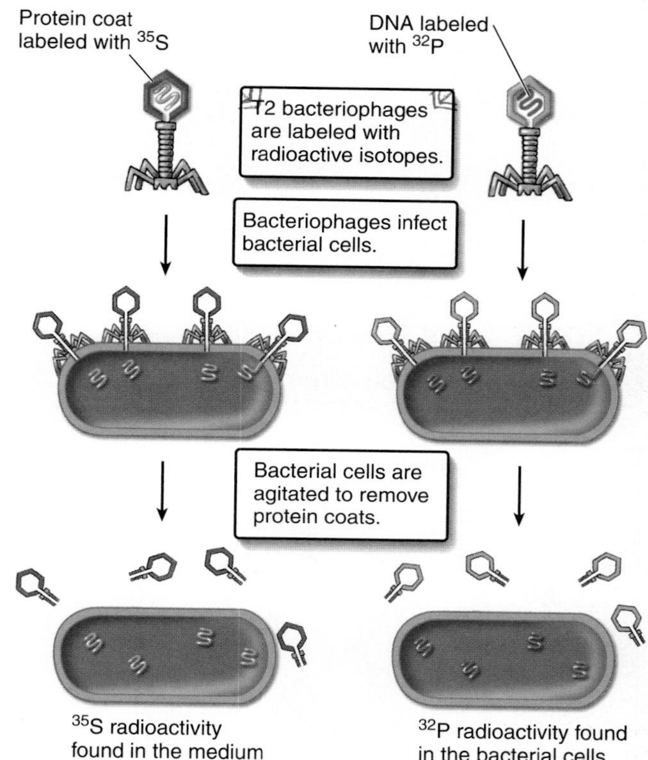
Protein coat labeled with ^{35}S
DNA labeled with ^{32}P
T2 bacteriophages are labeled with radioactive isotopes.
Bacteriophages infect bacterial cells.
Bacterial cells are agitated to remove protein coats.
^{35}S radioactivity found in the medium
^{32}P radioactivity found in the bacterial cells

Figure 11.2 The Hershey-Chase experiment.

The experiment that convinced most biologists that DNA is the genetic material was carried out soon after World War II, when radioactive isotopes were first becoming commonly available to researchers. Hershey and Chase used different radioactive labels to "tag" and track protein and DNA. They found that when bacterial viruses inserted their genes into bacteria to guide the production of new viruses, it was DNA and not protein that was inserted. More specifically, ^{35}S radioactivity did not enter infected bacterial cells and ^{32}P radioactivity did. Clearly the virus DNA, not the virus protein, was responsible for directing the production of new viruses.

IMPLICATION FOR YOU Household smoke detectors contain a very small amount (3 millionths of a gram) of the radioactive isotope Americium-241, a decay product of plutonium. Am-241 emits a stream of alpha particles that ionize oxygen and nitrogen atoms in the air, creating a small, steady electric current. When smoke enters the smoke detector, smoke particles absorb the alpha radiation; this halts ion production, causing the current to fall and setting off the alarm. Why do you think Am-241 is used, rather than some other, less expensive radioisotope?

Adenine (A)

Guanine (G)

Thymine (T)

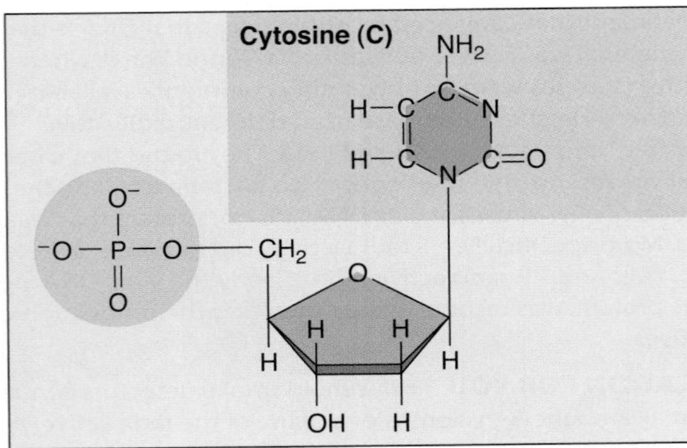

Figure 11.3 The four nucleotide subunits that make up DNA.

The nucleotide subunits of DNA are composed of three parts: a central five-carbon sugar called deoxyribose, a phosphate group, and an organic, nitrogen-containing base.

11.3 Discovering the Structure of DNA

LEARNING OBJECTIVE 11.3.1 Explain how Watson and Crick's proposed structure of DNA explained Chargaff's rule.

As it became clear that DNA stored the hereditary information, researchers began to question how a molecule like DNA could carry out the complex function of inheritance. Scientists at that time did not know what the DNA molecule looked like.

We now know that DNA is a long, chainlike molecule made up of subunits called **nucleotides.** As you can see in figure 11.3, each nucleotide has three parts: a central sugar called deoxyribose to which a phosphate (PO_4) group and an organic base are attached. The sugar (lavender pentagon structure) and the phosphate group (yellow-circled structure) are the same in every nucleotide of DNA. However, there are four different kinds of bases: two large ones with double-ring structures, and two small ones with single rings. The large bases, called **purines,** are **A** (adenine) and **G** (guanine). The small bases, called **pyrimidines,** are **C** (cytosine) and **T** (thymine). The carbon atoms that make up the sugar of the deoxyribose are numbered from 1′ to 5′, as shown in the top panel. The phosphate group binds to the 5′ carbon and the organic base binds to the 1′ carbon. You will learn about the significance of this numbering system later.

Early in the analysis of DNA, a key observation was made by Erwin Chargaff. He noted that DNA molecules always had equal amounts of purines and pyrimidines. In fact, with slight variations due to imprecision of measurement, the amount of A always equals the amount of T, and the amount of G always equals the amount of C. This observation (A = T, G = C), known as **Chargaff's rule,** suggested that DNA had a regular structure.

In the early 1950s, the British chemists Maurice Wilkins and Rosalind Franklin carried out the first X-ray diffraction experiments on DNA. In their experiments, DNA molecules bombarded with X-ray beams created a pattern on photographic film that looked like the ripples created by tossing a rock into a smooth lake (figure 11.4*a*). Wilkins and Franklin's results suggested that the DNA molecule had the shape of a coiled spring or a corkscrew, a form called a **helix.**

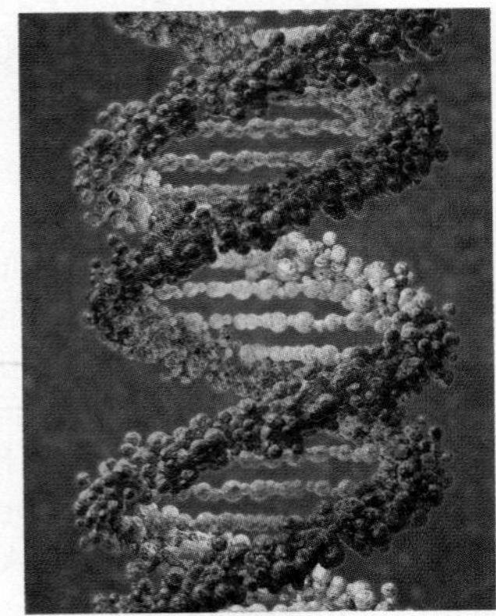

Model of DNA double helix

Franklin's work was shared with two researchers at Cambridge University, Francis Crick and James Watson, before it was published. Using Tinkertoy-like models of the bases, Watson and Crick deduced the structure of DNA (figure 11.4*b*): The DNA molecule is a **double helix,** a structure that resembles a winding staircase (figure 11.4*c*). The sugar and phosphate groups form the stringers of the staircase, and the bases of the nucleotides form the steps. The significance of Chargaff's rule is now clear, a direct reflection of this structure—every bulky purine on one strand is paired with a slender pyrimidine on the other strand. Specifically, A pairs with T, and G pairs with C.

Putting the Concept to Work

In a DNA double helix, why doesn't the purine adenine pair with the pyrimidine cytosine?

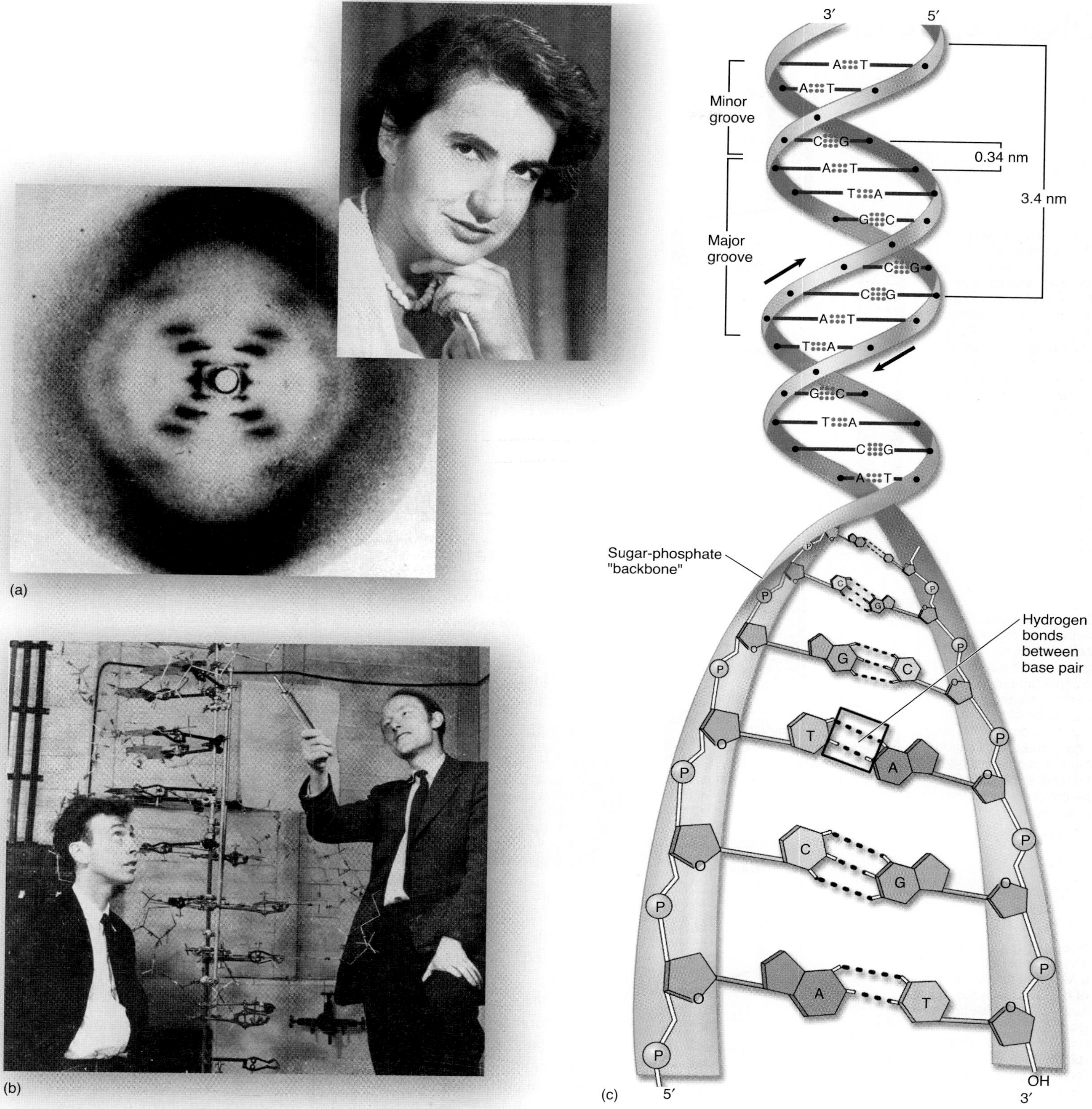

Figure 11.4 The DNA double helix.

(a) This X-ray diffraction photograph was made in 1953 by Rosalind Franklin (inset) in the laboratory of Maurice Wilkins. It suggested to Watson and Crick that the DNA molecule was a helix, like a winding staircase. (b) In 1953 Watson and Crick deduced the structure of DNA. James Watson (seated and peering up at their homemade model of the DNA molecule) was a young American postdoctoral student, and Francis Crick (pointing) was an English scientist. (c) The dimensions of the double helix were suggested by the X-ray diffraction studies. In a DNA duplex molecule, only two base pairs are possible: adenine (A) with thymine (T) and guanine (G) with cytosine (C). A G–C base pair has three hydrogen bonds; an A–T base pair has only two.

DNA Replication

Parent DNA

Replicating DNA

Conservative replication: The two strands of the double helix separate and serve as templates for the assembly of two new strands by base pairing A with T and G with C. After replicating, the original strands rejoin, preserving the parent DNA and forming an entirely new duplex.

Rejoined original DNA

Daughter DNA composed of two new strands

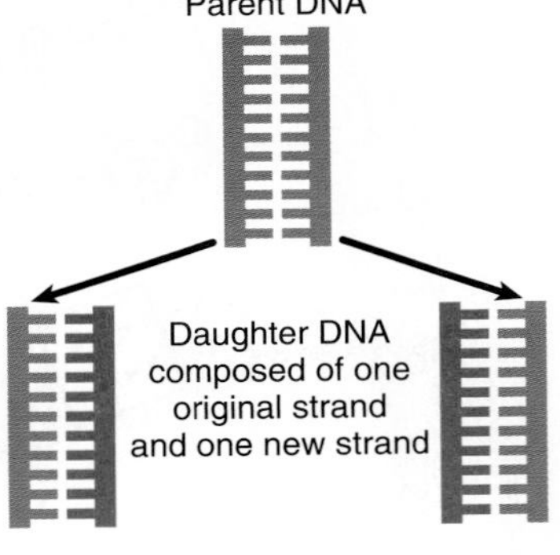

Semiconservative replication: The double helix need only "unzip" and assemble a new complementary chain along each single strand. The sequence of the original duplex is conserved after one round of replication, but the duplex itself is not. Instead, each strand of the parent duplex becomes part of another duplex.

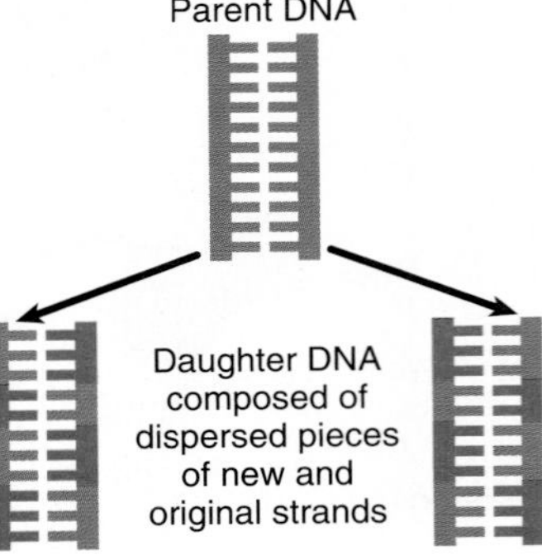

Dispersive replication: The original DNA serves as a template for the formation of new DNA strands, but the new and old DNA are dispersed among the two daughter strands. Each daughter strand is made up of sections of original strands and new strands.

Figure 11.5 Alternative mechanisms of DNA replication.

There are three possible alternatives as to how the DNA could serve as a template for the assembly of new DNA molecules. In all three, the original strands of DNA are colored blue, and the newly synthesized strands are colored red.

11.4 How DNA Copies Itself

LEARNING OBJECTIVE 11.4.1 Explain three ways in which DNA complementarity might be achieved during DNA replication.

What holds the two DNA strands together? The "glue" is provided by the weak hydrogen bonds that form between the bases that face each other from the two strands. That is why A pairs with T and not C. The A base can only form hydrogen bonds with the T base. Similarly, G can form hydrogen bonds with C but not T. In the Watson-Crick model of DNA, the two strands of the double helix are said to be *complementary* to each other. One chain of the helix can have any sequence of bases, of A, T, G, and C, but this sequence completely determines that of its partner in the helix. Each chain in the helix is a complementary mirror image of the other. This complementarity makes it possible for the DNA molecule to copy itself during cell division in a very direct manner; but there are several different ways that this could occur. Figure 11.5 walks you through three possible mechanisms of DNA replication.

Putting the Concept to Work

If the sequence of one strand of DNA is GTCCATCG, what is the sequence of its complementary strand?

The Meselson-Stahl Experiment

LEARNING OBJECTIVE 11.4.2 Describe how the Meselson-Stahl experiment revealed the true mode of DNA replication.

The three alternative hypotheses of DNA replication were tested in 1958 by Matthew Meselson and Franklin Stahl of the California Institute of Technology. These two scientists grew bacteria in a medium containing the heavy isotope of nitrogen, ^{15}N, which became incorporated into the bases of the bacterial DNA (figure 11.6). After several generations, samples were taken from this culture and grown in a medium containing the normal lighter isotope ^{14}N, which became incorporated into the newly replicating DNA. Bacterial samples were taken from the ^{14}N media at intervals. The DNA collected immediately after the transfer was all dense, as shown in test tube ❷. However, after the bacteria completed their first round of DNA replication, the density of their DNA had decreased to a value intermediate between ^{14}N-DNA and ^{15}N-DNA, as shown in test tube ❸. Why? Because after the first round of replication, each daughter DNA duplex was a hybrid possessing one of the heavy strands of the parent molecule and one light strand. Later, when this hybrid duplex replicated, it contributed one heavy strand to form another hybrid duplex and one light strand to form a light duplex, as shown in test tube ❹. Thus, this experiment clearly ruled out conservative and dispersive DNA replication, and confirmed that DNA replicates in a semiconservative manner.

Isotopes, as discussed on page 36, are atoms that contain varying numbers of neutrons. Isotopes have the same atomic number but different masses. In this experiment, ^{15}N contains one more neutron than ^{14}N and so it is heavier; DNA that contains ^{15}N is heavier.

Putting the Concept to Work

If DNA replication had been conservative rather than semiconservative, what results would Meselson and Stahl have seen?

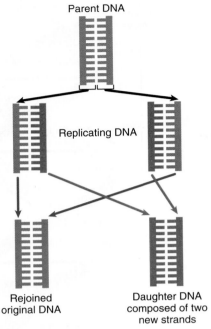

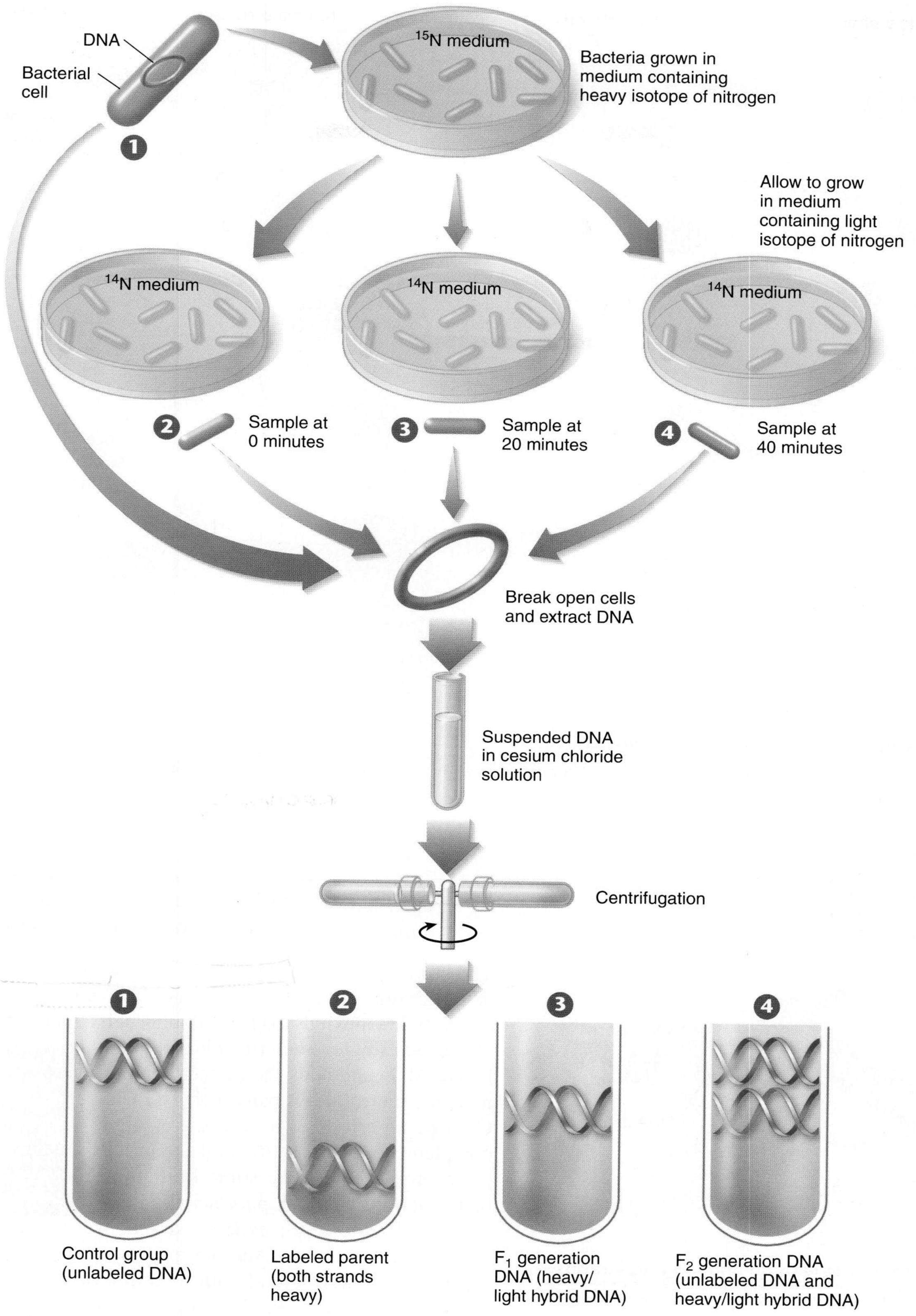

Figure 11.6 The Meselson-Stahl experiment.

Bacterial cells were grown for several generations in a medium containing a heavy isotope of nitrogen (^{15}N) and then were transferred to a new medium containing the normal lighter isotope (^{14}N). At various times thereafter, samples of the bacteria were collected, and their DNA was dissolved in a solution of cesium chloride, which was spun rapidly in a centrifuge. The centrifugal forces caused the heavy cesium ions to migrate toward the bottom of the centrifuge tube, creating a gradient of cesium concentration, and thus a gradation of density. Each DNA strand floats or sinks in the gradient until it reaches the position where its density exactly matches the density of the cesium there. The DNA with two heavy strands settled down toward the bottom of the tube. The DNA with two light strands settled higher up in the tube. The DNA with one heavy and one light strand settled in between the other two.

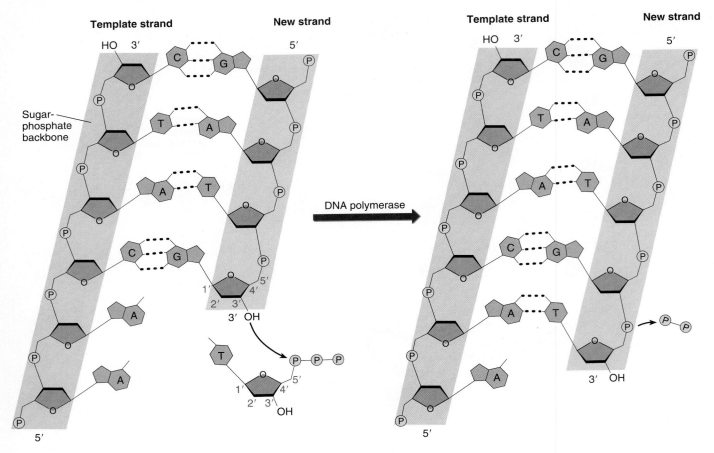

Figure 11.7 How nucleotides are added in DNA replication.

Nucleotides are added to the new growing strand of DNA by DNA polymerase. The addition of the nucleotides follows base pairing.

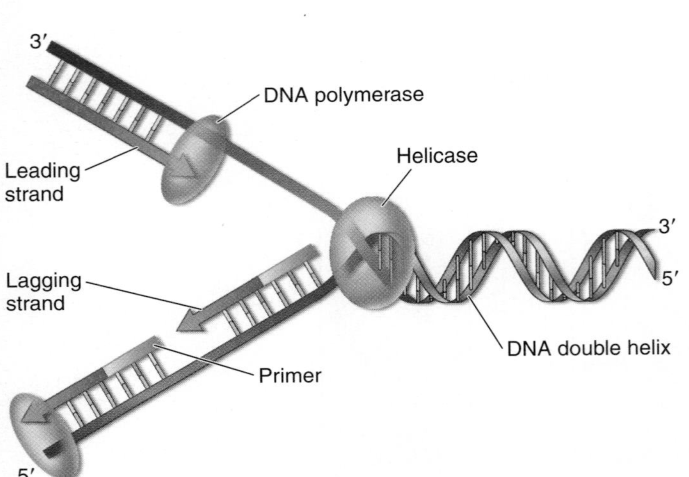

Figure 11.8 Building the leading and lagging strands.

DNA polymerase builds the leading strand as a continuous strand moving into the replication fork growing 5′ to 3′, but the lagging strand, also growing 5′ to 3′, is assembled moving away from the replication fork, in segments, each beginning with a primer.

How DNA Copies Itself

LEARNING OBJECTIVE 11.4.3 Describe the process of DNA replication, distinguishing between leading and lagging strands.

The copying of DNA before cell division is called **DNA replication** and is carried out by an enzyme called *DNA polymerase*. An enzyme called *helicase* first unwinds the DNA double helix, then DNA polymerase reads along each single strand (the blue strand in figure 11.7) and adds the correct complementary nucleotide (A pairs with T, G with C) at each position as it moves, creating a complementary strand (the pink strand).

This process of unwinding and separating the two strands of the DNA molecule happens again during protein synthesis. A section of the DNA that contains a gene is opened during transcription, discussed on page 207, and an RNA copy of the DNA is made by a different enzyme.

However, there are some limitations of the actions of DNA polymerase. First, it can only add to an existing strand; it cannot begin a strand. Another enzyme circumvents this difficulty by beginning the new strand with a section of nucleotides called a *primer*. These are the green segments in figure 11.8. This happens at the place where the parent DNA molecule becomes unzipped, called the *replication fork*. At the replication fork, the polymerase very actively shuttles several hundred nucleotides up one strand, building a new strand of DNA called the **leading strand,** adding on to the primer in a continuous fashion. The leading strand is the upper red strand in figure 11.8, the primer is off further to the left out of the frame of the diagram. The new strand is built when the phosphate group of a nucleotide, called the 5′ end, attaches to the sugar end, called the 3′ end, of the nucleotide at the end of the growing strand. The carbon atoms in the sugar component of a nucleotide have a numbering scheme, shown in figure 11.7 (or refer back to figure 11.3). In a nucleotide, the phosphate group is attached to the 5′ carbon atom of the sugar, and an OH group is attached to the 3′ carbon atom. So, each nucleotide has a 5′ end and a 3′ end, and when the nucleotides attach to each other in a long chain, there will be a 5′ phosphate end to the chain on one side and a 3′ OH end on the other side. In the DNA double helix, the two strands of nucleotides pair up in opposite orientations, with one strand running 5′ to 3′ and the other running 3′ to 5′.

The directionality of building the new strand is apparent in figure 11.7, where the phosphate group of the incoming T nucleotide attaches to the OH group of the sugar of the G nucleotide. The new strand assembles in a 5′ to 3′ direction, and new nucleotides can only be added to the 3′ end of an existing strand. This reveals a second limitation: DNA polymerase can only build a strand of DNA in one direction, and so it assembles the other DNA strand, called the **lagging strand,** in segments. Each lagging strand segment begins with a primer (the green segments you saw in figure 11.8), and the DNA polymerase then builds it away from the replication fork until it encounters the previous section.

Eukaryotic chromosomes each contain a single, very long molecule of DNA, one far too long to copy all the way from one end to the other with a single replication fork. Each eukaryotic chromosome is instead copied in sections of about 100,000 nucleotides, each with its own replication origin and fork.

Before the newly formed DNA molecules wind back into the double helix shape, the primers must be removed and the segments of DNA assembled in sections on the lagging strand need to be covalently linked together. The enzyme that performs this sealing function is *DNA ligase.* DNA ligase joins the ends of newly synthesized segments of DNA after the primers have been removed, resulting in one continuous strand of DNA. This process is summarized in *Essential Biological Process 11A*, with the DNA ligase in panel 3 sealing the gaps between the DNA sections of the lagging strand.

The enormous amount of DNA that resides within the cells of your body represents a long series of DNA replications, starting with the DNA of a single cell—the fertilized egg. Living cells have evolved many mechanisms to avoid errors during DNA replication and to preserve the DNA from damage. These mechanisms of DNA repair proofread the strands of each DNA molecule against one another for accuracy and correct any mistakes. But the proofreading is not perfect. If it were, no mistakes such as mutations would occur. Mutation will be discussed in more detail in the next section and in chapter 14, where we consider mutation as the raw material of evolution.

Putting the Concept to Work

If DNA polymerase cannot begin a strand, how does DNA replication get started?

Essential Biological Process 11A

DNA Replication

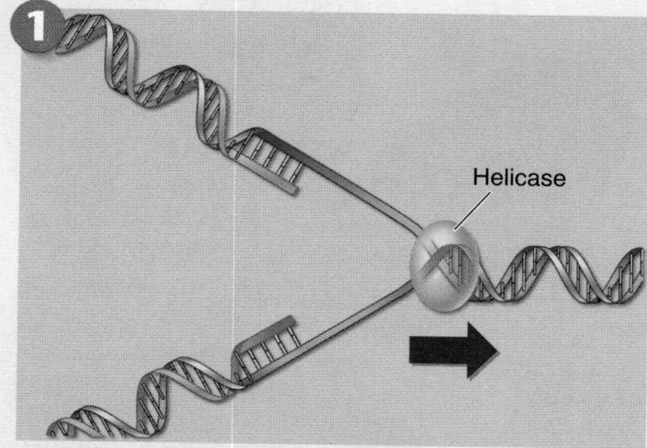

Helicase unwinds the DNA double helix for about 1,000 nucleotides.

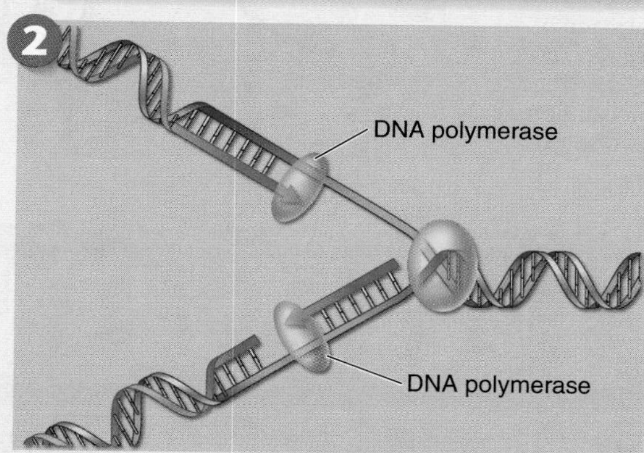

DNA polymerase assembles a complementary new strand on each old one, building the two strands in opposite directions.

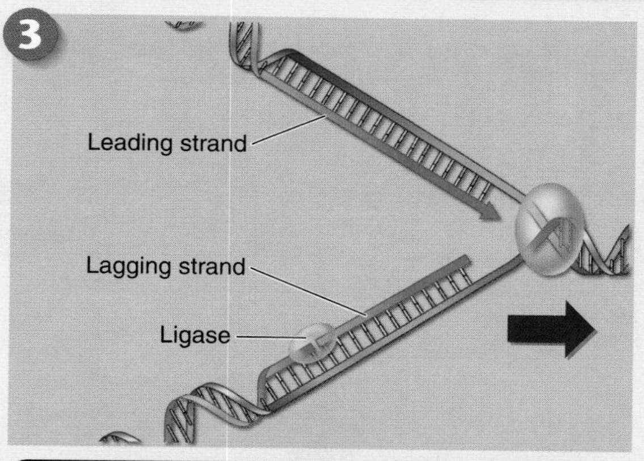

DNA ligase attaches one new strand to the previously replicated segment on the lagging strand, and helicase unwinds another segment.

Altering the Genetic Message

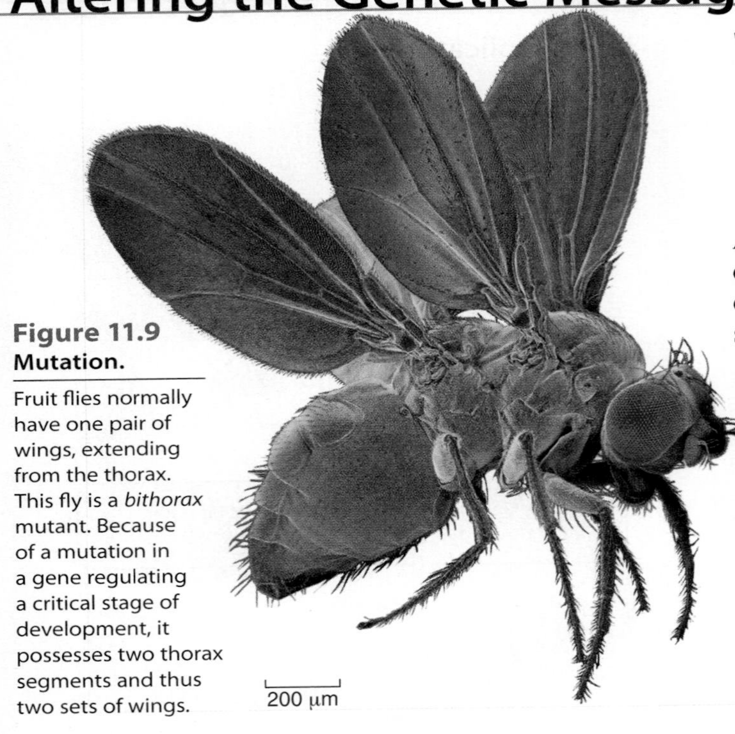

Figure 11.9 Mutation.

Fruit flies normally have one pair of wings, extending from the thorax. This fly is a *bithorax* mutant. Because of a mutation in a gene regulating a critical stage of development, it possesses two thorax segments and thus two sets of wings.

11.5 Mutation

LEARNING OBJECTIVE 11.5.1 Contrast the inheritance of somatic and germ-line mutations, and list four molecular events that can cause them.

A change in the content of the genetic message—the base sequence of one or more genes—is referred to as a **mutation.** As you learned in the previous section, DNA copies itself by forming complementary strands along single strands of DNA when they are separated. The template strand directs the formation of the new strand. However, this replication process is not foolproof. Sometimes errors are made, and these are called mutations. Some mutations alter the identity of a particular nucleotide, while others remove or add nucleotides to a gene. The cells of eukaryotes contain an enormous amount of DNA, and the mechanisms that protect and proofread the DNA are not perfect. If they were, no variation would be generated.

Mistakes Happen

In fact, cells do make mistakes during replication, as shown in figure 11.9. Other mutations occur because of DNA alteration by chemicals like those in cigarette smoke, or by radiation like the ultraviolet light from the sun or in tanning beds. However, mutations are rare. In humans, sequencing the genomes of an entire family has revealed that only about 60 of the 3 billion nucleotides of the genome are altered by mutation each generation. If changes were more common, the genetic instructions encoded in DNA would soon degrade into meaningless gibberish. Limited as it might seem, however, the steady trickle of change is the very stuff of evolution. Every difference in the genetic messages that specify different organisms arose as the result of genetic change.

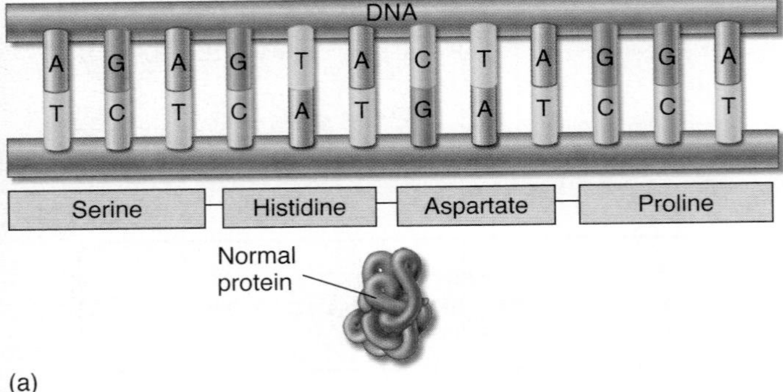

(a)

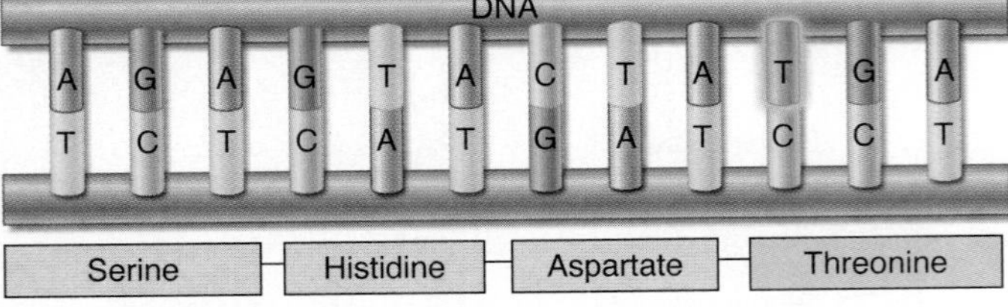

Base substitution (red) in DNA: changes proline to threonine in the protein.

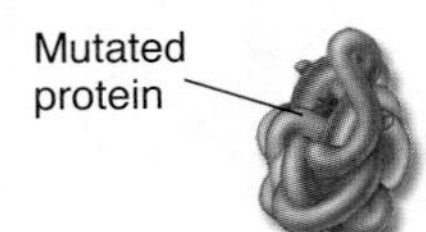

(b)

Figure 11.10 Base substitution mutation.

(a) Often, DNA sequences code for a particular protein. (b) A mutation that substitutes one base for another can result in a change in a single amino acid. This can produce a mutated protein that may not function the same as the normal protein.

Kinds of Mutation

Gene expression occurs in two steps: transcription, discussed on page 207, transfers the nucleotide message in the DNA to a molecule of RNA. In translation, discussed on page 208, the nucleotide message is converted into a string of amino acids that make up the protein.

The message that DNA carries in its genes is the "instructions" of how to make proteins. The sequence of nucleotides in a strand of DNA translates into the sequence of amino acids that makes up a protein. This process was introduced in section 10.5 on page 168. If the core message in the DNA is altered through mutation as shown in figure 11.10, where a T nucleotide (in red) is inserted instead of a G nucleotide during DNA replication, then the protein product can also be altered, sometimes to the point where it can no longer function properly. Because mutations can occur randomly in a cell's DNA, most mutations are detrimental, just as making a random change in a computer program usually worsens performance. The consequences of a detrimental mutation may be minor or catastrophic, depending on the function of the altered gene.

Mutations in Germ-Line Tissues. The effect of a mutation depends critically on the identity of the cell in which the mutation occurs. During the embryonic development of all multicellular organisms, there comes a point when cells destined to form gametes (germ-line cells) are segregated from those that will form the other cells of the body (somatic cells). Only when a mutation occurs within a germ-line cell is it passed to subsequent generations as part of the hereditary endowment of the gametes derived from that cell. Mutations in germ-line tissue are of enormous biological importance because they provide the raw material from which natural selection produces evolutionary change.

Mutations in Somatic Tissues. Change can occur only if there are new, different allele combinations available to replace the old. Mutation produces new alleles, and recombination puts the alleles together in different combinations. In animals, it is the occurrence of these two processes in germ-line tissue that is important to evolution, because mutations in somatic cells (somatic mutations) are not passed from one generation to the next. However, a somatic mutation may have drastic effects on the individual organism in which it occurs, because it is passed on to all of the cells that are descended from the original mutant cell. Thus, if a mutant lung cell divides, all cells derived from it will carry the mutation. Somatic mutations of lung cells are the principal cause of lung cancer.

Altering the Sequence of DNA. One category of mutational changes affects the message itself, producing alterations in the sequence of DNA nucleotides (**table 11.1**). If alterations involve only one or a few base pairs in the coding sequence, they are called **point mutations.** Sometimes the identity of a nucleotide changes (*base substitution*), while other times one or a few nucleotides are added (*insertion*) or lost (*deletion*). If an insertion or deletion throws the reading of the gene message out of register, a **frame-shift mutation** results. **Figure 11.10** shows a base substitution mutation that results in the change of an amino acid, from proline to threonine. This could be a minor change or catastrophic. However, suppose that this had been the deletion of a nucleotide, that the cytosine base nucleotide had been skipped during replication. This would shift the register of the DNA message (imagine removing the "w" from this sentence, yielding "*This oulds hiftt her egistero fth eDN Amessag*") and you can see the problem.

Many point mutations result from damage to the DNA caused by mutagens, usually radiation or chemicals. The latter is of particular importance because modern industrial societies often release many chemical mutagens into the environment.

The Importance of Genetic Change

All evolution begins with alterations in the genetic message that create new alleles or alter the organization of genes on chromosome. Some changes in germ-line tissue produce alterations that enable an organism to leave more offspring, and those changes tend to be preserved as the genetic endowment of future generations. Other changes reduce the ability of an organism to leave offspring. Those changes tend to be lost, as the organisms that carry them contribute fewer members to future generations. Evolution can be viewed as the selection of particular combinations of alleles from a pool of alternatives. The rate of evolution is ultimately limited by the rate at which these alternatives are generated. Genetic change through mutation and recombination provides the raw material for evolution.

Putting the Concept to Work

If somatic mutations are not inherited, why are they important?

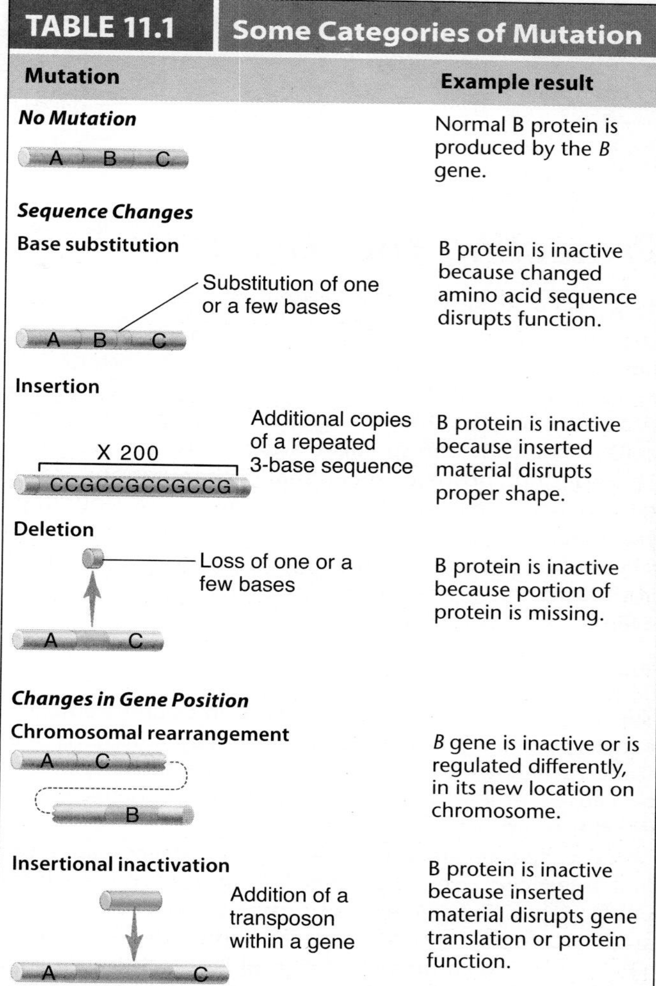

TABLE 11.1 Some Categories of Mutation

Mutation		Example result
No Mutation	A B C	Normal B protein is produced by the *B* gene.
Sequence Changes		
Base substitution	A B C — Substitution of one or a few bases	B protein is inactive because changed amino acid sequence disrupts function.
Insertion	X 200 CCGCCGCCGCCG — Additional copies of a repeated 3-base sequence	B protein is inactive because inserted material disrupts proper shape.
Deletion	A C — Loss of one or a few bases	B protein is inactive because portion of protein is missing.
Changes in Gene Position		
Chromosomal rearrangement	A C / B	*B* gene is inactive or is regulated differently, in its new location on chromosome.
Insertional inactivation	A C — Addition of a transposon within a gene	B protein is inactive because inserted material disrupts gene translation or protein function.

BIOLOGY & YOU

Almost All Inherited Mutations Occur in Males. Molecular analysis of DNA allows us to determine whether a mutation occurred in the mother or the father. The results are dramatic. In studies to determine the parent of origin, a total of 92 new human mutations were analyzed, and ALL were paternal. How can we account for a far higher mutation rate in males than in females? The explanation seems to lie in the far greater number of cell divisions in the male germ line. In females, germ cell divisions stop by the time of birth, while in males cell divisions are continuous, so that many divisions have occurred before an adult male's sperm is produced. Because most germ-line mutations are replication errors, the far greater number of replications in males leads to a much bigger opportunity for mistakes. This predicts that human mutation rates should increase with the age of the father. They do. At age 20, the mutation rate for a man is about 8 times the female rate. The difference is some 30-fold by age 30, and as much as 100-fold by age 40.

Biology and Staying Healthy

Protecting Your Genes

This text's discussion of changes in genes—mutations—has largely focused on heredity, how changes in the information encoded in DNA can affect offspring. It is important, however, to realize that inherited mutations occur only in germ-line tissue, in the cells that generate your eggs or sperm. Mutations in the other cells of your body, in so-called somatic tissues, are not inherited. This does not, however, mean that such mutations are not important. In fact, somatic mutations can have a disastrous impact upon your health, because they can lead to cancer. Protecting the DNA of your body's cells from damaging mutation is perhaps the most important thing you can do to prolong your life. Here we will examine two potential threats.

Smoking and Lung Cancer

The association of particular chemicals in cigarette smoke with lung cancer, particularly chemicals that are potent mutagens (see chapters 8 and 25), led researchers early on to suspect that lung cancer might be caused, at least in part, by the action of chemicals on the cells lining the lung.

The hypothesis that chemicals in tobacco cause cancer was first advanced over 200 years ago in 1761 by Dr. John Hill, an English physician. Hill noted unusual tumors of the nose in heavy snuff users and suggested tobacco had produced these cancers. In 1775, a London surgeon, Sir Percivall Pott, made a similar observation, noting that men who had been chimney sweeps exhibited frequent cancer of the scrotum. He suggested that soot and tars might be responsible. These observations led to the hypothesis that lung cancer results from the action of tars and other chemicals in tobacco smoke.

It was over a century before this hypothesis was directly tested. In 1915, Japanese doctor Katsusaburo Yamagiwa applied extracts of tar to the skin of 137 rabbits every two or three days for three months. Then he waited to see what would happen. After a year, cancers appeared at the site of application in seven of the rabbits. Yamagiwa had induced cancer with the tar, the first direct demonstration of chemical carcinogenesis. In the decades that followed, this approach demonstrated that many chemicals can cause cancer.

But do these lab studies apply to people? Do tars in cigarette smoke in fact induce lung cancer in humans? In 1949, the American physician Ernst Winder and the British epidemiologist Richard Doll independently reported that lung cancer showed a strong link to the smoking of cigarettes, which introduces tars into the lungs. Winder interviewed 684 lung cancer patients and 600 normal controls, asking whether each had ever smoked. Cancer rates were 40 times higher in heavy smokers than in nonsmokers. From these studies, it seemed likely as long as 50 years ago that tars and other chemicals in cigarette smoke induce cancer in the lungs of persistent smokers. While this suggestion was resisted by the tobacco industry, the evidence that has accumulated since these pioneering studies makes a clear case, and there is no longer any real doubt. Chemicals in cigarette smoke cause cancer.

As you will learn in chapter 25 (page 510), tars and other chemicals in cigarette smoke cause lung cancer by mutating DNA, disabling genes that in normal lung cells restrain cell division. Lacking these restraints, the altered lung cells begin to divide ceaselessly, and lung cancer results. Over 157,000 Americans died of lung cancer last year, and almost all of them were cigarette smokers.

If cigarette smoking is so dangerous, why do so many Americans smoke? Fully 23% of American men smoke, and 18% of women. Are they not aware of the danger? Of course they are. But they are not able to quit. Tobacco smoke, you see, also contains another chemical, nicotine, which is highly addictive. Basically, what happens is that a smoker's brain makes physiological compensations to overcome the effects of nicotine, and once these adjustments are made the brain does not function normally without nicotine. The body's physiological response to nicotine is profound and unavoidable; there is no way to prevent addiction to nicotine with willpower.

Many people attempting to quit smoking use patches containing nicotine to help them, the idea being that providing nicotine removes the craving for cigarettes. This is true, it does—as long as you keep using the patch. Actually, using such patches simply substitutes one (admittedly less dangerous) nicotine source for another. If you are going to quit smoking, there is no way to avoid the necessity of eliminating the drug to which you are addicted, nicotine. There is no easy way out. The only way to quit is to quit.

Clearly, if you do not smoke, you should not start. When asked what three things were most important to improve Americans' health, a prominent physician replied: "Don't smoke. Don't smoke. Don't smoke."

Tanning and Skin Cancer

Almost all cells in the human body undergo cell division, replacing themselves as they wear out. Some adult cells do this very frequently, others rarely if ever. Skin cells divide quite frequently. Exposed to a lot of wear and tear, they divide about every 27 days to replace dead or damaged cells. The skin sloughs off dead cells from the surface and replaces these with new cells from beneath. The average person will lose about 105 pounds of skin by the time he or she turns 70.

While skin can become damaged in many ways, the damage that seems to have the most long-term effect is caused by the sun. The skin contains cells called melanocytes that produce a pigment called melanin when exposed to UV light. Melanin produces a yellow-to-brown color in the skin. The type of melanin and the amount produced is genetically determined. People with darker skin types have more melanocytes and produce a melanin that is dark brown in color. Protected by UV-absorbing melanin, they almost never sunburn. Fair-skinned people have fewer melanocytes and produce melanin that is more yellow in color. Unprotected by melanin, these people sunburn easily and rarely tan. When cells on the body's surface are badly damaged by the sun, called a sunburn, the cells slough off. Recall the peeling that you experience if you have ever had a bad sunburn.

Up until the early 20th century, a tan was a condition that people went to great lengths to avoid. A tanned body was a sign of the working class, people who had to work in the sun. The wealthy elite avoided the sun, with pale skin being in fashion. All of this changed in the 1920s, when tans became a status symbol, with the wealthy able to travel to warm, sunny destinations, even in the middle of winter. That tan, bronzed glow that people would sit in the sun for hours to achieve was thought to be both healthy and attractive.

During the 1970s, doctors started to see an uptick in the number of cases of melanoma, a deadly form of skin cancer. New cases were increasing about 6% each year. Researchers proposed that UV rays from the sun were the underlying cause of this epidemic of skin cancer and warned people to avoid the sun when possible and protect themselves with sunscreen.

Malignant melanoma is the most deadly of skin cancers, although treatable if caught early. Melanoma is cancer of melanocyte cells. Melanoma lesions usually appear as shades of tan, brown, and black and often begin in or near a mole, and so changes in a mole is a symptom of melanoma. Melanoma is most prevalent in fair-skinned people, but unlike the other forms of skin cancer, it can also affect people with darker complexions.

The public has been slow to respond to warnings about avoiding sun exposure, perhaps because the cosmetic benefits of tanning are immediate while the health hazards are much delayed. The desire to achieve that tanned, bronzed body is as strong as ever.

A good tan requires regular exposure to the sun to maintain it, so indoor tanning salons have become popular. Tanning beds emit concentrated UV rays from two sides, allowing a person to tan in less time and in all weather conditions (sun, rain, snow). The indoor tanning business has grown in the U.S. to a $2-billion-a-year industry with an estimated 28 million Americans tanning annually.

People thought that building up a tan through the use of tanning beds would protect a person's skin from burning and would reduce the time exposed to the UV radiation, both leading to a reduced risk of skin cancer. However, recent research does not support these assumptions. A 2003 study of 106,000 Scandinavian women showed that exposure to UV rays in a tanning bed as little as once a month can increase your risk of melanoma by 55%, especially when the exposure is during early adulthood. Those women who were in their 20s and used sun lamps to tan were at the highest risk, about 150% higher than those who didn't use a tanning bed. As with other studies, fair-skinned women were at the greatest risk. In fact, tanning beds, even for those people who tan more easily, heighten the risk for skin cancer because people use the tanning beds year-round, increasing their cumulative exposure.

It is difficult to avoid the conclusion that to protect your genes you should avoid tanning beds. Like smoking cigarettes, excessive tanning is gambling with your life.

Inquiry & Analysis

Are Mutations Random or Directed By the Environment?

Once biologists appreciated that Mendelian traits were in fact alternative versions of DNA sequences, which resulted from mutations, a very important question arose and needed to be answered—Are mutations random events that might happen anywhere on a DNA chromosome, or are they directed to some degree by the environment? Do the mutagens in cigarettes, for example, damage DNA at random locations, or do they preferentially seek out and alter specific sites such as those regulating the cell cycle?

This key question was addressed and answered in an elegant and deceptively simple experiment carried out in 1943 by two of the pioneers of molecular genetics, Salvadore Luria and Max Delbruck. They chose to examine a particular mutation that occurs in laboratory strains of the bacterium *E. coli*. These bacterial cells are susceptible to T1 viruses, tiny chemical parasites that infect, multiply within, and kill the bacteria. If 10^5 bacterial cells are exposed to 10^{10} T1 viruses, and the mixture spread on a culture dish, not one cell grows—every single *E. coli* cell is infected and killed. However, if you repeat the experiment using 10^9 bacterial cells, lots of cells survive! When tested, these surviving cells prove to be mutants, resistant to T1 infection. The question is, did the T1 virus cause the mutations, or were the mutations present all along, too rare to be present in a sample of only 10^5 cells but common enough to be present in 10^9 cells?

To answer this question, Luria and Delbruck devised a simple experiment they called a "fluctuation test," illustrated here. Five cell generations are shown for each of four independent bacterial cultures, all tested for resistance in the fifth generation. If the T1 virus causes the mutations (top row), then each culture will have more or less the same number of resistant cells, with only a little fluctuation (that is, variation among the four). If, on the other hand, mutations are spontaneous and so equally likely to occur in any generation, then bacterial cultures in which the T1 resistance mutation occurs in earlier generations will possess far more resistant cells by the fifth generation than cultures in which the mutation occurs in later generations, resulting in wide fluctuation among the four cultures. The table presents the data they obtained for 20 individual cultures.

Number of Bacteria Resistant to T1 Virus

Culture number	Resistant colonies found	Culture number	Resistant colonies found
1	1	11	107
2	0	12	0
3	3	13	0
4	0	14	0
5	0	15	1
6	5	16	0
7	0	17	0
8	5	18	64
9	0	19	0
10	6	20	35

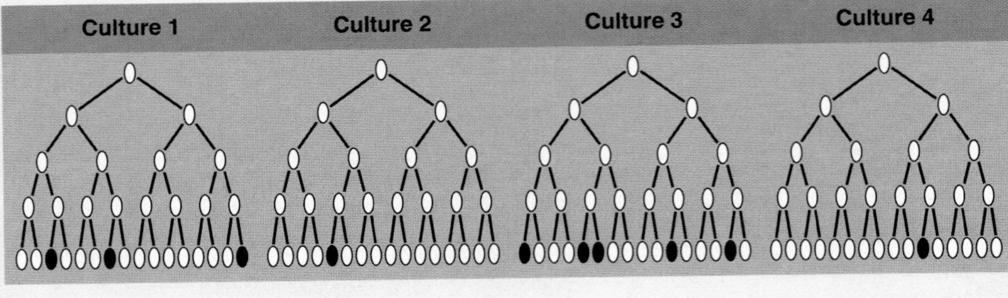

(a)

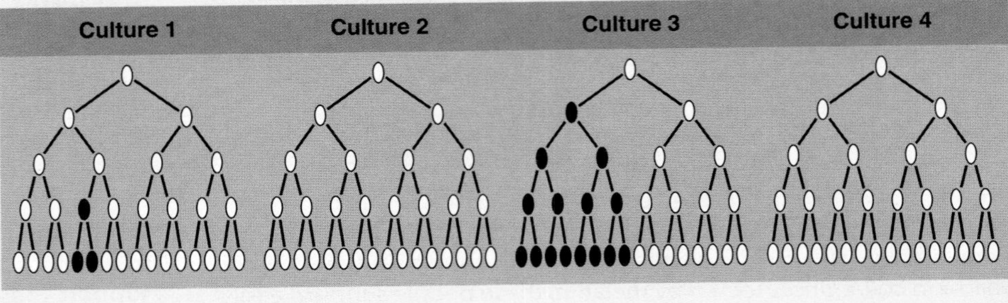

(b)

Analysis

1. **Interpreting Data** What is the mean number of T1-resistant bacteria found in the 20 individual cultures?

2. **Making Inferences**
   a. Comparing the twenty individual cultures, do the cultures exhibit similar numbers of T1-resistant bacterial cells?
   b. Which of the two alternative outcomes illustrated above, (*a*) or (*b*), is more similar to the outcome obtained by Luria and Delbruck in this experiment?

3. **Drawing Conclusions** Are these data consistent with the hypothesis that the mutation for T1 resistance among *E. coli* bacteria is caused by exposure to T1 virus? Explain.

Summary of Learning Outcomes

Genes Are Made of DNA

The Griffith Experiment

11.1.1 Using *Streptococcus pneumoniae* bacteria, Griffith showed that hereditary information that controls physical characteristics can be passed from one bacterium to another, even from a dead bacterium.

- By injecting mice with different strains of *S. pneumoniae,* Griffith determined that some strains were pathogenic, resulting in the mice's deaths. Bacteria of the pathogenic strains contained polysaccharide capsules (S strain), like the bacteria shown here from **figure 11.1,** while those without the capsules (R strain) were nonlethal. When Griffith mixed dead pathogenic bacteria (S), which usually would not cause death, and live nonpathogenic bacteria (R) and injected them into mice, the mice died. The dead mice contained living S strains.
- Something passed from the dead lethal bacteria to the live nonlethal bacteria, transforming them into pathogenic bacteria.

The Hereditary Material

11.2.1 Avery and colleagues showed that protein was not the source of this transformation. They replicated Griffith's experiment but removed all protein from the preparation. The virulent strain with its protein removed was still able to transform nonvirulent bacteria. This experimental result supported the hypothesis that DNA, not protein, was the transforming principle.

11.2.2 Using bacterial viruses, Hershey and Chase showed that genes were carried on DNA and not proteins. They used two different radioactively tagged preparations, DNA in one, as shown here from **figure 11.2,** and protein in the other. Each preparation was used to infect bacteria. When they screened the two bacterial cultures, they discovered that the infected bacteria contained radioactively tagged DNA.

Discovering the Structure of DNA

11.3.1 The structure of DNA was not known. The basic chemical components of DNA were determined to be nucleotides. Each nucleotide has a similar structure: a deoxyribose sugar attached to a phosphate group and one of four organic bases.

- Erwin Chargaff observed that two sets of bases are always present in equal amounts in a molecule of DNA (the amount of A nucleotides equals the amount of T nucleotides, and C nucleotides equals G nucleotides). This observation, called Chargaff's rule, gave some insight into the structure of DNA—that there was some regularity to the structure.
- Using X-ray diffraction, Rosalind Franklin and Maurice Wilkins were able to form a "picture" of DNA. The image suggested that the DNA molecule was coiled, a form called a helix.
- Using Chargaff's and Franklin's research, Watson and Crick argued that their data could best be explained if DNA is a double helix, two strands that are connected by base pairing between the nucleotide bases. An A nucleotide on one strand pairs with T on the other, and similarly G pairs with C.

DNA Replication

How DNA Copies Itself

11.4.1 The basis for the great accuracy of DNA replication is complementarity (A pairs only with T and C only with G)—if you know the sequence of one strand, the other strand's sequence is fully determined. However, there are several ways in which a single strand of DNA can serve as the template for production of the other strand.

11.4.2 Meselson and Stahl showed that DNA replicates semiconservatively, using each of the original strands as templates to form new strands. In semiconservative replication, each new strand of DNA consists of a template strand from the parent DNA and a newly synthesized strand that is complementary to the template stand.

11.4.3 In replication, the DNA molecule first unwinds by the actions of an enzyme called helicase. Each DNA strand is then copied by the actions of an enzyme called DNA polymerase. The two original strands serve as templates to the new DNA strands. DNA polymerase adds nucleotides to the new DNA strands that are complementary to the original single strands. DNA polymerase can only add on to an existing strand, and so the new strand begins after a section of nucleic acids called a primer is added. A different enzyme builds the primer. Nucleotides are added to the growing strand in a 5′ to 3′ direction.

- The point where the DNA separates is called the replication fork. Because nucleotides can only be added onto the 3′ end of the growing DNA strand, DNA copies in a continuous manner on one of the strands, called the leading strand, and in a discontinuous manner on the other strand, called the lagging strand. On the lagging strand, primers are inserted at the replication fork, and nucleotides are added in sections, as shown here on the lower strand from ***Essential Biological Process 11A.*** Before the new DNA strands rewind, the primers are removed and the DNA segments are linked together with another enzyme called DNA ligase.
- Errors can occur during the replication of DNA. The cell has many mechanisms to correct damage to the DNA or mistakes made during replication. This proofreading process compares one strand against its complementary strand and corrects errors, but this system is not foolproof.

Altering the Genetic Message

Mutation

11.5.1 A mutation is a change in the nucleotide sequence of the genetic message. Mutations that change one or only a few nucleotides are called point mutations. Some mutations cause only minor changes while others can have dramatic consequences.

Test Your Understanding

11.1.1 In his experiment, Frederick Griffith found that
a. hereditary information within a cell cannot be changed.
b. hereditary information can be added to cells from other cells.
c. mice infected with live R strains die.
d. mice infected with heat-killed S strains die.

11.2.2 The experiment performed by Alfred Hershey and Martha Chase showed that the molecule viruses use to specify new viruses is
a. a protein. **c.** ATP.
b. a carbohydrate. **d.** DNA.

11.3.1 Erwin Chargaff, Rosalind Franklin, Francis Crick, and James Watson all worked on pieces of information relating to the
a. structure of DNA. **c.** inheritance of DNA.
b. function of DNA. **d.** mutations of DNA.

11.3.1 The four DNA nucleotides are all different in terms of
a. their sizes.
b. the number of hydrogen bonds they can form with their base pair.
c. the type of nitrogen base.
d. the type of sugar.

11.3.1 Which of the following lists the organic bases found in the purine nucleotides?
a. adenine and cytosine **c.** cytosine and thymine
b. guanine and thymine **d.** adenine and guanine

11.4.1 If one strand of a DNA molecule has the base sequence ATTGCAT, its complementary strand will have the sequence
a. ATTGCAT. **c.** GCCATGC.
b. TAACGTA. **d.** CGGTACG.

11.4.2 Regarding the duplication of DNA, we now know that each double helix
a. reforms after replicating.
b. splits down the middle into two single strands, and each one then acts as a template to build its complement.
c. fragments into small chunks that duplicate and reassemble.
d. All of these are true for different types of DNA.

11.4.3 DNA polymerase can add nucleotides only to an existing chain, so ________________ is required.
a. a primer **c.** a lagging strand
b. helicase **d.** a leading strand

11.5.1 Genetic messages can be altered in two ways:
a. through semiconservative replication or conservative replication.
b. through the chromosome or through the protein.
c. by mutation or by transformation.
d. by activation or by repression.

11.5.1 Mutations can occur in
a. germ-line tissues and are passed on to future generations.
b. somatic tissues and are passed on to future generations.
c. germ-line tissues but not in somatic tissues.
d. somatic tissues but not in germ-line tissues.

Apply Your Understanding

11.5.1 What are some of the possible problems that could occur if the cytosine nucleotide indicated with the red arrow is accidentally replaced with an adenine nucleotide?

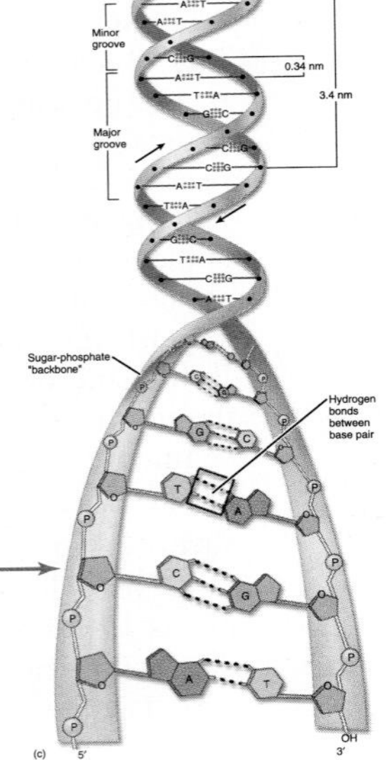

11.5.1 What types of mutations shown in the table result in a shift in the reading frame of the DNA? Explain.

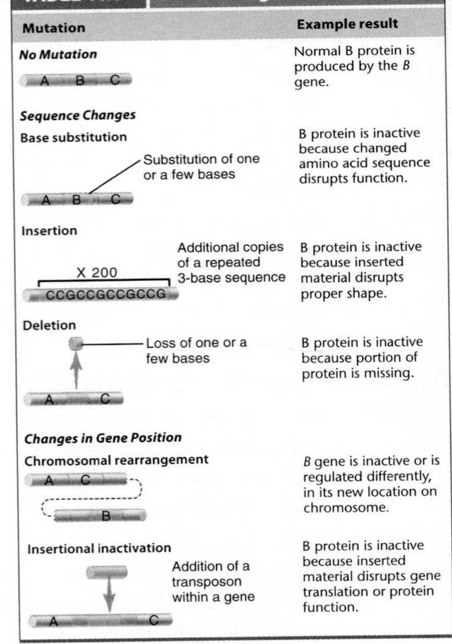

TABLE 11.1 Some Categories of Mutation

Mutation	Example result
No Mutation (A B C)	Normal B protein is produced by the *B* gene.
Sequence Changes	
Base substitution — Substitution of one or a few bases (A B C)	B protein is inactive because changed amino acid sequence disrupts function.
Insertion — Additional copies of a repeated 3-base sequence (X 200, CCGCCGCCGCCG)	B protein is inactive because inserted material disrupts proper shape.
Deletion — Loss of one or a few bases (A C)	B protein is inactive because portion of protein is missing.
Changes in Gene Position	
Chromosomal rearrangement (A C; B)	*B* gene is inactive or is regulated differently, in its new location on chromosome.
Insertional inactivation — Addition of a transposon within a gene (A C)	B protein is inactive because inserted material disrupts gene translation or protein function.

Synthesize What You Have Learned

11.2.1 The discovery that DNA is the hereditary material was an experimental journey rather than a flash of insight. Highlighting individual experiments, use the journey to defend the statement, attributed to Sir Isaac Newton in 1676 (though some say that Bernard of Chartres said it first, way back in about 1130!) that scientists build new ideas by "standing on the shoulders of giants."

11.5.1 Certain strains of bacteria are resistant to the antibiotic tetracycline, while other strains are sensitive to it. Design an experiment you would carry out to determine whether or not tetracycline resistance is an inherited trait specified by the DNA of the resistant strain.

Chapter 12

How Genes Work

CHAPTER AT A GLANCE

From Gene to Protein

12.1 The Central Dogma

12.2 Transcription

12.3 Translation

Essential Biological Process 12A: Translation

12.4 Gene Expression

Regulating Gene Expression

12.5 Transcriptional Control in Prokaryotes

12.6 Transcriptional Control in Eukaryotes

Essential Biological Process 12B: Control of Eukaryotic Gene Expression

12.7 RNA-Level Control

Biology and Staying Healthy: Silencing Genes to Treat Disease

Inquiry & Analysis: Building Proteins in a Test Tube

From Gene to Protein

12.1 The Central Dogma

LEARNING OBJECTIVE 12.1.1 State the "central dogma."

The discovery that genes are made of DNA, discussed in chapter 11, left unanswered the question of how the information in DNA is used. How does a string of nucleotides in a spiral molecule determine if you have red hair? We now know that the information in DNA is arrayed in little blocks, like entries in a dictionary, and each block is a gene that specifies the sequence of amino acids for a polypeptide. These polypeptides form the proteins that determine what a particular cell will be like.

All organisms, from the simplest bacteria to ourselves, use the same basic mechanism of reading and expressing genes, so fundamental to life as we know it that it is often referred to as the "central dogma": Information passes from the genes (DNA) to an RNA copy of the gene, and the RNA copy directs the sequential assembly of a chain of amino acids (figure 12.1). Said briefly, **DNA ⟶ RNA ⟶ protein.**

A cell uses four kinds of RNA in the synthesis of proteins: messenger RNA (mRNA), silencing RNA (siRNA), ribosomal RNA (rRNA), and transfer RNA (tRNA). These types of RNA are described in more detail later in this chapter.

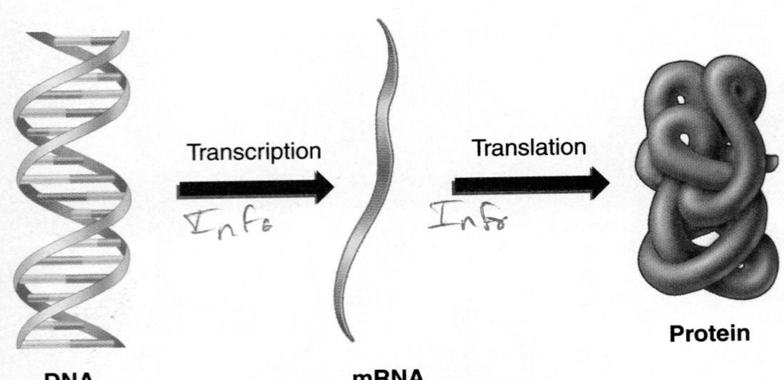

Figure 12.1 The central dogma: DNA to RNA to protein.

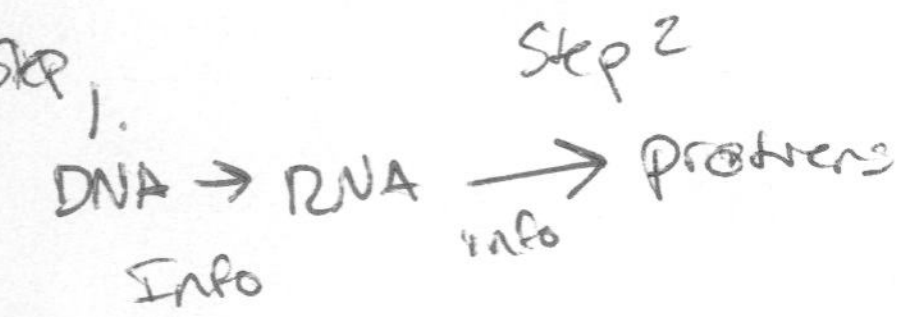

Transcription: An Overview

The first step of the central dogma is the transfer of information from DNA to RNA, which occurs when an mRNA copy of the gene is produced. Because the DNA sequence in the gene is transcribed into an RNA sequence, this stage is called *transcription.* Transcription is initiated when the enzyme *RNA polymerase* binds to a special nucleotide sequence called a *promoter* located at the beginning of a gene. Starting there, the RNA polymerase moves along the strand into the gene (figure 12.2). As it encounters each DNA nucleotide, it adds the corresponding complementary RNA nucleotide to a growing mRNA strand. This chain is a complementary transcript of the gene from which it was copied.

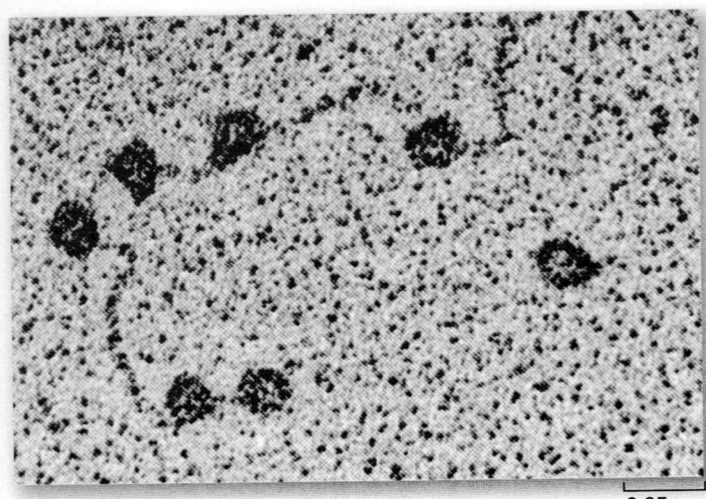

Figure 12.2 RNA polymerase.

In this electron micrograph, the dark circles are RNA polymerase molecules synthesizing RNA from a DNA template.

Translation: An Overview

The second step of the central dogma is the transfer of information from RNA to protein, which occurs when the information contained in the mRNA transcript is used to direct the sequence of amino acids during the synthesis of polypeptides by ribosomes. This process is called *translation* because the nucleotide sequence of the mRNA transcript is translated into an amino acid sequence in the polypeptide. Translation begins when an rRNA molecule within the ribosome recognizes and binds to a "start" sequence on the mRNA. The ribosome then moves along the mRNA molecule, three nucleotides at a time. Each group of three nucleotides is a code word that specifies which amino acid will be added to the growing polypeptide chain, and is recognized by a specific tRNA molecule. Small siRNA molecules help the cell fine-tune gene use by influencing which transcripts are translated. The use of information in DNA to direct the production of particular polypeptides is called **gene expression.**

Putting the Concept to Work

What four roles does RNA play in gene expression?

12.2 Transcription

LEARNING OBJECTIVE 12.2.1 Indicate the chemical direction in which an mRNA chain is assembled during transcription.

Just as an architect protects building plans from loss or damage by keeping them safe in a central place and issuing only blueprint copies to on-site workers, so your cells protect their DNA instructions by keeping them safe within a central DNA storage area, the nucleus. The DNA never leaves the nucleus. Instead, the process of **transcription** creates "blueprint" copies of particular genes that are sent out into the cell to direct the assembly of proteins (figure 12.3). These working copies of genes are made of ribonucleic acid (RNA) rather than DNA (see figures 3.10 and 3.11).

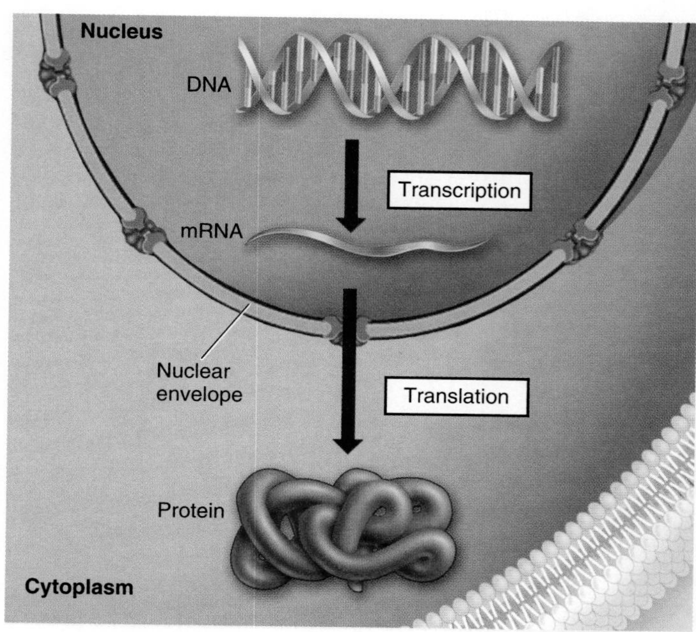

Figure 12.3 Overview of gene expression in a eukaryotic cell.

The Transcription Process

The RNA copy of a gene used in the cell to produce a polypeptide is called **messenger RNA (mRNA)**—it is the messenger that conveys the information from the nucleus to the cytoplasm. The copying process that makes the mRNA is called transcription—just as monks in monasteries used to make copies of manuscripts by faithfully transcribing each letter, so enzymes within the nuclei of your cells make mRNA copies of your genes by faithfully complementing each nucleotide.

In your cells, the transcriber is a large and very sophisticated protein called **RNA polymerase.** It binds to one strand of a DNA double helix at the promoter site and then moves along the DNA strand like a train engine on a track. Although DNA is double-stranded, the two strands have complementary rather than identical sequences, so RNA polymerase is able to bind only one of the two DNA strands (the one with the promoter-site sequence it recognizes). As RNA polymerase goes along the DNA strand it is copying, it pairs each nucleotide with its complementary RNA version (G with C, A with U—recall that RNA uses a nucleotide with uracil, U, in place of thymine). The mRNA chain is built in the 5′ to 3′ direction (figure 12.4).

The production of an RNA molecule during transcription is similar to the process of DNA replication, with the RNA chain of nucleotides growing in a 5′ to 3′ direction as is seen in DNA synthesis in figure 11.7 on page 196.

Putting the Concept to Work

Why is an mRNA chain assembled in only one direction?

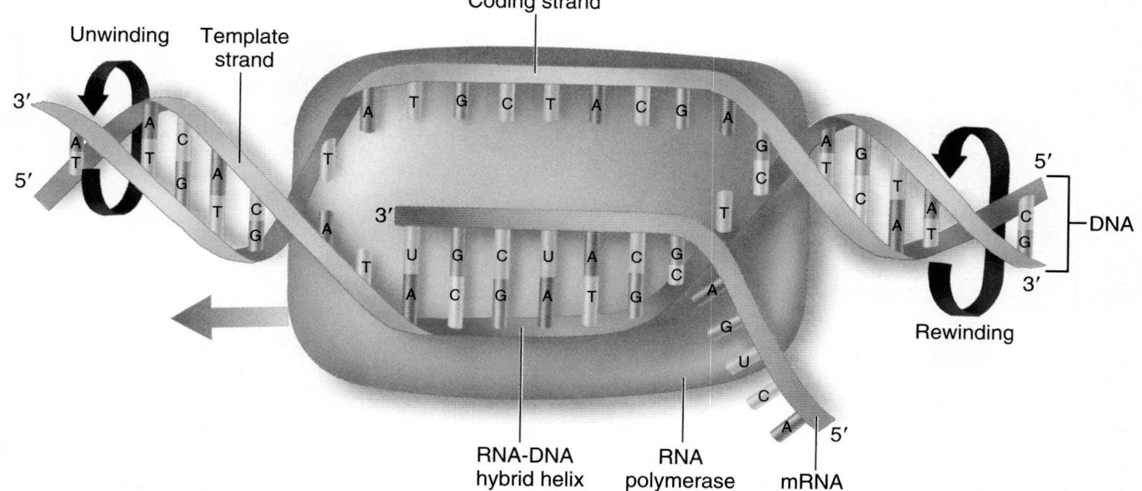

Figure 12.4 Transcription.

One of the strands of DNA functions as a template on which nucleotide building blocks are assembled into mRNA by RNA polymerase as it moves along the DNA strand.

12.3 Translation

The Genetic Code

LEARNING OBJECTIVE 12.3.1 Define codon and explain how to read one.

The essential lesson of genetics is that the information determining hereditary traits is encoded information, written within the chromosomes in blocks called genes. To read a gene, a cell must translate the information encoded in DNA into the language of proteins—that is, it must convert the order of the gene's nucleotides into the order of amino acids in a polypeptide, a process called **translation.** The rules that govern this translation are called the **genetic code.**

The mRNA nucleotide sequence is "read" by a ribosome in three nucleotide units called **codons.** Biologists worked out which codon corresponds to which amino acid by trial-and-error experiments carried out in test tubes. In these experiments, investigators used artificial mRNAs to direct the synthesis of polypeptides in the tube, and then looked to see the sequence of amino acids in the newly formed polypeptides. An mRNA that was a string of UUUUUU . . . , for example, produced a polypeptide that was a string of phenylalanine (Phe) amino acids, telling investigators that the codon UUU corresponded to the amino acid Phe. Most amino acids are specified by more than one codon. The entire genetic code dictionary is presented in figure 12.5.

The genetic code is universal, the same in practically all organisms. GUC codes for valine in bacteria, in fruit flies, in eagles, and in your own cells. The only exception biologists have ever found to this rule is in how cell organelles that contain DNA (mitochondria and chloroplasts) and a few microscopic protists read the "stop" codons. In every other instance, the same genetic code is employed by all living things.

Putting the Concept to Work

How many codons do not code for an amino acid?

Figure 12.5 The genetic code (RNA codons).

A codon consists of three nucleotides read in sequence. For example, ACU codes for threonine. To determine which amino acid corresponds to a codon, you read the chart first down the left side, then across the top, then down the right side. For the codon ACU, find the first letter, A, in the First Letter column; then follow the row over to the second letter, C, in the Second Letter row across the top; and then in that column trace down to the third letter, U, in the Third Letter column. Most amino acids are specified by more than one codon. For example, threonine is specified by four codons, which differ only in the third nucleotide (ACU, ACC, ACA, and ACG).

The Genetic Code

First Letter	Second Letter: U		C		A		G		Third Letter
U	UUU	Phenylalanine	UCU	Serine	UAU	Tyrosine	UGU	Cysteine	U
	UUC		UCC		UAC		UGC		C
	UUA	Leucine	UCA		UAA	Stop	UGA	Stop	A
	UUG		UCG		UAG	Stop	UGG	Tryptophan	G
C	CUU	Leucine	CCU	Proline	CAU	Histidine	CGU	Arginine	U
	CUC		CCC		CAC		CGC		C
	CUA		CCA		CAA	Glutamine	CGA		A
	CUG		CCG		CAG		CGG		G
A	AUU	Isoleucine	ACU	Threonine	AAU	Asparagine	AGU	Serine	U
	AUC		ACC		AAC		AGC		C
	AUA		ACA		AAA	Lysine	AGA	Arginine	A
	AUG	Methionine; Start	ACG		AAG		AGG		G
G	GUU	Valine	GCU	Alanine	GAU	Aspartate	GGU	Glycine	U
	GUC		GCC		GAC		GGC		C
	GUA		GCA		GAA	Glutamate	GGA		A
	GUG		GCG		GAG		GGG		G

Translating the RNA Message

LEARNING OBJECTIVE 12.3.2 Contrast the roles of tRNA and ribosomes in reading the genetic code.

The final result of the transcription process is the production of an mRNA copy of a gene. Like a photocopy, the mRNA can be used without damage or wear and tear on the original. After transcription of a gene is finished, the mRNA passes out of the nucleus into the cytoplasm through pores in the nuclear envelope. There, translation of the genetic message occurs. In translation, organelles called **ribosomes** use the mRNA produced by transcription to direct the synthesis of a polypeptide, following the genetic code.

The Protein-Making Factory. Ribosomes are the polypeptide-making factories of the cell. Ribosomes are very complex, containing over 50 different proteins (shown in gold in figure 12.6, top) and three chains of **ribosomal RNA (rRNA)** of some 3,000 nucleotides (shown in gray). It had been traditionally assumed that the proteins in a ribosome act as enzymes to catalyze the assembly process, with the RNA acting as a scaffold to position the proteins. Powerful atomic-resolution X-ray diffraction studies have unexpectedly revealed the many proteins of a ribosome to be scattered over its surface like decorations on a Christmas tree. The role of these proteins seems to be to stabilize the many bends and twists of the RNA chains. Importantly, there are no proteins on the inside of the ribosome where the chemistry of protein synthesis takes place—just twists of RNA. It is the ribosome's RNA, not its proteins, that catalyzes the synthesis of proteins!

Ribosomes are composed of two parts, or subunits, one nested into the other like a fist in the palm of your hand. The "fist" is the smaller of the two subunits, the pink structure in figure 12.6. Its rRNA has a short nucleotide sequence exposed on the surface of the subunit. This exposed sequence is identical to a sequence called the leader region that occurs at the beginning of all genes. Because of this, an mRNA molecule binds to the exposed rRNA of the small subunit like a fly sticking to flypaper.

The Key Role of tRNA. Directly adjacent to the exposed rRNA sequence are three small pockets or dents, designated the A, P, and E sites, in the surface of the ribosome shown in figure 12.6. These sites have just the right shape to bind yet a third kind of RNA molecule, **transfer RNA (tRNA).** It is tRNA molecules that bring amino acids to the ribosome used in making proteins. tRNA molecules are chains about 80 nucleotides long. The string of nucleotides folds back on itself, forming a three-looped structure shown in figure 12.7*a*. The looped structure further folds into a compact shape shown in figure 12.7*b*, with a three-nucleotide sequence at the bottom (the pink loop) and an amino acid attachment site at the top (the 3′ end).

The three-nucleotide sequence on the tRNA, called the **anticodon,** is very important: It is the complementary sequence to 1 of the 64 codons of the genetic code! Special enzymes, called *activating enzymes,* match amino acids in the cytoplasm with their proper tRNAs. The anticodon determines which amino acid will attach to a particular tRNA. Because the first dent in the ribosome, called the A site (the attachment site where amino-acid-bearing tRNAs will bind), is directly adjacent to where the mRNA binds to the rRNA, three nucleotides of the mRNA are positioned directly facing the anticodon of the tRNA. Like the address on a letter, the anticodon ensures that an amino acid is delivered to its correct "address" on the mRNA where the ribosome is assembling the polypeptide.

Putting the Concept to Work

How many different activating enzymes does a cell require?

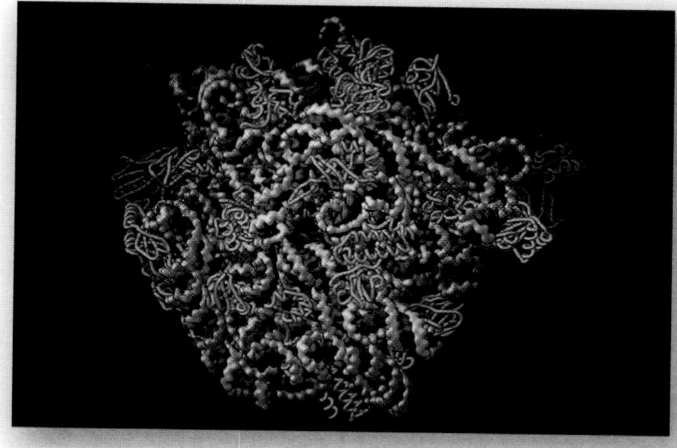

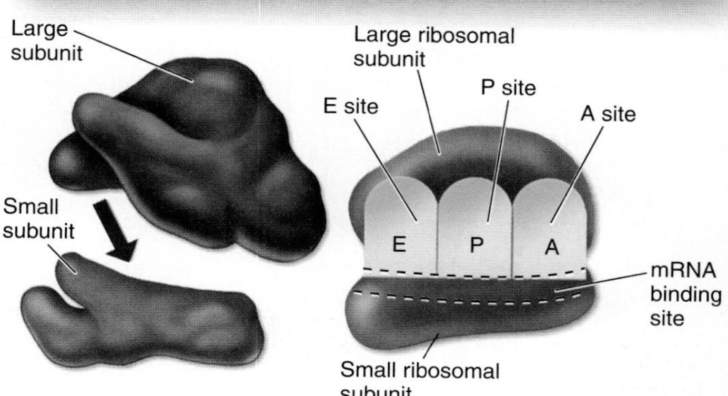

Figure 12.6 A ribosome is composed of two subunits.

The smaller subunit fits into a depression on the surface of the larger one. The A, P, and E sites on the ribosome play key roles in protein synthesis.

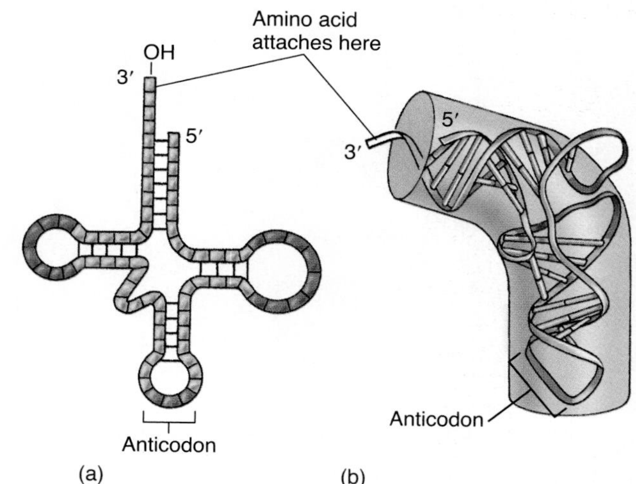

Figure 12.7 The structure of tRNA.

tRNA, like mRNA, is a long strand of nucleotides. However, unlike mRNA, hydrogen bonding occurs between its nucleotides, causing the strand to form hairpin loops, as seen in (a). The loops then fold up on each other to create the compact, three-dimensional shape seen in (b). Amino acids attach to the free, single-stranded —OH end of a tRNA molecule. A three-nucleotide sequence called the anticodon in the lower loop of tRNA interacts with a complementary codon on the mRNA.

Essential Biological Process 12A

Translation

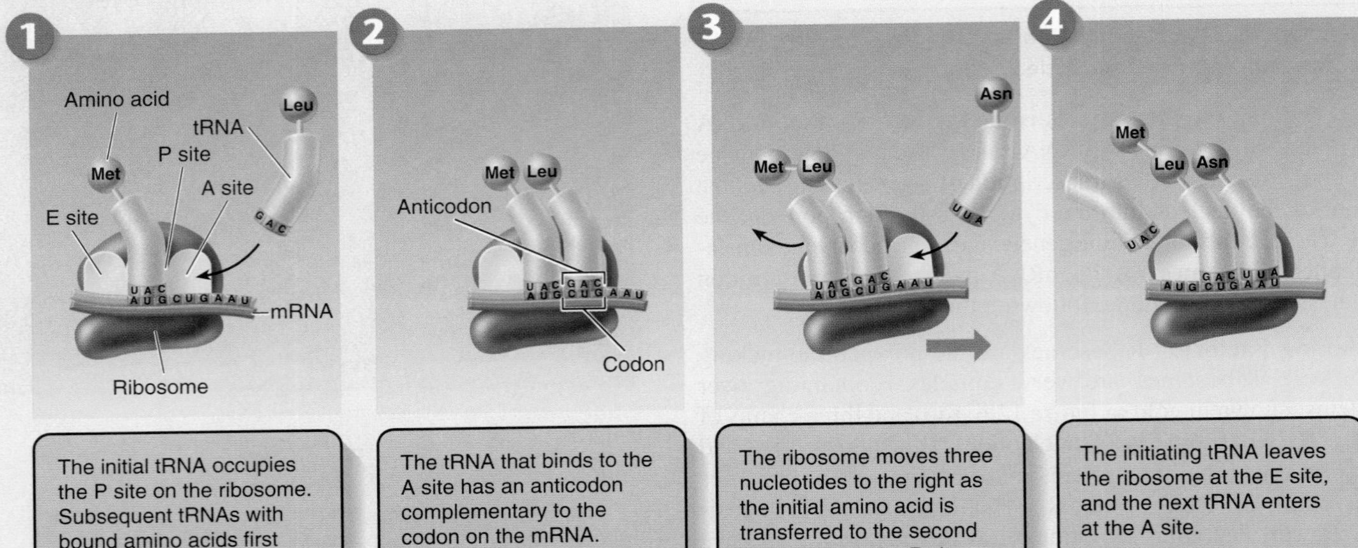

1
Amino acid
tRNA
Leu
P site
Met
A site
E site
UAC
AUGCUGAAU
mRNA
Ribosome
The initial tRNA occupies the P site on the ribosome. Subsequent tRNAs with bound amino acids first enter the ribosome at the A site.
2
Met
Leu
Anticodon
Codon
The tRNA that binds to the A site has an anticodon complementary to the codon on the mRNA.
3
Asn
Met
Leu
UUA
The ribosome moves three nucleotides to the right as the initial amino acid is transferred to the second amino acid at the P site.
4
Met
Leu
Asn
UAC
The initiating tRNA leaves the ribosome at the E site, and the next tRNA enters at the A site.

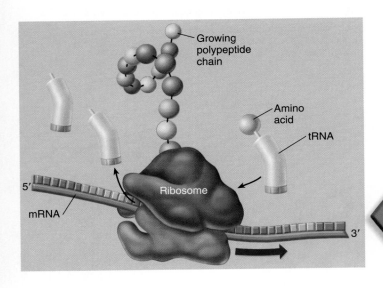

Figure 12.8 Ribosomes guide the translation process.
tRNA binds to an amino acid as determined by the anticodon sequence. Ribosomes bind the loaded tRNAs to their complementary sequences on the strand of mRNA. tRNA adds its amino acid to the growing polypeptide chain, which is released as the completed protein. The overall flow of genetic information is from DNA to mRNA to protein. For example, the polypeptide that is being formed in *Essential Biological Process 12A* began with the DNA nucleotide sequence TACGACTTA, which was transcribed into the mRNA sequence AUGCUGAAU. This sequence is then translated into a polypeptide composed of the amino acids methionine—leucine—asparagine.

Making the Polypeptide

LEARNING OBJECTIVE 12.3.3 Describe in detail how ribosomes guide the translation process.

Once an mRNA molecule has bound to the small ribosomal subunit, the other larger ribosomal subunit binds as well, forming a complete ribosome. The ribosome then begins the process of translation, shown in *Essential Biological Process 12A*. Panel 1 of the figure shows how the mRNA begins to thread through the ribosome like a string passing through the hole in a doughnut. The mRNA passes through in short spurts, three nucleotides at a time, and at each burst of movement a new three-nucleotide codon on the mRNA is positioned opposite the A site in the ribosome, where a tRNA molecule first binds, as shown in panel 2.

As each new tRNA brings in an amino acid to each new codon presented at the A site, the old tRNA paired with the previous codon is passed over to the P site where peptide bonds form between the incoming amino acid and the growing polypeptide chain. The tRNA in the P site eventually shifts to the E site (the exit site), as shown in panel 3, and the amino acid it carried is attached to the end of a growing amino acid chain. The tRNA is then released in panel 4. So as the ribosome proceeds down the mRNA, one tRNA after another is selected to match the sequence of mRNA codons and bring the amino acids into the ribosome, the growing polypeptide chain extending out from the ribosome (figure 12.8). Translation continues until a "stop" codon is encountered, which signals the end of the polypeptide. The ribosome complex falls apart, and the newly made polypeptide is released into the cell.

A peptide bond is the name given to the chemical bond that forms between two amino acids in a polypeptide, as discussed on page 53.

Putting the Concept to Work

In what order are the A, E, and P sites of a ribosome occupied by a particular amino acid?

12.4 Gene Expression

The central dogma, discussed in section 12.1, is the same in all organisms. **Figure 12.9** presents an overview of the components needed for the key processes of DNA replication, transcription, and translation and the products that are formed in each. In general, the components are the same, the processes are the same, and the products are the same whether in prokaryotes or eukaryotes. However, there are some differences in gene expression between the two types of cells.

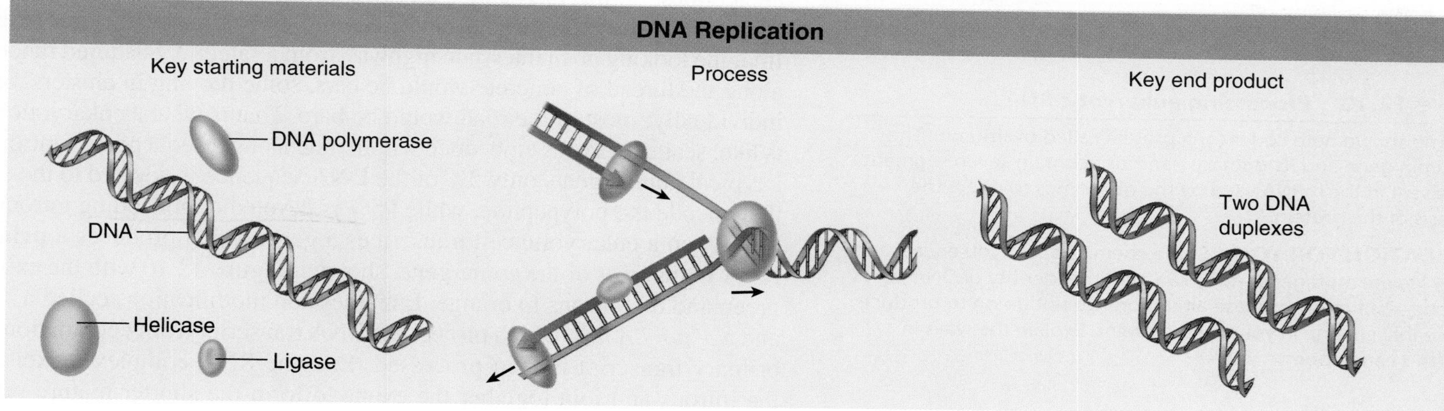

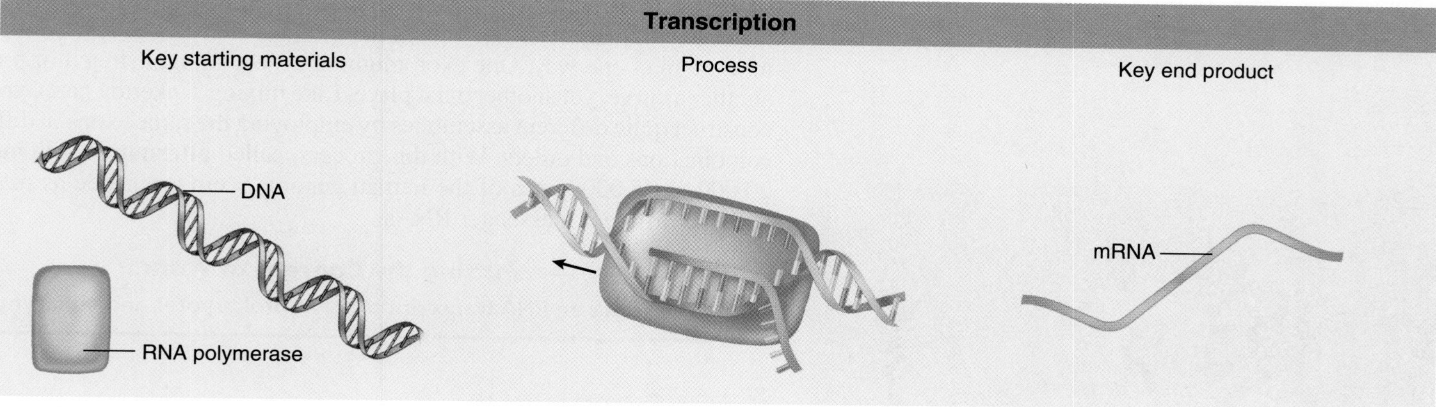

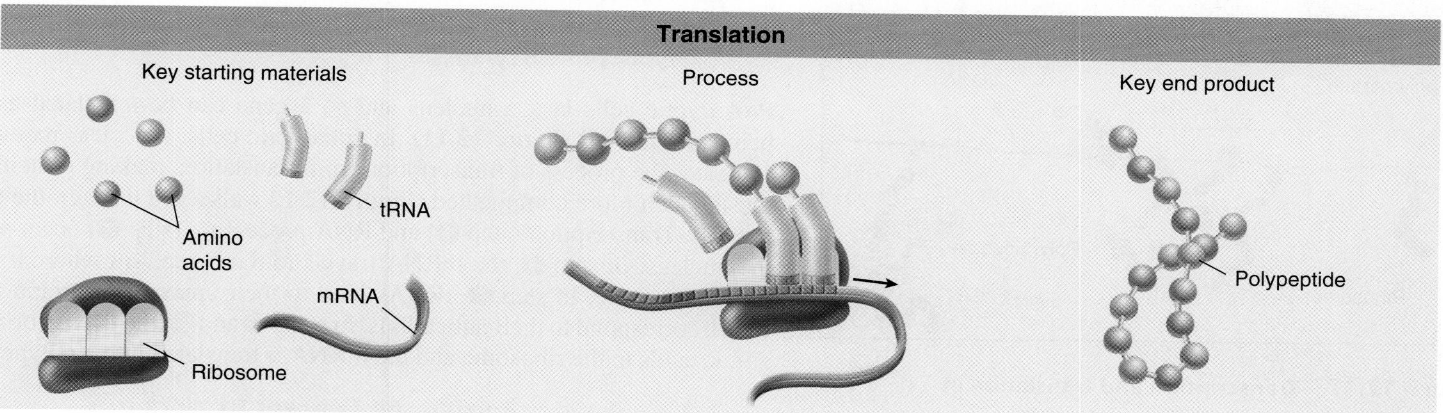

Figure 12.9 The processes of DNA replication, transcription, and translation.
These processes are generally the same in prokaryotes and eukaryotes.

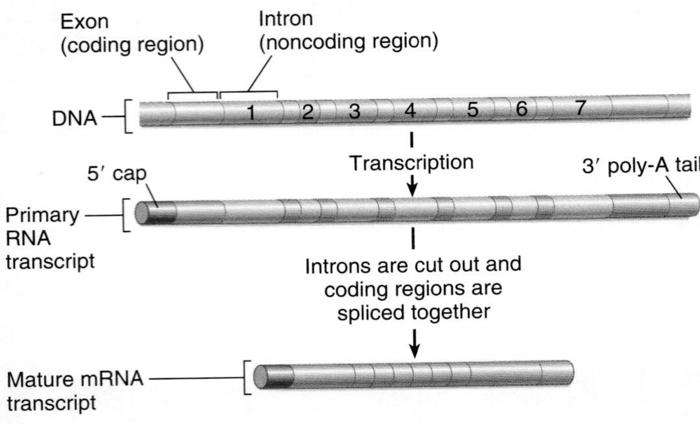

Figure 12.10 Processing eukaryotic RNA.

The gene shown here codes for a protein called ovalbumin. The ovalbumin gene and its primary transcript contain seven segments not present in the mRNA used by the ribosomes to direct the synthesis of the protein.

IMPLICATION FOR YOU Some chemicals that you encounter in daily life are mutagens—they can alter the identity of DNA bases in a gene—but many of these alterations do not go on to produce a noticeable change in your cells' proteins. Explain the ways in which this can happen.

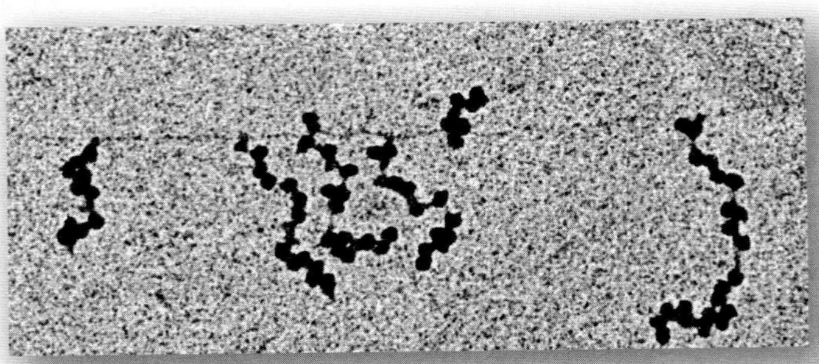

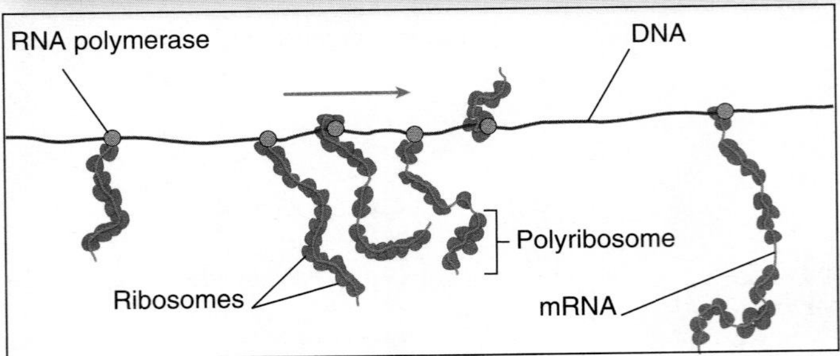

Figure 12.11 Transcription and translation in prokaryotes.

Ribosomes attach to an mRNA as it is formed, producing polyribosomes that translate the gene soon after it is transcribed.

Architecture of the Gene

LEARNING OBJECTIVE 12.4.1 Compare the architecture of prokaryotic and eukaryotic genes, explaining how introns allow alternative splicing.

In prokaryotes, a gene is an uninterrupted stretch of DNA nucleotides whose transcript is read three nucleotides at a time to make a chain of amino acids. In eukaryotes, by contrast, genes are fragmented. In these more complex genes, the DNA nucleotide sequences encoding the amino acid sequence of a polypeptide, called **exons,** are interrupted frequently by extraneous nucleotides, "extra stuff" called **introns.** In the segment of DNA illustrated in figure 12.10 the exons are the blue areas and the introns are the orange areas. Imagine looking at an interstate highway from a satellite. Scattered randomly along the thread of concrete would be cars, some moving in clusters, others individually; most of the road would be bare. That is what a eukaryotic gene is like: scattered exons embedded within much longer sequences of introns. In a typical human gene, only 5% of the DNA sequence is devoted to the exons that encode the polypeptide, while 95% is devoted to noncoding introns!

When a eukaryotic cell transcribes a gene, it first produces a **primary RNA transcript** of the entire gene, shown in figure 12.10 with the exons in green and the introns in orange. Enzymes add modifications called a *5′ cap* and a *3′ poly-A tail,* which protect the RNA transcript from degradation. The primary transcript is then processed: Enzyme-RNA complexes excise out the introns and join together the exons to form the shorter mature mRNA transcript that is actually translated into an amino acid chain.

If the introns are not translated into proteins, why have them? It appears that many human exons are functional modules that can be spliced together in more than one way. One exon might encode a straight stretch of protein, another a curve, yet another a flat place. Like mixing Tinkertoy parts, you can construct quite different assemblies by employing the same exons in different combinations and orders. With this process, called **alternative splicing,** the 20,000 to 25,000 genes of the human genome seem to encode as many as 120,000 different messenger RNAs.

Putting the Concept to Work

How does an RNA transcript differ in prokaryotes and eukaryotes?

Protein Synthesis

LEARNING OBJECTIVE 12.4.2 Describe the six stages of eukaryotic protein synthesis.

Prokaryotic cells lack a nucleus and so a gene can be translated as it is being transcribed (figure 12.11). In eukaryotic cells, a nuclear membrane separates the process of transcription from translation, making protein synthesis much more complicated. Figure 12.12 walks you through the entire process. Transcription (step ❶) and RNA processing (step ❷) occur within the nucleus. In step ❸, the mRNA travels to the cytoplasm where it binds to the ribosome. In step ❹, tRNAs bind to their appropriate amino acids, which correspond to their anticodons. In steps ❺ and ❻, the tRNAs bring the amino acids to the ribosome and the mRNA is translated into a polypeptide.

Putting the Concept to Work

Why is protein synthesis more complex in eukaryotes?

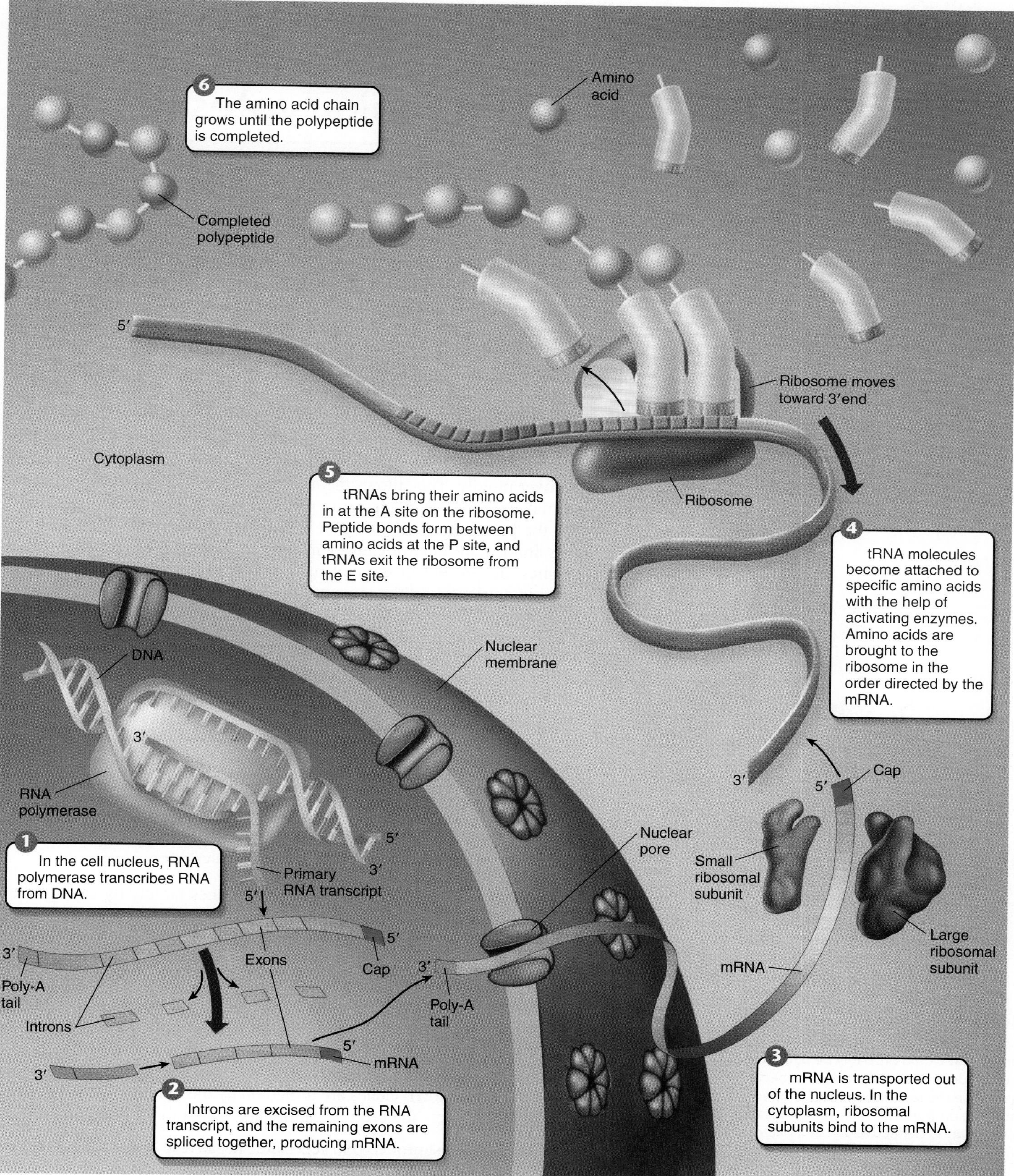

Figure 12.12 How protein synthesis works in eukaryotes.

Regulating Gene Expression

RNA polymerase
Repressor
P_{lac}
O
Gene 1
Gene 2
Gene 3
Promoter
Operator

(a) *lac* operon is "repressed"

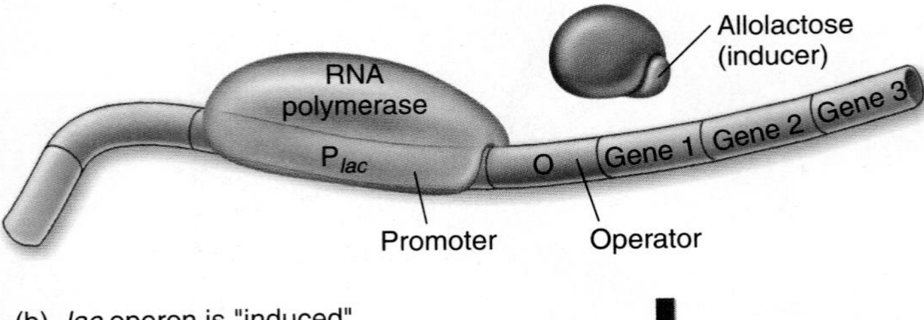

(b) *lac* operon is "induced"

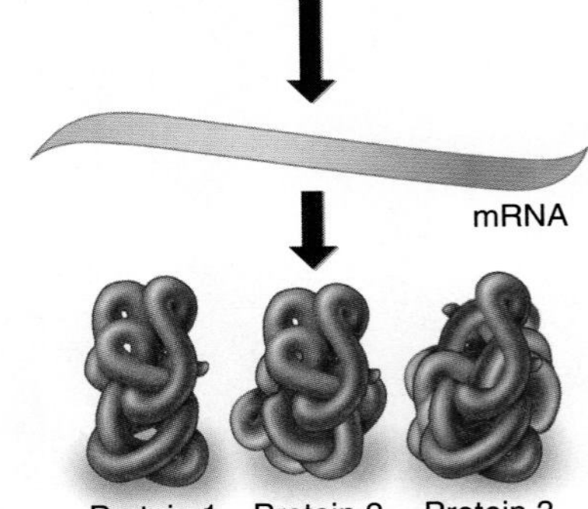

Figure 12.13 How the *lac* operon works.

(a) The *lac* operon is shut down ("repressed") when the repressor protein is bound to the operator site. Because promoter and operator sites overlap, RNA polymerase and the repressor cannot bind at the same time. (b) The *lac* operon is transcribed ("induced") when allolactose binds to the repressor protein changing its shape so that it can no longer sit on the operator site and block polymerase binding.

IMPLICATION FOR YOU Certain antibiotics act by interfering with transcription or translation in bacteria. The rifamycins are a group of drugs that would probably be administered to you if you were to come down with tuberculosis, a bacterial infection of your lungs. Unlike the repressor in the *lac* operon that binds to the operator site on the DNA, rifamycin binds to bacterial RNA polymerase. How can this effectively treat a bacterial infection like tuberculosis?

12.5 Transcriptional Control in Prokaryotes

LEARNING OBJECTIVE 12.5.1 Describe the fundamental goal of transcriptional control in prokaryotes.

Being able to translate a gene into a polypeptide is only part of gene expression. Every cell must also be able to regulate when particular genes are used. Imagine if every instrument in a symphony played at full volume all the time, all the horns blowing full blast and each drum beating as fast and loudly as it could! No symphony plays that way, because music is more than noise—it is the controlled expression of sound. In the same way, growth and development are due to the controlled expression of genes, each brought into play at the proper moment to achieve precise and delicate effects.

Control of gene expression is accomplished very differently in prokaryotes than in the cells of complex multicellular organisms. Prokaryotic cells have been shaped by evolution to grow and divide as rapidly as possible, enabling them to exploit transient resources. Proteins in prokaryotes turn over rapidly. This allows them to respond quickly to changes in their external environment by changing patterns of gene expression. In prokaryotes, the primary function of gene control is to adjust the cell's activities to its immediate environment. Changes in gene expression alter which enzymes are present in the cell in response to the quantity and type of available nutrients and the amount of oxygen present. Almost all of these changes are fully reversible, allowing the cell to adjust its enzyme levels up or down as the environment changes.

Putting the Concept to Work

Your body maintains quite constant internal conditions. Why might prokaryotic gene regulation not be suitable for you?

How Prokaryotes Turn Genes Off and On

LEARNING OBJECTIVE 12.5.2 Explain how activators and repressors work together to control transcription.

Prokaryotes control the expression of their genes largely by saying *when* individual genes are to be transcribed. At the beginning of each gene are special regulatory sites that act as points of control. Regulatory proteins within the cell bind to these sites, turning transcription of the gene off or on.

For a gene to be transcribed, the RNA polymerase has to bind to a **promoter,** a specific sequence of nucleotides on the DNA that signals the beginning of a gene. In prokaryotes, the expression of a gene is regulated by controlling the access of RNA polymerase to the gene's promoter. A gene is turned off by the binding of a **repressor** protein to the DNA, which blocks access to the promoter. Genes are turned on by the binding of an **activator,** a protein that makes the promoter more accessible to RNA polymerase.

Repressors. Most prokaryotic genes are "negatively" controlled: They are turned off except when needed. In these genes, the regulatory site is located between the place where the RNA polymerase binds to the DNA (the promoter site) and the beginning edge of the gene. When a regulatory protein called a repressor is bound to its regulatory site, called the *operator,* its presence blocks the movement of the polymerase toward the gene (figure 12.13). Imagine if you went to sit down to eat dinner and someone was already sitting in your chair—you could not begin your meal until this person was removed from your chair. In the same way, the polymerase cannot begin transcribing the gene until the repressor protein is removed.

To turn on a gene whose transcription is blocked by a repressor, cells use special "signal" molecules. The binding of the signal molecules to the repressor cause it to contort into a shape that doesn't fit DNA; the repressor falls off, removing the barrier to transcription.

A specific example demonstrating how repressor proteins work is the set of genes called the *lac* operon in the bacterium *Escherichia coli.* An **operon** is a segment of DNA containing a cluster of genes that are transcribed as a unit. The *lac* operon, shown in figure 12.13, consists of both protein-encoding genes (labeled genes 1, 2, and 3, which code for enzymes involved in breaking down the sugar lactose) and associated regulatory elements—the operator, the promoter, and other binding sites. When *E. coli* encounters the sugar lactose, a form of the sugar called allolactose binds to the repressor protein and induces a twist in its shape that causes the repressor to fall from the DNA (figure 12.13*b*); RNA polymerase, no longer blocked, starts to transcribe the genes needed to break down the lactose to get energy.

Activators. Because RNA polymerase binds to a specific promoter site on one strand of the DNA double helix, it is necessary that the DNA double helix unzip in the vicinity of this site for the polymerase protein to be able to sit down properly. This unzipping requires the assistance of a regulatory protein called an activator that binds to the DNA nearby and helps it unwind. Cells can turn the genes on and off by binding "signal" molecules to this activator protein. In the *lac* operon, a protein called catabolite activator protein (CAP) acts as an activator. CAP has to bind a signal molecule, cAMP, before it can associate with the DNA. Once the CAP/cAMP complex forms, as seen in figure 12.14, it binds to the DNA and makes the promoter more accessible to RNA polymerase.

Recall from the discussion on page 196 that the DNA is unwound by an enzyme called helicase. When the DNA is unwound, DNA polymerase has access to the DNA and can replicate it. Similarly, an activator allows RNA polymerase access to the gene.

Why bother with activators? Imagine if you had to eat every time you encountered food! Activator proteins enable a cell to cope with this sort of problem. Activators and repressors work together to control transcription. To understand how, let's consider the *lac* operon again, now shown in figure 12.15. When a bacterium encounters the sugar lactose, it may already have lots of energy in the form of glucose, as shown in panel ❶, and so does not need to break down more lactose. CAP can bind and activate gene transcription only when glucose levels are low. Because RNA polymerase requires the activator to function, the *lac* operon is not expressed. Also, if glucose is present and lactose is absent, not only is the activator CAP unable to bind, but also a repressor blocks the promoter, as shown in panel ❷. In the absence of both glucose and lactose, cAMP, the "low glucose" signal molecule (the green pie-shaped piece in panels ❸ and ❹) binds to CAP, and CAP is able to bind to the DNA. However, the repressor is still blocking transcription, as shown in panel ❸. When glucose is absent and lactose is present, then, and only then, the repressor is removed, the activator (CAP) is bound, and transcription proceeds, as shown in panel ❹.

Putting the Concept to Work

If lactose is added to their growth medium, bacterial cells that had contained no lactose-metabolizing enzymes abruptly possess them. How does this "enzyme induction" occur?

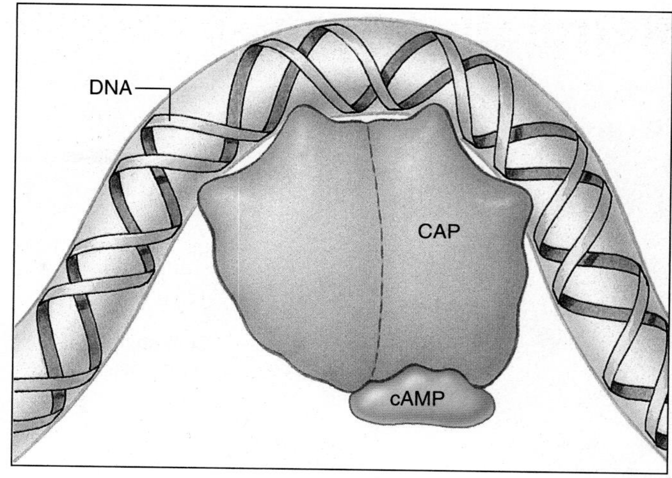

Figure 12.14 How an activator works.

Binding of the catabolite activator protein complex to DNA causes the DNA to bend around it. This increases the activity of RNA polymerase.

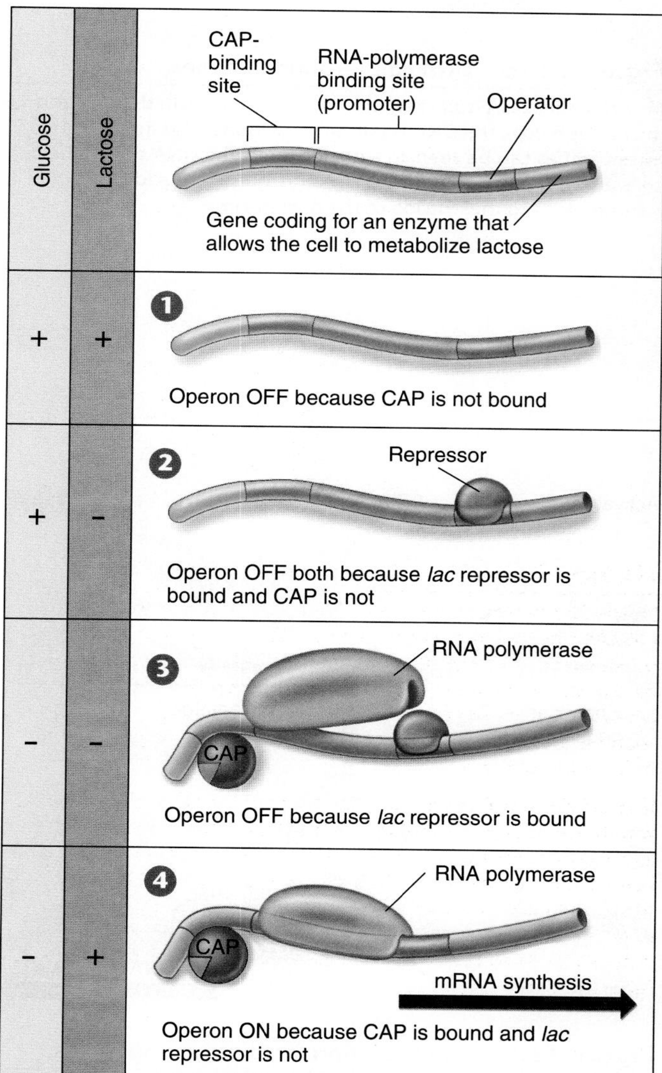

Figure 12.15 Activators and repressors at the *lac* operon.

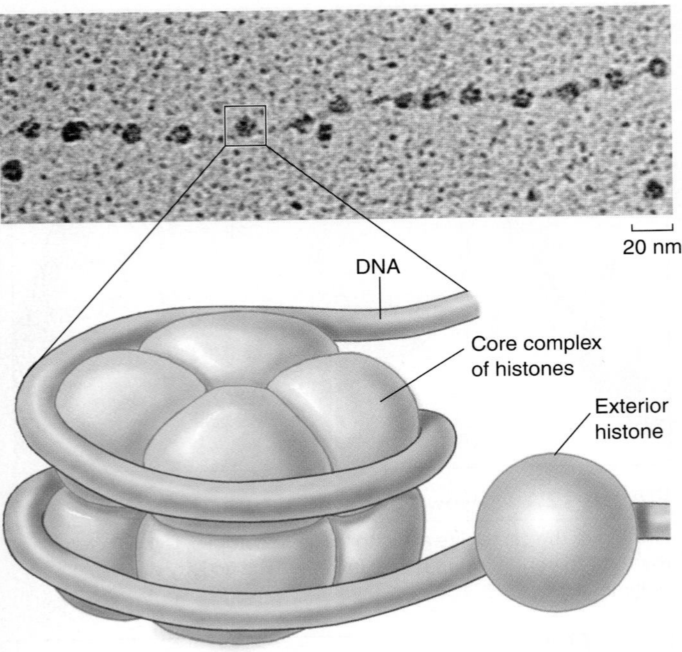

Figure 12.16 DNA coils around histones.

In chromatin, DNA is packaged into nucleosomes. In the electron micrograph (*top*), the DNA is partially unwound, and individual nucleosomes can be seen. In a nucleosome, the DNA double helix coils around a core complex of eight histones; one additional histone binds to the outside of the nucleosome.

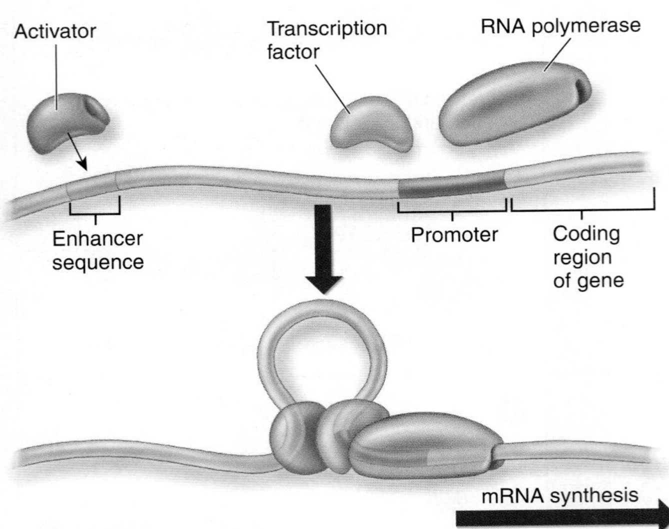

Figure 12.17 Transcription factors and enhancers.

The activator binding site, or enhancer, is often located far from the gene. The binding of an activator protein to the transcription factor is required for polymerase initiation.

12.6 Transcriptional Control in Eukaryotes

LEARNING OBJECTIVE 12.6.1 Describe the regulatory roles of histones and DNA methylation in eukaryotes.

Chromatin Structure

In multicellular organisms with relatively constant internal environments, the primary function of gene control in a cell is to participate in regulating the body as a whole. Some of these changes in gene expression compensate for changes in the physiological condition of the body. Others mediate the decisions that ultimately produce the body, ensuring that the right genes are expressed in the right cells at the right time during development.

The first hurdle faced by RNA polymerase in transcribing a eukaryotic gene is gaining access to it. As described in chapter 8, eukaryotic chromosomes consist of chromatin, a complex of DNA and protein. In chromatin, the DNA is packaged with histone proteins into nucleosomes (figure 12.16). During mitosis, nucleosomes wind, twist, and coil into chromosomes, but even during interphase when transcription is occurring, some sections of DNA remain as part of nucleosomes. These nucleosomes seem to block the binding of RNA polymerase and other proteins called transcription factors to the promoter site. Histones can be chemically modified to result in a greater condensation of the chromatin, making it even less accessible. Another chemical modification of the DNA—adding a methyl group ($—CH_3$) to cytosine nucleotides—blocks accidental transcription of "turned-off" genes. DNA methylation ensures that once a gene is turned off, it stays off.

Putting the Concept to Work

Do you think methylated genes would be found in nucleosomes?

Transcription Factors and Enhancers

LEARNING OBJECTIVE 12.6.2 Describe how transcription factors and enhancers regulate gene expression in eukaryotes.

Eukaryotic transcription requires not only the RNA polymerase molecule, but also a variety of other proteins, called *transcription factors,* that interact with the polymerase to form an *initiation complex.* Transcription factors are necessary for the assembly of the initiation complex and recruitment of RNA polymerase to a promoter (figure 12.17).

Although prokaryotic gene control sites are positioned immediately upstream of the coding region, eukaryotes can have regulatory sites located far from the gene. Eukaryotic activators can bind at distant sites called **enhancers,** and DNA bending to form a loop brings the activator in contact with the RNA polymerase/initiation complex (see figure 12.17).

Complex transcriptional control is only one aspect of gene regulation in eukaryotes. Other processes associated with translation, such as gene silencing, protein synthesis, and post-translational modification, are described in *Essential Biological Process 12B* and provide a cell the ability to produce finely graded responses to environmental and developmental signals.

Putting the Concept to Work

If an enhancer is located far from a gene, how can it control the gene's transcription?

Essential Biological Process 12B

Control of Eukaryotic Gene Expression

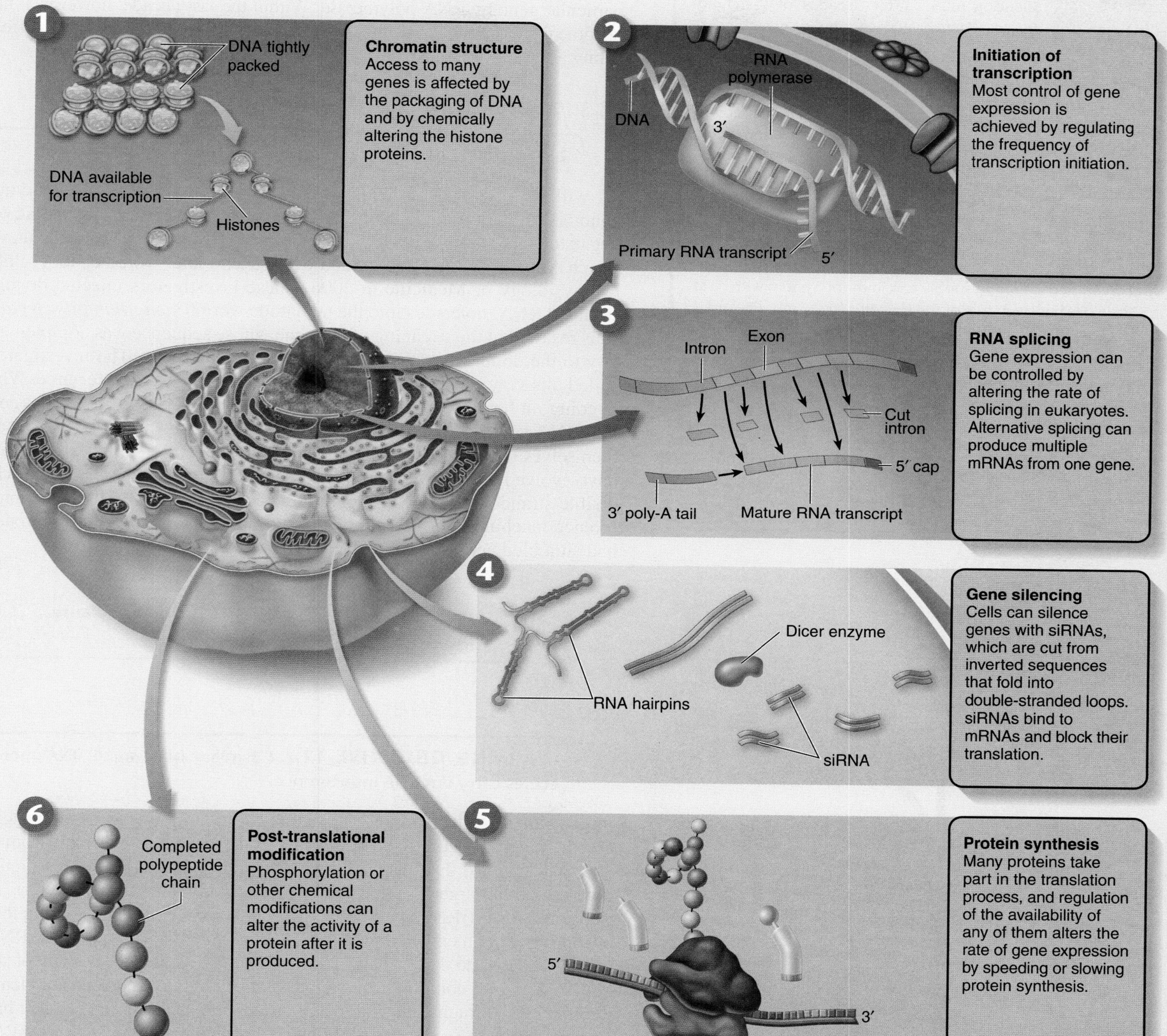

1
DNA tightly packed
DNA available for transcription
Histones
Chromatin structure
Access to many genes is affected by the packaging of DNA and by chemically altering the histone proteins.
2
RNA polymerase
DNA
3′
Primary RNA transcript
5′
Initiation of transcription
Most control of gene expression is achieved by regulating the frequency of transcription initiation.
3
Intron
Exon
Cut intron
5′ cap
3′ poly-A tail
Mature RNA transcript
RNA splicing
Gene expression can be controlled by altering the rate of splicing in eukaryotes. Alternative splicing can produce multiple mRNAs from one gene.
4
Dicer enzyme
RNA hairpins
siRNA
Gene silencing
Cells can silence genes with siRNAs, which are cut from inverted sequences that fold into double-stranded loops. siRNAs bind to mRNAs and block their translation.
5
5′
3′
Protein synthesis
Many proteins take part in the translation process, and regulation of the availability of any of them alters the rate of gene expression by speeding or slowing protein synthesis.
6
Completed polypeptide chain
Post-translational modification
Phosphorylation or other chemical modifications can alter the activity of a protein after it is produced.

IN THE NEWS

Silencing AIDS. After decades of searching unsuccessfully for an effective AIDS vaccine, researchers are turning to other approaches. One of the most promising centers on a 42-year-old American resident of Germany, who in 2008 was completely cured of AIDS. How? First, his immune system was wiped out with radiation and drugs, then he received blood stem cells (which make both circulating blood cells and immune system cells) from a person homozygous for a gene mutation known as *delta 32*. This mutation destroys the cell surface receptor called CCR5 that allows HIV to invade the immune system, so that people homozygous for it are immune to HIV infection and AIDS. Because the patient's own blood stem cells had been destroyed, these new ones reconstituted his blood supply and immune system with *delta 32* cells. He has been free of the HIV virus for 20 months and it appears he has been permanently cured of AIDS. Wiping out a person's immune system is far too dangerous as a general therapy (10%–30% die), but the success in this instance has encouraged researchers to try using RNA "scissors" as described on this page to cut out the *delta 32* gene from a patient's own blood stem cells and reinject them after wiping out only the patient's blood stem cells, not the entire immune system. Researchers report that the concept is working in monkeys.

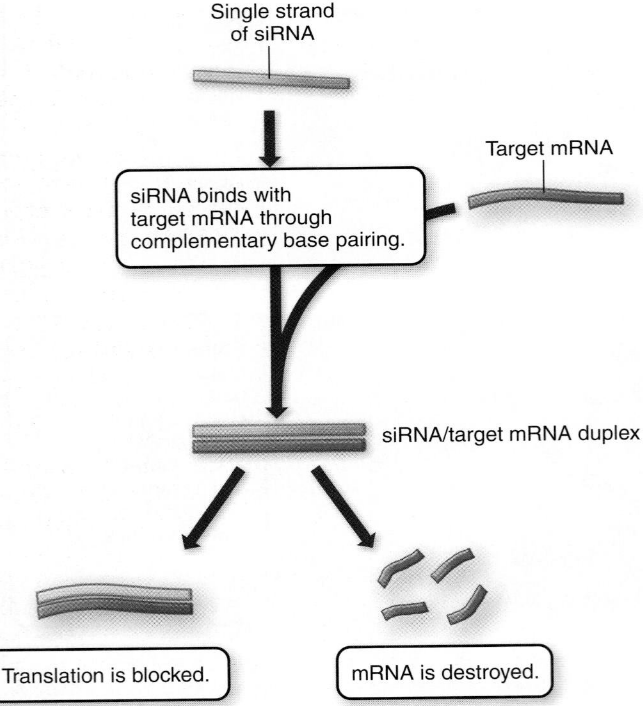

Figure 12.18 RNA interference.

RNA interference stops gene expression either by blocking the translation of the gene (on the left) or by targeting the mRNA for destruction before it can be translated.

12.7 RNA-Level Control

Thus far we have discussed gene regulation entirely in terms of proteins that regulate the start of transcription by blocking or activating the "reading" of a particular gene by RNA polymerase. Within the last decade, however, it has become increasingly clear that RNA molecules also regulate gene expression, acting after transcription as a second equally important level of control.

Discovery of RNA Interference

LEARNING OBJECTIVE 12.7.1 Define RNA interference.

As will be discussed in detail in chapter 13, the bulk of the eukaryotic genome is not translated into proteins. This finding was puzzling at first, but began to make sense in 1998, when a simple experiment was carried out, for which Americans Andrew Fire and Craig Mello later won the Nobel Prize in Physiology or Medicine in 2006. These investigators injected double-stranded RNA molecules into the nematode worm *Caenorhabditis elegans*. This resulted in the silencing of the gene whose sequence was complementary to the double-stranded RNA, and of no other gene. The investigators called this very specific effect **gene silencing,** or **RNA interference.** What is going on here? A group of viruses called RNA viruses, those that contain RNA as their hereditary storage molecule rather than DNA, replicate themselves through double-stranded intermediates. RNA interference may have evolved as a cellular defense mechanism against these viruses with double-stranded viral RNAs being targeted for destruction by RNA interference machinery. Without intending to do so, the nematode researchers had stumbled across this defense.

Putting the Concept to Work

How can attacking double-stranded DNA provide a defense against RNA viruses?

How RNA Interference Works

LEARNING OBJECTIVE 12.7.2 Explain how small RNA molecules carry out RNA interference.

Investigating interference, researchers noted that in the process of silencing a gene, plants produced short RNA molecules (ranging in length from 21 to 28 nucleotides) that matched the gene being silenced. Earlier researchers focusing on far larger messenger RNA (mRNA), transfer RNA (tRNA), and ribosomal RNA (rRNA) had not noticed these far smaller bits, tossing them out during experiments. These bits of RNA are called "small interfering RNA" or siRNA. How do these small fragments of RNA silence the activity of specific genes? In a complex way we are just beginning to understand clearly, the small RNA fragments bind to any mRNA molecules in the cell that have a complementary sequence. Silencing of the gene that produced this mRNA is achieved in one of two ways (figure 12.18): either the expression of the mRNA is inhibited by blocking its translation into protein, or the mRNA is simply destroyed. In either case, the specific gene that produced that mRNA fails to be expressed—it is silenced.

Putting the Concept to Work

If RNA is not double-stranded, how can siRNA bind to mRNA?

Biology and Staying Healthy

Silencing Genes to Treat Disease

The recent discovery that eukaryotes control their genes by selectively "silencing" particular gene transcripts has electrified biologists, as it opens exciting possibilities for treating disease and infection. Many diseases are caused by expression of one or more genes. AIDS for example requires the expression of several genes of the HIV virus. Many chronic human diseases result from excessively active genes. What if doctors could somehow shut these genes off?

The idea is simple. If you can isolate a gene involved in the disorder and determine its sequence, then in principle you could synthesize an RNA molecule with the sequence of the opposite or "antisense" strand. This RNA would thus have a sequence complementary to the messenger RNA produced by that gene. Introduced into cells, this synthesized RNA might be able to bind to the mRNA, creating a double-stranded RNA that could not be read by ribosomes. If an antisense therapy could be made to work and be delivered practically and inexpensively, the AIDS epidemic could be halted in its tracks. Indeed, any viral infection could be combatted in this way. Influenza is perhaps the greatest killer of all infectious diseases. A workable antisense therapy could provide a means of stamping out a bird flu epidemic before the virus spreads.

By far the most exciting promise of antisense gene silencing therapy is the possibility of a practical cancer therapy. Discussed in chapter 8, cancer kills more Americans than any other disease. We now know in considerable detail how cancer comes about. It results from damage to genes that regulate the cell cycle. The great promise of RNA gene silencing therapy comes from those cancer-causing gene mutations that increase the effectiveness of one or more "divide" signals. If these mutant genes could be silenced, the cancer could be shut down.

The prospect of using complementary RNA to silence troublesome genes has gotten a huge boost in the last few years from the discovery of a unique virus defense system in eukaryotes. In order to protect themselves from RNA virus infection, cells have a complex system for detecting, attacking, and destroying viral RNA. The system takes advantage of a subtle vulnerability of the infecting virus: at some point, in order to multiply within the infected cell, the virus must express its genes—it must make complementary copies of them that can serve as messenger RNAs to direct production of viral proteins. At that point, while the viral RNA molecule is double-stranded, the virus is vulnerable to attack: at no place in the cell is double-stranded RNA usually found, so by targeting double-stranded RNAs for immediate destruction, a cell can defeat viral infections.

Silencing genes with complementary RNA, dubbed "RNA interference," offers the exciting hope that successful treatment of many diseases may be literally at our doorstep. First, however, scientists must figure out how to make RNA interference therapies work. They are facing some formidable technical problems, not the least of which is to find a way to deliver the interfering RNA to, and into, the target cells. The problem is that RNA is rapidly broken down in the

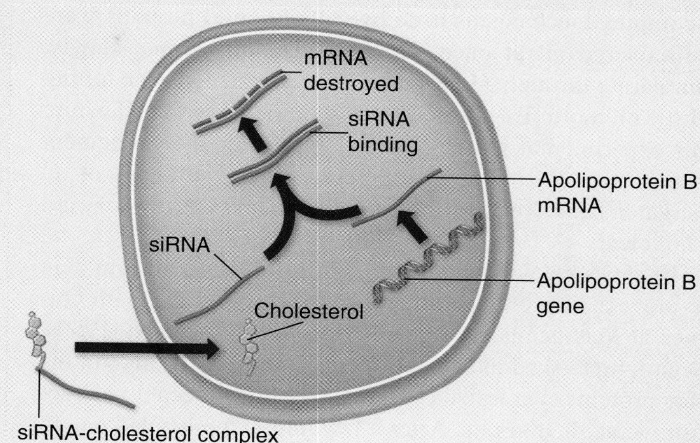

bloodstream, and most of the body's cells don't readily absorb it, even if it does reach them. Some researchers are attempting to package the RNA into viruses, although gene therapies that have attempted this approach can trigger an immune response and could even cause cancer. Gene therapy researchers have been seeking safer virus gene-delivery vehicles; what they learn will surely be put to good effect.

One interesting alternative approach is to modify the RNA to protect it and make it more easily taken up by cells. This work focuses on the mRNA that encodes apolipoprotein B, a molecule involved in the metabolism of cholesterol. High levels of apolipoprotein are found in people with high levels of cholesterol, associated with increased risk of coronary heart disease. Interfering RNAs that target apolipoprotein B mRNA result in destruction of the mRNA, and lower levels of cholesterol. To effectively deliver it to the body's tissues, researchers simply attached a molecule of cholesterol to each interfering RNA molecule (see diagram above). Levels of apolipoprotein B were reduced 50–70%, and blood cholesterol levels plummeted downward, to the same levels seen in cells from which the apolipoprotein B gene had been deleted. It is not clear if this approach will work for many other RNAs, but it looks promising.

A second major problem confronting those seeking to develop successful therapies based on RNA silencing of troublesome genes is one of specificity. It is very important that only the target gene be silenced. Before carrying out clinical trials involving large numbers of people, it is imperative that we be sure the interfering RNA will not shut down vital human genes as well as the targeted virus or cancer genes. Some studies suggest this will not be a problem, while in others, a range of "off-target" genes seem to be affected. This possibility will have to be carefully evaluated for each new therapy being developed.

Inquiry & Analysis

Building Proteins in a Test Tube

The complex mechanisms used by cells to build proteins were not discovered all at once. Our understanding came slowly, accumulating through a long series of experiments, each telling us a little bit more. To gain some sense of the incremental nature of this experimental journey, and to appreciate the excitement that each step gave, it is useful to step into the shoes of an investigator back when little was known and the way forward was not clear.

The shoes we will step into are those of Paul Zamecnik, an early pioneer in protein synthesis research. Working with colleagues at Massachusetts General Hospital in the early 1950s, Zamecnik first asked the most direct of questions: Where in the cell are proteins synthesized? To find out, they injected radioactive amino acids into rats. After a few hours, the labeled amino acids could be found as part of newly made proteins in the livers of the rats. And, if the livers were removed and checked only minutes after injection, radioactive-labeled proteins were found only associated with small particles in the cytoplasm. Composed of protein and RNA, these particles, later named ribosomes, had been discovered years earlier by electron microscope studies of cell components. This experiment identified them as the sites of protein synthesis in the cell.

After several years of trial-and-error tinkering, Zamecnik and his colleagues had worked out a "cell-free" protein-synthesis system that would lead to the synthesis of proteins in a test tube. It included ribosomes, mRNA, and ATP to provide energy. It also included a collection of required soluble "factors" isolated from homogenized rat cells that somehow worked with the ribosome to get the job done. When Zamecnik's team characterized these required factors, they found most of them to be proteins, as expected, but also present in the mix was a small RNA, very unexpected.

To see what this small RNA was doing, they performed the following experiment. In a test tube, they added various amounts of ^{14}C-leucine (that is, the radioactively labeled amino acid leucine) to the cell-free system containing the soluble factors, ribosomes, and ATP. After waiting a bit, they then isolated the small RNA from the mixture and checked it for radioactivity. You can see the results in graph (a) above.

In a follow-up experiment, they mixed the radioactive leucine-small RNA complex that this experiment had generated with cell extracts containing intact endoplasmic reticulum (that is, a cell system of ribosomes on membranes quite capable of making protein). Looking to see where the radioactive label now went, they then isolated the newly-made protein [red in graph (b)] as well as the small RNA [blue in graph (b)].

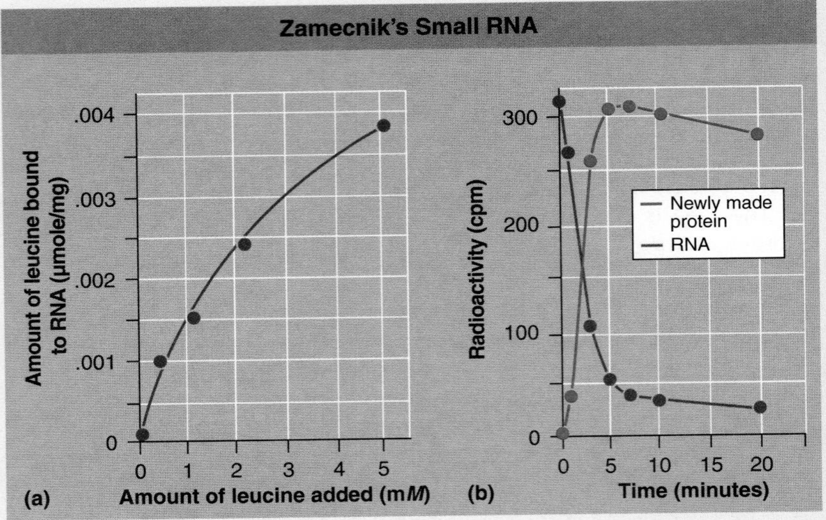

Analysis

EXPERIMENT A, shown in graph (a)

1. **Interpreting Data** Does the amount of leucine added to the test tube have an effect on the amount of leucine found bound to the small RNA?
2. **Making Inferences** Is the amount of leucine bound to small RNA proportional to the amount of leucine added to the mixture?
3. **Drawing Conclusions** Can you reasonably conclude from this result that the amino acid leucine is binding to the small RNA?

EXPERIMENT B, shown in graph (b)

1. **Interpreting Data**
   a. Monitoring radioactivity for 20 minutes after the addition of the radioactive leucine-small RNA complex to the cell extract, what happens to the level of radioactivity in the small RNA (blue)?
   b. Over the same period, what happens to the level of radioactivity in the newly made protein (red)?
2. **Making Inferences** Is the same amount of radioactivity being lost from the small RNA that is being gained by the newly made protein?
3. **Drawing Conclusions**
   a. Is it reasonable to conclude that the small RNA is donating its amino acid to the growing protein? [Hint: As a result of this experiment, the small RNA was called transfer RNA.]
   b. If you were to isolate the protein from this experiment made after 20 minutes, which amino acids would be radioactively labeled? Explain.

Summary of Learning Outcomes

From Gene to Protein

The Central Dogma

12.1.1 DNA is the storage site of genetic information in the cell. The process of gene expression, DNA to RNA to protein, is called the central dogma, shown here from **figure 12.1.**

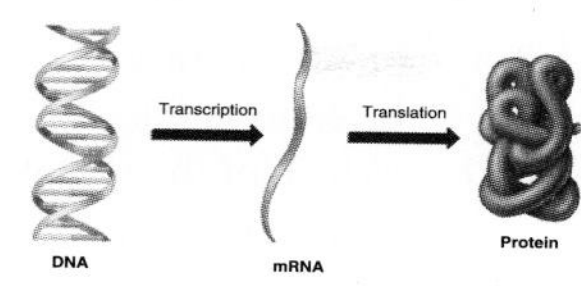

- Gene expression occurs in two stages using different types of RNA: transcription, where an mRNA copy is made from the DNA, and translation, where the information on the mRNA is translated into a protein using rRNA and tRNA.

Transcription

12.2.1 Transcription is the process of reading the DNA message. In transcription, DNA serves as a template for mRNA synthesis by an enzyme called RNA polymerase. RNA polymerase binds to one strand of the DNA at a site called the promoter. RNA polymerase adds complementary nucleotides onto the growing mRNA.

Translation

12.3.1 The message within the mRNA is coded in its sequence of nucleotides, which are read in three nucleotide units called codons. Codons correspond to particular amino acids. The rules that govern the translation of codons on the mRNA into amino acids are called the genetic code.

12.3.2 In translation, the mRNA carries the message to the cytoplasm. rRNA combines with proteins to form a structure called a ribosome, the platform on which proteins are assembled.

- A ribosome contains a small and a large subunit. Translation begins when the mRNA binds to the small ribosomal subunit, which triggers the binding of the large subunit to the small subunit, forming a complete ribosome. The ribosome has three sites, called A, P, and E, to which a third type of RNA, called transfer RNA (tRNA), binds.
- The tRNA molecules, like one shown here from **figure 12.7,** carry amino acids to the ribosome to build the polypeptide chain. The amino acid that attaches to the tRNA is determined by a three-nucleotide sequence on the tRNA called the anticodon.

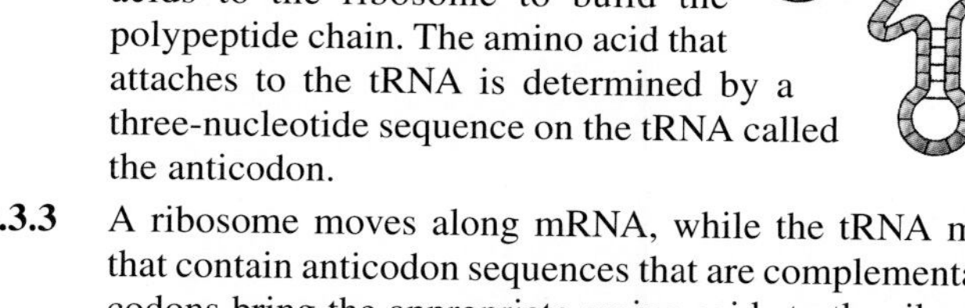

12.3.3 A ribosome moves along mRNA, while the tRNA molecules that contain anticodon sequences that are complementary to the codons bring the appropriate amino acids to the ribosome. An incoming tRNA first attaches to the A site, then moves to the P and E sites as the ribosome moves, leaving the A site open for the next tRNA. The amino acids add to the growing polypeptide chain.

- When a "stop" codon is reached, the ribosome dissociates and releases the polypeptide into the cell.

Gene Expression

12.4.1 Prokaryotic genes are contained within a stretch of DNA that is transcribed and translated in its entirety.

- Eukaryotic genes are fragmented, containing coding regions called exons, and noncoding regions called introns. The entire eukaryotic gene is transcribed into RNA, but the introns are spliced out before translation (shown here from **figure 12.10**).
- Exons can be spliced together in different ways, a process called alternative splicing, producing different protein products from the same sections of DNA.

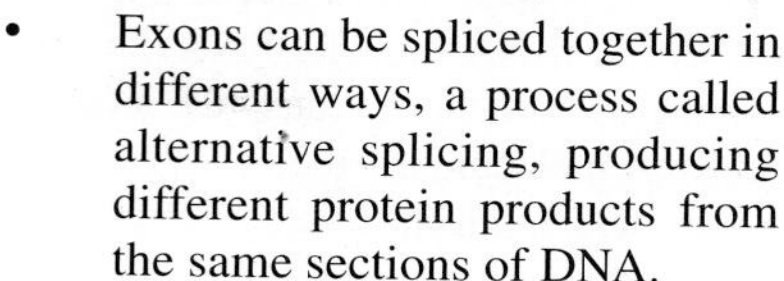

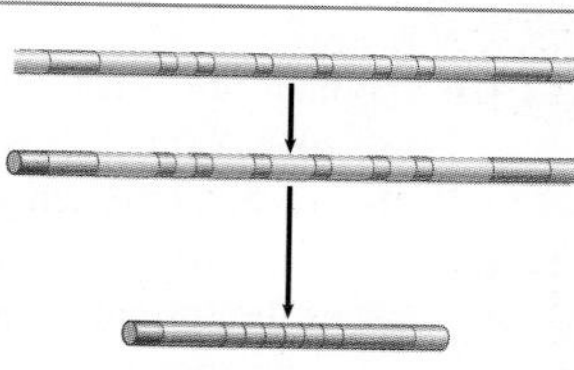

12.4.2 The process of protein synthesis is different in eukaryotes compared to prokaryotes. In prokaryotes, transcription and translation can occur simultaneously. Ribosomes attach to the mRNA as it is transcribed, beginning translation before transcription is completed. In eukaryotes, the RNA transcript is first produced and then processed (introns spliced out) in the nucleus. The mRNA then travels to the cytoplasm, where it is translated into a polypeptide.

Regulating Gene Expression

Transcriptional Control in Prokaryotes

12.5.1 Prokaryotes control the expression of genes by determining when they are transcribed.

12.5.2 In prokaryotic cells, genes are turned off when a repressor protein binds to a site called the operator and blocks the promoter, as shown here from **figure 12.13.**

- Some genes can be turned on only when a protein called an activator binds to the DNA and opens up the double helix so that RNA polymerase can bind to the promoter.
- The *lac* operon contains a cluster of genes that are involved in the breakdown of the sugar lactose. When the proteins produced by the *lac* operon genes are needed, an inducer molecule will bind to the repressor protein so it can't attach to the DNA, thereby freeing the promoter so that RNA polymerase can bind.
- The *lac* operon is also controlled by an activator. The activator alters the shape of DNA, which allows RNA polymerase to bind to the DNA. It is only when the activator binds to the DNA and the repressor is removed that the RNA polymerase can bind to the promoter.

Transcriptional Control in Eukaryotes

12.6.1 The coiling of DNA around histones restricts RNA polymerase's access to the DNA. Controlling gene expression may involve chemical modification of histones or methylation of the DNA itself that keeps a gene turned off.

12.6.2 In eukaryotic cells, transcription requires the binding of transcription factors before RNA polymerase can bind to the promoter. Eukaryotic genes are controlled from distant locations called enhancers. A regulatory protein binds to the enhancer region far from the gene and the DNA forms a loop, as shown here from **figure 12.17,** bringing the distant enhancer region into contact with the transcription factors. Eukaryotic cells have several levels of gene expression.

RNA-Level Control

12.7.1 RNA interference is gene silencing by blocking translation.

12.7.2 In RNA interference small bits of RNA, called siRNA, bind to mRNA in the cytoplasm, blocking translation or destroying mRNA.

Test Your Understanding

12.1.1 Which of the following is not a type of RNA?
a. nRNA (nuclear RNA) c. rRNA (ribosomal RNA)
b. mRNA (messenger RNA) d. tRNA (transfer RNA)

12.1.1 The site where RNA polymerase attaches to the DNA molecule to start the formation of an RNA molecule is called
a. a promoter. c. an intron.
b. an exon. d. an enhancer.

12.2.1 The process of obtaining a copy of the information in a gene as a strand of messenger RNA is called
a. polymerase. c. transcription.
b. expression. d. translation.

12.3.1 Each amino acid in a polypeptide is specified by
a. an enhancer. c. an rRNA molecule.
b. a promoter. d. a codon.

12.3.1 Which of the following statements is correct about the genetic code?
a. Every codon encodes an amino acid.
b. Each amino acid is encoded by only one codon.
c. A codon consists of three nucleotides.
d. A codon and its complementary anticodon have the same sequences.

12.3.2 If an mRNA codon reads UAC, its complementary anticodon will be
a. TUC. c. AUG.
b. ATG. d. UAC.

12.3.3 The process of taking the information on a strand of messenger RNA and building an amino acid chain, which will become all or part of a protein molecule, is called
a. polymerase. c. transcription.
b. expression. d. translation.

12.4.1 Which of the following statements is correct about eukaryotic gene expression?
a. mRNAs must have introns spliced out.
b. mRNAs contain the transcript of only one gene.
c. Introns make up 95% of a typical human gene.
d. All of the above.

12.5.1 Which of the following accurately describes gene regulation in prokaryotic cells?
a. All genes are on all the time in all cells, making the needed amino acid sequences.
b. Some genes are always off unless a promoter turns them on.
c. Some genes are always on unless a promoter turns them off.
d. Some genes remain off as long as a repressor is bound.

12.6.2 Which of the following is *not* a mechanism of controlling gene expression in eukaryotic cells?
a. blocking translation with siRNA
b. activating an enhancer
c. translating a gene as it is being transcribed
d. alternative splicing of the primary RNA transcript

Apply Your Understanding

12.1.1 This figure of the central dogma represents the general process of gene expression in prokaryotes and eukaryotes. However, the process is slightly more complex in eukaryotic cells. What step is missing here that occurs in eukaryotic cells but not in prokaryotic cells?

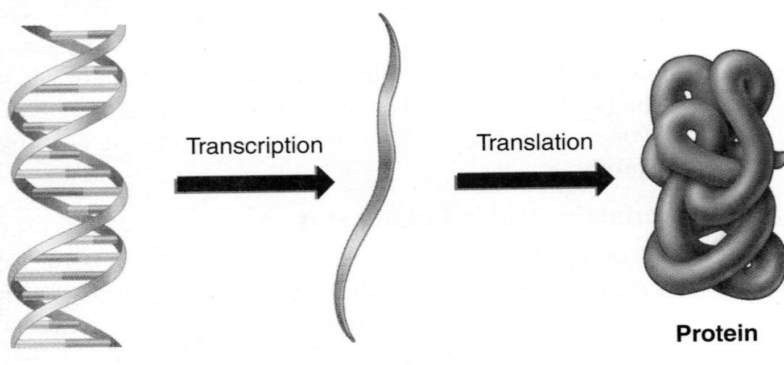

12.5.2 Can genes 1, 2, and 3 be transcribed? What would happen if an inducer molecule were present in the cell?

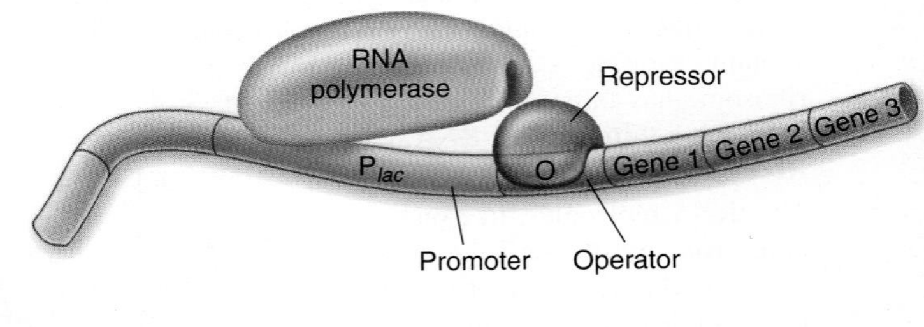

Synthesize What You Have Learned

12.3.1 On the television program *The X Files*, Agent Scully discovers an extraterrestrial life form that has a DNA genome like ours, but with a four-letter genetic code instead of the triplet genetic code that we earthlings possess. How many different amino acids would this extraterrestrial code be able to specify (assuming there were that many kinds of amino acids available on the extraterrestrial planet)? Why do you think the terrestrial code allows 64 combinations, when only 22 amino acids are common here on earth? Why do you think only 20 of them are common in proteins here on earth?

12.3.1 The nucleotide sequence of a hypothetical gene is:

TACATACTTAGTTACGTCGCCCGGAAATAT

a. What will be the sequence on the mRNA when it is transcribed?
b. What will be the amino acid sequence of the protein when it's translated?
c. What would happen to the amino acid chain if the highlighted nucleotide underwent a mutation and was changed to an A nucleotide?

12.5.1 What would happen if all the genes in a cell were always active?

Chapter 14

Evolution and Natural Selection

CHAPTER AT A GLANCE

Evolution
14.1 Darwin's Voyage on HMS *Beagle*
14.2 Darwin's Evidence
14.3 The Theory of Natural Selection

Darwin's Finches: Evolution in Action
14.4 The Beaks of Darwin's Finches
14.5 How Natural Selection Produces Diversity

The Theory of Evolution
14.6 The Evidence for Evolution
Today's Biology: Darwin and Moby Dick
14.7 Evolution's Critics
Today's Biology: Putting Intelligent Design to the Test

How Populations Evolve
14.8 Genetic Change in Populations
14.9 Agents of Evolution

Adaptation Within Populations
14.10 Sickle-Cell Disease
14.11 Peppered Moths and Industrial Melanism
14.12 Selection on Color in Guppies
Author's Corner: Are Bird-Killing Cats Nature's Way of Making Better Birds?

How Species Form
14.13 The Biological Species Concept
14.14 Isolating Mechanisms

Inquiry & Analysis: Does Natural Selection Act on Enzyme Polymorphism?

Evolution

Figure 14.1 The theory of evolution by natural selection was proposed by Charles Darwin.

This rediscovered photograph appears to be the last ever taken of the great biologist. It was taken in 1881, the year before Darwin died.

14.1 Darwin's Voyage on HMS *Beagle*

LEARNING OBJECTIVE 14.1.1 Recount the story of Darwin's voyage on the *Beagle*.

The great diversity of life on earth—ranging from bacteria to elephants and roses—is the result of a long process of **evolution,** the change that occurs in organisms' characteristics through time. In 1859 the English naturalist Charles Darwin (1809–82; figure 14.1) first suggested an explanation for why evolution occurs, a process he called *natural selection*. Biologists soon became convinced Darwin was right and now consider evolution one of the central concepts of the science of biology. In this chapter we examine Darwin and evolution in detail, as the concepts we encounter will provide a solid foundation for your exploration of the living world.

The theory of evolution proposes that a population can change over time, sometimes forming a new species. A **species** is a group of populations that possess similar characteristics and whose members can interbreed and produce fertile offspring. This famous theory provides a good example of how a scientist develops a hypothesis—in this case, a hypothesis of how evolution occurs—and how, after much testing, the hypothesis is eventually accepted as a theory.

Charles Robert Darwin was an English naturalist who, after years of study and observation, wrote in 1859 one of the most famous and influential books of all time. This book, *On the Origin of Species by Means of Natural Selection, or The Preservation of Favoured Races in the Struggle for Life,* created a sensation when it was published, and the ideas Darwin expressed in it have played a central role in the development of human thought ever since.

In Darwin's time, most people believed that the various kinds of organisms and their individual structures resulted from direct actions of the Creator. Species were thought to be specially created and unchangeable over the course of time. In contrast to these views, a number of earlier philosophers had presented the view that living things must have changed during the history of life on earth. Darwin proposed a concept he called natural selection as a coherent, logical explanation for this process. Darwin's book, as its title indicates, presented a conclusion that differed sharply from conventional wisdom. Although his theory did not challenge the existence of a Divine Creator, Darwin argued that this Creator did not simply create things and then leave them forever unchanged. Instead, Darwin's God expressed Himself through the operation of natural laws that produced change over time—evolution.

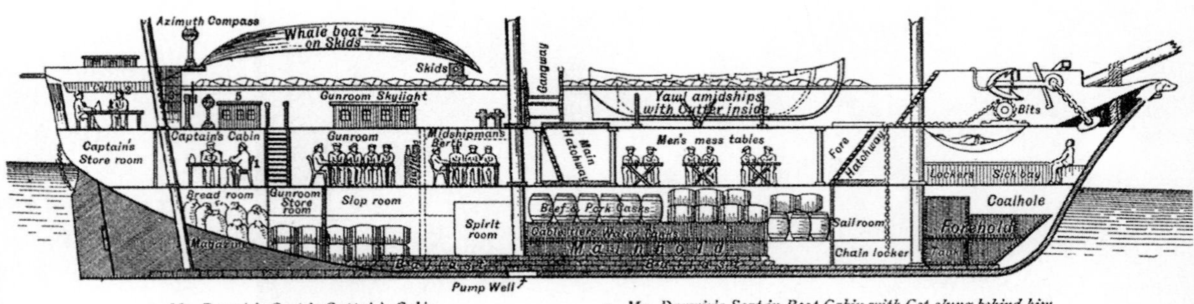

Figure 14.2 Cross section of HMS *Beagle*.

HMS *Beagle*, a 10-gun brig of 242 tons, only 90 feet in length, had a crew of 74 people! After he first saw the ship, Darwin wrote to his college professor Henslow: "The absolute want of room is an evil that nothing can surmount."

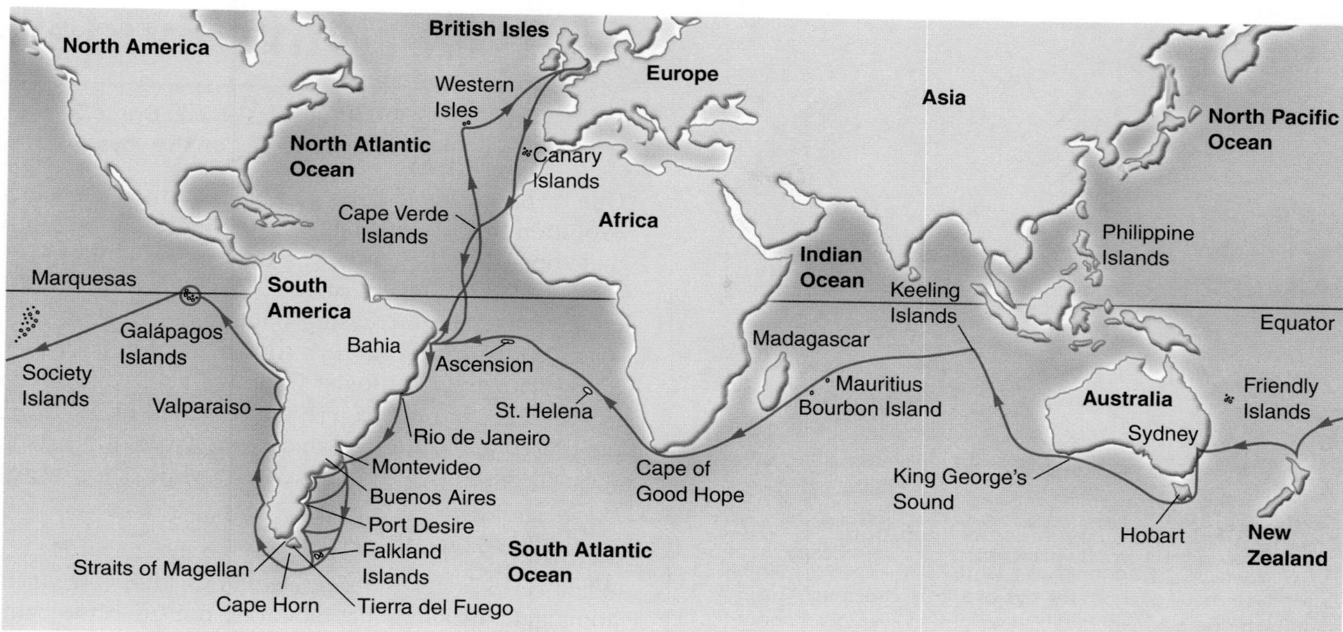

Figure 14.3 **The five-year voyage of HMS *Beagle*.**

Although the ship sailed around the world, most of the time was spent exploring the coasts and coastal islands of South America, such as the Galápagos Islands. Darwin's studies of the animals of these islands played a key role in the eventual development of his theory of evolution by means of natural selection.

IMPLICATION FOR YOU During Darwin's five years on HMS *Beagle,* he was confined to a ship that crammed 74 people into a very small space for months at a time. Have you ever lived in very tight quarters with others who were not members of your own family? If you were living in Darwin's time, would you have wanted to take this trip, mixing the promise of adventure with this very real sacrifice of privacy?

The story of Darwin and his theory begins in 1831, when he was 22 years old. The small British naval vessel HMS *Beagle* (figure 14.2) was about to set sail on a five-year navigational mapping expedition around the coasts of South America. The red arrows in figure 14.3 indicate the route taken by HMS *Beagle*. The young (26-year-old) captain of HMS *Beagle,* unable by British naval tradition to have social contact with his crew, and anticipating a voyage that would last many years, wanted a gentleman companion, someone to talk to. Indeed, the *Beagle*'s previous skipper had broken down and shot himself to death after three solitary years away from home.

On the recommendation of one of his professors at Cambridge University, Darwin, the son of a wealthy doctor and very much a gentleman, was selected to serve as the captain's companion, primarily to share his table at mealtime during every shipboard dinner of the long voyage. Darwin paid his own expenses, and even brought along a manservant.

Darwin took on the role of ship's naturalist (the official naturalist, a man named Robert McKormick, left the ship before the first year was out). During this long voyage, Darwin had the chance to study a wide variety of plants and animals on continents and islands and in distant seas. He was able to explore the biological richness of the tropical forests, examine extraordinary fossils at the southern tip of South America, and observe the remarkable series of related forms of life on the **Galápagos Islands.**

When Darwin returned from the voyage at the age of 27, he began a long period of study and contemplation. During the next 10 years, he published important books on several different subjects, including the formation of oceanic islands from coral reefs and the geology of South America. He then devoted eight years to a detailed study of barnacles, a group of small shelled marine animals that inhabit rocks and pilings, eventually writing a four-volume work on their classification and natural history. In 1842, Darwin and his family moved out of London to a country home at Down, in the county of Kent. In these pleasant surroundings, Darwin lived, studied, and wrote for the next 40 years.

Putting the Concept to Work

How long after his original voyage on HMS *Beagle* did Darwin publish *On the Origin of Species?*

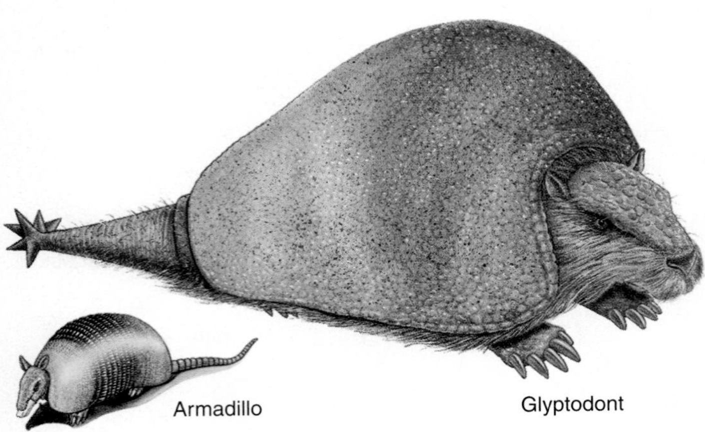

Figure 14.4 Fossil evidence of evolution.

The now-extinct glyptodont was a large 2,000-kilogram South American armadillo (about the size of a small car), much larger than the modern armadillo, which weighs an average of about 4.5 kilograms and is about the size of a house cat. The similarity of fossils such as the glyptodonts to living organisms found in the same regions suggested to Darwin that evolution had taken place.

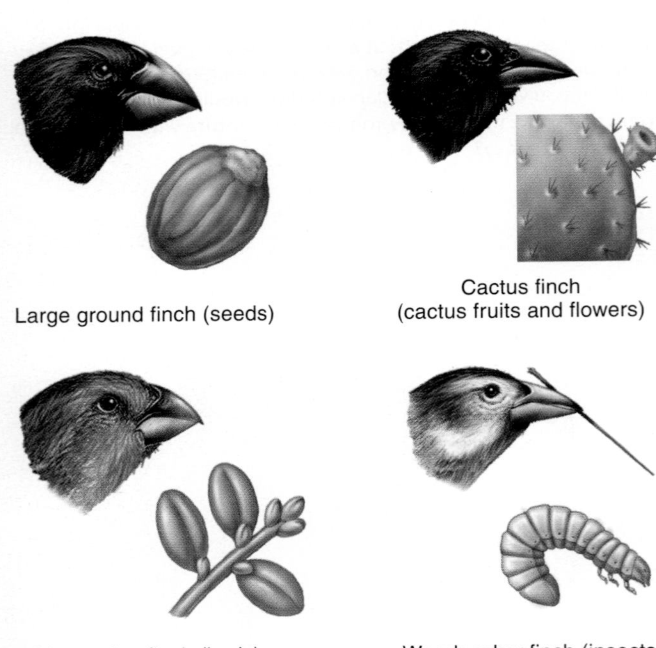

Figure 14.5 Four Galápagos finches and what they eat.

Darwin observed 14 different species of finches on the Galápagos Islands, differing mainly in their beaks and feeding habits. These four finches eat very different food items, and Darwin surmised that the very different shapes of their beaks represented evolutionary adaptations improving their ability to do so.

14.2 Darwin's Evidence

LEARNING OBJECTIVE 14.2.1 Describe the fossils and patterns of life Darwin observed on the voyage of HMS *Beagle*.

One of the obstacles that had blocked the acceptance of any theory of evolution in Darwin's day was the incorrect notion, widely believed at that time, that the earth was only a few thousand years old. The discovery of thick layers of rocks, evidence of extensive and prolonged erosion, and the increasing numbers of diverse and unfamiliar fossils discovered during Darwin's time made this assertion seem less and less likely. The great geologist Charles Lyell, whose *Principles of Geology* (1830) Darwin read eagerly as he sailed on HMS *Beagle,* outlined for the first time the story of an ancient world of plants and animals in flux, species constantly becoming extinct while others were emerging.

What Darwin Saw

When HMS *Beagle* set sail, Darwin was fully convinced that species were immutable, meaning that they were not subject to being changed. Indeed, it was not until two or three years after his return that he began to seriously consider the possibility that they could change. Nevertheless, during his five years on the ship, Darwin observed a number of phenomena that were of central importance to him in reaching his ultimate conclusion. For example, in the rich fossil beds of southern South America, he observed fossils of the extinct armadillo shown on the right in figure 14.4. They were surprisingly similar in form to the armadillos that still lived in the same area, shown on the left. Why would similar living and fossil organisms be in the same area unless the earlier form had given rise to the other? Later, Darwin's observations would be strengthened by the discovery of other fossils that show intermediate characteristics, pointing to successive change.

Repeatedly, Darwin saw that the characteristics of similar species varied somewhat from place to place. These geographical patterns suggested to him that organismal lineages change gradually as individuals move into new habitats. On the Galápagos Islands, 900 kilometers (540 miles) off the coast of Ecuador, Darwin encountered a variety of different finches on the islands. The 14 species, although related, differed slightly in appearance. Darwin felt it most reasonable to assume all these birds had descended from a common ancestor blown by winds from the South American mainland several million years ago. Eating different foods, on different islands, the species had changed in different ways, most notably in the size of their beaks. The larger beak of the ground finch in the upper left of figure 14.5 is better suited to crack open the large seeds it eats. As the generations descended from the common ancestor, these ground finches changed and adapted, what Darwin referred to as "descent with modification"—evolution.

In a more general sense, Darwin was struck by the fact that the plants and animals on these relatively young volcanic islands resembled those on the nearby coast of South America. If each one of these plants and animals had been created independently and simply placed on the Galápagos Islands, why didn't they resemble the plants and animals of islands with similar climates, such as those off the coast of Africa? Why did they resemble those of the adjacent South American coast instead?

Putting the Concept to Work

What did Darwin see on the Galápagos Islands that hinted at evolution?

14.3 The Theory of Natural Selection

LEARNING OBJECTIVE 14.3.1 Explain how Malthus's proposition implies that nature acts to limit population numbers, and how this leads to the process Darwin called natural selection.

It is one thing to observe the results of evolution but quite another to understand how it happens. Darwin's great achievement lies in his formulation of the hypothesis that evolution occurs because of natural selection.

Darwin and Malthus

Of key importance to the development of Darwin's insight was his study of Thomas Malthus's *Essay on the Principle of Population* (1798). In his book, Malthus pointed out that populations of plants and animals (including human beings) tend to increase geometrically, while their food supply increases only arithmetically. In a geometric progression, the elements increase by a constant factor; the blue line in figure 14.6 shows the progression 2, 6, 18, 54, . . . where each number is three times the preceding one. In an arithmetic progression, in contrast, the elements increase by a constant difference; the red line shows the progression 2, 4, 6, 8, . . . where each number is two greater than the preceding one.

Malthus's ideas about population growth will come into play again in chapter 19 on page 382 in relation to carrying capacity. Carrying capacity is the size at which a population stabilizes because of limited resources.

Because populations increase geometrically, virtually any kind of animal or plant would cover the entire surface of the world within a surprisingly short time, if it could reproduce unchecked. Instead, population sizes of species remain fairly constant year after year, because death limits population numbers. Malthus's conclusion provided the key ingredient for Darwin to develop the hypothesis that evolution occurs by natural selection.

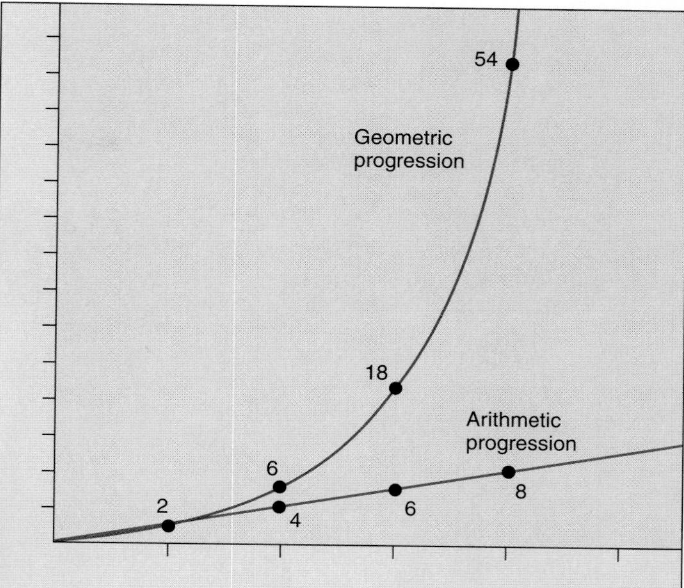

Figure 14.6 Geometric and arithmetic progressions.

An arithmetic progression increases by a constant difference (for example, units of 1 or 2 or 3), while a geometric progression increases by a constant factor (for example, by 2 or by 3 or by 4). Malthus contended that the human growth curve was geometric but the human food production curve was only arithmetic. Can you see the problems this difference would cause?

Natural Selection

Sparked by Malthus's ideas, Darwin saw that although every organism has the potential to produce more offspring than can survive, only a limited number actually do survive and produce further offspring. Many examples appear in nature. Sea turtles, for instance, will return to the beaches where they hatched to lay their eggs. Each female will lay about 100 eggs. The beach could be covered with thousands of hatchlings, like in figure 14.7, trying to make it to water's edge. Less than 10% will actually reach adulthood and return to this beach to reproduce. Darwin combined his observation with what he had seen on the voyage of HMS *Beagle,* as well as with his own experiences in breeding domestic animals, and made an important association: Those individuals that possess physical, behavioral, or other attributes that help them live in their environment are more likely to survive than those that do not have these characteristics. Darwin called this process **natural selection.** By surviving, they gain the opportunity to pass on their favorable characteristics to their offspring. As the frequency of these characteristics increases in the population, the nature of the population as a whole will gradually change, or evolve.

Variation enters a population through mutation, as discussed on pages 198 and 199. Without this variation, a population cannot evolve. Selection, artificial or natural, can only work on variation that exists in the population.

Figure 14.7 Sea turtle hatchlings.

These newly hatched sea turtles make their way to the ocean from their nests on the beach. Thousands of eggs may be laid on a beach during a spawning, but less than 10% of hatchlings will survive to adulthood. Natural predators, human egg poachers, and environmental challenges prevent the majority of offspring from surviving. As Darwin observed, sea turtles produce more offspring than will actually survive to reproduce.

Figure 14.8 Darwin greets his monkey ancestor.

In his time, Darwin was often portrayed unsympathetically, as in this drawing from an 1874 publication.

IMPLICATION FOR YOU In 2008 the Spanish parliament approved resolutions granting to gorillas, chimpanzees, and orangutans statutory rights currently applicable only to humans. This was the first time a country had taken such action. The resolutions were based on the Great Ape Project, a framework designed by scientists and philosophers to provide humans' closest relatives with the right to life, liberty, and protection from torture. Zoos could still legally hold apes, but living conditions must be "optimal." Using apes in performances will be illegal. The law will also ban using apes in potentially useful research if it might hurt the ape in any way. Do you think this resolution, particularly the last condition, should be adopted in the United States? Explain.

The driving force of evolution that Darwin identified has often been referred to as survival of the fittest. However, this is not to say the biggest or the strongest always survive. These characteristics may be favorable in one environment but less favorable in another. The organisms that are "best suited" to their particular environment survive more often, and therefore produce more offspring than others in the population, and in this sense are the "fittest."

Darwin's theory that evolution is caused by natural selection provides a simple and direct explanation of biological diversity, or why animals are different in different places—because habitats differ in their requirements and opportunities, the organisms with characteristics favored locally by natural selection will tend to vary in different places. As we will discuss later in section 14.9, there are five evolutionary forces that can affect biological diversity, although natural selection is the only evolutionary force that produces *adaptive* changes.

Darwin Drafts His Argument

Darwin drafted the overall argument for evolution by natural selection in a preliminary manuscript in 1842. After showing the manuscript to a few of his closest scientific friends, however, Darwin put it in a drawer and for 16 years turned to other research. No one knows for sure why Darwin did not publish his initial manuscript—it is very thorough and outlines his ideas in detail.

Wallace Has the Same Idea

The stimulus that finally brought Darwin's theory into print was an essay he received in 1858. A young English naturalist named Alfred Russel Wallace (1823–1913) sent the essay to Darwin from Malaysia; it concisely set forth the theory of evolution by means of natural selection, a theory Wallace had developed independently of Darwin. Like Darwin, Wallace had been greatly influenced by Malthus's 1798 book. After receiving Wallace's essay, Darwin arranged for a joint presentation of their ideas at a seminar in London. Neither attended the seminar: Wallace was still in Malaysia, and Darwin's young daughter drowned the day before the seminar took place. Darwin then expanded the 1842 manuscript he had written so long ago, and submitted it for publication the following year as *On the Origin of Species by Means of Natural Selection*.

Publication of Darwin's Theory

Darwin's book appeared in November 1859 and caused an immediate sensation. Although people had long accepted that humans closely resembled apes in many characteristics, the possibility that there might be a direct evolutionary relationship was unacceptable to many. Darwin did not actually discuss this idea in his book, but it followed directly from the principles he outlined. In a subsequent book, *The Descent of Man,* Darwin presented the argument directly, building a powerful case that humans and living apes have common ancestors. Many people were deeply disturbed with the suggestion that human beings were descended from the same ancestor as apes, and his book on evolution caused Darwin to become a victim of the satirists of his day—the cartoon in **figure 14.8** is a vivid example. Darwin's arguments for the theory of evolution by natural selection were so compelling, however, that his views were almost completely accepted among scientists after the 1860s.

Putting the Concept to Work

How did Malthus influence both Darwin and Wallace?

Darwin's Finches: Evolution in Action

14.4 The Beaks of Darwin's Finches

LEARNING OBJECTIVE 14.4.1 Contrast the work of Darwin and that of the Grants on Galápagos finch evolution.

Darwin's Galápagos finches played a key role in his argument for evolution by natural selection. He collected 31 specimens of finches from three islands when he visited the Galápagos Islands in 1835. Darwin, not an expert on birds, had trouble identifying the specimens. He believed by examining their beaks that his collection contained wrens, "gross-beaks," and blackbirds.

The Importance of the Beak

Upon Darwin's return to England, ornithologist John Gould examined the finches. Gould recognized that Darwin's collection was in fact a closely related group of distinct species, all similar to one another except for their beaks. In all, 14 species are now recognized, 13 from the Galápagos and one from far-distant Cocos Island. The ground finches with the larger beaks in **figure 14.9** feed on seeds that they crush in their beaks, whereas those with narrower beaks eat insects, including the warbler finch (named for its resemblance to a mainland bird). Other species include fruit and bud eaters, and species that feed on cactus fruits and the insects they attract; some populations of the sharp-beaked ground finch even include "vampires" that creep up on seabirds and use their sharp beaks to drink their blood. Perhaps most remarkable are the tool users, like the woodpecker finch you see in the upper left of the figure, that picks up a twig, cactus spine, or leaf stalk, trims it into shape with its beak, and then pokes it into dead branches to pry out grubs.

Figure 14.9 A diversity of finches on a single island.

Ten species of Darwin's finches from Isla Santa Cruz, one of the Galápagos Islands. The ten species show differences in beaks and feeding habits. The bird in the photograph above is a ground finch, its stout beak adapted for seed-eating. The differences between the ten species presumably arose when the finches arrived and encountered habitats lacking small birds. Scientists concluded that all of these birds derived from a single common ancestor.

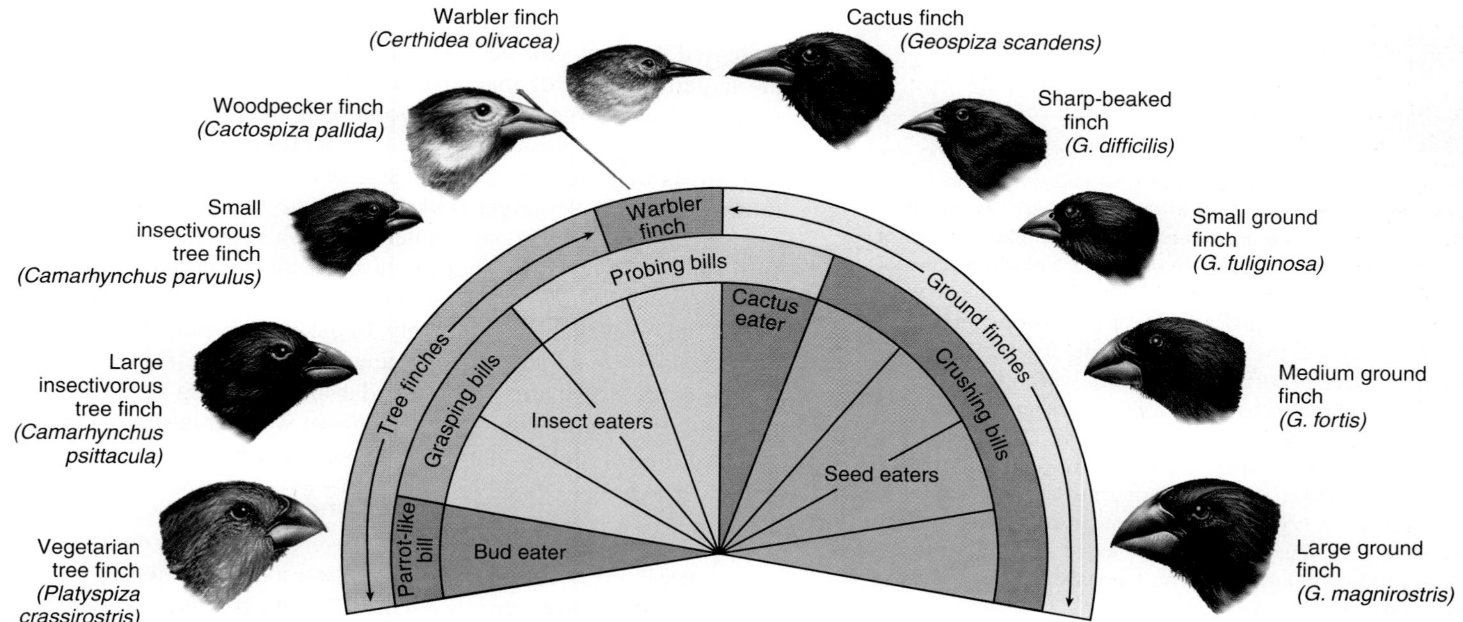

Figure 14.10 A gene shapes the beaks of Darwin's finches.

A cell-signalling molecule called "bone morphogenic protein 4" (BMP4) has been shown by DNA researchers to tailor the shape of the beak in Darwin's finches.

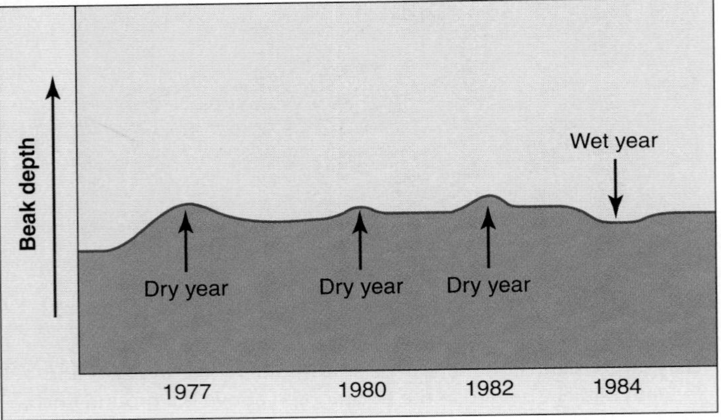

Figure 14.11 Evidence that natural selection alters beak size in *Geospiza fortis*.

In dry years, when only large, tough seeds were available, the mean beak size increased. In wet years, when many small seeds were available, smaller beaks became more common.

EVOLUTION

How Vampires Evolved. Anyone viewing the film *Twilight* could not help but wonder about vampires. Could vampires ever have evolved in the real world? Yes, and they have—in bats. There are three kinds of vampire bats, all of which employ a salivary enzyme called plasminogen activator to prevent blood from clotting as they eat. The common vampire bat, *Desmodus rotundus,* which laps the blood of mammals, has four copies of the gene that encodes this enzyme. There are other vampire bats: *Diaemus youngi,* which also feeds on mammals but prefers birds, and *Diphylla ecaudata,* which sticks to birds, have only one copy of the gene. DNA sequencing reveals that the four copies of the plasminogen activator gene possessed by the common vampire bat all lack a section called *Kringle 2,* which is present in this gene in both other species. Its deletion in *Desmodus* may have aided a dietary switch to mammalian blood. There are no human vampires, of course, but if there were it is a good bet they would also lack *Kringle 2.*

The differences in the beaks of Darwin's finches are due to differences in the genes of the birds. When biologists compare the DNA of large ground finches (with stout beaks for cracking large seeds) to the DNA of small ground finches (with more slender beaks), the only growth factor gene that is different in the DNA of the two species is *BMP4* (**figure 14.10** and **figure 1.13**). The difference is in how the gene is used. The large ground finches, with larger beaks, make more BMP4 protein than do the small ground finches.

The suitability of the beaks of the 14 finch species to their food source immediately suggested to Darwin that evolution had shaped them:

"*Seeing this gradation and diversity of structure in one small, intimately related group of birds, one might really fancy that from an original paucity of birds in this archipelago, one species has been taken and modified for different ends.*"

Checking to See if Darwin Was Right

If Darwin's suggestion that the beak of an ancestral finch had been "modified for different ends" is correct, then it ought to be possible to see the different species of finches acting out their evolutionary roles, each using its beak to acquire its particular food specialty. The four species that crush seeds within their beaks, for example, should feed on different seeds, with those with stouter beaks specializing on harder-to-crush seeds.

Starting in 1973, Peter and Rosemary Grant of Princeton University and generations of their students have studied the medium ground finch, *Geospiza fortis,* on a tiny island in the center of the Galápagos called Daphne Major. These finches feed on small tender seeds, abundantly available in wet years. The birds resort to larger, drier seeds that are harder to crush when small seeds are hard to find. Such lean times come during periods of dry weather, when plants produce few seeds, large or small.

By carefully measuring the beak shape of many birds every year, the Grants were able to assemble for the first time a detailed portrait of evolution in action. The Grants found that beak depth changed from one year to the next in a predictable fashion. During droughts, plants produced few seeds, and all available small seeds quickly were eaten, leaving large seeds as the major remaining source of food. As a result, birds with large beaks survived better, because they were better able to break open these large seeds. Consequently, the average beak depth of birds in the population increased the next year because this next generation included offspring of the large-beaked birds that survived. The offspring of the surviving "dry year" birds had larger beaks, an evolutionary response that led to the peaks you see in the graph in **figure 14.11**. The reason there are peaks and not plateaus is that the average beak size decreased again when wet seasons returned because the larger beak size was no longer more favorable when seeds were plentiful and so smaller-beaked birds survived to reproduce.

If the year-to-year changes in beak depth can be predicted by the pattern of dry years, then Darwin was right—natural selection influences beak size based on available food supply. In the study discussed here, birds with stout beaks have an advantage during dry periods, for they can break the large, dry seeds that are the only food available. When small seeds become plentiful once again with the return of wet weather, a smaller beak proves a more efficient tool for harvesting smaller seeds.

Putting the Concept to Work

How do you suppose the Grants were able to rule out the possibility that the changes they saw in beak dimensions simply reflect diet, with poorly fed birds having stouter beaks?

14.5 How Natural Selection Produces Diversity

LEARNING OBJECTIVE 14.5.1 Describe the four ecological niches occupied by Galápagos finches and their impact on the evolution of finch beaks.

Darwin believed that each Galápagos finch species had adapted to the particular foods and other conditions on the island it inhabited. Because each island presented different opportunities, a cluster of species resulted. Presumably, the ancestor of Darwin's finches reached these newly formed islands before other land birds, so that when it arrived, all of the niches where birds occur on the mainland were unoccupied. A *niche* is what a biologist calls the way a species makes a living—the biological (that is, other organisms) and physical (climate, food, shelter, etc.) conditions with which an organism interacts as it attempts to survive and reproduce. As the new arrivals to the Galápagos moved into vacant niches and adopted new lifestyles, they were subjected to diverse sets of selective pressures. Under these circumstances, the ancestral finches rapidly split into a series of populations, some of which evolved into separate species.

Competition between organisms that are utilizing the same niche cannot continue indefinitely. As discussed on pages 388-390, one of the participants dies out in competitive exclusion, or the niche is somehow divided.

The phenomenon by which a cluster of species change, as they occupy a series of different habitats within a region, is called *adaptive radiation.* Figure 14.12 shows how the 14 species of Darwin's finches on the Galápagos Islands and Cocos Island are thought to have evolved. The ancestral population, indicated by the base of the brackets, migrated to the islands about 2 million years ago and underwent adaptive radiation giving rise to the 14 different species. Such species clusters are often particularly impressive on island groups, in series of lakes, or in other sharply discontinuous habitats.

The 14 species of finches that inhabit the Galápagos Islands and Cocos Island fall into four groups, distinguished by niche:

1. **Ground finches.** There are six species of *Geospiza* ground finches. Most of the ground finches feed on seeds. The size of their beaks is related to the size of the seeds they eat. Some of the ground finches feed primarily on cactus flowers and fruits and have longer, larger, more pointed beaks.
2. **Tree finches.** There are five species of insect-eating tree finches. Four species have beaks that are suitable for feeding on insects. The woodpecker finch has a chisel-like beak. This unique bird carries around a twig or a cactus spine, which it uses to probe for insects in deep crevices.
3. **Vegetarian finch.** The very heavy beak of this bud-eating bird is used to wrench buds from branches.
4. **Warbler finches.** These birds play the same ecological role in Galápagos woods that warblers play on the mainland, searching continually over the leaves and branches for insects. They have a slender, warbler-like beak.

Putting the Concept to Work

A fifth very specialized niche is occupied by some populations of one species of ground finch—vampire finches that drink the blood of sea birds. Which ground finch species in figure 14.12 has the most suitable bill for this ecological niche?

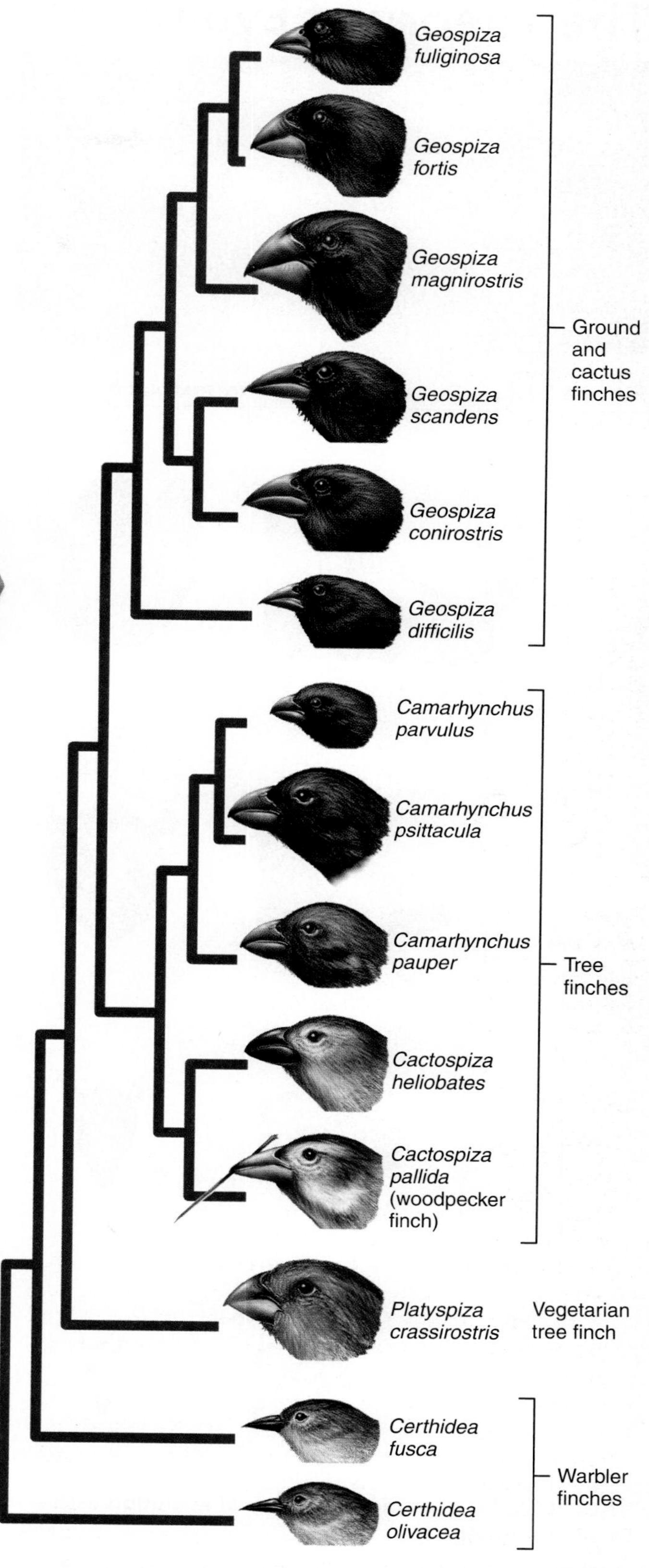

Figure 14.12 An evolutionary tree of Darwin's finches. This family tree was constructed by comparing DNA of the 14 species. Their position at the base of the finch tree suggests that warbler finches were among the first adaptive types to evolve in the Galápagos.

The Theory of Evolution

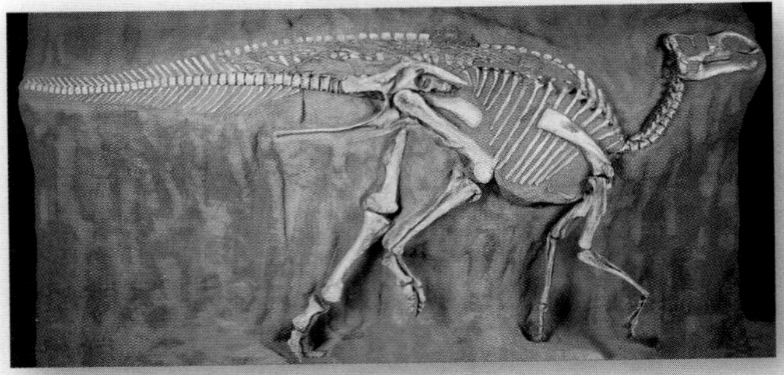

Figure 14.13 Dinosaur fossil of *Parasaurolophus.*

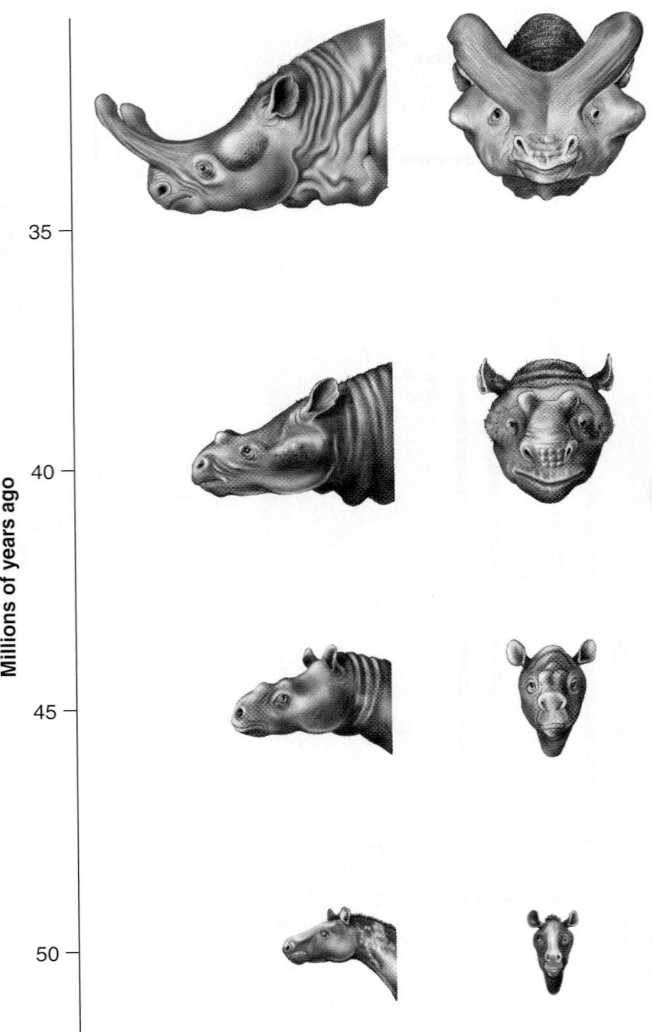

Figure 14.14 Testing the theory of evolution with fossil titanotheres.

Here you can trace the changes in a group of hoofed mammals known as titanotheres from about 50 million years ago (at the bottom) through 35 million years ago (at the top). During this time, the small, bony protuberance located above the nose 50 million years ago evolved into relatively large, blunt horns.

14.6 The Evidence for Evolution

LEARNING OBJECTIVE 14.6.1 Outline a four-step procedure to test the theory of evolution using fossil evidence.

The evidence that Darwin presented in *The Origin of Species* to support his theory of evolution was strong. We will now examine other lines of evidence supporting Darwin's theory, including information revealed by examining fossils, anatomical features, and molecules such as DNA and proteins.

The Fossil Record

The most direct evidence of evolution is found in the fossil record. **Fossils** are the preserved remains, tracks, or traces of once-living organisms. Fossils are created when organisms become buried in sediment. The calcium in bone or other hard tissue mineralizes, and the surrounding sediment eventually hardens to form rock. Most fossils are, in effect, skeletons, as shown by the dinosaur fossil in figure 14.13. In the rare cases when fossils form in very fine sediment, feathers may also be preserved. When remains are frozen or become suspended in amber (fossilized plant resin), however, the entire body may be preserved. The fossils contained in layers of sedimentary rock reveal a history of life on earth.

Isotopes are atoms that have the same number of protons but different numbers of neutrons. Some isotopes, called radioisotopes, are unstable and tend to break up into particles with lower atomic numbers. This decay of radioisotopes can be used to date materials, as discussed on page 36.

By dating the rock in which a fossil occurs, we can get an accurate idea of how old the fossil is. Rocks are dated by measuring the amount of certain radioisotopes in the rock. A radioisotope will break down, or decay, into other isotopes or elements. This occurs at a constant rate, and so the amount of a radioisotope present in the rock is an indication of the rock's age.

Using Fossils to Test the Theory of Evolution

If the theory of evolution is correct, then the fossils we see preserved in rock should represent a history of evolutionary change. The theory makes the clear prediction that a parade of successive changes should be seen, as first one change occurs and then another. If the theory of evolution is not correct, on the other hand, then such orderly change is not expected.

To test this prediction, biologists follow a very simple procedure:

1. *Assemble a collection of fossils of a particular group of organisms.* You might, for example, gather together a collection of fossil titanotheres, a hoofed mammal that lived about 50–35 million years ago.
2. *Date each of the fossils.* In dating the fossils, it is important to make no reference to what the fossil looks like. Imagine it as being concealed in a black box of rock, with only the box being dated.
3. *Order the fossils by their age.* Without looking in the "black boxes," place them in a series, beginning with the oldest and proceeding to the youngest.
4. *Now examine the fossils.* Do the differences between the fossils appear jumbled, or is there evidence of successive change as evolution predicts? You can judge for yourself in figure 14.14, which traces the

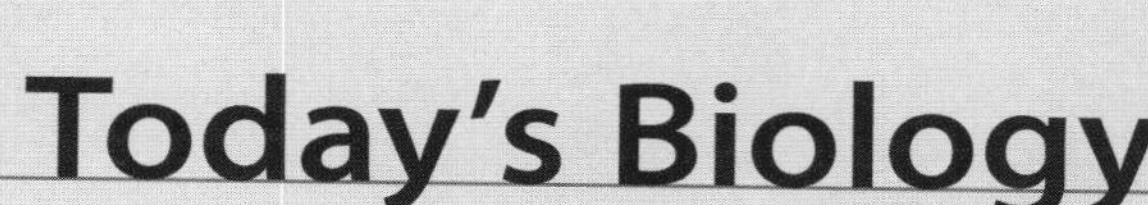

Darwin and Moby Dick

Moby Dick, the white whale hunted by Captain Ahab in Melville's novel, was a sperm whale. One of the ocean's great predators, a large sperm whale is a voracious meat-eater that may span over 60 feet and weigh 50 tons. A sperm whale is not a fish, though. Unlike the great white shark in *Jaws*, a whale has hairs (not many), and a female whale has milk-producing mammary glands with which it feeds its young. A sperm whale is a mammal, just as you are! This raises an interesting question. If Darwin is right about the fossil record reflecting life's evolutionary past, then fossils tell us mammals evolved from reptiles on land at about the time of the dinosaurs. How did they end up back in the water?

The evolutionary history of whales has long fascinated biologists, but only in recent years have fossils been discovered that reveal the answer to this intriguing question. A series of discoveries now allows biologists to trace the evolutionary history of the most colossal animals ever to live on earth back to their beginnings at the dawn of the Age of Mammals. Whales, it turns out, are the descendants of four-legged land mammals that reinvaded the sea some 50 million years ago, much as seals and walruses are doing today. It's pretty startling to realize that Moby Dick's evolutionary ancestor lived on the steppes of Asia and looked like a modest-sized pig a few feet long and weighing perhaps 50 pounds.

From what group of land mammals did whales arise? Researchers had long speculated that it might be a hoofed meat-eater with three toes known as a mesonychid, related to rhinoceroses. Subtle clues suggested this—the arrangement of ridges on the molar teeth, the positioning of the ear bones in the skull. But findings announced in 2001 reveal these subtle clues to have been misleading. Ankle bones from two newly described 50 million-year-old whale species discovered by Philip Gingerich of the University of Michigan are those of an artiodactyl, a four-toed mammal related to hippos, cattle, and pigs. Even more recently, Japanese researchers studying DNA have discovered unique genetic markers shared today only by whales and hippos.

Biologists now conclude that whales, like hippos, are descended from a group of early four-hoofed mammals called anthracotheres, modest-sized grazing animals with a piggish appearance abundant in Europe and Asia 50 million years ago.

In Pakistan in 1994, biologists discovered its descendant, the oldest known whale. The fossil was 49 million years old, had four legs, each with four-toed feet and a little hoof at the tip of each toe. Dubbed *Ambulocetus* (walking whale), it was sharp-toothed and about the size of a large sea lion. Analysis of the minerals in its teeth reveal it drank fresh water, so like a seal it was not yet completely a marine animal. Its nostrils were on the end of the snout, like a dog's.

Appearing in the fossil record a few million years later is *Rodhocetus*, also seal-like but with smaller hind limbs and the teeth of an ocean water drinker. Its nostrils are shifted higher on the skull, halfway towards the top of the head.

Almost 10 million years later, about 37 million years ago, we see the first representatives of *Basilosaurus*, a giant 60-foot-long serpent-like whale with shrunken hind legs still complete down to jointed knees and toes.

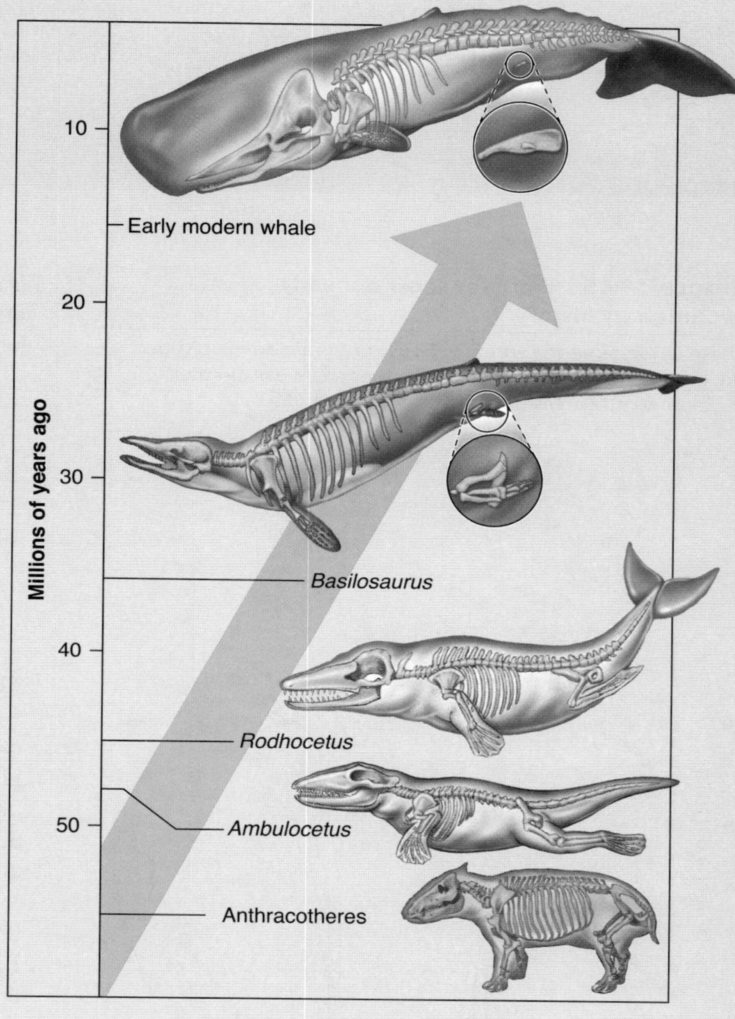

The earliest modern whales appear in the fossil record 15 million years ago. The nostrils are now in the top of the head, a "blowhole" that allows it to break the surface, inhale, and resubmerge without having to stop or tilt the head up. The hind legs are gone, with vestigial tiny bones remaining that are unattached to the pelvis. Still, today's whales retain all the genes used to code for legs—occasionally a whale is born having sprouted a leg or two.

So it seems to have taken 35 million years for a whale to evolve from the piglike ancestor of a hippopotamus—intermediate steps preserved in the fossil record for us to see. Darwin, who always believed that gaps in the vertebrate fossil record would eventually be filled in, would have been delighted.

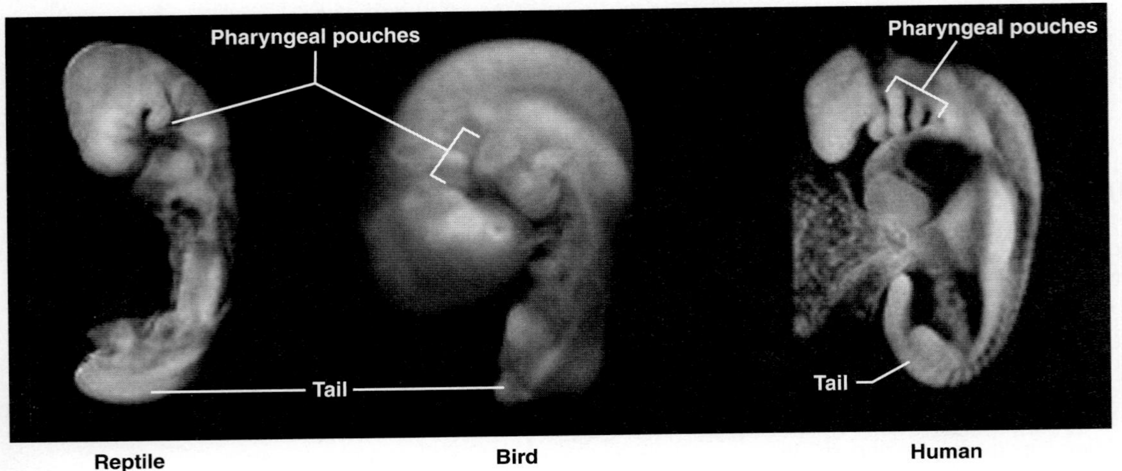

Figure 14.15 Embryos show our early evolutionary history.

These embryos, representing various vertebrate animals, show the primitive features that all vertebrates share early in their development, such as pharyngeal pouches and a tail.

fossils through time from the oldest at the bottom to the more recent at the top. During the 15 million years spanned by this collection of titanothere fossils, the small, bony protuberance located above the nose 50 million years ago evolved in a series of continuous changes into relatively large blunt horns.

It is important not to miss the key point of the result you see illustrated in figure 14.14: Evolution is an observation, not a conclusion. Because the dating of the samples is independent of what the samples are like, *successive change through time is a data statement*. While the statement that evolution is the result of natural selection is a theory advanced by Darwin, the statement that evolution has occurred is a factual observation.

Putting the Concept to Work

If titanothere horns had *not* evolved continuously, how would you expect the fossil data analysis to have come out?

The Anatomical Record

LEARNING OBJECTIVE 14.6.2 Discriminate between analogous and homologous structures.

Much of the evolutionary history of vertebrates can be seen in the way in which their embryos develop. Figure 14.15 shows three different embryos early in development, and as you can see, all vertebrate embryos have pharyngeal pouches (in fish, these develop into gill slits); also every vertebrate embryo has a long bony tail, even if the tail is not present in the fully developed animal. These relict developmental forms strongly suggest that all vertebrates share a basic set of developmental instructions.

As vertebrates have evolved, the same bones are sometimes still there but put to different uses, their presence betraying their evolutionary past. For example, the forelimbs of vertebrates are all **homologous structures;** that is, although the structures and functions of the bones have diverged, they are derived from the same body part present in a common ancestor. You can see in figure 14.16 how the bones of the forelimb have been modified to make up the human forearm, wrist, and fingers, the wing of the bat, the full leg of the horse, and the paddle in the fin of the porpoise.

Not all similar features are homologous. Sometimes features found in different lineages come to resemble each other as a result of parallel evolutionary adaptations to similar environments. This form of evolutionary change is referred to as *convergent evolution,* and these similar-looking features are called **analogous structures.** For example, the wings of birds, pterosaurs, and bats are analogous structures, with different bones modified through natural selection to serve the same function and therefore produce wings that look the same.

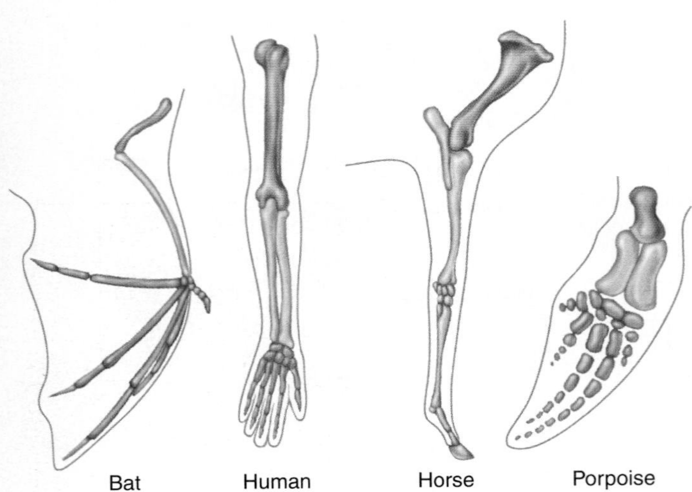

Figure 14.16 Homology among vertebrate limbs.

Homologies among the forelimbs of four mammals show the ways in which the proportions of the bones have changed in relation to the particular way of life of each organism. Although considerable differences can be seen in form and function, the same basic bones are present in each forelimb.

IMPLICATION FOR YOU Sometimes homologous structures are put to no use at all, like the human appendix. The great apes, our closest relatives, have an appendix much larger than ours attached to the gut tube, which holds bacteria used in digesting the cellulose cell walls of the plants eaten by these primates. Your appendix is a vestigial version of this structure that now serves no function in your digestion of food.

Putting the Concept to Work

If similar features are either homologous or analogous, how can both be used as arguments supporting evolution?

The Molecular Record

LEARNING OBJECTIVE 14.6.3 Describe the protein and DNA evidence supporting the hypothesis of evolutionary divergence.

Traces of our evolutionary past are also evident at the molecular level. We possess the same set of color vision genes as our ancestors, only more complex, and during early development we employ pattern formation genes that all animals share. Indeed, if you think about it, the fact that organisms have evolved from a series of simpler ancestors implies that a record of evolutionary change is present in the cells of each of us, in our DNA. According to evolutionary theory, new alleles arise from older ones by mutation and come to predominance through favorable selection. A series of evolutionary changes thus implies a continual accumulation of genetic changes in the DNA. Thus, evolutionary theory makes a clear prediction: Organisms that are more distantly related should have accumulated a greater number of evolutionary differences than two species that are more closely related.

This prediction is now subject to direct test. Recent DNA research allows us to directly compare the genomes of different organisms. The result is clear: For a broad array of vertebrates, the more distantly related two organisms are, the greater their genomic difference. This research is described later in this chapter on page 264.

Our knowledge of the molecular record is expanding with the advancements made in genomics. The sequencing of genomes, discussed on page 224, allows scientists to compare the DNA of closely and distantly related organisms.

This same pattern of divergence can be clearly seen at the protein level. Comparing the hemoglobin amino acid sequence of different species with the human sequence in figure 14.17, you can see that species more closely related to humans have fewer differences in the amino acid structure of their hemoglobin. Macaques, primates closely related to humans, have fewer differences from humans (only 8 different amino acids) than do more distantly related mammals like dogs (which have 32 different amino acids). Nonmammalian terrestrial vertebrates differ from us even more, and marine vertebrates are the most different of all.

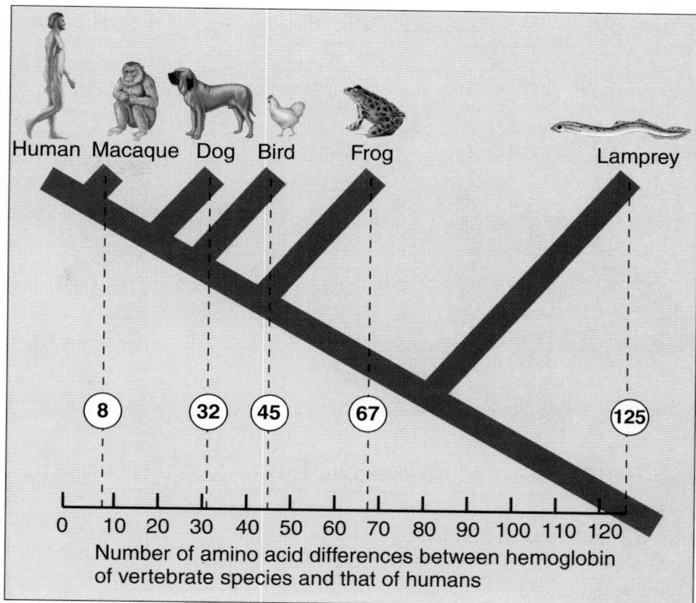

Figure 14.17 Molecules reflect evolutionary divergence.

The greater the evolutionary distance from humans (as revealed by the *blue* evolutionary tree based on the fossil record), the greater the number of amino acid differences in the vertebrate hemoglobin polypeptide.

Molecular Clocks. This same pattern is seen when the DNA sequence of an individual gene is compared over a much broader array of organisms. One well-studied case is the mammalian *cytochrome c* gene (cytochrome *c* is a protein that plays a key role in oxidative metabolism). Figure 14.18 compares the time when two species diverged on the *x* axis to the number of differences in their *cytochrome c* gene on the *y* axis. To practice using this data set, go back about 75 million years ago to find a common ancestor for humans and rodents—in that time there have been about 60 base substitutions in cytochrome *c*. This graph reveals a very important finding: Evolutionary changes appear to accumulate in cytochrome *c* at a constant rate, as indicated by the straightness of the blue line connecting the points. This constancy is sometimes referred to as a molecular clock. Most proteins for which data are available appear to accumulate changes over time in this fashion, although different proteins can evolve at very different rates.

The central dogma, DNA-RNA-protein, is discussed on page 206, and describes the information pathway used by cells. Mutations in DNA that occur over time can affect protein products and those changes can be traced in the DNA itself and in the proteins.

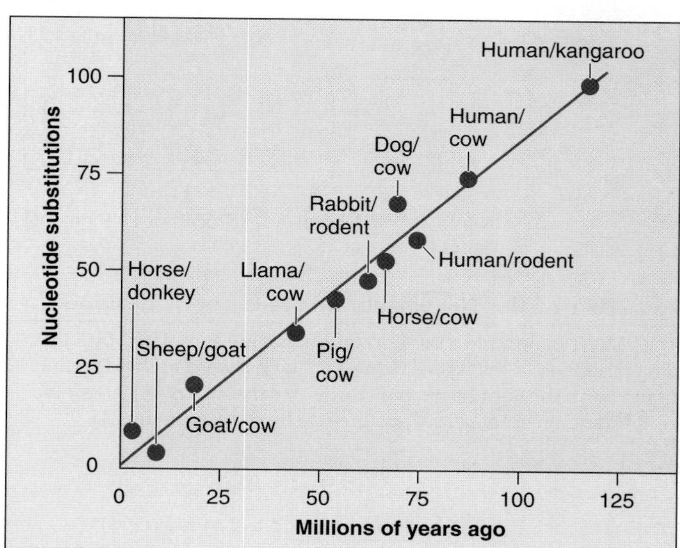

Figure 14.18 The molecular clock of cytochrome *c*.

When the time since each pair of organisms presumably diverged is plotted against the number of nucleotide differences in cytochrome *c*, the result is a straight line, suggesting that the *cytochrome c* gene is evolving at a constant rate.

Putting the Concept to Work

Can you propose a nonevolutionary explanation of the constant rate at which genes like cytochrome *c* accumulate mutations?

14.7 Evolution's Critics

LEARNING OBJECTIVE 14.7.1 Evaluate the scientific merit of common criticisms of Darwin's theory of evolution.

Critics of evolution have raised a variety of objections to Darwin's theory of evolution by natural selection:

1. **Evolution is not solidly demonstrated.** *"Evolution is just a theory,"* critics point out, as if theory meant lack of knowledge, some kind of guess. Scientists, however, use the word theory in a very different sense than the general public does (see section 1.6). Theories are the solid ground of science, supported with much experimental evidence and that of which we are most certain. Few of us doubt the theory of gravity because it is "just a theory."
2. **There are no fossil intermediates.** *"No one ever saw a fin on the way to becoming a leg,"* critics claim, pointing to the many gaps in the fossil record in Darwin's day. Since then, however, most fossil intermediates in vertebrate evolution have indeed been found. A clear line of fossils now traces the transition between whales and hoofed mammals, between reptiles and mammals, and between apes and humans. The fossil evidence of evolution between major forms is compelling (figure 14.19).
3. **The intelligent design argument.** *"The organs of living creatures are too complex for a random process to have produced them."* This classic "argument from design" was first proposed nearly 200 years ago by William Paley in his book *Natural Theology*—the existence of a clock is evidence of the existence of a clockmaker, Paley argues. Similarly, Darwin's critics argue that organs like the mammalian ear are too complex to be due to blind evolution. There must have been a designer. Biologists do not agree. Complex structures like the mammalian ear evolved as a progression of slight improvements. The intermediates in the evolution of the mammalian ear are well documented in the fossil record, each favored by natural selection because they each had value—being able to amplify sound a little is better than not being able to amplify it at all. Nor is the solution always optimal, as your own eyes attest. As you can see in the blown-up image in figure 14.20, the receptor cells in the human eye are actually facing backward to the stimulus (light). No intelligent designer would design an eye backward!
4. **Evolution violates the second law of thermodynamics.** *"A jumble of soda cans doesn't by itself jump neatly into a stack—things become more disorganized due to random events, not more organized."* Biologists point out that this argument ignores what the second law really says: Disorder increases *in a closed system,* which the earth most certainly is not. Energy enters the biosphere from the sun, fueling life and all the processes that organize it.
5. **Proteins are too improbable.** *"Hemoglobin has 141 amino acids. The probability that the first one would be leucine is 1/20, and that all 141 would be the ones they are by chance is $(1/20)^{141}$, an impossibly rare event."* You cannot use probability to argue backward. The probability that a student in a classroom has a particular birthday is 1/365; arguing this way, the probability that everyone in a class of 50 would have the birthdays they do is $(1/365)^{50}$—and yet there the class sits.

Figure 14.19 An intermediate fossil.

The animal that produced this fossil is an extinct lobe-finned fish (genus *Tiktaalik*) that lived approximately 375 million years ago. Coined by its discoverer as a "fishopod," it clearly has some characteristics that are fishlike, similar to fish that lived about 380 million years ago, and others that are more like early tetrapods, which lived about 365 million years ago. *Tiktaalik* appears to be a transitional animal, between fish and amphibians.

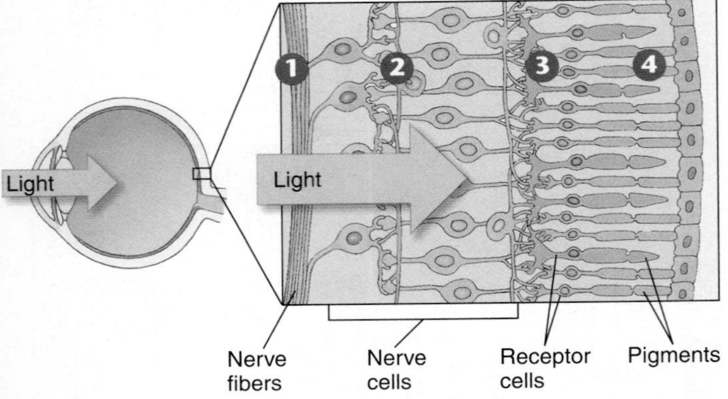

Figure 14.20 The vertebrate eye is poorly designed.

The visual pigments in a vertebrate eye that are stimulated by light are embedded in the retinal tissue, facing backward to the direction of the light. The light has to pass through nerve fibers ❶, nerve cells ❷, and receptor cells ❸, before reaching the pigments ❹.

The Irreducible Complexity Fallacy

The century-and-a-half-old "intelligent design" argument of William Paley has been recently articulated in a new molecular guise. Today's proponents of intelligent design now argue that the intricate molecular machinery of our cells is so elaborate that it cannot be explained by evolution from simpler stages—it is "irreducibly complex." Each part of a molecular machine plays a vital role. Remove just one, they claim, and cell molecular machinery cannot function.

As an example of such an irreducibly complex system, intelligent design advocates point to the series of more than a dozen blood clotting proteins that act in our body to cause blood to clot around a wound. Take out any step in the complex cascade of reactions that leads to coagulation of blood, they say, and your body's blood would leak out from a cut like water from a ruptured pipe. If dozens of different proteins all must work correctly to clot blood, how could natural selection act to fashion any one of the individual proteins? No one protein does anything on its own, just as a portion of a watch doesn't tell time. Like Paley's watch, the blood clotting system must have been designed all at once, as a single functioning machine.

What's wrong with this argument, as evolutionary scientists have been quick to point out, is that evolution acts on the system, not its parts. Natural selection can evolve a complex system because at every stage of its evolution, the system functions. Parts that improve function are added, and, because of later changes, eventually become essential, in the same way that the second rung of a ladder becomes essential once you have added a third.

The mammalian blood clotting system, for example, has evolved in stages from much simpler systems (**figure 14.21**). The core of the vertebrate clotting system, called the "common pathway" (highlighted in blue), evolved at the dawn of the vertebrates approximately 600 million years ago, and is found today in lampreys, the most primitive fish. As vertebrates evolved, proteins were added to the clotting system, improving its efficiency. The so-called extrinsic pathway (highlighted in pink), triggered by substances released from damaged tissues, was added 500 million years ago. Each step in the pathway amplifies what goes before, so adding the extrinsic pathway greatly increases the amplification and thus the sensitivity of the system. Fifty million years later, a third component was added, the so-called intrinsic pathway (highlighted in tan). It is triggered by contact with the jagged surfaces produced by injury. Again, amplification and sensitivity were increased to ultimately end up with blood clots formed by the cross linking of fibrin (highlighted in green). At each stage as the clotting system evolved to become more complex, its overall performance came to depend on the added elements. Mammalian clotting, which utilizes all three pathways, no longer functions if any one of them is disabled. Blood clotting has become "irreducibly complex"—as the result of Darwinian evolution. Intelligent design proponents claim that complex cellular and molecular processes can't be explained by Darwinism. Indeed, examination of the human genome reveals that the cluster of blood clotting genes arose through duplication of genes, with increasing amounts of change. The evolution of the blood clotting system is an observation, not a surmise. Its irreducible complexity is a fallacy.

Putting the Concept to Work

Is the theory of intelligent design a scientific theory? Explain.

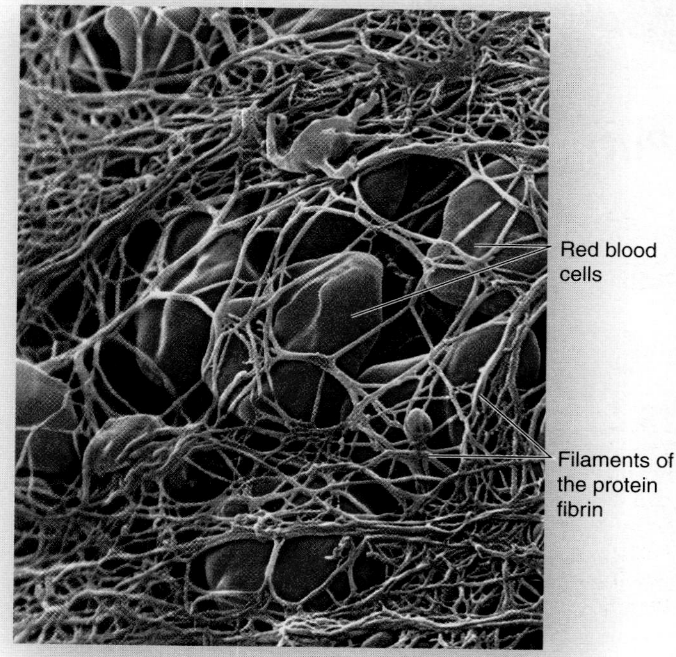

(a) A blood clot

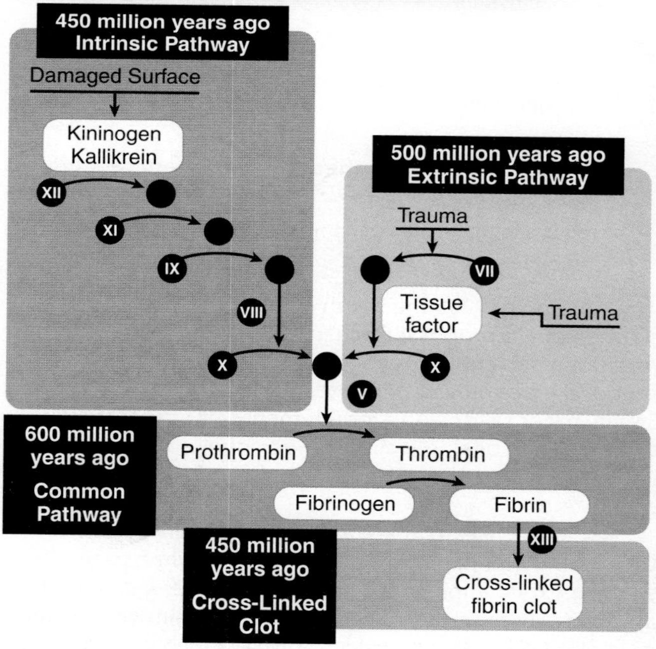

(b) The blood clotting system

Figure 14.21 How blood clotting evolved.

The blood clotting system evolved in steps, with new proteins adding on to the preceding step.

Today's Biology

Putting Intelligent Design to the Test

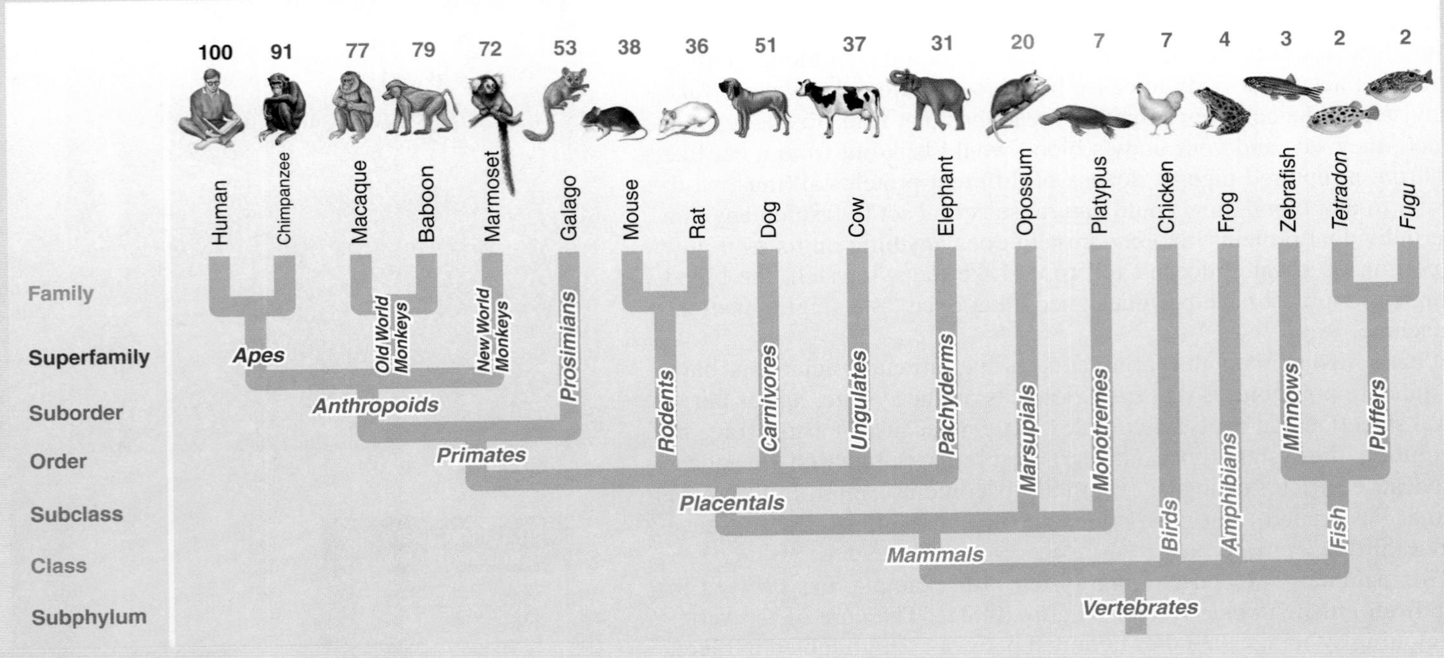

Genomic similarity reflects evolutionary relatedness.

The number above each organism is the percent of the nucleotides in selected regions of that organism's genome that match those of the same regions in the human genome.

In the spring of 2006 the South Carolina Board of Education rejected a state panel's proposal to change high school standards by calling on students to critically analyze evolution. The Board stated it felt the proposal was a ploy to promote the avoidance of teaching evolution. Similar proposals to add a requirement that students critically analyze evolution had been rejected earlier in the year by the Utah and Ohio Boards of Education, and are currently under consideration in several other states.

What are we to make of this? Surely no scientist can object to critically analyzing any theory. That is what science is all about, seeking explanations for what can be observed, tested, replicated, and possibly falsified. Indeed, biologists claim that Darwin's theory of evolution has been subjected to as much critical analysis as any theory in the history of science.

So why the objection to this change in high school standards? Because many scientists and teachers, apparently including the South Carolina Board of Education, feel the change is simply intended to promote the teaching of a non-scientific alternative to evolution in classrooms.

This distinction between an assertion that can be tested and one that cannot goes to the very nature of science. Actually, nothing makes this difference more clear cut than the critical analysis so sought after by South Carolina's critics of evolution. So let's do it. Let's put Darwin to the test.

As explained earlier in the chapter, if Darwin's assertion is correct, that organisms evolved from ancestral species, then we should be able to track evolutionary changes in our DNA. The variation that we see between species reflects adaptations to environmental challenges, adaptations that result from changes in DNA. Therefore, a series of evolutionary changes should be reflected in an accumulation of genetic changes in the DNA. This hypothesis, that evolutionary changes reflect accumulated changes in DNA, leads to the following prediction: Two species that are more distantly related (for example, humans and mice) should have accumulated a greater number of evolutionary differences than two species that are more closely related (say, humans and chimpanzees).

So have they? Let's compare vertebrate species to see. The "family tree" above shows how biologists believe 18 different vertebrate species are related. Apes and monkeys, because they are in the same order (primates), are considered more closely related to each other than either are to members of another order, such as mice and rats (rodents).

The wealth of genomes (a genome is all the DNA that an organism possesses) that have been sequenced since completion of the human genome project allows us to directly compare the DNA of these 18 vertebrates. To reduce the size of the task, investigators at the National Human Genome Research Institute working at the University of California, Santa Cruz, focused on 44 so-called ENCODE regions scattered around the vertebrate genomes. These regions, corresponding to 30 Mb (megabase, or million bases) or roughly 1% of the total human genome, were selected to be representative of the genome as a whole, containing protein-encoding genes as well as noncoding DNA.

For each vertebrate species, the investigators determined the similarity of its DNA to that of humans—that is, the percent of the nucleotides in that organism's 44 ENCODE regions which match those of the human genome.

You can see the result in each instance presented as a number above the picture of each organism on the vertebrate family tree. As Darwin's theory predicts, the closer the relatives, the less the genomic difference we see. The chimpanzee genome is more like the human genome (91% for these ENCODE regions) than the monkey genomes are (72 to 79%). Furthermore, these five genomes, all in the primate order, are more like each other than any are to those of another order, such as rodents (mouse and rat).

In general, as you proceed through the taxonomic categories of the vertebrate family tree from very distant relatives on the right (some in the same class as humans) to very close ones on the left (in the same family), you can see clearly that genomic similarity increases as taxonomic distance decreases—just as Darwin's theory predicts. The prediction of evolutionary theory is solidly confirmed.

The analysis does not have to stop here. The evolutionary history of the vertebrates is quite well known from fossils, and because many of these fossils have been independently dated using tools such as radioisotope dating, it is possible to recast the analysis in terms of concrete intervals of time, and assess directly whether or not vertebrate genomes accumulate more differences over longer periods of time as Darwin's theory predicts.

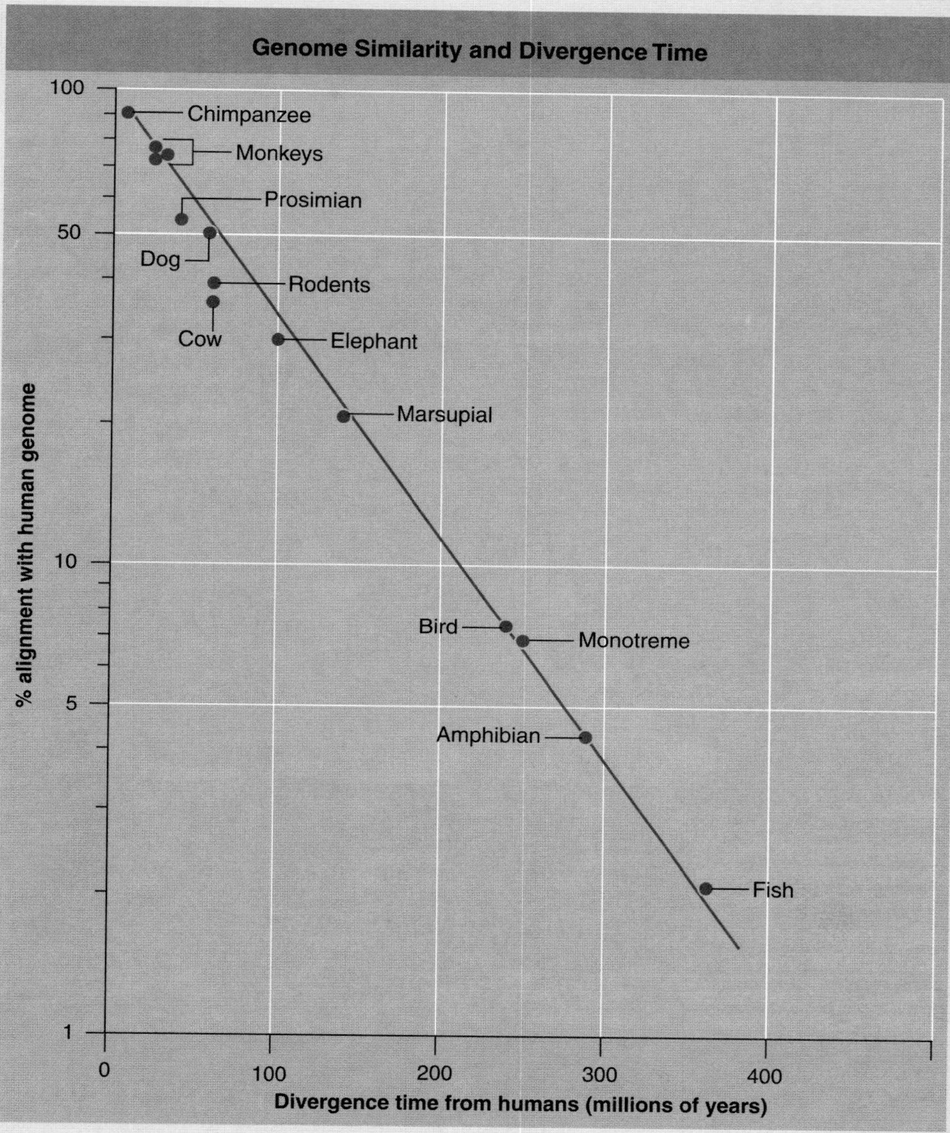

For each of the 18 vertebrates being analyzed, the graph shown here plots genomic similarity—how alike the DNA sequence of the vertebrate's ENCODE regions are to those of the human genome—against divergence time (that is, how many millions of years have elapsed since that vertebrate and humans shared a common ancestor in the fossil record). Thus the last common ancestor shared by chickens and humans was an early reptile called a dicynodont that lived some 250 million years ago; since then the genomes of the two species have changed so much that only 7% of their ENCODE sequences are still the same.

The result seen in the graph is striking and very clear: Over their more than 300 million year history, vertebrates have accumulated more and more genetic change in their DNA. "Descent with modification" was Darwin's definition of evolution, and that is exactly what we see in the graph. The evolution of the vertebrate genome is not a theory, but an observation.

The wealth of data made available by the human genome project has allowed a powerful test of Darwin's prediction. The conclusion to which the test leads us is that evolution is an observed fact, clearly revealed in the DNA of vertebrates.

This is the sort of critical analysis that science requires, and that the theory of evolution has again passed. Anyone suggesting that a nonscientific alternative to evolution, such as Intelligent Design, offers an alternative scientific explanation to evolution is welcome to subject it to the same sort of critical analysis you have seen employed here. Can you think of a way to do so? It is precisely because the assertion of intelligent design cannot be critically analyzed—it does not make any testable prediction—that it is not science and has no place in science classrooms.

How Populations Evolve

14.8 Genetic Change in Populations

LEARNING OBJECTIVE 14.8.1 **State the Hardy-Weinberg rule and its five assumptions.**

Darwin and his contemporaries were puzzled why dominant **alleles** (alternative forms of a gene) did not drive recessive alleles out of populations. The solution to this puzzle was explained in 1908 by G. H. Hardy and W. Weinberg. Hardy and Weinberg studied **allele frequencies** (the proportion of alleles of a particular type in a population) in a population's *gene pool,* which is the sum of all of the genes in a population, including all alleles in all individuals. Hardy and Weinberg pointed out that in a large population in which there is random mating, and in the absence of forces that change allele frequencies, the original genotype proportions remain constant from generation to generation. Dominant alleles do not, in fact, replace recessive ones. Because their proportions do not change, the genotypes are said to be in **Hardy-Weinberg equilibrium.**

Figure 14.22 **Hardy-Weinberg equilibrium.**

In the absence of factors that alter them, the frequencies of gametes, genotypes, and phenotypes remain constant generation after generation. The example shown here involves a population of 1,000 cats, in which 160 are white and 840 are black. White cats are *bb*, and black cats are *BB* or *Bb*. The potential crosses in this cat population can be determined using a Punnett square analysis.

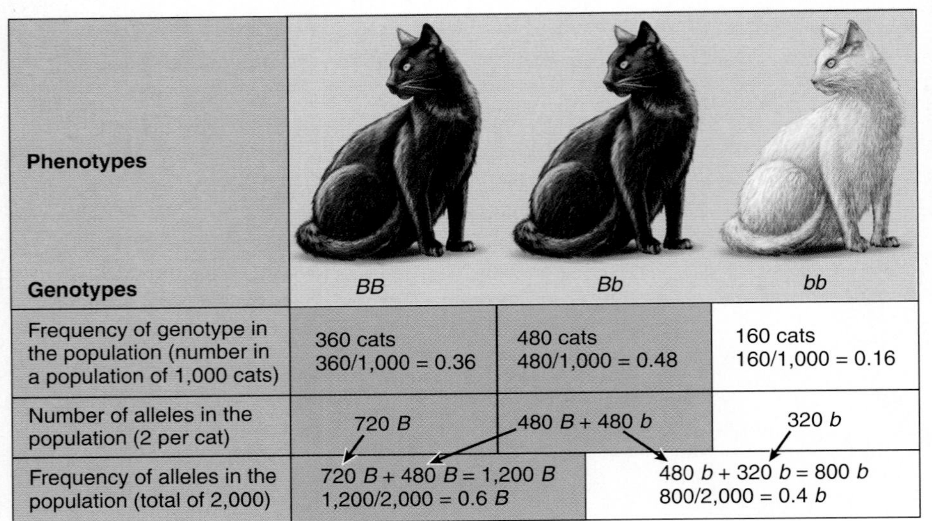

Phenotypes			
Genotypes	*BB*	*Bb*	*bb*
Frequency of genotype in the population (number in a population of 1,000 cats)	360 cats 360/1,000 = 0.36	480 cats 480/1,000 = 0.48	160 cats 160/1,000 = 0.16
Number of alleles in the population (2 per cat)	720 *B*	480 *B* + 480 *b*	320 *b*
Frequency of alleles in the population (total of 2,000)	720 *B* + 480 *B* = 1,200 *B* 1,200/2,000 = 0.6 *B*		480 *b* + 320 *b* = 800 *b* 800/2,000 = 0.4 *b*

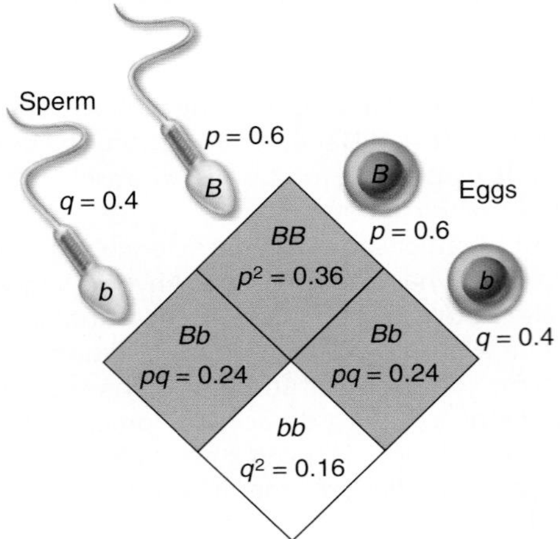

The Hardy-Weinberg rule is viewed as a baseline to which the frequencies of alleles in a population can be compared. If the allele frequencies are not changing (they are in Hardy-Weinberg equilibrium), the population is not evolving. If, however, allele frequencies are sampled at one point in time and they differ greatly from what would be expected under Hardy-Weinberg equilibrium, then the population is undergoing evolutionary change.

Hardy and Weinberg came to their conclusion by analyzing the frequencies of alleles in successive generations. The **frequency** of something is defined as the proportion of individuals with a certain characteristic, compared to the entire population. Thus, in the population of 1,000 cats shown in figure 14.22, there are 840 black cats and 160 white cats. To determine the frequency of black cats, divide 840 by 1,000 (840/1,000), which is 0.84. The frequency of white cats is 160/1,000 = 0.16.

Knowing the frequency of the phenotype, one can calculate the frequency of the genotypes and alleles in the population. By convention, the frequency of the dominant (and usually more common) of two alleles (in this case *B* for the black allele) is designated by the letter p and that of the recessive allele (*b* for the white allele) by the letter q. Because there are only two alleles, the sum of p and q must always equal 1 ($p + q = 1$).

In algebraic terms, the Hardy-Weinberg equilibrium is written as an equation. For a gene with two alternative alleles. *B* (frequency p) and *b* (frequency q), the equation looks like this:

p^2	+	$2pq$	+	q^2	=	1
Individuals homozygous for allele ***B***		Individuals heterozygous for alleles ***B*** and ***b***		Individuals homozygous for allele ***b***		

You will notice that not only does the sum of the allele frequencies p and q add up to 1, but so does the sum of the frequencies of genotypes.

Hardy-Weinberg Assumptions

The Hardy-Weinberg rule is based on certain assumptions. The equation on the facing page is true only if the following five assumptions are met:

1. The size of the population is very large or effectively infinite.
2. Individuals mate with one another at random.
3. There is no mutation.
4. There is no input of new copies of any allele from any extraneous source (such as migration from a nearby population) or losses of copies of alleles through emigration (individuals leaving the population).
5. All alleles are replaced equally from generation to generation (natural selection is not occurring).

Many populations, and most human populations, are large and randomly mating with respect to most traits (a few traits affecting appearance undergo strong sexual selection in humans). Thus, many populations are similar to the ideal population envisioned by Hardy and Weinberg. For some genes, however, the observed proportion of heterozygotes does not match the value calculated from the allele frequencies. When this occurs, it indicates that something is acting on the population to alter one or more of the genotypic frequencies, whether it is selection, nonrandom mating, migration, or some other factor. The factors that can affect the frequencies of alleles in a population are discussed in detail later in this chapter.

Case Study: Cystic Fibrosis in Humans

How valid are the predictions made by the Hardy-Weinberg equation? For many genes, they prove to be very accurate. As an example, consider the recessive allele responsible for the serious human disease cystic fibrosis. This allele (q) is present in Caucasians in North America at a frequency of 0.022. What proportion of Caucasian North Americans, therefore, is expected to express this trait? The frequency of double-recessive individuals (q^2) is expected to be:

$$q^2 = 0.022 \times 0.022 = 0.00048$$

which equals 0.48 in every 1,000 individuals or about 1 in every 2,000 individuals, very close to real estimates.

What proportion is expected to be heterozygous carriers? If the frequency of the recessive allele q is 0.022, then the frequency of the dominant allele p must be $p = 1 - q$ or:

$$p = 1 - 0.022 = 0.978$$

The frequency of heterozygous individuals ($2pq$) is thus expected to be:

$$2 \times 0.978 \times 0.022 = 0.043$$

It is estimated that 12 million individuals in the United States are carriers of the cystic fibrosis allele. In a population of 292 million people, that is a frequency of 0.041, very close to projections using the Hardy-Weinberg equation.

Putting the Concept to Work

Does the sum of allele frequencies always equal the sum of genotype frequencies? Discuss.

IN THE NEWS

Why Doesn't Natural Selection Eliminate Cystic Fibrosis? As you learned in this chapter, the frequency of the allele responsible for cystic fibrosis in the United States indicates that it is in Hardy-Weinberg equilibrium, and thus not undergoing evolutionary change. Why hasn't natural selection acted to eliminate cystic fibrosis from the human population? Recent experiments on mice offer an answer. They suggest that the nearly 5% of all Caucasians who carry just one copy of the *cf* allele—and thus don't suffer from the disease—are protected against another deadly scourge: cholera. A geneticist in Barcelona, Spain, announced results in 2008 indicating that the *cf* mutation known as *delta-F508*—a deletion of three DNA base pairs from among the 250,000 that make up the gene of the allele form responsible for half of all cases of cystic fibrosis—arose at least 52,000 years ago. This was before the settlement of Europe by modern humans but after humans migrated to Asia (among modern-day East Asians, only 1 in 100,000 develop the disease). The survival of this harmful allele among human populations for so long suggests that there must be a selective advantage to the disorder. A few months later, a University of North Carolina researcher announced results indicating what that advantage might be: The *cf* mutation offers increased resistance to deadly epidemics of cholera, by lessening the diarrhea that kills people with this disease. The researcher found that laboratory mice with one copy of the *cf* allele had half as many functioning chloride channels as normal mice, and so lost only half as much body water to diarrhea when injected with cholera toxin. While not suffering cystic fibrosis, he suggests, early Europeans with one *cf* allele were better able to survive the killing dehydration of cholera. Why wasn't this an advantage in East Asians? Because one *cf* allele also makes a person lose more salt in their sweat, and in hot climates excessive salt loss would result. It seems that chronic salt loss was a graver problem than occasional exposure to cholera, and because of this, natural selection in Asia favored the lesser of two evils.

TABLE 14.1 Agents of Evolution

Factor		Description
Mutation	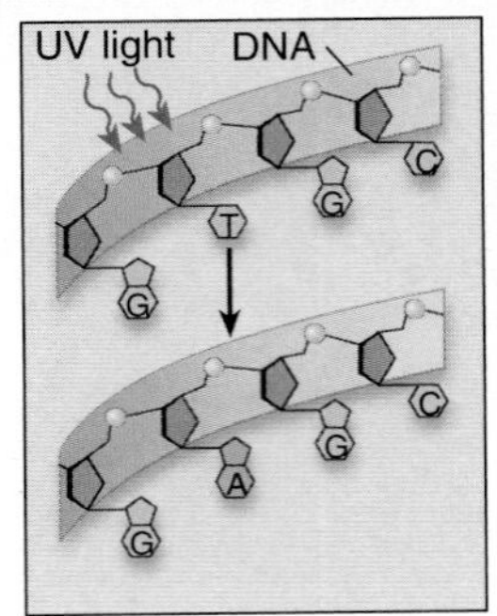	The ultimate source of genetic variation. Individual mutations occur so rarely that mutation alone does not change allele frequency much.
Migration		A very potent agent of change. Migration acts to promote evolutionary change by enabling populations that exchange members to converge toward one another. This bee carries pollen from one population of flowers to another.
Genetic drift		Chance events may result in the loss of individuals and therefore the loss of alleles in a population. Usually occurs only in very small populations. A small number of alleles can also impact a newly formed population, such as the founder effect on an island.
Nonrandom mating	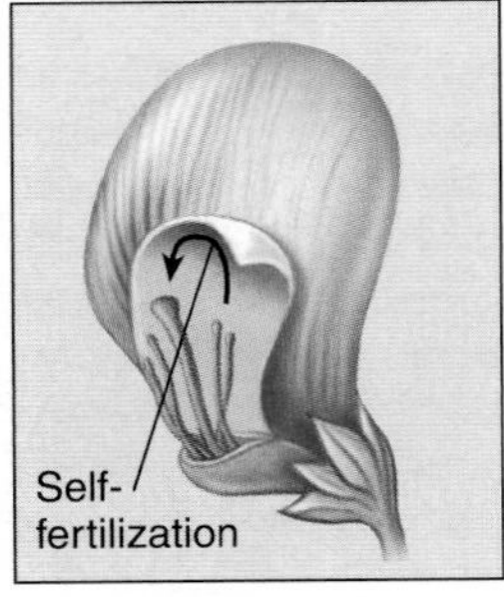	Inbreeding is the most common form of non-random mating. It does not alter allele frequency but decreases the proportion of heterozygotes (2*pq*). See text for explanation.
Selection	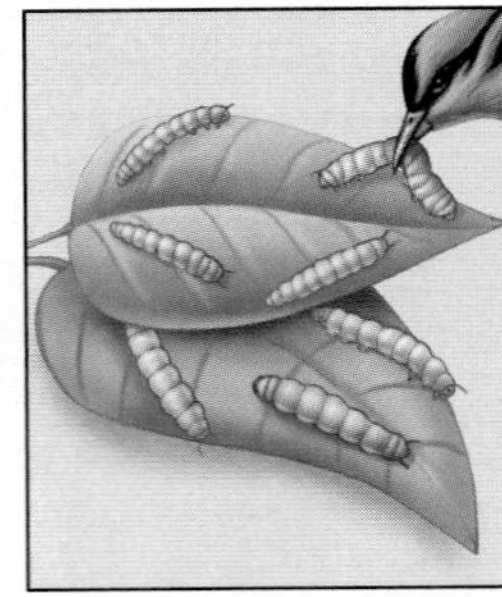	The only form that produces *adaptive* evolutionary changes. Only rapid for allele frequency greater than .01.

14.9 Agents of Evolution

LEARNING OBJECTIVE 14.9.1 Discuss five evolutionary forces that have the potential to significantly alter allele and genotype frequencies in populations.

Many factors can alter allele frequencies. But only five alter the proportions of homozygotes and heterozygotes enough to produce significant deviations from the proportions predicted by the Hardy-Weinberg rule (**table 14.1**):

1. Mutation
2. Migration
3. Genetic drift
4. Nonrandom mating
5. Selection

Mutation

A **mutation** is a change in a nucleotide sequence in DNA. For example, a T nucleotide could undergo a mutation and be replaced with an A nucleotide. Mutation from one allele to another obviously can change the proportions of particular alleles in a population. But mutation rates are generally too low to significantly alter Hardy-Weinberg proportions of common alleles. Many genes mutate 1 to 10 times per 100,000 cell divisions. Some of these mutations are harmful, while others are neutral or, even rarer, beneficial. Also, the mutations must affect the DNA of the germ cells (egg and sperm), or the mutation will not be passed on to offspring. The mutation rate is so slow that few populations are around long enough to accumulate significant numbers of mutations. However, no matter how rare, mutation is the ultimate source of genetic variation in a population.

Migration

Migration is defined in genetic terms as the movement of individuals between populations. It can be a powerful force, upsetting the genetic stability of natural populations. Migration includes movement of individuals into a population, called *immigration,* or the movement of individuals out of a population, called *emigration.* If the characteristics of the newly arrived individuals differ from those already there, and if the newly arrived individuals adapt to survive in the new area and mate successfully, then the genetic composition of the receiving population may be altered.

Sometimes migration is not obvious. Subtle movements include the drifting of gametes of plants, or of the immature stages of marine organisms, from one place to another. For example, a bee can carry pollen from a flower in one population to a flower in another population. By doing this, the bee may be introducing new alleles into a population. However it occurs, migration can alter the genetic characteristics of populations and cause a population to be out of Hardy-Weinberg equilibrium. Thus, migration can cause evolutionary change. The magnitude of effects of migration is based on two factors: (1) the proportion of migrants in the population, and (2) the difference in allele frequencies between the migrants and the original population. The actual evolutionary impact of migration is difficult to assess, and depends heavily on the selective forces prevailing at the different places where the populations occur.

Genetic Drift

In small populations, the frequencies of particular alleles may be changed drastically by chance alone. In an extreme case, individual alleles of a given gene may all be represented in few individuals, and may be accidentally lost if those individuals fail to reproduce or die. This loss of individuals and their alleles is due to random events rather than the fitness of the individuals carrying those alleles. This is not to say that alleles are always lost with genetic drift, but allele frequencies appear to change randomly, as if the frequencies were drifting; thus, random changes in allele frequencies is known as **genetic drift.** A series of small populations that are isolated from one another may come to differ strongly as a result of genetic drift.

When one or a few individuals migrate and become the founders of a new, isolated population at some distance from their place of origin, the alleles that they carry, even if rare in the source population, will become a significant fraction of the new population's genetic endowment. This is called the **founder effect.** As a result of the founder effect, rare alleles and combinations often become more common in new, isolated populations. The founder effect is particularly important in the evolution of organisms that occur on oceanic islands, such as the Galápagos Islands which Darwin visited. Most of the kinds of organisms that occur in such areas were probably derived from one or a few initial founders. In a similar way, isolated human populations are often dominated by the genetic features that were characteristic of their founders, particularly if only a few individuals were involved initially (figure 14.23).

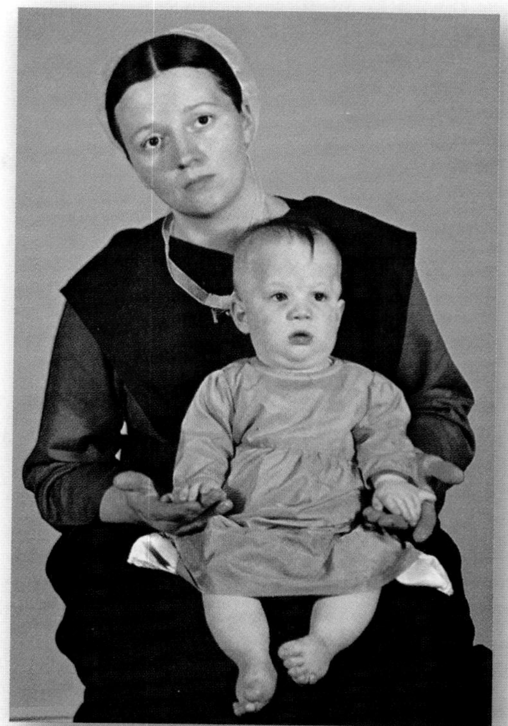

Figure 14.23 The founder effect.
This Amish woman is holding her child, who has Ellis-van Creveld syndrome. The characteristic symptoms are short limbs, dwarfed stature, and extra fingers. This disorder was introduced in the Amish community by one of its founders in the eighteenth century and persists to this day because of reproductive isolation.

Nonrandom Mating

Individuals with certain genotypes sometimes mate with one another either more or less frequently than would be expected on a random basis, a phenomenon known as **nonrandom mating.** One type of nonrandom mating is **inbreeding,** or mating with relatives, such as in the self-fertilization of a flower. Inbreeding increases the proportions of individuals that are homozygous because no individuals mate with any genotype but their own. As a result, inbred populations contain more homozygous individuals than predicted by the Hardy-Weinberg rule. This is why populations of self-fertilizing plants contain so many more homozygous individuals than outcrossing plants, which have a higher proportion of heterozygous individuals. Nonrandom mating alters genotype frequencies but not allele frequencies—the alleles are just distributed differently among the offspring.

Selection

As Darwin pointed out, some individuals leave behind more progeny than others, and the likelihood they will do so is affected by their inherited characteristics. The result of this process is called **selection** and was familiar even in Darwin's day to breeders of domestic animals. In so-called **artificial selection,** the breeder selects for the desired characteristics. For example, mating larger animals with each other produces offspring that are larger. In **natural selection,** Darwin suggested the environment plays this role, with conditions in nature determining which kinds of individuals in a population are the most fit (best suited to their environment) and so affecting the proportions of genes among individuals of future populations. The environment imposes the conditions that determine the results of selection and, thus, the direction of evolution.

Putting the Concept to Work

If a population is in Hardy-Weinberg equilibrium, is it evolving?

Why Cheetahs Are All Alike. Even if organisms do not move from place to place, occasionally their populations may be drastically reduced in size from flooding, drought, or other natural catastrophes, a form of genetic drift. The surviving individuals constitute a random genetic sample of the original population. Such a restriction in genetic variability has been termed the bottleneck effect. The very low levels of genetic variability seen in African cheetahs (*Acinonyx jubatus*) today is thought to reflect a near-extinction event 10,000 years ago. Only a few individuals are thought to have survived, and among them they represented only a tiny portion of the species's genetic variation—less than that seen in deliberately inbred strains of laboratory mice. African cheetahs are so genetically similar that they don't reject each other's skin grafts! Unfortunately, this lack of genetic variability is considered to be a significant contributing factor to a lack of disease resistance in African cheetahs. In 1983 a productive and healthy Oregon breeding colony of cheetahs was nearly wiped out by an epidemic of corona virus, a virus that kills less than 1% of infected domestic cats. Cheetah populations have simply lost the alleles that make other cat groups resistant. This vulnerability of cheetahs to disease is leading to a modern decline that threatens both natural and captive populations with extinction.

Kinds of Selection

LEARNING OBJECTIVE 14.9.2 Compare the operations of stabilizing, disruptive, and directional selection.

Selection operates in natural populations of a species as skill does in a football game. In any individual game, it can be difficult to predict the winner, because chance can play an important role in the outcome. But over a long season, the teams with the most skillful players usually win the most games. In nature, those individuals best suited to their environments tend to win the evolutionary game by leaving the most offspring, although chance can play a major role in the life of any one individual. While you cannot predict the fate of any one individual, just as you cannot predict "heads" or "tails" in any one coin toss, it is possible to predict which trait will tend to become more common in populations of a species. For example, it is possible to predict the proportion of heads after many coin tosses.

In nature, many traits, perhaps most, are affected by more than one gene. The interactions between genes are typically complex, as you saw in chapter 10. For example, alleles of many different genes play a role in determining human height (see figure 10.12). In such cases, selection operates on all the genes, influencing most strongly those that make the greatest contribution to the phenotype. How selection changes the population depends on which genotypes are favored. Three types of natural selection have been identified: stabilizing selection, disruptive selection, and directional selection. Figure 14.24 shows the results of these three types of selection on body size.

Figure 14.24 Three kinds of natural selection.

In the top panels, the *blue* areas indicate the phenotypes that are being selected for and the *red* areas are the phenotypes that are not being preferentially selected for. The bottom panels show the phenotypic results of the selection. (a) In *stabilizing selection,* individuals with midrange phenotypes are favored, with selection acting against both ends of the range of phenotypes. (b) In *disruptive selection,* individuals in the middle of the range of phenotypes of a certain trait are selected against, and the extreme forms of the trait are favored. (c) In *directional selection,* individuals concentrated toward one extreme of the array of phenotypes are favored.

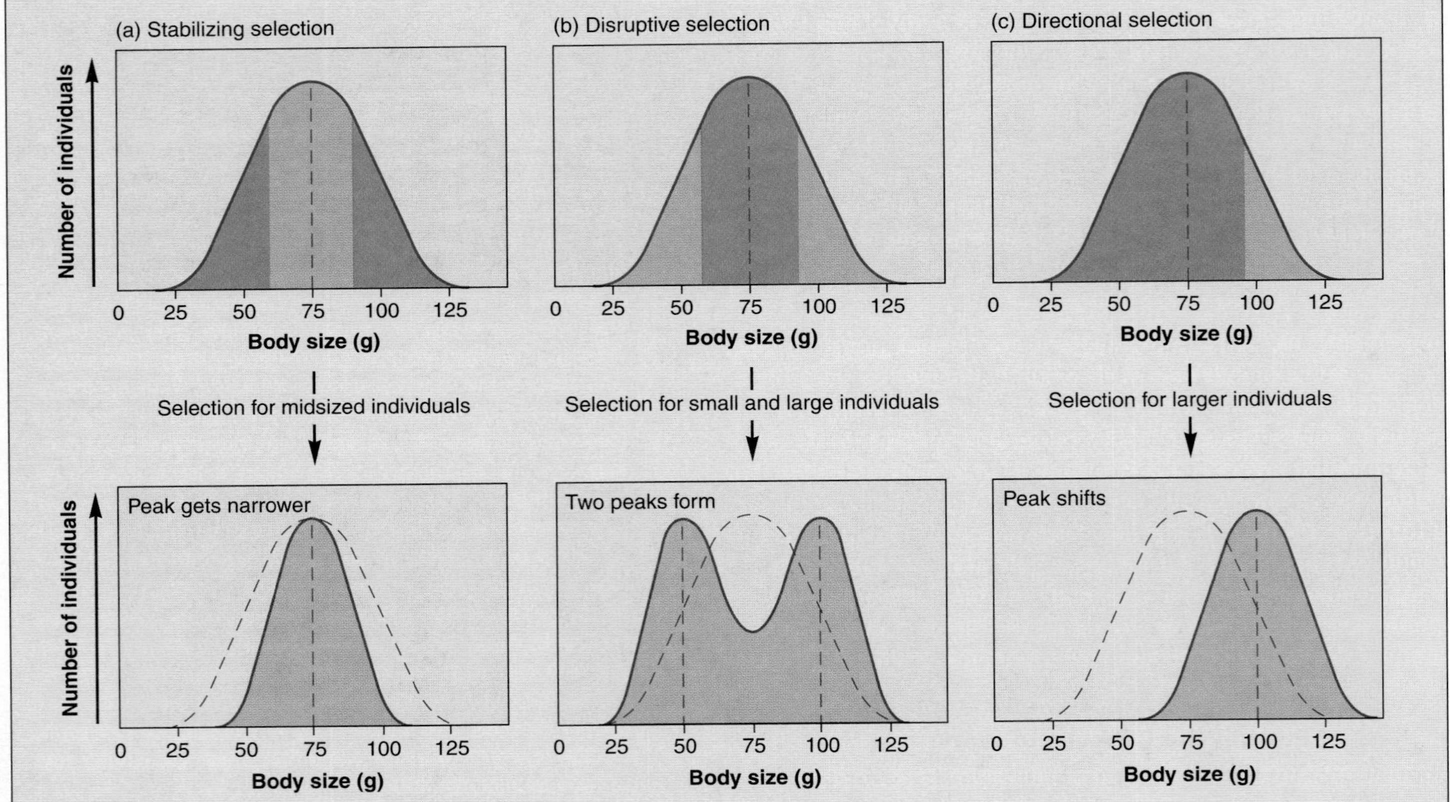

Stabilizing Selection

When selection acts to eliminate both extremes from an array of phenotypes—for example, eliminating the larger and smaller body sizes (**figure 14.24*a***)—the result is an increase in the frequency of the already common intermediate phenotype (a midsized body). This is called **stabilizing selection.** In effect, selection is operating to prevent change away from the middle range of values. In a classic study carried out after an "uncommonly severe storm of snow, rain, and sleet" on February 1, 1898, 136 starving English sparrows were collected and brought to the laboratory of H. C. Bumpus at Brown University in Providence, Rhode Island. Of these, 64 died and 72 survived. Bumpus took standard measurements on all the birds. He found that among the female birds that perished were many more individuals that had extreme measurements, either very large or very small. Selection had acted most strongly against these "extreme-sized" birds. Stabilizing selection does not change which phenotype is the most common of the population—the average-sized birds were already the most common phenotype—but rather makes it even more common by eliminating extremes. Many examples similar to Bumpus's female sparrows are known. In humans, infants with intermediate weight at birth have the highest survival rate (**figure 14.25*a***).

Disruptive Selection

In some situations, selection acts to eliminate the intermediate type (**figure 14.24*b***), resulting in the two more extreme phenotypes becoming more common in the population. This type of selection is called **disruptive selection.** A clear example is the different beak sizes of the African black-bellied seedcracker finch *Pyrenestes ostrinus* (**figure 14.25*b***). Populations of these birds contain individuals with large and small beaks, but very few individuals with intermediate-sized beaks. As their name implies, these birds feed on seeds, and the available seeds fall into two size categories: large and small. Only large-beaked birds, like the one on the left in the figure, can open the tough shells of large seeds, whereas birds with the smallest beaks, like the one on the right, are more adept at handling small seeds. Birds with intermediate-sized beaks are at a disadvantage with both seed types: unable to open large seeds and too clumsy to efficiently process small seeds. Consequently, selection acts to eliminate the intermediate phenotypes, partitioning the population into two distinct groups.

Directional Selection

When selection acts to eliminate one extreme from an array of phenotypes (**figure 14.24*c***), the alleles determining this extreme become less frequent in the population. This form of selection is called **directional selection.** An experiment set up to test directional selection is shown in **figure 14.25*c***. In the *Drosophila* population, flies that flew toward light, a behavior called phototropism, were eliminated from the population. The remaining flies were mated and the experiment repeated. After 20 generations of selected mating, flies exhibiting phototropism were far less frequent in the population.

Putting the Concept to Work

Selection for faster racehorses is no longer very successful, although it used to be. Can you think of a reason why, and what might be done to increase the success of such breeding programs?

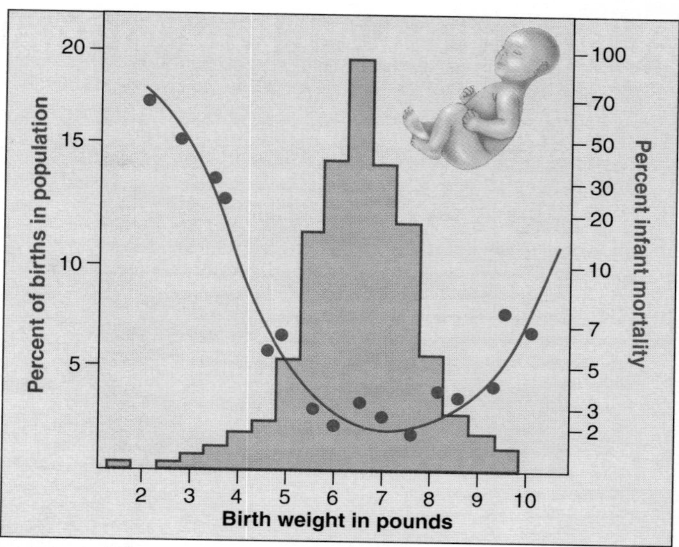

(a) Stabilizing selection for birth weight. The death rate among human babies is lowest at an intermediate birth weight between 7 and 8 pounds indicated by the *red* line. The intermediate weights are also the most common in the population, indicated by the *blue* area. Larger and smaller babies both occur less frequently and have a greater tendency to die at or near birth.

(b) Disruptive selection for large and small beaks. Differences in beak size in the black-bellied seedcracker finch of West Africa are the result of disruptive selection for two distinct food sources.

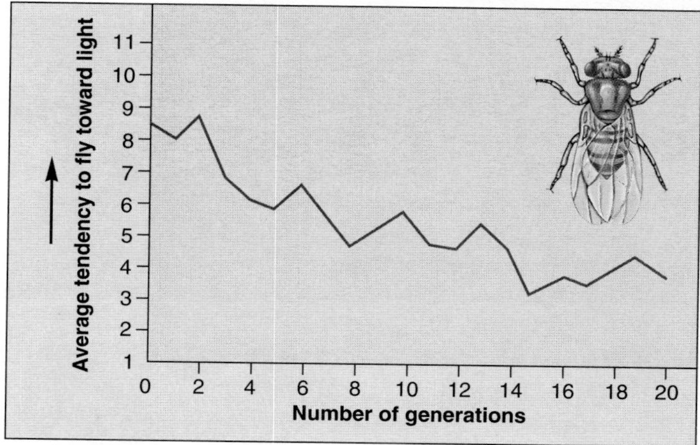

(c) Directional selection for negative phototropism in *Drosophila*. Individuals of the fly *Drosophila* were selectively bred. Flies that moved toward light were discarded; only flies that moved away from light were used as parents for the next generation. After 20 generations, the offspring had an ever greater tendency to avoid light.

Figure 14.25 Examples of selection.

Adaptation Within Populations

The Presbyterian Hospital, Chicago, Ill.

EXAMINATION OF BLOOD.

Case Number
Name of Patient Noel
Date 12/31, 1904
Room or Ward 7

MACROSCOPICAL AND QUANTITATIVE.

Appearance pale
Coagulability
Erythrocytes per cu. mm. (Thoma Zeiss). 2,880,000
Leucocytes per cu. mm. (Thoma Zeiss). 15,250
Hemoglobin (Von Fleischi) 50%
Specific gravity
Color index
Volume index

MICROSCOPICAL.

Fresh Specimen.

Erythrocytes—Color
Size irregular
Shape very irregular
Rouleaux formation
Leucocytes—Apparent increase in number
Ratio of granular to non-granular
Fibrin
Blood-platelets
Pigment
Plasmodium malariæ
Miscellaneous

Figure 14.26 The first known patient with sickle-cell disease.

Dr. Ernest Irons's blood examination report on his patient Walter Clement Noel, December 31, 1904, described his oddly shaped red blood cells.

14.10 Sickle-Cell Disease

LEARNING OBJECTIVE 14.10.1 Explain how stabilizing selection maintains sickle-cell disease in Central Africa.

In the time since Darwin suggested the pivotal role of natural selection in evolution, many examples have been found in which natural selection is clearly acting to change the genetic makeup of species, just as Darwin predicted. Here we will examine three examples: sickle-cell disease (a defect in human hemoglobin proteins), industrial melanism in European moths, and color selection in South American guppy populations.

Sickle-cell disease (which used to be called sickle-cell anemia) is a hereditary disease affecting hemoglobin molecules in the blood. It was first detected in 1904 in Chicago in a blood examination of an individual complaining of tiredness. You can see the original doctor's report in figure 14.26. The disorder arises as a result of a single nucleotide change in the gene encoding β-hemoglobin, one of the key proteins used by red blood cells to transport oxygen. The sickle-cell mutation changes the sixth amino acid in the β-hemoglobin chain (position B6) from glutamic acid (very polar) to valine (nonpolar). The unhappy result of this change is that the nonpolar *valine* at position B6, protruding from a corner of the hemoglobin molecule, fits nicely into a nonpolar pocket on the opposite side of another hemoglobin molecule; the nonpolar regions associate with each other. As the two-molecule unit that forms still has both a B6 valine and an opposite nonpolar pocket, other hemoglobins clump on, and long chains form as in figure 14.27*a*. The result is the deformed "sickle-shaped" red blood cell you see in figure 14.27*b*. In normal hemoglobin, by contrast, the polar amino acid *glutamic acid* occurs at position B6. This polar amino acid is not attracted to the nonpolar pocket, so no hemoglobin clumping occurs, and the cells are normal in shape, as in figure 14.27*c*.

Persons homozygous for the sickle-cell genetic mutation (referred to as the *s* allele) in the β-hemoglobin gene often have a reduced life span. This is because red blood cells that are sickled do not flow smoothly through the tiny capillaries but instead jam up and block blood flow, which interferes with oxygen transport. Heterozygous individuals, who have both a defective and a normal form of the gene, make enough functional hemoglobin to keep their red blood cells healthy.

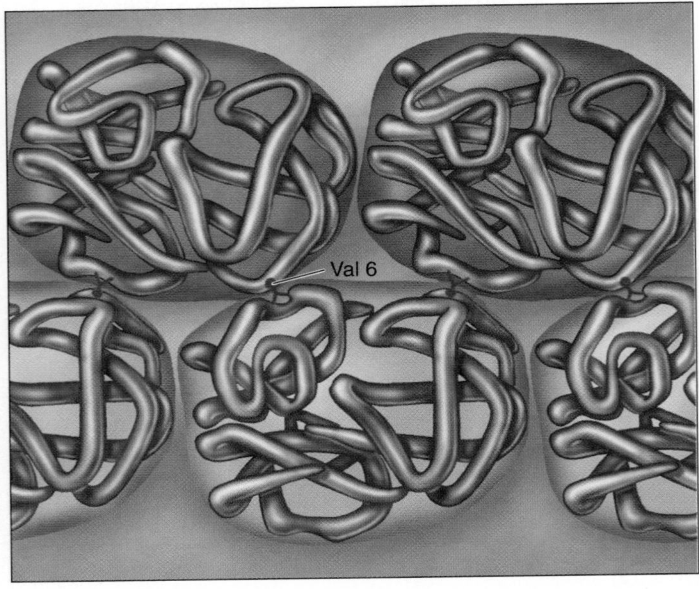

(a)

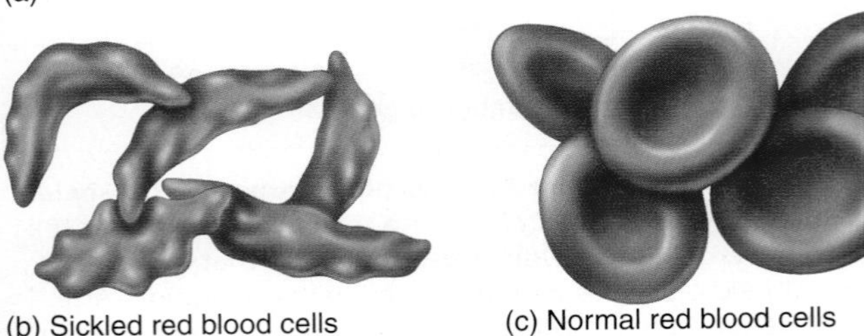

(b) Sickled red blood cells

(c) Normal red blood cells

Figure 14.27 Why the sickle-cell mutation causes hemoglobin to clump.

The Puzzle: Why So Common?

The disorder is now known to have originated in Central Africa, where the frequency of the sickle-cell allele is about 0.12. One in 100 people is homozygous for the defective allele and develops the fatal disorder. Sickle-cell disease affects roughly two African Americans out of every thousand but is almost unknown among other racial groups.

If Darwin is right, and natural selection drives evolution, then why has natural selection not acted against the defective allele in Africa and eliminated it from the human population there? Why is this potentially fatal allele instead relatively common there?

The Answer: Stabilizing Selection

The defective *s* allele has not been eliminated from Central Africa because people who are heterozygous for the sickle-cell allele are much less susceptible to malaria, one of the leading causes of death in Central Africa. Examine the maps in figure 14.28, and you will see the relationship between sickle-cell disease and malaria clearly. The upper map shows the frequency of the sickle-cell allele, the darker green areas indicating a 10% to 20% frequency of the allele. The map on the bottom indicates the distribution of malaria in dark orange. Clearly, the areas that are colored in darker green on the upper map overlap many of the dark orange areas in the map at the bottom. Although the population pays a high price—the many individuals in each generation who are homozygous for the sickle-cell allele die—the deaths are far fewer than would occur due to malaria if the heterozygous individuals were not malaria resistant. One in 5 individuals (20%) are heterozygous and survive malaria, while only 1 in 100 (1%) are homozygous and die of sickle-cell disease. Similar inheritance patterns of the sickle-cell allele are found in other countries frequently exposed to malaria, such as areas around the Mediterranean, India, and Indonesia. Natural selection has favored the sickle-cell allele in Central Africa and other areas hit by malaria because the payoff in survival of heterozygotes more than makes up for the price in death of homozygotes. This phenomenon is an example of **heterozygote advantage.**

Stabilizing selection (also called *balancing selection*) is thus acting on the sickle-cell allele: (1) selection tends to eliminate the sickle-cell allele because of its lethal effects on homozygous individuals, and (2) selection tends to favor the sickle-cell allele because it protects heterozygotes from malaria. Like a manager balancing a store's inventory, natural selection increases the frequency of an allele as long as there is something to be gained by it, until the cost balances the benefit.

Stabilizing selection occurs because malarial resistance counterbalances lethal sickle-cell disease. Malaria is a tropical disease that has essentially been eradicated in the United States since the early 1950s, and stabilizing selection has not favored the sickle-cell allele here. Africans brought to America several centuries ago have not gained any evolutionary advantage in all that time from being heterozygous for the sickle-cell allele. There is no benefit to being resistant to malaria if there is no danger of getting malaria anyway. As a result, the selection against the sickle-cell allele in America is not counterbalanced by any advantage, and the allele has become less common among African Americans than among native Africans living in Central Africa.

Stabilizing selection is thought to have influenced many other human genes in a similar fashion. The recessive *cf* allele causing cystic fibrosis is unusually common in northwestern Europeans. As discussed in the "In the News" feature on page 267, heterozygotes for the *cf* allele are protected from the dehydration caused by cholera, and the *cf* allele provides other advantages as well. Apparently the bacterium causing typhoid fever uses the healthy version of the CFTR protein (see page 86) to enter the cells it infects, but it cannot use the cystic fibrosis version of the protein. As with sickle-cell disease, heterozygotes are protected.

Putting the Concept to Work

The rare *c* allele of β-hemoglobin provides even more protection from malaria when homozygous than the *s* allele does, but leads to severe sickle-cell disease when heterozygous with the *s* allele (although not with the normal allele). Can you suggest a reason why the *c* allele is rare in Africa and the *s* allele is not?

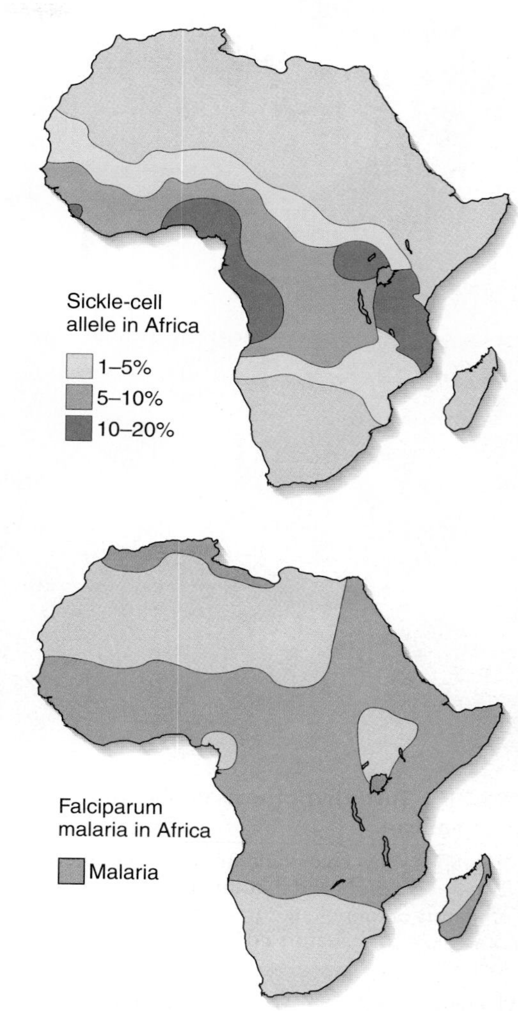

Figure 14.28 How stabilizing selection maintains sickle-cell disease.

The diagrams show the frequency of the sickle-cell allele (*top*) and the distribution of falciparum malaria (*bottom*). Falciparum malaria is one of the most devastating forms of the often fatal disease. As you can see, its distribution in Africa is closely correlated with that of the allele of the sickle-cell characteristic.

IMPLICATION FOR YOU 1 in 500 African Americans have sickle-cell disease (SCD). Although there is no cure, the antitumor drug hydroxyurea can be used to block expression of the disorder. Administration of hydroxyurea reverses the course of hemoglobin development, inducing the reading of the fetal hemoglobin gene in place of the adult hemoglobin gene, and in so doing preventing sickling in SCD patients. Can you suggest a reason why the substitution of fetal for adult hemoglobin might prevent sickling and so block expression of the disorder? If you yourself were to take hydroxyurea so that you expressed fetal rather than adult hemoglobin, what effect would you expect on your ability to run a race? (Please don't actually do this!)

Figure 14.29 Tutt's hypothesis explaining industrial melanism.

These photographs show color variants of the peppered moth (*Biston betularia*). Tutt proposed that the dark moth is more visible to predators on unpolluted trees (*top*), while the light moth is more visible to predators on bark blackened by industrial pollution (*bottom*).

IMPLICATION FOR YOU Peppered moths are creatures of the woodland. The moths you find in your house are much smaller, about the size of the end of your pinky. There are two very common types you may find in your home, Indian meal moths (called pantry moths) and clothes moths, whose larvae eat clothing. You can usually deal with clothes moths with ironing, vacuuming, moth balls, or by using chemical poisons called pyrethrins. Indian meal moths are a different story altogether, as you don't want the poison or smell of moth balls on your food. How can you rid your kitchen of a pantry moth infestation? After careful cleaning, you can use a commercial moth trap loaded with pheromones (powerful sexual attractants). It's a rare pantry moth that can resist their call. They fly in and can't fly back out and soon the trap will contain every moth in your kitchen. Why is this approach not also effective in blocking the damage caused by an infestation of clothing moths in your closets?

14.11 Peppered Moths and Industrial Melanism

LEARNING OBJECTIVE 14.11.1 **Assess the evidence that natural selection has led to melanism in moths.**

The peppered moth, *Biston betularia,* is a European moth that rests on tree trunks during the day. Until the mid-nineteenth century, almost every captured individual of this species had light-colored wings. From that time on, individuals with dark-colored wings increased in frequency in the moth populations near industrialized centers, until they made up almost 100% of these populations. Dark individuals had a dominant allele that was present but very rare in populations before 1850. Biologists soon noticed that in industrialized regions where the dark moths were common, the tree trunks were darkened almost black by the soot of pollution. Dark moths were much less conspicuous resting on them than light moths were. In addition, air pollution that was spreading in the industrialized regions had killed many of the light-colored lichens on tree trunks, making the trunks darker.

Selection for Melanism

Can Darwin's theory explain the increase in the frequency of the dark allele? Why did dark moths gain a survival advantage around 1850? An amateur moth collector named J. W. Tutt proposed in 1896 what became the most commonly accepted hypothesis explaining the decline of the light-colored moths. He suggested that light forms were more visible to predators on sooty trees that had lost their lichens. Consequently, birds ate the light moths resting on the trunks of darkened trees during the day. The dark forms, in contrast, were at an advantage because they were camouflaged (**figure 14.29**). Although Tutt initially had no evidence, British ecologist Bernard Kettlewell tested the hypothesis in the 1950s by rearing populations of peppered moths with equal numbers of dark and light individuals. Kettlewell then released these populations into two sets of woods: one near heavily polluted Birmingham, the other in unpolluted Dorset. Kettlewell set up traps in the woods to see how many of both kinds of moths survived. To evaluate his results, he had marked the released moths with a dot of paint on the underside of their wings, where birds could not see it.

In the polluted area near Birmingham, Kettlewell trapped 19% of the light moths, but 40% of the dark ones. This indicated that dark moths had a far better chance of surviving in these polluted woods, where the tree trunks were dark. In the relatively unpolluted Dorset woods, Kettlewell recovered 12.5% of the light moths but only 6% of the dark ones. This indicated that where the tree trunks were still light-colored, light moths had a much better chance of survival. Kettlewell later solidified his argument by placing dead moths on trees and filming birds looking for food. Sometimes the birds actually passed right over a moth that was the same color as its background.

Industrial Melanism

Industrial melanism is a term used to describe the evolutionary process in which darker individuals come to predominate over lighter individuals since the industrial revolution as a result of natural selection. The process is widely believed to have taken place because the dark organisms are better concealed from their predators in habitats that have been darkened by soot and other forms of industrial pollution, as suggested by Kettlewell.

Dozens of other species of moths have changed in the same way as the peppered moth in industrialized areas throughout Eurasia and North America, with dark forms becoming more common from the mid-nineteenth century onward as industrialization spread.

Selection Against Melanism

As of the second half of the twentieth century, with the widespread implementation of pollution controls, these trends are reversing, not only for the peppered moth in many areas in England but also for many other species of moths throughout the northern continents. These examples provide some of the best-documented instances of changes in allelic frequencies of natural populations as a result of natural selection due to specific factors in the environment.

In England, the air pollution promoting industrial melanism began to reverse following enactment of Clean Air legislation in 1956. Beginning in 1959, the *Biston* population at Caldy Common outside Liverpool has been sampled each year. The frequency of the melanic (dark) form dropped from a high of 94% in 1960 to a low of 19% in 1995 (**figure 14.30**). Similar reversals have been documented at numerous other locations throughout England. The drop correlates well with a drop in air pollution, particularly with tree-darkening sulfur dioxide and suspended particulates.

Interestingly, the same reversal of industrial melanism appears to have occurred in America during the same time that it was happening in England. Industrial melanism in the American subspecies of the peppered moth was not as widespread as in England, but it has been well documented at a rural field station near Detroit. Of 576 peppered moths collected there from 1959 to 1961, 515 were melanic, a frequency of 89%. The American Clean Air Act, passed in 1963, led to significant reductions in air pollution. Resampled in 1994, the Detroit field station peppered moth population had only 15% melanic moths! The moths in Liverpool and Detroit, both part of the same natural experiment, exhibit strong evidence of natural selection.

Reconsidering the Target of Natural Selection

Tutt's hypothesis, widely accepted in the light of Kettlewell's studies, is currently being reevaluated. The problem is that the recent selection against melanism does not appear to correlate with changes in tree lichens. At Caldy Common, the light form of the peppered moth began its increase in frequency long before lichens began to reappear on the trees. At the Detroit field station, the lichens never changed significantly as the dark moths first became dominant and then declined over the last 30 years. In fact, investigators have not been able to find peppered moths on Detroit trees at all, whether covered with lichens or not. Wherever the moths rest during the day, it does not appear to be on tree bark. Some evidence suggests they rest on leaves on the treetops, but no one is sure.

The action of selection may depend on other differences between light and dark forms of the peppered moth as well as their wing coloration. Researchers report, for example, a clear difference in their ability to survive as caterpillars under a variety of conditions. Perhaps natural selection is also targeting the caterpillars rather than the adults. While we can't yet say exactly what the targets of selection are, researchers are actively investigating this, one of the best-documented instances of natural selection in action.

Putting the Concept to Work

If birds aren't eating noncryptic moths, is there evidence of selection? What is it?

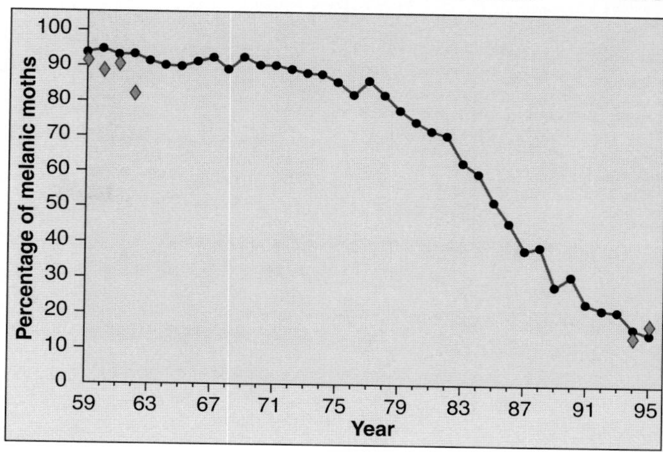

Figure 14.30 Selection against melanism.

The dots indicate the frequency of melanic *Biston betularia* moths at Caldy Common in England, sampled continuously from 1959 to 1995. Red diamonds indicate frequencies of melanic *B. betularia* in Michigan from 1959 to 1962 and from 1994 to 1995.

Natural Selection for Melanism in Mice. Melanism isn't restricted to just insects. Many mammals have melanic forms that are subject to natural selection in much the same way as moths. The coat color of desert pocket mice that live on differently colored rock habitats provides a clear-cut example of natural selection acting on melanism. In Arizona and New Mexico, these small wild pocket mice live in isolated black volcanic lava beds and the pale soils between them. Melanin synthesis during hair development of pocket mice is regulated by the receptor gene *MC1R*. Mutations that disable *MC1R* lead to melanism. Such mutations are dominant alleles, so whenever they are present in a population, dark pocket mice are seen. When wild populations of pocket mice were surveyed by biologists from the University of Arizona, there was a striking correlation between coat color and the color of the rock on which the population of pocket mice lived. As you can see in the upper photographs, the close match between coat color and background color gives the mice cryptic protection from avian predators, particularly owls. These mice are very visible when placed in the opposite habitats (lower photos).

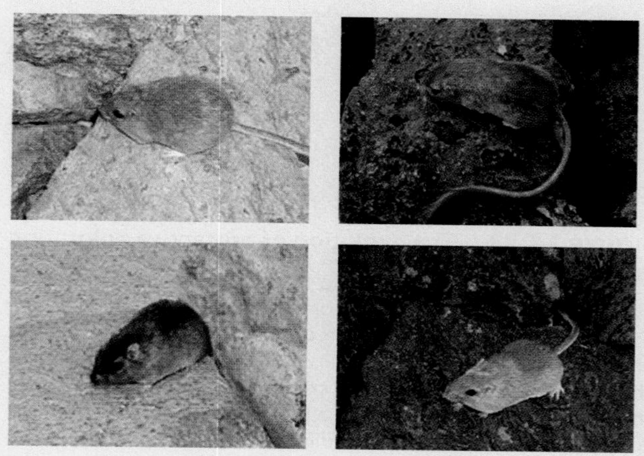

14.12 Selection on Color in Guppies

LEARNING OBJECTIVE 14.12.1 Analyze how predation might be altering coloration in Trinidad guppies.

To study evolution, biologists have traditionally investigated what has happened in the past, sometimes many millions of years ago, relying on observation rather than experiments to examine ideas about past events. Nonetheless, evolutionary biology is not entirely an observational science. In some circumstances evolutionary change can occur rapidly. Consequently, it is possible to establish experimental studies to test evolutionary hypotheses in real time. Although laboratory studies on fruit flies and other organisms have been common for more than 50 years, it has only been in recent years that scientists have started conducting experimental studies of evolution in nature. One excellent example of how observations of the natural world can be combined with rigorous experiments in the lab and in the field concerns research on the guppy, *Poecilia reticulata.*

Guppies Live in Different Environments

The guppy is a popular aquarium fish because of its bright coloration and prolific reproduction. In nature, guppies are found in small streams in northeastern South America and the nearby island of Trinidad. In Trinidad, guppies are found in many mountain streams. One interesting feature of several streams is that they have waterfalls. Amazingly, guppies and some other fish are capable of colonizing portions of the stream above the waterfall. The killifish, *Rivulus hartii,* is a particularly good colonizer; apparently on rainy nights, it will wriggle out of the stream and move through the damp leaf litter. Guppies are not so proficient, but they are good at swimming upstream. During flood seasons, rivers sometimes overflow their banks, creating secondary channels that move through the forest. During these occasions, guppies may be able to move upstream and invade pools above waterfalls. By contrast, not all species are capable of such dispersal and thus are only found in these streams below the first waterfall. One species whose distribution is restricted by waterfalls is the pike cichlid, *Crenicichla alta,* a voracious predator that feeds on other fish, including guppies.

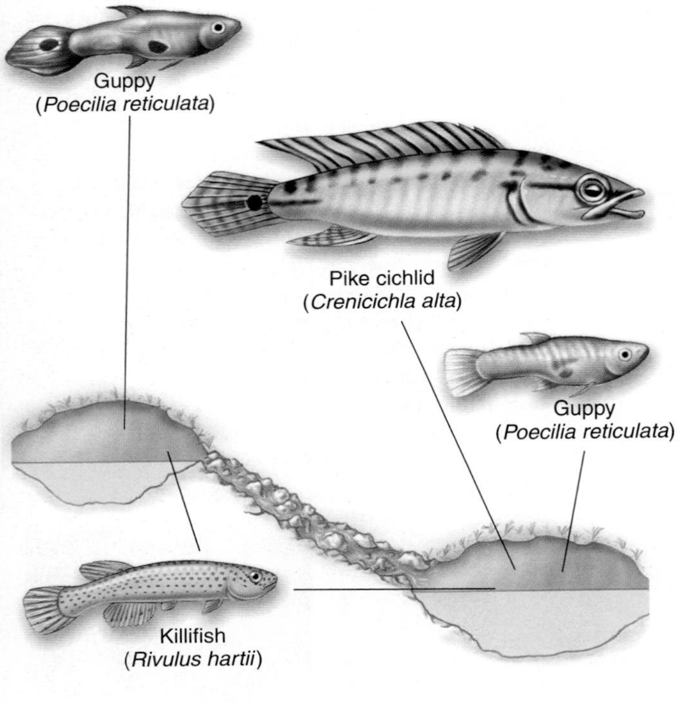

Because of these barriers to dispersal, guppies can be found in two very different environments. The guppies you see living in pools just below the waterfalls in **figure 14.31** are faced with predation by the pike cichlid. This substantial risk keeps rates of survival relatively low. By contrast, in similar pools just above the waterfall, the only predator present is the killifish, which only rarely preys on guppies. Guppy populations above and below waterfalls exhibit many differences. In the high-predation pools, male guppies exhibit the drab coloration you see in the guppies below the waterfall in **figure 14.31**. Moreover, they tend to reproduce at a younger age and attain relatively smaller adult sizes. By contrast, male fish above the waterfall in the figure display gaudy colors that they use to court females. Adults mature later and grow to larger sizes.

These differences suggest the function of natural selection. In the low-predation environment, males display gaudy colors and spots that help in mating. Moreover, larger males are most successful at holding territories and mating with females, and larger females lay more eggs. Thus, in the absence of predators, larger and more colorful fish may have produced

Guppy (*Poecilia reticulata*)
Pike cichlid (*Crenicichla alta*)
Guppy (*Poecilia reticulata*)
Killifish (*Rivulus hartii*)

Figure 14.31 The evolution of protective coloration in guppies.

In pools below waterfalls where predation is high, male guppies (*Poecilia reticulata*) are drab colored. In the absence of the highly predatory pike cichlid (*Crenicichla alta*), male guppies in pools above waterfalls are much more colorful and attractive to females. The killifish (*Rivulus hartii*) is also a predator but only rarely eats guppies. The evolution of these differences in guppies can be experimentally tested.

more offspring, leading to the evolution of those traits. In pools below the waterfall, however, natural selection would favor different traits. Colorful males are likely to attract the attention of the pike cichlid, and high predation rates mean that most fish live short lives; thus, individuals that are more drab and shunt energy into early reproduction, rather than into growth to a larger size, are likely to be favored by natural selection.

The Experiments

Although the differences between guppies living above and below the waterfalls suggest that they represent evolutionary responses to differences in the strength of predation, alternative explanations are possible. Perhaps, for example, only very large fish are capable of swimming upstream past the waterfall to colonize pools. If this were the case, then the new population would be established solely by individuals with genes for large size.

Laboratory Experiment. The only way to rule out such alternative possibilities is to conduct a controlled experiment. John Endler, now of the University of California, Santa Barbara, conducted the first experiments in large pools in laboratory greenhouses. At the start of the experiment, a group of 2,000 guppies was divided equally among 10 large pools. Six months later, pike cichlids were added to four of the pools and killifish to another four, with the remaining two pools left to serve as "no predator" controls. Fourteen months later (which corresponds to 10 guppy generations), the scientists compared the populations. You can see their results in figure 14.32*a*. The guppies in the killifish pools (the blue line) and control pools (the green line) were notably large, brightly colored fish with about 13 colorful spots per individual. In contrast, the guppies in the pike cichlid pools (the red line) were smaller and drab in coloration, with a reduced number of spots (about 9 per fish). These results clearly suggest that predation can lead to rapid evolutionary change, but do these laboratory experiments reflect what occurs in nature?

A control experiment, as discussed on page 23, is an experiment in which no variable is altered. It is usually run in parallel with an experiment in which a variable has been changed in order to test a hypothesis.

Field Experiment. To find out, Endler and colleagues—including David Reznick, now at the University of California, Riverside—located two streams that had guppies in pools below a waterfall, but not above it (see the photograph in figure 14.32*b*). As in other Trinidadian streams, the pike cichlid was present in the lower pools, but only the killifish was found above the waterfalls. The scientists then transplanted guppies to the upper pools and returned at several-year intervals to monitor the populations. Despite originating from populations in which predation levels were high, the transplanted populations rapidly evolved the traits characteristic of low-predation guppies: they matured late, attained greater size and had brighter colors. Control populations in the lower pools, by contrast, continued to be drab and matured early and at smaller sizes. Laboratory studies confirmed that the differences between the populations were the result of genetic differences. These results demonstrate that substantial evolutionary change can occur in less than 12 years. The results give strong support to the theory of evolution by natural selection.

Putting the Concept to Work

How might increasing the numbers of pike cichlids in a population of guppies influence the evolution of color in the guppies?

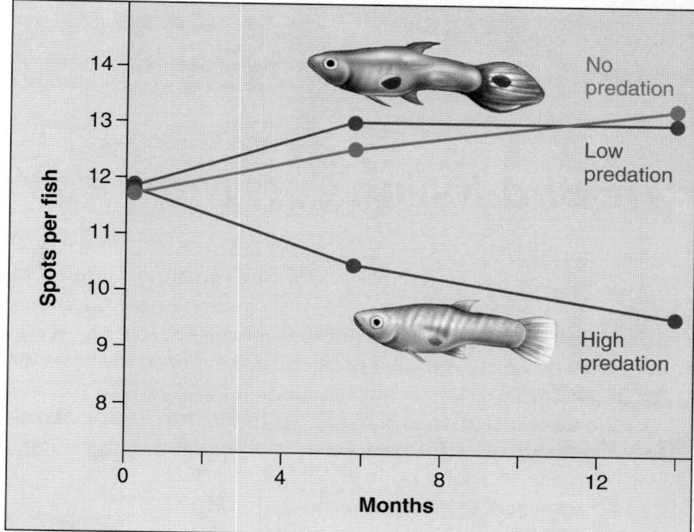

(a)

(b)

Figure 14.32 Evolutionary change in spot number.

(a) Guppies raised in low-predation or no-predation environments in laboratory greenhouses had a greater number of spots, whereas selection in more dangerous environments, like the pools with the highly predatory pike cichlid, led to less conspicuous fish. (b) The same results are seen in field experiments conducted in pools above and below waterfalls.

IMPLICATION FOR YOU Many people raise guppies as a hobby. Purchasing a few fish at the local pet store can soon lead to a very large number of guppies in your fish tank, as they breed prodigiously. After several generations of such breedings, however, sickly and deformed individuals begin to be seen in increasing numbers. What might be happening? Have you ever raised goldfish? Did this ever happen to your goldfish?

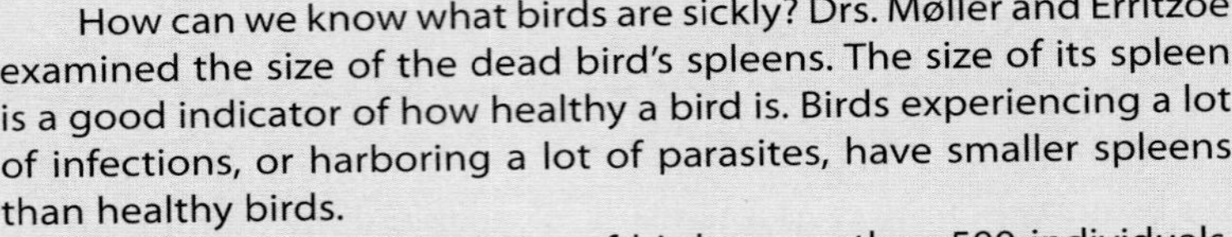

Author's Corner

Are Bird-Killing Cats Nature's Way of Making Better Birds?

Death is not pretty, early in the morning on the doorstep. A small dead bird was left at our front door one morning, lying by the newspaper as if it might at any moment fly away. I knew it would not. Like other birds before it, it was a gift to our household by Feisty, a cat who lives with us. Feisty is a killer of birds, and every so often he leaves one for us, like rent.

We have four cats, and the other three, true housecats, would not know what to do with a bird. Feisty is different, a long-haired gray Persian with the soul of a hunter. While the other three cats sleep safely in the house with us, Feisty spends most nights outside, prowling.

Feisty's nocturnal donations are not well received by my family. More than once it has been suggested, as we donate the bird to the trash can, that perhaps Feisty would be happier living in the country.

As a biologist I try to take a more scientific view. I tell my girls that getting rid of Feisty is unwarranted, because hunting cats like Feisty actually help birds, in a Darwinian sort of way. Like an evolutionary quality control check, I explain, predators ensure that only those individuals of a population that are better suited to their environment contribute to the next generation, by the simple expedient of removing the lesser suited. By taking the birds who are least able to escape predation—the sick and the old—Feisty culls the local bird population, leaving it on average a little better off.

That's what I tell my girls. It all makes sense, from a biological point of view, and it is a story they have heard before, in movies like *Never Cry Wolf*, and *The Lion King*. So Feisty is given a reprieve, and survives to hunt another night.

What I haven't told my girls is how little evidence actually backs up this pretty defense of Feisty's behavior. My explanation may be couched in scientific language, but without proof this "predator-as-purifier" tale is no more than a hypothesis. It might be true, and then again it might not. By such thin string has Feisty's future with our family hung.

Recently the string became a strong cable. Two French biologists put the hypothesis I had been using to defend Feisty to the test. To my great relief, it was supported.

Drs. Anders Møller and Johannes Erritzoe of the Université Pierre et Marie Curie in Paris devised a simple way to test the hypothesis. They compared the health of birds killed by domestic cats like Feisty with that of birds killed in accidents such as flying into glass windows or moving cars. Glass windows do not select for the weak or infirm—a healthy bird flies into a glass window and breaks its neck just as easily as a sickly bird. If cats are actually selecting the less-healthy birds, then their prey should include a larger proportion of sickly individuals than those felled by flying into glass windows.

How can we know what birds are sickly? Drs. Møller and Erritzoe examined the size of the dead bird's spleens. The size of its spleen is a good indicator of how healthy a bird is. Birds experiencing a lot of infections, or harboring a lot of parasites, have smaller spleens than healthy birds.

They examined 18 species of birds, more than 500 individuals. In all but two species (robins and goldcrests) they found that the spleens of birds killed by cats were significantly smaller than those killed accidentally. We're not splitting hairs here, talking about some minor statistical difference. Spleens were on average a third smaller in cat-killed birds. In five bird species (blackcaps, house sparrows, lesser whitethroats, skylarks, and spotted flycatchers), the spleens of birds pounced on by cats were less than half the size of those killed by flying at speed into glass windows or moving cars.

As a control to be sure that additional factors were not operating, the Paris biologists checked for other differences between birds killed by cats and birds killed accidentally. Weight, sex, and wing length, all of which you could imagine might be important, were not significant. Cat-killed birds had, on average, the same weight, proportion of females, and wing length as accident-killed birds.

One other factor did make a difference: age. About 50% of the birds killed accidentally were young, while fully 70% of the birds killed by cats were. Apparently it's not quite so easy to catch an experienced old codger as it is a callow youth.

So Feisty was just doing Darwin's duty, I pleaded, informing my girls that the birds he catches would soon have died anyway. But a dead bird on a doorstep argues louder than any science, and they remained unconvinced.

They are my daughters, and thus not ones to give in without a fight. Scouring the Internet, they assembled this counter-argument: Predatory house cats not unlike Feisty, as well as feral cats (domesticated cats that have been abandoned to the wild), are causing major problems for native bird populations of England, New Zealand, and Australia, as well as here in the United States. Although house cats like Feisty have the predatory instincts of their ancestors, they seem to lack the restraint that their wild relatives have. Most wild cats hunt only when hungry, but pet and feral cats seem to "love the kill," not killing for food but for sport.

So Darwin and I lost this argument. It seems I must restrict Feisty's hunting expeditions after all. While a little pruning may benefit a bird population, wholesale slaughter only devastates it. I will always see a lion whenever I look at Feisty on the prowl, but it will be a lion restricted to indoor hunting.

How Species Form

14.13 The Biological Species Concept

LEARNING OBJECTIVE 14.13.1 Define the biological species concept.

A key aspect of Darwin's theory of evolution is his proposal that small adaptations (what is called microevolution) lead ultimately to large-scale changes leading to species formation and higher taxonomic groups (macroevolution). The way natural selection leads to the formation of new species has been thoroughly documented by biologists, who have observed the stages of the species-forming process, or **speciation,** in many different plants and animals. Speciation usually involves successive change: first, local populations become increasingly specialized; then, if they become different enough, natural selection may act to keep them that way.

Before we can discuss how one species gives rise to another, we need to understand exactly what a species is. The **biological species concept** defines species as "groups of actually or potentially interbreeding natural populations which are reproductively isolated from other such groups." In other words, the biological species concept says that a species is composed of populations whose members mate with each other and produce fertile offspring—or would do so if they came into contact. Conversely, populations whose members do not mate with each other or who cannot produce fertile offspring are said to be **reproductively isolated** and, thus, members of different species.

What causes reproductive isolation? If organisms cannot interbreed or cannot produce fertile offspring, they clearly belong to different species. However, some populations that are considered to be separate species can interbreed and produce fertile offspring, but they ordinarily do not do so under natural conditions. They are still considered to be reproductively isolated in that genes from one species generally will not be able to enter the gene pool of the other species. Table 14.2 summarizes the steps at which barriers to successful reproduction may occur. Examine this table carefully. We will return to it throughout our discussion of species formation. Such barriers are termed **reproductive isolating mechanisms** because they prevent genetic exchange between species. We will first discuss *prezygotic isolating mechanisms,* those that prevent the formation of zygotes. Then we will examine *postzygotic isolating mechanisms,* those that prevent the proper functioning of zygotes after they have formed.

Even though the definition of what constitutes a species is of fundamental importance to evolutionary biology, this issue has still not been completely settled and is currently the subject of considerable research and debate. For example, the biological species concept has had a number of problems. Plants of different species cross-fertilize and produce fertile hybrids at much higher frequencies than first thought. Hybridization also occurs in animal populations. This is not to say that hybridization is rampant, but it is common enough to cast doubt about whether reproductive isolation is the only force maintaining the integrity of species.

Putting the Concept to Work

Studies of DNA reveal that modern humans interbred with Neanderthals. Does this mean the two were the same species?

TABLE 14.2 Isolating Mechanisms

Mechanism		Description
Prezygotic Isolating Mechanisms		
Geographic isolation		Species occur in different areas, which are often separated by a physical barrier such as a river or mountain range.
Ecological isolation	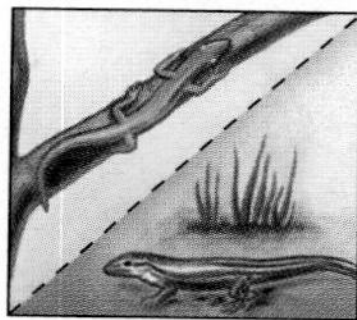	Species occur in the same area, but they occupy different habitats. Survival of hybrids is low because they are not adapted to either environment of their parents.
Temporal isolation		Species reproduce in different seasons or at different times of the day.
Behavioral isolation		Species differ in their mating rituals.
Mechanical isolation	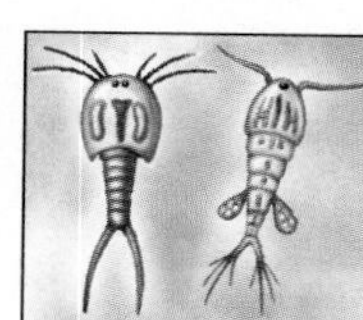	Structural differences between species prevent mating.
Prevention of gamete fusion	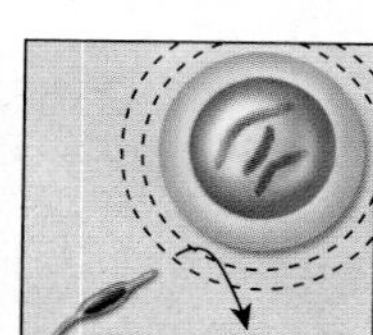	Gametes of one species function poorly with the gametes of another species or within the reproductive tract of another species.
Postzygotic Isolating Mechanisms		
Hybrid inviability or infertility		Hybrid embryos do not develop properly, hybrid adults do not survive in nature, or hybrid adults are sterile or have reduced fertility.

14.14 Isolating Mechanisms

LEARNING OBJECTIVE 14.14.1 Describe five prezygotic isolating mechanisms, comparing them to postzygotic mechanisms.

Prezygotic Isolating Mechanisms

Geographical Isolation. This mechanism is perhaps the easiest to understand; species that exist in different areas are not able to interbreed. The two populations of flowers in the first panel of table 14.2 are separated by a mountain range and so would not be capable of interbreeding.

Ecological Isolation. Even if two species occur in the same area, they may utilize different portions of the environment and thus not hybridize because they do not encounter each other, like the lizards in the second panel of table 14.2. One lives on the ground and the other in the trees. Another example in nature is the ranges of lions and tigers in India. Their ranges overlapped until about 150 years ago. Even when they did overlap, however, there were no records of natural hybrids. Lions stayed mainly in the open grassland and hunted in groups called prides; tigers tended to be solitary creatures of the forest. Because of their ecological and behavioral differences, lions and tigers rarely came into direct contact with each other, even though their ranges overlapped thousands of square kilometers. Figure 14.33 shows that hybrids are possible; the liger shown in figure 14.33*c* is a hybrid of a male lion and a female tiger (a tigon is the hybrid of a male tiger and a female lion). These matings do not occur in the wild but can happen in artificial environments such as zoos.

(a)

(b)

(c)

Figure 14.33 Lions and tigers are ecologically isolated.

The ranges of lions and tigers used to overlap in India. However, lions and tigers do not hybridize in the wild because they utilize different portions of the habitat. (a) Tigers are solitary animals that live in the forest, whereas (b) lions live in open grassland. (c) Hybrids, such as this liger, have been successfully produced in captivity, but hybridization does not occur in the wild.

Temporal Isolation. *Lactuca graminifolia* and *L. canadensis,* two species of wild lettuce, grow together along roadsides throughout the southeastern United States. Hybrids between these two species are easily made experimentally and are completely fertile. But such hybrids are rare in nature because *L. graminifolia* flowers in early spring and *L. canadensis* flowers in summer. This is called temporal isolation and is shown in the third panel in table 14.2. When the blooming periods of these two species overlap, as they do occasionally, the two species do form hybrids, which may become locally abundant.

Behavioral Isolation. In chapter 21, we will consider the often elaborate courtship and mating rituals of some groups of animals, which tend to keep these species distinct in nature even if they inhabit the same places. This behavioral isolation is pictured in the fourth panel of table 14.2. For example, mallard and pintail ducks are perhaps the two most common freshwater ducks in North America. In captivity they produce completely fertile offspring, but in nature they nest side-by-side and rarely hybridize.

Mechanical Isolation. The prevention of mating due to structural differences between related species of animals and plants is called mechanical isolation and is shown in panel five of table 14.2. Flowers of related species of plants often differ significantly in their proportions and structures. Some of these differences limit the transfer of pollen from one plant species to another. For example, bees may pick up the pollen of one species on a certain place on their bodies; if this area does not come into contact with the receptive structures of the flowers of another plant species, the pollen is not transferred.

As discussed on page 336, the flower contains the sexual structures in a group of plants called angiosperms. The male gametes, called pollen, are produced on one part of the flower and the female gametes, eggs, are produced on another part of the flower.

Prevention of Gamete Fusion. In animals that shed their gametes directly into water, eggs and sperm derived from different species may not attract one another. Many land animals may not hybridize successfully because the sperm of one species may function so poorly within the reproductive tract of another that fertilization never takes place. In plants, the growth of pollen tubes may be impeded in species hybrids. In both plants and animals, the operation of such isolating mechanisms prevents the union of gametes even after mating.

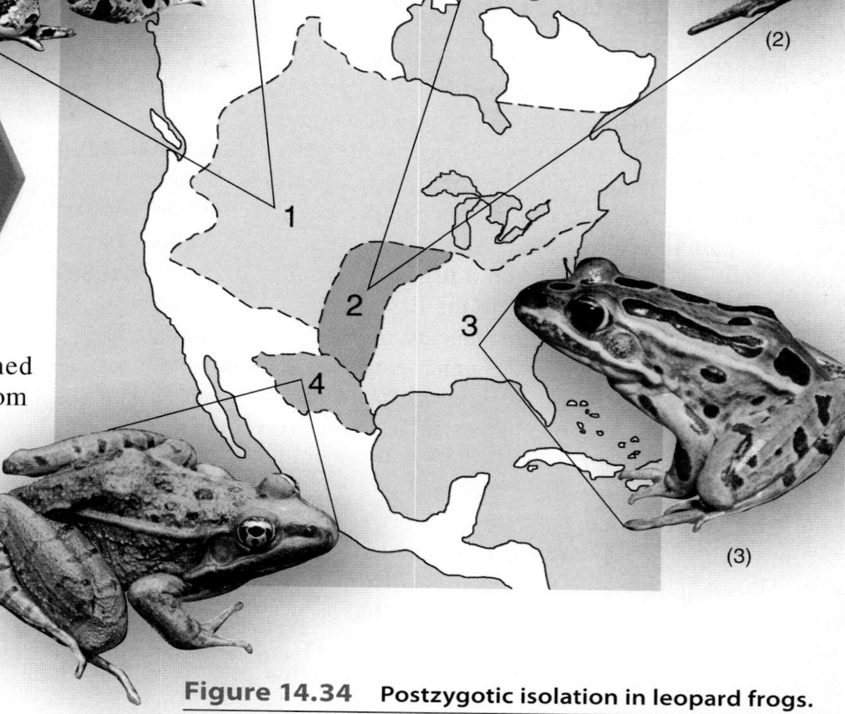

Figure 14.34 Postzygotic isolation in leopard frogs.

Numbers indicate the following species in the geographic ranges shown: (1) *Rana pipiens;* (2) *Rana blairi;* (3) *Rana sphenocephala;* (4) *Rana berlandieri.* These four species resemble one another closely in their external features. Their status as separate species was first suspected when hybrids between them were found to produce defective embryos in the laboratory. Subsequent research revealed that the mating calls of the four species differ substantially, indicating that the species have both pre- and postzygotic isolating mechanisms.

Postzygotic Isolating Mechanisms

If hybrid matings do occur, and zygotes are produced, many factors may still prevent those zygotes from developing into normally functioning, fertile individuals. In hybrids, the genetic complements of two species may be so different that they cannot function together normally in embryonic development. For example, hybridization between sheep and goats usually produces embryos that die in the earliest developmental stages.

Figure 14.34 shows four species of leopard frogs (genus *Rana*) and their ranges throughout North America. It was assumed for a long time that they constituted a single species. However, careful examination revealed that although the frogs appear similar, successful mating between them is rare because of problems that occur as the fertilized eggs develop. Many of the hybrid combinations cannot be produced even in the laboratory.

Even if hybrids survive the embryo stage, however, they may not develop normally. If the hybrids are weaker than their parents, they will almost certainly be eliminated in nature. Even if they are vigorous and strong, as in the case of the mule, a hybrid between a female horse and a male donkey, they may still be sterile and thus incapable of contributing to succeeding generations. Sterility may result in hybrids because the development of sex organs may be abnormal, because the chromosomes derived from the respective parents may not pair properly, or from a variety of other causes.

Putting the Concept to Work

Why do ligers and tigons not occur in the wild?

IN THE NEWS

Why Does a Wolf Not Cross the Road? Geographical isolation need not involve massive barriers like mountain ranges. Constructing a road across a forest creates a barrier that many animals cannot cross. Anyone traveling by car who counts the roadkill can see one reason why. A less obvious reason is that many animals simply don't like to be close to the humans that roads bring to the forest. A recent study of wolves in Wisconsin has revealed that road density has been a critical factor in the disappearance of breeding wolf populations in that state. The critical density, measured in several studies extending back a century, seems to be roughly 0.5 km of road per square km of forest. At higher road densities, radio-collared wolves simply move away to regions where they can live farther from roads.

Inquiry & Analysis

Does Natural Selection Act on Enzyme Polymorphism?

The essence of Darwin's theory of evolution is that, in nature, selection favors some gene alternatives over others. Many studies of natural selection have focused on genes encoding enzymes because populations in nature tend to possess many alternative alleles of their enzymes (a phenomenon called *enzyme polymorphism*). Often investigators have looked to see if weather influences which alleles are more common in natural populations. A particularly nice example of such a study was carried out on a fish, the mummichog (*Fundulus heteroclitus*), which ranges along the East Coast of North America. Researchers studied allele frequencies of the gene encoding the enzyme lactate dehydrogenase, which catalyzes the conversion of pyruvate to lactate. As you learned in chapter 7, this reaction is a key step in energy metabolism, particularly when oxygen is in short supply. There are two common alleles of lactate dehydrogenase in these fish populations, with allele *a* being a better catalyst at lower temperatures than allele *b*.

In an experiment, investigators sampled the frequency of allele *a* in 41 fish populations located over 14 degrees of latitude, from Jacksonville, Florida (31° North), to Bar Harbor, Maine (44° North). Annual mean water temperatures change 1° C per degree change in latitude. The survey is designed to test a prediction of the hypothesis that natural selection acts on this enzyme polymorphism. If it does, then you would expect that allele *a,* producing a better "low-temperature" enzyme, would be more common in the colder waters of the more northern latitudes. The graph on the right presents the results of this survey. The points on the graph are derived from pie chart data such as shown for 20 populations in the map (a **pie chart diagram** assigns a slice of the pie to each variable; the size of the slice is proportional to the contribution made by that variable to the total). The blue line on the graph is the line that best fits the data (a **"best-fit" line,** also called a **regression line,** is determined statistically by a process called *regression analysis*).

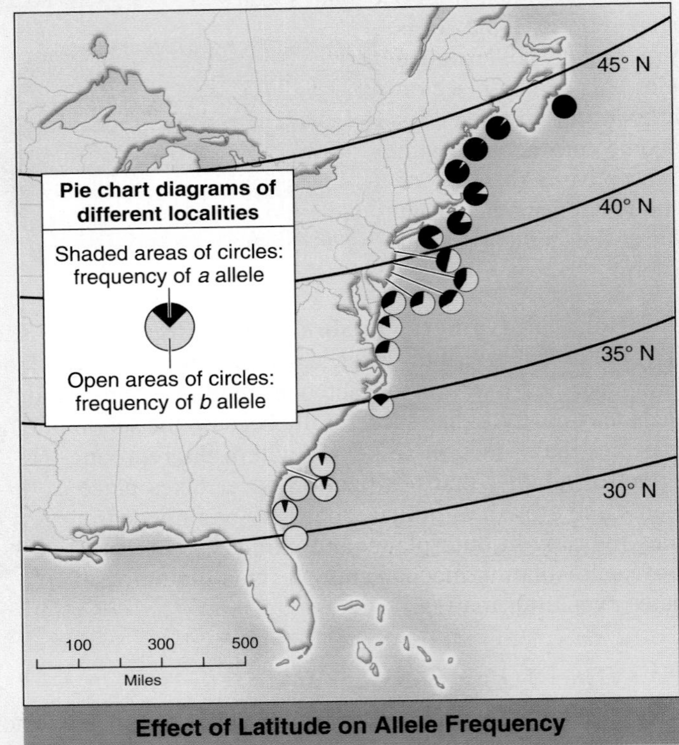

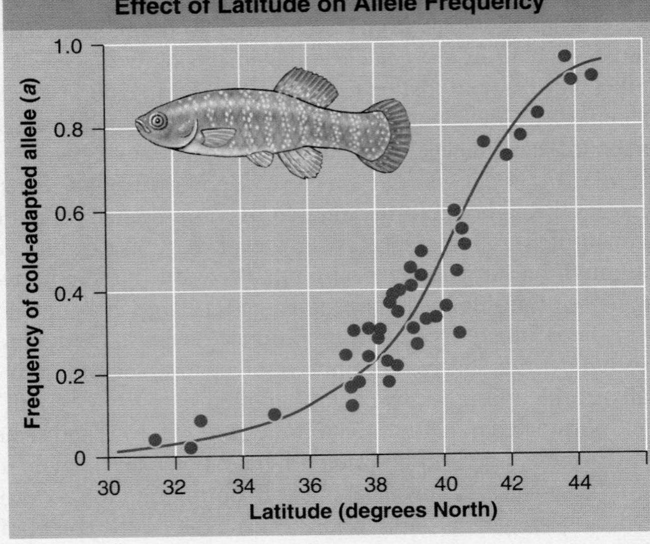

Analysis

1. **Applying Concepts**
   a. In the fish population located at 35° N latitude, what is the frequency of the *a* allele? Locate this point on the graph.
   b. Compare the frequency of allele *a* among fish captured in waters at 44° N latitude with the frequency among fish captured at 31° N latitude. Is there a pattern? Describe it.
2. **Interpreting Data** At what latitude do fish populations exhibit the greatest variability in allele *a* frequency?
3. **Making Inferences**
   a. Are fish populations in cold waters at 44° N latitude more or less likely to contain heterozygous individuals than fish populations in warm waters at 31° N latitude?
   b. Where along this latitudinal gradient in the frequency of allele *a* would you expect to find the highest frequency of heterozygous individuals? Why?
4. **Drawing Conclusions** Are the differences in population frequencies of allele *a* consistent with the hypothesis that natural selection is acting on the alleles encoding this enzyme? Explain.

Summary of Learning Outcomes

Evolution

Darwin's Voyage on HMS *Beagle*

14.1.1 Darwin's theory that evolution is a consequence of natural selection is overwhelmingly accepted by scientists and is considered to be a central concept of the science of biology.

Darwin's Evidence

14.2.1 The fossils and patterns of life that Darwin observed on his voyage eventually convinced him that evolution had taken place.

The Theory of Natural Selection

14.3.1 Key to Darwin's hypothesis was the observation by Malthus that the food supply limits population growth. A population grows only as large as can be supported by available food, which limits geometric growth of a population.

- Using Malthus's observations and his own, Darwin proposed that individuals that are better suited to their environments survive to produce offspring, gaining the opportunity to pass their characteristics on to future generations, what Darwin called natural selection.

Darwin's Finches: Evolution in Action

The Beaks of Darwin's Finches

14.4.1 By observing the different sizes and shapes of beaks in the closely related finches of the Galápagos Islands and correlating the beaks with the types of food consumed, Darwin concluded that the birds' beaks were modified from an ancestral species based on the food available, each suited to its food supply. Scientists have identified a gene, *BMP4*, that is expressed differently in birds with differently shaped beaks.

How Natural Selection Produces Diversity

14.5.1 The 14 species of finches found on the Galápagos Islands off the coast of South America descended from a mainland species, long-ago migrants that adapted to conditions on the islands, filling unoccupied niches in a variety of ways.

The Theory of Evolution

The Evidence for Evolution

14.6.1 The fossil record provides a clear record of successive evolutionary change. The titanothere, shown here from **figure 14.14**, and its ancestors are known only from the fossil record, which in many cases reveals organisms that are intermediate in form.

14.6.2 The evidence for evolution includes the anatomical record, which reveals similarities in structures between species. Homologous structures are similar in structure but differ in their functions. Analogous structures are similar in function but differ in their underlying structure.

14.6.3 The molecular record traces changes in the genomes and proteins of species.

Evolution's Critics

14.7.1 Darwin's theory of evolution through natural selection has always had its critics. Their criticisms of the theory of evolution, however, are without scientific merit.

How Populations Evolve

Genetic Change in Populations

14.8.1 If a population follows the five assumptions of Hardy-Weinberg, the frequencies of alleles within the population will not change. However, if a population is small, has selective mating, experiences mutations or migrations, or is under the influence of natural selection, allele frequencies will be different from those predicted by the Hardy-Weinberg rule.

Agents of Evolution

14.9.1 Five evolutionary forces act on populations to change their allele and genotype frequencies: (1) Mutations are changes in DNA. (2) Migrations are the movements of individuals or alleles into or out of a population. (3) Genetic drift is the random loss of alleles in a population due to chance occurrences. In the founder effect, a small group of individuals establishes a new population such that their alleles become common in the newly established population. (4) Nonrandom mating occurs when individuals seek out mates based on certain traits. (5) Selection occurs when individuals with certain traits leave more offspring because their traits allow them to better respond to the challenges of their environment.

14.9.2 Selection can act on the genes in a population in several different ways. Stabilizing selection tends to reduce extreme phenotypes, disruptive selection tends to reduce intermediate phenotypes, and directional selection tends to reduce one extreme phenotype.

Adaptation Within Populations

Sickle-Cell Disease

14.10.1 Sickle-cell disease is an example of a disease maintained in human populations by natural selection. In areas with malaria, people who are heterozygous for the sickle-cell trait survive better than individuals with either of the two homozygous phenotypes.

Peppered Moths and Industrial Melanism

14.11.1 Natural selection favors the dark form of the peppered moth in areas of heavy pollution.

Selection on Color in Guppies

14.12.1 Experiments have shown that selection pressure from predation resulted in evolutionary change in guppies—drab-colored fish where there is predation and brightly colored fish, like the fish here from **figure 14.31**, when there was no selection pressure.

How Species Form

The Biological Species Concept

14.13.1 The biological species concept defines a species as a group of organisms that are capable of mating with each other and producing fertile offspring. If they cannot mate, or mate but produce sterile offspring, they are said to be reproductively isolated.

Isolating Mechanisms

14.14.1 There are two types of isolating mechanisms: prezygotic mechanisms prevent the formation of a hybrid zygote; postzygotic mechanisms prevent development of a hybrid zygote or result in sterile offspring.

Test Your Understanding

14.3.1 Darwin was greatly influenced by Thomas Malthus who observed that
a. food supplies increase geometrically.
b. populations increase arithmetically.
c. populations are capable of geometric increase, yet remain at constant levels.
d. the food supply usually increases faster than the population that depends on it.

14.3.1 Darwin proposed that individuals with traits that help them live in their immediate environment are more likely to survive and reproduce than individuals without those traits. He called this
a. natural selection. **c.** the theory of evolution.
b. arithmetic progression. **d.** geometric progression.

14.4.1 A great deal of research has been done on Darwin's finches over the last 70 years. The research
a. seems to contradict Darwin's original ideas.
b. seems to agree with Darwin's original ideas.
c. does not show any clear patterns that support or refute Darwin's original ideas.
d. suggests a different explanation for evolution of finches.

14.5.1 The process whereby a cluster of species change and diversify as they occupy a variety of niches in a certain region is called
a. the founder effect. **c.** convergent evolution.
b. a molecular clock. **d.** adaptive radiation.

14.6.2 One of the major sources of evidence for evolution is in the comparative anatomy of organisms. Features that look different but have similar structural origin are called
a. homologous structures. **c.** vestigial structures.
b. analogous structures. **d.** equivalent structures.

14.8.1 A large group of organisms lives in a large, stable ecosystem. There is no competition for resources. Individuals show no mate preferences. All organisms appear to be identical except for a few individuals in the most recent generation of offspring that exhibit a different fur coat color and pattern. The ecosystem and population are geographically isolated from other populations of the same organism. Which Hardy-Weinberg assumption has been violated?
a. large population size
b. random mating within the population
c. no mutation within the population
d. no input of new alleles from outside or loss of alleles

14.8.1 A population of 1,000 individuals has 200 individuals who show a homozygous recessive phenotype and 800 individuals who express the dominant phenotype. What is the frequency of homozygous recessive individuals in this population?
a. 0.20 **c.** 0.45
b. 0.30 **d.** 0.55

14.9.1 A chance event occurs that causes a population to lose some individuals (they died)—hence, a loss of alleles in the population results from
a. mutation. **c.** selection.
b. migration. **d.** genetic drift.

14.9.2 Selection that causes one extreme phenotype to be more frequent in a population is an example of
a. disruptive selection. **c.** directional selection.
b. stabilizing selection. **d.** equivalent selection.

14.13.1 A key element of Ernst Mayr's biological species concept is
a. homologous isolation. **c.** convergent isolation.
b. divergent isolation. **d.** reproductive isolation.

Apply Your Understanding

14.9.2 Because of prolonged drought, the trees on an island are producing nuts that are much smaller with thicker and harder shells. What will happen to the birds that depend on the nuts for food? What type of selection will result?

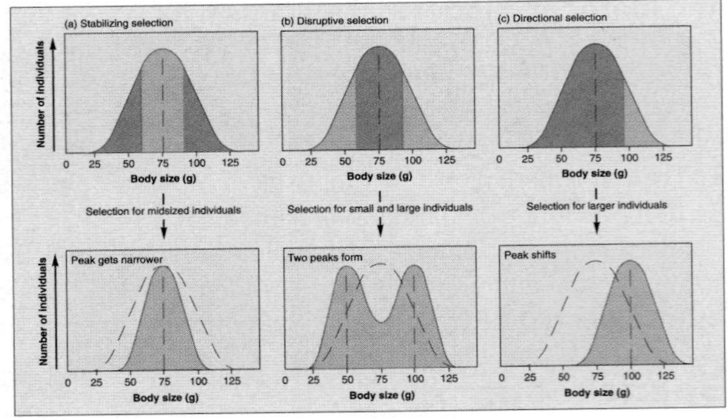

14.14.1 A very heavy rainstorm floods a mountain river, changing its course and digging a deep canyon through the soft soils of the meadow in the valley below. How could mice populations on either side of the valley be affected?

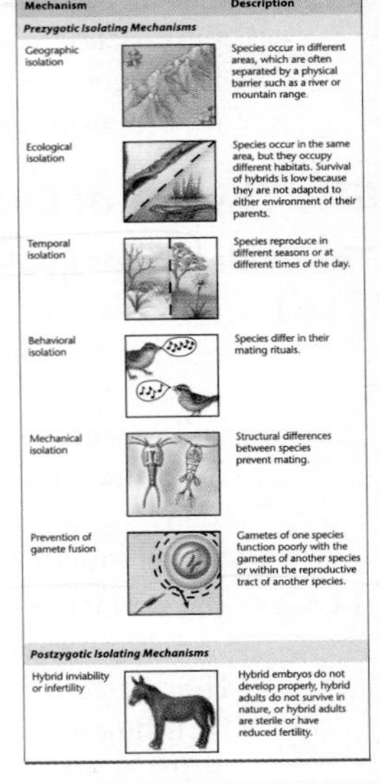

TABLE 14.2 Isolating Mechanisms

Mechanism	Description
Prezygotic Isolating Mechanisms	
Geographic isolation	Species occur in different areas, which are often separated by a physical barrier such as a river or mountain range.
Ecological isolation	Species occur in the same area, but they occupy different habitats. Survival of hybrids is low because they are not adapted to either environment of their parents.
Temporal isolation	Species reproduce in different seasons or at different times of the day.
Behavioral isolation	Species differ in their mating rituals.
Mechanical isolation	Structural differences between species prevent mating.
Prevention of gamete fusion	Gametes of one species function poorly with the gametes of another species or within the reproductive tract of another species.
Postzygotic Isolating Mechanisms	
Hybrid inviability or infertility	Hybrid embryos do not develop properly, hybrid adults do not survive in nature, or hybrid adults are sterile or have reduced fertility.

Synthesize What You Have Learned

14.3.1 Can natural selection occur among genetically identical clones? Explain your reasoning.

14.6.1 The evolutionary histories of some groups of related organisms indicate change from larger to smaller organisms over time, such as the glyptodont to the armadillo, or the mammoth to the elephant. Yet other groups of related organisms have exhibited over the same geological periods a trend of increased sizes of species, such as the tiny eohippus to the horse. Explain how this can occur.

14.7.1 In a courtroom in 2005, biologist Ken Miller criticized the claims of intelligent design. After noting that 99.9% of the organisms that have ever lived on earth are now extinct, he said that "an intelligent designer who designed things, 99.9% of which didn't last, certainly wouldn't be very intelligent." Evaluate Miller's criticism.

Chapter 19

Populations and Communities

CHAPTER AT A GLANCE

Ecology
19.1 What Is Ecology?

Populations
19.2 Population Range
19.3 Population Distribution
19.4 Population Growth
Today's Biology: The War Against Urban Deer
19.5 The Influence of Population Density
19.6 Life History Adaptations
19.7 Population Demography

How Competition Shapes Communities
19.8 Communities
19.9 The Niche and Competition

Species Interact in Many Ways
19.10 Coevolution and Symbiosis
19.11 Predation
19.12 Plant and Animal Defenses
19.13 Mimicry
Today's Biology: Invasion of the Killer Bees

Community Stability
19.14 Ecological Succession

Inquiry & Analysis: Are Island Populations of Song Sparrows Density Dependent?

Ecology

Figure 19.1 A redwood community.

(a) The redwood forest of coastal California and southwestern Oregon is dominated by the population of redwoods *(Sequoia sempervirens)*. Other species in the redwood community include (b) redwood sorrel *(Oxalis oregana)*, (c) sword ferns *(Polystichum munitum)*, and (d) ground beetles *(Scaphinotus velutinus)*, this one feeding on a slug on a sword fern leaf.

19.1 What Is Ecology?

Ecology is the study of how organisms interact with each other and with their environment. Ecology also encompasses the study of the distribution and abundance of organisms, which includes population growth and the limits and influences on population growth. The word *ecology* was coined in 1866 by the great German biologist Ernst Haeckel and comes from the Greek words *oikos* (house, place where one lives) and *logos* (study of). Our study of ecology, then, is a study of the house in which we live. Do not forget this simple analogy built into the word ecology—most of our environmental problems could be avoided if we treated the world in which we live the same way we treat our own homes. Would you pollute your own house?

Levels of Ecological Organization

LEARNING OBJECTIVE 19.1.1 Describe the six levels of organization of organisms.

The discussion of the hierarchical organization of life on pages 18 and 19 began at the cellular level and traced the increasing complexity of life up through the levels to ecosystems. In this chapter, we pick up the hierarchy at the population level.

Ecologists consider groups of organisms at six progressively more encompassing levels of organization. As mentioned in chapter 1, new characteristics called *emergent properties* arise at each higher level, resulting from the way components of each level interact.

1. **Populations.** Individuals of the same species that live together are members of a population. They potentially interbreed with one another, share the same habitat, and use the same pool of resources the habitat provides.
2. **Species.** All populations of a particular kind of organism form a species. Populations of the species can interact and affect the ecological characteristics of the species as a whole.
3. **Communities.** Populations of different species that live together in the same place are called communities. Different species typically use different resources within the habitat they share (**figure 19.1**).
4. **Ecosystems.** A community and the nonliving factors with which it interacts is called an **ecosystem.** An ecosystem is affected by the flow of energy, ultimately derived from the sun, and the cycling of the essential elements on which the lives of its constituent organisms depend. The redwood forest community pictured in **figure 19.1** is part of an ecosystem, where the giant trees and other organisms interact with each other and with their physical surroundings.
5. **Biomes.** Biomes are major terrestrial assemblages of plants, animals, and microorganisms that occur over wide geographical areas that have distinct physical characteristics. Examples include deserts, tropical rain forests, and grasslands. Similar types of groupings occur in marine and freshwater habitats.
6. **The biosphere.** All the world's biomes, along with its marine and freshwater assemblages, together constitute an interactive system we call the biosphere. Changes in one biome can have profound consequences for others.

Although we include biomes and the biosphere as higher levels of ecological organization in this list of organizational levels, the *ecosystem* is viewed as the "basic functional unit," in much the same way the cell, rather than tissues or organs, is considered the basic unit of living organisms.

Some ecologists, called *population ecologists,* focus on a particular species and how its populations grow. Other ecologists, called *community ecologists,* study how the different species living in a place interact with one another. Still other ecologists, called *systems ecologists,* are interested in how biological communities interact with their physical environment.

We will begin our study of ecology by examining populations and communities. We will then work our way up the hierarchy by examining ecosystems and biomes, ending with a critical look at the condition of the biosphere.

Putting the Concept to Work

What is the difference between a community and an ecosystem?

The Environmental Challenge

LEARNING OBJECTIVE 19.1.2 Discuss how the environmental challenges of a particular region impact its species.

The nature of the physical environment determines to a great extent which organisms live in a particular climate or region. The following are four key elements of the environment:

Temperature. Most organisms are adapted to live within a relatively narrow range of temperatures and will not thrive if temperatures are colder or warmer. The growing season of plants, for example, is strongly influenced by temperature.

Water. All organisms require water. On land, water is often scarce, so patterns of rainfall have a major influence on life.

Sunlight. Almost all ecosystems rely on energy captured by photosynthesis and so the availability of sunlight influences the amount of life an ecosystem can support, particularly below the surface in marine environments.

Soil. The physical consistency, pH, and the availability of minerals in the soil often severely limit plant growth, particularly the amount of nitrogen and phosphorus present in the soil.

During the course of a day, a season, or a lifetime, an individual organism must cope with a range of living conditions. Many organisms are able to adapt to environmental change by making physiological, morphological, or behavioral adjustments. For example, you sweat when it is hot, increasing heat loss through evaporation and thus preventing overheating. Morphological adaptations in some mammals may include growing a thicker coat of fur in winter (**figure 19.2**). And, many animals deal with variations in the environment through behavior, such as moving from one place to another, thereby avoiding areas that are unsuitable. For example, a tropical lizard manages to maintain a fairly uniform body temperature by basking in the sunlight but then retreating to the shade when it becomes too hot (**figure 19.3**). These physiological, morphological, and behavioral abilities are a product of natural selection acting in a particular environmental setting over time, which explains why an individual organism that is moved to a different environment may not survive.

Putting the Concept to Work

Are deep-sea ecosystems affected by changes in the intensity of sunlight from winter to summer?

Figure 19.2 Wolf in winter.

This gray wolf grows a thicker coat of fur in the winter to insulate its body. Escaping body heat is trapped in the air surrounding the hairs of its coat, holding in heat and thus helping to maintain the wolf's body temperature in the cold winter.

IMPLICATION FOR YOU Fur isn't the only way to keep warm. Emperor penguins survive the long, frigid, Antarctic winter wearing a coat of downy feathers. Sperm whales diving down to the ultra-cold ocean depths keep warm with a thick layer of insulating blubber. How do you keep warm outside on cold winter days?

Figure 19.3 Costa Rican lizard.

This green iguana escapes to the shade in the heat of the day, helping to keep its body cooler as the temperature outside rises.

Populations

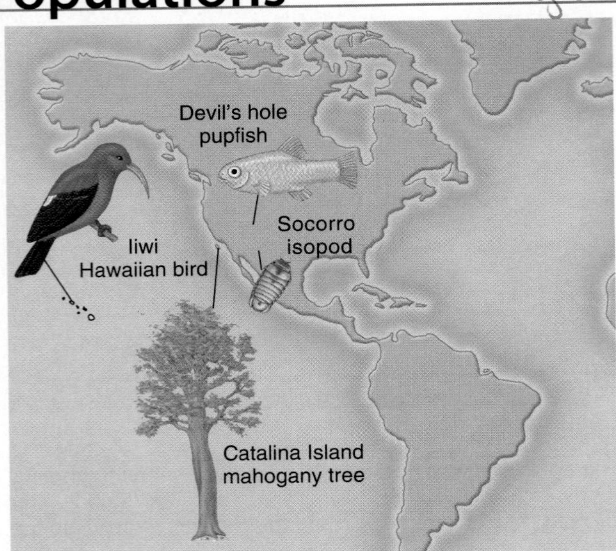

Figure 19.4 Species that occur in only one place.

These species, and many others, are only found in a single population. All are endangered species, and should anything happen to their single habitat, the population, and the species, would go extinct.

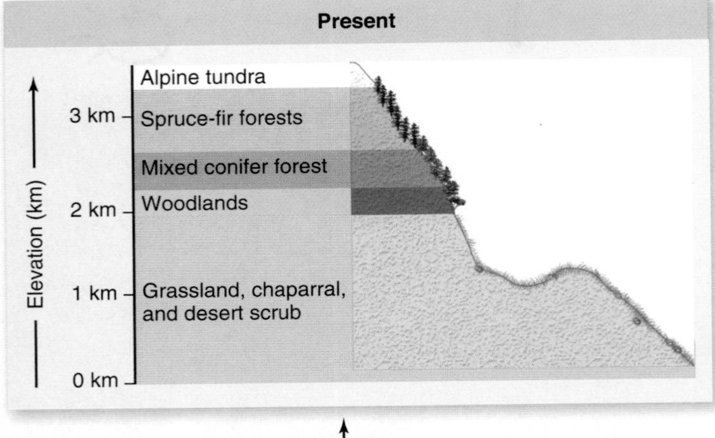

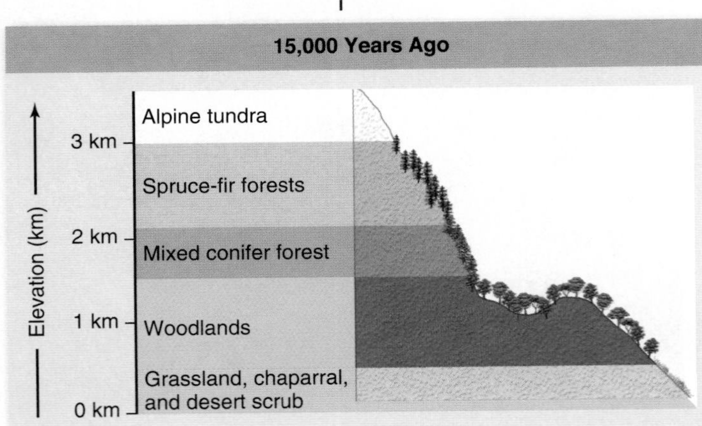

Figure 19.5 Altitudinal shifts in population ranges in the mountains of southwestern North America.

19.2 Population Range

Populations

LEARNING OBJECTIVE 19.2.1 Identify and describe five key characteristics of populations.

Organisms live as members of **populations,** groups of individuals that occur together at one place and time. Whether the population is a group of birds, insects, plants, or humans, ecologists can study several key elements of populations and learn more about them.

The term "population" can be defined narrowly or broadly. This flexibility allows us to speak in similar terms of the world's human population, the population of protists in the gut of an individual termite, or the population of deer that inhabit a forest. Five aspects of populations are particularly important: *population range*, which is the area throughout which a population occurs, *population distribution*, which is the pattern of spacing of individuals within that range, *population size*, which is the number of individuals a population contains, *population density*, which is how many individuals share an area, and *population growth*, which describes whether a population is growing or shrinking, and at what rate. We will consider each in turn.

Putting the Concept to Work

What is the difference between the range and the distribution of a species?

Population Ranges

LEARNING OBJECTIVE 19.2.2 State what factors determine the range of a species.

No population, not even one composed of humans, occurs in all habitats throughout the world. Most species, in fact, have relatively limited geographic ranges, and the range of some species is minuscule (**figure 19.4**): The Devil's Hole pupfish, for example, lives in a single hot water spring in southern Nevada, and the Socorro isopod is known from a single spring system in New Mexico. At the other extreme, some species are widely distributed. For example, the common dolphin (***Delphinus delphis***) is found throughout all of the world's oceans.

Organisms must be adapted for the environment in which they occur. Polar bears are exquisitely adapted to survive the cold of the Arctic, but you won't find them in the tropical rain forest. Certain prokaryotes can live in the near-boiling waters of Yellowstone's geysers, but they do not occur in cooler streams nearby. Each population has its own requirements—temperature, humidity, certain types of food, and a host of other factors—that determine where it can live and reproduce and where it can't. When the environment changes, ranges may expand or contract in response. For example, the range for trees that survive better in colder temperatures shifts farther up a mountain when climates become warmer (**figure 19.5**).

Putting the Concept to Work

Why might the range of penguins not include Greenland or arctic ice?

19.3 Population Distribution

LEARNING OBJECTIVE 19.3.1 Describe three ways individuals may be distributed within a population.

A key characteristic affecting a species's range is the way in which individuals of its populations are distributed. They may be randomly spaced, uniformly spaced, or clumped (**figure 19.6**).

Randomly Spaced

Individuals are randomly spaced within populations when they do not interact strongly with one another or with nonuniform aspects of their environment. Random distributions are not common in nature. Some species of trees, however, appear to exhibit random distributions in Panamanian rain forests (**figure 19.6*b***).

Uniformly Spaced

Uniform spacing within a population may often, but not always, result from competition for resources. The means by which it is accomplished, however, varies.

Among plants, uniform spacing results when closely spaced individuals compete for available sunlight, nutrients, or water (**figure 19.6*b***). These contests can be direct, as when one plant casts a shadow over another, or indirect, as when two plants compete by extracting nutrients or water from a shared area. In addition, some plants, such as creosote, produce chemicals in the surrounding soil that are toxic to other members of their species. In all of these cases, only plants that are spaced an adequate distance from each other will be able to coexist, leading to uniform spacing.

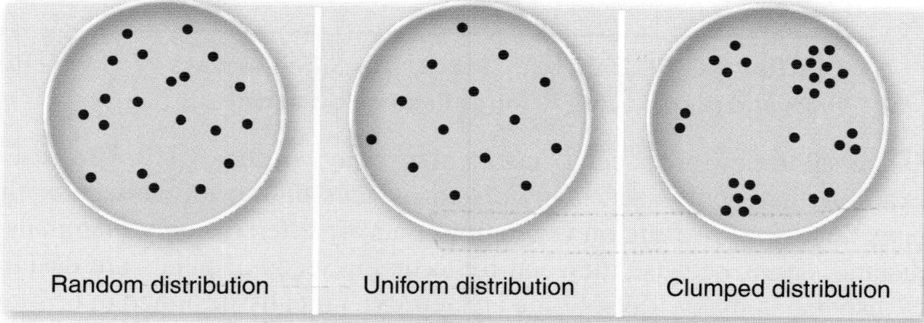

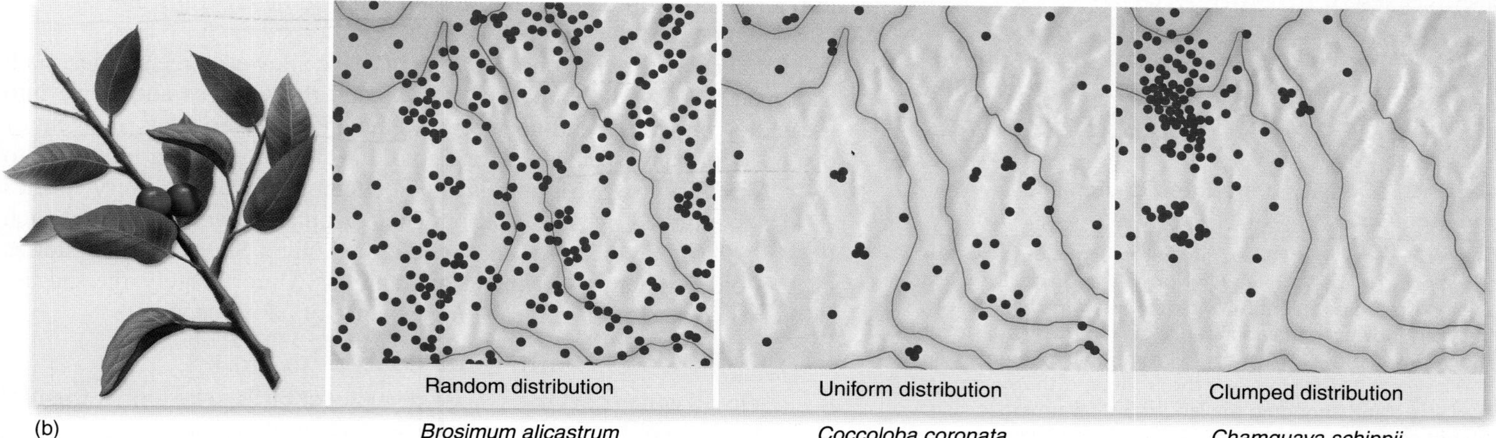

Figure 19.6 Population distribution.

The different patterns of spacing are exhibited by (a) different arrangements of bacterial colonies and (b) three different species of trees from the same locality in Panama.

Source: Data from Elizabeth Losos, Center for Tropical Forest Science, Smithsonian Tropical Research Institute.

Figure 19.7 Uniform distribution in a population of gannets off the coast of New Zealand.

Figure 19.8 Density-dependent dispersal by swarming locusts.

The swarming insects you see here are migratory locusts, *Locusta migratoria,* moving across farmland in North Africa in 1988. In most years, the locusts are not plentiful and do not swarm. In particularly favorable years, however, the abundance of resources leads to high population densities, the locusts exhibit hormonal differences, and take off as a swarm. Dispersing over the landscape, the swarm eats every available plant, denuding the landscape. Swarming locusts, although not common in North America, are a legendary plague of large areas of Africa and Eurasia.

In animals, uniform spacing often results from behavioral interactions. In many species, individuals defend a territory from which other individuals are excluded. These territories provide the owner with exclusive access to resources such as food, water, hiding refuges, or mates, and individuals tend to be evenly spaced across the habitat (**figure 19.7**).

Clumped Spacing

Individuals clump into groups or clusters in response to uneven distribution of resources in their immediate environments (see **figure 19.6*b***). Clumped distributions are common in nature because individual animals, plants, and microorganisms tend to prefer microhabitats defined by soil type, moisture, or other aspects of the environment to which they are best adapted.

Social interactions also can lead to clumped distributions. Many species live and move around in large groups, which go by a variety of names (for example, flock, herd, pride). Such groupings can provide many advantages, including increased awareness of and defense against predators, decreased energetic cost of moving through air and water, and access to the knowledge of all group members.

At a broader scale, populations are often most densely-populated in the interior of their range and less densely distributed toward the edges. Such patterns usually result from the manner in which the environment changes in different areas. Populations are often best adapted to the conditions in the interior of their distribution. As environmental conditions change, individuals are less well-adapted, and thus densities decrease.

Putting the Concept to Work

Describe what sort of interaction with other animals might lead to uniform spacing, and what sort to clumped spacing.

Dispersal Mechanisms

LEARNING OBJECTIVE 19.3.2 Describe the ways in which animals and plants achieve long-distance dispersal.

Dispersal to new areas can occur in many ways (**figure 19.8**). Lizards, for example, have colonized many distant islands due to individuals or their eggs floating or drifting on vegetation. Bats are often the only mammals on distant islands because they can fly to them. Seeds of plants are designed to disperse in many ways: Some are aerodynamically designed to be blown long distances by the wind; others have structures that stick to the fur or feathers of animals, so that they are carried long distances before falling to the ground. Still others enclose their seeds in fleshy fruits that can pass through the digestive systems of animals.

By altering the environment, humans have allowed some species, such as coyotes and white-tailed deer, to expand their ranges and move into areas they previously did not occupy. Humans have served as an agent of dispersal for many species. For example, 100 starlings were introduced into New York City in 1896 in a misguided attempt to establish every species of bird mentioned by Shakespeare. Their population steadily spread such that by 1980, they occurred throughout the United States. Similar stories can be told for many other plants and animals. Unfortunately, the success of these invaders often comes at the expense of native species.

Putting the Concept to Work

Would you expect the species diversity of birds to be higher than that of reptiles on isolated islands like Tahiti? Explain.

19.4 Population Growth

LEARNING OBJECTIVE 19.4.1 Differentiate population size, population density, and population growth.

Within its range, a species typically is found living in local populations, separated to at least some extent from other populations of that species. In this section, we will focus on the factors that influence whether a population will grow or shrink, and at what rate. These factors are also important when considering our own population. Although we humans picture ourselves as different from populations of animals living in the wild, factors that affect wild populations affect human populations in similar ways.

One of the critical properties of any population is its **population size**—the number of individuals in the population. For example, if an entire species consists of only one or a few small populations, that species is likely to become extinct, especially if it occurs in areas that have been or are being radically changed. In addition to population size, **population density**—the number of individuals that occur in a unit area, such as per square kilometer—is often an important characteristic. The density of a population, how closely individuals associate with each other, is an indication of how they live. For example, animals that live in large groups, such as herds of wildebeests, may find safety in numbers (figure 19.9). In addition to size and density, another key characteristic of any population is its capacity to grow. To understand populations we must consider what factors in nature promote or limit **population growth.**

The simplest model of population growth defines a population's growth rate (the change in its numbers over time) as the difference between the birthrate and the death rate, corrected for any movement of individuals into (immigration) or out of (emigration) the population. Movements of individuals can have a major impact on population growth rates. For example, the increase in human population in the United States during the closing decades of the twentieth century was mostly due to immigrants. Less than half of the increase came from the reproduction of the people already living there.

Putting the Concept to Work

Explain how the density of a population may affect its size.

(a)

(b)

Figure 19.9 Population density.

(a) Siberian tigers occupy enormous territories (typically 60–100 km^2 for an adult male) because of the relative lack of prey, especially in winter. (b) This Serengeti wildebeest herd numbers over 1 million animals.

The Exponential Growth Model

LEARNING OBJECTIVE 19.4.2 Contrast exponential and logistic growth.

The innate capacity for growth of any population is exponential, which can result in *exponential growth* (see figure 19.11). Even when a population's growth rate remains constant, the actual increase in the *number* of individuals in the population accelerates rapidly; the larger a population is, the faster it grows. This sort of growth pattern is similar to that obtained by compounding interest on an investment. In practice, such patterns prevail only for short periods, usually when an organism reaches a new habitat with abundant resources. Natural examples include dandelions reaching the lawns of North America from Europe for the first time; algae colonizing a newly formed pond; or the first plants arriving on an island recently thrust up from the sea. Figure 19.10 shows the establishment of tree populations in the British Isles after the glaciers receded in the Northern Hemisphere 20,000 years ago. The tree population grew at an exponential rate.

Pollen accumulation rate (grains/cm^2/year): 0, 10,000, 20,000, 30,000, 40,000, 50,000
Years after colonizing: 0, 250, 500

Figure 19.10 Exponential growth in a tree population.

These data present the exponential growth of Scotch pine trees after glaciers receded from the Norfolk region of Great Britain. The size of the population was estimated based on the rate of pollen accumulation in lake sediments.

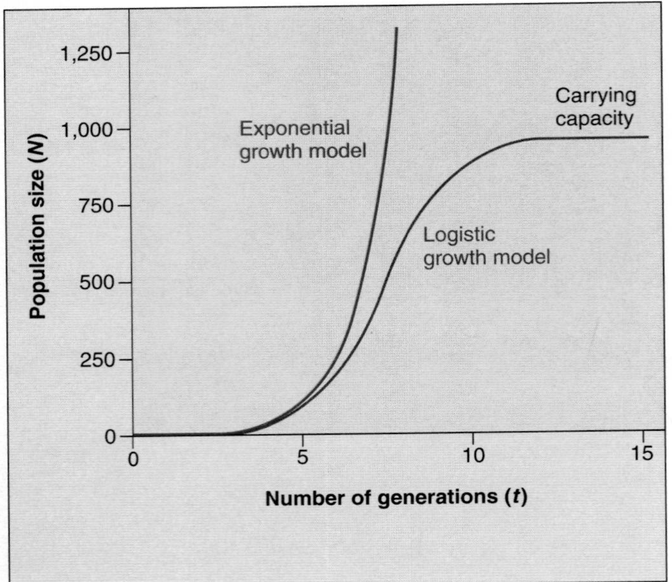

Figure 19.11 Two models of population growth.

The *red line* illustrates the exponential growth model for a population. The *blue line* illustrates the logistic growth model. At first, logistic growth accelerates exponentially, and then, as resources become limiting, the birthrate decreases or the death rate increases, and growth slows. Growth ceases when the death rate equals the birthrate. The carrying capacity ultimately depends on the resources available in the environment.

Carrying Capacity

No matter how rapidly populations grow, they eventually reach a limit imposed by shortages of important environmental factors such as space, light, water, or nutrients and will experience *logistic growth.* A population usually ultimately stabilizes at a certain size, called the **carrying capacity** of the particular place where it lives, and the size of the population levels off, like the flat portion of the blue line in **figure 19.11**. The carrying capacity is the maximum number of individuals that an area can support.

The Logistic Growth Model

As a population approaches its carrying capacity, its rate of growth slows greatly as fewer and fewer resources remain for each new individual to use, until the population size levels off at or near the carrying capacity. The growth curve of such a population, which is always limited by one or more factors in the environment, is approximated by an S-shaped sigmoid growth curve, the blue line in **figure 19.11**. The curve is called "sigmoid" because its shape has a double curve like the letter *S.* As the size of a population stabilizes at the carrying capacity, its rate of growth slows down, eventually coming to a halt. The fur seal population in **figure 19.12** has a carrying capacity of about 10,000 breeding male seals.

Processes such as competition for resources, emigration, and the accumulation of toxic wastes all tend to increase as a population approaches its carrying capacity for a particular habitat. The resources for which the members of the population are competing may be food, shelter, light, mating sites, mates, or any other factor needed to survive and reproduce.

Putting the Concept to Work

What is the expected growth rate of a population living at the carrying capacity of its environment? What must happen to convert logistic into exponential growth?

BIOLOGY & YOU

Living Exponentially. Throughout most of human history, the size of the world's human population has been limited by food availability. Two thousand years ago, some 130 million people populated the earth. It took a thousand years for that number to double, and it was 1650 before it doubled again, to about 500 million. In all these years, the human population grew only slowly, limited by the earth's ability to support it. That all changed in the early 1700s with the advent of the industrial revolution. For the first time, technology gave humans control over the food supply, removing the limit to earth's carrying capacity and unleashing exponential growth. Although the human birthrate has remained unchanged for the last 300 years at about 30 per 1,000 per year, the death rate has fallen from 20 per thousand per year to its present level of 13. The difference between birth and death rates means the human population grows unchecked at 1% to 2% a year, leading to today's population of 7 billion. This year about 80 million more will be added, and the population will double in the next 60 years. How long do you think this exponential growth can continue? What do you think will happen then?

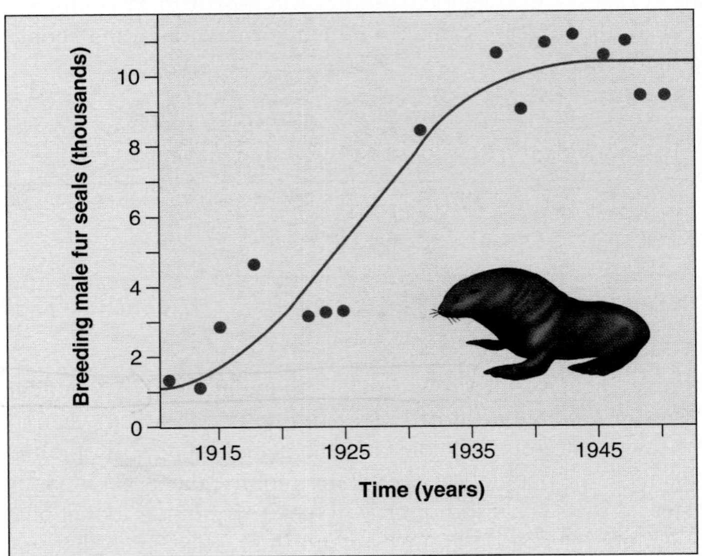

Figure 19.12 Most natural populations exhibit logistic growth.

These data present the history of a fur seal (*Callorhinus ursinus*) population on St. Paul Island, Alaska. Driven almost to extinction by hunting in the late 1800s, the fur seal made a comeback after hunting was banned in 1911. Today the number of breeding males with "harems" oscillates around 10,000 individuals, presumably the carrying capacity of the island.

Today's Biology

The War Against Urban Deer

Early in the 20th century, white-tailed deer were rare. Uncontrolled hunting had reduced their numbers to about 500,000 nationwide, and some states had no deer at all. In order to protect the remaining deer, laws were passed in the 1920s and 1930s to restrict hunting, particularly of does (females). This course of action seemed sensible, but ignored a fundamental fact about deer: Deer reproduce quickly. A doe matures at 2 or 3 years, and then typically gives birth to twins each year for 10 or more years.

Any student of biology could have predicted what would happen, what would *have* to happen, if hunting were severely restricted. Since Malthus and Darwin, biologists have recognized that populations that grow unchecked do not increase in a linear fashion, but exponentially. That is to say, the population does not increase the same amount each year, but rather grows by ever-greater amounts as the babies have babies, like compounding interest. A deer herd that has plenty to eat and is not hunted by humans or other predators will double in size every three years!

With the restrictions on hunting, deer populations indeed began to grow. Numbers of white-tailed deer rebounded slowly at first, then more and more quickly. In the last few decades, deer numbers have literally exploded, and now exceed 30 million nationwide. There are more deer today than at any time in our nation's history.

Much of the growth in the national deer population has occurred near urban areas. Deer have adapted well to encroaching suburbia, for two reasons:

1. **Growth of suburbs.** Paradoxically, land development tends to improve deer food supplies. Because the reproduction and survival of deer depend directly upon the quality of the food available to them, the improved food has led to more deer. Deer browse on leaves, and require large quantities of new growth with high nutritional content to maintain normal reproduction. Deer populations 40 years ago rarely grew large, for the simple reason that most of the trees in an undisturbed forest are old and only the undergrowth provides suitable food. It is because land development usually involves clearing land that urban development leads to increased deer food supplies. There are far fewer trees, but the trees are new growth, and very munchable. So are garden shrubs. Deer eat very, very well in suburbia.
2. **Restriction of hunting.** Nobody wants someone shooting at deer near their kids. Not surprisingly, then, most of the areas in which deer populations are growing most rapidly have been declared off limits to hunters. Removing their only significant predator—hunters—allows deer populations to grow unchecked.

Anyone who lives in the suburbs knows the result of providing ample food and no hunting: lots of deer. "A deer in the backyard is wonderful," says wildlife biologist William Porter. "Twenty-five deer in the backyard is a problem." Nancy Hoffstetter of the Saint Louis suburb Town and Country has been quoted as saying, "I consider them long-legged rats."

What should we do to respond to this plague of deer? You can't just "remove" the deer to some forest far from the suburb. Why won't this humane approach work? Other deer from surrounding areas just take their place! Imagine trying to empty people from a prime section of a new baseball stadium by physically removing individuals one at a time. You would never get anywhere, because other people would just crowd in. For every deer removed, there are two eager to get in the chow line and have a good meal.

There were only two real options open to lower deer numbers: decrease the birthrate or increase the death rate.

Decreasing the birthrate is certainly the most ethically palatable approach. However, deer birth control has proven impractical. Every female deer must be captured for the first dose, and redarted for each subsequent booster shot. Only in very small isolated populations is this practical. Nor is there any effective oral contraceptive for deer.

This leaves increasing the death rate. On more remote forest land, laws can be passed that extend the hunting season, increase the bag limit, and encourage the shooting of antlerless females. But there is no hunting in suburbs. In suburbs the only realistic approach is to thin out the local herds. How? In the summer of 2009, a 76-year-old housewife from a Cleveland suburb discovered a faun nestled in her garden, picked up a shovel and beat it to death. She was arrested and fined for cruelty—no one wants this type of "bambicide." In suburbs throughout the country, the thinning is being done with professional sharpshooters. Deer are still safe in people's backyards, but the herds are being culled by taking deer from nearby open fields.

Killing the cute deer in your backyard is not ideal, but fawns and other deer starving to death is every bit as unpleasant an option, and if local deer herds continue to grow, that is what is going to happen. A lot more deer will die, a lot more miserably. Can you think of any better solution to this haunting problem?

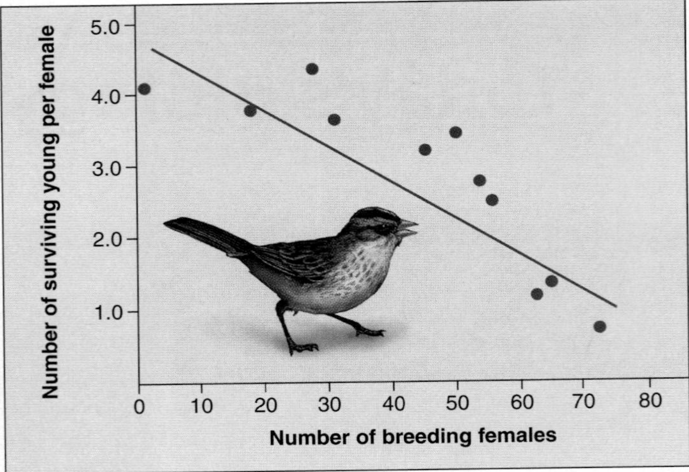

Figure 19.13 Density-dependent effects.

Reproductive success of the song sparrow (*Melospiza melodia*) decreases as population size increases.

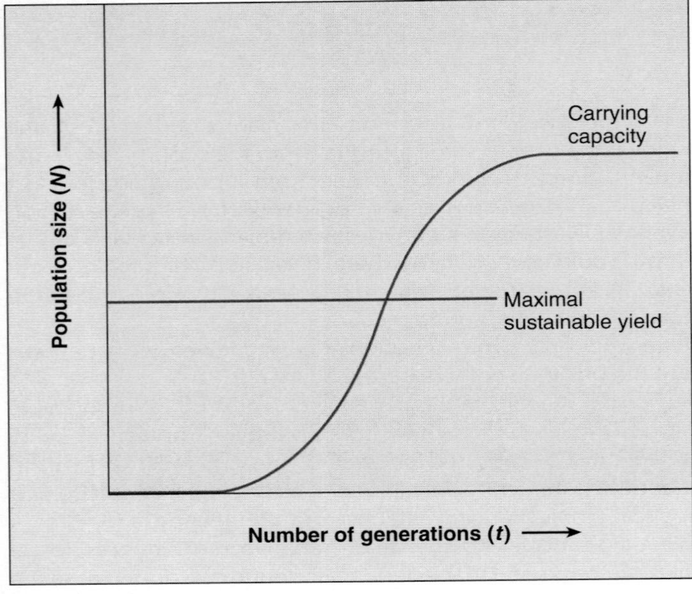

Figure 19.14 Maximal sustainable yield.

The goal of harvesting organisms for commercial purposes is to harvest just enough organisms to maximize current yields but also to sustain the population for future yields. Harvesting the organisms when the population is in the rapid growth phase of the sigmoidal curve, but not overharvesting, will result in sustained yields.

IMPLICATION FOR YOU Do you like tuna steaks? Atlantic bluefin tuna (*Thunnus thynnus*) are among the largest bony fishes in the ocean (reaching over 10 feet long and weights of 1,200 pounds) and are prized catches of commercial fishers. Not surprisingly, their numbers have fallen dramatically due to the calamitous overexploitation of Atlantic populations of this species. The bluefins are now protected in the western Atlantic, but not in the eastern Atlantic, even though tagging of fish confirms that they go back and forth. Do you think the Atlantic bluefin population will be sustainable under this policy?

19.5 The Influence of Population Density

LEARNING OBJECTIVE 19.5.1 Differentiate between density-dependent and density-independent effects on population growth.

Many factors act to regulate the growth of populations in nature. Some of these factors act independently of the size of the population; others do not.

Density-Independent Effects

Effects that are independent of the size of a population and act to regulate its growth are called **density-independent effects.** A variety of factors may affect populations in a density-independent manner. Most of these are aspects of the external environment such as weather (extremely cold winters, droughts, storms, floods) and physical disruptions (volcanic eruptions and fire). Individuals often will be affected by these activities regardless of the size of the population. Populations that occur in areas in which such events occur relatively frequently will display erratic population growth patterns, increasing rapidly when conditions are relatively good, but suffering extreme reductions whenever the environment turns hostile.

Density-Dependent Effects

Effects that are dependent on the size of the population and act to regulate its growth are called **density-dependent effects.** Among animals, these effects may be accompanied by hormonal changes that can alter behavior that will directly affect the ultimate size of the population. One striking example occurs in migratory locusts ("short-horned" grasshoppers, which you encountered in **figure 19.8** earlier in this chapter). When they become crowded, the locusts produce hormones that cause them to enter a migratory phase; the locusts take off as a swarm (as pictured at the beginning of this chapter) and fly long distances to new habitats. Density-dependent effects, in general, have an increasing effect as population size increases. For example, as the population of song sparrows in **figure 19.13** grows, the individuals in the population compete with increasing intensity for limited resources. Darwin proposed that these effects result in natural selection and improved adaptation as individuals compete for the limiting factors.

Maximizing Population Productivity

In natural systems that are exploited by humans, such as fisheries, the aim is to maximize productivity by exploiting the population early in the rising portion of its sigmoid growth curve. At such times, populations and individuals are growing rapidly, and net productivity—in terms of the amount of material incorporated into the bodies of these organisms—is highest. The point of *maximal sustainable yield* (the red line in **figure 19.14**) lies partway up the sigmoid curve. Harvesting the population of an economically desirable species near this point will result in the best sustained yields. Overharvesting a population that is smaller than this critical size can destroy its productivity for many years or even drive it to extinction.

Putting the Concept to Work

Are density-dependent effects more or less pronounced as population size increases? Can density-independent effects result in natural selection?

19.6 Life History Adaptations

LEARNING OBJECTIVE 19.6.1 Contrast *r*-selected and *K*-selected adaptations.

Populations of many species, including annual plants, some insects, and most bacteria, can have very fast rates of growth when not limited by dwindling environmental resources. Habitats with more available resources than the population requires favor very rapid reproduction rates, which often approximate the exponential growth model discussed earlier. In mathematical formulas used to calculate population growth rates, the maximum growth rate is indicated by ***r***.

Populations of most animals have much slower rates of growth with numbers limited by available resources. Growth slows as available resources become limiting, producing a sigmoid growth curve approximating the logistic growth model discussed earlier. Habitats with limited resources lead to more intense competition for resources, and favor individuals that can survive and successfully reproduce more efficiently. The number of individuals that can survive at this limit is the carrying capacity of the environment. In mathematical formulas used to calculate population growth rates, the carrying capacity is indicated by ***K***.

The complete life cycle of an organism constitutes its life history. Life histories are very diverse, with different organisms having different adaptations in response to their environments. Some life history adaptations of a population favor very rapid growth in a habitat with abundant resources, or in unpredictable or volatile environments in which organisms have to take advantage of the resources when they are available. In these situations reproducing early, producing many small offspring that mature quickly, and engaging in other aspects of "big bang" reproduction are favored. Using the terms of the exponential model, these adaptations that favor a high rate of increase, approaching the maximum growth rate or *r*, are called ***r*-selected adaptations.** Examples of organisms displaying *r*-selected life history adaptations include dandelions, aphids, mice, and cockroaches (figure 19.15).

Other life history adaptations favor survival in an environment in which individuals are competing for limited resources. These features include reproducing late, having small numbers of larger-sized offspring that mature slowly and receive intensive parental care, and other aspects of "carrying capacity" reproduction. In terms of the logistic model, these adaptations favoring reproduction near the carrying capacity of the environment or *K*, are called ***K*-selected adaptations.** Examples of organisms displaying *K*-selected life history adaptations include coconut palms, whooping cranes, and whales.

In general, populations living in rapidly changing habitats tend to exhibit *r*-selected adaptations, whereas populations of closely related organisms living in more stable and competitive habitats exhibit more *K*-selected adaptations. Most natural populations show life history adaptations that exist along a continuum, ranging from completely *r*-selected traits to completely *K*-selected traits. Table 19.1 outlines the adaptations at the extreme ends of the continuum.

Putting the Concept to Work

Would you expect a mosquito to exhibit more *r*-selected or more *K*-selected adaptations? Explain why.

Figure 19.15 The consequences of exponential growth.

All organisms have the potential to produce populations larger than those that actually occur in nature. The German cockroach *(Blatella germanica)*, a major household pest, produces 80 young every six months. If every cockroach that hatched survived for three generations, kitchens might look like this theoretical culinary nightmare concocted by the Smithsonian Museum of Natural History.

TABLE 19.1 *r*-Selected and *K*-Selected Life History Adaptations

Adaptation	*r*-Selected Populations	*K*-Selected Populations
Age at first reproduction	Early	Late
Homeostatic capability	Limited	Often extensive
Life span	Short	Long
Maturation time	Short	Long
Mortality rate	Often high	Usually low
Number of offspring produced per reproductive episode	Many	Few
Number of reproductions per lifetime	Usually one	Often several
Parental care	None	Often extensive
Size of offspring or eggs	Small	Large

Figure 19.16 Age structure in different types of populations.

The grass you see in this photo is an annual plant. The individual plants are all the same age because they die every year. By contrast, the herd of bison contains individuals of varying ages because they can survive from year to year.

19.7 Population Demography

LEARNING OBJECTIVE 19.7.1 Explain how the growth rate of a population is influenced by its age structure, fecundity, and mortality.

Demography is the statistical study of populations. Demography is the science that helps predict how population sizes will change in the future. Populations grow if births outnumber deaths and shrink if deaths outnumber births. Because birth and death rates also depend on age and sex, the future size of a population depends on its present age structure and sex ratio.

Age Structure

Many annual plants and insects time their reproduction to particular seasons of the year and then die. All members of these populations are the same age. Perennial plants and longer-lived animals contain individuals of more than one generation, so that in any given year individuals of different ages are reproducing within the population (figure 19.16). A group of individuals of the same age is referred to as a **cohort.**

Within a population, every cohort has a characteristic birthrate, or **fecundity,** defined as the number of offspring produced in a standard time (for example, per year), and a characteristic death rate, or **mortality,** the number of individuals that die in that period. The rate of a population's growth depends on the difference between these two rates.

The relative number of individuals in each cohort defines a population's age structure. A population with a large proportion of young individuals tends to grow rapidly because an increasing proportion of its individuals are reproductive. A population with more females usually also tends to grow more rapidly. However, among monogamous species like many birds, pairs often form long-lasting reproductive relationships, and a reduction in the number of males can directly reduce the number of births. The proportion of males to females in a population is its **sex ratio.**

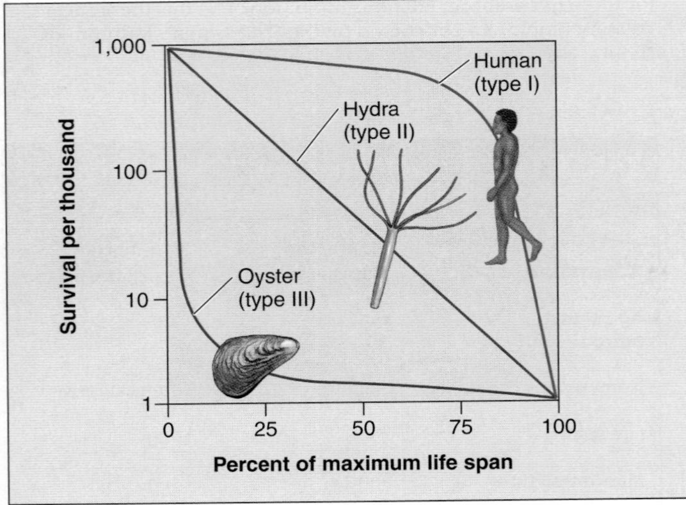

Figure 19.17 Survivorship curves.

By convention, survival (the *vertical axis*) is plotted on a log scale. In hydra, animals related to jellyfish, individuals are equally likely to die at any age, as indicated by the straight survivorship curve (the blue line, type II). Oysters, like plants, produce vast numbers of offspring, only a few of which live to reproduce. However, once they become established as reproductive individuals, their mortality is extremely low (red line, type III survivorship curve). Even though human babies are susceptible to death at relatively high rates, mortality in humans, as in many animals and protists, rises in the postreproductive years (green line, type I survivorship curve).

Mortality and Survivorship Curves

A population's intrinsic rate of increase depends on the ages of the organisms in it and the reproductive performance of the individuals in the various age groups. When a population lives in a constant environment for a few generations, its **age distribution**—the proportion of individuals in different age categories—tends to stabilize. This distribution differs greatly from species to species and even, to some extent, from population to population within a given species. A population whose size remains fairly constant through time is called a stable population. In such a population, births plus immigration must balance deaths plus emigration.

One way to express the age distribution characteristics of populations is through a **survivorship curve.** Survivorship is defined as the percentage of an original population that survives to a given age. Examples of different kinds of survivorship curves are shown in figure 19.17.

Putting the Concept to Work

If fecundity increases, does the population growth rate go up or down?

How Competition Shapes Communities

19.8 Communities

LEARNING OBJECTIVE 19.8.1 Contrast individualistic and holistic concepts of community.

The term **community** refers to the mix of species that occur at any particular locality. Some communities contain many species (**figure 19.18**), while others contain only a few species, such as in the near-boiling waters of Yellowstone's geysers (where a limited number of microbial species live). Communities can be characterized either by their constituent species, a list of all species present in the community, or by their properties, such as species richness (the number of different species present) or primary productivity (the amount of solar energy captured through photosynthesis and stored as organic compounds).

Interactions among community members govern many ecological and evolutionary processes. These interactions, such as predation (**figure 19.18*b***) and competition (**figure 19.18*c***), affect the population biology of particular species, as well as the ways in which energy and nutrients are used in the ecosystem. As discussed further in chapter 20, an *ecosystem* includes a community of living organisms and the nonliving components that surround them.

Scientists study biological communities in many ways, ranging from detailed observations to elaborate, large-scale experiments. In some cases, such studies focus on the entire community, whereas in other cases only a subset of species that are likely to interact with each other are studied. Regardless of how they are studied, two views exist on the makeup and functioning of communities.

The *individualistic concept* of communities, first championed by H. A. Gleason of the University of Chicago early in the twentieth century, holds that a community is nothing more than an aggregation of species that happen to coexist in one place. By contrast, the *holistic concept* of communities, which can be traced to the work of F. E. Clements, also about a century ago, views communities as an integrated unit. In this sense, the community could be viewed as a superorganism whose constituent species have coevolved to the extent that they function as a part of a greater whole, just as the kidneys, heart, and lungs all function together within an animal's body. In this view, then, a community would amount to more than the sum of its parts.

Most ecologists today favor the individualistic concept. For the most part, species seem to respond independently to changing environmental conditions. As a result, community composition changes gradually across landscapes as some species appear and become more abundant, while others decrease in abundance and eventually disappear. Competition is an important factor that affects individuals and in so doing affects the community.

Putting the Concept to Work

Why is the individualistic concept of communities supported by the fact that species respond independently to changing environmental conditions?

(a)

(b)

(c)

Figure 19.18 A Tanzanian savanna community.

A community consists of all the species—plants, animals, fungi, protists, and prokaryotes—that occur at a locality. (a) A savanna community in Lake Manyara National Park in Tanzania. Species within a community interact with each other, such as through (b) predation or (c) competition for a resource.

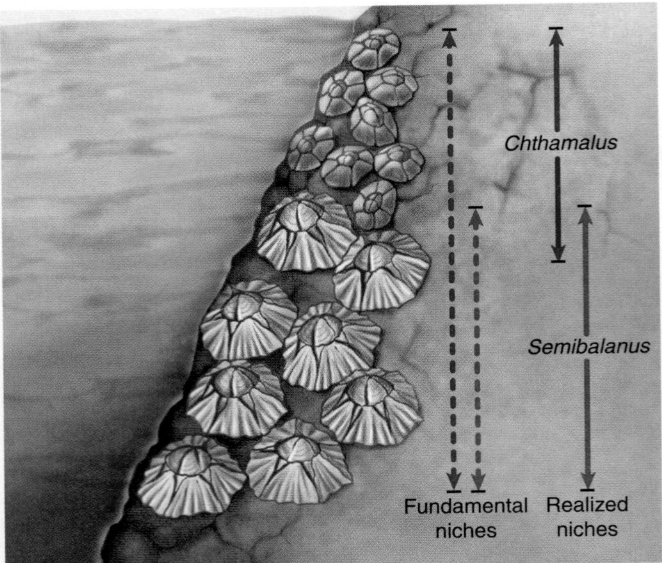

Figure 19.19 Competition among two species of barnacles limits niche use.

Chthamalus can live in both deep and shallow zones (its fundamental niche), but *Semibalanus* forces *Chthamalus* out of the part of its fundamental niche that overlaps the realized niche of *Semibalanus*.

19.9 The Niche and Competition

LEARNING OBJECTIVE 19.9.1 Contrast the fundamental niche and the realized niche.

Within a community, each organism occupies a particular biological role, or **niche.** The niche an organism occupies is the sum total of all the ways it uses the resources of its environment, including space, food, and many other factors of the environment. A niche may be described in terms of space utilization, food consumption, temperature range, appropriate conditions for mating, requirements for moisture, and other factors. *Niche* is not synonymous with **habitat,** the place where an organism lives. *Habitat* is a place, and *niche* is a pattern of living. Many species can share a habitat, but as we shall see, no two species can long occupy exactly the same niche.

Sometimes species are not able to occupy their entire niche because of the presence or absence of other species. **Competition** describes the interaction when two organisms attempt to use the same resource when there is not enough of the resource to satisfy both. Competition between individuals of different species is called **interspecific competition.** Interspecific competition is often greatest between organisms that obtain their food in similar ways and between organisms that are more similar. Another type of competition, called **intraspecific competition,** is competition between individuals of the same species.

The Realized Niche

Because of competition, organisms may not be able to occupy the entire niche they are theoretically capable of using, called the **fundamental niche** (or theoretical niche). The actual niche the organism is able to occupy in the presence of competitors is called its **realized niche.**

In a classic study, J. H. Connell of the University of California, Santa Barbara, investigated competitive interactions between two species of barnacles that grow together on rocks along the coast of Scotland. Barnacles are marine animals (crustaceans) that have free-swimming larvae. The larvae eventually settle down, cementing themselves to rocks and remaining attached for the rest of their lives. Of the two species Connell studied, *Chthamalus stellatus* (the smaller barnacle in figure 19.19) lives in shallower water, where tidal action often exposes it to air, and *Semibalanus balanoides* (the larger barnacle) lives at lower depths, where it is rarely exposed to the atmosphere. In the deeper zone, *Semibalanus* could always outcompete *Chthamalus* by crowding it off the rocks, undercutting it, and replacing it even where it had begun to grow. When Connell removed *Semibalanus* from the area, however, *Chthamalus* was easily able to occupy the deeper zone, indicating that no physiological or other general obstacles prevented it from becoming established there. In contrast, *Semibalanus* could not survive in the shallow-water habitats where *Chthamalus* normally occurs; it evidently does not have the special physiological and morphological adaptations that allow *Chthamalus* to occupy this zone. Thus, the fundamental niche of the barnacle *Chthamalus* in Connell's experiments in Scotland included that of *Semibalanus* (the red dashed arrow), but its realized niche was much narrower (the red solid arrow) because *Chthamalus* was outcompeted by *Semibalanus* in its fundamental niche.

Putting the Concept to Work

What happens to the unoccupied part of a fundamental niche?

IN THE NEWS

Beavers Back in Britain. The highlands of Scotland, once heavily timbered, were lumbered so intensively centuries ago that the mountains were denuded of trees. Starting a few decades ago, the highlands began the long road back. A major program of tree replanting was started, and today woodlands have begun to again pepper the highlands. Many of the deer and other forest inhabitants that used to frequent Scottish highland forests are now seen there again—but not beavers. For 400 years there have been no beavers in Scotland, or indeed anywhere in Great Britain—they disappeared in the seventeenth century, at the dawn of the Industrial Revolution. This raises a very interesting question: Does the absence of beavers imply that beavers cannot compete successfully for habitat in Great Britain—that the new replanted Scottish highlands are outside a beaver's fundamental niche? Or might the reborn Scottish highlands simply be outside today's realized niche for beavers, unoccupied only because there are no beavers around in the highlands these days to do the job? To answer this question, British government conservationists in 2009 released into the highlands of western Scotland four wild beaver families that had been trapped in Norway and quarantined for six months. These intrepid colonizers will soon settle the issue, creating new wetland habitats or disappearing again into the highland mists.

Competitive Exclusion

LEARNING OBJECTIVE 19.9.2 State the principle of competitive exclusion.

In classic experiments carried out between 1934 and 1935, Russian ecologist G. F. Gause studied competition among three species of *Paramecium,* a tiny protist. All three species grew well alone in culture tubes (**figure 19.20*a***), preying on bacteria and yeasts that fed on oatmeal suspended in the culture fluid. However, when Gause grew *P. aurelia* together with *P. caudatum* in the same culture tube (**figure 19.20*b***), the numbers of *P. caudatum* (the green line) always declined to extinction, leaving *P. aurelia* the only survivor. Why? Gause found *P. aurelia* was able to grow six times faster than its competitor, *P. caudatum,* because it was able to better use the limited available resources.

From experiments such as this, Gause formulated what is now called the *principle of competitive exclusion.* This principle states that if two species are competing for a resource, the species that uses the resource more efficiently will eventually eliminate the other locally—no two species with the same niche can coexist.

Putting the Concept to Work

If two species attempt to occupy the same niche, how can you tell which one will be eliminated?

Niche Overlap

LEARNING OBJECTIVE 19.9.3 Explain why niche overlap may lead to character displacement.

In a revealing experiment, Gause challenged *P. caudatum*—the defeated species in his earlier experiments—with a third species, *P. bursaria.* Because he expected these two species to also compete for the limited bacterial food supply, Gause thought one would win out, as had happened in his previous experiments. But that's not what happened. Instead, both species survived in the culture tubes (**figure 19.20*c***); the paramecia found a way to divide the food resources. How did they do it? In the upper part of the culture tubes, where the oxygen concentration and bacterial density were high, *P. caudatum* dominated because it was better able to feed on bacteria. However, in the lower part of the tubes, the lower oxygen concentration favored the growth of a different potential food, yeast, and *P. bursaria* was better able to eat this food. The fundamental niche of each species was the whole culture tube, but the realized niche of each species was only a portion of the tube. This graph also demonstrates the negative effect competition had on the participants: Competition was always detrimental to both species involved. Both species more than doubled their densities when grown without a competitor as when grown together.

Gause's principle of competitive exclusion can be restated to say that no two species can occupy the same niche indefinitely when resources are limiting. When two species are able to coexist on a long-term basis, either resources are not limited or their niches differ in one or more features; otherwise, one species outcompetes the other and the extinction of the second species inevitably results through competitive exclusion.

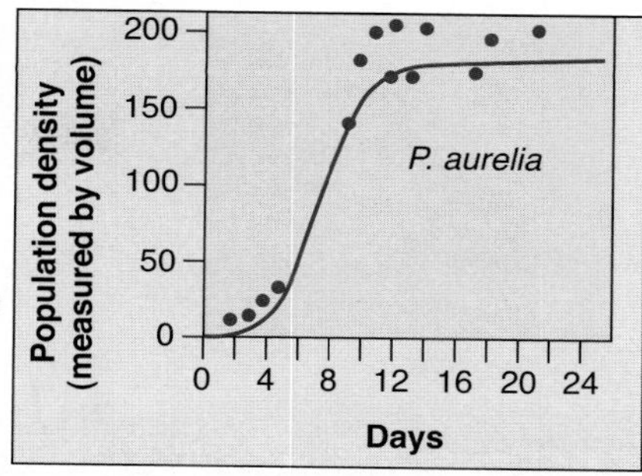

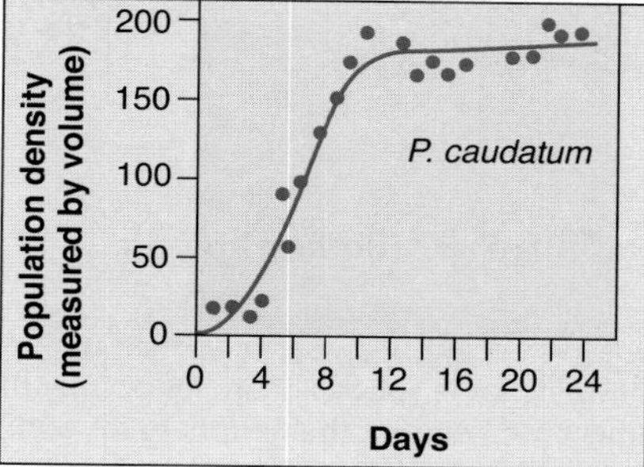

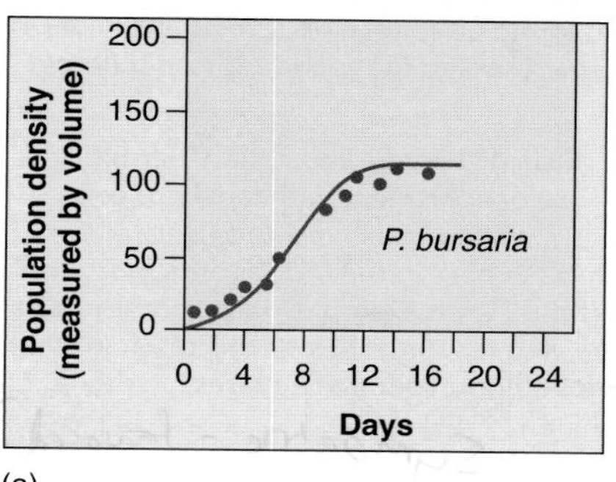

(a)

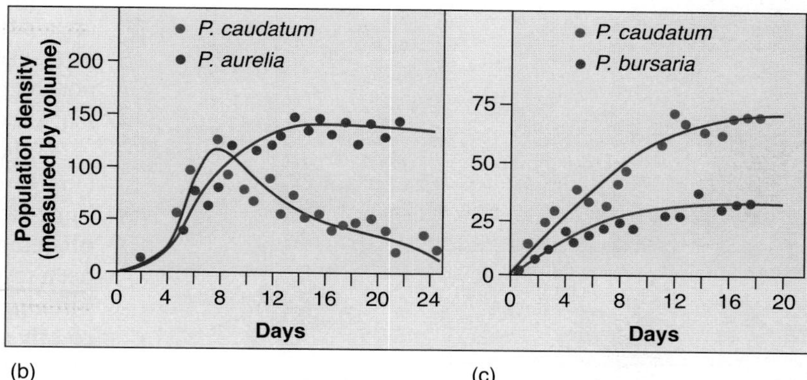

(b) (c)

Figure 19.20 Competitive exclusion among three species of *Paramecium*.

In the microscopic world, *Paramecium* is a ferocious predator. Paramecia eat by ingesting their prey; their plasma membranes surround bacterial or yeast cells, forming a food vacuole containing the prey cell. In his experiments, (a) Gause found that three species of *Paramecium* grew well alone in culture tubes. (b) However, *P. caudatum* declined to extinction when grown with *P. aurelia* because they shared the same realized niche, and *P. aurelia* outcompeted *P. caudatum* for food resources. (c) *P. caudatum* and *P. bursaria* were able to coexist, although in smaller populations, because the two have different realized niches and thus avoid competition.

Figure 19.21 Resource partitioning among lizard species.

Species of *Anolis* lizards in the Caribbean partition their tree habitats in a variety of ways. Some species of anoles occupy the canopy of trees (a), others use twigs on the periphery (b), and still others are found at the base of the trunk (c). In addition, some use grassy areas in the open (d). This same pattern of resource partitioning has evolved independently on different Caribbean islands.

IMPLICATION FOR YOU Few of us live solitary hermit-like lives. Instead we share a house or apartment with family or college roommates. Doing this, we share many resources: water (for showers and baths), food (what's in the fridge), and, most important of all, space (who uses the TV, for example, or the bathroom). How do you partition your living resources? Does this result in "character displacement" behavior among your living mates?

Resource Partitioning

Gause's exclusion principle has a very important consequence: Persistent and intense competition between two species is rare in natural communities. Either one species drives the other to extinction, or natural selection reduces the competition between them, such as through **resource partitioning** (dividing up resources to create two realized niches). In resource partitioning, species that live in the same geographical area avoid competition by living in different portions of the habitat or by using different food or other resources. A clear example of this is seen in *Anolis* lizards (figure 19.21), where species may live in different parts of a tree habitat to avoid competition for food and space with other species that may live on the twigs, trunks, or grass.

Resource partitioning can often be seen in closely related species that occupy the same geographical area. Called **sympatric species** (Greek, *syn,* same, and *patria,* country), these species avoid competition by evolving different adaptations to use different portions of the habitat, food or other resources. Closely related species that do not live in the same geographical area, called **allopatric species** (Greek, *allos,* other, and *patria,* country), often use the same habitat locations and food resources—because they are not in competition, natural selection does not favor evolutionary changes that subdivide their niche.

When a pair of closely related species occur in the same place, they tend to exhibit greater differences in morphology and behavior than the same two species do when living in different areas. Called **character displacement,** the differences between sympatric species are thought to have been favored by natural selection as a mechanism to facilitate resource partitioning and thus reduce competition. Character displacement can be seen clearly among Darwin's finches. The two Galápagos finches in figure 19.22 have beaks of similar size when each is living on an island where the other does not occur. On islands where they are found living together, the two species have evolved beaks of different sizes, one adapted to larger seeds, the other to smaller ones. In essence, the two finches have subdivided the food niche, creating two new smaller niches. By partitioning the available food resources, the two species have avoided direct competition with each other, and so are able to live together in the same habitat.

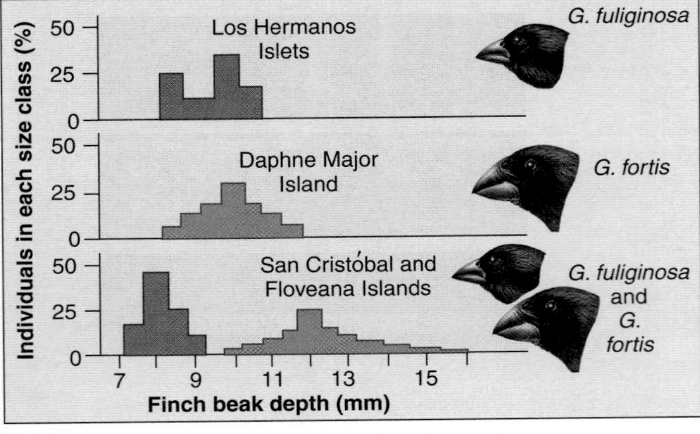

Figure 19.22 Character displacement.

These two species of Galápagos finches (genus *Geospiza*) have beaks of similar sizes when living apart, but different sizes when living together.

Putting the Concept to Work

Does character displacement occur between allopatric species?

Species Interact in Many Ways

19.10 Coevolution and Symbiosis

LEARNING OBJECTIVE 19.10.1 Explain the difference between evolution and coevolution.

The previous section described the "winner take all" results of competition between two species whose niches overlap. Other relationships in nature are less competitive and more cooperative.

Coevolution

The plants, animals, protists, fungi, and prokaryotes that live together in communities have changed and adjusted to one another continually over millions of years. For example, many features of flowering plants have evolved in relation to the dispersal of the plant's gametes by animals (**figure 19.23**). These animals, in turn, have evolved a number of special traits that enable them to obtain food or other resources efficiently from the plants they visit, often from their flowers. In addition, the seeds of many flowering plants have features that make them more likely to be dispersed to new areas of favorable habitat.

Such interactions, which involve the long-term, mutual evolutionary adjustment of the characteristics of the members of biological communities, are examples of **coevolution.** Coevolution is the adaptation of two or more species to each other. In this section, we consider the many ways species interact, some of which involve coevolution.

Putting the Concept to Work

What is the minimal number of species that may be involved in a coevolutionary relationship?

Figure 19.23 Pollination by bat.

Many flowering plants have coevolved with other species to facilitate pollen transfer. Insects are widely known as pollinators, but they're not the only ones. Notice the cargo of pollen on the bat's snout.

Symbiosis Is Widespread

LEARNING OBJECTIVE 19.10.2 Describe the three major kinds of symbiotic relationships.

In symbiotic relationships, two or more kinds of organisms live together in often elaborate and more or less permanent relationships. All symbiotic relationships carry the potential for coevolution between the organisms involved, and in many instances the results of this coevolution are fascinating. Examples of symbiosis include lichens, which are associations of certain fungi with green algae or cyanobacteria. Other important examples are mycorrhizae, the associations between fungi and the roots of most kinds of plants. The fungi expedite the plant's absorption of certain nutrients, and the plants in turn provide the fungi with carbohydrates. Similarly, root nodules that occur in legumes and certain other kinds of plants contain bacteria that fix atmospheric nitrogen and make it available to their host plants.

As you will recall from the discussion on page 319, mycorrhizae are symbiotic relationships between fungi and the roots of plants; lichens are symbiotic relationships between fungi and a photosynthetic partner such as cyanobacteria or green algae.

In the tropics, leaf-cutter ants are often so abundant that they can remove a quarter or more of the total leaf surface of the plants in a given area. They

BIOLOGY & YOU

Your Little Friends. The 10 trillion bacteria that live in the human gut have evolved over millions of years to live in symbiosis with the human digestive system. One such bacterium, *Bacteroides thetaiotaomicron*, salvages energy from complex polysaccharide sugars that are otherwise nondigestible by humans, benefiting both itself and its host. Another, *Bacteroides fragilis*, offers protection from inflammatory bowel diseases, estimated to affect one million Americans. When *B. fragilis* detects the presence of the pathogenic bacterium *Helicobacter* that causes the disease, it releases a polysaccharide "symbiosis factor" which signals the human immune system to begin producing a chemical defense in the gut against *Helicobacter*. So while it is useful to eliminate disease-causing bacteria from our bodies with antibiotics, in some instances disease may result from the absence of beneficial bacteria and their symbiotic good effects. The frequency of inflammatory bowl diseases has skyrocketed in the last 50 years, as antibiotic use became prevalent. Perhaps there is a downside to living without our little friends.

Figure 19.24 The pistol shrimp defends the coral, which he calls home—an example of mutualism.

Figure 19.25 Oxpeckers eat insects off an impala—an example of commensalism.

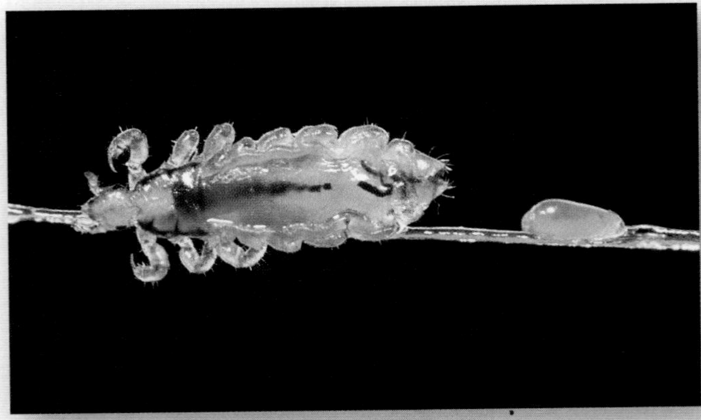

Figure 19.26 The head louse, shown here with its egg, feeds on its host and is an example of parasitism.

do not eat these leaves directly; rather, they take them to underground nests, where they chew them up and inoculate them with the spores of particular fungi. These fungi are cultivated by the ants and brought from one specially prepared bed to another, where they grow and reproduce. In turn, the fungi constitute the primary food of the ants and their larvae. The relationship between leaf-cutter ants and these fungi is an excellent example of symbiosis.

The major kinds of symbiotic relationships include (1) **mutualism,** in which both participating species benefit; (2) **commensalism,** in which one species benefits while the other neither benefits nor is harmed; and (3) **parasitism,** in which one species benefits but the other is harmed. Parasitism can also be viewed as a form of predation, although the organism that is preyed upon does not necessarily die.

Mutualism

Mutualism is a symbiotic relationship in which both species benefit. The pistol shrimp patrolling the surface of the coral in figure 19.24 is defending its homestead from sea stars, which prey on coral. When it encounters a sea star on the coral, the shrimp attacks, pinching the sea star's spines and tube feet and making loud snapping sounds with its enlarged pincers. The loud popping sounds, which have given the shrimp its name, are so intense they stun small fish. Protection from being eaten by sea stars certainly provides a benefit to the coral. The shrimp also clearly benefit, obtaining food and shelter from the coral. Because both parties benefit, their relationship is an example of mutualism.

Commensalism

Commensalism is a symbiotic relationship that benefits one species and neither hurts nor helps the other. The best-known examples of commensalism involve the relationships between certain small tropical fishes and sea anemones, marine animals that have stinging tentacles (see chapter 18). These fish have evolved the ability to live among the tentacles of sea anemones, even though these tentacles would quickly paralyze other fishes that touched them. The fishes feed on the detritus left from the meals of the host anemone, remaining uninjured under remarkable circumstances. In another example, birds called oxpeckers eat ticks and other insects off of grazing animals (figure 19.25). In this symbiotic relationship, the oxpeckers receive a clear benefit in the form of nutrition. If the removal of the ticks benefits the impala, then the relationship is mutually beneficial and the relationship would be considered a form of mutualism. However, there is no evidence that this is so. In this instance, as in most examples of commensalism, it is difficult to be certain whether the partner receives a benefit or not.

Parasitism

Parasitism is a symbiotic relationship which benefits one species at the expense of the other. Typically the parasite is much smaller than its host, and remains closely associated with it. Parasitism is sometimes considered a special kind of predator-prey relationship in which the predator is much smaller than the prey, but unlike a predator, the parasite typically does not kill its host. Parasites are very common among animals. The head louse you see in figure 19.26, for example, is one of two types of sucking lice that parasitize humans.

Putting the Concept to Work

Ants protecting aphids but also eating the "honeydew" the aphids excrete is an example of what type of symbiotic relationship?

19.11 Predation

LEARNING OBJECTIVE 19.11.1 Discuss the ways predators can effect prey populations.

Species that live together in a community interact in many ways, one of which is to eat one another. **Predation** is the consuming of one organism by another. The organism doing the eating is called the *predator*, while the organism being eaten is the *prey*. Examples of predation include a leopard capturing and eating an antelope, a whale grazing on millions of microscopic ocean plankton, and locusts eating the leaves of plants.

In nature, predators often have large effects on prey populations. Some of the most dramatic examples involve situations in which humans have either added or eliminated predators from an area. For example, the elimination of large carnivores from much of the eastern United States has led to population explosions of white-tailed deer, which strip the habitat of all edible plant life within their reach. Similarly, when sea otters were hunted to near extinction on the western coast of the United States, populations of sea urchins, a principal prey item of the otters, exploded. Appearances, however, sometimes can be deceiving. On Isle Royale in Lake Superior, moose reached the island by crossing over ice in an unusually cold winter and multiplied freely there in isolation. When wolves later reached the island by crossing over the ice, naturalists widely assumed that the wolves were playing a key role in controlling the moose population. More careful studies have demonstrated that this is not in fact the case. The moose that the wolves eat are, for the most part, old or diseased animals that would not survive long anyway. In general, the moose are controlled by food availability, disease, and other factors rather than by the wolves (figure 19.27).

Figure 19.27 Wolves chasing a moose—what will the outcome be?

On Isle Royale, Michigan, a large pack of wolves pursue a moose. They chased this moose for almost 2 kilometers; it then turned and faced the wolves, who by that time were exhausted from running through chest-deep snow. The wolves lay down, and the moose walked away.

Putting the Concept to Work

Explain why deer are far more common in New Jersey than in Montana.

Predator/Prey Cycles

LEARNING OBJECTIVE 19.11.2 Evaluate which factors are responsible for predator-prey oscillations.

Why doesn't a predator exterminate its prey, and then become extinct itself, having nothing left to eat? This is just what happens in laboratory experiments, such as the experiment shown in figure 19.28, where the predator, *Didinium* (red line) often exterminates its prey, *Paramecium* (blue line). However, if refuges are provided for the prey, its population drops to low levels but not to extinction. Low prey population levels then provide inadequate food for the predators, causing the predator population to decrease. When this occurs, the prey population can recover. In this way, predator and prey populations cycle in their abundance.

Population cycles are characteristic of some species of small mammals, such as lemmings, and they appear to be stimulated, at least in some situations, by their predators. Ecologists have studied cycles in hare populations since the 1920s. They have found that the North American snowshoe hare, *Lepus americanus,* follows a "10-year cycle" (in reality, it varies from

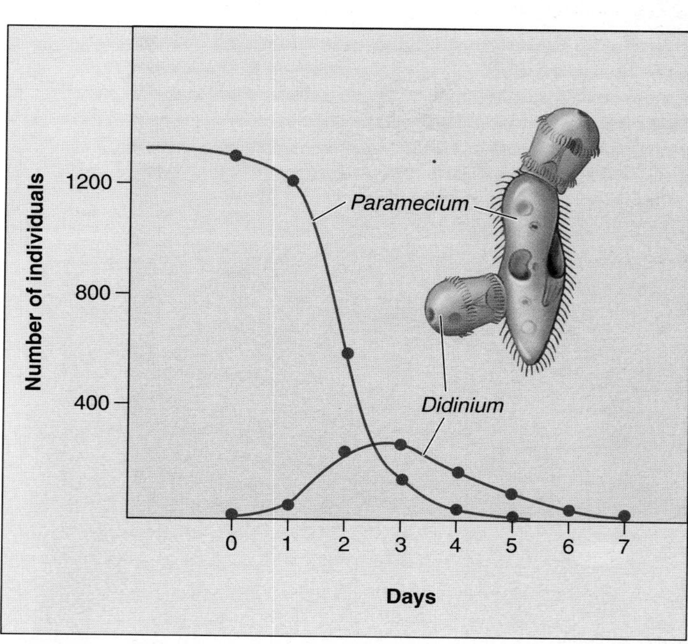

Figure 19.28 Predator-prey in the microscopic world.

When the predatory *Didinium* is added to a *Paramecium* population, the numbers of *Didinium* initially rise, while the numbers of *Paramecium* steadily fall. As the *Paramecium* population is depleted, however, the *Didinium* individuals also die.

(a)

Snowshoe hare
Lynx
160
120
80
40
0
Number of pelts (in thousands)
1845 1855 1865 1875 1885 1895 1905 1915 1925 1935
Year

(b)

Figure 19.29 A predator-prey cycle.

(a) A snowshoe hare being chased by a lynx. (b) The numbers of lynxes and snowshoe hares oscillate in tune with each other in northern Canada. The data are based on numbers of animal pelts from 1845 to 1935. As the number of hares grows, so does the number of lynxes, with the cycle repeating about every 10 years. Both predators (lynxes) and available food resources control the number of hares. The number of lynxes is controlled by the availability of prey (snowshoe hares).

Figure 19.30 Predation reduces competition.

When a key predator, starfish (*Pisaster*), is removed from a coastal ecosystem, fiercely competitive mussels explode in growth, effectively crowding out seven other indigenous species.

8 to 11 years). Its numbers fall 10-fold to 30-fold in a typical cycle, and 100-fold changes can occur. Two factors appear to be generating the cycle: food plants and predators.

1. **Food plants.** The preferred foods of snowshoe hares are willow and birch twigs. As hare density increases, the quantity of these twigs decreases, leading to a precipitous decline in willow and birch twig abundance. The result is that hares are forced to feed on high-fiber (low-quality) food, causing lower birthrates, low juvenile survivorship, low growth rates, and a corresponding fall in hare abundance.
2. **Predators.** A key predator of the snowshoe hare is the Canada lynx, *Lynx canadensis*. The Canada lynx shows a "10-year cycle" of abundance that seems remarkably entrained to the hare abundance cycle (figure 19.29). As hare numbers increase, lynx numbers do, too, rising in response to the increased availability of lynx food. When hare numbers fall, so do lynx numbers, their food supply depleted.

Which factor is responsible for the predator-prey oscillations? Do increasing numbers of hares lead to overharvesting of plants (a hare-plant cycle), or do increasing numbers of lynx lead to overharvesting of hares (a hare-lynx cycle)? Field experiments have shown that both factors can affect the cycle, which, in practice, seems to be generated by the interaction between the two factors.

Putting the Concept to Work

What do you expect will happen to hare numbers in an experimental plot if predators are excluded from the plot?

Predation Reduces Competition

LEARNING OBJECTIVE 19.11.3 Explain why the removal of a predator reduces diversity.

Predator-prey interactions are an essential factor in the maintenance of communities that are rich and diverse in species. The predators prevent or greatly reduce competitive exclusion by reducing the numbers of individuals of competing species. For example, in preying selectively on bivalves in marine intertidal habitats, sea stars prevent bivalves from monopolizing such habitats, opening up space for many other organisms. When sea stars are removed, species diversity falls precipitously, the sea floor community coming to be dominated by a few species of bivalves (figure 19.30). Because predation tends to reduce competition in natural communities, it is usually a mistake to attempt to eliminate a major predator such as sea stars, wolves, or mountain lions from a community. The result is to decrease rather than increase the biological diversity of the community, the opposite of what is intended.

The predatory-prey relationship is not the only factor that affects biodiversity. As you will see in chapter 22, page 455, several factors are responsible for the loss of biodiversity, including habitat loss, overexploitation, and introduced species.

Putting the Concept to Work

How would you expect the biodiversity of Yellowstone National Park to respond to the reintroduction of wolves in the last decade?

19.12 Plant and Animal Defenses

LEARNING OBJECTIVE 19.12.1 Describe the ways plants and animals defend themselves from predators.

Plant Defenses

Plants have evolved many mechanisms to defend themselves from their predators, called herbivores. The most obvious are thorns, spines, and prickles. Chemical defenses are even more crucial, and are widespread in plants. Mustard oils, which give the sharp pungent taste to mustard, capers, cabbage, and horseradish, are toxic to many groups of insects. Interestingly, certain groups of herbivores have developed the ability to feed on these plants without harm, thereby avoiding competition with other herbivores. For example, cabbage butterfly caterpillars (subfamily Pierinae) feed almost exclusively on plants of the mustard and caper families (figure 19.31).

Figure 19.31 Insect herbivores are well suited to their hosts.

Although mustard oils protect plants in the mustard family against most herbivores, the caterpillars of the cabbage butterfly (*Pieris rapae*) are able to break down the mustard oil compounds.

Animal Defenses

Some animals that feed on chemically protected plants can concentrate and store the protective chemicals. Monarch butterflies contain protective chemicals because the caterpillars feed on plants of the milkweed family. In addition, animals also manufacture and use a startling array of defensive substances. Bees, wasps, predatory bugs, scorpions, spiders, and many other arthropods use chemicals to defend themselves and to kill their prey. Similar chemical defenses have also evolved among both marine animals, such as jellyfish, and vertebrates, including venomous snakes, lizards, fishes, and some birds. The poison-dart frogs of the family Dendrobatidae produce toxic alkaloids in the mucus that covers their brightly colored skin (figure 19.32). Some of these toxins are so powerful that a few micrograms will kill a person if injected into the bloodstream.

Figure 19.32 Warning coloration serves as a defense mechanism in Dendrobatidae.

The skin coloration of this poison dart frog warns potential predators of the toxic mucus covering the skin, and predators keep their distance.

Defensive Coloration. Many animals that use chemical defenses are brightly colored (see figure 19.32), advertising their poisonous nature with an ecological strategy known as **warning coloration** or **aposematic coloration.** How does a predator know not to eat brightly colored organisms? By learning. One attempt is rarely repeated. Organisms that lack specific chemical defenses are seldom brightly colored. In fact, many have **cryptic coloration**—color that blends with the surroundings and thus hides the individual from predators (figure 19.33).

Figure 19.33 Cryptic coloration.

An inchworm caterpillar (family Geometridae) closely resembles a twig.

Coevolution of Predator and Prey

Predation can exert strong selective pressures on prey populations. Any feature that acts to decrease the probability of capture should thus be strongly favored by natural selection. In turn, the evolution of such features by prey would be expected to encourage natural selection to then favor counteradaptations in their predator populations. In this way, a coevolutionary arms race may ensue, in which predators and prey are continually evolving better defenses and better means of circumventing these defenses. Herbivores that are able to feed on mustard, milkweed, and dogbane are predators that have acquired counteradaptations to the chemicals produced by the plants.

Putting the Concept to Work

Explain which sorts of animals might have aposematic coloration, and which cryptic coloration.

(a) Model

(b) Batesian mimic

Figure 19.34 A Batesian mimic.

(a) The model. Monarch butterflies (*Danaus plexippus*) are protected from birds and other predators by the cardiac glycosides they incorporate from the milkweeds and dogbanes they feed on as larvae. Adult monarch butterflies advertise their poisonous nature with warning coloration. (b) The mimic. Viceroy butterflies, *Limenitis archippus,* are Batesian mimics of the poisonous monarch. Although the viceroy is not related to the monarch, it looks a lot like it, so predators that have learned not to eat distasteful monarchs avoid viceroys, too.

EVOLUTION

Wandering Mimics. Batesian mimicry also occurs in vertebrates. Probably the most famous case is the nonvenomous scarlet kingsnake, whose red, black, and yellow bands mimic those of the venomous eastern coral snake. Paradoxically, the scarlet kingsnake is found hundreds of miles away from the range of its coral snake model. Why is this a paradox? Theory tells us that mimics should not occur in areas where their model is absent, because predators there would not be under selection to avoid the dangerous banding pattern. So how can scarlet kingsnakes get away with disobeying the rules? It turns out that they don't—male kingsnakes have simply dispersed far from regions where both snakes are present. Researchers have found that, once separated, natural selection promotes the evolution of scarlet kingsnakes that look less like their model in the model-free area.

19.13 Mimicry

During the course of their evolution, many unprotected (nonpoisonous) species have come to resemble distasteful ones that exhibit aposematic coloration. Also, protected species can mimic each other, or organisms can have adaptations that mimic body parts. These types of mimicry are discussed below.

Batesian Mimicry

LEARNING OBJECTIVE 19.13.1 Explain the relationship of a Batesian mimic to its model.

Batesian mimicry is named for Henry Bates, the nineteenth-century British naturalist who first brought this type of mimicry to general attention in 1857. In his journeys to the Amazon region of South America, Bates discovered many palatable insects that resembled brightly colored, distasteful species. He reasoned that the mimics are avoided by predators, who are fooled by the disguise into thinking the mimic actually is the distasteful model.

Many of the best-known examples of Batesian mimicry occur among butterflies and moths. Obviously, predators in systems of this kind must use visual cues to hunt for their prey; otherwise, similar color patterns would not matter to potential predators. There is also increasing evidence indicating that Batesian mimicry can also involve nonvisual cues, such as olfaction, although such examples are less obvious to humans.

The kinds of butterflies that provide the models in Batesian mimicry are, not surprisingly, members of groups whose caterpillars feed only on one or a few closely related plant families. The plant families on which they feed are strongly protected by toxic chemicals. The model butterflies incorporate the poisonous molecules from these plants into their bodies. The mimic butterflies, in contrast, belong to groups in which the feeding habits of the caterpillars are not so restricted. As caterpillars, these butterflies feed on a number of different plant families unprotected by toxic chemicals.

One often-studied mimic among North American butterflies is the viceroy, *Limenitis archippus* (**figure 19.34*b***). This butterfly, which resembles the poisonous monarch (in **figure 19.34*a***), ranges from central Canada through much of the United States and into Mexico. The caterpillars feed on willows and cottonwoods, and neither caterpillars nor adults were thought to be distasteful to birds, although recent findings may dispute this. Interestingly, the Batesian mimicry seen in the adult viceroy butterfly does not extend to the caterpillars. Viceroy caterpillars are camouflaged on leaves, resembling bird droppings, whereas the monarch's distasteful caterpillars are very conspicuous.

Putting the Concept to Work

Explain why other butterfly species mimic Monarch butterflies.

Müllerian Mimicry

LEARNING OBJECTIVE 19.13.2 Explain the relationship of a Müllerian mimic to its model.

Another kind of mimicry, **Müllerian mimicry,** was named for German biologist Fritz Müller, who first described it in 1878. In Müllerian mimicry, several unrelated but protected animal species come to resemble one another (**figure 19.35**). Thus, different kinds of stinging wasps have yellow-and-black-

Figure 19.35 Müllerian mimics.

Because the color patterns of these insects are very similar, and because they all sting, they are Müllerian mimics. The yellow jacket (a), the masarid wasp (b), the sand wasp (c), and the anthidiine bee (d) all act as models for each other, strongly reinforcing the color pattern that they all share.

IMPLICATION FOR YOU A close relative of the yellow jacket is the European hornet, *Vespa crabro,* introduced to the eastern United States in 1840. It is the only true hornet in North America. It also has a yellow and black banded body. Do you think it is a Müllerian mimic? How would you decide?

striped abdomens, but they may not all be descended from a common yellow-and-black-striped ancestor. In general, yellow and black and bright red tend to be common color patterns that warn predators relying on vision. If animals that are all poisonous or dangerous resemble one another, they gain an advantage because a predator learns more quickly to avoid them. In both Batesian and Müllerian mimicry, mimic and model must not only look alike but also act alike if predators are to be deceived. For example, the members of several families of insects that resemble wasps behave surprisingly like the wasps they mimic, flying often and actively from place to place.

Self-Mimicry

Another type of mimicry, called **self-mimicry,** involves adaptations in which one animal body part comes to resemble another body part. This type of mimicry is used by both prey and predators. In prey, it is used to increase survival during an attack. For example, many moths, butterflies, and fish have coloration patterns with "eyespots" (figure 19.36). In some cases, these eyespots startle a predator, allowing the prey time to escape, or they present a false target for the predator's attack, for example attacking the tail where the eyespots appear instead of the head. Predators may also use mimicry to simulate bait to lure prey in. For example, some predators have accessory body parts that look like food, such as the tongue of the alligator snapping turtle that looks like a wriggly worm. The wormlike tongue attracts prey and brings them in close enough for a successful attack.

Putting the Concept to Work

Explain why many wasps and bees tend to look alike.

Figure 19.36 Self-mimicry.

The eyespots on the wings of this moth may startle predators or may be a pattern that predators are instinctively afraid of, because the eyespots resemble the eyes of predators' predators.

Invasion of the Killer Bees

One of the harshest lessons of environmental biology is that the unexpected does happen. Precisely because science operates at the edge of what we know, scientists sometimes stumble over the unexpected. This lesson has been brought clearly to mind in recent years, with reports of killer bees being discovered east of the Mississippi River.

In the continental United States, we are used to the mild-mannered European honeybee, a subspecies called *Apis mellifera mellifera*. The African variety, subspecies *A. m. scutela*, looks very much like them, but they are hardly mild mannered. They are in fact very aggressive critters with a chip on their shoulder, and when swarming do not have to be provoked to start trouble.

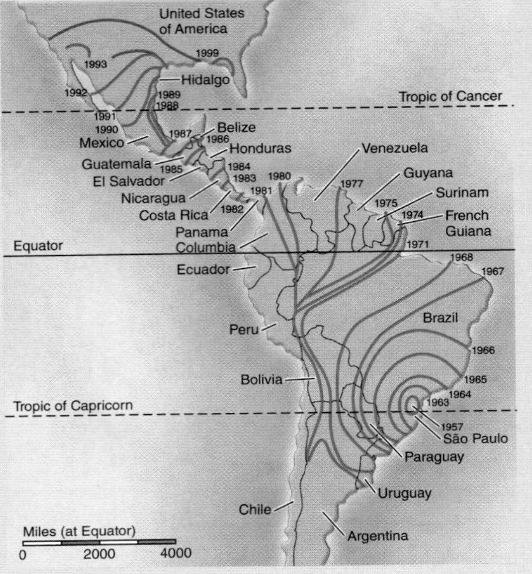

A few individuals may see you at a distance, "lose it," and lead thousands of bees in a concerted attempt to do you in. The only thing you can do is run—fast. They will keep after you for up to a mile. It doesn't do any good to duck under water, as they just wait for you to surface.

They are nicknamed "killer" bees not because any one sting is worse than the European kind, but rather because so many of the bees try to sting you. An average human can survive no more than 300 bee stings. A horrible total of more than 8,000 bee stings is not unusual for a killer bee attack. An American graduate student attacked and killed in a Costa Rican jungle had 10,000 stings.

Killer bees remind us of the "law of unintended consequences" because their invasion of this continent is the direct result of scientists stumbling over the unexpected.

Killer bees were brought from Africa to Brazil over 50 years ago by a prominent Brazilian scientist, Warwick Estevan Kerr. A famous geneticist, Kerr is the only Brazilian to be a member of the U.S. National Academy of Sciences. What he was doing in 1956, at the request of the Brazilian government, was attempting to establish tropical bees in Brazil to expand the commercial bee industry (bees pollinate crops and make commercial honey in the process). African bees seemed ideal candidates, better adapted to the tropics than European bees and more prolific honey producers.

Kerr established a quarantined colony of African bees at a remote field station outside the city of Rio Claro, several hundred miles from his university at São Paulo. Although he had brought back many queens from South Africa, the colony came to be dominated by the offspring of a single very productive queen from Tanzania. Kerr noted at the time that she appeared unusually aggressive.

In the fall of 1957, the field station was visited by a beekeeper. As no one else was around that day, the visitor performed the routine courtesy of tending the hives. A hive with a queen in it has a set of bars across the door so the queen can't get out. Called a "queen excluder," the bars are far enough apart that the smaller worker bees can squeeze through. Once a queen starts to lay eggs, she never leaves the hive, so there is little point in slowing down entry of workers to the hive, and the queen excluder is routinely removed. On that day, the visitor saw the Tanzanian queen laying eggs in the African colony hive, and so removed the queen excluder.

One and a half days later, when a staff member inspected the African colony, the Tanzanian queen and 26 of her daughter queens had decamped. Out into the neighboring forest they went. And that's what was unexpected. European queen bees never leave the hive after they have started to lay eggs. No one could have guessed that the Tanzanian queen would behave differently. But she did.

By 1970 the superaggressive African bees had blanketed Brazil, totally replacing local colonies. They reached Central America by 1980, Mexico by 1986, and Texas by 1990, having conquered 5 million square miles in 33 years. In the process they killed an estimated 1,000 people and over 100,000 cows. The first American to be killed, a rancher named Lino Lopez, died of multiple stings in Texas in 1993.

All during the 1990s, the bees continued their invasion of the United States. All of Arizona and much of Texas has been occupied. A few years ago, Los Angeles county was officially declared colonized, and it looks like African bees will eventually move at least halfway up the state of California.

Soon, however, the invasion is predicted to cease, on a line roughly from San Francisco, California, to Richmond, Virginia. Winter cold is expected to limit any further northward advance of the invading hoards.

For the states below this line, sure as the sun rises, the bees are coming, not caring one bit that they were unanticipated. The deep lesson—that unexpected things do happen—is being driven home by millions of tiny aggressive teachers.

Community Stability

19.14 Ecological Succession

LEARNING OBJECTIVE 19.14.1 **Explain what succession is and why it happens.**

Marked changes in habitat can result in the orderly replacement of one community with another, from simple to complex, in a process known as **succession.** This process is familiar to anyone who has seen a vacant lot or cleared woods slowly become occupied by an increasing number of plants, or a pond become dry land as it is filled with vegetation encroaching from the sides.

Secondary Succession

If a wooded area is cleared and left alone, plants slowly reclaim the area. Eventually traces of the clearing disappear and the area is again woods. Similarly, intense flooding may clear a stream bed of many organisms, leaving mostly sand and rock; afterward, the bed is progressively reinhabited by protists, invertebrates, and other aquatic organisms. This kind of succession, which occurs in areas where an existing community has been disturbed, is called **secondary succession.** Humans are often responsible for initiating secondary succession, such as when a fire has burned off an area or in abandoned agricultural fields.

Primary Succession

In contrast, **primary succession** occurs on bare, lifeless substrate, such as rocks. Primary succession occurs in lakes left behind after the retreat of glaciers, on volcanic islands that rise above the sea, and on land exposed by retreating glaciers. Primary succession on glacial moraines provides an example. The graph in **figure 19.37** shows how nitrogen concentrations change in the soil as primary succession occurs. On bare, mineral-poor soil, lichens grow first, forming small pockets of soil. Acidic secretions from the lichens help to break down the substrate and add to the accumulation of soil. Mosses then colonize these pockets of soil (**figure 19.37*a***), eventually building up enough nutrients in the soil for alder shrubs to take hold (**figure 19.37*b***). These first plants to appear form a **pioneering community.** Over 100 years, the alders (**figure 19.37*c*** and ***photo***) build up the soil nitrogen levels until spruce are able to thrive, eventually crowding out the alder and forming a dense spruce forest (**figure 19.37*d***).

Primary successions end with a community called a **climax community,** whose populations remain relatively stable and are characteristic of the region as a whole.

Why Succession Happens

Succession happens because species alter the habitat and the resources available in it, often in ways that favor other species. As ecosystems mature, and more *K*-selected species replace *r*-selected ones, species richness and total biomass increase but net productivity decreases.

Putting the Concept to Work

Does step (d) in figure 19.37 indicate a pioneering or a climax community? What is the effect of succession on net productivity?

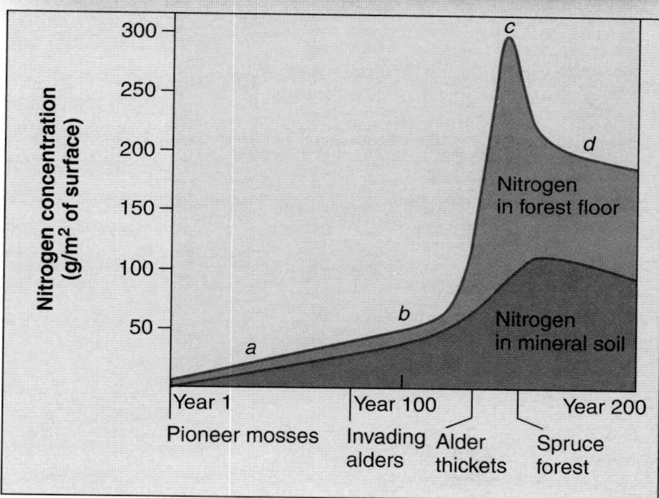

Figure 19.37 **Plant succession produces progressive changes in the soil.**

Initially the glacial moraine at Glacier Bay, Alaska, had little soil nitrogen, but nitrogen-fixing alders (shown in the photo) led to a buildup of nitrogen in the soil, encouraging the subsequent growth of the conifer forest. The graph breaks down the steps of primary succession. (a) The first invaders after the glaciers retreat are pioneering mosses with nitrogen-fixing mutualistic microbes. (b) Within 20 years, young alder shrubs take hold. (c) Rapidly fixing nitrogen, they soon form dense thickets (in photo). (d) As soil nitrogen levels rise, spruce crowd out the mature alders, forming a forest.

IMPLICATION FOR YOU Plant succession occurs wherever habitats are disturbed, even in your own backyard. If you are wildly interested in this, you can demonstrate it for yourself. In the fall, dig up an area of your yard about the size of a dining room table, turning all the soil over and removing as many plants as possible. The following summer, lay out a 1-meter wide path across the disturbed area and onward an equal distance into the untouched yard; this is called a transect line. Inventory the plants you find within the transect, classifying them as either abundant, occasional, or absent. How do the disturbed and untouched areas compare?

Inquiry & Analysis

Are Island Populations of Song Sparrows Density Dependent?

When island populations are isolated, receiving no visitors from other populations, they provide an attractive opportunity to test the degree to which a population's growth rate is affected by its size. A population's size can influence the rate at which it grows because increased numbers of individuals within a population tend to deplete available resources, leading to an increased risk of death by deprivation. Also, predators tend to focus their attention on common prey, resulting in increasing rates of mortality as populations grow. However, simply knowing that a population is decreasing in numbers does not tell you that the decrease has been caused by the size of the population. Many factors such as severe weather, volcanic eruption, and human disturbance can influence island population sizes too.

The graph to the right displays data collected from 13 song sparrow populations on Mandarte Island (see map below). In an attempt to gauge the impact of population size on the evolutionary success of these populations, each population was censured, and its juvenile mortality rate estimated. On the graph, these juvenile mortality rates have been plotted against the number of breeding adults in each population. Although the data appear scattered, the "best-fit" regression line is statistically significant (**statistically significant** means that there is a less than 5% chance that there is in fact no correlation between dependent and independent variables).

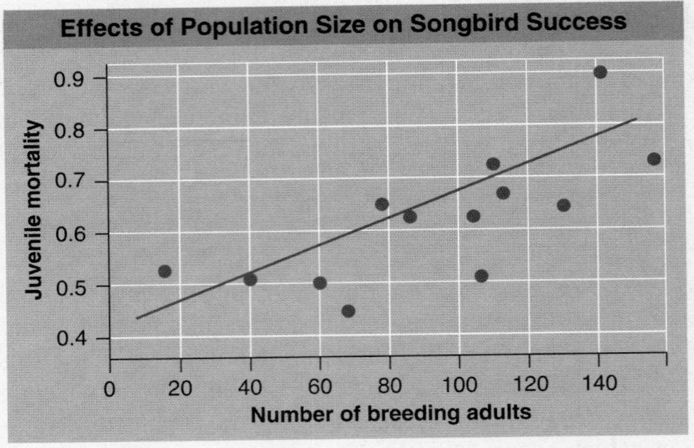

Analysis

1. **Analyzing Scattered Data** What is the size of the song sparrow population (based on breeding adults) with the lowest juvenile mortality? with the greatest?
2. **Interpreting Data**
   a. What is the average juvenile mortality of all 13 populations, estimated from the 13 points on the graph?
   b. How many populations were observed to have juvenile mortality rates *below* this average value? What is the average size of these populations?
   c. How many populations were observed to have juvenile mortality rates *above* this average value? What is the average size of these populations?
3. **Making Inferences** Are the populations with lower juvenile mortality bigger or smaller than the populations with higher juvenile mortality?
4. **Drawing Conclusions** Do the population sizes of these song sparrows appear to exhibit density dependence?

Summary of Learning Outcomes

Ecology

What Is Ecology?

19.1.1 Ecology is the study of how the organisms that live in a place interact with each other and with their physical environment. There are six levels of ecological organization: populations, species, communities, ecosystems, biomes, and the biosphere.

- An ecosystem is a dynamic ecological system composed of a community and the nonliving factors with which it interacts.

19.1.2 Individual organisms must cope with a range of environmental conditions, including temperature (**figure 19.2**), moisture, sunlight, soil, and other organisms.

Populations

Population Range

19.2.1 A population is a group of individuals of the same species that live together and influence each other's survival.

19.2.2 The area a population occupies is referred to as that population's range, which can change in response to environmental changes.

Population Distribution

19.3.1 Availability of resources largely determines how individuals are distributed within populations.

19.3.2 Dispersal to new areas can establish new populations.

Population Growth

19.4.1 Population size, density (**figure 19.9**), and growth are other key characteristics of populations.

19.4.2 Exponential growth occurs in a population when no factors are limiting its growth. When resources are limiting, a population increases in size to the carrying capacity of the environment, and then stabilizes, a pattern called logistic growth that exhibits a sigmoid growth curve.

The Influence of Population Density

19.5.1 Factors such as weather and physical disruptions are density-independent effects and act on population growth, regardless of population size. Density-dependent effects are factors, such as resources, that are affected by increases in population size. As resources are used up, individuals die off and reduce the size of the population. A population is less affected by losses during the rising portion of the sigmoid growth curve, a point called the maximal sustainable yield.

Life History Adaptations

19.6.1 Populations whose resources are abundant experience little competition and reproduce rapidly; these organisms favor near-exponential growth and exhibit *r*-selected adaptations. Populations that experience competition over limited resources favor logistic growth and tend to be more reproductively efficient and exhibit *K*-selected adaptations.

Population Demography

19.7.1 The growth rate of a population is a sensitive function of its age structure. Survivorship curves illustrate the impact of mortality rates among different age groups in a population.

How Competition Shapes Communities

Communities

19.8.1 The array of organisms that live together in an area is called a community. These individuals compete and cooperate with each other to make the community stable.

The Niche and Competition

19.9.1 A niche is defined as the way an organism uses all available resources in its environment. Competition limits an organism from using its entire niche, as shown here from **figure 19.19**.

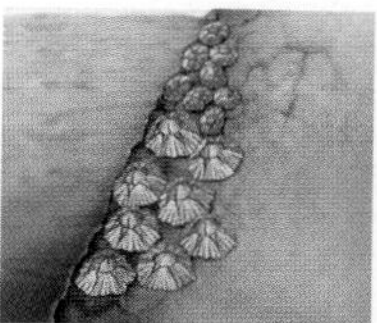

19.9.2 Two results are possible when species try to use the same niche. First, one species can outcompete the other, driving it to extinction in a process called competitive exclusion.

19.9.3 Or, the two species can divide the niche into smaller niches, called resource partitioning. As each species adapts to its portion of the niche, resource partitioning can affect morphological characteristics, called character displacement.

Species Interact in Many Ways

Coevolution and Symbiosis

19.10.1 Coevolution is the long-term evolutionary adjustment of two or more species to each other.

19.10.2 Symbiotic relationships involve two or more organisms of different species that live together and form a somewhat permanent relationship. The major kinds of symbioses are mutualism, commensalism, and parasitism.

Predation

19.11.1 In predator-prey relationships, the predator kills and consumes the prey. Sometimes, in the absence of a predator, a prey population can grow rapidly. Other times, relationships between predators and prey are more complicated.

19.11.2 Predator and prey populations often exhibit cycles, the prey population being hunted to a low number, which begins to negatively affect predator population size.

19.11.3 Predators also act to maintain diversity in a community.

Plant and Animal Defenses

19.12.1 Plants and animals have evolved both morphological and chemical defenses against their predators, as shown here from **figure 19.32**.

Mimicry

19.13.1 Mimicry is where one organism takes advantage of the warning coloration of another organism. Batesian mimicry is where a harmless species has come to resemble a harmful species.

19.13.2 Müllerian mimicry is where a group of harmful species has a similar warning coloration pattern.

Community Stability

Ecological Succession

19.14.1 Succession is the replacement of one community with another. Secondary succession occurs following the disturbance of an existing community, and primary succession is the emergence of a pioneering community where no life existed before.

Test Your Understanding

19.1.1 In the levels of ecological organization, the lowest level, composed of individuals of a single species who live near each other, share the same resources, and can potentially mate, is called a(n)
a. population. **c.** ecosystem.
b. community **d.** biome.

19.4.2 When the number of organisms in a population remains more or less the same over time in the specific place where these organisms live, it is said that this population of organisms has reached its
a. dispersion. **c.** carrying capacity.
b. biotic potential. **d.** population density.

19.5.1 Which of the following is a density-dependent effect on a population?
a. earthquake
b. increased competition for food
c. habitat destruction by humans
d. seasonal flooding

19.6.1 Which of the following traits is *not* a characteristic of an organism that has *K*-selected adaptations?
a. short life span
b. few offspring per breeding season
c. extensive parental care of offspring
d. low mortality rate

19.8.1 All the organisms that live in the same location (fungi, protists, bacteria, archaea, animals, and plants) make up a(n)
a. biome.
b. population.
c. ecosystem.
d. community.

19.9.3 For similar species to occupy the same space, their niches must be different in some way. One way for these species to both survive is
a. competitive exclusion.
b. interspecific competition.
c. resource partitioning.
d. intraspecific competition.

19.10.2 A relationship between two species where one species benefits and the other is neither hurt nor helped is known as
a. parasitism.
b. commensalism.
c. mutualism.
d. competition.

19.11.3 Predators can assist in maintaining the species diversity of an area by
a. increasing competitive exclusion between prey species.
b. decreasing competitive exclusion between prey species.
c. not affecting competitive exclusion between prey species.
d. decreasing resource partitioning between prey species.

19.12.1 The bright colors of poison-dart frogs is an example of
a. aposematic coloration.
b. character displacement.
c. cryptic coloration.
d. Batesian mimicry.

19.14.1 Succession that occurs on abandoned agricultural fields is best described as
a. coevolution.
b. character displacement.
c. secondary succession.
d. prairie succession.

Apply Your Understanding

19.4.2 What factors in an environment could cause the carrying capacity of a population to decrease? Explain why. How might this apply to the world's human population?

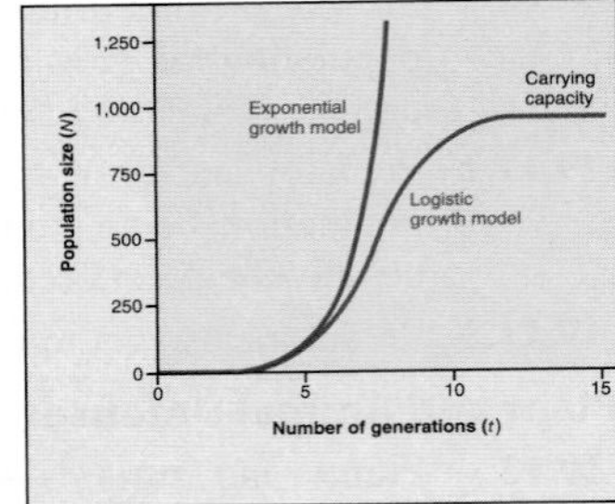

19.9.1 How would the realized niche change for *Chthamalus* if *Semibalanus* was removed from the community? How would the realized niche change for *Semibalanus* if *Chthamalus* was removed from the community?

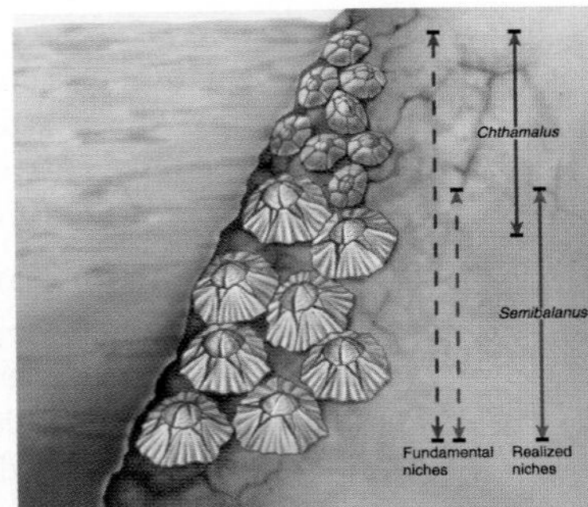

Synthesize What You Have Learned

19.4.2 Many U.S. communities struggle with issues of deer overpopulation. Even in dense housing developments, people complain that deer eat all the flowers in family gardens, and traffic accidents involving hitting deer are increasingly common on suburb streets. Explain the cause of this problem. What sort of remedy would you propose?

19.5.1 Give at least two examples, from your own area, of limiting factors on a population that are density-dependent factors, and two that are density-independent factors on the same population.

19.10.1 There are many examples of coevolution between flowering plants and their pollinators. A group of flowers, often referred to as carrion flowers, smell like a dead, rotting animal. What insects do you think pollinate these flowers? Explain why you think so.

19.14.1 Why are climax communities rare?

Chapter 20

Ecosystems

CHAPTER AT A GLANCE

The Energy in Ecosystems
- **20.1** Energy Flows Through Ecosystems
- **20.2** Ecological Pyramids

Materials Cycle Within Ecosystems
- **20.3** The Water Cycle
- **20.4** The Carbon Cycle
- **20.5** The Nitrogen and Phosphorus Cycles

How Weather Shapes Ecosystems
- **20.6** The Sun and Atmospheric Circulation
- **20.7** Latitude and Elevation
- **20.8** Patterns of Circulation in the Ocean

Major Kinds of Ecosystems
- **20.9** Ocean Ecosystems
- **20.10** Freshwater Ecosystems
- **20.11** Land Ecosystems

Inquiry & Analysis: Does Clear-Cutting Forests Cause Permanent Damage?

The Energy in Ecosystems

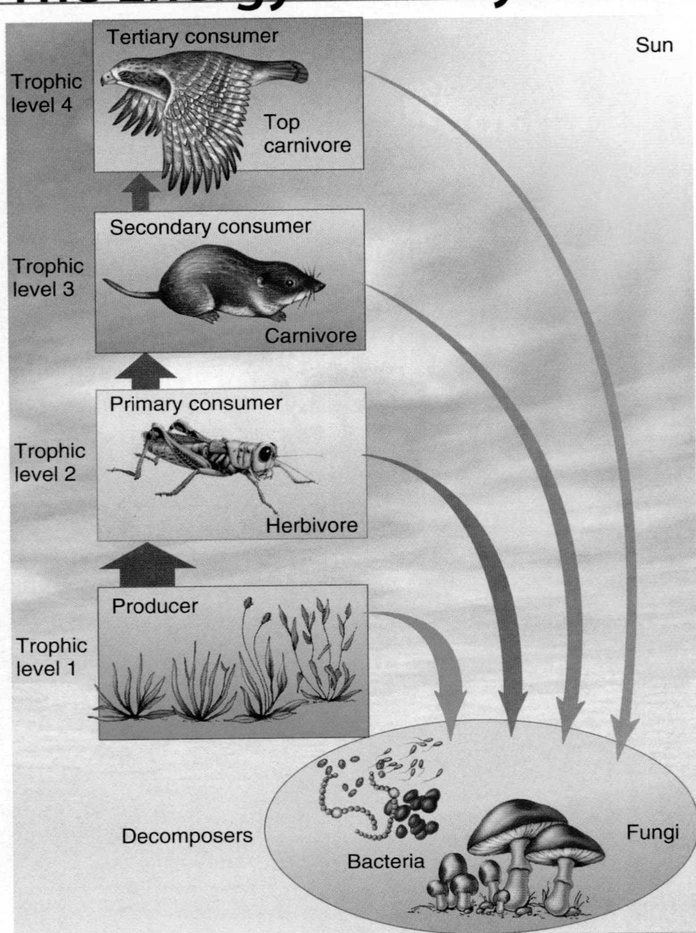

Figure 20.1 Trophic levels within an ecosystem.

Ecologists assign all the members of a community to various trophic levels based on feeding relationships.

20.1 Energy Flows Through Ecosystems

What Is an Ecosystem?

LEARNING OBJECTIVE 20.1.1 Distinguish among community, habitat, and ecosystem.

The ecosystem is the most complex level of biological organization. The biosphere includes all the ecosystems on earth. The earth is a closed system with respect to chemicals but an open system in terms of energy. The organisms in ecosystems regulate the capture and expenditure of energy and the cycling of chemicals. All organisms depend on the ability of photosynthetic organisms to recycle the basic components of life.

Ecologists, the scientists who study ecology, view the world as a patchwork quilt of different environments, all bordering on and interacting with one another. Consider for a moment a patch of forest, the sort of place a deer might live. Ecologists call the collection of creatures that live in a particular place a **community**—all the animals, plants, fungi, and microorganisms that live together in a forest, for example, are the forest community. Ecologists call the place where a community lives its **habitat**—the soil, and the water flowing through it, are key components of the forest habitat. The sum of these two, community and habitat, is an ecological system, or **ecosystem.** An ecosystem is a largely self-sustaining collection of organisms and their physical environment. An ecosystem can be as large as a forest or as small as a tide pool.

Putting the Concept to Work

Is your family a community and your home its habitat? Discuss.

The Path of Energy: Who Eats Whom in Ecosystems

LEARNING OBJECTIVE 20.1.2 Trace the path of energy through the trophic levels of an ecosystem.

Energy flows into the biological world from the sun, which shines a constant beam of light on our earth. Life exists on earth because some of that light energy can be captured and transformed into chemical energy through the process of photosynthesis and used to make organic molecules such as carbohydrates, nucleic acids, proteins, and fats. These organic molecules are what we call food. Living organisms use the energy in food to make new materials for growth, to repair damaged tissues, to reproduce, and to do a myriad of other things requiring energy.

You can think of all the organisms in an ecosystem as chemical machines fueled by energy captured in photosynthesis. The organisms that first capture the energy, the **producers,** are plants, algae and some bacteria, which produce their own energy-storing molecules by carrying out photosynthesis. They are also referred to as *autotrophs.* All other organisms in an ecosystem are **consumers,** obtaining energy-storing molecules by consuming plants or other animals, and are referred to as *heterotrophs.* Ecologists assign every organism in an ecosystem to a trophic (or feeding) level, depending on the source of its energy. A **trophic level** is composed of those

BIOLOGY & YOU

Your Own Personal Ecosystem. You may not realize it, but you are a walking ecosystem. Tiny, eight-legged mites nestle head down inside the follicles of your eye lashes, feasting unnoticed on skin cells. Microscopic bacteria live on your tongue, teeth, and skin. There are about 3.3 pounds of bacteria living in your gut. Most of the time we share our bodies harmoniously with these other inhabitants, a balanced ecological community. A few examples of the neighbors with whom you share your body: **1.** Over 500 species of bacteria live inside your gut, breaking down carbohydrates for you, making essential vitamins like K and B_{12}, and crowding out harmful bacteria. **2.** Bacteria that inhabit the vagina secrete lactic acid, which fends off hostile invaders like pathogenic *Candida* yeast. **3.** A flat, wingless insect called a head louse has been found attached to a strand of human hair 10,000 years old. Less than a tenth of an inch long, head lice suck on your blood, cementing their eggs, or nits, to your hair.

organisms within an ecosystem whose source of energy is the same number of consumption "steps" away from the sun. Thus, as shown in figure 20.1, a plant's trophic level is 1, while *herbivores* (animals that graze on plants) are in trophic level 2, and *carnivores* (animals that eat these grazers) are in trophic level 3. Higher trophic levels exist for carnivores that eat other carnivores (trophic level 4 in figure 20.1). Food energy passes through an ecosystem from one trophic level to another. When the path is a simple linear progression, like the links of a chain, it is called a **food chain.** The chain ends with *decomposers,* who break down dead organisms, or their excretions, and return the organic matter to the soil.

Producers

The lowest trophic level of any ecosystem is occupied by the producers (figure 20.2*a*)—green plants in most land ecosystems (and, usually, algae in aquatic ecosystems). Plants use the energy of the sun to build energy-rich sugar molecules. They also absorb carbon dioxide from the air, and nitrogen and other key substances from the soil, and use them to build biological molecules. It is important to realize that plants consume as well as produce. The roots of a plant, for example, do not carry out photosynthesis—there is no sunlight underground. Roots obtain their energy the same way you do, by using energy-storing molecules produced elsewhere (in this case, in the leaves of the plant).

Herbivores

At the second trophic level are **herbivores,** animals that eat plants (figure 20.2*a*). They are the *primary consumers* of ecosystems. Deer and horses are herbivores, and so are rhinoceroses, chickens (primarily herbivores), and caterpillars. Most herbivores rely on "helpers" to aid in the digestion of cellulose, a structural material found in plants. A cow, for instance, has a thriving colony of bacteria in its gut that digests cellulose. So does a termite. Humans cannot digest cellulose because we lack these bacteria—that is why a cow can live on a diet of grass and you cannot.

Carnivores

At the third trophic level are animals that eat herbivores, called **carnivores** (meat-eaters). They are the *secondary consumers* of ecosystems. Tigers and wolves are carnivores (figure 20.2*b*), and so are mosquitoes and blue jays. Some animals, like bears and humans, eat both plants and animals and are called **omnivores** (figure 20.2*c*). They use the simple sugars and starches stored in plants as food but not the cellulose. Many complex ecosystems contain a fourth trophic level, composed of animals that consume other carnivores. They are called *tertiary consumers,* or *top carnivores.* A weasel that eats a blue jay is a tertiary consumer. Only rarely do ecosystems contain more than four trophic levels, for reasons we will discuss later.

(a) Producers and herbivores

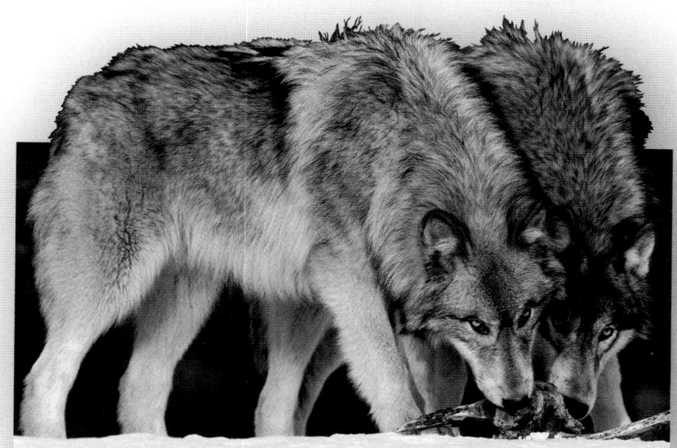

(b) Carnivores

(c) Omnivore

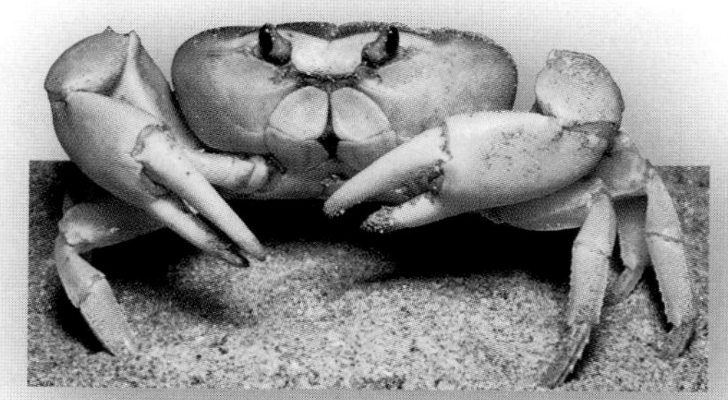

(d) Detritivore

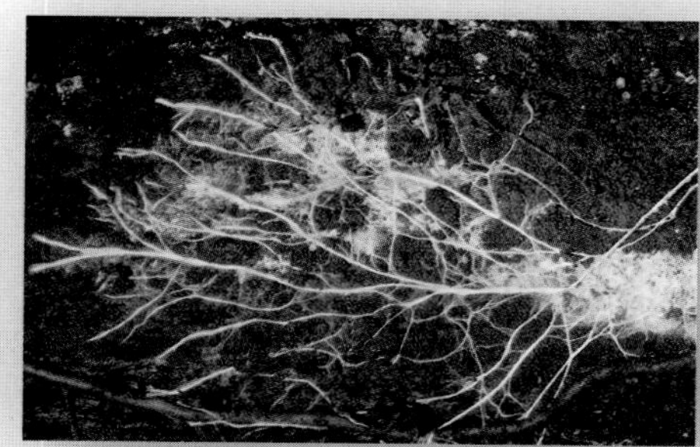

(e) Decomposer

Figure 20.2 Members of the food chain.

(a) The East African grasslands are covered by a dense growth of grasses, the primary producers. Grazing herbivores like these zebras obtain their food from plants. (b) These wolves are carnivores that live in North American forests. (c) This grizzly bear is an omnivore, this one fishing for salmon. (d) This crab is a detritivore. (e) Fungi, such as this basidiomycete growing through the soil, and bacteria are the primary decomposers of terrestrial ecosystems.

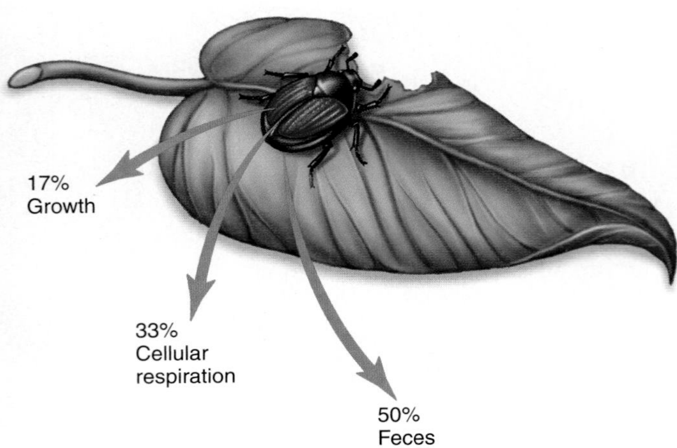

Figure 20.3 How heterotrophs use food energy.

A heterotroph assimilates only a fraction of the energy it consumes. For example, if a "bite" is composed of 500 Joules of energy (1 Joule = 0.239 calories), about 50%, 250 J, is lost in feces, about 33%, 165 J, is used to fuel cellular respiration, and about 17%, 85 J, is converted into consumer biomass. Only this 85 J (or roughly 20 calories) is available to the next trophic level.

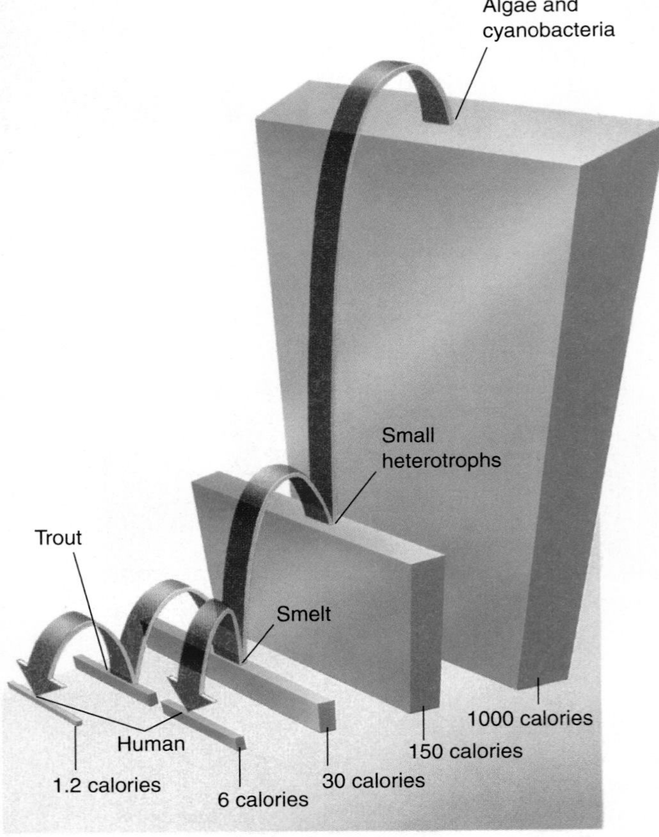

Figure 20.4 Energy loss in an ecosystem.

In a classic study of Cayuga Lake in New York, Lamont Cole of Cornell University measured the path of energy precisely at all points in the food web.

Detritivores and Decomposers

In every ecosystem there is a special class of consumers that include **detritivores** (figure 20.2*d*), organisms that eat dead organisms (also referred to as scavengers) and **decomposers,** organisms that break down organic substances making the nutrients available to other organisms (figure 20.2*e*). Worms and vultures are examples of detritivores. Bacteria and fungi are the principal decomposers in land ecosystems.

Energy Flows Through Trophic Levels

How much energy passes through an ecosystem? **Primary productivity** is the total amount of light energy converted by photosynthetic organisms into organic compounds in a given area per unit of time. An ecosystem's **net primary productivity** is the total amount of energy fixed by photosynthesis per unit of time, minus that which is expended by photosynthetic organisms to fuel metabolic activities. In short, it is the energy stored in organic compounds that is available to heterotrophs. The total weight of all an ecosystem's organisms, called its **biomass,** increases as a result of the ecosystem's net productivity.

When a plant uses the energy from sunlight to make structural molecules such as cellulose, it loses a lot of the energy as heat. In fact, only about half of the energy captured by the plant ends up stored in its molecules. The other half of the energy is lost. This is the first of many such losses as the energy passes through the ecosystem. When the energy flow through an ecosystem is measured at each trophic level, we find that 80% to 95% of the energy available at one trophic level is not transferred to the next. In other words, only 5% to 20% of the available energy passes from one trophic level to the next. For example, the amount of energy that ends up in the beetle's body in figure 20.3 is approximately only 17% of the energy present in the plant molecules it eats. Similarly, when a carnivore eats the herbivore, a comparable amount of energy is lost from the amount of energy present in the herbivore's molecules. This is why food chains generally consist of only three or four steps. So much energy is lost at each step that little usable energy remains after it has been incorporated into the bodies of organisms at four successive trophic levels.

How energy flows through an ecosystem can be seen by tracing the red arrows in figure 20.4. Each green block represents the energy obtained by a different trophic level, with the producers (the algae and cyanobacteria) being the largest block. Researchers calculated that about 150 of each 1,000 calories of potential energy fixed by algae and cyanobacteria are transferred into the bodies of small heterotrophs (animal plankton). Of these, about 30 calories are incorporated into the bodies of the principal secondary consumers of the system (a type of small fish called a smelt). If humans eat the smelt, they gain about 6 of the 1,000 calories that originally entered the system. If trout eat the smelt and humans eat the trout, humans gain only about 1.2 of the 1,000 calories originally captured by the producers.

Thus, in most ecosystems, the path of energy is not a simple linear one, because individual animals often feed at several trophic levels. This creates a more complicated path of energy flow called a **food web** (figure 20.5).

Putting the Concept to Work

What trophic level do you occupy in a food chain? Explain.

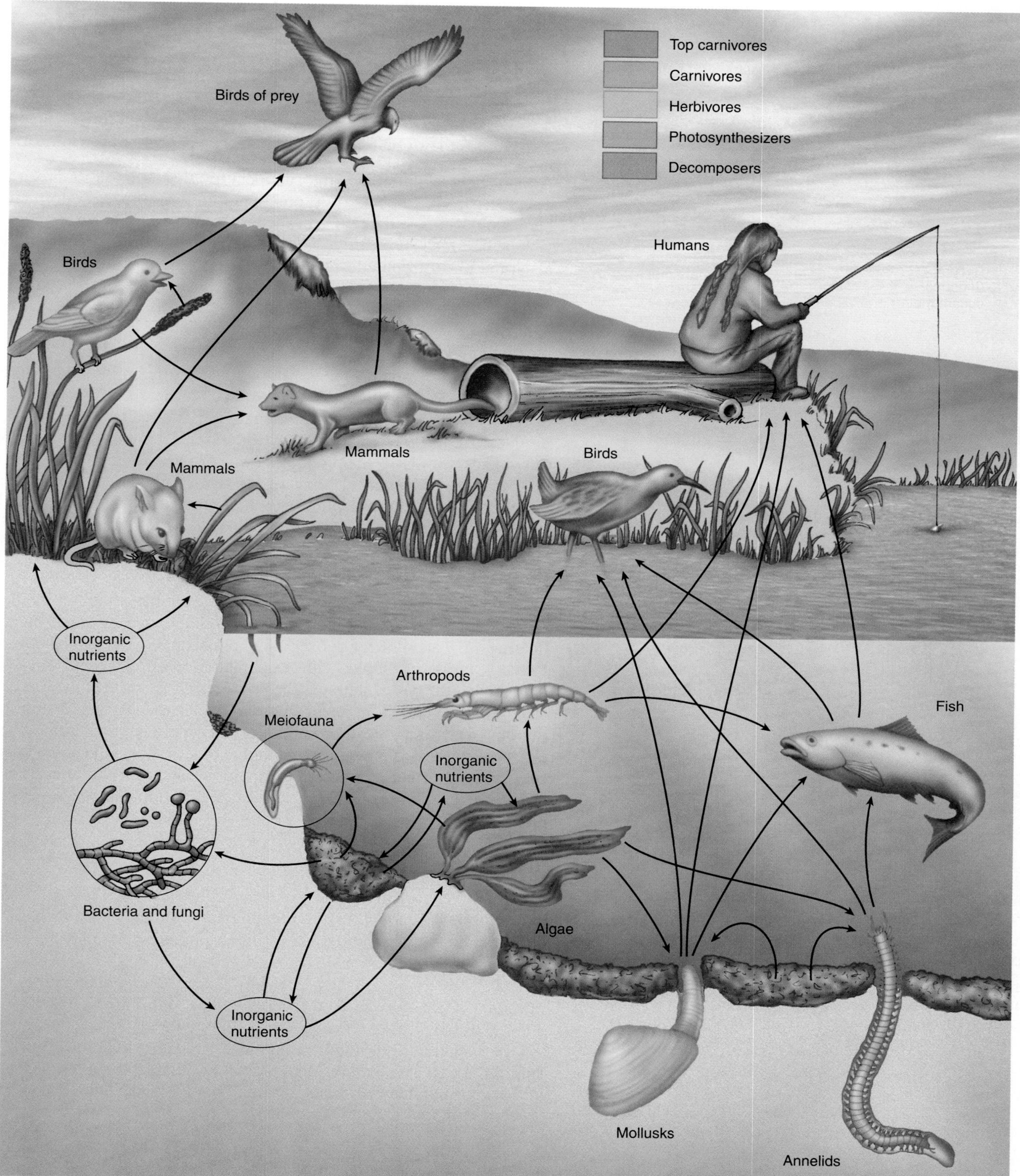

Figure 20.5 A food web.

A food web is much more complicated than a linear food chain. The path of energy passes from one trophic level to another and back again in complex ways.

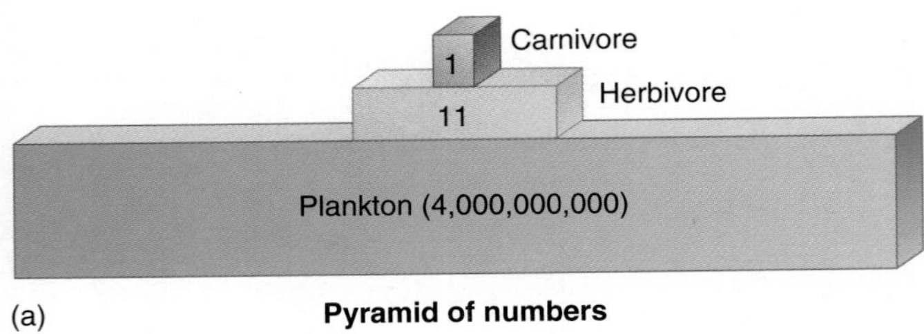

(a) **Pyramid of numbers**

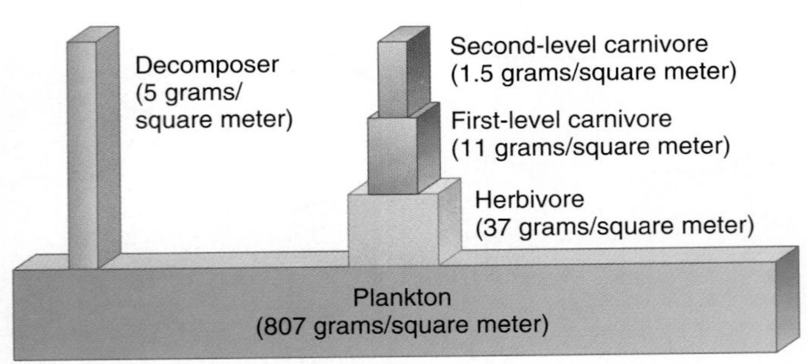

(b)

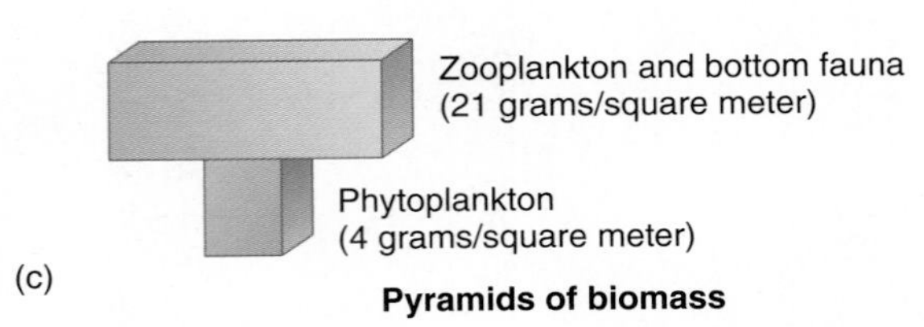

(c) **Pyramids of biomass**

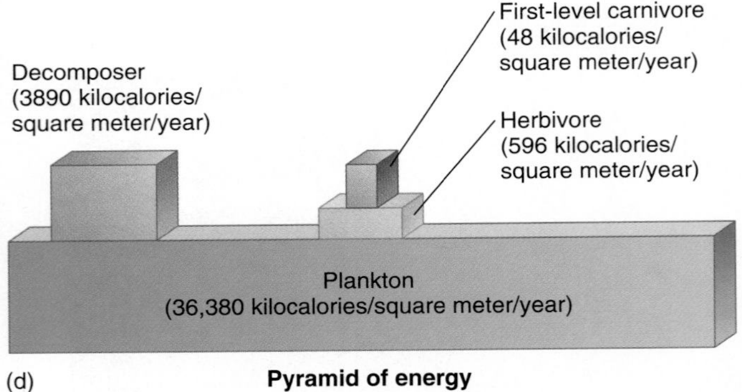

(d) **Pyramid of energy**

Figure 20.6 Ecological pyramids.

Ecological pyramids measure different characteristics of each trophic level. In these aquatic ecosystems, plankton are the primary producers. (a) Pyramid of numbers. Pyramids of biomass, both normal (b) and inverted (c). (d) Pyramid of energy.

20.2 Ecological Pyramids

LEARNING OBJECTIVE 20.2.1 Explain why the biomass of primary producers (photosynthesizers) tends to be greater than that of the herbivores that consume them, and why herbivore biomass tends to be greater than that of the carnivores that consume them.

A plant fixes about 1% of the sun's energy that falls on its green parts. The successive members of a food chain, in turn, process into their own bodies on average about 10% of the energy available in the organisms on which they feed. For this reason, there are generally far more individuals at the lower trophic levels of any ecosystem than at the higher levels. Similarly, the biomass of the primary producers present in a given ecosystem is greater than the biomass of the primary consumers, with successive trophic levels having a lower and lower biomass and so less and less potential energy.

These key ecological relationships appear as pyramids when expressed as diagrams. Ecologists speak of "pyramids of numbers," where the sizes of the blocks reflect the number of individuals at each trophic level. The producers in the green box of **figure 20.6*a*** represent the largest number of individuals. Similarly, the producers (plankton) represent the largest group in "pyramids of biomass," shown in **figure 20.6*b***. The inverted pyramid in **figure 20.6*c*** is an exception and is discussed below. The "pyramid of energy" in **figure 20.6*d*** shows the producers as the largest block.

Inverted Pyramids

Some aquatic ecosystems have inverted biomass pyramids, like in **figure 20.6*c***. In a planktonic ecosystem—dominated by small organisms floating in water—the turnover of photosynthetic phytoplankton at the lowest level is very rapid, with zooplankton consuming phytoplankton so quickly that the phytoplankton (the producers at the base of the food chain) can never develop a large population size. Because the phytoplankton reproduce very rapidly, the community can support a population of heterotrophs that is larger in biomass and more numerous than the phytoplankton. However, don't confuse the sizes of these bars with the energy present at each level. The zooplankton that eat the phytoplankton are present in greater numbers but contain about only 10% of the energy.

Top Carnivores

The loss of energy that occurs at each trophic level places a limit on how many top-level carnivores a community can support. As we have seen, only about one-thousandth of the energy captured by photosynthesis passes all the way through a three-stage food chain to a tertiary consumer such as a snake or hawk. This explains why there are no predators that subsist on lions—the biomass of these animals is simply insufficient to support another trophic level.

In the pyramid of numbers, top-level predators tend to be fairly large animals. Thus, the small residual biomass available at the top of the pyramid is concentrated in a relatively small number of individuals.

Putting the Concept to Work

Explain how the pyramid of biomass can be inverted in oceans when the pyramid of energy is not.

Materials Cycle Within Ecosystems

20.3 The Water Cycle

LEARNING OBJECTIVE 20.3.1 Contrast the environmental and organismic water cycles.

Unlike energy, which flows through the earth's ecosystems in one direction (from the sun to producers to consumers), the physical components of ecosystems are passed around and reused within ecosystems. Ecologists speak of such constant reuse as recycling or, more commonly, cycling. Materials that are constantly recycled include all the chemicals that make up the soil, water, and air. While many are important, the proper cycling of four materials is particularly critical to the health of any ecosystem: water, carbon, and the soil nutrients nitrogen and phosphorus.

The paths of water, carbon, and soil nutrients as they pass from the environment to living organisms and back form closed circles, or cycles. In each cycle, the chemical resides for a time in an organism and then returns to the nonliving environment, often referred to as a *biogeochemical cycle.*

Of all the nonliving components of an ecosystem, water has the greatest influence on the living portion. The availability of water and the way in which it cycles in an ecosystem in large measure determines the biological richness of that ecosystem—the kinds of creatures that live there and how many of each.

Water cycles within an ecosystem in two ways: the environmental water cycle and the organismic water cycle. Both cycles are shown in **figure 20.7**.

BIOLOGY & YOU

You and the Water Cycle. How many gallons of water do you personally consume in a day? Take a guess. Here are some numbers to help you make an estimate: *bath*: 40 gallons; *shower*: 2 gallons per minute; *teeth brushing*: 1 gallon; *hands/face washing*: 1 gallon; *dishwasher*: 15 gallons/load; *clothes machine load*: 25 gallons/load; *toilet flush*: 3 gallons; *glasses of water drunk*: 1/16 gallon/glass. Your per-capita water use (*per* is Latin for "by" and *capita* is Latin for "head") can rapidly become quite alarming—and the number you get from a calculation like this is quite likely an underestimation. It does not take into account everything you use water for, such as cooking, washing your dog, or cleaning muddy shoes. You might water your lawn, wash your car, or leave the water running while you brush your teeth. It all adds up. Even using water conservation measures such as low-flow shower heads and toilets, few of us have a per-capita water use less than 100 gallons a day.

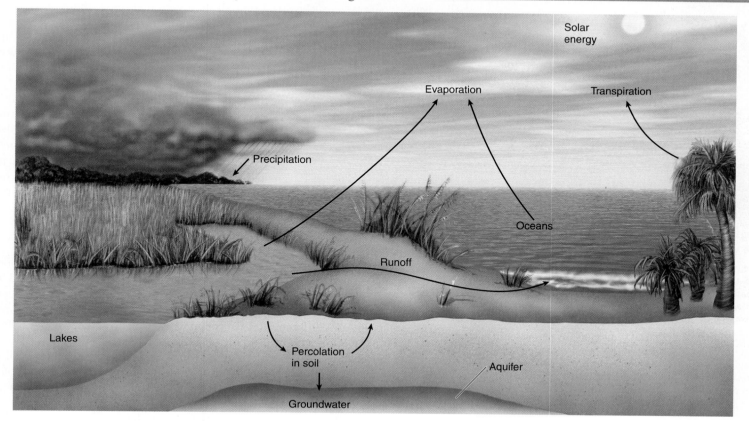

Figure 20.7 The water cycle.

Precipitation on land eventually makes its way to the ocean via groundwater, lakes, and rivers. Solar energy causes evaporation, adding water to the atmosphere. Plants give off excess water through transpiration, also adding water to the atmosphere. Atmospheric water falls as rain or snow over land and oceans, completing the water cycle.

The Environmental Water Cycle

In the environmental water cycle, water vapor in the atmosphere condenses and falls to the earth's surface as rain or snow (called precipitation in figure 20.7). Heated there by the sun, it reenters the atmosphere by **evaporation** from lakes, rivers, and oceans, where it condenses and falls to the earth again.

The Organismic Water Cycle

In the organismic water cycle, surface water does not return directly to the atmosphere. Instead, it is taken up by the roots of plants. After passing through the plant, the water reenters the atmosphere through tiny openings (stomata) in the leaves, evaporating from their surface. This evaporation from leaf surfaces is called **transpiration.** Transpiration is driven by the sun: it's heat creates wind currents that draw moisture from the plant by passing air over the leaves.

The mechanism of transpiration is described in more detail on pages 629 and 630. Air moving across the stomata in the leaves causes water to evaporate from the leaf tissue. The water in the leaves is replaced by water passing into the roots.

Breaking the Cycle

In very dense forest ecosystems, such as tropical rain forests, more than 90% of the moisture in the ecosystem is taken up by plants and then transpired back into the air. Because so many plants in a rain forest are doing this, the vegetation is the primary source of local rainfall. In a very real sense, these plants create their own rain: The moisture that travels up from the plants into the atmosphere falls back to earth as rain.

Where forests are cut down, the organismic water cycle is broken, and moisture is not returned to the atmosphere. Water drains off to the sea instead of rising to the clouds and falling again on the forest. During his expeditions from 1799–1805, the great German explorer Alexander von Humboldt reported that stripping the trees from a tropical rain forest in Colombia prevented water from returning to the atmosphere and created a semiarid desert. It is a tragedy of our time that many tropical areas rain forests are being clear-cut or burned in the name of "development" (figure 20.8).

Figure 20.8 Burning or clear-cutting forests breaks the water cycle.

The high density and large size of plants in a forest translate into great quantities of water being transpired to the atmosphere, creating rain over the forests. In this way, rain forests perpetuate the wet climate that supports them. Tropical deforestation permanently alters the climate in these areas, creating arid zones.

IMPLICATION FOR YOU Proponents of clear-cutting suggest that this practice, if followed by planting neat rows of lumber tree seedlings, actually improves the forest, as it allows "plantation forestry," making future lumbering much more efficient. What do you think of this argument?

Groundwater

Much less obvious than the surface waters seen in streams, lakes, and ponds is the groundwater, which occurs in permeable, saturated, underground layers of rock, sand, and gravel called *aquifers.* In many areas, groundwater is the most important water reservoir; for example, in the United States, more than 96% of all freshwater is groundwater, which provides about 50% of the population with its drinking water.

Because of the greater rate at which groundwater is being used, the increasing chemical pollution of groundwater is a very serious problem. Pesticides, herbicides, and fertilizers are key sources of groundwater pollution. Because of the large volume of water, its slow rate of turnover, and its inaccessibility, removing pollutants from aquifers is virtually impossible.

Putting the Concept to Work

How does clear-cutting break the environmental water cycle?

20.4 The Carbon Cycle

LEARNING OBJECTIVE 20.4.1 Contrast the effects of respiration, erosion, and combustion on the carbon cycle.

The earth's atmosphere contains plentiful carbon, present as carbon dioxide (CO_2) gas. This carbon cycles between the atmosphere and living organisms, often being locked up for long periods of time in organisms or deep underground. The cycle is begun by plants that use CO_2 in photosynthesis to build organic molecules—in effect, they trap the carbon atoms of CO_2 within the living world. The carbon atoms are returned to the atmosphere's pool of CO_2 through respiration, combustion, and erosion, as shown in figure 20.9.

Carbon dioxide is generated at two points during cellular respiration. First, two molecules of CO_2 are produced in the oxidation of pyruvate to acetyl-CoA, discussed on page 121. Another four molecules of CO_2 are produced in the Krebs cycle, discussed on page 122.

Respiration

All organisms in ecosystems respire—that is, they extract energy from organic food molecules, which involves stripping away the carbon atoms and combining them with oxygen to form CO_2. This end product of respiration is released into the atmosphere.

Combustion

Plants that become buried in sediment may be transformed by pressure into coal or oil. The carbon originally trapped by these plants is only released back into the atmosphere when the coal or oil (called **fossil fuels**) is burned.

Human activity is causing the carbon cycle to become unbalanced. As described on page 454, the influx of large amounts of carbon dioxide into the atmosphere from the burning of fossil fuels is causing atmospheric temperatures to rise, a process called global warming.

Erosion

Very large amounts of carbon are present in limestone, formed from calcium carbonate shells of marine organisms. When the limestone becomes exposed to weather and erodes, the carbon washes back and is dissolved again in oceans.

Putting the Concept to Work

How is carbon released into the atmosphere from plants?

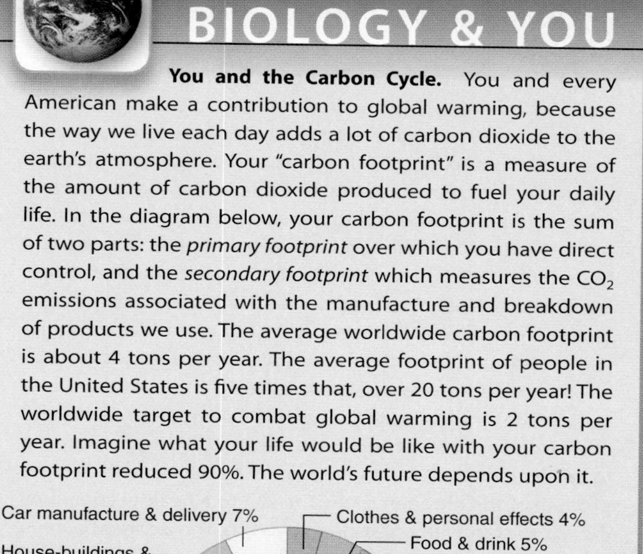

BIOLOGY & YOU

You and the Carbon Cycle. You and every American make a contribution to global warming, because the way we live each day adds a lot of carbon dioxide to the earth's atmosphere. Your "carbon footprint" is a measure of the amount of carbon dioxide produced to fuel your daily life. In the diagram below, your carbon footprint is the sum of two parts: the *primary footprint* over which you have direct control, and the *secondary footprint* which measures the CO_2 emissions associated with the manufacture and breakdown of products we use. The average worldwide carbon footprint is about 4 tons per year. The average footprint of people in the United States is five times that, over 20 tons per year! The worldwide target to combat global warming is 2 tons per year. Imagine what your life would be like with your carbon footprint reduced 90%. The world's future depends upon it.

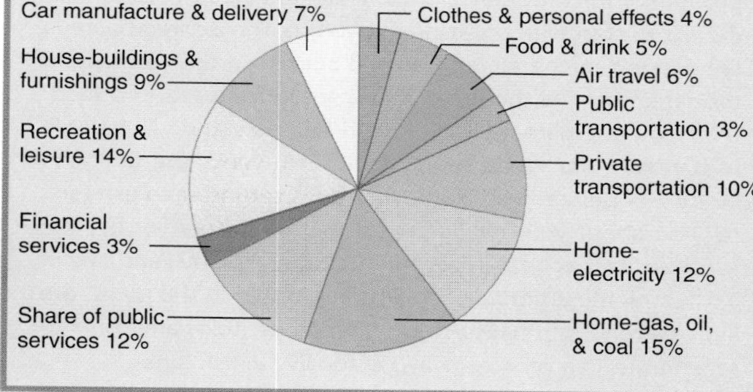

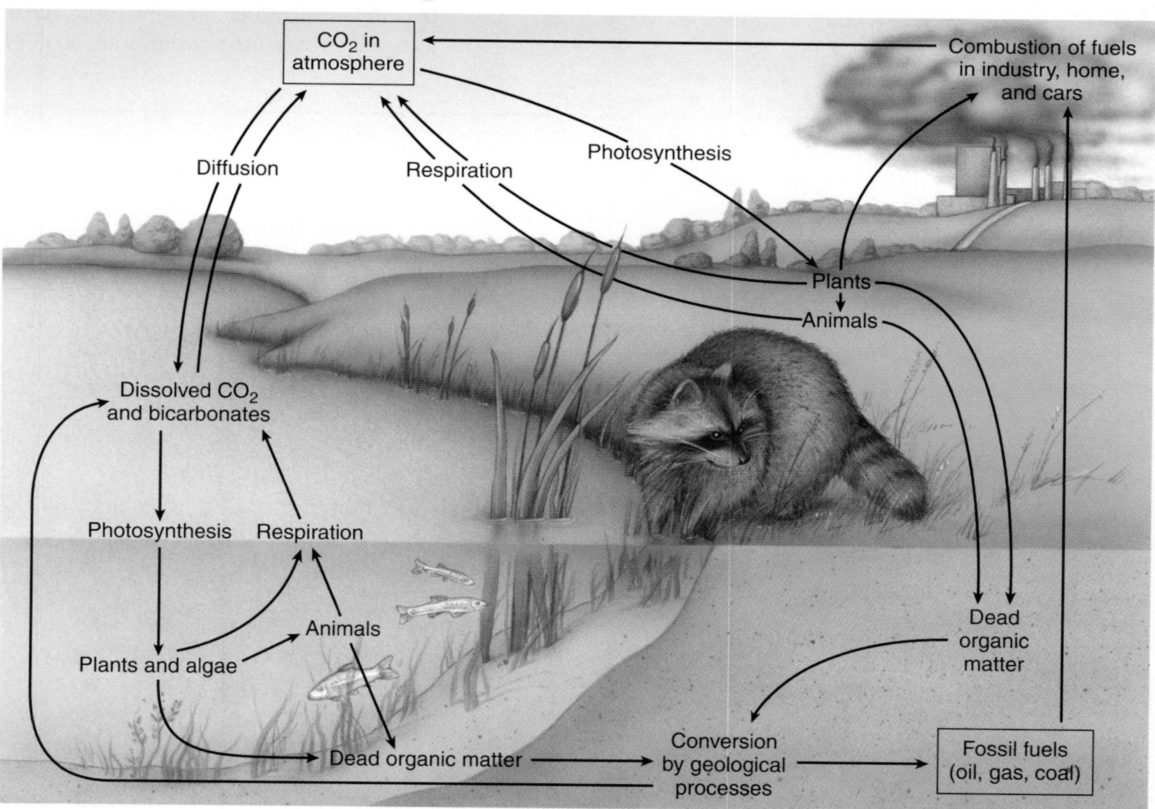

Figure 20.9
The carbon cycle.
Carbon from the atmosphere and from water is fixed by photosynthetic organisms and returned through respiration, combustion, and erosion.

BIOLOGY & YOU

You and the Nitrogen Cycle. As a way to step back and see the larger picture of how the nitrogen cycle affects your life, imagine setting up an aquarium tank with many fish. To care for the fish, plants, and other aquatic life you add to the tank, you have to provide light (for the plants) and fish food (for the critters). If that is all you do, however, the fish will soon die. Why? Although fish get along fine in rivers and lakes, a fish tank is a confined body of water, and that makes a critical difference. Fish food contains a lot of protein. A combination of uneaten fish food, decaying plant life, and urine and feces excreted by the fish will soon cause a toxic buildup of ammonia in the tank. *Nitrosomonas* bacteria in the water convert the ammonia into the chemical compound nitrite, and other *Nitrobacter* bacteria oxidize the nitrite, adding an oxygen to produce nitrate, much less harmful to the fish and the end product of the nitrogen cycle. The key to a healthy aquarium, then, is to start with only one or two fish. The desired bacteria are present in the air, and so will start to grow naturally in the tank water as the fish begin to produce waste products. Over time the bacteria will grow in numbers and will be able to handle more waste products. In 6–8 weeks the tank can be fully populated with fish. What does setting up a fish tank tell you about your nitrogen cycle? Our nitrogen wastes are "cleaned" by bacteria in sewage treatment plants, and like in a fish tank the ammonia concentrations within the plants are kept low enough that bacteria can convert toxic ammonia to safe nitrate. In a very real way, we too live in fish tanks.

20.5 The Nitrogen and Phosphorus Cycles

LEARNING OBJECTIVE 20.5.1 Compare the nitrogen and phosphorus cycles.

The Nitrogen Cycle

Earth's atmosphere is 78.08% nitrogen gas (N_2), but most living organisms are unable to use the N_2 so plentifully available in the air surrounding them. The two nitrogen atoms of N_2 are bound together by a particularly strong "triple" covalent bond that is very difficult to break. Luckily, a few kinds of bacteria can break this triple bond and bind nitrogen atoms to hydrogen, forming "fixed" nitrogen, ammonia (NH_3), in a process called **nitrogen fixation.**

> **Recall from the discussion of covalent bonds on page 38, that a triple covalent bond involves the sharing of three pairs of electrons. This is a lot of energy holding together two atoms, which is why the bond holding the nitrogen atoms together in nitrogen gas is so difficult to break.**

Bacteria evolved the ability to fix nitrogen early in the history of life, before photosynthesis had introduced oxygen gas into the earth's atmosphere, and that is still the only way the bacteria are able to do it—even a trace of oxygen poisons the process. In today's world, awash with oxygen, these bacteria live encased within bubbles called cysts that admit no oxygen or within special airtight cells in nodules of tissue on the roots of beans, aspen trees, and a few other plants. Figure 20.10 shows the workings of the nitrogen cycle.

The growth of plants in ecosystems is often severely limited by the availability of "fixed" nitrogen in the soil, which is why farmers fertilize fields. Today most fixed nitrogen added to soils by farmers is produced in factories by industrial rather than bacterial nitrogen fixation—this industrial process today accounts for a prodigious 30% of the entire nitrogen cycle.

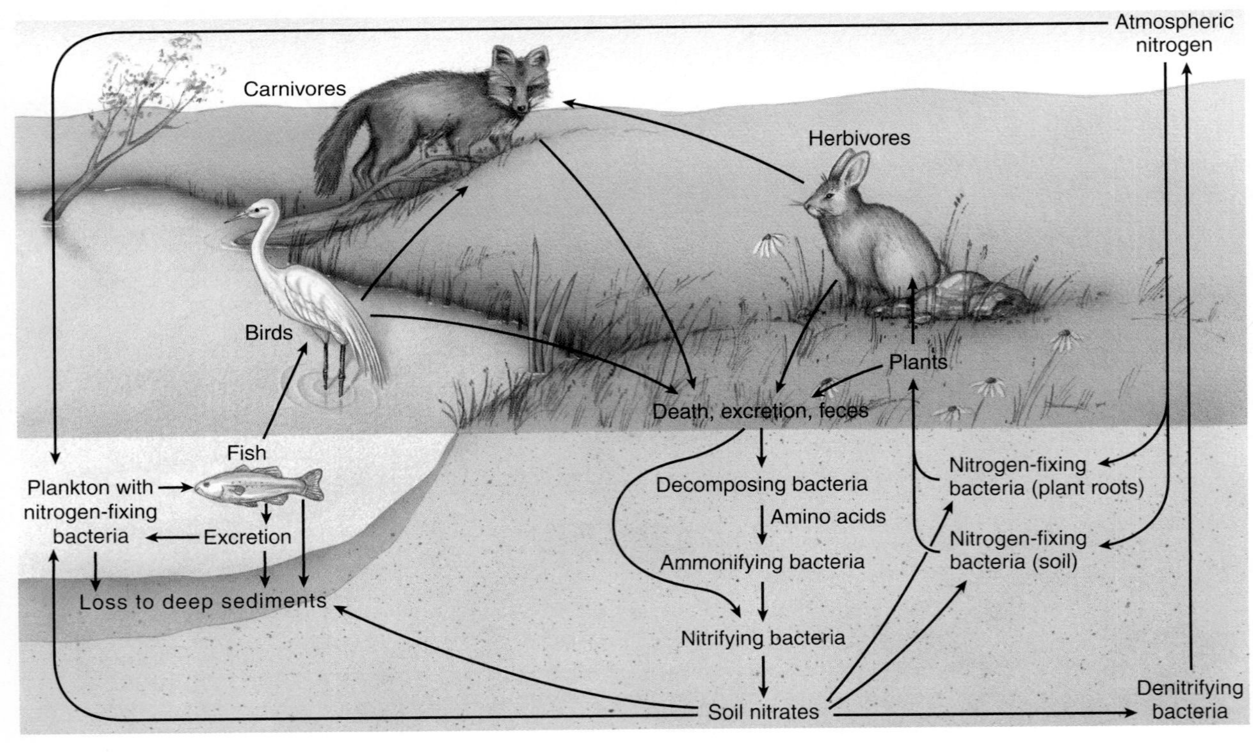

Figure 20.10
The nitrogen cycle.
Relatively few kinds of organisms—all of them bacteria—can convert atmospheric nitrogen into forms that can be used for biological processes.

Figure 20.11
The phosphorus cycle.

Phosphorus plays a critical role in plant nutrition; next to nitrogen, phosphorus is the element most likely to be so scarce that it limits plant growth.

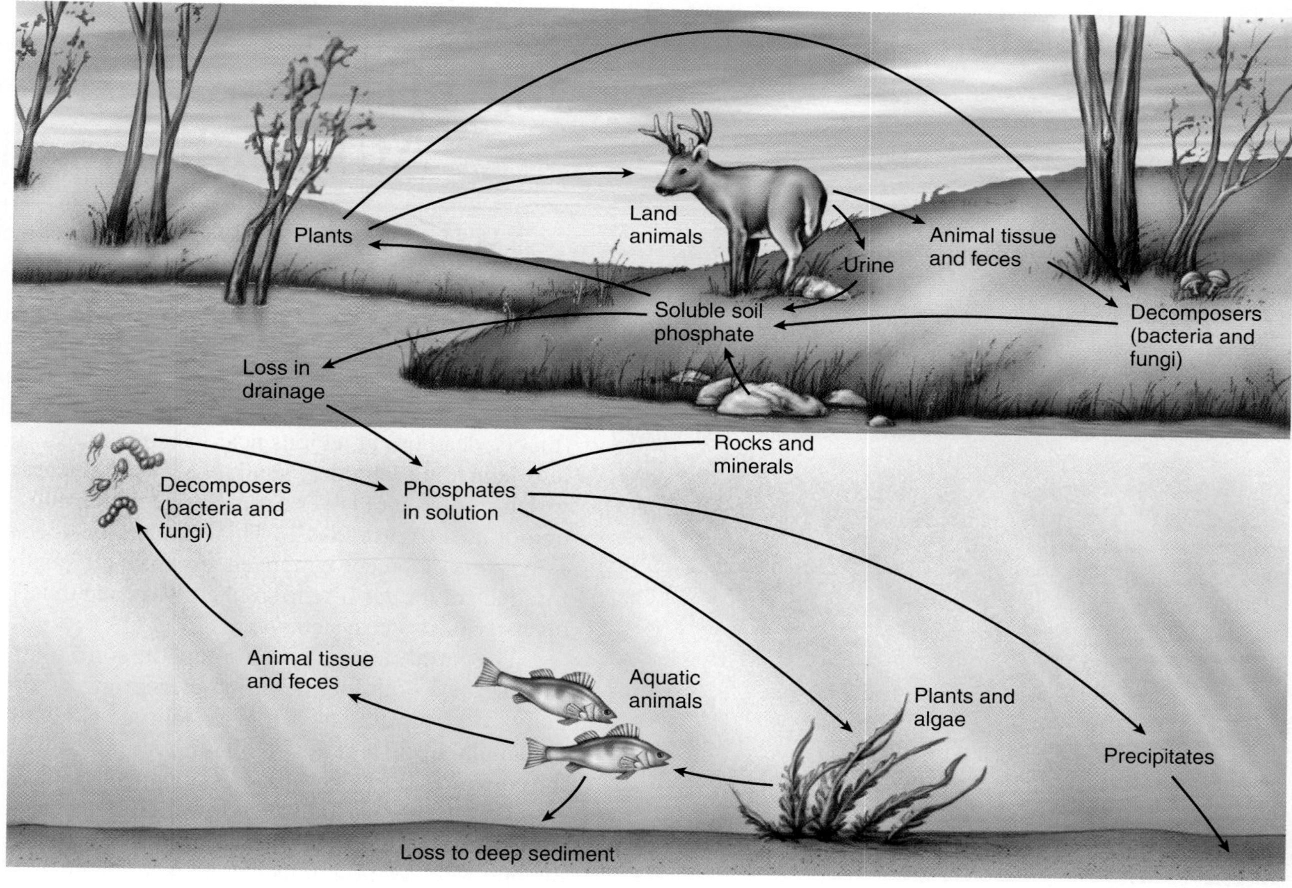

The Phosphorus Cycle

Phosphorus is an essential element in all living organisms, a key part of both ATP and DNA. Phosphorus is often in very limited supply in the soil of particular ecosystems, and because phosphorus does not form a gas, none is available in the atmosphere. Most phosphorus exists in soil and rock as the mineral calcium phosphate, which dissolves in water to form phosphate ions, as shown in **figure 20.11**. These phosphate ions are absorbed by the roots of plants and used by them to build organic molecules like ATP and DNA. When the plants and animals die and decay, bacteria in the soil convert the organic phosphorus back into phosphate ions, completing the cycle.

The phosphorus level in freshwater lake ecosystems is often quite low, preventing much growth of photosynthetic algae in these systems. Pollution of a lake by the inadvertent addition of phosphorus to its waters (agricultural fertilizers and many commercial detergents are rich in phosphorus) first produces a green scum of algal growth on the surface of the lake, and then proceeds to "kill" the lake: As aging algae die, bacteria feeding on the dead algae cells use up so much of the lake's dissolved oxygen that fish and invertebrate animals suffocate. Such rapid, uncontrolled growth caused by excessive nutrients in an aquatic ecosystem is called **eutrophication.**

Putting the Concept to Work

If air is 78% nitrogen gas, why is plant growth often severely limited by available nitrogen?

BIOLOGY & YOU

You and the Phosphorus Cycle. Most of us have little direct impact on the phosphorus cycle, with one glaring exception: fertilizing lawns and gardens. Soils in most states already have an adequate amount of phosphorus to grow healthy lawns and gardens. Adding more phosphorus in fertilizers does not benefit the plants. Instead, the extra phosphorus runs off in rainwater and is washed down the nearest street or storm drain, ending up in your local lake or river. Soon the phosphorus produces algal blooms, a green scum over what was once clear water. States like Minnesota have passed laws that meet this problem head on. Starting in 2005, it became illegal to use fertilizers containing phosphorus on lawns anywhere in Minnesota. If you want to help keep phosphorus levels down in your community, look at the bag or box of fertilizer before you buy it. On its label there is a string of three numbers that list its percent nitrogen, phosphorus, and potassium content, in that order. A "0" in the middle means a phosphorus-free fertilizer.

How Weather Shapes Ecosystems

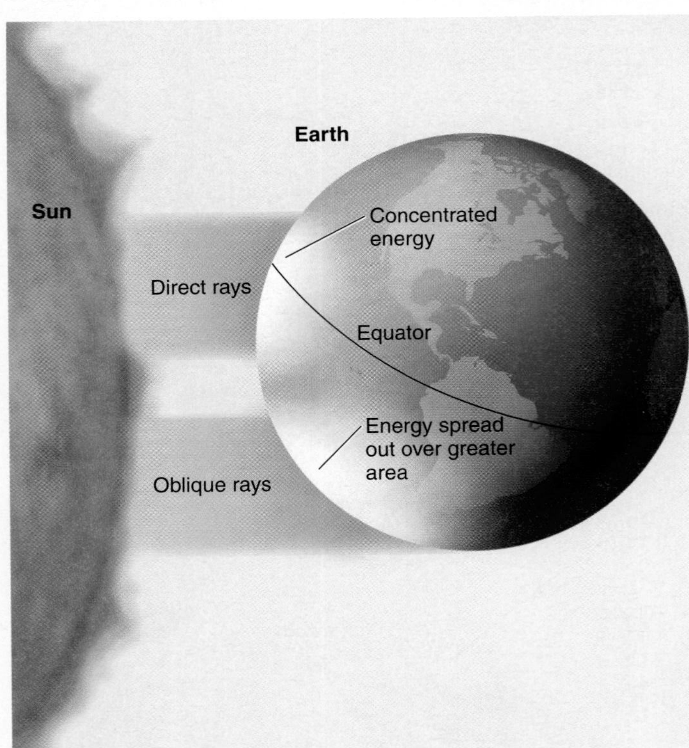

Figure 20.12 Latitude affects climate.

The relationship between the earth and sun is critical in determining the nature and distribution of life on earth. The tropics are warmer than the temperate regions because the sun's rays strike at a direct angle, providing more energy per unit of area.

20.6 The Sun and Atmospheric Circulation

LEARNING OBJECTIVE 20.6.1 Describe how the sun drives circulation of the atmosphere.

The world contains a wide variety of ecosystems because its climate varies a great deal from place to place. On a given day, Miami and Boston often have very different weather. There is no mystery about this. The tropics are warmer than the temperate regions because the sun's rays arrive almost perpendicular (that is, dead on) at regions near the equator. As you move from the equator into temperate latitudes, sunlight strikes the earth at more oblique angles, which spreads it out over a much greater area, thus providing less energy per unit of area (figure 20.12). This simple fact—because the earth is a sphere, some parts of it receive more energy from the sun than others—is responsible for much of the earth's different climates and thus, indirectly, for much of the diversity of its ecosystems.

The earth's annual orbit around the sun and its daily rotation on its own axis are also both important in determining world climate. Because of the daily cycle, the climate at a given latitude is relatively constant. Because of the annual cycle and the inclination of the earth's axis, all parts away from the equator experience a progression of seasons. In summer in the Southern Hemisphere, the earth is tilted toward the sun as shown in figure 20.12, and rays hit more directly leading to higher temperatures. As the earth reaches the opposite position in its annual orbit, the Northern Hemisphere receives more direct rays from the sun and experiences summer.

The major atmospheric circulation patterns result from the interactions between six large air masses. These great air masses (shown as circulating arrows in figure 20.13) occur in pairs, with one air mass of the pair occurring in the northern latitudes and the other occurring in the southern latitudes. These air masses affect climate because the rising and falling of an air mass influence its temperature, which, in turn, influences its moisture-holding capacity.

Near the equator, warm air rises and flows toward the poles (indicated by arrows at the equator that rise and circle toward the poles). As it rises and cools, this air loses most of its moisture because cool air holds less water vapor than warm air. (This explains why it rains so much in the tropics where the air is warm.) When this air has traveled to about 30 degrees N (north) and S (south) latitudes, the cool, dry air sinks and becomes reheated, soaking up water like a sponge as it warms, producing a broad zone of low rainfall. It is no accident that all of the great deserts of the world lie near 30 degrees N or 30 degrees S latitude. Air at these latitudes is still warmer than it is in the polar regions, and thus it continues to flow toward the poles. At about 60 degrees N and S latitudes, air rises and cools and sheds its moisture, and such are the locations of the great temperate forests of the world. Finally, this rising air descends near the poles, producing zones of very low precipitation.

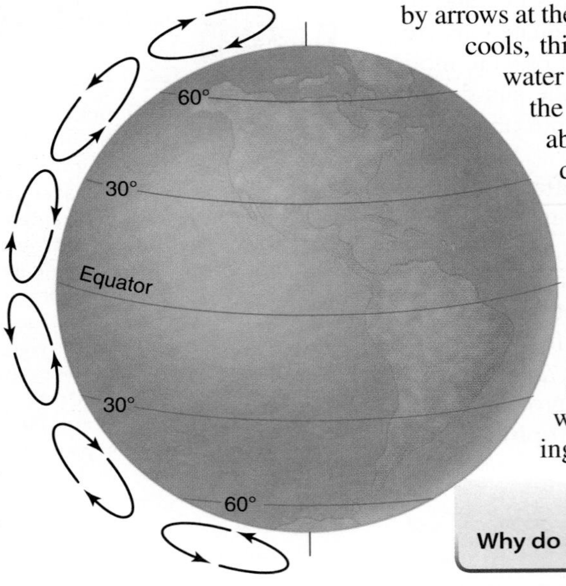

Figure 20.13 Air rises at the equator and then falls.

The pattern of air movement out from and back to the earth's surface forms three pairs of great cycles.

Putting the Concept to Work

Why do all the earth's great deserts lie near 30° N or 30° S latitude?

20.7 Latitude and Elevation

LEARNING OBJECTIVE 20.7.1 Describe a rain shadow and explain why changes in latitude and elevation have similar effects on ecosystems.

Temperatures are higher in tropical ecosystems for a simple reason: more sunlight per unit area falls on tropical latitudes (see figure 20.12). Solar radiation is most intense when the sun is directly overhead, and this occurs only in the tropics, where sunlight strikes the equator perpendicularly. Temperature also varies with elevation, with higher altitudes becoming progressively colder. At any given latitude, air temperature falls about 6°C for every 1,000-meter increase in elevation. The ecological consequences of temperature varying with elevation are the same as temperature varying with latitude. Figure 20.14 illustrates this principle, comparing changes in ecosystems that occur with increasing latitudes in North America with the ecosystem changes that occur with increasing elevation at the tropics. A 1,000-meter increase in elevation on a mountain in southern Mexico (figure 20.14*b*) results in a temperature drop equal to that of an 880-kilometer increase in latitude on the North American continent (figure 20.14*a*). This is why the "timberline" (the elevation above which trees do not grow) occurs at progressively lower elevations as one moves farther from the equator.

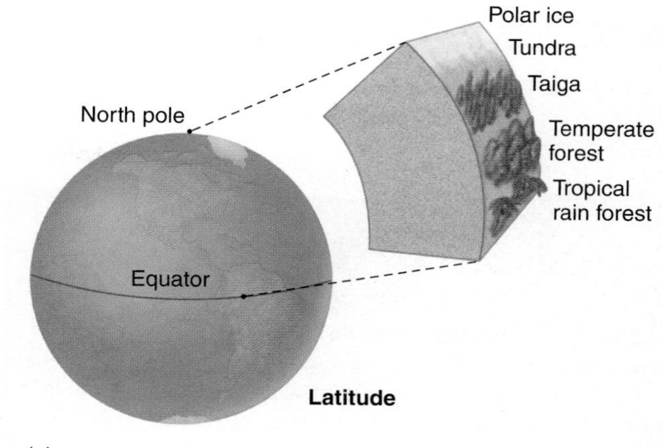

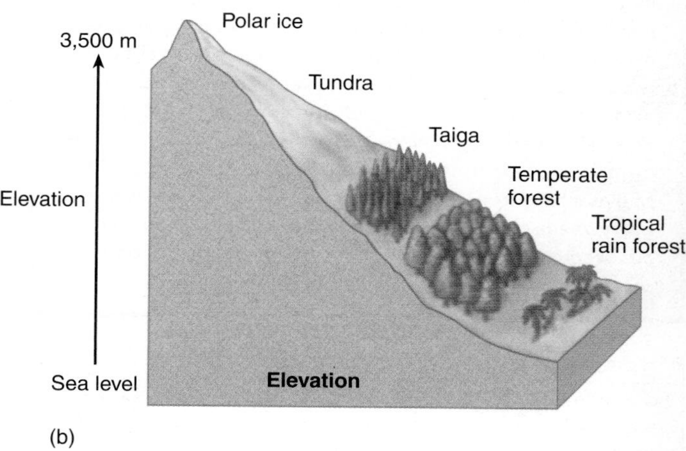

Figure 20.14 How elevation affects ecosystems.

The same land ecosystems that normally occur as latitude increases north and south of the equator at sea level (a) can occur in the tropics as elevation increases (b).

Rain Shadows

When a moving body of air encounters a mountain (figure 20.15), it is forced upward, and as it is cooled at higher elevations the air's moisture-holding capacity decreases, producing the rain you see on the windward side of the mountains—the side from which the wind is blowing. The effect on the other side of the mountain—the leeward side—is quite different. As the air passes the peak and descends on the far side of the mountains, it is warmed, so its moisture-holding capacity increases. Sucking up all available moisture, the air dries the surrounding landscape, often producing a desert. This effect, called a **rain shadow,** is responsible for deserts such as Death Valley, which is in the rain shadow of Mount Whitney, the tallest mountain in the Sierra Nevada.

Similar effects can occur on a larger scale. Regional climates are areas that are located on different parts of the globe but share similar climates because of similar geography. A so-called Mediterranean climate results when winds blow from a cool ocean onto warm land during the summer. As a result, the air's moisture-holding capacity is increased and precipitation is blocked, similar to what occurs on the leeward side of mountains. This effect accounts for dry, hot summers and cool, moist winters in areas with a Mediterranean climate such as portions of southern California or Oregon, central Chile, southwestern Australia, and the Cape region of South Africa. Such a climate is unusual on a world scale. In the regions where it occurs, many unusual kinds of endemic (local in distribution) plants and animals have evolved.

Figure 20.15 The rain shadow effect.

Moisture-laden winds from the Pacific Ocean rise and are cooled when they encounter the Sierra Nevada. As they cool, their moisture-holding capacity decreases and precipitation occurs. As the air descends on the east side of the range, it warms, its moisture-holding capacity increases, and the air picks up moisture from its surroundings. As a result, arid conditions prevail on the east side of these mountains.

Putting the Concept to Work

Death Valley, within 160 miles of the Pacific Ocean, is one of the driest places on earth. How could it be so dry, if it is so close to so much water?

IN THE NEWS

Message in a Bottle. Scientists learned of the huge gyres that form ocean currents long before satellites allowed them to measure mid-ocean currents. Instead, researchers tossed thousands of plastic cards and bottles with messages inside into the sea, hoping they would drift with the current and wash up on a beach somewhere. Messages in these "drift bottles" would ask the discoverer to notify scientists, allowing ocean scientists to track which way surface currents were moving. Using a similar approach, researcher Curtis Ebbesmeyer maps ocean currents in a semiwacky but wildly interesting way: by studying movements of random junk. With help from a worldwide army of beachcombers he organized in the 1990s, Ebbesmeyer has documented spills of everything from onions to hockey gloves. Plastic is found everywhere, even in mid-ocean far from any land. Our oceans are becoming a huge refuse dump. The message in a bottle, it seems, is that we should clean up our act.

20.8 Patterns of Circulation in the Ocean

LEARNING OBJECTIVE 20.8.1 Explain how patterns of oceanic circulation are created and how they affect adjacent lands.

Patterns of ocean circulation are determined by solar energy. The radiant input of heat from the sun sets the atmosphere in motion as already described, and then the winds set the ocean in motion. Oceanic circulation is dominated by the movement of surface waters in huge spiral patterns called gyres, which move around the subtropical zones of high pressure between approximately 30 degrees north and south latitudes. These gyres, indicated by the red and blue arrows in **figure 20.16**, move clockwise in the Northern Hemisphere and counterclockwise in the Southern Hemisphere. The ways they redistribute heat profoundly affects life not only in the oceans but also on coastal lands. For example, the Gulf Stream, in the North Atlantic (a red-colored arrow in the figure below, meaning it carries warm waters), swings away from North America near North Carolina, reaching Europe near the southern British Isles. Because of the Gulf Stream, western Europe is much warmer and more temperate than eastern North America at similar latitudes.

Putting the Concept to Work

Where does the energy of waves pounding a beach come from?

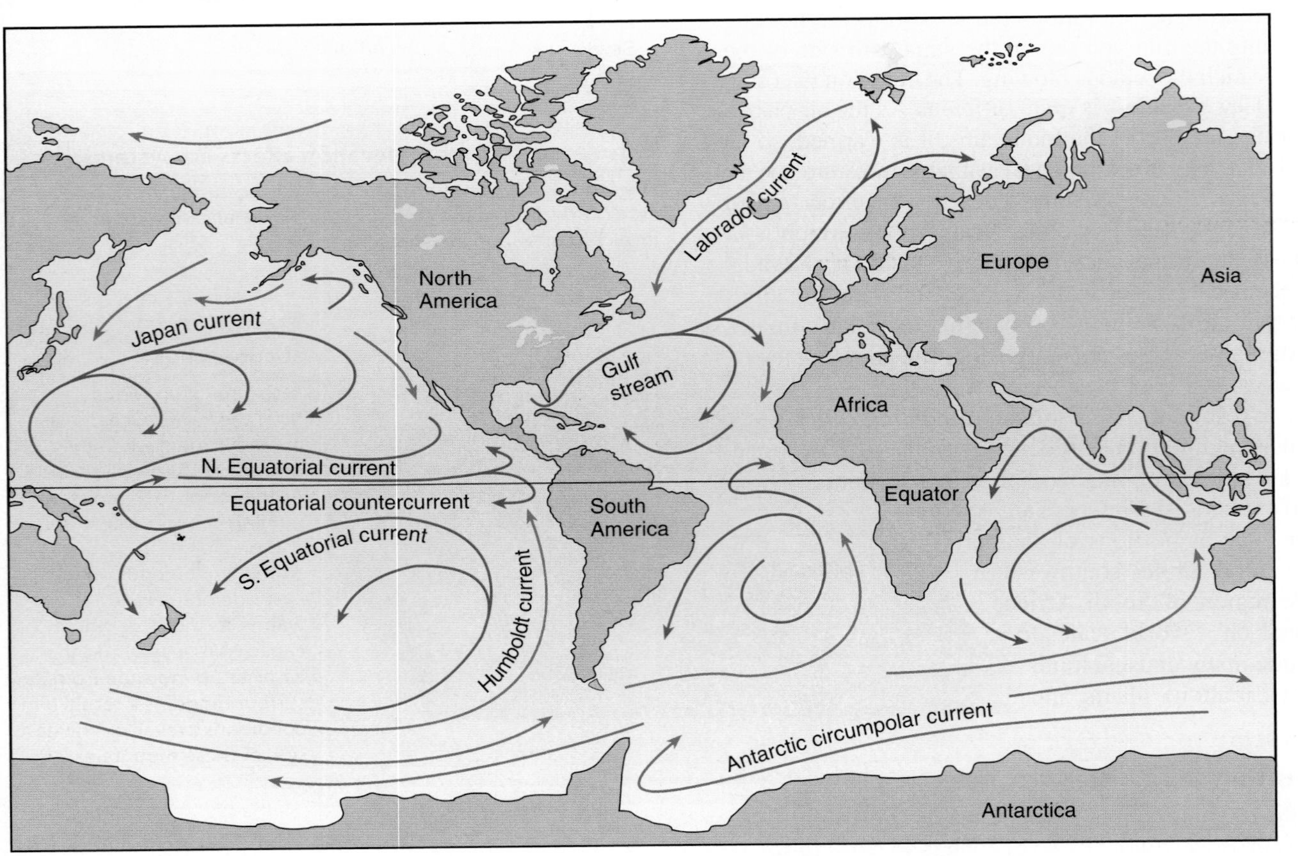

Figure 20.16 Oceanic circulation.

The circulation in the oceans moves in great surface spiral patterns called gyres; oceanic circulation affects the climate on adjacent lands.

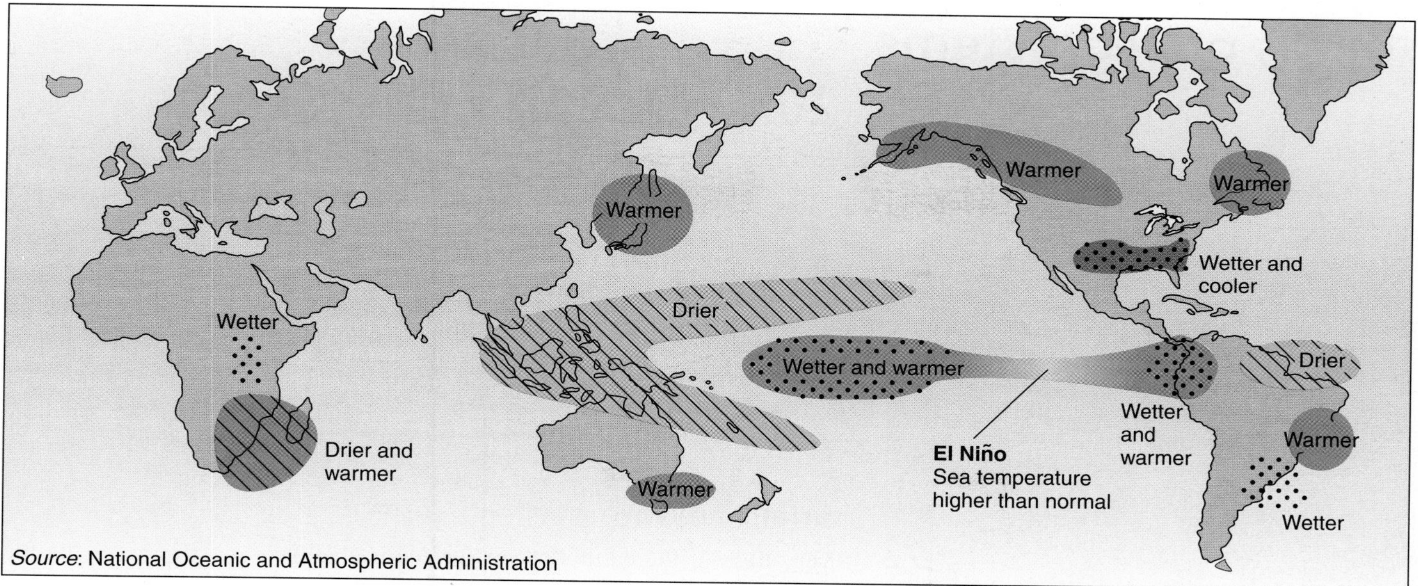

Figure 20.17 An El Niño winter.

El Niño currents produce unusual weather patterns all over the world as warm waters from the western Pacific move eastward.

El Niño and Ocean Ecology

LEARNING OBJECTIVE 20.8.2 Describe El Niño and explain its cause, and impact.

Every Christmas a warm current sweeps down the coast of Peru and Ecuador from the tropics, reducing the fish population slightly and giving local fishers some time off. The local fishers named this Christmas current *El Niño* (literally, "the child," after the Christ Child). A dramatic version of the same phenomenon occurs every two to seven years, felt on a global scale.

Scientists now have a pretty good idea of what goes on in an El Niño. Normally the Pacific Ocean is fanned by constantly blowing east-to-west trade winds. These winds push warm surface water away from the ocean's eastern side (Peru, Ecuador, and Chile) and allow cold water to well up from the depths in its place, carrying nutrients that feed plankton and hence fish. This warm surface water piles up in the west, around Australia and the Philippines, making it several degrees warmer and a meter or so higher than the eastern side of the ocean. But if the winds slacken briefly, warm water begins to slosh back across the ocean (indicated by the darker red band stretching between Australia and the northern coast of South America in **figure 20.17**), causing an El Niño.

The end result is to shift the weather systems of the western Pacific Ocean 6,000 kilometers eastward. The tropical rainstorms that usually drench Indonesia and the Philippines soak the western edge of South America, leaving the previously rainy areas in drought (indicated by the light pink, hatched areas in **figure 20.17**).

Putting the Concept to Work

Why does the El Niño ocean circulation affect weather in the American Midwest?

IN THE NEWS

El Niño and Global Warming. El Niño, the unusual rise in sea-surface temperatures in the equatorial Pacific Ocean, visited three times from 1991 to 1998, an unwanted guest that wouldn't go away. In between, temperatures never went quite back to normal, as if it were all one long El Niño. This has led some scientists like Kevin Trenberth at the National Center for Atmospheric Research in Boulder, Colorado, to speculate that the apparent increase in El Niño events may be linked to warmer ocean temperatures resulting from global warming. He believes that as global warming drives temperatures higher, ocean currents and weather systems are not able to release all the extra heat getting pumped into tropical seas. El Niño, in his view, acts as a kind of pressure release valve, expelling the excess heat. As global warming becomes more pronounced, El Niño events become more intense and frequent. Other scientists suspect that the recent upturn in El Niño events are a statistical blip—we would have expected to see one to two events between 1991 and 1998 anyway. Without better computer models or decades of data, we are not going to know with any certainty who is right.

Major Kinds of Ecosystems

20.9 Ocean Ecosystems

LEARNING OBJECTIVE 20.9.1 Compare the communities that occupy shallow waters, open-sea surface, and deep-sea waters.

Most of the earth's surface—nearly three-quarters—is covered by water. The seas have an average depth of more than 3 kilometers, and they are, for the most part, cold and dark. Photosynthetic organisms are confined to the upper few hundred meters because light does not penetrate any deeper. Almost all organisms that live below this level feed on organic debris that rains downward. The three main kinds of marine ecosystems are shallow waters, open-sea surface, and deep-sea waters (**figure 20.18**).

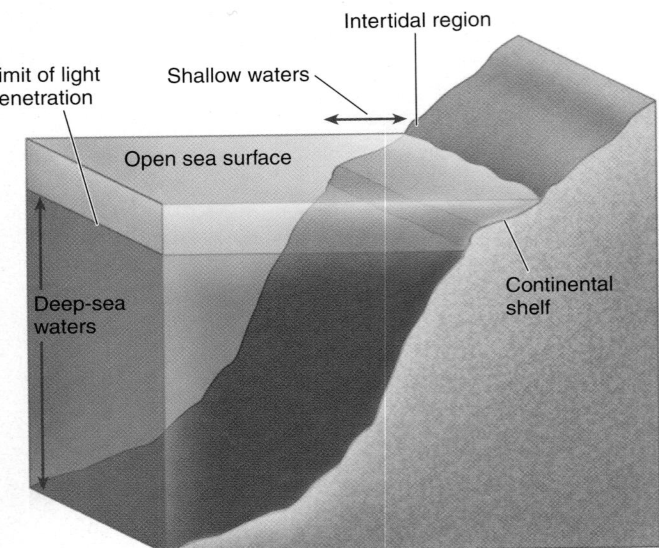

Figure 20.18 Ocean ecosystems.

There are three primary ecosystems found in the earth's oceans. Shallow water ecosystems occur along the shoreline and at areas of coral reefs. Open sea surface ecosystems occur in the upper 100 meters where light can penetrate. Finally, deep-sea water ecosystems are bottom areas below 300 meters.

Shallow Waters

Very little of the earth's ocean surface is shallow—mostly that along the shoreline—but this small area contains many more species than other parts of the ocean (**figure 20.19*a***). The world's great commercial fisheries occur on banks in the coastal zones, where nutrients derived from the land are more abundant than in the open ocean. Part of this zone consists of the **intertidal region,** which is exposed to the air whenever the tides recede. Partly enclosed bodies of water, such as those that often form at river mouths and in coastal bays, where the salinity is intermediate between that of seawater and freshwater, are called **estuaries.** Estuaries are among the most naturally fertile areas in the world, often containing rich stands of submerged and emergent plants, algae, and microscopic organisms. They provide the breeding grounds for most of the coastal fish and shellfish that are harvested both in the estuaries and in open water.

Open-Sea Surface

Drifting freely in the upper, better-illuminated waters of the ocean is a diverse biological community of microscopic organisms. Most of the plankton occurs in the top 100 meters of the sea. Many fish swim in these waters as well, feeding on the plankton and one another (**figure 20.19*b***). Some members of the plankton, including algae and some bacteria, are photosynthetic and are called phytoplankton. Collectively, these organisms are responsible for about 40% of all photosynthesis that takes place on

(a)

(b)

Figure 20.19 Shallow waters and open sea surface.

(a) Fish and many other kinds of animals find food and shelter among the coral in the coastal waters of some regions. (b) The upper layers of the open ocean contain plankton and large schools of fish, like these bigeye snappers.

earth. Over half of this is carried out by organisms less than 10 micrometers in diameter—at the lower limits of size for organisms—and almost all of it near the surface of the sea, in the zone into which light from the surface penetrates freely.

Deep-Sea Waters

In the deep waters of the sea, below 300 meters, little light penetrates. Very few organisms live there, compared to the rest of the ocean, but those that do include some of the most bizarre organisms found anywhere on earth. Many deep-sea inhabitants have bioluminescent (light-producing) body parts that they use to communicate or to attract prey (**figure 20.20*a***).

The supply of oxygen can often be critical in the deep ocean, and as water temperatures become warmer, the water holds less oxygen. For this reason, the amount of available oxygen becomes an important limiting factor for deep-sea organisms in warmer marine regions of the globe. Carbon dioxide, in contrast, is almost never limited in the deep ocean. The distribution of minerals is much more uniform in the ocean than it is on land, where individual soils reflect the composition of the parent rocks from which they have weathered.

Frigid and bare, the floors of the deep sea have long been considered a biological desert. Recent close-up looks taken by marine biologists, however, paint a different picture (**figure 20.20*b***). The ocean floor is teeming with life. Often kilometers deep, thriving in pitch darkness under enormous pressure, crowds of marine invertebrates have been found in hundreds of deep samples from the Atlantic and Pacific. Rough estimates of deep-sea diversity have soared to hundreds of thousands of species. Many appear endemic (local). The diversity of species is so high it may rival that of tropical rain forests! This profusion is unexpected. New species usually require some kind of barrier to diverge (see chapter 14), and the ocean floor seems boringly uniform. However, little migration occurs among deep populations, and this lack of movement may encourage local specialization and species formation. A patchy environment may also contribute to species formation there; deep-sea ecologists find evidence that fine but nonetheless formidable resource barriers arise in the deep sea.

No light falls in the deep ocean. From where do deep-sea organisms obtain their energy? While some utilize energy falling to the ocean floor as debris from above, other deep-sea organisms are autotrophic, gaining their energy from **hydrothermal vent systems,** areas in which seawater circulates through porous rock surrounding fissures where molten material from beneath the earth's crust comes close to the surface. Hydrothermal vent systems, also called deep-sea vents, support a broad array of heterotrophic life (**figure 20.20*c***). Water in the area of these hydrothermal vents is heated to temperatures in excess of 350°C, and contains high concentrations of hydrogen sulfide. Prokaryotes that live by these deep-sea vents obtain energy and produce carbohydrates through chemosynthesis instead of photosynthesis. Like plants, they are autotrophs; they extract energy from hydrogen sulfide to manufacture food, much as a plant extracts energy from the sun to manufacture its food. These prokaryotes live symbiotically within the tissues of heterotrophs that live around the deep-sea vents. The animals provide a place for the prokaryotes to live and obtain nutrients, and the prokaryotes supply the animal with organic compounds to use as food.

Putting the Concept to Work

How can bacteria living near deep-sea vents be autotrophs, when no light penetrates so deep?

(a)

(c)

(b)

Figure 20.20 Deep-sea waters.

(a) The luminous spot below the eye of this deep-sea fish results from the presence of a symbiotic colony of luminous bacteria. (b) Looking for all the world like some undersea sunflower, these two sea anemones (actually animals) use a glass-sponge stalk to catch "marine snow," food particles raining down on the ocean floor from the ocean surface several kilometers above. (c) These giant beardworms live along vents where water jets from fissures at 350°C and then cools to the 2°C of the surrounding water.

IMPLICATION FOR YOU No sunlight penetrates to the bottom of the deep sea. Why do you think that fish in this subphotic region have eyes, often extremely large, rather than evolution having selected for no eyes, as it has done for freshwater fish that inhabit deep dark caves?

Figure 20.21 Freshwater organism.

Some organisms, such as this giant waterbug with eggs on its back, can only live in freshwater habitats.

20.10 Freshwater Ecosystems

LEARNING OBJECTIVE 20.10.1 Differentiate the ecological zones of a freshwater lake and explain the cause of the lake's spring and fall overturns.

Freshwater ecosystems (lakes, ponds, rivers, and wetlands) are distinct from both ocean and land ecosystems, and they are very limited in area. Inland lakes cover about 1.8% of the earth's surface and rivers, streams, and wetlands about 0.4%. All freshwater habitats are strongly connected to land habitats, with marshes and swamps (wetlands) constituting intermediate habitats. In addition, a large amount of organic and inorganic material continually enters bodies of freshwater from communities growing on the land nearby. Many kinds of organisms are restricted to freshwater habitats (figure 20.21). When they occur in rivers and streams, they must be able to attach themselves in such a way as to resist or avoid the effects of current or risk being swept away.

Like the ocean, ponds and lakes have three zones in which organisms live (figure 20.22*a*): a shallow "edge" zone (the littoral zone), an open-water surface zone (the limnetic zone), and a deep-water zone where light does not penetrate (the profundal zone). Also, lakes can be divided into two categories, based on their production of organic material. In **oligotrophic lakes** (figure 20.22*b*), organic matter and nutrients are relatively scarce. Such lakes are often deep, and their deep waters are always rich in

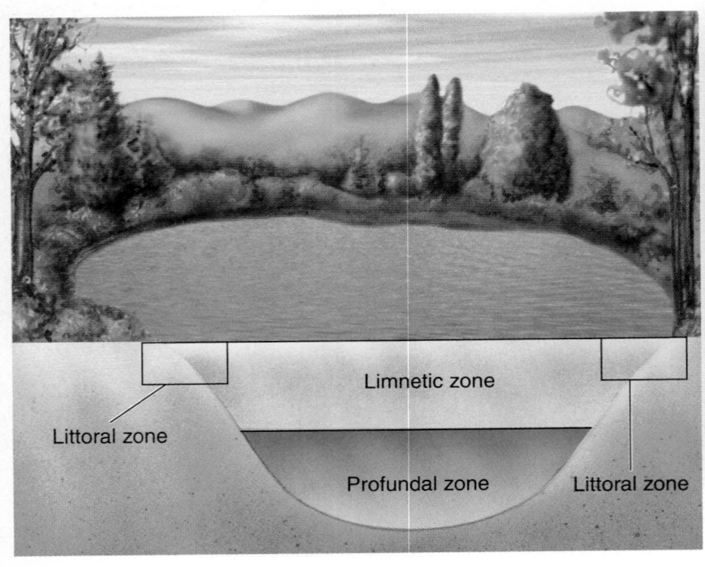

(a)

(b) Oligotrophic lake

(c) Eutrophic lake

Figure 20.22 Characteristics of ponds and lakes.

(a) Ponds and lakes can be divided into three zones based on the types of organisms that live in each. A shallow "edge" (littoral) zone lines the periphery of the lake where attached algae and their insect herbivores live. An open-water surface (limnetic) zone lies across the entire lake and is inhabited by floating algae, zooplankton, and fish. A dark, deep-water (profundal) zone overlies the sediments at the bottom of the lake. The profundal zone contains numerous bacteria and wormlike organisms that consume dead debris settling at the bottom of the lake. Lakes can be oligotrophic (b), containing scarce amounts of organic material, or eutrophic (c), containing abundant amounts of organic material.

oxygen. Oligotrophic lakes are highly susceptible to pollution from excess phosphorus from such sources as fertilizer runoff, sewage, and detergents. **Eutrophic lakes,** on the other hand, have an abundant supply of minerals and organic matter (figure 20.22*c*). Oxygen is depleted at the lower depths in the summer because of the abundant organic material and high rate at which aerobic decomposers in the lower layer use oxygen. These stagnant waters circulate to the surface in the fall (during the fall overturn, as discussed below) and are then infused with more oxygen.

Aerobic decomposers consume dead organisms as a means of acquiring energy. Because they carry out aerobic respiration, they need oxygen as the final electron acceptor in the electron transport chain, as discussed on page 124. Their active metabolism uses up a lot of oxygen.

Thermal stratification, characteristic of the larger lakes in temperate regions, is the process whereby water at a temperature of 4°C (which is when water is most dense) sinks beneath water that is either warmer or cooler. Follow through the changes in a large lake in figure 20.23 beginning in winter ❶, where water at 4°C sinks beneath cooler water that freezes at the surface at 0°C. Below the ice, the water remains between 0° and 4°C, and plants and animals survive there. In spring ❷, as the ice melts, the surface water is warmed to 4°C and sinks below the cooler water, bringing the cooler water to the top with nutrients from the lake's lower regions. This process is known as the *spring overturn.*

In summer ❸, warmer water forms a layer over the cooler water that lies below. In the area between these two layers, called the thermocline, temperature changes abruptly. You may have experienced the existence of these layers if you have dived into a pond in temperate regions in the summer. Depending on the climate of the particular area, the warm upper layer may become as much as 20 meters thick during the summer. In autumn ❹, its surface temperature drops until it reaches that of the cooler layer underneath—4°C. When this occurs, the upper and lower layers mix—a process called the fall overturn. Therefore, colder waters reach the surfaces of lakes in the spring and fall, bringing up fresh supplies of dissolved nutrients.

BIOLOGY & YOU

Putting Thermal Stratification to Work: Ice Fishing. When a large lake freezes in winter, it doesn't freeze solid like a huge ice cube. Only the surface freezes. Beneath its hard skin lies cold, dense water where game fish like pickerel, walleye, and pike thrive all winter long. Ice fishing is the activity of catching these fish with lines and fish hooks through a small opening augured through the ice. Some hardy ice anglers sit on a stool in the open on a frozen lake; other less adventurous souls await a catch in a heated cabin on the ice, some with bunks, kitchens, and portable bathrooms! Ice fishing has long been a popular solitary pastime in Finland, Norway, and Sweden, with fish houses a rare occurrence. In the United States, by contrast, ice fishing is often a social activity, with fish houses rented out by the day in states like Minnesota or Wisconsin—indeed, any state with lakes and long cold winters. Winter fishing makes up nearly one-fourth of the annual catch in Wisconsin. Some confident but reckless ice fishers will walk out on 2.5 inches of ice, but because the thickness of ice can vary across an area, a full 4 inches of good ice is recommended—"thick and blue, tried and true." If you are on a snowmobile (it can be a long way from a lake's edge out to its center) you need 6 inches of ice; in a pickup or car, you must have 12–14 inches if you don't want your vehicle to join the fishes you seek to catch.

Putting the Concept to Work

If you break through the ice on a large lake in winter and dive in, does it get warmer or colder as you swim deeper?

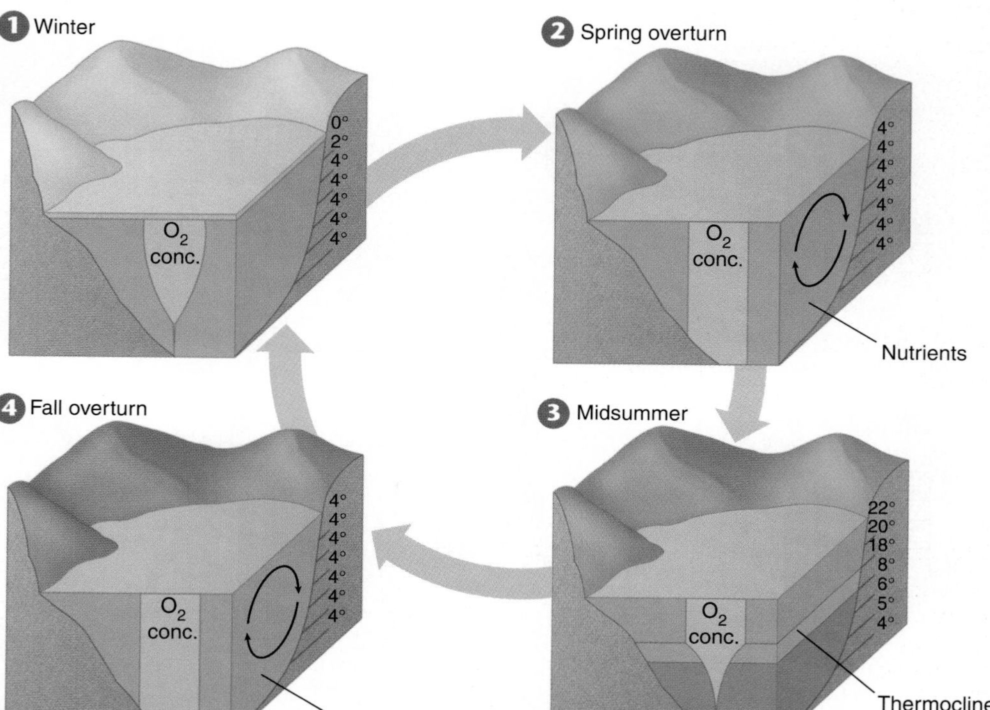

Figure 20.23 Spring and fall overturns in freshwater ponds or lakes.

The pattern of stratification in a large pond or lake in temperate regions is upset in the spring and fall overturns. Of the three layers of water shown in midsummer (*lower right*), the densest water occurs at 4°C. The warmer water at the surface is less dense. The thermocline is the zone of abrupt change in temperature that lies between them. In summer and winter, oxygen concentrations are lower at greater depths, whereas in the spring and fall, they are more similar at all depths.

20.11 Land Ecosystems

LEARNING OBJECTIVE 20.11.1 Identify the seven most widespread terrestrial biomes and describe how each is defined by temperature and rainfall patterns.

Biomes are major types of ecosystems that occur on land. Each biome occurs over a broad area and is characterized by a particular climate and a defined group of organisms. While biomes can be classified in a number of ways, the seven most widely occurring biomes (**figure 20.24**) are (1) tropical rain forest, (2) savanna, (3) desert, (4) temperate grassland, (5) temperate deciduous forest, (6) taiga, and (7) tundra. The reason that there are seven primary biomes, and not one or 80, is that they have evolved to suit the climate of the region, and the earth has seven principal climates. The seven biomes differ remarkably from one another but show many consistencies within; a particular biome often looks similar and contains many of the same types of organisms, wherever it occurs on earth.

There are seven other less widespread biomes also shown in **figure 20.24**: chaparral; polar ice; mountain zone; temperate evergreen forest; warm, moist evergreen forest; tropical monsoon forest; and semidesert.

If there were no mountains and no climatic effects caused by the irregular outlines of the continents and by different sea temperatures, each biome would form an even belt around the globe. In fact, their distribution is greatly affected by these factors, especially by elevation. Thus, the summits of the Rocky Mountains are covered with a vegetation type that resembles tundra, whereas other forest types that resemble taiga

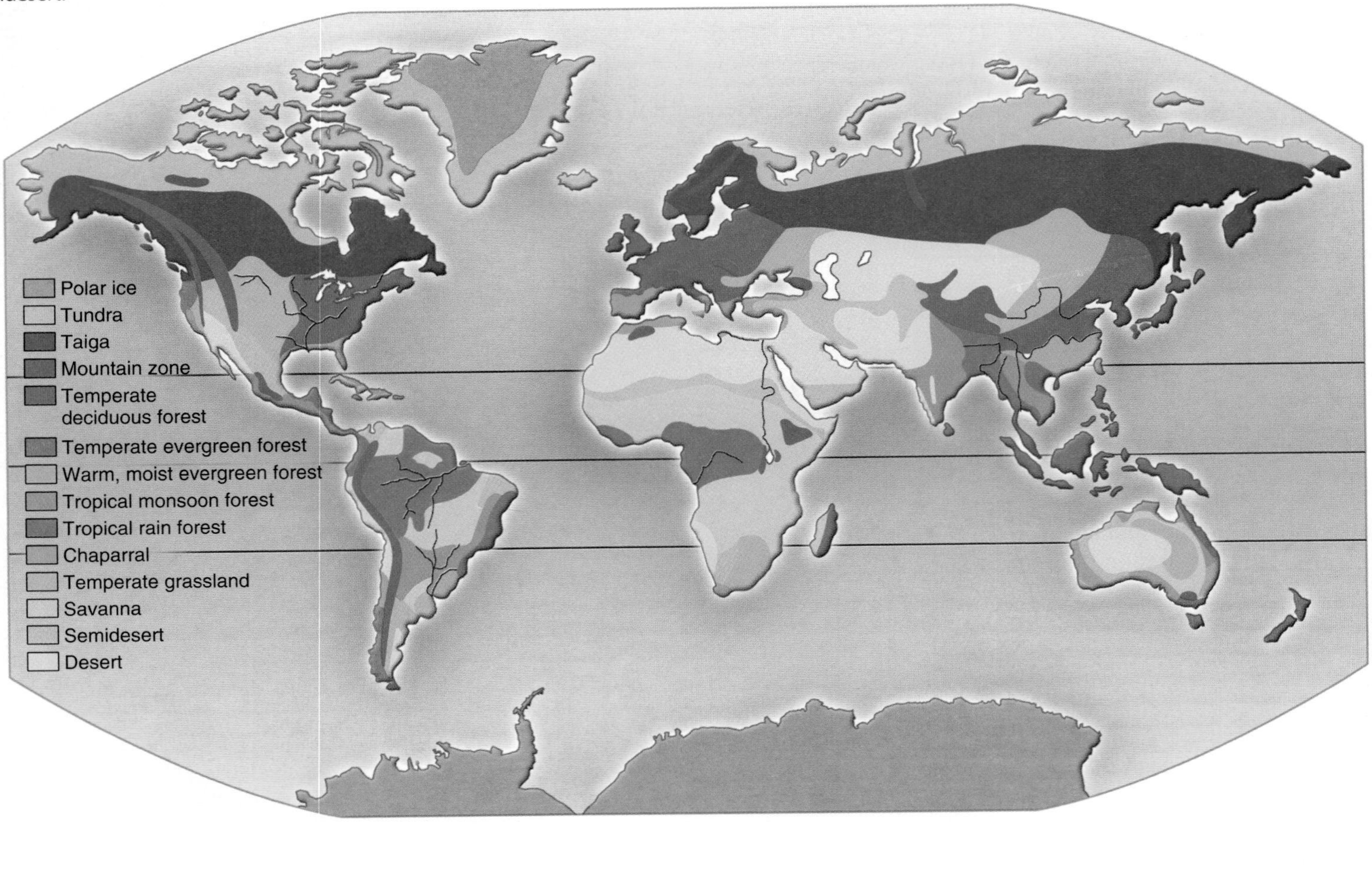

Figure 20.24 Distribution of the earth's biomes.

The seven primary types of biomes are tropical rain forest, savanna, desert, temperate grassland, temperate deciduous forest, taiga, and tundra. In addition, seven less widespread biomes are chaparral, polar ice, mountain zone (photo *above*), temperate evergreen forest, warm, moist evergreen forest, tropical monsoon forest, and semidesert.

occur farther down. It is for reasons such as these that the distributions of the biomes are so irregular. One trend that is apparent is that those biomes that normally occur at high latitudes also follow an altitudinal gradient along mountains. That is, biomes found far north and far south of the equator at sea level also occur in the tropics but at high mountain elevations (see **figure 20.14**).

Lush Tropical Rain Forests

Rain forests, which experience over 250 centimeters of rain a year, are the richest ecosystems on earth (**figure 20.25**). They contain at least half of the earth's species of terrestrial plants and animals—more than 2 million species! In a single square mile of tropical forest in Rondonia, Brazil, there are 1,200 species of butterflies—twice the total number found in the United States and Canada combined. The communities that make up tropical rain forests are diverse in that each kind of animal, plant, or microorganism is often represented in a given area by very few individuals. There are extensive tropical rain forests in South America, Africa, and Southeast Asia. But the world's tropical rain forests are being destroyed, and with them, countless species, many of them never seen by humans. Perhaps a quarter of the world's species will disappear with the rain forests during the lifetime of many of us.

Figure 20.25 Tropical rain forest.

Savannas: Dry Tropical Grasslands

In the dry climates that border the tropics are found the world's great grasslands, called **savannas.** Landscapes are open, often with widely spaced trees, and rainfall (75 to 125 cm annually) is seasonal. Many of the animals and plants are active only during the rainy season. The huge herds of grazing animals that inhabit the African savanna are familiar to all of us (**figure 20.26**). Such animal communities occurred in the temperate grasslands of North America during the Pleistocene epoch but have persisted mainly in Africa. On a global scale, the savanna biome is transitional between tropical rain forest and desert. As these savannas are increasingly converted to agricultural use to feed rapidly expanding human populations in subtropical areas, their inhabitants are finding it difficult to survive. The elephant, rhino, and cheetah are now endangered species; the lion and giraffe will soon follow them.

Figure 20.26 Savanna.

Deserts: Burning Hot Sands

In the interior of continents are found the world's great deserts, especially in Africa (the Sahara), Asia (the Gobi), and Australia (the Great Sandy Desert). **Deserts** are dry places where less than 25 centimeters of rain falls in a year—an amount so low that vegetation is sparse and survival depends on water conservation (**figure 20.27**). One quarter of the world's land surface is desert. The plants and animals that live in deserts may restrict their activity to favorable times of the year, when water is present. To avoid high temperatures, most desert vertebrates live in deep, cool, and sometimes even somewhat moist burrows. Those that are active over a greater portion of the year emerge only at night, when temperatures are relatively cool. Some, such as camels, can drink large quantities of water when it is available and then survive long, dry periods. Many animals simply migrate to or through the desert, where they exploit food that may be abundant seasonally.

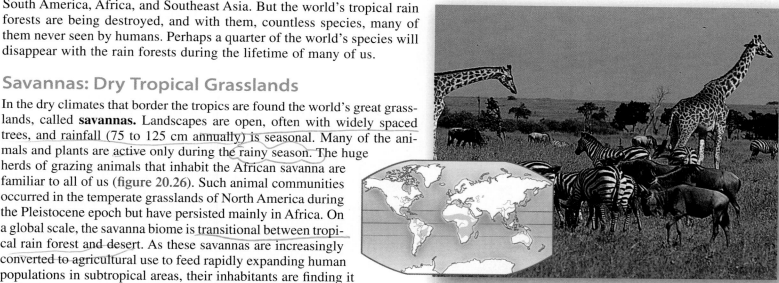

Figure 20.27 Desert.

Figure 20.28 Temperate grassland.

Grasslands: Seas of Grass

Halfway between the equator and the poles are temperate regions where rich **grasslands** grow. These grasslands once covered much of the interior of North America, and they were widespread in Eurasia and South America as well. Such grasslands are often highly productive when converted to agriculture. Many of the rich agricultural lands in the United States and southern Canada were originally occupied by **prairies,** another name for temperate grasslands. These natural temperate grasslands are one of the biomes adapted to periodic fire.

The roots of perennial grasses characteristically penetrate far into the soil, and grassland soils tend to be deep and fertile. Temperate grasslands are often populated by herds of grazing mammals. In North America, the prairies were once inhabited by huge herds of bison and pronghorns (figure 20.28). The herds are almost all gone now, with most of the prairies having been converted to the richest agricultural region on earth.

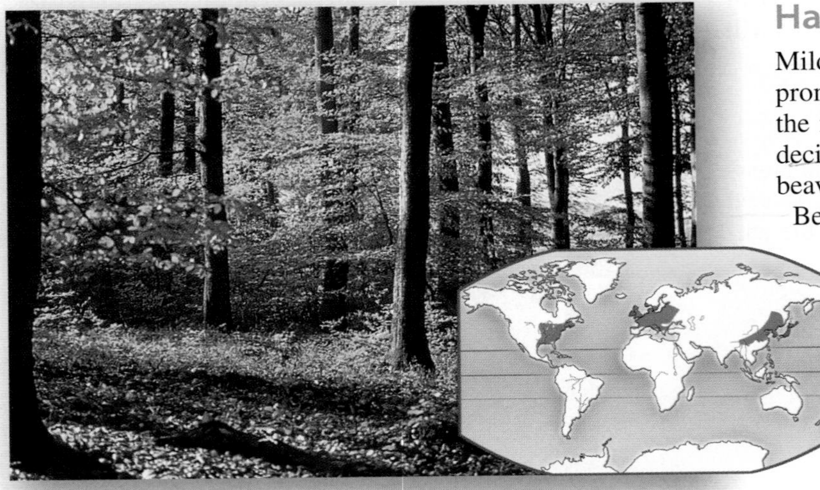

Figure 20.29 Temperate deciduous forest.

Deciduous Forests: Rich Hardwood Forests

Mild climates (warm summers and cool winters) and plentiful rains promote the growth of **deciduous** ("hardwood") **forests** in Eurasia, the northeastern United States, and eastern Canada (figure 20.29). A deciduous tree is one that drops its leaves in the winter. Deer, bears, beavers, and raccoons are the familiar animals of the temperate regions. Because the temperate deciduous forests represent the remnants of more extensive forests that stretched across North America and Eurasia several million years ago, these remaining areas—especially those in eastern Asia and eastern North America—share animals and plants that were once more widespread. Alligators, for example, are found only in China and in the southeastern United States. The deciduous forest in eastern Asia is rich in species because climatic conditions have remained constant.

Figure 20.30 Taiga.

Taiga: Trackless Conifer Forests

A great ring of northern forests of coniferous trees (spruce, hemlock, larch, and fir) extends across vast areas of Asia and North America. Coniferous trees are ones with leaves like needles that are kept all year long. This ecosystem, called **taiga,** is one of the largest on earth (figure 20.30). Here, the winters are long and cold. Rain, often as little as in hot deserts, falls in the summer. Because it has too short a growing season for farming, few people live there. Many large mammals, including elk, moose, deer, and such carnivores as wolves, bears, lynx, and wolverines, live in the taiga. Traditionally, fur trapping has been extensive in this region. Lumber production is also important. Marshes, lakes, and ponds are common and are often fringed by willows or birches. Most of the trees occur in dense stands of one or a few species.

Tundra: Cold Boggy Plains

In the far north, above the great coniferous forests and below the polar ice, there are few trees. There the grassland, called **tundra,** is open, windswept, and often boggy (**figure 20.31**). Enormous in extent, this ecosystem covers one-fifth of the earth's land surface. Very little rain or snow falls. When rain does fall during the brief arctic summer, it sits on frozen ground, creating a sea of boggy ground. **Permafrost,** or permanent ice, usually exists within a meter of the surface. Trees are small and are mostly confined to the margins of streams and lakes. Large grazing mammals, including musk-oxen, caribou, reindeer, and carnivores such as wolves, foxes, and lynx, live in the tundra. Lemming populations rise and fall on a long-term cycle, with important effects on the animals that prey on them.

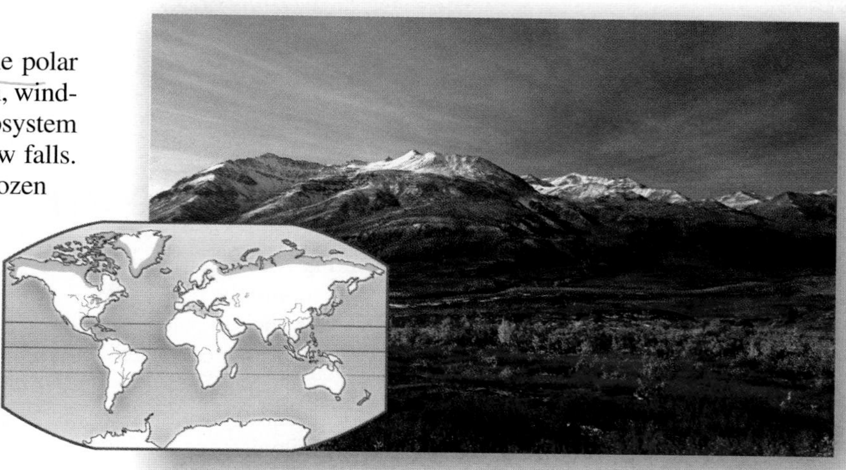

Figure 20.31 Tundra.

Chaparral

Chaparral consists of evergreen, often spiny shrubs and low trees that form communities in regions with what is called a "Mediterranean," dry summer climate. These regions include California, central Chile, the Cape region of South Africa, southwestern Australia, and the Mediterranean area itself (**figure 20.32**). Many plant species found in chaparral can germinate only when they have been exposed to the hot temperatures generated during a fire. The chaparral of California and adjacent regions is historically derived from deciduous forests.

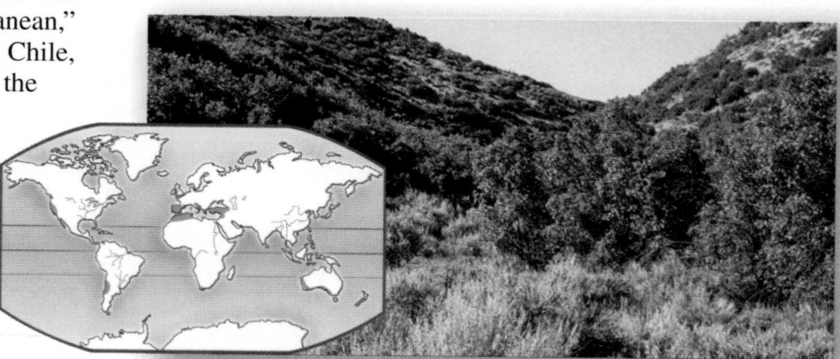

Figure 20.32 Chaparral.

Polar Ice Caps

Polar ice caps lie over the Arctic Ocean in the north and Antarctica in the south (**figure 20.33**). The poles receive almost no precipitation, so although ice is abundant, freshwater is scarce. The sun barely rises in the winter months. Life in Antarctica is largely limited to the coasts. Because the Antarctic ice cap lies over a landmass, it is not warmed by the latent heat of circulating ocean water and becomes very cold, so only prokaryotes, algae, and some small insects inhabit the vast Antarctic interior.

Figure 20.33 Polar ice.

Tropical Monsoon Forest

Tropical upland forests (**figure 20.34**) occur in the tropics and semitropics at slightly higher latitudes than rain forests or where local climates are drier. Most trees in these forests are deciduous, losing many of their leaves during the dry season. This loss of leaves allows sunlight to penetrate to the understory and ground levels of the forest, where a dense layer of shrubs and small trees grow rapidly. Rainfall is typically very seasonal, measuring several inches daily in the monsoon season and approaching drought conditions in the dry season, particularly in locations far from oceans, such as in central India.

Putting the Concept to Work

In what biome do you live? How many others have you visited?

Figure 20.34 Tropical monsoon forest.

Inquiry & Analysis

Does Clear-Cutting Forests Cause Permanent Damage?

The lumber industry practice called "clear-cutting" has been common in many states. Loggers find it more efficient to simply remove all trees from a watershed, and sort the logs out later, than to selectively cut only the most desirable mature trees. While the open cuts seem a desolation to the casual observer, the loggers claim that new forests can become established more readily in the open cut as sunlight now more easily reaches seedlings at ground level. Ecologists counter that clear-cutting fundamentally changes the forest in ways which cannot be easily reversed.

Who is right? The most direct way to find out is to try it, clear-cut an area and watch it very carefully. Just this sort of massive field test was carried out in a now-classic experiment at the Hubbard Brook Experimental Forest in New Hampshire. Hubbard Brook is the central stream of a large watershed that drains a region of temperate deciduous forest in northern New Hampshire. The research team, led by then-Dartmouth College professors Herbert Bormann and Gene Likens, first gathered a great deal of information about the forest watershed. Starting in 1963, they censused the trees, measured the flow of water through the watershed, and carefully documented the levels of minerals and other nutrients in the water leaving the ecosystem via Hubbard Brook. To keep track, they constructed concrete dams across each of the six streams that drain the forest and monitored the runoff, chemically analyzing samples. The undisturbed forest proved very efficient at retaining nitrogen and other nutrients. The small amounts of nutrients that entered the ecosystem in rain and snow were approximately equal to the amounts of nutrients that ran out of the valleys into Hubbard Brook.

Now came the test. In the winter of 1965 the investigators felled all the trees and shrubs in 48 acres drained by one stream (as shown in the photo), and examined the water running off. The immediate effect was dramatic: the amount of water running out of the valley increased by 40%. Water that otherwise would have been taken up by vegetation and released into the atmosphere through evaporation was now simply running off. It was clear that the forest was not retaining water as well, but what about the soil nutrients, the key to future forest fertility?

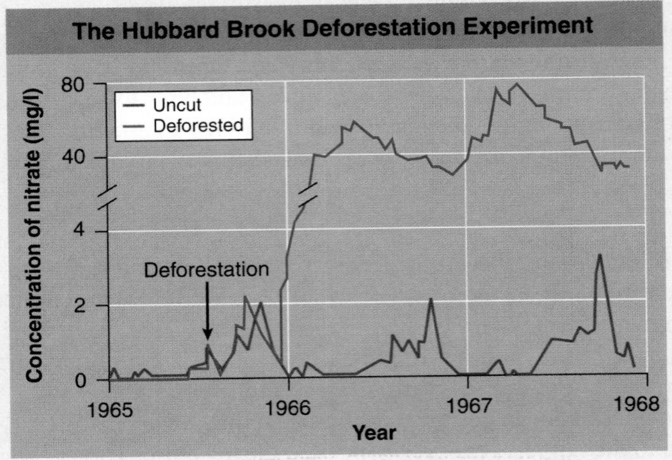

The red line in the graph above shows nitrogen minerals leaving the ecosystem in the runoff water of the stream draining the clear-cut area; the blue line shows the nitrogen runoff in a neighboring stream draining an adjacent uncut portion of the forest.

Analysis

1. **Applying Concepts**
   Scale. What is the significance of the break in the vertical axis between 4 and 40?
2. **Interpreting Data**
   a. What is the approximate concentration of nitrogen in the runoff of the uncut valley before cutting? of the cut valley before cutting?
   b. What is the approximate concentration of nitrogen in the runoff of the uncut valley one year after cutting? of the clear-cut valley one year after cutting?
3. **Making Inferences**
   a. Is there any yearly pattern to the nitrogen runoff in the uncut forest? Can you explain it?
   b. How does the loss of nitrogen from the ecosystem in the clear-cut forest compare with nitrogen loss from the uncut forest?
4. **Drawing Conclusions**
   a. What is the impact of this forest's trees upon its ability to retain nitrogen?
   b. Has clear-cutting harmed this ecosystem? Explain.

Summary of Learning Outcomes

The Energy in Ecosystems

Energy Flows Through Ecosystems

20.1.1 An ecosystem includes the community and the habitat present in a particular area.

20.1.2 Energy constantly flows into an ecosystem from the sun, and is passed among organisms in a food chain. Energy from the sun is captured by photosynthetic producers, which are eaten by herbivores, which are in turn eaten by carnivores, as shown here from **figure 20.1**. Organisms at all trophic levels die and are consumed by detritivores and decomposers. A food chain is organized linearly, but in nature the flow of energy is often more complex, and is called a food web.

- An ecosystem's net primary productivity is the total amount of energy that is captured by producers. Energy is lost at every level in a food chain, such that only about 5% to 20% of available energy is passed on to the next trophic level.

Ecological Pyramids

20.2.1 Because energy is lost at every step as it passes up through the trophic levels of the food chain, there tends to be more individuals at the lower trophic levels. Similarly, the amount of biomass is also less at the higher trophic levels, as is the amount of energy. Ecological pyramids illustrate this distribution of number of individuals, biomass, and energy.

Materials Cycle Within Ecosystems

The Water Cycle

20.3.1 Physical components of the ecosystem cycle through the ecosystem, being used then recycled and reused, in a process called a biogeochemical cycle.

- Water cycles through ecosystems in two ways: the environmental cycle and the organismic cycle. In the environmental cycle, shown here from **figure 20.7**, water cycles from the atmosphere as precipitation, where it falls to the earth and reenters the atmosphere through evaporation. In the organismic cycle, water cycles through plants, entering through the roots and leaving as water vapor by transpiration. Groundwater held in underground aquifers cycles more slowly through the water cycle.

The Carbon Cycle

20.4.1 Carbon cycles from the atmosphere through plants, via carbon fixation of CO_2 in photosynthesis. Carbon then returns to the atmosphere as CO_2 via cellular respiration, but some carbon is also stored in the tissues of the organisms. Eventually, this carbon reenters the atmosphere by the burning of fossil fuels and by diffusion after erosion.

The Nitrogen and Phosphorus Cycles

20.5.1 Nitrogen gas in the atmosphere cannot be readily used by organisms and needs to be fixed by certain types of bacteria into ammonia and nitrate that is then used by plants. Animals eat plants that have taken up the fixed nitrogen. Nitrogen reenters the ecosystem through decomposition and animal excretions.

- Phosphorus also cycles through the ecosystem and may limit growth when not available or it can cause problems in aquatic ecosystems when found in excess amounts. Phosphorus is not a gas and so does not cycle through the atmosphere. Instead it cycles from soil and rock through plants and back to the soil.

How Weather Shapes Ecosystems

The Sun and Atmospheric Circulation

20.6.1 The heating power of the sun drives circulation of the atmosphere, causing certain parts of the globe, such as the tropics, to have larger amounts of precipitation.

Latitude and Elevation

20.7.1 Temperature and precipitation are similarly affected by elevation and latitude. Changes in ecosystems from the equator to the poles are similarly reflected in the changes in ecosystems from sea level to mountaintops, as shown here from **figure 20.14**. Changes in temperature cause the rain shadow effect, where precipitation is deposited on the windward side of mountains, and deserts form on the leeward side.

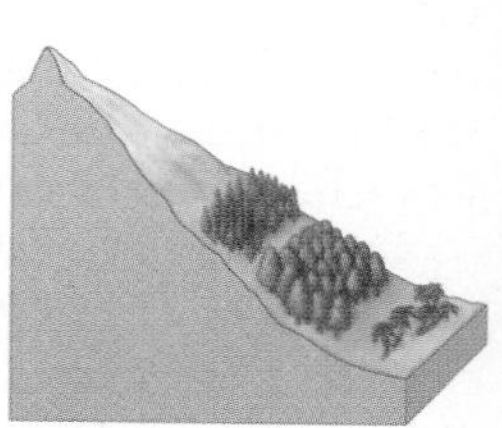

Patterns of Circulation in the Ocean

20.8.1 The earth's oceans circulate in huge gyres that distribute warmer and cooler waters to different areas of the world. These ocean patterns affect climates across the globe.

20.8.2 During an El Niño, warm waters from the western Pacific move eastward.

Major Kinds of Ecosystems

Ocean Ecosystems

20.9.1 There are three primary ocean ecosystems: shallow waters, open-sea surfaces, and deep-sea waters (**figure 20.18**).

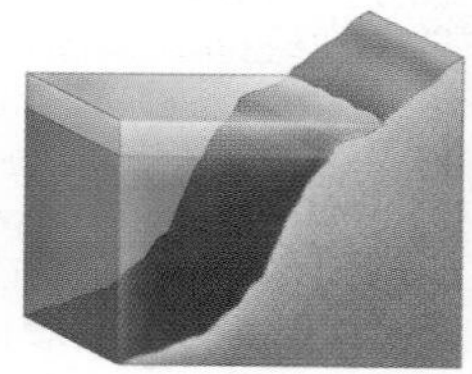

Freshwater Ecosystems

20.10.1 Freshwater ecosystems cover 2% of the earth's surface and are closely tied to the terrestrial environments that surround them. Freshwater ecosystems are affected by light, temperature, and nutrients. The penetration of light divides a lake into three zones with varying amounts of light. Temperature variations in a lake, called thermal stratification, also bring about an overturning of the lake that distributes nutrients.

Land Ecosystems

20.11.1 Biomes are terrestrial communities found throughout the world (**figure 20.24**). Each biome contains its own characteristic group of organisms based on temperature and rainfall patterns.

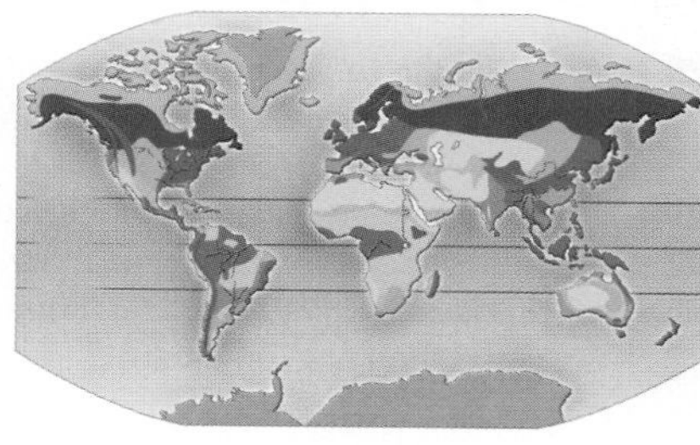

Test Your Understanding

20.1.2 Energy from the sun is captured and converted into chemical energy by

a. herbivores. **c.** producers.
b. carnivores. **d.** detritivores.

20.1.2 As energy is transferred from one trophic level to the next, substantial amounts of energy are lost to/as

a. undigestible biomass. **c.** metabolism.
b. heat. **d.** All of the above.

20.2.1 The number of carnivores found at the top of an ecological pyramid is limited by the

a. number of organisms above the top carnivores.
b. number of trophic levels below the producers.
c. biomass of the decomposers.
d. amount of energy transferred to the top carnivores.

20.3.1 Hydrologists, scientists who study the movements and cycles of water, refer to the return of water from the ground to the air as evapotranspiration. The first part of the word refers to evaporation. The second part of the word refers to transpiration, which is evaporation of water

a. from plants.
b. through animal perspiration.
c. off the ground shaded by plants.
d. from the surface of rivers.

20.4.1 The carbon cycle includes a store of carbon as fossil fuels that is released through

a. respiration. **c.** erosion.
b. combustion. **d.** All of the above.

20.5.1 The element phosphorus is needed in organisms to build

a. proteins. **c.** ATP.
b. carbohydrates. **d.** steroids.

20.7.1 A rain shadow results in

a. extremely wet conditions due to the lack of wind over a mountain range.
b. dry air moving toward the poles that cools and sinks in regions 15 to 30 degrees north/south latitude.
c. global polar regions that rarely receive moisture from the warmer, tropical regions, and are therefore drier.
d. desert conditions on the downwind side of a mountain due to increased moisture-holding capacity of the winds as the air heats up.

20.7.1 As one travels from northern Canada south to the United States, the timberline increases in elevation. This is because as latitude

a. increases, temperature increases.
b. decreases, temperature increases.
c. increases, humidity decreases.
d. decreases, humidity increases.

20.10.1 In freshwater lakes during the summer, layers of sudden temperature change called _____ form.

a. eutrophy **c.** oligotrophy
b. the profundal zone **d.** the thermocline

20.11.1 Which of the following biomes is *not* found south of the equator?

a. polar ice cap **c.** tundra
b. savanna **d.** tropical monsoon forest

Apply Your Understanding

20.1.2 In the example shown here, algae harvest 1,000 calories of energy from sunlight. Explain the probable efficiency if you were to eat, respectively, (1) the algae itself, (2) the heterotrophs, (3) the smelt, or (4) the trout. How many more people could be fed if they all ate algae? Assuming there were enough algae, why can't we survive by eating just algae?

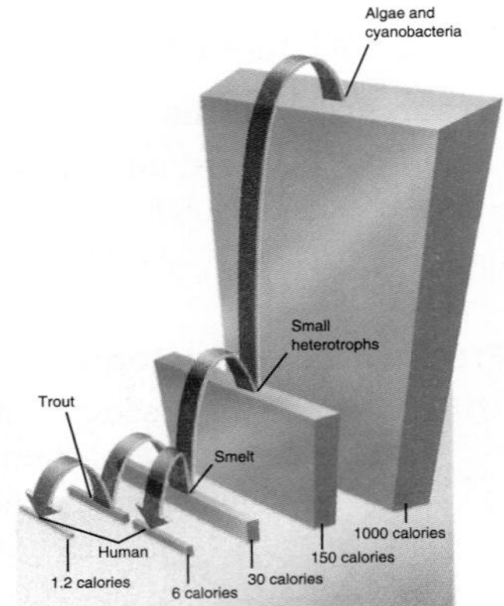

20.3.1 Imagine that you are a molecule of water. Describe the journey of your existence, starting with falling as part of a raindrop onto the earth, and ending in a cloud ready to fall again. Be sure to take a trip through a plant along the way.

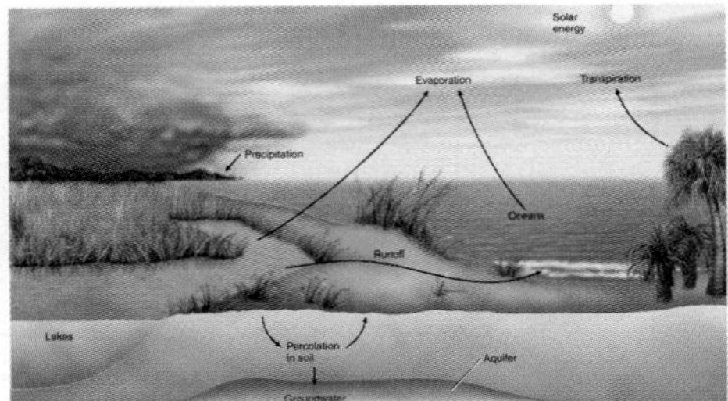

Synthesize What You Have Learned

20.1.2 Given the amount of sunlight that hits the plants on our planet, and the capacity of plants for rapid growth and reproduction, how come we aren't all hip deep in plants?

20.1.2 Many experiments by ecologists have shown that species-rich communities are more productive than species-poor ones. If this is so, why is American farming, based almost entirely on monoculture, so productive?

20.7.1 Why do increasing latitude and increasing elevation each affect which plant species grow in a place, and why do the two factors do so in the same way?

20.11.1 Pick two different biomes that you personally have encountered. Compare and contrast the sunshine, rainfall, major temperature features, and the plants and animals found there.

Chapter 22

Human Influences on the Living World

CHAPTER AT A GLANCE

Global Change

22.1 Pollution

22.2 Acid Precipitation

22.3 Global Warming

22.4 Loss of Biodiversity

Today's Biology: The Global Decline in Amphibians

22.5 The Ozone Hole

Saving Our Environment

22.6 Reducing Pollution

22.7 Preserving Nonreplaceable Resources

22.8 Curbing Population Growth

Solving Environmental Problems

22.9 Preserving Endangered Species

22.10 Finding Cleaner Sources of Energy

22.11 Individuals Can Make the Difference

Inquiry & Analysis: How Real Is Global Warming?

Global Change

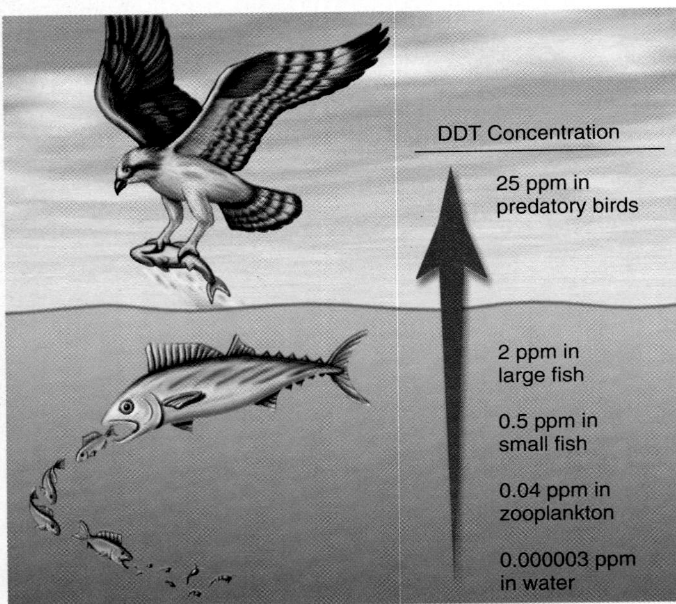

Figure 22.1 Biological magnification of DDT.

Because DDT accumulates in animal fat, the compound becomes increasingly concentrated in higher levels of the food chain.

22.1 Pollution

LEARNING OBJECTIVE 22.1.1 Explain how modern industry and agriculture are leading to higher levels of chemical pollution.

Our world is one highly interactive biosphere, and damage done to any one ecosystem can have ill effects on many others. Burning high-sulfur coal in Illinois kills trees in Vermont, while dumping refrigerator coolants in New York destroys atmospheric ozone over Antarctica and leads to increased skin cancer in Madrid. Biologists call such widespread effects on the worldwide ecosystem **global change.** The pattern of global change that has become evident within recent years, including chemical pollution, acid precipitation, the ozone hole, the greenhouse effect, and the loss of biodiversity, is one of the most serious problems facing humanity's future.

Chemical Pollution

The problem posed by chemical pollution has grown very serious in recent years, both because of the growth of heavy industry and because of an overly casual attitude in industrialized countries. Chemicals are released into both the air and into water; therefore, their effects are far reaching.

Air Pollution. Air pollution is a major problem in the world's cities. In Mexico City, oxygen is sold routinely on street corners for patrons to inhale. Cities such as New York, Boston, and Philadelphia are known as gray-air cities because most of the air pollutants are sulfur oxides emitted by industry. Cities such as Los Angeles, however, are called brown-air cities because the air pollutants undergo chemical reactions in the sunlight to form smog.

Water Pollution. Disposing of chemicals into the water, a "flushing it down the sink" approach, doesn't work in today's crowded world. There is simply not enough water available to dilute the many substances that the enormous human population produces continuously. Lakes and rivers throughout the world are becoming increasingly polluted with sewage, fertilizers, and insecticides that wash from the land to the water in great quantities.

Agricultural Chemicals

The spread of "modern" agriculture has caused very large amounts of many kinds of new chemicals to be introduced into the global ecosystem, particularly pesticides, herbicides, and fertilizers. Chlorinated hydrocarbons like DDT accumulate in animal fat tissue, so as they pass through a food chain, they become increasingly concentrated, a process called **biological magnification.** Figure 22.1 shows how a minute concentration of DDT in plankton increases to significant levels as it is passed up through this aquatic food chain. DDT caused serious ecological problems, leading to the production of thin, fragile eggshells in many predatory bird species such as peregrine falcons, bald eagles, osprey, and brown pelicans. In the late 1960s, DDT was banned in the United States in time to save the birds from extinction. DDT is still widely used in the tropics.

Food chains, as discussed on page 405, track the path of energy through an ecosystem from the sun through the trophic levels, based on who eats whom.

Putting the Concept to Work

Why is DDT, widely used in the tropics, banned in the USA?

BIOLOGY & YOU

Do You Use Bottled Water? One sort of chemical pollution that many of us contribute to without thinking about it is drinking bottled water packaged in plastic. Bottled water is purified water or spring water, popular in the United States both because water is a healthy choice instead of soft drinks and because bottles can be purchased conveniently in stores or vending machines. Americans buy some 28 billion water bottles a year, consuming more bottled water than beer, even though in the United States tap water quality is as high as bottled water, and an awful lot cheaper. Bottled water typically costs \$1 to \$2 per bottle (90% of the cost is making the bottle, label, and cap), while tap water is essentially free. Why do the Sierra Club, the World Wildlife Fund, and other conservation groups urge you to consume less bottled water? Because the bottles, made of plastic, do not degrade and 80% are not recycled—they simply accumulate by the billions in refuse dumps, landfills, and the world's oceans. Adding to the environmental damage, producing the bottles creates more than 2.5 million tons of CO_2 each year, an estimated 250 grams for each bottle. That's like filling a quarter of every bottle with oil and burning it. If you want to do your bit to curb global warming and pollution, drink more tap water.

22.2 Acid Precipitation

LEARNING OBJECTIVE 22.2.1 Explain the sources and consequences of acid precipitation.

The smokestacks you see in figure 22.2 are those of a power plant that burns coal, sending the smoke high into the atmosphere through these tall stacks. The smoke contains high concentrations of sulfur dioxide and other sulfates, which produce acid when they combine with water vapor in the air. The first tall stacks were introduced in Britain in the mid-1950s, and the design rapidly spread through Europe and the United States. The intent of having tall smokestacks was to release the sulfur-rich smoke high in the atmosphere, where winds would disperse and dilute it.

However, in the 1970s scientists began noticing that the acids from the sulfur-rich smoke were having devastating effects. Throughout northern Europe, lakes were reported to have suffered drastic drops in biodiversity, some even becoming devoid of life. The trees of the great Black Forest of Germany were dying—and the damage was not limited to Europe. In the eastern United States and Canada, many of the forests and lakes have been seriously damaged.

It turns out that when the sulfur introduced into the upper atmosphere combined with water vapor to produce sulfuric acid, the acid was taken far from its source, but it later fell along with water as acidic rain and snow. This pollution-acidified precipitation is called **acid rain** (but the term acid precipitation is actually more correct). Natural rainwater rarely has a pH lower than 5.6; however, rain and snow in many areas of the United States have pH values less than 5.3, and in the northeastern United States, pHs of 3.0 have been recorded.

The pH scale, discussed on page 44, is a measurement of the amount of hydrogen ions (H^+) in a solution on a scale from 0 to 14. The lower the value, the more acidic the solution.

Acid precipitation destroys life. Many of the forests of the northeastern United States and Canada have been seriously damaged. In fact, it is now estimated that at least 1.4 million acres of forests in the Northern Hemisphere have been adversely affected by acid precipitation (figure 22.3). In addition, thousands of lakes in Sweden and Norway no longer support fish—these lakes are now eerily clear. In the northeastern United States and Canada, tens of thousands of lakes are dying biologically as their pH levels fall to below 5.0, so acidic that many fish species and other aquatic animals die, unable to reproduce.

Acidification of the world's oceans driven by rising levels of carbon dioxide in the atmosphere is creating an even more serious problem. CO_2 dissolves in water to form carbonic acid, lowering the pH. Ocean acidification will lower ocean water pH by 0.5 pH units by 2100 at current rates. Marine organisms like shellfish and coral that use calcium carbonate to form structures will be disastrously affected, their shells dissolving at the lower pH.

The solution seems like it would be easy—clean up the sulfur and CO_2 emissions. But there have been serious problems with implementing this solution. The polluter and the recipient of the pollution are far from one another, and neither wants to pay so much for what they view as someone else's problem. In the U.S., legislation has begun to address this problem by mandating some cleaning of emissions, but laws capping CO_2 emissions by taxing them have yet to be passed.

Putting the Concept to Work

How can burning coal be responsible for acid rain, when coal has been burned for centuries, while acid rain was unknown before 1950? Explain.

Figure 22.2 Tall stacks export pollution.

Tall stacks, as seen in this coal-burning power plant, send pollution far up into the atmosphere.

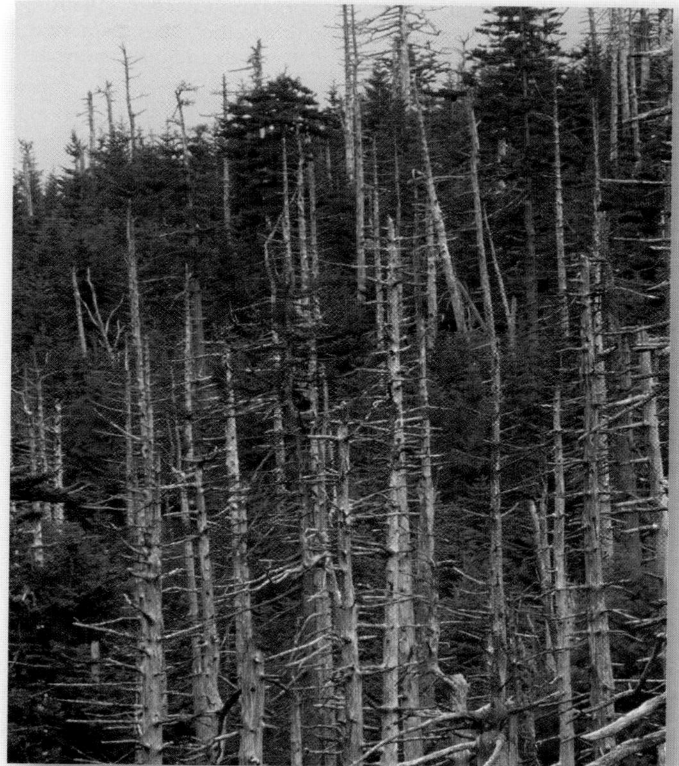

Figure 22.3 Acid precipitation.

Acid precipitation is killing many of the trees in North American and European forests. Much of the damage is done to the mycorrhizae, fungi growing within the cells of the tree roots. Trees need mycorrhizae in order to extract nutrients from the soil.

IMPLICATION FOR YOU When you breathe in the air in a New England forest, you are exposed to the same acidified moisture that is killing the trees in North American forests. Why do you suppose it doesn't kill you?

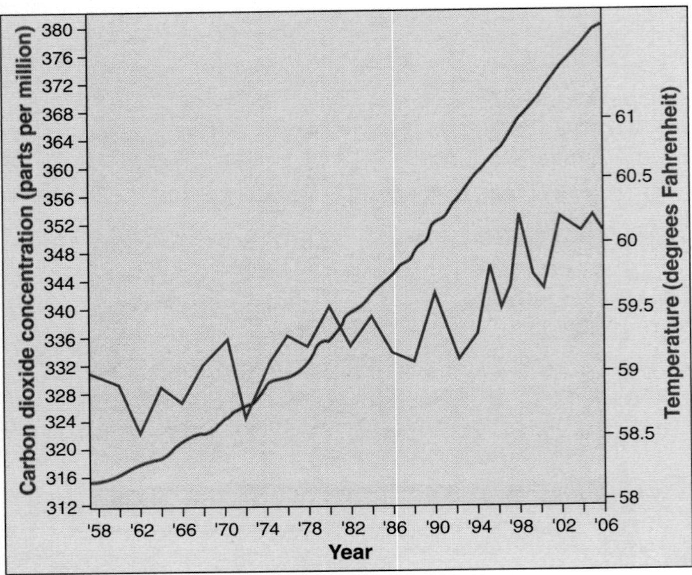

Figure 22.4 The greenhouse effect.

The concentration of carbon dioxide in the atmosphere has shown a steady increase for many years *(blue line)*. The *red line* shows the average global temperature for the same period of time. Note the general increase in temperature since the 1950s and, specifically, the sharp rise beginning in the 1980s. Data from the National Center for Atmospheric Research and other sources.

22.3 Global Warming

LEARNING OBJECTIVE 22.3.1 Assess the proposition that global warming is the consequence of increased CO_2 in the atmosphere.

For over 150 years, much of the growth of our industrial society has been fueled by burning fossil fuels—coal, oil, and gas. Coal, oil, and gas are the remains of ancient plants, transformed by pressure and time into carbon-rich "fossil fuels." When such fossil fuels are burned, this carbon is combined with oxygen atoms, producing carbon dioxide (CO_2). Industrial society's burning of fossil fuels has released huge amounts of carbon dioxide into the atmosphere. No one paid any attention to this because the carbon dioxide was thought to be harmless and because the atmosphere was thought to be a limitless reservoir, able to absorb and disperse any amount. It turns out neither assumption is true, and in recent decades the levels of carbon dioxide in the atmosphere have risen sharply and are continuing to rise.

What is alarming is that the carbon dioxide doesn't just sit in the air doing nothing. The chemical bonds in carbon dioxide molecules transmit radiant energy from the sun but trap the longer wavelengths of infrared light, or heat, that are reflected off the earth's surface, and prevent them from radiating back into space. This creates what is known as the **greenhouse effect.** Planets that lack this type of "trapping" atmosphere are much colder than those that possess one. If the earth did not have a "trapping" atmosphere, the average earth temperature would be about –20°C, instead of the actual +15°C.

Global Warming Due to Greenhouse Gases

The rise in average global temperatures during recent decades, a profound change in the earth's atmosphere referred to as **global warming**, is correlated with increased carbon dioxide concentrations in the atmosphere (figure 22.4). The suggestion that global warming might in fact be caused by the accumulation of greenhouse gases (carbon dioxide, CFCs, nitrogen oxides, and methane) in the atmosphere has been controversial, and is examined in detail in the Inquiry & Analysis feature at the end of this chapter. After serious examination of the evidence, the overwhelming consensus among scientists is that, indeed, greenhouse gases are causing global warming.

Increases in the amounts of greenhouse gases increase average global temperatures from 1° to 4°C, which could have serious impact on rain patterns, prime agricultural lands, and sea levels.

Effects on Rain Patterns. Global warming is predicted to have a major effect on rainfall patterns. Areas that have already been experiencing droughts may see even less rain, contributing to even greater water shortages.

Effects on Agriculture. Warmer temperatures and increased levels of carbon dioxide in the atmosphere would be expected to increase the yields of some crops, while having a negative impact on others. Droughts that may result from global warming will also negatively affect crops.

Rising Sea Levels. Much of the water on earth is locked into ice in glaciers and polar ice caps. As global temperatures increase, these large stores of ice have begun to melt. Most of the water from the melted glaciers ends up in the oceans, causing water levels to rise. Higher water levels can be expected to cause increased flooding of low-lying lands.

Putting the Concept to Work

Do you expect the melting of the polar ice cap covering the North Pole to raise global sea levels significantly? Explain.

IN THE NEWS

Clean Coal. The key problem we must face in combating global warming is the world's growing thirst for cheap energy. While we in the United States begin to search for effective ways to obtain large amounts of energy without burning fossil fuels, the problem is spiraling out of control. India and China are initiating large-scale commercial projects that would tap enormous but inaccessible coal reserves by burning the coal where it lies, deep below the earth's surface. The amount of carbon dioxide released by such burning would be staggering. Such underground coal gasification was pioneered by the Russians in the 1930s. Because underground gasification produces no sulfur oxide or nitrogen oxide, and the ash stays underground, the U.S. Coal Industry has taken to calling the process "clean coal." They suggest that the carbon dioxide released by the burning of underground coal can be captured and then sequestered (that is, locked away from the atmosphere) by pumping it back into the underground void left by burning the coal. The problem, ignored in television ads promoting governmental incentives for clean coal development in the United States, is that carbon sequestration costs a lot of money. This makes the energy obtained from underground coal gasification much more expensive, a strong incentive to skip this step. A clear-sighted government environmental policy would tie any financial incentive for coal gasification to caps on carbon emissions. Otherwise, governmental support of coal gasification may accelerate rather than slow the speed of climate change.

22.4 Loss of Biodiversity

LEARNING OBJECTIVE 22.4.1 Identify the three main causes of today's loss of biodiversity.

Just as death is as necessary to a normal life cycle as reproduction, so extinction is as normal and necessary to a stable world ecosystem as species formation. Most species, probably all, go extinct eventually. More than 99% of species known to science (most from the fossil record) are now extinct. However, current rates of extinctions are alarmingly high. The extinction rate for birds and mammals was about one species every decade from 1600 to 1700, but it rose to one species every year during the period from 1850 to 1950, and four species per year between 1986 and 1990. It is this increase in the rate of extinction that is the heart of the **biodiversity** crisis.

Factors Responsible for Extinction

What factors are responsible for extinction? Studying a wide array of recorded extinctions, biologists have identified three factors that seem to play a key role in many extinctions: habitat loss, species overexploitation, and introduced species (**figure 22.5**).

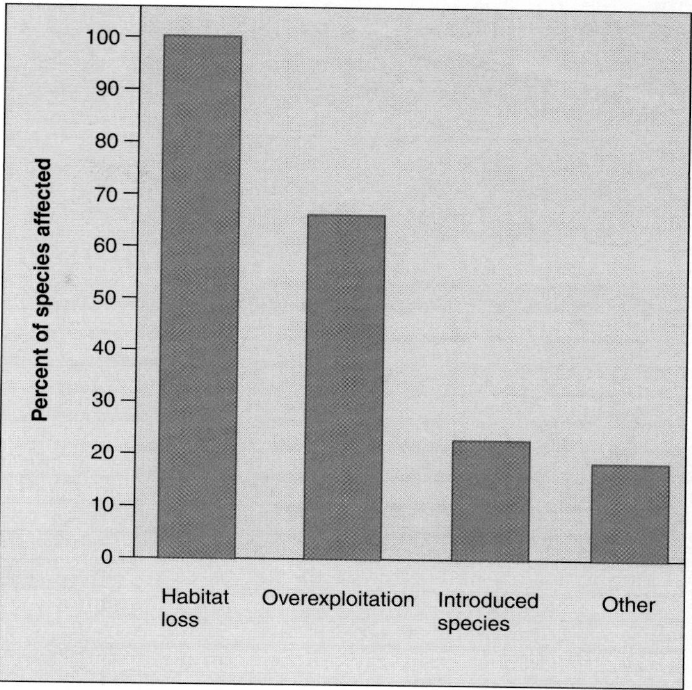

Figure 22.5 Factors responsible for animal extinction.

These data represent known extinctions of mammals in Australia, Asia, and the Americas. Some extinctions have more than one cause.

Habitat Loss. Habitat loss is the single most important cause of extinction. Given the tremendous amounts of ongoing destruction of all types of habitat, from rain forest to ocean floor, this should come as no surprise. Natural habitats may be adversely affected by human influences in four ways: (1) destruction, (2) pollution, (3) human disruption, and (4) habitat fragmentation (dividing up the habitat into small isolated areas). For example, habitat destruction in Madagascar is rapidly endangering species that live in the rain forest (**figure 22.6**).

Species Overexploitation. Species that are hunted or harvested by humans have historically been at grave risk of extinction, even when the species populations are initially very abundant. There are many examples in our recent history of overexploitation: passenger pigeons, bison, many species of whales, and mahogany trees are but a few.

Introduced Species. Occasionally a new species will enter a habitat and colonize it, usually at the expense of native species. Colonization occurs in nature, but it is rare; however, humans have made this process more common, with devastating ecological consequence. The introduction of exotic species has wiped out or threatened many native populations. Species introductions occur in many ways, usually unintentionally. Plants and animals can be transported in nursery plants, in the ballast of large ocean vessels, as stowaways in boats, cars, and planes, and as beetle larvae within wood products. These species enter new environments where they have no native predators to keep their population sizes in check. Free to populate the habitat, they crowd out native species.

Putting the Concept to Work

Name one species of animal or plant driven extinct in your lifetime.

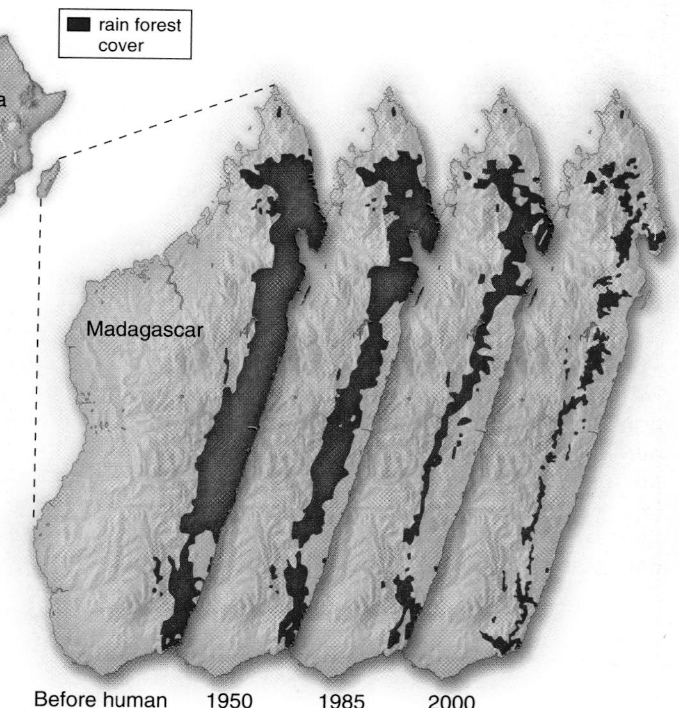

Figure 22.6 Extinction and habitat destruction.

The rain forest covering the eastern coast of Madagascar, an island off the coast of East Africa, has been progressively destroyed as the island's human population has grown. Ninety percent of the original forest cover is now gone. Many species have become extinct, and many others are threatened, including 16 of Madagascar's 31 primate species.

The Global Decline in Amphibians

Sometimes important things happen, right before our eyes, without anyone noticing. That thought occurred to David Bradford as he stood looking at a quiet lake high in the Sierra Nevada Mountains of California in the summer of 1988. Bradford, a biologist, had hiked all day to get to the lake, and when he got there his worst fears were confirmed. The lake was on a list of mountain lakes that Bradford had been visiting that summer in Sequoia-Kings Canyon National Parks while looking for a little frog with yellow legs. The frog's scientific name was *Rana muscosa,* and it had lived in the lakes of the parks for as long as anyone had kept records. But this silent summer evening, the little frog was gone. The last major census of the frog's populations within the parks had been taken in the mid-1970s, and *R. muscosa* had been everywhere, a common inhabitant of the many freshwater ponds and lakes within the parks. Now, for some reason Bradford did not understand, the frogs had disappeared from 98% of the ponds that had been their homes.

After Bradford reported this puzzling disappearance to other biologists, an alarming pattern soon became evident. Throughout the world, local populations of amphibians (frogs, toads, and salamanders) were becoming extinct. Waves of extinction have swept through high-elevation amphibian populations in the western United States, and have also cut through the frog populations of Central America and coastal Australia.

Amphibians have been around for 350 million years, since long before the dinosaurs. Their sudden disappearance from so many of their natural homes sounded an alarm among biologists. What are we doing to our world? If amphibians cannot survive the world we are making, can we?

In 1998 the U.S. National Research Council brought scientists together from many disciplines in a serious attempt to address the problem. After years of intensive investigation, they have begun to sort out the reasons for the global decline in amphibians. Like many important questions in science, this one does not have a simple answer.

Five factors seem to be contributing in a major way to the worldwide amphibian decline: (1) habitat deterioration and destruction, particularly clear-cutting of forests, which drastically lowers the humidity (water in the air) that amphibians require; (2) the introduction of exotic species that outcompete local amphibian populations; (3) chemical pollutants that are toxic to amphibians; (4) fatal infections by pathogens; and (5) global warming, which is making some habitats unsuitable.

Infection by parasites appears to have played a particularly important role in the western United States and coastal Australia. Amphibian ecology expert James Collins of Arizona State University has reported one clear instance of infection leading to amphibian decline. When Collins examined populations of salamanders living on the Kaibab Plateau along the Grand Canyon rim, he found many sick salamanders. Their skin was covered with white pustules, and most infected ones died, their hearts and spleens collapsed. The infectious agent proved to be a virus common in fish called a ranavirus. Ranavirus isolated by Collins from one sick salamander would cause the disease in a healthy salamander, so there was no doubt that ranavirus was the culprit responsible for the salamander decline on the Kaibab Plateau.

Ranavirus outbreaks eliminate small populations, but in larger ones a few individuals survive infection, sloughing off their pustule-laden skin. These populations slowly recover.

A second kind of infection, very common in Australia but also seen in the United States, is having more widespread effects. Populations infected with this microbe, a kind of fungus called a chytrid (pronounced "kit-rid," see chapter 16), do not recover. Usually a harmless soil fungus that decomposes plant material, this particular chytrid (with the Latin name of *Batrachochytrium dendrobatidis*) is far from harmless to amphibians. It dissolves and absorbs the keratinous mouthparts of amphibian larvae, killing them.

This killer chytrid appeared in Australia near Melbourne in the early 1980s. Now almost all Australia is affected. How did the disease spread so rapidly? Apparently it traveled by truck. Infected frogs moved all across Australia in wooden boxes with bunches of bananas. In one year, 5,000 frogs were collected from banana crates in one Melbourne market alone.

In other parts of the world, infection does not seem to play as important a role as acid precipitation, habitat loss, and introduction of exotic species. This complex pattern of cause and effect only serves to emphasize the take-home lesson: Worldwide amphibian decline has no one culprit. Instead, all five factors play important roles. It is their total impact that has shifted the worldwide balance toward extinction.

To reverse the trend toward extinction, we must work to lessen the impact of all of these factors. It is important that we not get discouraged at the size of the job, however. Any progress we make on any one factor will help shift the balance back toward survival. Extinction is only inevitable if we let it be.

22.5 The Ozone Hole

LEARNING OBJECTIVE 22.5.1 Explain how CFCs caused the ozone hole over Antarctica, and describe the consequences.

For 2 billion years, life was trapped in the oceans because radiation from the sun seared the earth's surface unchecked. Nothing could survive that bath of destructive energy. Living things were able to leave the oceans and colonize the surface of the earth only after a protective shield of ozone (O_3) had been added to the atmosphere by photosynthesis. Imagine if that shield were taken away. Alarmingly, it appears that we are destroying it ourselves. Starting in 1975, the earth's ozone shield began to disintegrate. Over the South Pole in September of that year, satellite photos revealed that the ozone concentration was unexpectedly low. It was as if some "ozone eater" were chewing it up in the Antarctic sky, leaving a mysterious zone of lower-than-normal ozone concentration, an **ozone hole.** For many years after that, more of the ozone was depleted, and the hole grew bigger and deeper. The satellite image in figure 22.7 shows lower levels of ozone as purple—the ozone hole completely covers Antarctica.

What is eating the ozone? Scientists soon discovered that the culprit was a class of chemicals that everyone had thought to be harmless: **chlorofluorocarbons (CFCs).** Throughout the world, CFCs are used in large amounts as coolants in refrigerators and air conditioners, as the gas in aerosol dispensers, and as the foaming agent in Styrofoam containers. All of these CFCs eventually escape into the atmosphere, but no one worried about this until recently, because CFCs were thought to be chemically inert.

It turned out that the CFCs were causing mischief the chemists had not imagined. High over the South and North Poles, nearly 50 kilometers up, where it is very, very cold, the CFCs stick to frozen water vapor and act as catalysts of a chemical reaction. Just as an enzyme carries out a reaction in your cells without being changed itself, so the CFCs catalyze the conversion of ozone (O_3) into oxygen (O_2) without being used up themselves. Oxygen gas, unlike ozone, does not provide a protective shield. The drop in ozone worldwide is now over 3%.

Ultraviolet radiation is a serious human health concern. Every 1% drop in the atmospheric ozone content is estimated to lead to a 6% increase in the incidence of skin cancers. At middle latitudes, the drop of approximately 3% that has occurred worldwide is estimated to have led to an increase of perhaps as much as 20% in lethal melanoma skin cancers.

Experts generally agree that levels of ozone-killing chemicals in the upper atmosphere are leveling off since more than 180 countries in the 1980s signed an international agreement phasing out the manufacture of CFCs. Current computer models suggest the Antarctic ozone hole should disappear by 2065, and the lesser-damaged ozone layer over the Arctic should recover by about 2023.

Putting the Concept to Work

If the % drop in atmospheric ozone over the U.S. falls to 2% of 1975 levels by your 30th birthday, what will the level of lethal melanoma skin cancers be then, relative to what it is today?

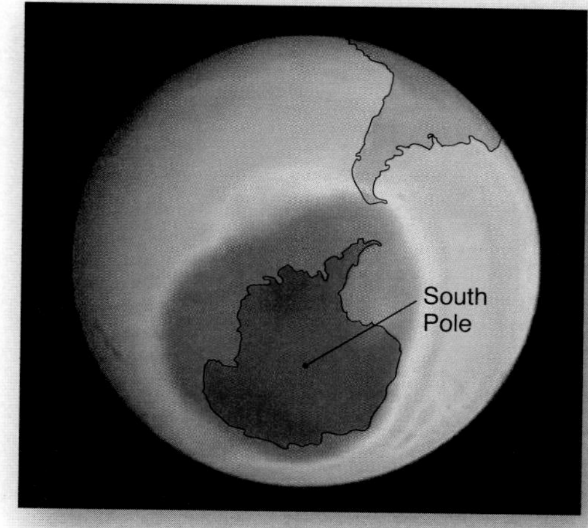

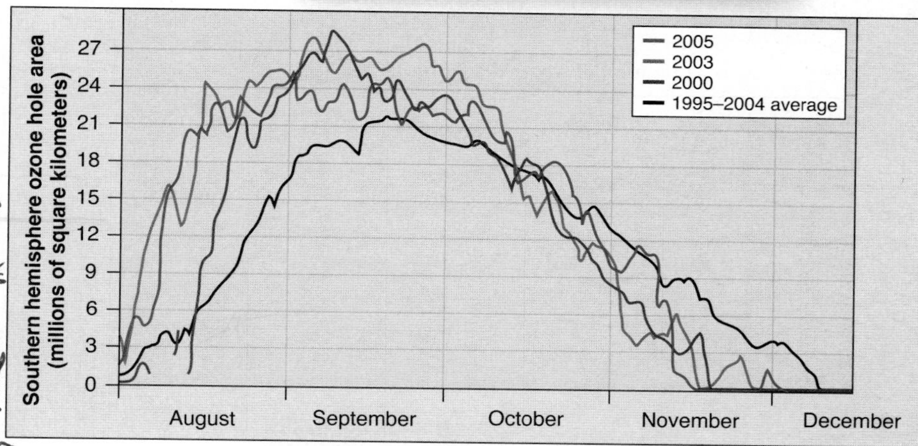

Figure 22.7 The ozone hole over Antarctica.

For decades NASA satellites have tracked the extent of ozone depletion over Antarctica. Every year since 1975 an ozone "hole" has appeared in August when sunlight triggers chemical reactions in cold air trapped over the South Pole during Antarctic winter. The hole intensifies during September before tailing off as temperatures rise in November–December. In 2000, the 28.4-million-square-kilometer hole (*purple* in the satellite image) covered an area larger than the United States, Canada, and Mexico combined. In September 2000, the hole extended over Punta Arenas, a city of about 120,000 people in southern Chile, exposing residents to very high levels of UV radiation.

IMPLICATION FOR YOU The ozone hole reached its largest average recording in 2006, at 26.6 million square kilometers. The ozone hole was still nearly as large in 2008, at 25.2 million square kilometers average. However, levels of CFCs over Antarctica in 2008 had decreased 3.8% from their peak in 2000. Based on these CFC levels, would you expect the size of the ozone hole to continue to decrease over the next few years? Explain your reasoning.

Saving Our Environment

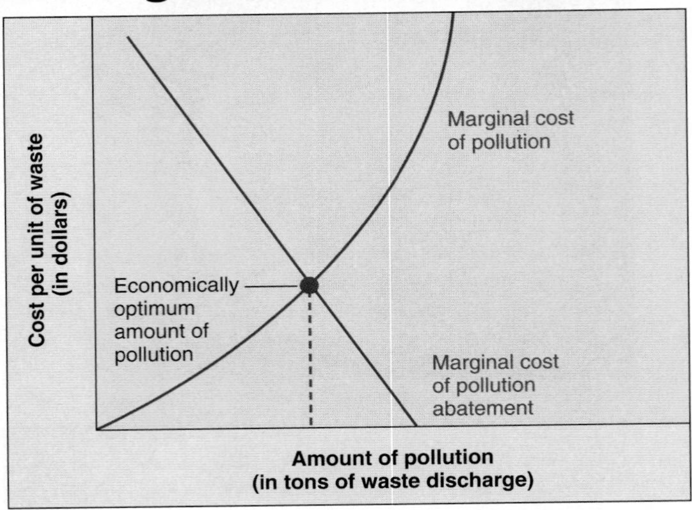

Figure 22.8 Is there an optimum amount of pollution?

Economists identify the "optimum" amount of pollution as the point at which eliminating the next unit of pollution (the marginal cost of pollution abatement) equals the cost in damages caused by that unit of pollution (the marginal cost of pollution).

22.6 Reducing Pollution

LEARNING OBJECTIVE 22.6.1 Describe how economists estimate the "optimal" level of pollution, and how it might be achieved.

To solve the problem of industrial and atmospheric pollution, it is first necessary to understand the cause of the problem. In essence, it is a failure of our economy to set a proper price on environmental health. The economy of the United States (and much of the rest of the industrial world) is based on a simple feedback system of supply and demand. As a commodity gets scarce, its price goes up, and this added profit acts as an incentive for more of the item to be produced; if too much is produced, the price falls and less of it is made because it is no longer as profitable to produce it.

This system works very well and is responsible for the economic strength of our nation, but it has one great weakness. If demand is set by price, then it is very important that all the costs be included in the price. Imagine that the person selling the item were able to pass off part of the production cost to a third person. The seller would then be able to set a lower price and sell more of the item! Driven by the lower price, the buyer would purchase more than if all the costs had been factored into the price.

Unfortunately, that sort of pricing error is what has driven the pollution of the environment by industry. The true costs of energy and of the many products of industry are composed of direct production costs, such as materials and wages, and of indirect costs, such as pollution of the ecosystem. These indirect costs are not always taken into account when setting prices. Economists have identified an "optimum" amount of pollution based on how much it costs to reduce pollution versus the social and environmental cost of allowing pollution. The economically optimum amount of pollution is indicated by the blue dot in figure 22.8. If more pollution than the optimum is allowed, the social cost is too high, but if less than the optimum is allowed, the economic cost is too high.

Pollution Laws and Taxes

In the last 20 years, laws have begun to significantly curb pollution by setting stiff standards for what can be released into the environment. For example, all cars are required to have effective catalytic converters to eliminate automobile smog. Similarly, the Clean Air Act of 1990 requires that power plants eliminate sulfur emissions, typically by installing scrubbers on their smokestacks. The cost of the scrubbers increases the price of the energy. The new, higher costs are closer to the true costs, lowering consumption to more appropriate levels.

A second approach to curbing pollution has been to increase the consumer costs directly by placing a tax on the pollution, in effect an artificial price hike imposed by the government as a tax added to the price of production. This added cost lowers consumption too, but by adjusting the tax, the government can attempt to balance the conflicting demands of environmental safety and economic growth to achieve "optimal" pollution. Such taxes, often imposed as "cap-and-trade pollution permits," are becoming an increasingly important part of antipollution laws.

Putting the Concept to Work

Explain why the "optimum amount of pollution" is not zero.

BIOLOGY & YOU

Green Living. Few of us think of ourselves as sources of pollution, although all of us are. The production of the food we eat often involves the release into the environment of pesticides, herbicides, and other agricultural chemicals. The plastic products we use expose us to bisphenol A and other chemicals. As important as these sources of pollution are, however, our most serious individual impact comes from our use of fossil fuel energy. Burning fossil fuels pollutes the atmosphere with carbon dioxide and other greenhouse gases that are the root cause of global climate change. You can lessen your impact on environmental pollution and global warming in a variety of ways that are collectively coming to be called "green living." One simple way is to favor organic foods, those produced without extensive use of agricultural chemicals. Also, don't drive when you can walk or share a ride. Another very important contribution you can make is to go on a home energy diet. Replace incandescent light bulbs with compact fluorescent bulbs. Turn up the thermostat on your air conditioner (air conditioners account for 16% of residential electricity consumption), and turn heating down at night in the winter. Don't take overlong showers or run the dishwasher half-full. Each aspect of green living seems small, but if all of us were to live this way, it could have a major impact. We will not succeed unless every one of us gets involved.

22.7 Preserving Nonreplaceable Resources

LEARNING OBJECTIVE 22.7.1 Evaluate the importance of three nonreplaceable resources.

Among the many ways ecosystems are being damaged, one problem stands out as more serious than all the rest: consuming or destroying resources that we all share in common but cannot replace (**figure 22.9**).

Topsoil

Soil is composed of a mixture of rocks and minerals with partially decayed organic matter called humus. Plant growth is strongly affected by soil composition. Minerals like nitrogen and phosphorus are critical to plant growth, and are abundant in humus-rich soils. Our midwestern farm belt sits astride what was once a great prairie. The soil of that ecosystem accumulated bit by bit from countless generations of animals and plants until, by the time humans came to plow, the humus-rich soil extended down several feet.

We cannot replace this rich **topsoil,** the capital upon which our country's greatness is built, yet we are allowing it to be lost at a rate of centimeters every decade. Our country has lost one-quarter of its topsoil since 1950! By repeatedly tilling (turning the soil over) to eliminate weeds, we permit rain to wash more and more of the topsoil away, into rivers and eventually out to sea. New approaches are desperately needed to lessen the reliance on intensive cultivation. Some possible solutions include using genetic engineering to make crops resistant to weed-killing herbicides, and terracing to recapture lost topsoil.

BIOLOGY & YOU

Organic Farming. Organic farming is a form of agriculture that avoids the use of synthetic chemicals. The use of fertilizers and pesticides is strictly limited, as are plant growth regulators and livestock feed additives. Organic farming relies upon crop rotation and green manure to provide nitrogen and nutrients to crops, instead of applying synthetic fertilizers. Insects are fought using biological pest control rather than synthetic pesticides. Weeds are eliminated from fields by mechanical cultivation rather than herbicides. Genetically modified (GM) crops are avoided, primarily because most GM crops like Roundup-ready soybeans have been created so that synthetic herbicides can be used more extensively (there is nothing inherently nonorganic about a DNA modification as such). Approximately 2% of total world farmland is now farmed organically. However, while ecologically very desirable, organic farming is controversial. It produces as little as half the output of high-yield conventional farming, suggesting that organic farming may be incapable of feeding a rapidly growing world population.

Figure 22.9 The tragedy of the commons.

In a now-famous essay, ecologist Garrett Hardin argues that destruction of the environment is driven by freedom without responsibility.

Reprinted with permission from "The Tragedy of the Commons," by G. Hardin, Science, 162, p. 1244. Copyright 1968 AAAS.

"Freedom in a Commons Brings Ruin to All"

The essence of Hardin's original essay:

Picture a pasture open to all. It is expected that each herdsman will try to keep as many cattle as possible on [this] commons....What is the utility...of adding one more animal?...Since the herdsman receives all the proceeds from the sale of the additional animal, the positive utility [to the herdsman] is nearly +1.... Since, however, the effects of overgrazing are shared by all the herdsmen, the negative utility for any particular decision-making herdsman is only a fraction of -1. Adding together the...partial utilities, the rational herdsman concludes that the only sensible course for him to pursue is to add another animal to [the] herd. And another; and another.... Therein is the tragedy. Each man is locked into a system that [causes] him to increase his herd without limit—in a world that is limited....Freedom in a commons brings ruin to all.

—G. Hardin, "The Tragedy of the Commons," *Science* **162,** 1243 (1968), p. 1244

(a)

(b)

(c)

Figure 22.10 Tropical rain forest destruction.

(a) These fires are destroying the rain forest in Brazil, which is being cleared for cattle pasture. (b) The flames are so widespread and so high that their smoke can be viewed from space. (c) The consequences of deforestation can be seen on these middle-elevation slopes in Ecuador. The slopes now support only low-grade pastures where they used to support highly productive forest.

Groundwater

A second resource that we cannot replace is **groundwater,** water trapped beneath the soil within porous rock reservoirs called aquifers. This water seeped into its underground reservoir very slowly during the last ice age over 12,000 years ago. We should not waste it, for we cannot replace it.

In most areas of the United States, local governments exert relatively little control over the use of groundwater. As a result, a very large portion is wasted watering lawns, washing cars, and running fountains. A great deal more is inadvertently being polluted by poor disposal of chemical wastes—and once pollution enters the groundwater, there is no effective means of removing it. Some cities, like Phoenix and Las Vegas, may completely deplete their groundwater within several decades.

Biodiversity

The number of species in danger of extinction during your lifetime is far greater than the number that became extinct with the dinosaurs. This disastrous loss of biodiversity is important because as these species disappear, so does our chance to learn about them and their possible benefits for ourselves. The fact that our entire supply of food is based on 20 kinds of plants, out of the 250,000 available, should give us pause. Like burning a library without reading the books, we don't know what it is we waste. All we can be sure of is that we cannot retrieve it. Extinction is forever.

Over the last 20 years, about half of the world's tropical rain forests have been either burned to make pasture land or cut for timber (**figure 22.10**). Over 6 million square kilometers have been destroyed. Every year the rate of loss increases as the human population in the tropics grows. About 160,000 square kilometers were cut each year in the 1990s, a rate greater than 0.6 hectares (1.5 acres) per second! At this rate, all the rain forests of the world will be gone in your lifetime. In the process, it is estimated that one-fifth or more of the world's species of animals and plants will become extinct—more than a million species. This would be an extinction event unparalleled since the Age of Dinosaurs.

You should not be lulled into thinking that loss of biodiversity is a problem limited to the tropics. The ancient forests of the Pacific Northwest are being cut at a ferocious rate today. At the current rate, very little will remain in a decade. Nor is the problem restricted to one area. Throughout our country, natural forests are being "clear-cut," replaced by pure stands of lumber trees planted in rows like so many lines of corn. It is difficult to scold those living in the tropics when we do such a poor job of preserving our own country's biodiversity.

But what is so bad about losing species? What is the value of biodiversity? Loss of a species entails three costs: (1) the direct economic value of the products we might have obtained from species; (2) the indirect economic value of benefits produced by species without our consuming them, such as nutrient recycling in ecosystems; and (3) their ethical and aesthetic value. It is not difficult to see the value in protecting species that we use to obtain food, medicine, clothing, energy, and shelter, but other species are vitally important to maintaining healthy ecosystems; by destroying biodiversity, we are creating conditions of instability and lessened productivity. Other species add beauty to the living world, no less crucial because it is hard to set a price upon.

Putting the Concept to Work

Do you think it is bad to lose a species like wild horses, whose overbreeding harms the environment? Explain.

22.8 Curbing Population Growth

LEARNING OBJECTIVE 22.8.1 Describe the growth of the human population over the last 10,000 years.

If we were to solve all the problems mentioned in this chapter, we would merely buy time to address the fundamental problem: there are getting to be too many of us.

Humans first reached North America at least 12,000 to 13,000 years ago, crossing the narrow straits between Siberia and Alaska and moving swiftly to the southern tip of South America. By 10,000 years ago, when the continental ice sheets withdrew and agriculture first developed, about 5 million people lived on earth, distributed over all the continents except Antarctica. With the new and much more dependable sources of food that became available through agriculture, the human population began to grow more rapidly. By the time of Christ, 2,000 years ago, an estimated 130 million people lived on earth. By the year 1650, the world's population had doubled, and doubled again, reaching 500 million. Starting in the early 1700s, changes in technology have given humans more control over their food supply, led to the development of cures for many diseases, and produced improvements in shelter and storage capabilities that make humans less vulnerable to climatic uncertainties. Recall from chapter 19 that populations grow exponentially until they reach the limits of their environment, called the carrying capacity. These changes that occurred since the 1700s allowed humans to expand the carrying capacity of the habitats in which they lived and thus to escape the confines of logistic growth and reenter the exponential phase of the sigmoidal growth curve, shown by the explosive growth in figure 22.11.

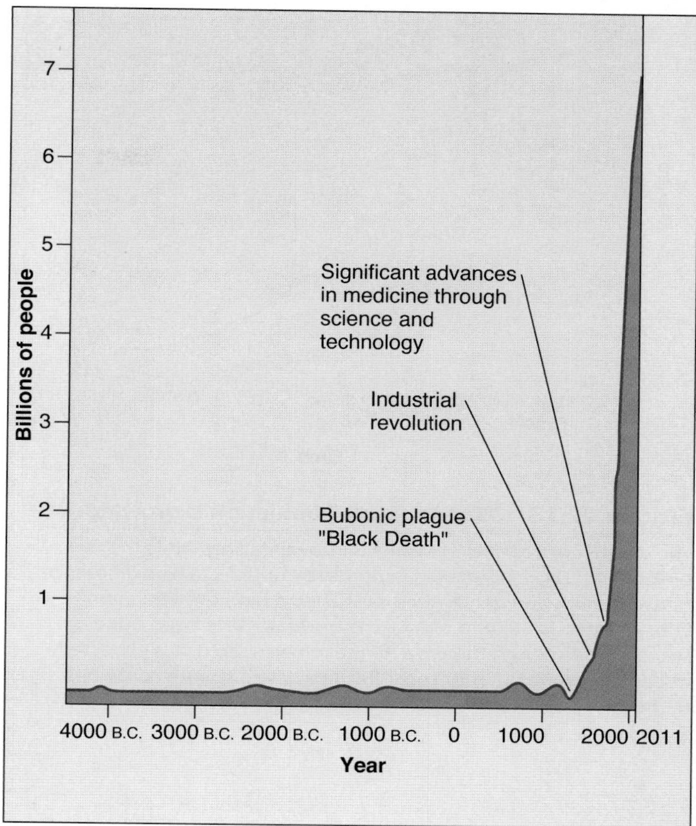

Figure 22.11 Growth curve of the human population. Over the past 300 years, the world population has been growing steadily. Currently, there are about 7 billion people on the earth.

Although the human population has grown explosively for the last 300 years, the average human birthrate has stabilized at about 18 births per year per 1,000 people worldwide. However, with the spread of better sanitation and improved medical techniques, the death rate has fallen steadily, to its present level of 2 per 1,000 per year. The difference between birth and death rates amounts to a population growth rate of 1.1% per year, which seems like a small number, but it is not, given the large population size (figure 22.12).

Figure 22.12 Mexico City has a population of about 20 million people.

The world population reached 7 billion people in 2011, and the annual increase now amounts to about 77 million people, which leads to a doubling of the world population in about 61 years. Put another way, about 219,000 people are added to the world population each day, or almost 152 every minute. At this rate, the world's population will continue to grow and perhaps stabilize at a figure around 10 billion. Such growth cannot continue, because our world cannot support it. Just as a cancer cannot grow unabated in your body without eventually killing you, so humanity cannot continue to grow unchecked in the biosphere without killing it.

Most countries are devoting considerable attention to slowing the growth rate of their populations and there are genuine signs of progress, but the world population may still gain another 1 to 4 billion people before it stabilizes. No one knows whether the world can support so many people indefinitely. Finding a way to do so is the greatest task facing humanity. The quality of life that will be available for your children in this new century will depend to a large extent on our success.

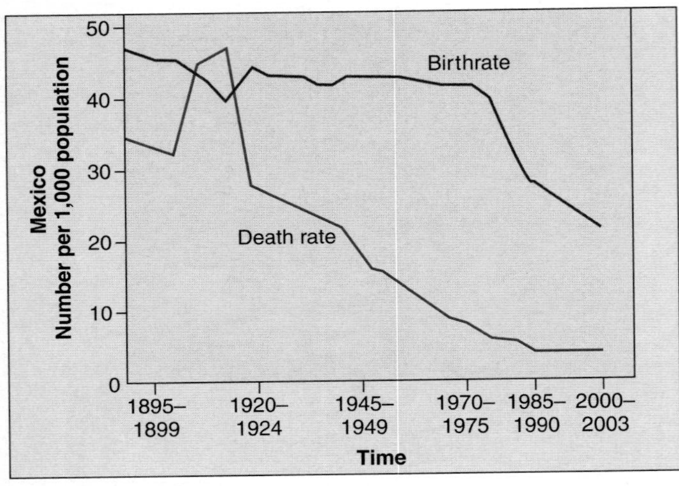

Figure 22.13 Why Mexico's population is growing.

The death rate (*red line*) in Mexico has been falling, while the birthrate (*blue line*) remained fairly steady until 1970. The difference between birth and death rates has fueled a high growth rate. Efforts begun in 1970 to reduce the birthrate have been quite successful. Although the growth rate remains rapid, it is expected to begin leveling off in the near future as the birthrate continues to drop.

Population Growth Rate Has Been Declining

The world population growth rate has been declining, from a high of 2.0% in the period 1965–70 to 1.1% in 2009. Nonetheless, because of the larger population, this amounts to an increase of 77 million people per year to the world population, compared to 53 million per year in the 1960s.

The United Nations attributes the decline to increased family planning efforts and the increased economic power and social status of women. As family size decreases in developing countries, education programs improve, leading to increased education levels for women, which in turn tends to result in further decreases in family size.

No one knows whether the world can sustain today's population of over 7 billion people, much less the far greater numbers expected in the future. If we are to avoid catastrophic increases in death rates, such as the tragedy we are seeing in sub-Saharan Africa, the birthrates must continue to fall dramatically.

Putting the Concept to Work

What is the human population growth rate today? Is this fast? Explain.

Population Pyramids

LEARNING OBJECTIVE 22.8.2 Explain why population pyramids with broader bases indicate more rapid future population growth.

While the human population as a whole continues to grow rapidly, this growth is not occurring uniformly over the planet. Some countries, like Mexico, are currently growing rapidly. Figure 22.13 shows how Mexico's birthrate, while declining (the blue line), still greatly exceeds its death rate (the red line). There is often a correlation in how developed a country is and how rapidly its population grows. Table 22.1, on the next page, compares three countries that differ in their levels of development. Ethiopia, a developing country, has a higher fertility rate, which results in a higher birthrate than either Brazil or the United States. But Ethiopia also has a much higher infant mortality rate and a lower life expectancy. Overall, the population in Ethiopia will double much more quickly than the population of Brazil or the United States. The rate at which a population can be expected to grow in the

Figure 22.14 Population pyramids.

Population pyramids are graphed according to a population's age distribution. Kenya's pyramid has a broad base because of the great number of individuals below child-bearing age. When all of the young people begin to bear children, the population will experience rapid growth. The 2005 U.S. pyramid demonstrates a larger number of individuals in the "baby boom" cohort—the pyramid bulges because of an increase in births between 1945 and 1964, as shown at the base of the 1964 pyramid. The 25 to 34 cohort in the 1964 pyramid represents people born during the Depression and is smaller in size than the cohorts in the preceding and following years.

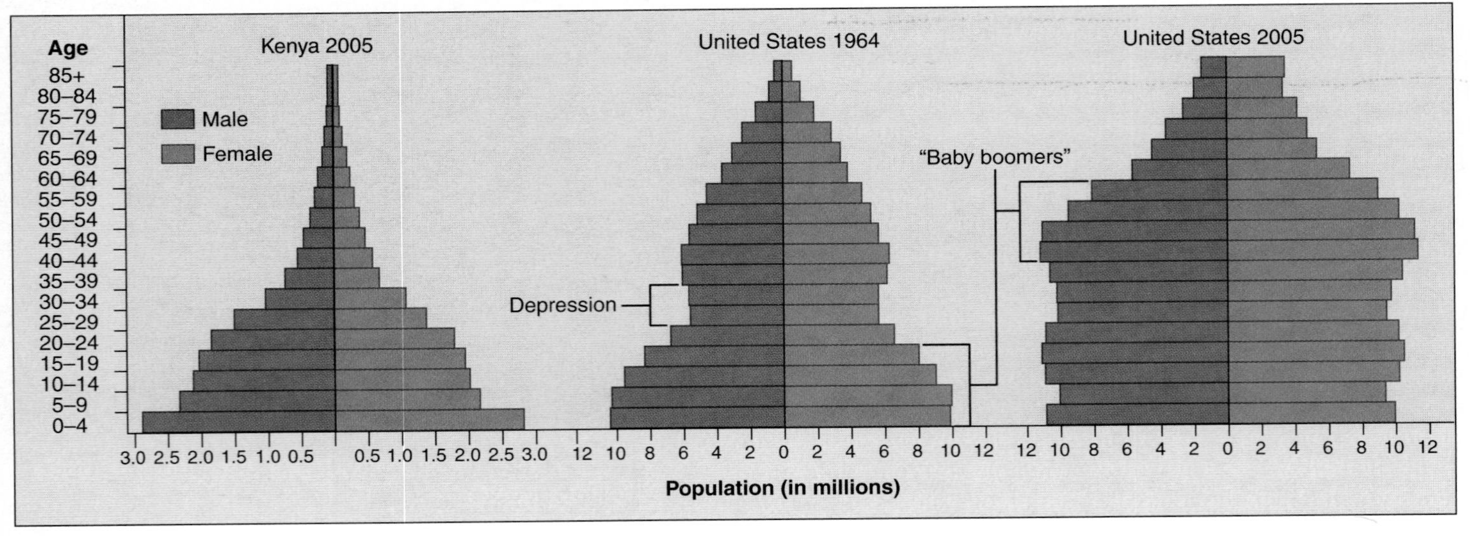

TABLE 22.1 A Comparison of 2006 Population Data in Developed and Developing Countries

	United States (highly developed)	Brazil (moderately developed)	Ethiopia (developing)
Fertility rate	2.1	2.3	5.4
Doubling time at current rate (yr)	72.2	55.5	27.9
Infant mortality rate (infant deaths/1,000 births)	6.5	27	77
Life expectancy (yr)	78	72	49
Per capita income (U.S. dollar equivalent)	\$44,260	\$8,800	\$1,190

future can be assessed graphically by means of a population pyramid—a bar graph displaying the numbers of people in each age category (some examples are shown in figure 22.14). Males are conventionally shown to the left of the vertical age axis (colored blue here) and females to the right (colored red). In most human population pyramids, the number of older females is disproportionately large compared with the number of older males, because females in most regions have a longer life expectancy than males. This is apparent in the upper portion of the 2005 U.S. pyramid.

Viewing such a pyramid, one can predict demographic trends in births and deaths. In general, rectangular pyramids are characteristic of countries whose populations are stable; their numbers are neither growing nor shrinking. A triangular pyramid, like the 2005 Kenya pyramid, is characteristic of a country that will exhibit rapid future growth, as most of its population has not yet entered the child-bearing years. Inverted triangles indicate shrinking populations.

Compare the differences in the population pyramids for the United States and Kenya in figure 22.14. In the somewhat more rectangular population pyramid for the United States in 2005, the cohort (group of individuals) 40 to 59 years old represents the "baby boom," the large number of babies born following World War II. The very triangular pyramid of Kenya, by contrast, predicts explosive future growth. The population of Kenya is predicted to double in less than 20 years. It is important to note that these estimates do not take into account the huge impact that natural disasters and epidemics such as AIDS will have on population sizes (figure 22.15).

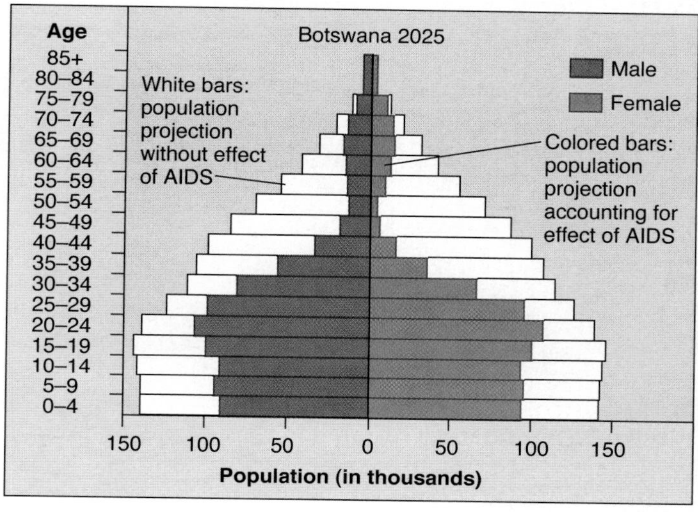

Figure 22.15 Projected AIDS effect on Botswana population (year 2025).

The Level of Consumption in the Developed World Is Also a Problem

The wealthiest 20% of the world's population accounts for 86% of the world's consumption of resources and produces 53% of the world's carbon dioxide emissions, whereas the poorest 20% of the world is responsible for only 1.3% of consumption and 3% of CO_2 emissions.

One way of quantifying this disparity is by calculating what has been termed the **ecological footprint,** which is the amount of productive land required to support an individual at the standard of living of a particular population through the course of his or her life. As figure 22.16 illustrates, the ecological footprint of an individual in the United States is more than 10 times greater than that of someone in India. Based on these measurements, researchers have calculated that resource use by humans is now one-third greater than the amount that nature can sustainably replace; if all humans lived at the standard of living in the developed world, two additional planet earths would be needed.

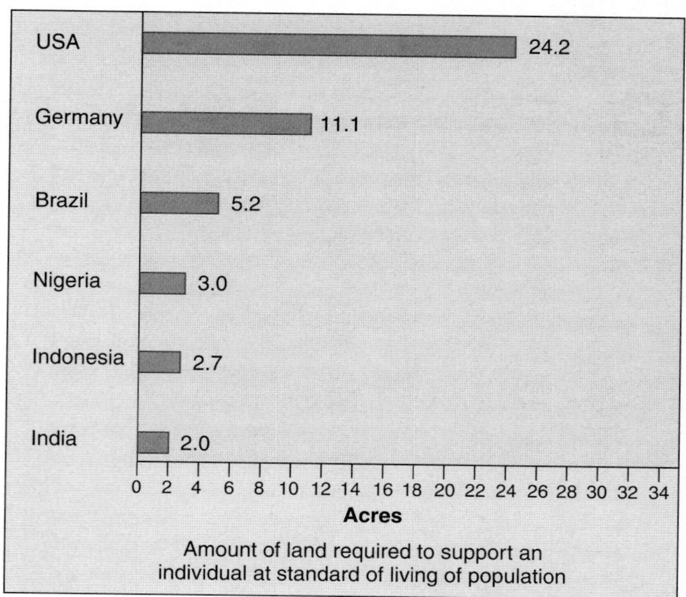

Figure 22.16 Ecological footprint of individuals in different countries in 2003.

Putting the Concept to Work

What is the downside of a triangular population pyramid?

Solving Environmental Problems

(a)

(b)

Figure 22.17 Habitat restoration.

The University of Wisconsin-Madison Arboretum has pioneered restoration ecology. (a) The restoration of the prairie was at an early stage in November, 1935. (b) The prairie as it looks today. This picture was taken at approximately the same location as the 1935 photograph.

BIOLOGY & YOU

Endangered Species Fur. Do you have $50,000 to spare? That's a typical penalty for breaking the Endangered Species Act of 1973, which outlaws trade of any product from an endangered animal. Suppose you have a genuine leopard skin fur coat and want to sell it. You list the coat on eBay with no restrictions and sell it to someone in another state or country. Not only does this violate eBay policies, you have just broken a federal law. Although once widely available, fur from leopards and other large cats like tigers and cheetahs is now banned—even fur garments made as long as 30 years ago. Virtually every bear species is endangered, as are many types of seal and otter. Endangered plants are protected too. Digging up a cactus plant you encounter on a desert hike can be a crime! The list of protected species under the Endangered Species Act is lengthy and complex, containing about 2,000 species of mammals, birds, fish, insects and other invertebrates, and plants. So unless you are positive the fur garment, purse, or throw rug you want to buy or sell is not from an animal listed as endangered or threatened, you should first check to be certain.

22.9 Preserving Endangered Species

LEARNING OBJECTIVE 22.9.1 Explain how the design of recovery plans for endangered species is related in each instance to the cause of species loss.

Once you understand the reasons a particular species is endangered, it becomes possible to think of designing a recovery plan. If the cause is commercial overharvesting, regulations can be designed to lessen the impact and protect the threatened species. If the cause is habitat loss, plans can be instituted to restore lost habitat. Loss of genetic variability in isolated subpopulations can be countered by transplanting individuals from genetically different populations. Populations in immediate danger of extinction can be captured, introduced into a captive breeding program, and later reintroduced to other suitable habitats.

Habitat Restoration

Conservation biology typically concerns itself with preserving populations and species in danger of decline or extinction. However, in many situations conservation is no longer an option. The clear-cutting of the temperate forests of Washington State leaves little behind to conserve, nor does converting a piece of land into a wheat field or an asphalt parking lot. Redeeming these situations requires restoration rather than conservation. Three quite different sorts of habitat restoration programs might be undertaken, depending very much on the cause of the habitat loss.

Pristine Restoration. In situations where all species have been effectively removed, one might attempt to restore the plants and animals that are believed to be the natural inhabitants of the area, when such information is available. Restoring abandoned farmland to prairie (**figure 22.17**) requires that you know the identity of all of the original inhabitants, and the ecologies of each of the species. We rarely have this much information, so no restoration is truly pristine.

Removing Introduced Species. Sometimes the habitat of a species has been destroyed by a single introduced species. In such a case, habitat restoration involves removal of the introduced species. For example, Lake Victoria, Africa, was home to over 300 species of cichlid fishes, small perchlike fishes that display incredible diversity. However, in 1954 the Nile perch, a commercial fish with a voracious appetite, was introduced into Lake Victoria. This resulted in the loss of over 70% of cichlid species, including all open-water species.

Restoration of the once-diverse cichlid fishes to Lake Victoria will require that the Nile perch population (as well as other introduced species such as water hyacinth plants) be brought under control or removed, as well as breeding and restocking the endangered species.

Cleanup and Rehabilitation. Habitats seriously degraded by chemical pollution cannot be restored until the pollution is cleaned up. The successful restoration of the Nashua River in New England, discussed in section 22.11, is one example of how a concerted effort can succeed in restoring a heavily polluted habitat to a relatively pristine condition.

Captive Propagation

Recovery programs, particularly those focused on one or a few species, often must involve direct intervention in natural populations to avoid an immediate threat of extinction. Introducing wild-caught individuals into captive breeding programs is being used in an attempt to save the black-footed ferret and California condor populations in immediate danger of disappearing. Several other such captive propagation programs have had success.

Case History: The Peregrine Falcon. U.S. populations of birds of prey such as the peregrine falcon (*Falco peregrinus*) began an abrupt decline shortly after World War II. Of the approximately 350 breeding pairs east of the Mississippi River in 1942, all had disappeared by 1960. The culprit proved to be the chemical pesticide DDT and related organochlorine pesticides. Birds of prey are particularly vulnerable to DDT because they feed at the top of the food chain, where DDT becomes concentrated (see the discussion of biological magnification in section 22.1). DDT interferes with the deposition of calcium in the bird's eggshells, causing most eggs to break before they hatch.

The use of DDT was banned by federal law in 1972, causing levels of DDT in the eastern United States to fall quickly. Because there were no peregrine falcons left in the eastern United States to reestablish a natural population, falcons from other parts of the country were used to establish a captive breeding program at Cornell University in 1970. By the end of 1986, over 850 birds had been released in 13 eastern states, producing an astonishingly strong recovery (**figure 22.18**).

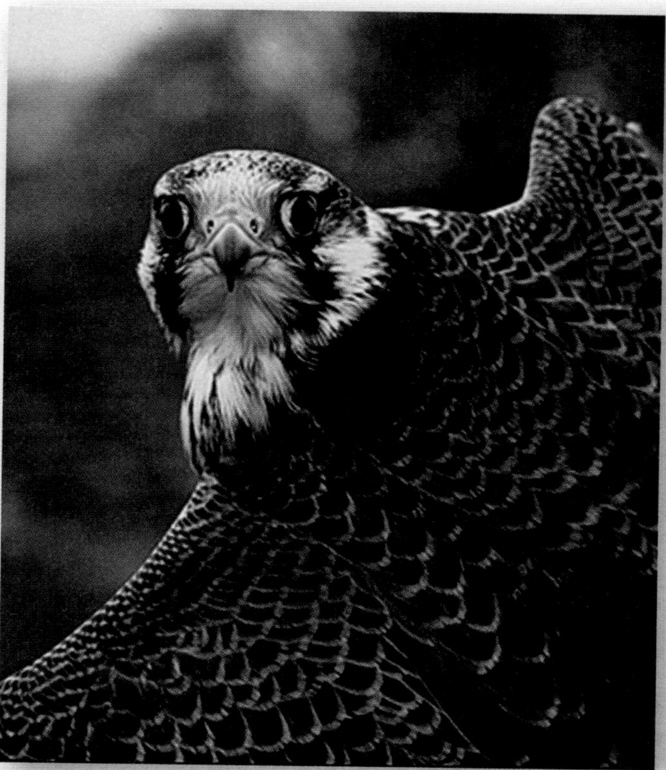

Figure 22.18 Captive propagation.

The reestablishment of peregrine falcon populations in the eastern United States is a success story for captive propagation programs.

Sustaining Genetic Diversity

One of the chief obstacles to a successful species recovery program is that a species is generally in serious trouble by the time a recovery program is instituted. When populations become very small, much of their genetic diversity is lost. If a program is to have any chance of success, it must sustain as much genetic diversity as possible.

Case History: The Black Rhino. Three of the five species of rhinoceros are critically endangered. The three Asian species live in a forest habitat that is rapidly being destroyed, while the two African species are illegally killed for their horns. Fewer than 22,000 individuals of all five species survive today. The problem is intensified by the fact that many of the remaining animals live in very small, isolated populations. The 4,000 wild-living individuals of the black rhino, *Diceros bicornis* (**figure 22.19**), live in approximately 75 small, widely separated groups that are adapted to local conditions throughout the species's range. The West African subspecies of black rhino was recently declared extinct, and the three surviving subspecies appear to have low genetic variability. Analysis of mitochondrial DNA suggests that in these populations most individuals are genetically very similar.

Small populations are at greater risk of extinction. Genetic drift, as discussed on page 269, is caused by random events that eliminate individuals, and therefore alleles, from a population and can be devastating if that population is small to begin with.

This lack of genetic variability represents one of the greatest challenges to the future of the species. Much of the range of the black rhino is still open and not yet subject to human encroachment. To have any significant chance of success, a species recovery program will have to find a way to sustain the genetic diversity that remains in this species.

Figure 22.19 Sustaining genetic diversity.

The black rhino is highly endangered, living in 75 small, widely separated populations. Only about 4,000 individuals survive in the wild. Conservation biologists have the difficult job of finding ways to preserve genetic diversity in small, isolated populations.

IMPLICATION FOR YOU A basic problem faced by black rhinos is that the species has lost much of its genetic diversity as its numbers have decreased. Do you think that expanding the size of today's small rhino populations would fix this problem?

Figure 22.20 Preserving keystone species.

The flying fox is a keystone species in many Old World tropical islands. It pollinates many of the plants, and is a key disperser of seeds. Its elimination by hunting and habitat loss is having a devastating effect on the ecosystems of many South Pacific islands.

IMPLICATION FOR YOU Can you think of a keystone species that plays a key role in natural ecosystems in your area? How would you go about confirming that it is indeed a keystone species?

Heterozygosity could be best maintained by bringing all black rhinos together in a single breeding population, but this is not a practical possibility. A more feasible solution would be to move individuals between populations. Managing the black rhino populations for genetic diversity could prevent the fatal loss of genetic variation.

Preserving Keystone Species

Keystone species are species that exert a particularly strong influence on the structure and functioning of their ecosystem. Their removal can have disastrous consequences.

Case History: Flying Foxes. The severe decline of many species of pteropodid bats, or "flying foxes," in the Old World tropics is an example of how the loss of a keystone species can have dramatic effects on the other species living within an ecosystem, sometimes even leading to a cascade of further extinctions (**figure 22.20**). These bats have very close relationships with important plant species on the islands of the Pacific and Indian Oceans. Widespread on the islands of the South Pacific, flying foxes are the most important—and often the only—pollinators and seed dispersers. A study in Samoa found that 80% to 100% of the seeds landing on the ground during the dry season were deposited by flying foxes. Many species are entirely dependent on these bats for pollination.

Flying foxes are being driven to extinction by human hunting. They are hunted for food and by orchard farmers, who consider them pests. Flying foxes are particularly vulnerable because they live in large, easily seen groups of up to a million individuals. Because they move in predictable patterns and can be tracked to their home roost, hunters can easily bag thousands at a time.

In Guam, where the two local species of flying fox have recently been driven extinct or nearly so, the impact on the ecosystem appears to be substantial. Many plant species are not fruiting, or are doing so only marginally, with fewer fruits than normal. Attempts to preserve flying fox populations are underway. In each instance, legal protection, captive breeding programs, and habitat preservation are key ingredients to successful programs.

Conservation of Ecosystems

Habitat fragmentation is one of the most pervasive enemies of biodiversity conservation efforts. Some species simply require large patches of habitat to thrive, and conservation efforts that cannot provide suitable habitat of such a size are doomed to failure. It has become clear that species placed in isolated patches of habitat are lost far more rapidly than species placed in large preserves. As a result, conservation biologists have promoted the creation, particularly in the tropics, of so-called mega-reserves, large areas of land containing a core of one or more undisturbed habitats (**figure 22.21**).

However, ample land to form mega-reserves may not be available. In these cases, the linking together of habitat islands through the use of corridors is proving an option. Corridors are areas with suitable vegetation and topography between habitats that allow animals to wander outside of their home ranges. Corridors allow for seasonal migrations, the dispersal of juveniles into new territories, and the expansion of growing populations.

Figure 22.21 A mega-reserve.

The Baviaanskloof mega-reserve in South Africa's Eastern Cape Province includes 270,000 hectares of unspoiled terrain, habitat for many species of plants and animals.

Putting the Concept to Work

Explain the importance of keystone species to biodiversity.

22.10 Finding Cleaner Sources of Energy

LEARNING OBJECTIVE 22.10.1 Discuss renewable alternatives to fossil fuels, and evaluate what role biomass may play.

Modern society's propensity to burn fossil fuels has recycled an enormous amount of CO_2 back into the earth's atmosphere. To gain some idea, focus for a moment on your own personal contribution to the carbon cycle. Every mile you drive your car releases about a pound of CO_2 into the air. How many miles do you drive in a year? You see the point? Think about the natural gas that heats your home, the electricity that lights it (mostly generated by the burning of fossil fuels). Your life is having a significant impact on the earth's carbon balance. And you are not alone. Three hundred million other Americans are having a similar impact. In 2006 we saw reductions in carbon dioxide emission in the United States, but Americans still released nearly 6 billion metric tons of carbon dioxide into earth's atmosphere from the burning of fossil fuels (5,973,000,000,000,000 pounds!).

This massive flow of carbon dioxide into the atmosphere is having an unintended and very grave consequence—the earth is getting warmer. What can we do about it? For now the best way to avoid contributing to global warming will be to switch to *alternative energy sources* that don't add to the atmosphere's load of CO_2.

Many countries are turning to nuclear power for their energy needs. Over 75% of France's electricity is now produced by nuclear power plants. In theory nuclear power can provide plentiful, cheap energy, but nuclear power presents several problems—safety, waste disposal, security—that must be overcome if it is to provide a significant portion of the world's energy (**figure 22.22**).

Figure 22.22 Three Mile Island nuclear power plant.

Since a nuclear accident here in 1979, the building of nuclear power stations in the United States has slowed dramatically.

Alternative Energy Sources

A variety of other sources of cleaner energy can help reduce our use of fossil fuels. Many of these are *renewable energy*—sources of energy such as solar power that are naturally replenished. The solar panels in **figure 22.23*a*** capture the energy of sunlight to heat water or other fluids and make steam that turns a turbine, generating electricity. Smaller applications use solar panels connected to photovoltaic cells, which convert solar energy directly into electricity. Other sources of renewable energy include wind (**figure 22.23*b***), and biomass, plants like corn and sugar cane that can be used to produce ethanol, replacing gasoline in cars.

Looking Closer at Ethanol

Ethanol is a simple two-carbon alcohol, CH_3CH_2OH—the same alcohol found in beer and wine. Rich in energy-storing C—H bonds, ethanol makes a good fuel. Burning a gallon of ethanol in your car releases about 80% as much car-powering energy as burning a gallon of gasoline. Ethanol is typically added to gasoline rather than burned by itself.

How can we burn ethanol and not add more CO_2 to the atmosphere? Focus on the word "more." Ethanol is produced through yeast fermentation of sugars found in plants, the same fermentation process that is used to make beer and wine. If our automobiles burn carbon molecules recently produced via photosynthesis by living plants, then they are simply returning to the atmosphere the CO_2 recently extracted from it! No net increase in atmospheric CO_2 occurs.

(a)

(b)

Figure 22.23 Alternate energy sources.

(a) Solar energy uses large mirrors to collect energy from the sun. These solar panels absorb heat from the sun that is used to boil water (or other fluids), which creates steam. The steam turns large turbines (not pictured), generating electricity. (b) Wind-powered energy is an old technology modernized for large-scale use. Large wind fields harness the kinetic energy in wind, converting it into electricity.

Figure 22.24 The starch in corn kernels is used in ethanol production.

Figure 22.25 The challenge of our future.

The girl gazing from this now-classic National Geographic photo faces an uncertain future. An Afghani refugee, the whims of war destroyed her home, her family, and all that was familiar to her. Her expression carries a message about our own future: The problems humanity faces on an increasingly unstable, overcrowded, and polluted earth are no longer hypothetical. They are with us today and demand solutions. As a concerned citizen, your first task must be to clearly understand the nature of the problems. You cannot hope to preserve what you do not understand. The world's environmental problems are acute, and a knowledge of biology is an essential tool you will need to contribute to the effort to solve them. It has been said that we do not inherit the earth from our parents—we borrow it from our children. We must preserve for them a world in which they can live. That is our challenge for the future, and it is a challenge that must be met soon. In many parts of the world, the future is happening right now.

To understand this, focus on where the carbon atoms come from. Burning a fossil fuel like gasoline releases into the atmosphere stores of carbon that had been trapped for thousands of years as oil buried deep in the earth. Burning ethanol also releases carbon, but in this case the carbon dioxide released into the atmosphere has just been taken from it. Think of the atmosphere as a fountain. A fountain recycles the water it shoots into the air. The level of water in the pool stays the same because the water added to the pool by the falling spray is recycled back to the pump to shoot up again. That is how ethanol works with regard to carbon dioxide emissions. Carbon dioxide is taken from the atmosphere and used by the plant to build plant tissue; that tissue is then used to make ethanol. Now imagine that there is a nearby tank of water (representing fossil fuels), and that water from the tank is pumped into the fountain's pool. Not only will the tank become depleted, but the pool will overflow (too much carbon dioxide). That is what happens when fossil fuels are burned.

In the United States, commercial ethanol fuel is traditionally produced by fermenting sugars obtained from starch stored in corn kernels (**figure 22.24**). How might we get ethanol from the rest of the corn plant—the stalk, leaves, and cob? They are made largely of three nonstarch organic molecules: 40% cellulose, 40% hemicellulose, and 10% lignins.

Focus first on the cellulose. Fully one-half of all the organic carbon in the living world is cellulose. Like starch, cellulose consists of chains of glucose sugars linked together. Why not use the sugars in cellulose to make ethanol? Because there is a subtle but very important chemical difference between starch and cellulose. Each of the glucose sugars in a starch molecule has six carbon atoms arranged in a ring like a group of children holding hands in a circle. In a cellulose molecule, the rings of the glucose molecules are inside-out, as if the children are facing with their backs to the center of the circle. Yeast enzymes do not attack links between these kinds of sugars. To use cellulose to produce ethanol, bioengineers must find a way to teach yeasts to break these links.

There are microbes with enzymes that can do this, otherwise cows could not survive by eating grass, nor termites wood. Using the sort of genetic engineering technology discussed in chapter 13, it is possible to "bioengineer" a yeast to be able to ferment cellulose. Researchers in Spain have succeeded in commercially producing ethanol from cellulose biomass. They added DNA taken from plant-digesting bacteria in the gut of termites to yeast—DNA containing the genes these bacteria use to break down cellulose and free sugars.

Nor should we forget hemicellulose, which contains one-fifth of the corn plant's carbon. Hemicellulose is like cellulose, but with five-carbon sugars. Genetically-engineered bacteria containing the enzymes necessary to break down hemicellulose into free five-carbon sugars have already been constructed, so this approach seems rich with promise.

In addition to corn, there are other fast-growing plants that could be dedicated to fuel production, including switchgrass and trees such as hybrid poplar and willows. These plants can be grown on lands that are not suitable for row crops like corn, especially erosion-prone soils. Sawdust and paper pulp could also be used to produce ethanol, as could leaves and yard waste and the paper and cardboard that make up the bulk of municipal dumps.

This is a problem that urgently needs to be addressed. Meeting environmental challenges like modern society's need for energy is not an option but a necessity, for you and each student reading these words (**figure 22.25**).

Putting the Concept to Work

Burning a gallon of ethanol releases about the same amount of CO_2 as burning a gallon of gasoline, so why is ethanol a more desirable fuel?

22.11 Individuals Can Make the Difference

LEARNING OBJECTIVE 22.11.1 Recount how Lake Washington and the Nashua River were restored through individual action.

The development of appropriate solutions to the world's environmental problems must rest partly on the shoulders of politicians, economists, bankers, and engineers—many kinds of public and commercial activity will be required. However, it is important not to lose sight of the key role often played by informed individuals in solving environmental problems. Often one person has made the difference; two examples serve to illustrate the point.

The Nashua River

Running through the heart of New England, the Nashua River was severely polluted by mills established in Massachusetts in the early 1900s. By the 1960s, the river was clogged with pollution and declared ecologically dead. When Marion Stoddart moved to a town along the river in 1962, she was appalled. She approached the state about setting aside a "greenway" (trees running the length of the river on both sides), but the state wasn't interested in buying land along a filthy river. So Stoddart organized the Nashua River Cleanup Committee and began a campaign to ban the dumping of chemicals and wastes into the river. The committee presented bottles of dirty river water to politicians, spoke at town meetings, recruited businesspeople to help finance a waste treatment plant, and began to clean garbage from the Nashua's banks. This citizen's campaign, coordinated by Stoddart, greatly aided passage of the Massachusetts Clean Water Act of 1966. Industrial dumping into the river is now banned, and the river has largely recovered (**figure 22.26**).

Figure 22.26 Cleaning up the Nashua River.

The Nashua River, seen on the left in the 1960s, was severely polluted because factories set up along its banks dumped their wastes directly into the river. Seen on the right today, the river is mostly clean.

Lake Washington

A large, 86-square-kilometer freshwater lake east of Seattle, Lake Washington became surrounded by Seattle suburbs in the building boom following the Second World War. Between 1940 and 1953, a ring of 10 municipal sewage plants discharged their treated effluent into the lake. Safe enough to drink, the effluent was believed "harmless." By the mid-1950s a great deal of effluent had been dumped into the lake (try multiplying 80 million liters/day × 365 days/year × 10 years). In 1954, an ecology professor at the University of Washington in Seattle, W. T. Edmondson, noted that his research students were reporting filamentous blue-green algae growing in the lake. Such algae require plentiful nutrients, which deep freshwater lakes usually lack—the sewage had been fertilizing the lake! Edmondson, alarmed, began a campaign in 1956 to educate public officials to the danger: Bacteria decomposing dead algae would soon so deplete the lake's oxygen that the lake would die. After five years, joint municipal taxes financed the building of a sewer to carry the effluent out to sea. The lake is now clean (**figure 22.27**).

Figure 22.27 Lake Washington, Seattle.

Lake Washington in Seattle is surrounded by residences, businesses, and industries. By the 1950s, the dumping of sewage and the runoff of fertilizers had caused an algal bloom in the lake, which would eventually deplete the lake's oxygen. Efforts to reverse this effect and clean up the lake were started by W. T. Edmondson of the University of Washington in 1956. The lake is now clean.

IMPLICATION FOR YOU It is easy to become discouraged when considering the world's many environmental problems, but do not lose track of the single most important conclusion that emerges from our examination of these problems—the fact that each is solvable. A polluted lake can be cleaned; a dirty smokestack can be altered to remove noxious gas; waste of key resources can be stopped. What is required is a clear understanding of the problem and a commitment to doing something about it. The extent to which U.S. families recycle aluminum cans and newspapers is evidence of the degree to which people want to become part of the solution, rather than part of the problem. What do you recycle? What other items could you be recycling?

Putting the Concept to Work

Why didn't Professor Edmondson simply recommend that the municipalities around Lake Washington poison the algae growing in the lake with chemicals that don't harm humans, in order to return the lake's water to its pristine state?

Inquiry & Analysis

How Real Is Global Warming?

The controversy over global warming has two aspects. The first contentious issue is the claim that global temperatures are rising significantly, a profound change in the earth's atmosphere and oceans referred to as "global warming." The second contentious issue is the assertion that global warming is the consequence of elevated concentrations of carbon dioxide in the atmosphere as a consequence of the widespread burning of fossil fuels.

Resolution of the second issue requires detailed science and is only now reaching consensus acceptance. Resolution of the first issue is a simpler proposition, because it is, in essence, a data statement. The graph to the right displays the data in question, global air temperatures for the last century and a half. Temperature data is collected from measuring stations across the globe, as shown in the image below, and averaged. The bars of the histogram represent mean yearly global air temperatures for each year since 1850. In order to dampen the effects of random year-to-year variations and so better reveal accumulating influences, the data are presented as an anomaly histogram (in an **anomaly histogram,** each bar presents the deviation of the value during that period from the average value determined for some standard period). In this instance, the anomaly histogram shows the deviation of each year's global mean air temperature from the mean of these values observed over a standard 30-year period between 1961 and 1990.

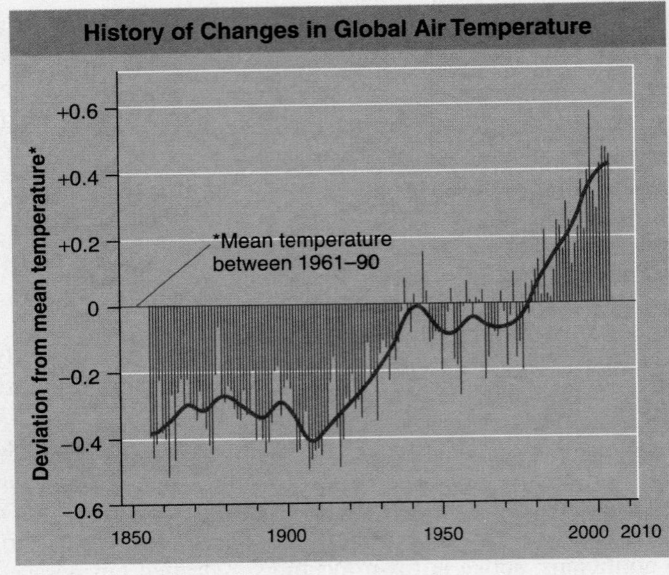

Analysis

1. **Applying Concepts** What fraction of the 155 years do not deviate from the 1961–1990 mean value? What fraction deviates more than +0.2°C? more than −0.2°C? more than +0.4°C? more than −0.4°C?
2. **Interpreting Data**
   a. Of the years that deviate more than +0.2°C, how many are before 1940? between 1940 and 1980? after 1980? What fraction occur after 1980?
   b. Of the years that deviate more than +0.4°C, how many are before 1980? after 2000? What fraction occur after 2000?
   c. Of the years that deviate more than −0.2°C, how many are before 1940? between 1940 and 1980? after 1980? What fraction occur before 1940?
   d. Of the years that deviate more than −0.4°C, how many are before 1940? 1900? What fraction occur before 1900?
3. **Making Inferences** If you were to pick a year at random between 1850 and 1900, would it be most likely to deviate +0.2, +0.4, 0, −0.2, or −0.4? a year between 1900 and 1940? a year after 1980?
4. **Drawing Conclusions** Has the global air temperature been warming progressively over the last century and a half?

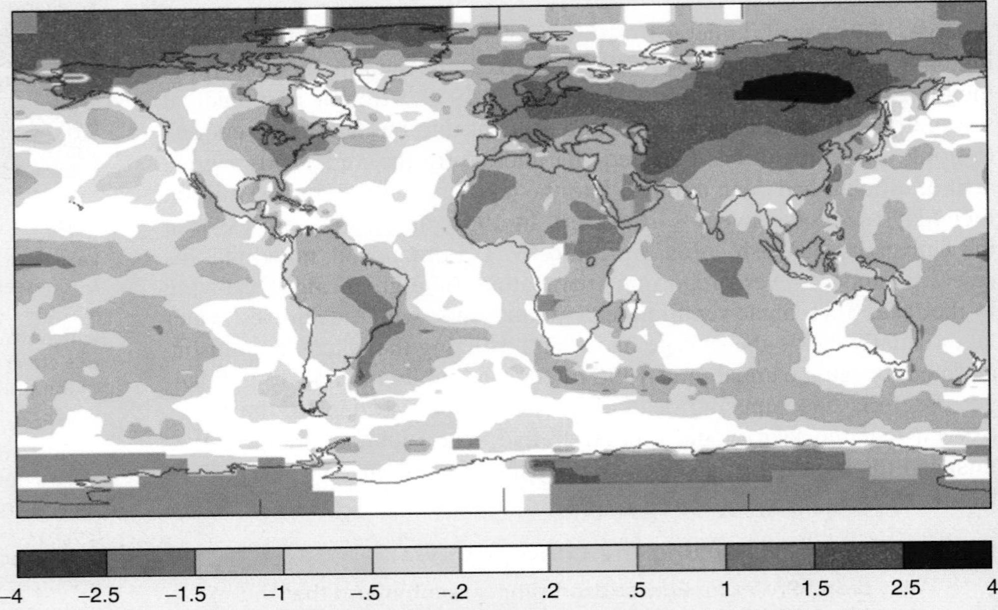

Global variation in deviations from average mean temperature from 1951 to 1980

Summary of Learning Outcomes

Global Change

Pollution

22.1.1 All over the world, increasing industrialization is leading to higher levels of pollution. Pollution leads to global change because its effects can spread far from the source. Air and water become polluted when chemicals that are harmful to organisms are released into the ecosystem. The use of agricultural chemicals, such as pesticides, herbicides, and fertilizers, has been widespread with devastating effects on animals. Biological magnification occurs when harmful chemicals become more concentrated as they pass up through the food chain, as shown here from **figure 22.1**.

Acid Precipitation

22.2.1 The burning of coal releases sulfur into the atmosphere, where it combines with water vapor to form sulfuric acid. This acid falls back to earth in rain and snow, commonly called acid rain, far from the source of the pollution, killing animals and vegetation (**figure 22.3**).

Global Warming

22.3.1 Humanity's burning of fossil fuels has greatly increased levels of carbon dioxide in the atmosphere, where it traps infrared light (heat) from the sun, a phenomenon known as the greenhouse effect. As a result, the average global temperatures have been steadily increasing as CO_2 levels increase in the atmosphere, a process known as global warming. Global warming is predicted to have major impacts on global rain patterns, agriculture, and sea levels.

Loss of Biodiversity

22.4.1 The current rate of species extinction is alarmingly high. Three factors mostly responsible include loss of habitat, overexploitation, and the introduction of new species. Of these, loss of habitat is the most devastating.

The Ozone Hole

22.5.1 Ozone (O_3) forms a protective shield in the earth's upper atmosphere that blocks out harmful UV rays from the sun. In the mid-1970s, scientists determined that ozone was being depleted. The culprit, chlorofluorocarbons (CFCs), used in refrigeration systems, reacts with ozone, converting it to oxygen gas (O_2), which doesn't block UV rays. Termed the ozone hole, this reduction in ozone over and extending from the South Pole, as shown here from **figure 22.7**, is resulting in dangerously high levels of radiation reaching the earth. This drop in O_3 levels is also resulting in an increase in the incidence of skin cancer.

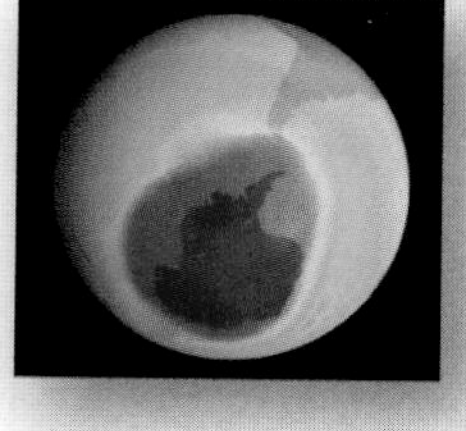

Saving Our Environment

Reducing Pollution

22.6.1 Human activities are placing severe stress on the biosphere. Reducing pollution requires examining the costs associated with pollution. Antipollution laws and pollution taxes are ways to begin factoring in the costs of pollution.

Preserving Nonreplaceable Resources

22.7.1 The consumption or destruction of nonreplaceable resources is perhaps the most serious problem humans face. Topsoil, necessary for agriculture, is being depleted rapidly. Groundwater, which percolates through the soil to underground reservoirs, is our primary source of drinking water, but it is being wasted and polluted. Biodiversity is being reduced through extinctions, due primarily to loss of habitat, such as rain forests (seen in **figure 22.10**).

Curbing Population Growth

22.8.1 The problem at the core of our environmental concerns is the rapid growth of the world's human population. Technology has allowed the human population to grow exponentially for the last 300 years to a current population of about 7 billion.

22.8.2 Human populations grow at different rates, with developing countries' populations growing more rapidly than developed countries' populations, as tracked using population pyramids. Disease and natural disasters can affect regional population growth projections.

- Although population growth rates are lower for developed countries, it takes more resources to support populations in developed countries.

Solving Environmental Problems

Preserving Endangered Species

22.9.1 In an attempt to slow the loss of biodiversity, recovery programs are under way, designed to save endangered species (**figure 22.19**). These programs include habitat restoration, breeding in captivity, sustaining genetic diversity, preserving keystone species, and conservation of ecosystems.

Finding Cleaner Sources of Energy

22.10.1 The burning of fossil fuels leads to pollution, depletion of valuable resources, and global warming. Alternative sources of energy are needed, and some countries have looked to nuclear power, but nuclear power has its own drawbacks. Renewable energy sources such as solar and wind power and ethanol are promising alternatives.

Individuals Can Make the Difference

22.11.1 There are environmental success stories, where one or a few individuals made a difference and reversed an ecological disaster.

Test Your Understanding

22.1.1 "Gray-air cities" are the result of
a. biological magnification of air pollutants.
b. chlorinated hydrocarbons as a major air pollutant.
c. pesticides as a major air pollutant.
d. sulfur oxides as a major air pollutant.

22.2.1 The main cause of acid rain is
a. car and truck exhaust.
b. coal-powered industry.
c. chlorofluorocarbons.
d. chlorinated hydrocarbons.

22.3.1 Global warming affects all of the following except
a. rain patterns.
b. sea levels.
c. ozone levels.
d. agriculture.

22.4.1 The factor most responsible for present-day extinctions is
a. habitat loss.
b. overexploitation of species.
c. introduction of new species.
d. All are equally responsible.

22.5.1 Destruction of the ozone layer is due to
a. car and truck exhaust.
b. coal-powered industry.
c. chlorofluorocarbons.
d. chlorinated hydrocarbons.

22.6.1 Free-market economies often promote pollution. This is because
a. environmental costs are hardly ever recognized as part of the economy.
b. supply never keeps up with demand, so industry must increase output to address the demand.
c. the costs of energy and raw materials are so variable.
d. laws controlling pollution are unenforceable.

22.7.1 Preserving biodiversity is
a. needed to preserve possible direct value from species, such as new medicines.
b. not needed as extinction is a "natural" cycle and should not be disturbed.
c. needed to make sure all niches are filled.
d. not needed as it interferes with industrial development.

22.8.1 Which factor is *not* responsible for the large increase in the human population over the last 300 or so years?
a. larger and more reliable food reserves from the modernization of farming techniques
b. decreasing mortality rate due to improvements in medicine
c. increasing amounts of open space as countries develop
d. increased sanitation practices

22.9.1 Removal of the endangered black-footed ferret and California condor populations from the wild for breeding programs in zoos and field laboratories are examples of preservation through
a. pristine restoration.
b. habitat restoration.
c. habitat rehabilitation.
d. captive propagation.

22.9.1 If the removal of a species causes an ecosystem to collapse, that species is known as a(n)
a. keystone species.
b. endangered species.
c. threatened species.
d. None of the above.

Apply Your Understanding

22.4.1 Your friend tells you that his father complains that environmentalists are trying to save "every confounded bug and weed on the planet." He says, "Things have always gone extinct, why should now be any different?" Use the graph to frame a response to your friend's father.

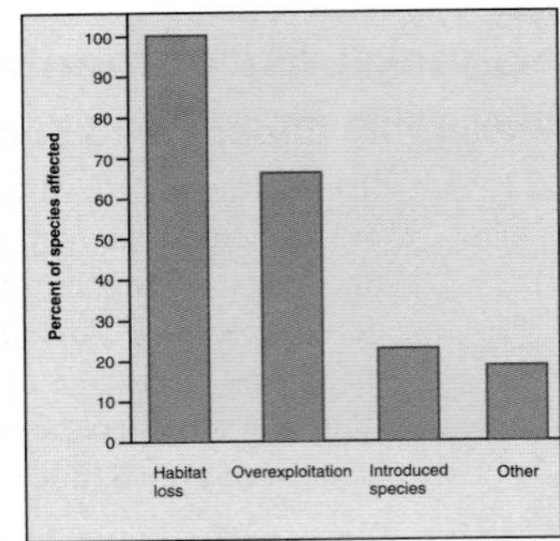

22.8.1 Discuss the human growth curve on the left in terms of the "carrying capacity" graph on the right.

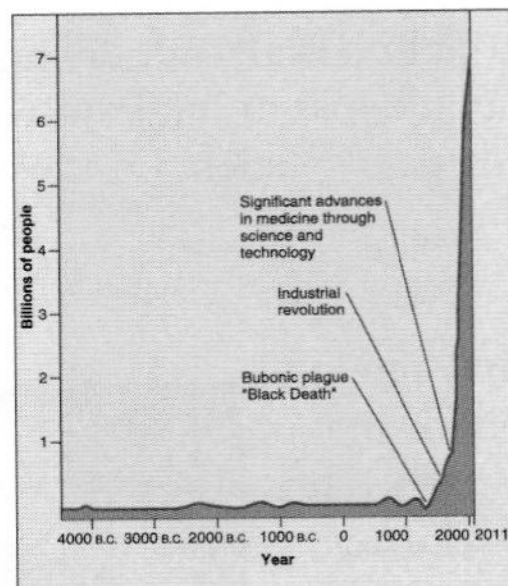

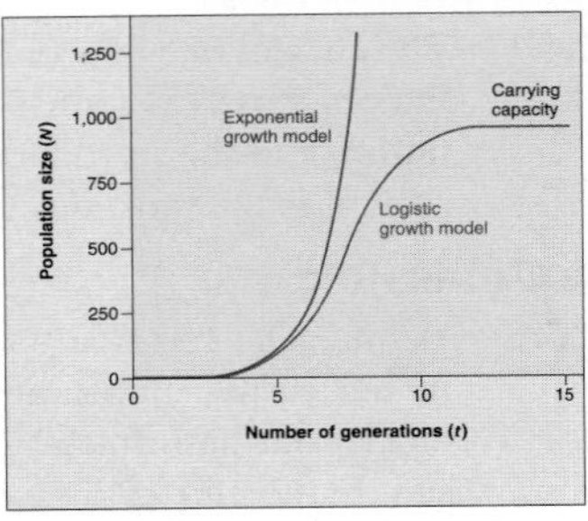

Synthesize What You Have Learned

22.1.1 Explain why being exposed to even very tiny amounts of chemical pollutants like BPA that mimic estrogen can, over time, be hazardous to your health. Should one sex be more concerned than the other?

22.6.1 Economists tend to look at the world in terms of costs. They say, "If you increase pollution, then you increase the social costs to people's health, but if you try to decrease pollution, then you increase the economic costs of cleaning it up." Discuss whether you think these two costs are paid equally by the same set of people.

22.11.1 Consider the stories of Marion Stoddart, W. T. Edmondson, and the following statement: "Never doubt that a small group of thoughtful, committed citizens can change the world, indeed it's the only thing that ever has."—Margaret Mead, anthropologist. What *could* you do to make your neighborhood/area/community a better, healthier place? What *will* you do?

Chapter 23

The Animal Body and How It Moves

CHAPTER AT A GLANCE

The Animal Body Plan
23.1 Organization of the Vertebrate Body
Tissues of the Vertebrate Body
23.2 Epithelium Is Protective Tissue
23.3 Connective Tissue Carries Out Various Functions
23.4 Muscle Tissue Lets the Body Move
23.5 Nerve Tissue Conducts Signals Rapidly
The Skeletal and Muscular Systems
23.6 Types of Skeletons
23.7 Muscles and How They Work
Biology and Staying Healthy: The Author Works Out
Inquiry & Analysis: Which Mode of Locomotion Is the Most Efficient?

The Animal Body Plan

23.1 Organization of the Vertebrate Body

LEARNING OBJECTIVE 23.1.1 **Describe the four general classes of tissues, and how they are organized into organs.**

All vertebrates and other coelomates have the same general architecture: a long internal tube (the gut or digestive system) that extends from mouth to anus, which is suspended within an internal body cavity called the *coelom.* The coelom of many terrestrial vertebrates is divided into two parts: the *thoracic cavity,* which contains the heart and lungs, and the *abdominal cavity,* which contains the stomach, intestines, and liver. The vertebrate body is supported by an internal scaffold, or skeleton, made up of jointed bones or cartilage.

Like all animals, the vertebrate body is composed of cells—over 10 to 100 trillion of them in your body. It's difficult to picture how large this number actually is. A line of 10 trillion cars would stretch from the earth to the sun and back 100 times! Not all of these cells in your body are the same, of course. If they were, we would not be bodies but amorphous blobs. Vertebrate bodies contain over 100 different kinds of cells.

Figure 23.1 **Vertebrate tissue types.**

The four basic classes of tissue are epithelial, nerve, connective, and muscle.

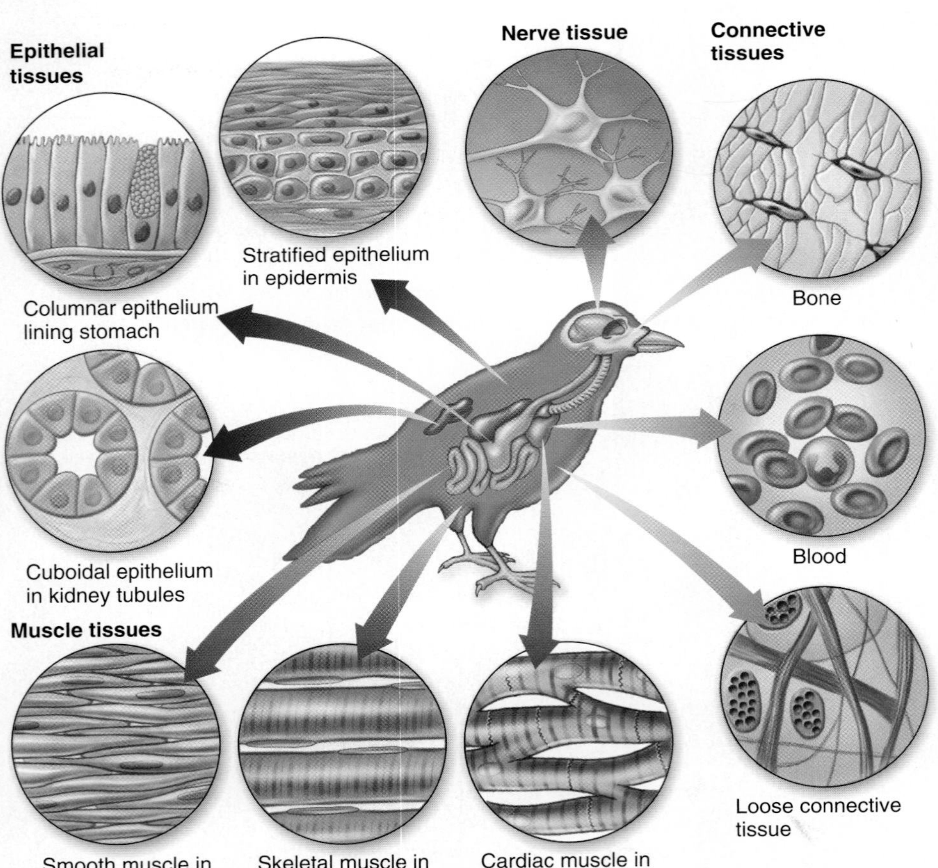

Tissues

Groups of cells of the same type are organized within the body into **tissues,** which are the structural and functional units of the vertebrate body. A tissue is a group of cells of the same type that performs a particular function. It is possible to assemble many different kinds of tissue from 100 cell types, but biologists have traditionally grouped adult tissues into four general classes: *epithelial, connective, muscle,* and *nerve tissue* (**figure 23.1**).

Organs

Organs are body structures composed of several different tissues grouped together into a larger structural and functional unit, just as a factory is a group of people with different jobs who work together to make something. The heart is an organ. It contains cardiac muscle tissue wrapped in connective tissue and joined to many nerves. All of these tissues work together to pump blood through the body: The cardiac muscles contract, which squeezes the heart to push the blood; the connective tissues act as a bag to hold the heart in the proper shape and ensure that the different chambers of the heart squeeze in the proper order; and the nerves control the rate at which the heart beats. No single tissue can do the job of the heart, any more than one piston can do the job of an automobile engine.

Putting the Concept to Work

Name a human organ other than the heart. What tissues is it made of?

Organ Systems

LEARNING OBJECTIVE 23.1.2 Describe the principal organ systems of the vertebrate body.

An **organ system** is a group of organs that work together to carry out an important function (figure 23.2). For example, the vertebrate digestive system is an organ system composed of individual organs that break up food (beaks or teeth), pass the food to the stomach (esophagus), break down the food (stomach and intestine), absorb the food (intestine), and expel the solid residue (rectum). If all of these organs do their job right, the body obtains energy and necessary building materials from food. The digestive system is a particularly complex organ system with many different organs consisting of many different types of cells, all working together to carry out a complex function.

The vertebrate body contains 11 principal organ systems:

1. **Skeletal.** The most distinguishing feature of the vertebrate body is its internal skeleton made of cartilage or bone. The skeletal system protects the body and provides support for locomotion and movement. Its principal components are bones, cartilage, and ligaments. Like arthropods, vertebrates have jointed appendages—arms, hands, legs, and feet.

Jointed appendages, as discussed on page 356, were a key evolutionary innovation in arthropods that is maintained in the vertebrates. The term arthropods comes from two Greek words, *arthros,* jointed, and *podes,* feet.

2. **Circulatory.** The circulatory system transports oxygen, nutrients, and chemical signals to the cells of the body and removes carbon dioxide, chemical wastes, and water. Its principal components are the heart, blood vessels, and blood.
3. **Endocrine.** The endocrine system coordinates and integrates the activities of the body through the release of hormones. Its principal components are the pituitary, adrenal, thyroid, and other ductless glands.
4. **Nervous.** The activities of the body are coordinated by the nervous system. Its principal components are the nerves, sense organs, brain, and spinal cord.
5. **Respiratory.** The respiratory system captures oxygen and exchanges gases and is composed of the lungs, trachea, and other air passageways.
6. **Immune.** The immune system removes foreign bodies from the bloodstream using special cells, such as lymphocytes and macrophages.
7. **Digestive.** The digestive system captures soluble nutrients from ingested food. Its principal components are the mouth, esophagus, stomach, intestines, liver, and pancreas.
8. **Urinary.** The urinary system removes metabolic wastes from the bloodstream. Its principal components are the kidneys, bladder, and associated ducts.
9. **Muscular.** The muscular system produces movement, both within the body and of its limbs. Its principal components are skeletal muscle, cardiac muscle, and smooth muscle.
10. **Reproductive.** The reproductive system carries out reproduction. Its principal components are the testes in males, ovaries in females, and associated reproductive structures.
11. **Integumentary.** The integumentary system covers and protects the body. Its principal components are the skin, hair, nails, and sweat glands.

Putting the Concept to Work

Which organ systems extend throughout all of the major parts of the human body?

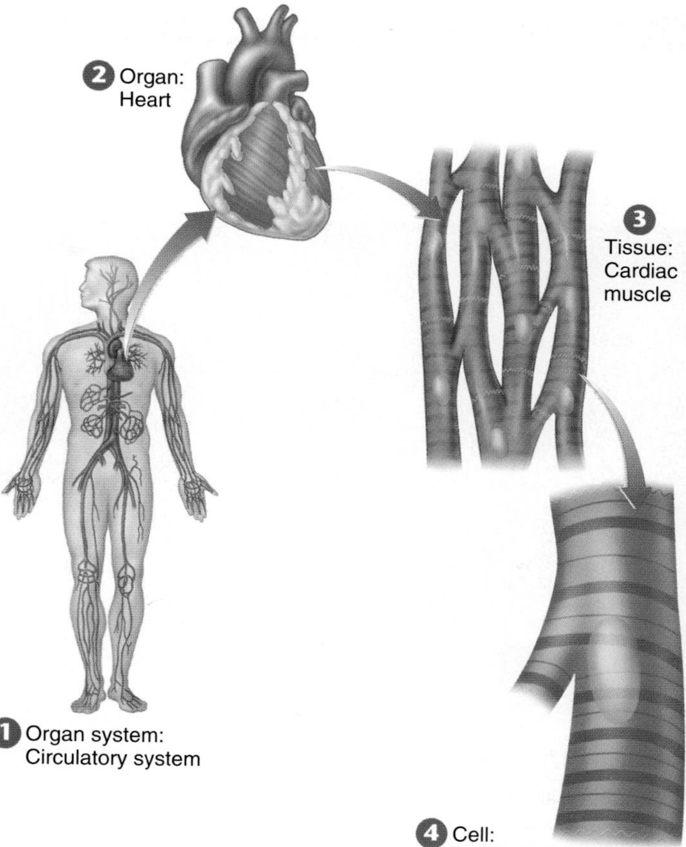

Figure 23.2 Levels of organization within the vertebrate body.

1 The circulatory system you see illustrated here is an example of an organ system. 2 The heart is one of several organs that work together to carry out the function of circulation for the body. 3 Within an organ like the heart, individual tissues like cardiac muscle function together with other tissues. 4 Particular cell types, like cardiac muscle cells, operate together with other similar types of cells to form each kind of tissue.

EVOLUTION

Regrowing Complex Organs. Many vertebrates, such as newts, can renew damaged parts of their bodies, but mammals like us cannot. The only example of a mammal being able to regrow a large complex organ is antler growth. Deer antlers are large structures made of living bone, cartilage, blood vessels, and fibrous tissue, covered in skin. Each year antlers grow in the summer (they are said to be "in velvet"), die in the fall (the hard bone is used for fighting), are shed in the winter, and then regenerate in the spring. Unlike the regenerative processes of newts, antler growth does not involve reversal of the differentiated state, but rather local activation of stem cells. Researchers are seeking to understand this process, hoping it may someday be possible to activate organ renewal of damaged human tissues.

Tissues of the Vertebrate Body

23.2 Epithelium Is Protective Tissue

LEARNING OBJECTIVE 23.2.1 Describe the three types of vertebrate epithelial cells and how they function.

Tissues are the basic building blocks of the animal body. We begin our discussion of tissues with one located on the body's surfaces, epithelium. Epithelial cells are the guards and protectors of the body. They cover both internal and external surfaces of the body, and determine which substances enter the body and which do not. The body's epithelial layers function in three ways:

1. They *protect underlying tissues* from water loss and mechanical damage. Because epithelium encases all the body's surfaces, every substance that enters or leaves the body must cross an epithelial layer, even one as thick as the gila monster's in figure 23.3.
2. They *provide sensory surfaces*. Many of a vertebrate's sense organs are modified epithelial cells.
3. They *secrete materials*. Most secretory glands are derived from pockets of epithelial cells that pinch together during embryonic development.

Figure 23.3 The epithelium prevents dehydration.

The tough, scaly skin of this gila monster provides a layer of protection against dehydration and injury. For all land-dwelling vertebrates, the relative impermeability of the surface epithelium (the epidermis) to water offers essential protection from dehydration and from airborne pathogens (disease-causing organisms).

Types of Epithelial Cells and Epithelial Tissues

Epithelial cells are classified into three types according to their shapes: squamous, cuboidal, and columnar. Layers of epithelial tissue are usually only one or a few cells thick. Individual epithelial cells possess only a small amount of cytoplasm and have a relatively low metabolic rate. A characteristic of all epithelia is that sheets of cells are tightly bound together, with very little space between them. This forms the barrier that is key to their functioning.

Like animals, plants also have a surface layer of protective epithelial cells, some of which are specialized for different functions, as described on page 620.

The cells of epithelial layers are constantly being replaced throughout the life of the organism. The cells lining the digestive tract, for example, are continuously replaced every few days. The epidermis, the epithelium that forms the skin, is renewed every two weeks.

There are two general kinds of epithelial tissue. First, the membranes that line the lungs and the major cavities of the body are a **simple epithelium** only a single cell layer thick. These single-celled layers are surfaces across which many materials must pass, entering and leaving the body's compartments. Second, the skin, or epidermis, is a **stratified epithelium** composed of more-complex epithelial cells several layers thick. Multilayers are necessary to provide adequate cushioning and protection and to enable the skin to continuously replace its cells.

A type of simple epithelial tissue that has a secretory function is cuboidal epithelium, which is found in the **glands** of the body. Endocrine glands secrete hormones into the blood. Exocrine glands (those with ducts that open to the body's outside) secrete sweat, milk, saliva, and digestive enzymes.

Putting the Concept to Work

In what way is your skin like the bark of a tree? In what way is it different?

BIOLOGY & YOU

Dandruff. Have you ever had dandruff? You know, the white flaky stuff on your collar and shoulders. If so, you are not alone. Many, if not most, Americans experience dandruff at one time or another. Dandruff is the shedding of excessive dead skin cells from the scalp. It is normal for skin cells to die and flake off, producing small flakes too tiny to see—the epidermal layer continually replaces itself from its inside, pushing cells outward where they eventually die and flake off. However, in people with dandruff this process is greatly accelerated, with skin cells maturing and shedding in two to seven days as opposed to around a month in people without dandruff. Dead skin cells build up so fast that they are shed in large, oily clumps which appear as white flakes. What causes dandruff? A scalp fungus called *Malassezia globosa*. It metabolizes skin oils, producing a by-product that triggers an inflammatory response in susceptible persons, leading to accelerated division of skin cells. Shampoos control dandruff in different ways: Sebulex uses salicylic acid to remove dead skin cells from the scalp and slow cell division; Head and Shoulders uses zinc pyrithione to kill the *Malassezia* fungus; Selsun Blue uses selenium sulfide to achieve the results of both salicylic acid and zinc pyrithione. All reduce flaking dramatically.

23.3 Connective Tissue Carries Out Various Functions

LEARNING OBJECTIVE 23.3.1 Describe the three functional categories of connective tissue and their structural features.

The cells of **connective tissue** provide the vertebrate body with its structural building blocks and also with its most potent defenses. These cells are sometimes densely packed together, and sometimes loosely arrayed. Although very diverse, all connective tissues share a key common structural feature: They all have abundant extracellular **matrix** material between widely spaced cells.

Immune Connective Tissue Defends the Body

The cells of the immune system, the many kinds of "white blood cells," roam the body within the bloodstream. They are mobile hunters of invading microorganisms and cancer cells. The two principal kinds of immune system cells are **macrophages,** which engulf and digest invading microorganisms, and **lymphocytes,** which attack virus-infected cells or make antibodies that tag cells for destruction. Immune cells are carried through the body in a fluid matrix, called *plasma.*

Skeletal Connective Tissue Supports the Body

Three kinds of connective tissue are the principal components of the skeletal system: fibrous connective tissue, cartilage, and bone. Although composed of similar cells, they differ in the nature of the matrix that is laid down between individual cells.

1. **Fibrous connective tissue.** The most common kind of connective tissue in the vertebrate body is fibrous connective tissue. It is composed of flat, irregularly branching cells called **fibroblasts** that secrete structurally strong proteins like collagen into the spaces between the cells. Fibroblasts are active in wound healing; scar tissue, for example, possesses a collagen matrix.
2. **Cartilage.** In cartilage, a collagen matrix between cartilage cells (technically called *chondrocytes*) forms in long parallel arrays along the lines of mechanical stress. What results is a firm and flexible tissue of great strength (figure 23.4), just as strands of nylon molecules laid down in long, parallel arrays produce strong, flexible ropes.
3. **Bone.** Bone is similar to cartilage, except the collagen fibers are coated with a calcium phosphate salt, making the tissue rigid.

Blood and Fat Cells: Transport and Storage

The third general class of connective tissue is made up of cells that are specialized to accumulate and transport particular molecules. They include the fat-accumulating cells of **adipose tissue**, and red blood cells, called **erythrocytes,** that function in transport and storage. About 5 billion erythrocytes are present in every milliliter of your blood.

Putting the Concept to Work

What is the common structural feature of all connective tissues?

BIOLOGY & YOU

Getting Fat. It will come as no surprise to you that overeating can make you fat. Is this because overeating triggers the production of more fat cells, or because the fat cells get larger? It turns out, both situations occur. You are born with a predetermined number of fat cells, with women generally inheriting more than men. The number then grows through childhood until late puberty, after which it is pretty much set. It was generally thought that the only difference between obese people and non-obese people was that obese people's fat cells were filled up to capacity. When overweight people lose weight, they empty their fat cells, but the fat cells don't go away. They are still there, like little sponges waiting to refill. We now know that we can—and do—"grow" more fat cells in adulthood, and that overweight and obese people do in fact have more fat cells. It turns out that when fat cells expand to their maximum size, this triggers cell division, producing an increase in the actual number of fat cells. It is one of the curses of dieters, that these new cells do not go away when you lose weight. Dieting may shrink the cells, but dieters tend to regain lost weight rapidly. If you wind up with a lot of extra fat cells, you have to work harder than lean people to keep excess weight off. It does not seem fair, and it is not fun, but it is important to good health. You CAN lose weight and keep it off with commitment and determination.

Figure 23.4 Cartilage: skeletal connective tissue.

The entire skeleton of this Caribbean reef shark is made of cartilage, a strong but flexible type of connective tissue. In other vertebrates, cartilage is found in joints, noses, and external ears.

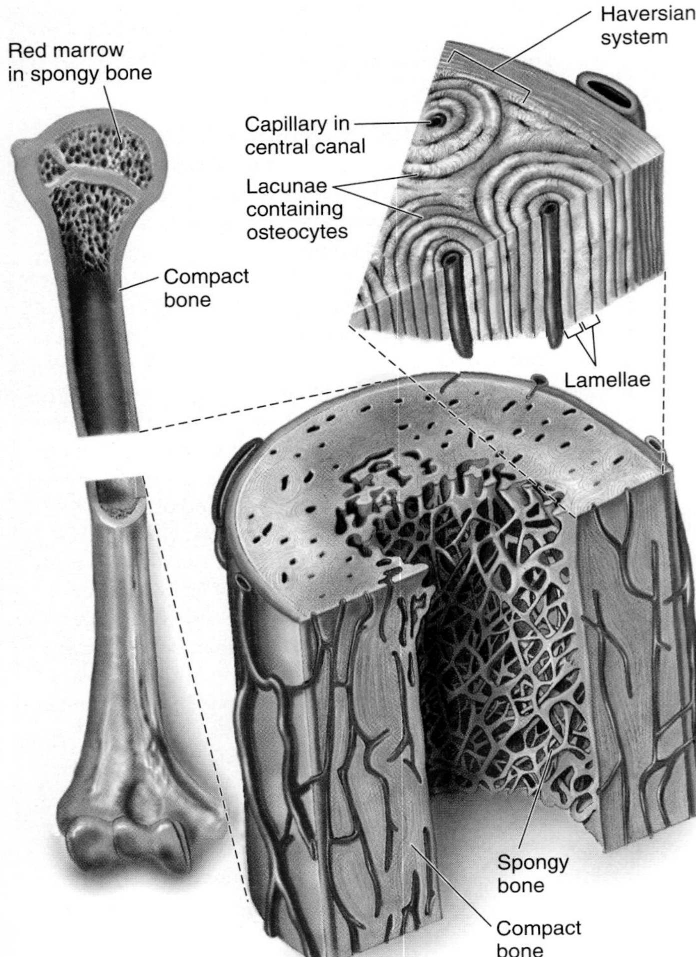

Figure 23.5 The structure of bone.

Some parts of bones are dense and compact, giving the bone strength. Other parts are spongy, with a more open lattice; red blood cells form in the bone marrow. Osteocytes, which are mature osteoblasts, lie in tight spaces called lacunae.

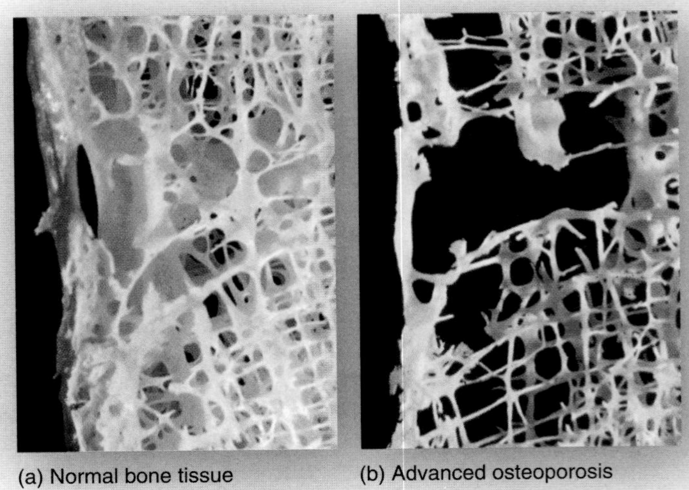

Figure 23.6 Osteoporosis.

Common in older women, osteoporosis is a bone disorder in which bones progressively lose minerals.

A Closer Look at Bone

LEARNING OBJECTIVE 23.3.2 Describe the dynamic structure of bone, contrasting osteoblasts and osteoclasts.

Bone consists of living bone cells embedded within an inert matrix composed of the structural protein collagen coated with a calcium phosphate salt called *hydroxyapatite*. Why coat the collagen fibers with calcium salts? The construction of bone is similar to that of fiberglass, a composite composed of glass fibers embedded in epoxy glue: Small, needle-shaped crystals of hydroxyapatite surround and impregnate collagen fibers within bone. No crack can penetrate far into bone because any stress that breaks a hard hydroxyapatite crystal passes into the collagenous matrix, which dissipates the stress before it encounters another crystal.

Most of us think of bones as solid and rocklike. But actually, bone is a dynamic tissue that is constantly being reconstructed. The cross section through a bone in figure 23.5 shows that the outer layer of bone is very dense and compact and so is called **compact bone.** The interior is less compact, with a more open lattice structure, and is called **spongy bone.** Red blood cells form in the red marrow of spongy bone. New bone is formed in two stages: First, collagen is secreted by cells called **osteoblasts,** which lay down a matrix of fibers along lines of stress. Then calcium minerals impregnate the fibers. Bone is laid down in thin, concentric layers, like layers of paint on an old pipe. The layers form as a series of tubes around a narrow channel called a **central canal,** also called a *Haversian canal,* which runs parallel to the length of the bone (figure 23.5). The many central canals within a bone are all interconnected and contain blood vessels and nerves that provide a lifeline to its living, bone-forming cells.

When bone is first formed in the embryo, osteoblasts use a cartilage skeleton as a template for bone formation. During childhood, bones grow actively. The total bone mass in a healthy young adult, by contrast, does not increase much from one year to the next. This does not mean change is not occurring. Large amounts of calcium and thousands of **osteocytes** (mature osteoblasts) are constantly being removed and replaced, but total bone mass does not change because deposit and removal take place at about the same rate.

Two cell types are responsible for this dynamic bone "remodeling": *Osteoblasts* deposit bone, and **osteoclasts** secrete enzymes that digest the organic matrix of bone, liberating calcium for reabsorption by the bloodstream. The dynamic remodeling of bone adjusts bone strength to workload, new bone being formed along lines of stress. When a bone is subjected to compression, mineral deposition by osteoblasts exceeds withdrawals by osteoclasts. That is why long-distance runners slowly increase the distances they attempt, to allow their bones to strengthen along lines of stress, lest stress fractures cripple them.

Bone contains large stores of calcium ions, and as you will see on pages 592 and 593, the body draws on these calcium stores when needed for body functions. When calcium levels in the blood drop, the body will actually break down bone tissue, releasing calcium.

As a person ages, the backbone and other bones tend to decline in mass. Excessive bone loss is a condition called **osteoporosis.** After the onset of osteoporosis, the replacement of calcium and other minerals lags behind withdrawal, causing the bone tissue to gradually erode. Compare the normal bone in figure 23.6*a* with bone from a person with osteoporosis in figure 23.6*b*. Eventually the bones become brittle and easily broken. Women are four times more likely to develop osteoporosis than men are.

Putting the Concept to Work

How do the bones of a runner's legs adjust strength to workload?

23.4 Muscle Tissue Lets the Body Move

LEARNING OBJECTIVE 23.4.1 Compare smooth, skeletal, and cardiac muscle.

Muscle cells are the motors of the vertebrate body. The distinguishing characteristic of muscle cells, the thing that makes them unique, is the abundance of contractible protein fibers within them. These fibers, called **myofilaments,** are made of the proteins actin and myosin. Crammed in like the fibers of a rope, they take up practically the entire volume of the muscle cell. When actin and myosin slide past each other, the muscle contracts. Like slamming a spring-loaded door, the shortening of all of these fibers together within a muscle cell can produce considerable force. The process of muscle contraction will be discussed later in this chapter.

Figure 23.7 Locomotion.

The animal body achieves a complex activity, locomotion, by coordinating the activities of nerves, muscles, and bones to propel itself through its environment. Animals are unrivaled among the inhabitants of the living world in their ability to move about from one place to another, swimming, burrowing, crawling, slithering, sliding, walking, jumping, running, gliding, soaring, and flying. This sidewinder rattlesnake can move surprisingly rapidly over the desert sand by a coordinated series of muscle contractions, throwing its long body into a series of sinuous curves.

Smooth Muscle

Smooth muscle cells are long and spindle-shaped, each containing a single nucleus. Smooth muscle tissue is organized into sheets of cells. In some tissues, smooth muscle cells contract only when they are stimulated by a nerve or hormone. Examples are the muscles that line the walls of many blood vessels and those that make up the iris of the vertebrate eye. In other smooth muscle tissue, such as that found in the wall of the gut, the individual cells contract spontaneously, leading to a slow, steady contraction of the tissue.

Skeletal Muscle

Skeletal muscles are attached to and move the bones of the skeleton when they contract during body movement (figure 23.7). Skeletal muscle cells are produced during development by the fusion of several cells at their ends to form a very long fiber still containing all the original nuclei. Each **muscle fiber** consists of many elongated **myofibrils** composed of myofilaments of the proteins actin and myosin (figure 23.8). The arrangement of actin and myosin gives the muscle fibers a banded appearance, called *striations*.

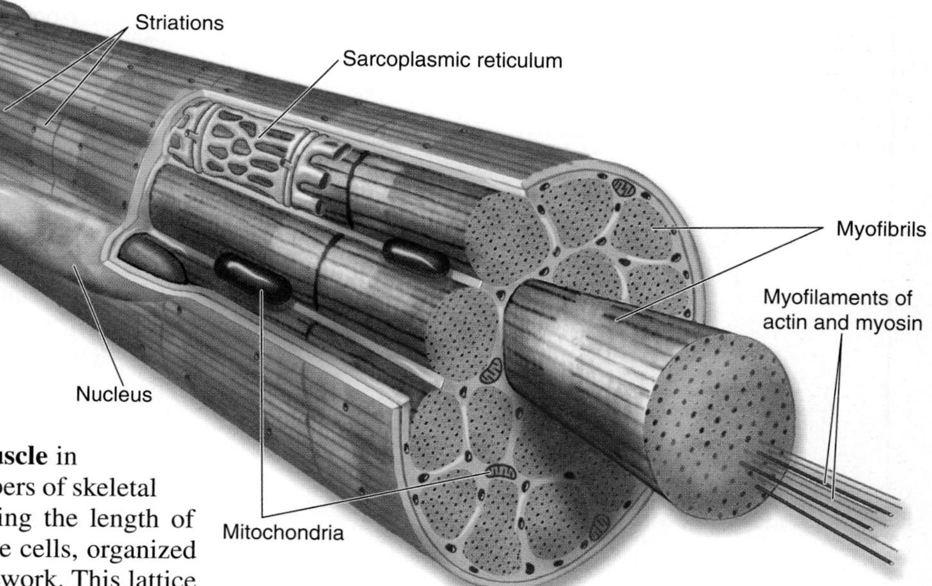

Figure 23.8 A skeletal muscle fiber, or muscle cell.

Each muscle is composed of bundles of muscle cells, or fibers. Each fiber is composed of many myofibrils, which are each, in turn, composed of myofilaments. Muscle cells have a modified endoplasmic reticulum called the sarcoplasmic reticulum that is involved in the regulation of calcium ions in muscles.

Cardiac Muscle

The vertebrate heart is composed of striated **cardiac muscle** in which the fibers are arranged very differently from the fibers of skeletal muscle. Instead of very long, multinucleate cells running the length of the muscle, heart muscle is composed of chains of single cells, organized into fibers that branch and interconnect, forming a latticework. This lattice structure is critical to the way heart muscle functions, as electrical impulses pass from cell to cell through small openings called gap junctions, causing the heart to contract in an orderly pulsation.

Putting the Concept to Work

What is the difference between a myofilament and a myofibril?

TABLE 23.1 Types of Neurons

Neuron	Typical Location	Function
❶ Sensory neurons	Eyes; ears; surface of skin	Receive information about body's condition and external environment; send impulses from sensory receptors to CNS
❷ Motor neurons	Brain and spinal cord	Stimulate muscles and glands; conduct impulses out of CNS toward muscles and glands
❸ Association neurons	Brain and spinal cord	Integrate information; conduct impulses between neurons within CNS

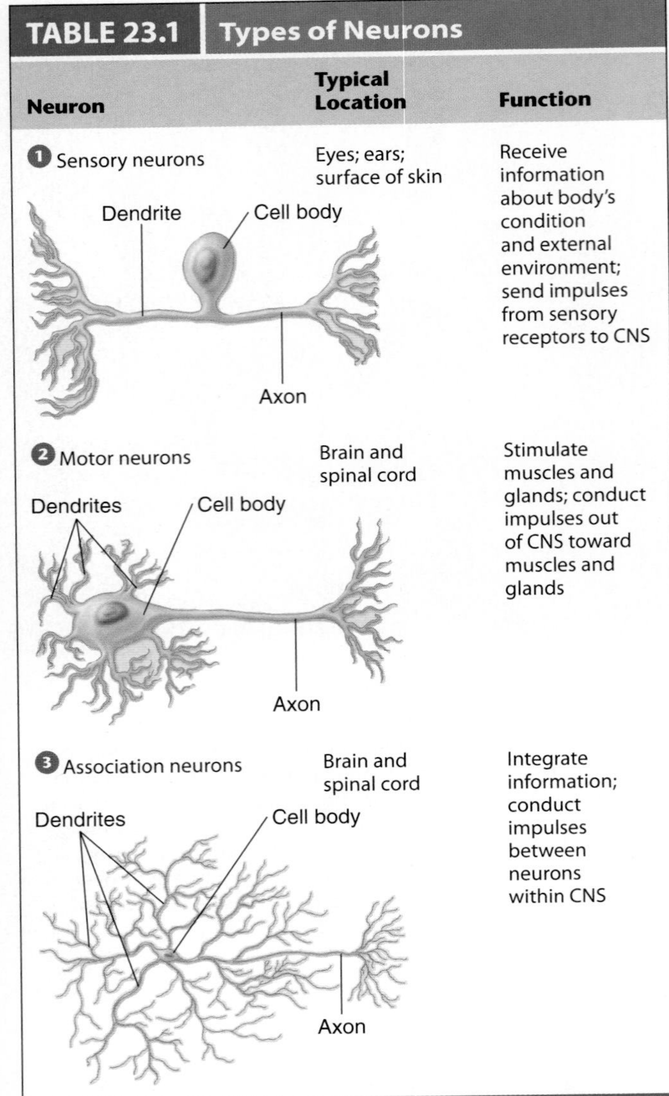

23.5 Nerve Tissue Conducts Signals Rapidly

LEARNING OBJECTIVE 23.5.1 Describe the three-part body of a typical neuron, and outline the functions of the three general categories of neuron.

Nerve tissue, the fourth major class of vertebrate tissue, is composed of two kinds of cells: (1) **neurons,** which are specialized for the rapid transmission of nerve impulses from one organ to another, and (2) supporting **glial cells,** which supply the neurons with nutrients, support, and insulation.

Neurons have a highly specialized cell architecture that enables them to conduct signals rapidly throughout the body. Their plasma membranes are rich in ion-selective channels that maintain a voltage difference between the interior and the exterior of the cell, the equivalent of a battery. When ion channels in a local area of the membrane open, ions flood in from the exterior, temporarily wiping out the charge difference. This process, called depolarization, tends to open nearby voltage-sensitive channels in the neuron membrane, resulting in a wave of electrical activity that travels down the entire length of the neuron as a nerve impulse.

Ions pass in and out of cells. As discussed on page 564, Na^+ and K^+ ion gradients are established by the actions of the Na^+/K^+ pump. Na^+ is pumped out of the cell and K^+ is pumped into the cell. When specific ion channels open, the ions flow down their concentration gradients.

Each neuron is composed of three parts, as illustrated in figure 23.9: (1) a **cell body,** which contains the nucleus; (2) threadlike extensions called **dendrites** extending from the cell body, which act as antennae, bringing nerve impulses to the cell body from other cells or sensory systems; and (3) a single, long extension called an **axon,** which carries nerve impulses away from the cell body. Axons often carry nerve impulses for considerable distances: The axons that extend from the skull to the pelvis in a giraffe are about 3 meters long!

The body contains neurons of various sizes and shapes. Some are tiny and have only a few projections, others are bushy and have more projections, and still others have extensions that are meters long. However, all fit into one of three general categories of neurons as shown in table 23.1. *Sensory neurons* ❶ generally carry electrical impulses from the body to the central nervous system (CNS), the brain and spinal cord. *Motor neurons* ❷ generally carry electrical impulses from the central nervous system to the muscles. *Association neurons* ❸ occur within the central nervous system and act as a "connector" between sensory and motor neurons. These will be discussed in more detail in chapter 29. Neurons are not normally in direct contact with one another. Instead, a tiny gap called a **synapse** separates them. Neurons communicate with other neurons by passing chemical signals called **neurotransmitters** across the gap.

Vertebrate nerves appear as fine white threads when viewed with the naked eye, but they are actually composed of bundles of axons. Like a telephone trunk cable, nerves include large numbers of independent communication channels—bundles composed of hundreds of axons, each connecting a nerve cell to a muscle fiber or other type of cell. It is important not to confuse a nerve with a neuron. A nerve is made up of the axons of many neurons, just as a cable is made of many wires.

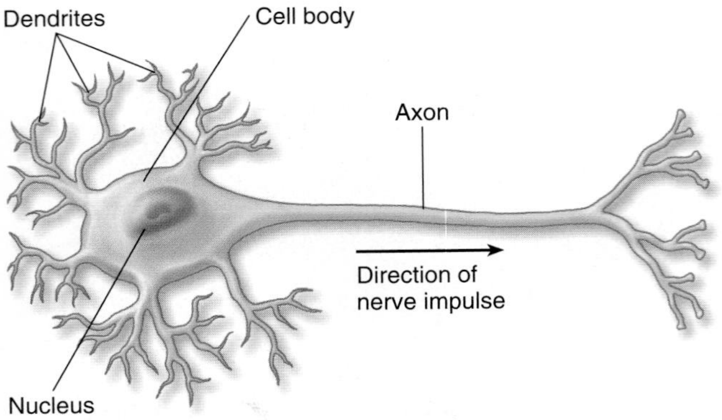

Figure 23.9 Neurons carry nerve impulses.

Neurons carry nerve impulses, which are electrical signals, from their initiation in dendrites, to the cell body, and down the length of the axon, where they may pass the signal to a neighboring cell.

Putting the Concept to Work

If you were to slice through a slender nerve thread within muscle tissue, what part or parts of its neurons would you damage?

The Skeletal and Muscular Systems

23.6 Types of Skeletons

LEARNING OBJECTIVE 23.6.1 Describe and contrast the three principal types of animal skeletal systems.

With muscles alone, the animal body could not move—it would simply pulsate as its muscles contracted and relaxed in futile cycles. For a muscle to produce movement, it must direct its force against another object. Animals are able to move because the opposite ends of their muscles are attached to a rigid scaffold, or **skeleton,** so that the muscles have something to pull against. There are three types of skeletal systems in the animal kingdom: hydraulic skeletons, exoskeletons, and endoskeletons.

Hydraulic skeletons are found in soft-bodied invertebrates such as earthworms and jellyfish. In this case, a fluid-filled cavity is encircled by muscle fibers that raise the pressure of the fluid when they contract. The earthworm in figure 23.10 moves forward by a wave of contractions of circular muscles that begins anteriorly and compresses the body, so that the fluid pressure pushes it forward. Contractions of longitudinal muscles then pull the rest of the body along.

Exoskeletons surround the body as a rigid hard case to which muscles attach internally. When a muscle contracts, it moves the section of exoskeleton to which it is attached. Arthropods, such as crustaceans (figure 23.11) and insects, have exoskeletons made of the polysaccharide *chitin.* An animal with an exoskeleton cannot grow too large because its exoskeleton would have to become thicker and heavier to prevent collapse. If an insect were the size of an elephant, its exoskeleton would have to be so thick and heavy it would hardly be able to move.

Endoskeletons, found in vertebrates and echinoderms, are rigid internal skeletons to which muscles are attached. Vertebrates have a soft, flexible exterior that stretches to accommodate the movements of their skeleton. The endoskeleton of some vertebrates is made of cartilage but in many others it is composed of bone (figure 23.12). Unlike chitin, bone is a cellular, living tissue capable of growth, self-repair, and remodeling in response to physical stresses.

Putting the Concept to Work

In what way would your athletic training be different, if your skeleton were made of chitin rather than bone?

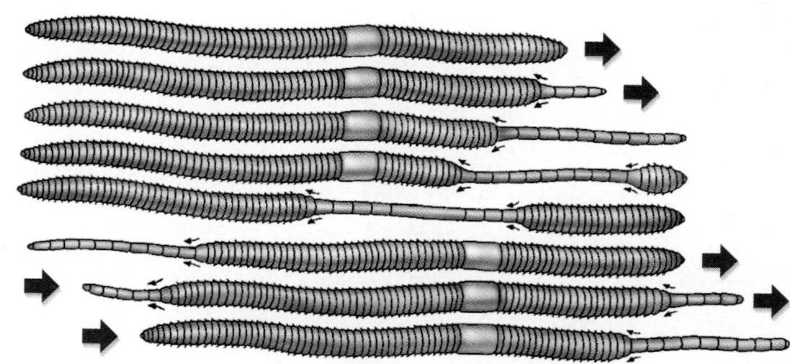

Figure 23.10 Earthworms have a hydraulic skeleton.

When an earthworm's circular muscles contract, the internal fluid presses on the longitudinal muscles, which then stretch to elongate segments of the earthworm. A wave of contractions down the body of the earthworm produces forward movement.

Figure 23.11 Crustaceans have an exoskeleton.

The exoskeleton of this rock crab is bright orange.

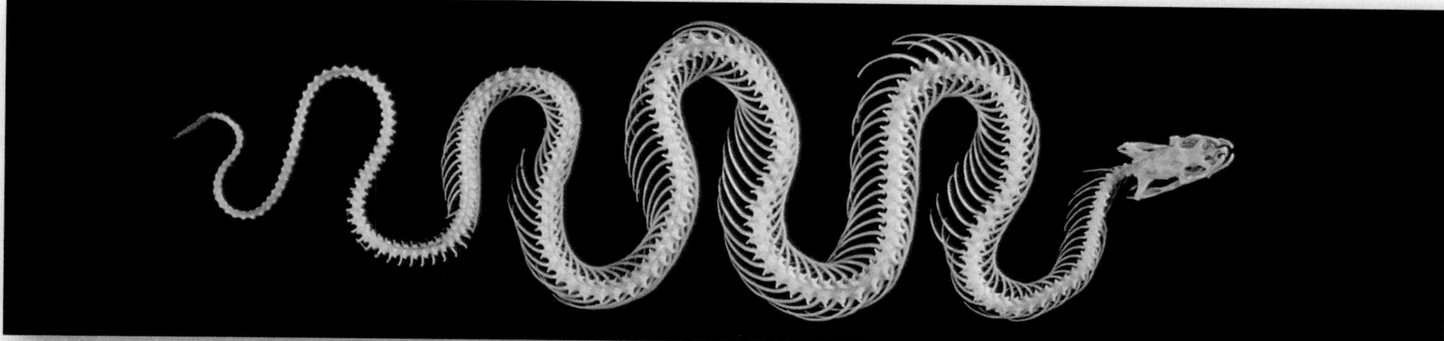

Figure 23.12 Snakes have an endoskeleton.

The endoskeleton of most vertebrates is made of bone. A snake's skeleton is specialized for quick lateral movement.

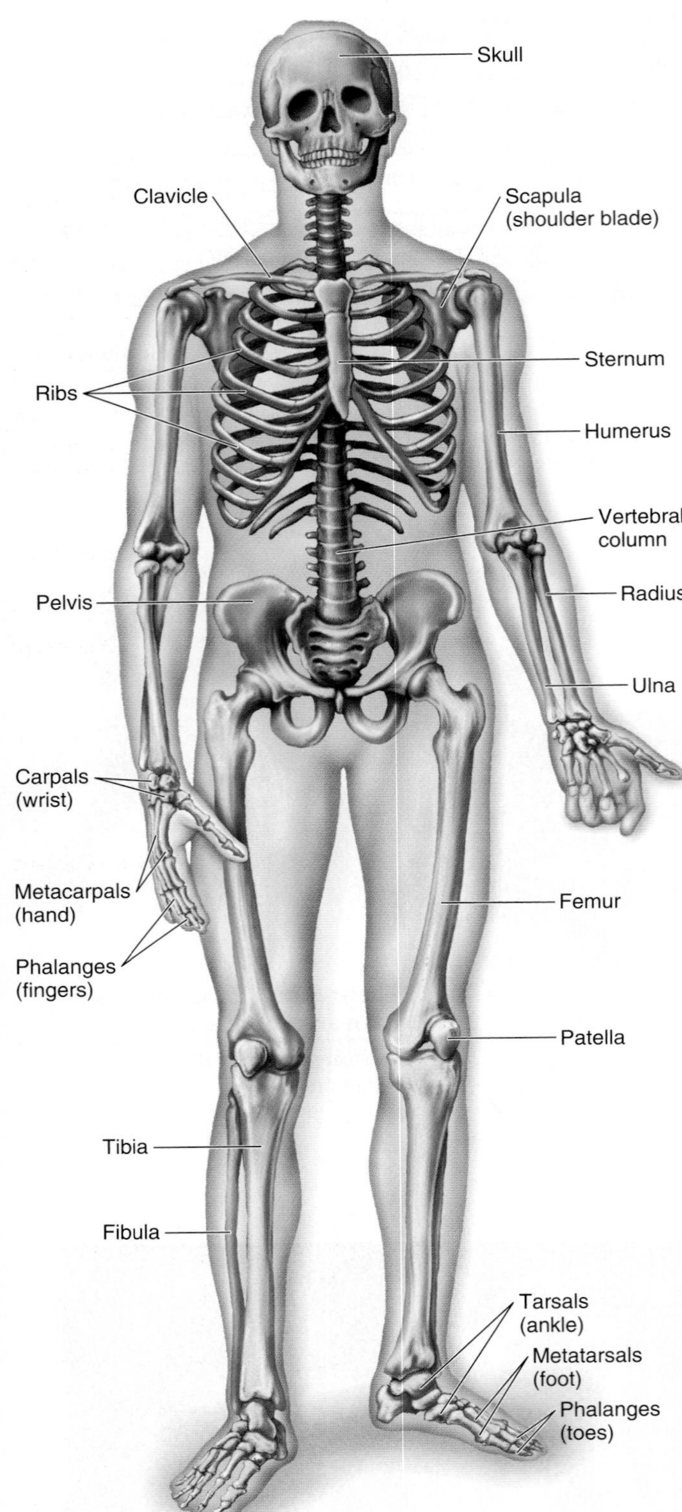

Figure 23.13 Axial and appendicular skeletons.

The axial skeleton is shown in *purple,* and the appendicular skeleton is shown in *tan.* Some of the joints are shown in *green.*

A Vertebrate Endoskeleton: The Human Skeleton

LEARNING OBJECTIVE 23.6.2 **Contrast the axial and appendicular human skeletons and their main classes of joints.**

The human skeleton is made up of 206 individual bones. If you saw them as a pile of bones jumbled together, it would be hard to make any sense of them. To understand the skeleton, it is necessary to group the 206 bones according to their function and position in the body. The 80 bones of the **axial skeleton,** the purple-colored bones in figure 23.13, support the main body axis, while the remaining 126 bones of the **appendicular skeleton,** the tan-colored bones, support the arms and legs. These two skeletons function more or less independently—that is, the muscles controlling the axial skeleton (postural muscles) are managed by the brain separately from those controlling the appendages (manipulatory muscles).

The Axial Skeleton

The axial skeleton is made up of the skull, vertebral column (backbone), and rib cage, which includes the sternum. Of the skull's 28 bones, only 8 form the cranium, which encases the brain; the rest are facial bones and middle ear bones.

The skull is attached to the upper end of the vertebral column, which is also called the spine. The spine is made up of 26 individual bones called vertebrae, stacked one on top of the other to provide a flexible column surrounding and protecting the spinal cord. Curving forward from the vertebrae are 12 pairs of ribs, attached at the front to the sternum, or breastbone, and forming a protective cage around the heart and lungs.

The Appendicular Skeleton

The 126 bones of the appendicular skeleton are attached to the axial skeleton at the shoulders and hips. The shoulder, or **pectoral girdle,** is composed of two large, flat shoulder blades, each connected to the top of the sternum by a slender, curved collarbone (clavicle). The arms are attached to the pectoral girdle; each arm and hand contains 30 bones. The clavicle is the most frequently broken bone of the body. Can you guess why? Because if you fall on an outstretched arm, a large component of the force is transmitted to the clavicle.

The **pelvic girdle** forms a bowl that provides strong connections for the legs, which must bear the weight of the body. Each leg and foot contains a total of 30 bones.

Joints are points where two bones come together. They confer flexibility to the rigid endoskeleton, allowing a range of motion determined by the type of joint. There are three main classes of joints, based on mobility. *Immovable joints,* such as the sutures of the skull, are capable of little to no movement. *Slightly movable joints,* such as the joints between vertebrae in the spine, allow the bones some movement. And *freely movable joints* allow a range of motion and are seen in the limbs (for example, the shoulder, elbow, hip, knee), the jaw, and fingers and toes. Depending on the type of joint, bones are held together at the joint by cartilage, fibrous connective tissue, or a fibrous capsule filled with a lubricating fluid.

Putting the Concept to Work

If skull sutures are incapable of movement, why have them?

23.7 Muscles and How They Work

LEARNING OBJECTIVE 23.7.1 Describe the structure and functioning of a skeletal muscle and its filaments.

Three kinds of muscle together form the vertebrate muscular system. As we have discussed, the vertebrate body is able to move because *skeletal muscles* pull the bones with considerable force. The heart pumps because of the contraction of *cardiac muscle.* Food moves through the intestines because of the rhythmic contractions of *smooth muscle.*

Actions of Skeletal Muscle

Skeletal muscles move the bones of the skeleton. Some of the major human muscles are labeled on the right in figure 23.14. Muscles are attached to bones by straps of dense connective tissue called **tendons.** Bones pivot about flexible connections called joints, pulled back and forth by the muscles attached to them. Each muscle pulls on a specific bone. One end of the muscle, the *origin,* is attached by a tendon to a bone that remains stationary during a contraction. This provides an object against which the muscle can pull. The other end of the muscle, the *insertion,* is attached to a bone that moves if the muscle contracts. For example, the origin and insertion for the sartorius muscle are labeled on the left in figure 23.14. This muscle helps bend the leg at the hip, bringing the knee to the chest. The origin of the muscle is at the hip and stays stationary. The insertion is just below the knee, such that when the muscle contracts (gets shorter) the knee is pulled up toward the chest.

Muscles can only pull, not push, because myofibrils contract rather than expand. For this reason, the muscles that extend across movable joints of vertebrates are attached in opposing pairs, called flexors and extensors, which, when contracted, move the bones in different directions. As you can see in figure 23.15, when the **flexor** muscle at the back of your upper leg contracts, the lower leg is moved closer to the thigh. When the **extensor** muscle at the front of your upper leg contracts, the lower leg is moved in the opposite direction, away from the thigh.

Muscle Filaments

Recall from figure 23.8 that myofibrils are composed of bundles of myofilaments. Far too fine to see with the naked eye, the individual myofilaments of vertebrate muscles are only 8 to 12 nanometers thick. Each is a long, threadlike filament of the proteins actin or myosin. An **actin filament** consists of two strings of actin molecules wrapped around one another, like two strands of pearls loosely wound together. A **myosin filament** is about twice as long as an actin filament and is composed of bundles of myosin molecules. A myosin molecule consists of two polypeptide chains wound about each other. Each polypeptide chain has a shape somewhat like that of a golf club: a very long rod with a globular region, or "head." This odd structure is the key to how muscles work.

Actin isn't found only in muscle cells. All animal cells contain some actin filaments as components of the cytoskeleton, discussed on page 80. The cytoskeleton helps maintain the shape of animal cells.

Putting the Concept to Work

Why can a muscle pull, but not push? If your arm muscles cannot push, how do your arms manage to do so?

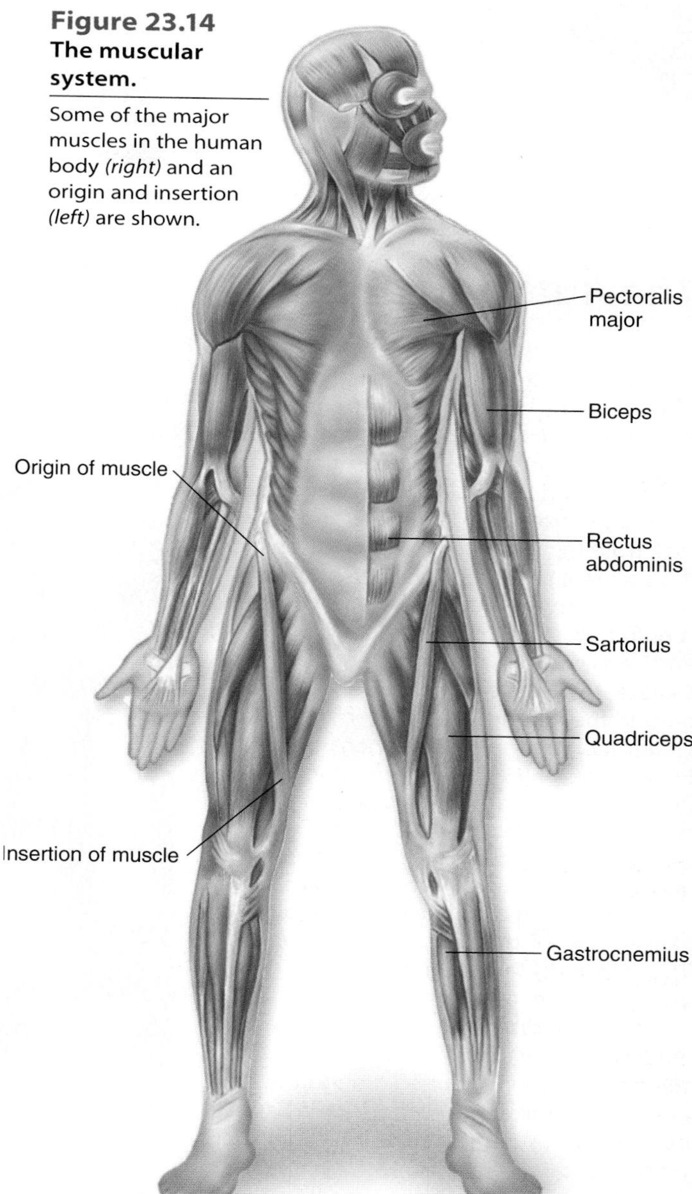

Figure 23.14 The muscular system.

Some of the major muscles in the human body *(right)* and an origin and insertion *(left)* are shown.

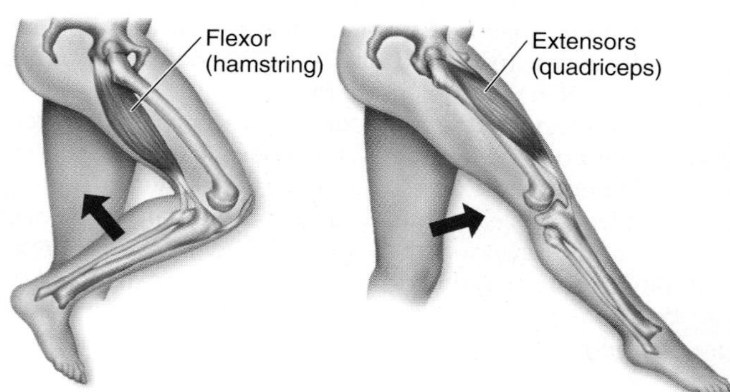

Figure 23.15 Flexor and extensor muscles.

Limb movement is always the result of muscle contraction, never muscle extension. Muscles that retract limbs are called flexors; those that extend limbs are called extensors.

The Author Works Out

No one seeing the ring of fat decorating my middle would take me for a runner. Only in my memory do I get up with the robins, lace up my running shoes, bounce out the front door, and run the streets around Washington University before going to work. Now my 5-K runs are 30-year-old memories. Any mention I make of my running in a race only evokes screams of laughter from my daughters, and an arch look from my wife. Memory is cruelest when it is accurate.

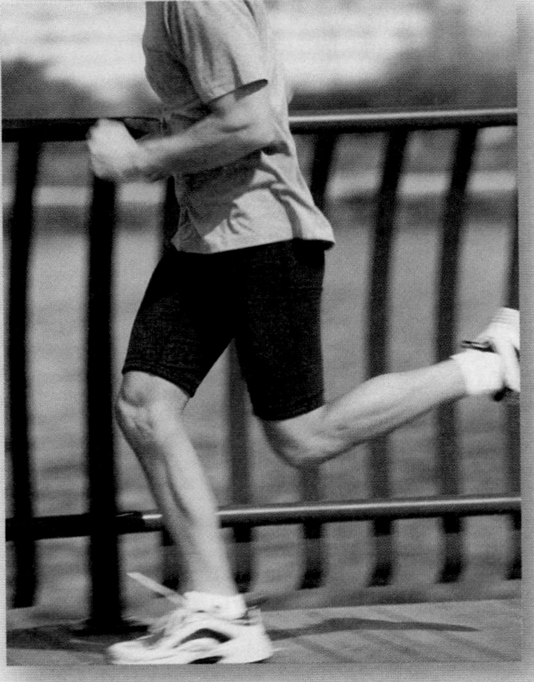

I remember clearly the day I stopped running. It was a cool fall morning in 1978, and I was part of a mob running a 5-K (that's 5 kilometers for the uninitiated) race, winding around the hills near the university. I started to get flashes of pain in my legs below the knees—like shin splints, but much worse. Imagine fire pouring on your bones. Did I stop running? No. Like a bonehead I kept going, "working through the pain," and finished the race. I have never run a race since.

I had pulled a muscle in my thigh, which caused part of the pain. But that wasn't all. The pain in my lower legs wasn't shin splints, and didn't go away. A trip to the doctor revealed multiple stress fractures in both legs. The X rays of my legs looked like tiny threads had been wrapped around the shaft of each bone, like the red stripe on a barber's pole. It was summer before I could walk without pain.

What went wrong? Isn't running supposed to be GOOD for you? Not if you run improperly. In my enthusiasm to be healthy, I ignored some simple rules and paid the price. The biology lesson I ignored had to do with how bones grow. The long bones of your legs are not made of stone, solid and permanent. They are dynamic structures, constantly being re-formed and strengthened in response to the stresses to which you subject them.

To understand how bone grows, we first need to recall a bit about what bone is like. Bone, as you have learned in this chapter, is made of fibers of a flexible protein called collagen stuck together to form cartilage. While an embryo, all your bones are made of cartilage. As your body develops, the collagen fibers become impregnated with tiny needle-shaped crystals of calcium phosphate, turning the cartilage into bone. The crystals are brittle but rigid, giving bone great strength. Collagen is flexible but weak, but like the epoxy of fiberglass, it acts to spread any stress over many crystals, making bone resistant to fracture. As a result, bone is both strong and flexible.

When you subject a bone in your body to stress—say, by running—the bone grows so as to withstand the greater workload. How does the bone "know" just where to add more material? When stress deforms the collagen fibers of a leg bone, the interior of the collagen fibers becomes exposed, like opening your jacket and exposing your shirt. The fiber interior produces a minute electrical charge. Cells called fibroblasts are attracted to the electricity like bugs to night lights, and secrete more collagen there. As a result, new collagen fibers are laid down on a bone along the lines of stress. Slowly, over months, calcium phosphate crystals convert the new collagen to new bone. In your legs, the new bone forms along the long stress lines that curve down along the shank of the bone.

Now go back 30 years, and visualize me pounding happily down the concrete pavement each morning. I had only recently begun to run on the sidewalk, and for an hour or more at a stretch. Every stride I took those mornings was a blow to my shinbones, a stress to which my bones no doubt began to respond by forming collagen along the spiral lines of stress. Had I run on a softer surface, the daily stress would have been far less severe. Had I gradually increased my running, new bone would have had time to form properly in response to the added stress. I gave my leg bones a lot of stress, and no time to respond to it. I pushed them too hard, too fast, and they gave way.

Nor was my improper running limited to overstressed leg bones. Remember that pulled thigh muscle? In my excessive enthusiasm, I never warmed up before I ran. I was having too much fun to worry about such details. Wiser now, I am sure the pulled thigh muscle was a direct result of failing to properly stretch and warm up before running.

I was reminded of that pulled muscle recently, listening to a good friend of my wife's describe how she sets out early each morning for a long run without stretching or warming up. I can see her in my mind's eye, bundled up warmly on the cooler mornings, an enthusiastic gazelle pounding down the pavement in search of good health. Unless she uses more sense than I did, she may fail to find it.

How Myofilaments Contract

LEARNING OBJECTIVE 23.7.2 Describe the sliding filament model of muscle contraction.

The **sliding filament model** of muscle contraction, illustrated in figure 23.16, describes how actin and myosin cause muscles to contract. Focus on the knob-shaped myosin head in panel 1. When a muscle contraction begins, the heads of the myosin filaments, which are attached to actin, move first. Like flexing your hand downward at the wrist, the heads bend backward and inward, as shown in panel 2. This moves the myosin heads closer to their rodlike backbones in the direction of the flex. In itself, this myosin head-flex accomplishes nothing—but because the myosin head is attached to the actin filament, the actin filament is pulled along with the myosin head as it flexes. This causes the actin filament to slide by the myosin filament in the direction of the flex (indicated by the arrows in panel 2). As one myosin head after another flexes, the myosin in effect "walks" step by step along the actin.

Each step uses a molecule of ATP to recock the myosin head (shown in panel 3) before it attaches to the actin again, ready for the next flex. It is important to note that ATP hydrolysis does not occur at the same time as the power stroke in the cycle. The hydrolysis of ATP to cock the myosin head is like your thumb cocking the spring-loaded hammer of an old-fashioned revolver, contributing the energy for when you pull the trigger later.

ATP is the energy currency of the cell, as discussed on page 98. An ATP molecule contains high-energy bonds that hold the phosphate groups together. The breaking of the outermost phosphate bond releases a burst of energy that resets the myosin heads.

How does this sliding of actin past myosin lead to myofibril contraction and muscle cell movement? The actin filament is anchored at one end, at a position in striated muscle called the Z line, indicated by the lavender-colored bars toward the edges in figure 23.17. Two Z lines with the actin and myosin filaments in between make up a contractile unit called a **sarcomere.** Because it is tethered like this, the actin cannot simply move off. Instead, the actin pulls the anchor with it! As actin moves past myosin, it drags the Z line toward the myosin. The secret of muscle contraction is that each myosin is interposed between two pairs of actin filaments, which are anchored at both ends to Z lines, as shown in panel 1 of figure 23.17. One moving to the left and the other to the right, the two pairs of actin molecules drag the Z lines toward each other as they slide past the myosin core, shown in panel 2. As the Z lines are pulled closer together, the plasma membranes to which they are attached move toward one another, and the cell contracts.

Putting the Concept to Work

To which molecule of a muscle fiber does ATP contribute its energy, and to do precisely what?

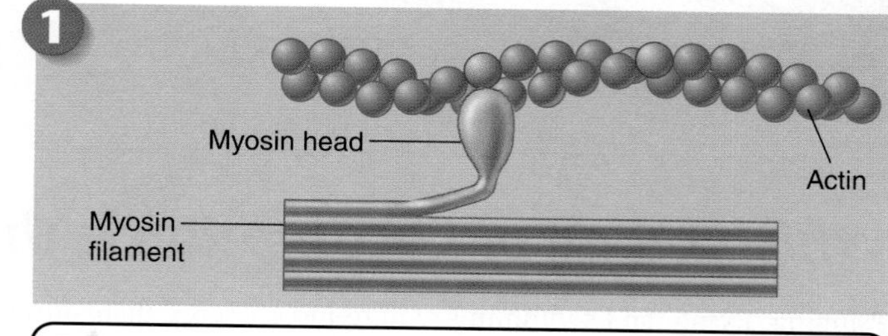

The myosin head is attached to actin.

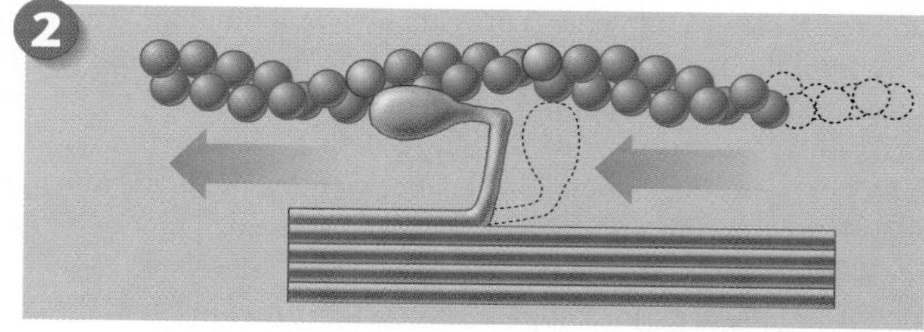

The myosin head flexes, advancing the actin filament.

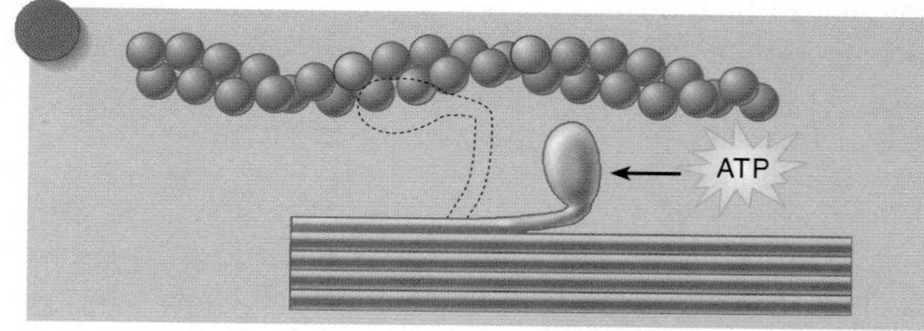

The myosin head releases and unflexes, powered by ATP. The myosin head is then able to reattach to actin, farther along the fiber.

Figure 23.16 How myofilament contraction works.

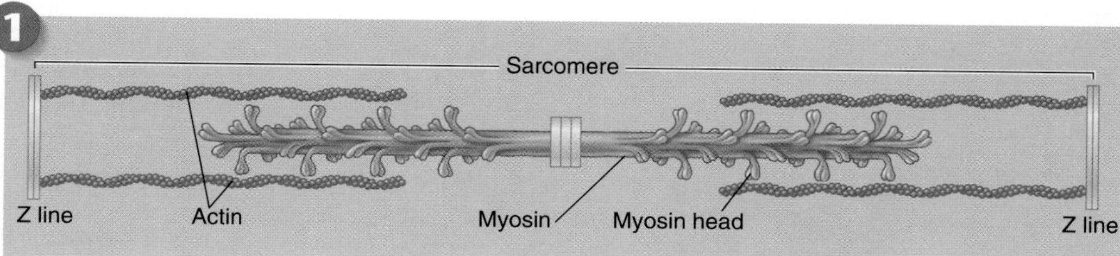

The heads on the two ends of the myosin filament are oriented in opposite directions.

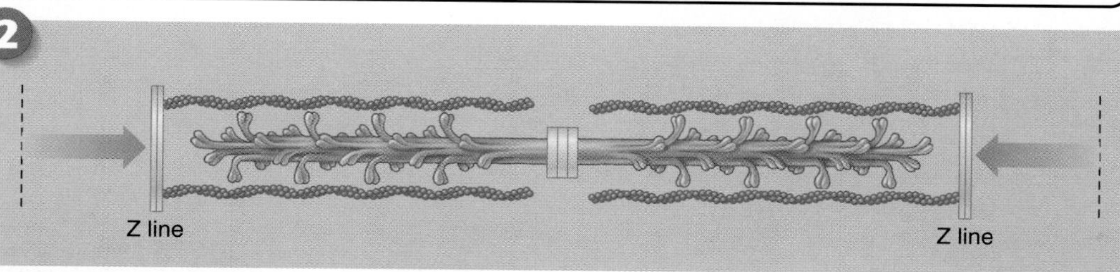

Thus, as the right-hand end of the myosin filament "walks" along the actin filaments, pulling them and their attached Z line leftward toward the center, the left-hand end of the same myosin filament "walks" along the actin filaments, pulling them and their attached Z line rightward toward the center. The result is that both Z lines move toward the center—and contraction occurs.

Figure 23.17 The sliding filament model of muscle contraction.

Inquiry & Analysis

Which Mode of Locomotion Is the Most Efficient?

Running, flying, and swimming require more energy than sitting still, but how do they compare? The greatest differences between moving on land, in the air, and in water result from the differences in support and resistance to movement provided by water and air. The weight of a swimming animal is fully supported by the surrounding water, and no effort goes into supporting the body, while running and flying animals must support the full weight of their bodies. On the other hand, water presents considerable resistance to movement, air much less, so that flying and running require less energy to push the medium out of the way.

A simple way to compare the costs of moving for different animals is to determine how much energy it takes to move. The energy cost to run, fly, or swim is in each case the energy required to move one unit of body mass over one unit of distance with that mode of locomotion. (Energy is measured in the **metric system** as a **kilocalorie** (**kcal**) or technically 4.184 kilojoules [note that the Calorie measured in food diets and written with a capital C is equivalent to 1 kcal]; body mass is measured in kilograms, where one kilogram [**kg**] is 2.2 pounds; distance is measured in kilometers, where one kilometer [**km**] is 0.62 miles). The graph to the right displays three such "cost-of-motion" studies. The blue squares are running, the red circles are flying, and the green triangles are swimming. In each study, the line is drawn as the statistical "best-fit" for the points. Some animals like humans have data in two lines, as they both run (well) and swim (poorly). Ducks have data in all three lines, as they not only fly (very well), but also run and swim (poorly).

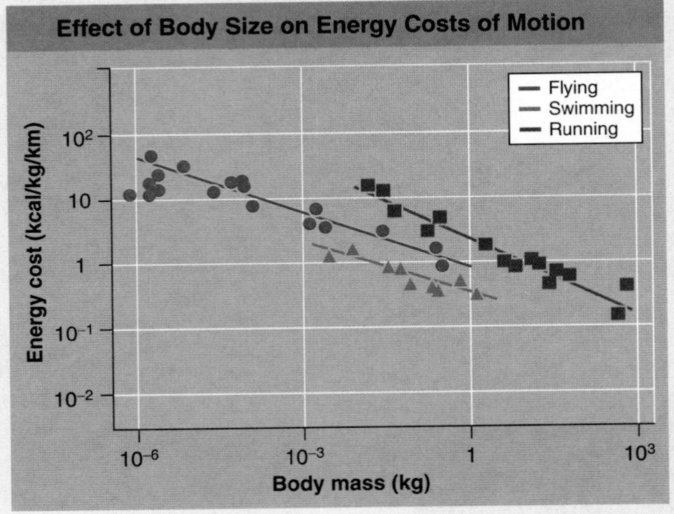

Analysis

1. **Applying Concepts** Do the three modes of locomotion have the same or different costs?
2. **Interpreting Data**
   a. For any given mode of locomotion, what is the impact of body mass on cost of moving?
   b. Is the impact of body mass the same for all three modes of locomotion? If not, which mode's cost is least affected by body mass? Why do you think this is so?
3. **Making Inferences**
   a. Comparing the energy costs of running versus flying for animals of the same body mass, which mode of locomotion is the most expensive? Why would you expect this to be so?
   b. Comparing the energy costs of swimming to flying, which uses the least energy? Why would you expect this to be so?
4. **Drawing Conclusions** In general, which mode of locomotion is the most efficient? the least efficient? Why do you think this is so?

Summary of Learning Outcomes

The Animal Body Plan

Organization of the Vertebrate Body

23.1.1 All vertebrates and some invertebrates have the same general architecture: a tube (the gut or digestive system) suspended in a cavity (the coelom) that in many terrestrial vertebrates is divided into a thoracic cavity and an abdominal cavity.

- The vertebrate body is composed of cells that exhibit increasing levels of structural and functional complexity.

23.1.2 Cells that group together into tissues act as functional units. Organs of the body are composed of several different kinds of tissues that act together to perform a higher level of function. Organs work together in an organ system to perform larger-scale body functions.

Tissues of the Vertebrate Body

Epithelium Is Protective Tissue

23.2.1 Epithelial tissue is composed of different types of epithelial cells. It covers internal and external surfaces of the body and provides protection.

- The structure of the epithelium determines its function. Some types of epithelium are a single layer of cells through which substances can pass. Some epithelium is stratified, providing protection. Cuboidal epithelium lines glands in the body and has a secretory function, producing and releasing hormones into the blood.

Connective Tissue Carries Out Various Functions

23.3.1 The connective tissues of the body are very diverse in structure and function, but all are composed of cells embedded in an extracellular matrix. The matrix may be hard as in bone, flexible as in fibrous connective tissue, adipose tissue, and cartilage, or fluid as in blood.

- Immune connective tissue contains white blood cells that float in the blood plasma and protect the body from infection.
- Skeletal connective tissues—such as fibrous connective tissue, cartilage (which makes up the skeleton of sharks, shown here from figure 23.4), and bone—provide structural support of the body.

- Adipose tissue stores fat deposits, and red blood cells, erythrocytes, transport substances throughout the body.

23.3.2 Bone is a living tissue. Bone cells called osteoblasts lay down a fibrous matrix. Calcium minerals then impregnate the fibers, causing the matrix to harden into compact bone.

Muscle Tissue Lets the Body Move

23.4.1 Muscle tissue is dynamic tissue; it contracts, causing the body to move. There are three types of muscle tissue: smooth, skeletal, and cardiac muscle. All three types of muscle contain actin and myosin myofilaments but differ in the organization of the myofilaments.

- Smooth muscle cells are long, spindle-shaped cells organized into sheets. Smooth muscle is found in the walls of blood vessels, in the iris of the vertebrate eye, and in the walls of the digestive system.
- Skeletal muscle cells are fused into long fibers. Skeletal muscle is attached to the skeleton, so when the muscle contracts, the skeleton moves.
- Cells of cardiac muscle found in the heart are interconnected so that they contract together in an orderly pulsation.

Nerve Tissue Conducts Signals Rapidly

23.5.1 Nerve tissue is composed of neurons and supporting glial cells. Neurons have three parts: branching dendrites, the cell body that contains the nucleus, and a long axon. Neurons carry electrical impulses from one area of the body to another. The electrical impulse travels down the length of the neuron's axon by the movement of ions across the plasma membrane. There are three categories of neurons: sensory neurons that carry impulses to the central nervous system, motor neurons that carry impulses from the central nervous system to muscles, and association neurons that act as connectors within the central nervous system.

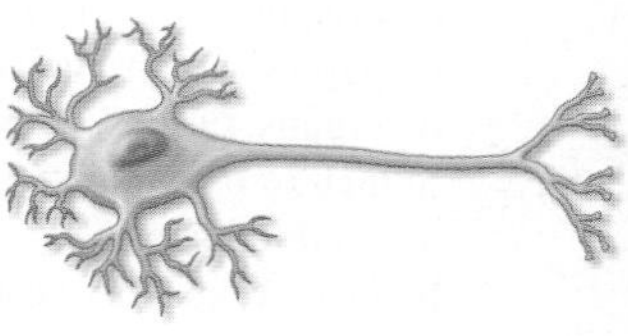

The Skeletal and Muscular Systems

Types of Skeletons

23.6.1 The skeletal system provides a framework on which muscles act to move the body. Soft-bodied invertebrates have hydraulic skeletons, where muscles act on a fluid-filled cavity.

- Arthropods have exoskeletons, where muscles attach from within to the hard outer covering of the body.

23.6.2 Vertebrates and echinoderms have endoskeletons, where muscles attach to bones or cartilage inside the body. The human skeleton has 206 individual bones that make up the axial and appendicular skeletons.

Muscles and How They Work

23.7.1 Skeletal muscles attach to the skeleton at two points. The end that attaches to the stationary bone is called the origin. The muscle passes over a joint and attaches to another bone at a point called the insertion. As the muscle contracts, the insertion is brought closer to the origin and the joint flexes. Muscles act in opposing pairs to flex or extend a joint.

23.7.2 Myofibrils are composed of bundles of actin and myosin. During muscle contraction, myosin attaches to actin (as shown here from figure 23.16).

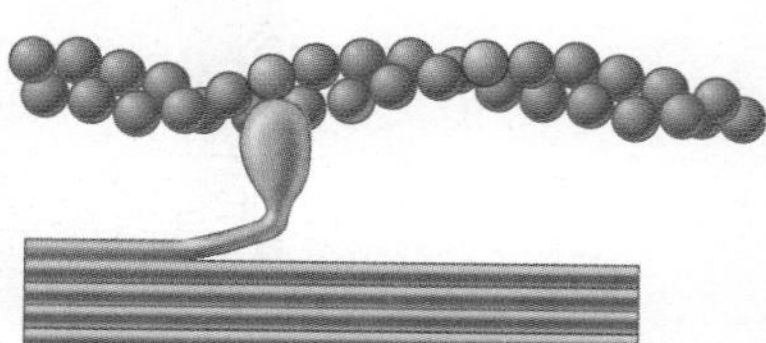

- A flexing myosin filament pulls the actin along its length, causing the myofilaments to slide past each other. Actin myofilaments are anchored at each end to a structure called the Z line. As the actin slides along the myosin, the anchor points are brought closer together, resulting in a shortening of the muscle. Energy from ATP causes the myofilaments to dissociate and reset, triggering the sliding motion again.

Test Your Understanding

23.1.1 Which of the following contains the heart and lungs in a vertebrate body?
a. the coelom
b. the gut
c. the thoracic cavity
d. the abdominal cavity

23.1.2 Which of the following is the correct organization sequence from smallest to largest in animals?
a. cells, tissues, organs, organ systems, organism
b. organism, organ systems, organs, tissues, cells
c. tissues, organs, cells, organ systems, organism
d. organs, tissues, cells, organism, organ systems

23.2.1 Which of the following is *not* a function of the epithelial tissue?
a. secrete materials
b. provide sensory surfaces
c. move the body
d. protect underlying tissue from damage and dehydration

23.3.1 An example of connective tissue is
a. nerve cells in your fingers.
b. skin cells.
c. brain cells.
d. red blood cells.

23.3.2 When a person has osteoporosis, the work of _____ falls behind the work of _____.
a. osteoclasts; osteoblasts
b. osteoclasts; collagen
c. osteoblasts; osteoclasts
d. osteoblasts; collagen

23.4.1 The type of muscle used to move the leg when walking is
a. skeletal.
b. cardiac.
c. smooth.
d. All of the above.

23.5.1 Nerve impulses pass from one nerve cell to another by the use of
a. hormones.
b. neurotransmitters.
c. pheromones.
d. calcium ions.

23.6.2 The vertebral column is part of the
a. appendicular skeleton.
b. axial skeleton.
c. hydraulic skeleton.
d. exoskeleton.

23.7.1 Movement of a limb in two directions requires a pair of muscles because
a. a single muscle can only pull and not push.
b. a single muscle can only push and not pull.
c. moving a limb requires more force than one muscle can generate.
d. None of the above.

23.7.2 ATP is required for muscle contraction to
a. pull the actin along the myosin fiber.
b. pull the myosin along the actin fiber.
c. to reset the myosin head so it can reattach to the actin.
d. All answers above are correct; ATP is required at several different stages in the contraction of the muscle.

Apply Your Understanding

23.3.2 Areas of normal bone are composed of an open lattice framework of minerals, including calcium. Why wouldn't it be more sensible for bones to be solid?

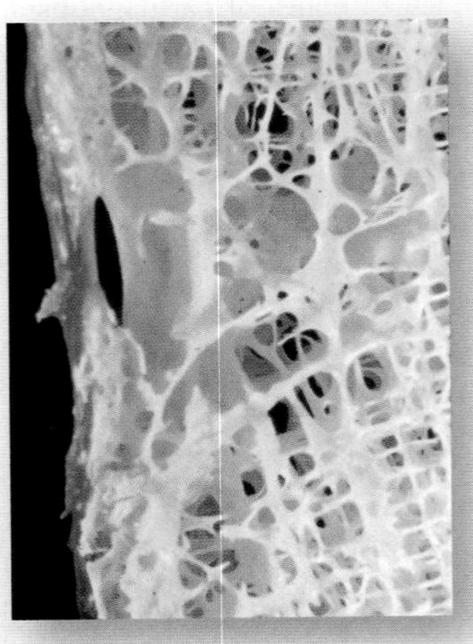

23.6.2 The bones of your head and trunk form three cagelike structures: the skull, the rib cage, and the pelvic girdle. What is the functional importance of this arrangement?

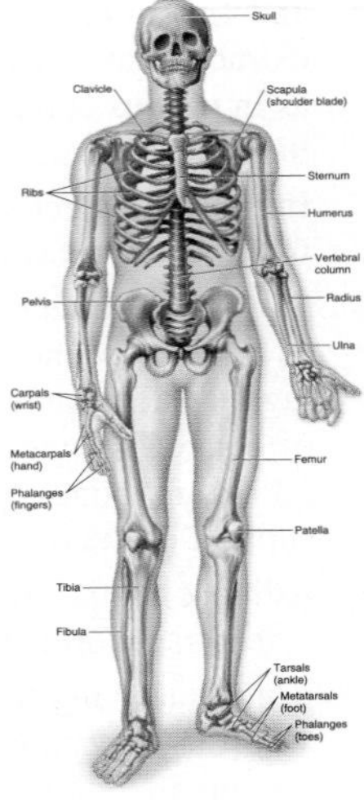

Synthesize What You Have Learned

23.1.1 Imagine that you are designing a living organism, some type of vertebrate. Explain briefly how the four types of tissue are all necessary to your design.

23.7.2 When you are exercising rapidly, such as playing tennis, dancing to fast music, or doing aerobics, you begin to breathe rapidly and your heart rate increases. If you continue, you become "out of breath" and flushed. Why does your body respond in this fashion?

Chapter 26

The Path of Food Through the Animal Body

CHAPTER AT A GLANCE

Food Energy and Essential Nutrients

26.1 Food for Energy and Growth

Digestion

26.2 Types of Digestive Systems

26.3 Vertebrate Digestive Systems

26.4 The Mouth and Teeth

26.5 The Esophagus and Stomach

26.6 The Small and Large Intestines

26.7 Accessory Digestive Organs

Inquiry & Analysis: Why Do Diabetics Excrete Glucose in Their Urine?

Food Energy and Essential Nutrients

26.1 Food for Energy and Growth

LEARNING OBJECTIVE 26.1.1 Discuss how a balanced diet influences the BMI and why this is important.

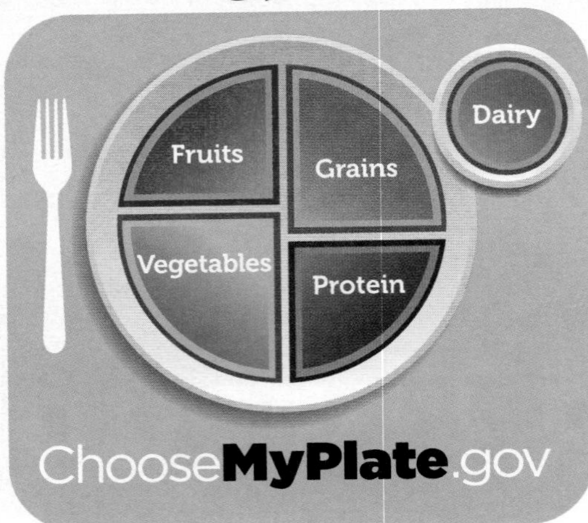

Figure 26.1 The nutrition plate.

The U.S. Department of Agriculture guidelines for a healthy diet utilize a "food plate" icon, organized the way people eat. It is recommended that one-half of your dietary plate be filled with fruits and vegetables, the other half with whole grains and lean protein. Fat is to be avoided in all choices. Dairy, indicated on the side, should favor low-fat items as well, such as skim milk and yogurt. Filling half the plate with fruit and vegetables reduces calories. The plate emphasizes whole grains rather than refined grains such as white rice or white bread, which are stripped of nutrients such as vitamins, fiber, and iron.

The food animals eat provides both a source of energy and essential molecules such as certain amino acids and fats that the animal body is not able to manufacture for itself. An optimal diet contains a balance of fruits, vegetables, grains, protein, and dairy, as recommended by the federal government's "nutrition plate" in figure 26.1. The plate is intended as a general guideline of what a person should eat. About half of a person's diet should be fruits and vegetables, and the other half should contain proteins, whole grains, and dairy. Fats are recommended in small amounts because they have a far greater number of energy-rich carbon–hydrogen bonds and thus a much higher energy content per gram than carbohydrates or proteins.

Carbohydrates are obtained primarily from grains (the brown section), fruits (the red section), and vegetables (the green section). On average, carbohydrates contain 4.1 calories per gram; fats, by comparison, contain 9.3 calories per gram, over twice as much. Dietary fats are obtained from oils, margarine, and butter and are abundant in fried foods, meats, and processed snack foods, such as potato chips and crackers. Like carbohydrates, proteins have 4.1 calories per gram and can be obtained from many foods, including dairy products, poultry, meat (the blue and purple sections), and grains.

Being significantly overweight is often the result of high-fat diets, in which fats constitute over 35% of the total caloric intake. The international standard measure of appropriate body weight is the body mass index (BMI), estimated as your body weight in kilograms, divided by your height in meters squared. A BMI chart is presented in figure 26.2. To determine your BMI, find your height in the left-hand column (in feet and inches) and trace it across to the column with your weight (in pounds). A BMI value of 25 (dark blue boxes) and above is considered overweight and 30 or over is considered obese. In the United States, the National Institutes of Health estimated in 2004 that 66% of adults, 133.6 million Americans, were overweight, with a body mass index of 25 or more. Of those individuals, 63.6 million were considered obese with a body mass index of 30 or greater. Being overweight is highly correlated with coronary heart disease, diabetes, and many other disorders. However, a BMI of less than 18.5, often resulting from eating disorders like anorexia nervosa, is also unhealthy.

All animals must eat. Even an animal that is completely at rest requires energy to support its metabolism. This minimum rate of energy consumption, called the *basal metabolic rate* (BMR), is relatively constant for a given individual. Exercise raises the metabolic rate above the basal levels, so the amount of energy the body requires per day is determined not only by the BMR but also by the level of physical activity. Energy that is not used for metabolism or exercise is stored as fat. Therefore, energy needs can be altered by the choice of diet (caloric intake) and the amount of energy expended in exercise.

Putting the Concept to Work

Calculate your personal body mass index. Are you overweight?

IN THE NEWS

The Peanut Butter Debate. Severe malnutrition occurs in some 20 million children in Africa and South Asia every year. A new type of ready-to-use food is changing the way severe malnutrition is treated. At therapeutic feeding centers, children are given a quick health checkup and, if malnourished, a silvery packet. Open and squeeze the packet and out pours 92 grams of a brown paste that looks like dark peanut butter. Called Plumpy'nut, it's made of roasted ground peanuts combined with vegetable oil, milk powder, sugar, and a mix of minerals and vitamins. One serving has 550 calories and plenty of proteins, vitamins, and minerals. Plumpy'nut has a long shelf life, does not need to be mixed with water as powdered milk treatments do (local water may be unavailable or unhealthy), and is simple for mothers to give children at home—and children love the sweet, sticky stuff. Eighty percent of severely malnourished children recover when fed Plumpy'nut. But should peanut butter-like pastes, like Plumpy'nut, be distributed far more widely, given to children at risk of malnutrition? The cost of attempting to *prevent* malnutrition in this way would be high ($55 per child in 2007). Many argue that the approach is not cost-effective and widespread use would make poor countries totally dependent on foreign aid. One solution, discussed by the World Health Organization in 2008, is to produce Plumpy'nut locally, and more cheaply—for instance, by replacing the powdered milk (the most expensive ingredient) with soy.

25 OVERWEIGHT LIMIT   OVERWEIGHT

WEIGHT / HEIGHT	100	105	110	115	120	125	130	135	140	145	150	155	160	165	170	175	180	185	190	195	200	205
5' 0"	20	21	21	22	23	24	25	26	27	28	29	30	31	32	33	34	35	36	37	38	39	40
5' 1"	19	20	21	22	23	24	25	26	26	27	28	29	30	31	32	33	34	35	36	37	38	39
5' 2"	18	19	20	21	22	23	24	25	26	27	27	28	29	30	31	32	33	34	35	36	37	37
5' 3"	18	19	19	20	21	22	23	24	25	26	27	27	28	29	30	31	32	33	34	35	35	36
5' 4"	17	18	19	20	21	21	22	23	24	25	26	27	27	28	29	30	31	32	33	33	34	35
5' 5"	17	17	18	19	20	21	22	22	23	24	25	26	27	27	28	29	30	31	32	32	33	34
5' 6"	16	17	18	19	19	20	21	22	23	23	24	25	26	27	27	28	29	30	31	31	32	33
5' 7"	16	16	17	18	19	20	20	21	22	23	23	24	25	26	27	27	28	29	30	31	31	32
5' 8"	15	16	17	17	18	19	20	21	21	22	23	24	24	25	26	27	27	28	29	30	30	31
5' 9"	15	16	16	17	18	18	19	20	21	21	22	23	24	24	25	26	27	27	28	29	30	30
5' 10"	14	15	16	17	17	18	19	19	20	21	22	22	23	24	24	25	26	27	27	28	29	29
5' 11"	14	15	15	16	17	17	18	19	20	20	21	22	22	23	24	24	25	26	26	27	28	29
6' 0"	14	14	15	16	16	17	18	18	19	20	20	21	22	22	23	24	24	25	26	26	27	28
6' 1"	13	14	15	15	16	16	17	18	18	19	20	20	21	22	22	23	24	24	25	26	26	27
6' 2"	13	13	14	15	15	16	17	17	18	19	19	20	21	21	22	22	23	24	24	25	26	26
6' 3"	12	13	14	14	15	16	16	17	17	18	19	19	20	21	21	22	22	23	24	24	25	26
6' 4"	12	13	13	14	15	16	16	16	17	18	18	19	19	20	21	21	22	23	23	24	24	25

Figure 26.2 Are you overweight?

This chart presents the body mass index (BMI) values used by federal health authorities to determine who is overweight. Your body mass index is at the intersection of your height and weight.

Essential Substances for Growth

LEARNING OBJECTIVE 26.1.2 Explain why we require essential amino acids, trace elements, and vitamins.

Over the course of their evolution, many animals have lost the ability to manufacture certain substances they need. Mosquitoes, for example, cannot manufacture cholesterol and must obtain it in their diet—human blood is rich in cholesterol. Humans are unable to manufacture 8 of the 20 amino acids used to make proteins: lysine, tryptophan, threonine, methionine, phenylalanine, leucine, isoleucine, and valine. These amino acids, called **essential amino acids,** must therefore be obtained from proteins in the food we eat.

Trace Elements. In addition to supplying energy, food must also supply the body with a wide variety of **trace elements,** which are minerals required in very small amounts. Among the trace elements are iodine (a component of thyroid hormone), cobalt (a component of vitamin B_{12}), zinc and molybdenum (components of enzymes), manganese, and selenium.

Vitamins. Essential organic substances that are used in trace amounts are called **vitamins.** Humans require at least 13 different vitamins. Humans, monkeys, and guinea pigs, for example, lack the ability to synthesize ascorbic acid (vitamin C) and will develop the potentially fatal disease called scurvy—characterized by weakness, spongy gums, and bleeding of the skin and mucous membranes—if vitamin C is not supplied in their diets.

Putting the Concept to Work

Why are only eight of the 20 amino acids called essential?

Vitamin Supplements: Nutrition in a Pill? It seems like wherever we go these days, we are bombarded with advertisements touting the health benefits of food supplements. Megadoses of vitamin C are said to aid in avoiding colds, and supplements of antioxidant vitamins (A, C, and E) are said to help prevent heart attacks and cancer. Is any of this true? Do dietary supplements make us healthier? According to most health professionals, the answer is no. The American Heart Association states that healthy people get adequate nutrients by eating a healthy diet, and recommend no supplements. Clinical trials are under way to see if increased vitamin antioxidant intake may have an overall benefit, but in early results, a large placebo-controlled, randomized study failed to show any benefit from vitamin E on heart disease. While dietary supplements may be necessary if you are a vegetarian or consume less than 1,600 calories a day, it appears they are wasted on most of us. The lone exception: omega-3 fatty acid supplements, which have been associated with decreased risk of heart disease. If you don't eat fish (salmon, herring, and trout are rich in omega-3), the American Heart Association suggests this supplement may be of value.

Digestion

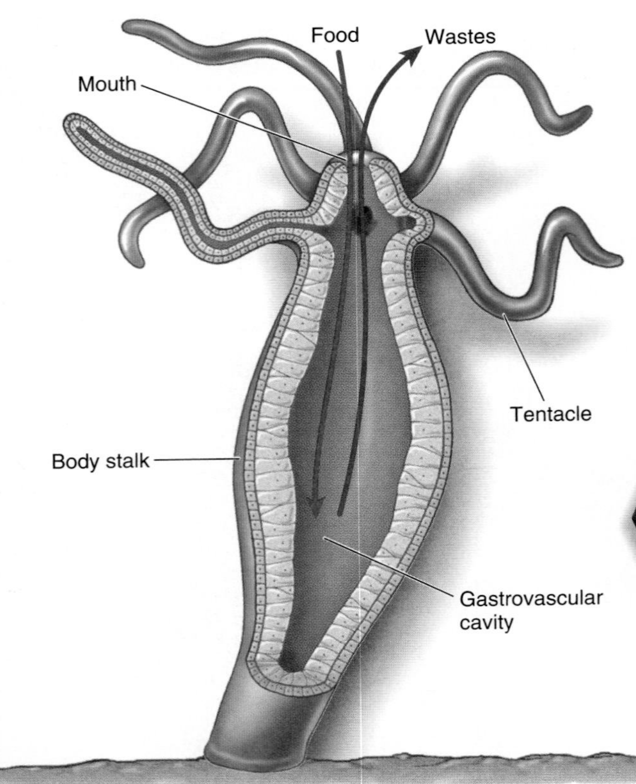

Figure 26.3 The gastrovascular cavity of *Hydra.*

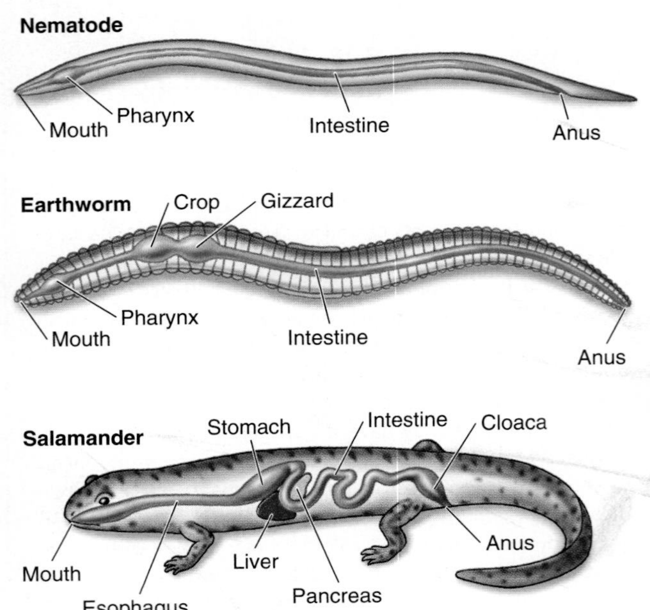

Figure 26.4 One-way digestive tracts.

One-way movement through the digestive tract allows different regions of the digestive system to become specialized for different functions.

26.2 Types of Digestive Systems

LEARNING OBJECTIVE 26.2.1 Contrast intracellular and extracellular digestion, and the digestive tract.

Heterotrophs are divided into three groups on the basis of their food sources. Animals that eat plants exclusively are classified as **herbivores;** common examples include cows, horses, rabbits, and sparrows. Animals that are meat eaters, such as cats, eagles, trout, and frogs, are **carnivores. Omnivores** are animals that eat both plants and other animals. We humans are omnivores, as are pigs, bears, and crows.

> The type of cell in sponges that absorbs food and breaks it down is a choanocyte, described in the Phylum Facts on page 348. The beating of its flagellum brings water and food toward the cell where food particles are trapped, brought into the cell, and digested.

Single-celled organisms and lower animals, like sponges, digest their food intracellularly, breaking down food particles with digestive enzymes inside their cells. Other animals digest their food extracellularly, within a digestive cavity. In this case, the digestive enzymes are released into a cavity that is continuous with the animal's external environment. In flatworms (such as *Planaria*) and cnidarians, like the hydra in figure 26.3, the digestive cavity has only one opening at the top that serves as both mouth (the red arrow) and anus (the blue arrow). There can be no specialization within this type of digestive system, called a *gastrovascular cavity,* because every cell is exposed to all stages of food digestion.

Specialization occurs when the digestive tract, or alimentary canal, has a separate mouth and anus, so that transport of food is one way. Three examples are shown in figure 26.4. The most primitive digestive tract is seen in nematodes (phylum Nematoda), where it is simply a tubular *gut* lined by an epithelial membrane. Earthworms (phylum Annelida) have a digestive tract specialized in different regions for the ingestion, storage (crop), fragmentation (gizzard), digestion, and absorption of food (intestine). All higher animals, like the salamander, show similar specializations.

The ingested food may be stored in a specialized region of the digestive tract or may first be subjected to physical fragmentation through the chewing action of teeth (in the mouth of many vertebrates) or the grinding action of pebbles (in the gizzard of earthworms and birds). The process of chemical digestion occurs primarily in the intestine, breaking down the larger food molecules of polysaccharides, fats, and proteins into smaller subunits. Chemical digestion involves hydrolysis reactions that liberate the subunits—primarily monosaccharides, amino acids, and fatty acids—from the food. These products of chemical digestion pass through the epithelial lining of the gut and ultimately into the blood, in a process known as absorption. Any molecules in the food that are not absorbed cannot be used by the animal. These waste products are excreted from the body through the anus.

> As discussed in chapter 3, page 51, the chemical bonds in carbohydrates, proteins, and fats are broken down by the addition of water molecules, a process called hydrolysis.

Putting the Concept to Work

Why does specialization not occur within the digestive tract of flatworms (refer to figure 24.1), when it does in earthworms?

26.3 Vertebrate Digestive Systems

LEARNING OBJECTIVE 26.3.1 Describe the elements of the vertebrate digestive system, and the layers of the digestive tract.

In humans and other vertebrates, the digestive system consists of a tubular gastrointestinal tract and accessory digestive organs (figure 26.5). Working through the figure from the top down, the initial components of the gastrointestinal tract are the mouth and the pharynx, which is the common passage of the oral and nasal cavities. The pharynx leads to the esophagus, a muscular tube that delivers food to the stomach. From the stomach, where some preliminary digestion occurs, food passes to the first part of the small intestine, where a battery of digestive enzymes continues the digestive process. Accessory digestive organs, such as the liver, gallbladder, and pancreas aid in digestion. The products of digestion pass across the wall of the small intestine into the bloodstream. The small intestine empties what remains into the large intestine, also called the colon, where water and minerals continue to be absorbed. In most vertebrates other than mammals, the waste products emerge from the large intestine into a cavity called the cloaca (see the salamander in figure 26.4), which also receives the products of the urinary and reproductive systems. In mammals, the urogenital products are separated from the fecal material in the large intestine; the fecal material enters the rectum and is expelled through the anus.

The tubular gastrointestinal tract of a vertebrate has a characteristic layered structure (figure 26.6). Working from the inside (the lumen) outward, the innermost layer is the mucosa, an epithelium that lines the lumen. The next major tissue layer, composed of connective tissue, is called the submucosa. Just outside the submucosa is the muscularis, which consists of a double layer of smooth muscles. The muscles in the inner layer have a circular orientation, and those in the outer layer are arranged longitudinally. An outer connective tissue layer, the serosa, covers the external surface of the tract. Nerves, intertwined in regions called plexuses, are located in the submucosa and help regulate the gastrointestinal activities.

In general, carnivores have shorter intestines for their size than do herbivores. A short intestine is adequate for a carnivore, but herbivores ingest a large amount of plant cellulose, which resists digestion. These animals have a long, convoluted small intestine. In addition, mammals called *ruminants* (such as cows) that consume grass and other vegetation have stomachs with multiple chambers, where microorganisms aid in the digestion of cellulose. The first chamber is the *rumen*, which serves as a fermentation vat where microbes digest cellulose. These animals will then regurgitate and rechew the contents of the rumen, breaking down more and more of the cellulose. This activity is called rumination, or "chewing the cud." The cud is then swallowed into another chamber of the stomach where digestion continues. Other herbivores, including rabbits and horses, also digest cellulose with the aid of bacteria, in a blind pouch called the *cecum* located at the beginning of the large intestine. Because the cecum is located beyond the stomach, regurgitation of its contents is impossible. However, rodents and rabbits eat their feces, thus passing food through their digestive tract a second time and so allowing the digested cellulose to be absorbed.

Putting the Concept to Work

How is the function of a rumen different from that of a cecum?

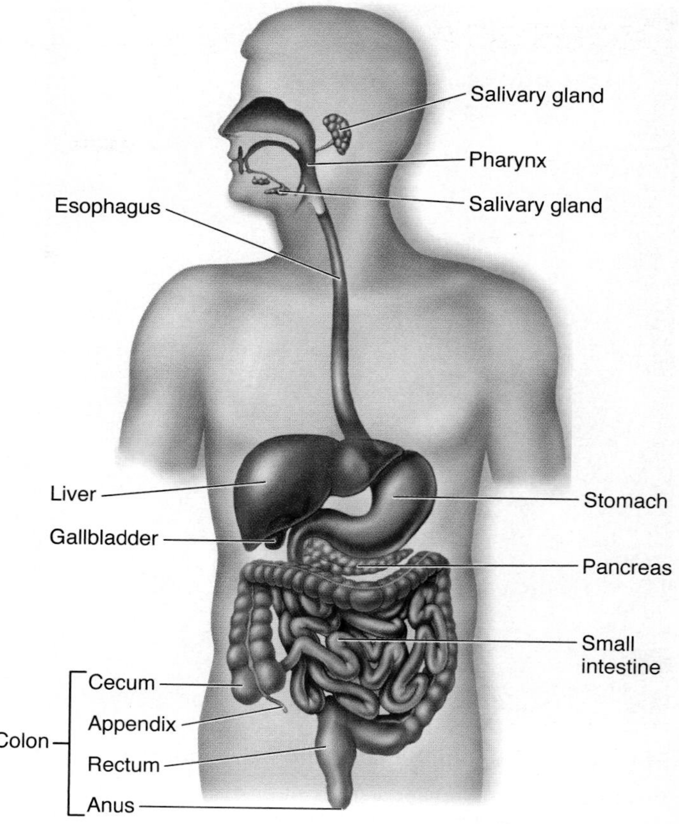

Figure 26.5 The human digestive system.

The tubular gastrointestinal tract and accessory digestive organs are shown. The colon extends from the cecum to the anus.

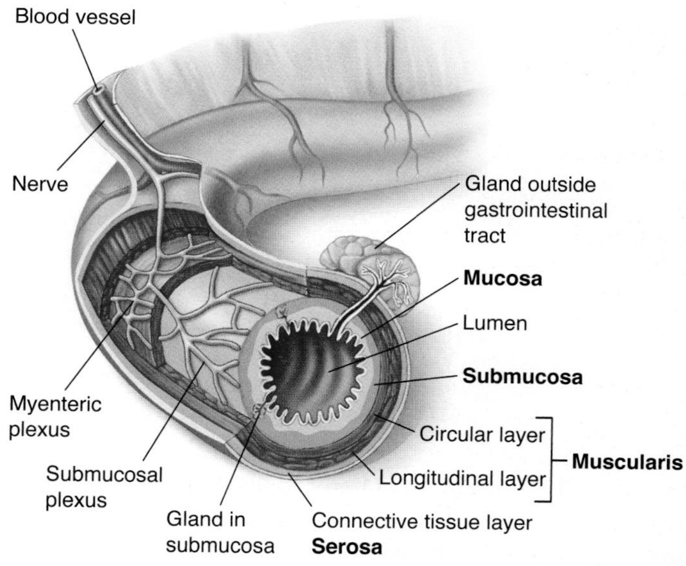

Figure 26.6 The layers of the gastrointestinal tract.

The mucosa contains a lining epithelium, the submucosa is composed of connective tissue (as is the outer serosa layer), and the muscularis consists of smooth muscles.

26.4 The Mouth and Teeth

Specializations of the digestive systems in different kinds of vertebrates reflect differences in the way these animals live. Many vertebrates have teeth (figure 26.7), and chewing (mastication) breaks up food into small particles and mixes it with fluid secretions. Birds, which lack teeth, break up food in a stomach chamber called the gizzard. The gizzard contains small pebbles ingested by the bird which are churned together with the food by muscular action. This churning grinds up the seeds and other hard plant material into smaller bits that can be digested more easily in the intestine.

Figure 26.7 Beginning the digestive journey.

There are no photosynthetic animals. All animals must continuously consume plants or other animals in order to live. The passage of food on its journey into and through a mammal begins with the teeth. The grass in this prairie dog's mouth will be chewed before it is ingested and converted within the prairie dog's cells to body tissue, energy, and refuse.

Vertebrate Teeth

LEARNING OBJECTIVE 26.4.1 Describe the interior structure of a tooth, and the functions of the four kinds of vertebrate teeth.

Reptiles and fish have homodont dentition (teeth that are all the same). However, most mammals have heterodont dentition (teeth of different specialized types): Incisors are chisel-shaped teeth used for nipping and biting; "canines" are sharp, pointed teeth used for tearing food; and premolars (bicuspids) and molars usually have flattened, ridged surfaces used for grinding and crushing food. The front teeth in the upper and lower jaws of mammals are incisors. On each side of the incisors are the canines. Behind the canines are premolars and then molars.

This general pattern of heterodont dentition is modified in different mammals depending on their diet (figure 26.8). For example, in carnivorous mammals the canines are prominent, and the premolars and molars are more blade-like, with sharp edges adapted for cutting and shearing. Carnivores often tear off pieces of their prey but have little need to chew them, because digestive enzymes can act directly on animal cells. (Have you ever noticed how a cat or dog gulps down its food?) By contrast, grass-eating herbivores, such as cows and horses, must pulverize the cellulose cell walls of plant tissue before digesting it. In these mammals, the incisors are used to cut grass and other plants, the canines are reduced or absent, and the premolars and molars are large, flat teeth with complex ridges for grinding.

Humans are omnivores, and human teeth are adapted for eating both plant and animal food. Viewed simply, humans are carnivores in the front of the mouth and herbivores in the back. Children have only 20 teeth, but these deciduous teeth are lost during childhood and are replaced by 32 adult teeth. The third molars are the wisdom teeth, which usually grow in during the late teens or early twenties, when a person is assumed to have gained some "wisdom."

As you can see in figure 26.9, the tooth is a living organ, composed of connective tissue, nerves, and blood vessels, held in place by cementum, a bonelike substance that anchors the tooth in the jaw. The interior of the tooth contains connective tissue called pulp that extends into the root canals and contains nerves and blood vessels. A layer of calcified tissue called dentin surrounds the pulp cavity. The portion of the tooth that projects above the gums is called the crown and is covered with an extremely hard, nonliving substance called enamel. Enamel protects the tooth against abrasion and acids that are produced by bacteria living in the mouth. Cavities form when bacterial acids break down the enamel, allowing bacteria to infect the inner tissues of the tooth.

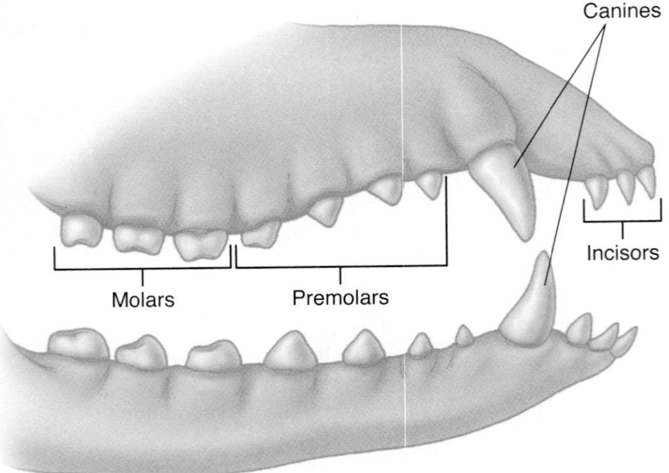

Figure 26.8 Diagram of heterodont dentition.

Different mammals have specific variations of heterodont dentition, depending on whether the mammal is an herbivore, carnivore, or omnivore. In this carnivore, the canines are prominent, and the premolars and molars are pointed—adaptations for tearing and ripping food. In herbivores, some of the incisors are large, the canines are reduced or absent, and the premolars and molars are flattened—adaptations for nipping and grinding vegetation.

Putting the Concept to Work

Why does brushing your teeth prevent tooth decay?

Processing Food in the Mouth

LEARNING OBJECTIVE 26.4.2 Describe the role of saliva, and the stages of the swallowing process.

Inside the mouth, the tongue mixes food with a mucous solution, called **saliva.** In humans, three pairs of salivary glands secrete saliva into the mouth through ducts in the mouth's mucosal lining. Saliva moistens and lubricates the food so that it is easier to swallow and does not abrade the tissue it passes on its way through the esophagus. Saliva also contains the hydrolytic enzyme *salivary amylase,* which initiates the breakdown of the polysaccharide starch into the disaccharide maltose. This digestion is usually minimal in humans, however, because most people don't chew their food very long.

The secretions of the salivary glands are controlled by the nervous system, which in humans maintains a constant flow of about half a milliliter of saliva per minute when the mouth is empty of food. This continuous secretion keeps the mouth moist. The presence of food in the mouth triggers an increased rate of saliva secretion, as taste-sensitive neurons in the mouth send impulses to the brain, which responds by stimulating the salivary glands. The most potent stimuli are acidic solutions; lemon juice, for example, can increase the rate of salivation eightfold. The sight, sound, or smell of food can stimulate salivation markedly in dogs, but in humans these stimuli are much less effective than thinking or talking about food.

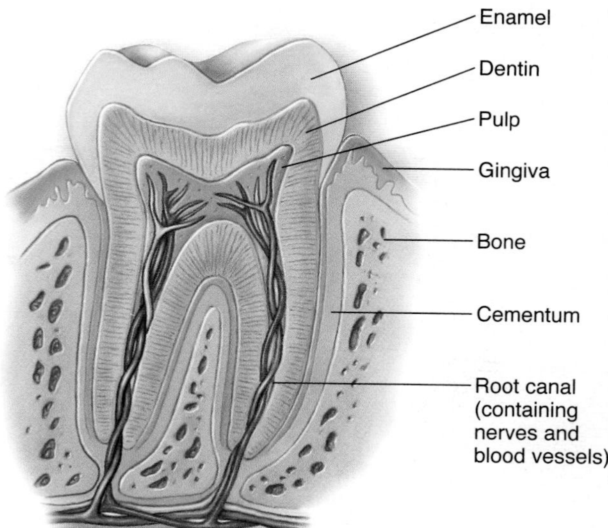

Figure 26.9 Human teeth.

Each vertebrate tooth is alive, with a central pulp containing nerves and blood vessels. The actual chewing surface is a hard enamel layered over the softer dentin, which forms the body of the tooth.

Swallowing

When food is ready to be swallowed, the tongue moves it to the back of the mouth. In mammals, the process of swallowing begins when the soft palate elevates, pushing against the back wall of the pharynx (**figure 26.10**). Elevation of the soft palate seals off the nasal cavity and prevents food from entering it ❶. Pressure against the pharynx stimulates neurons within its walls, which send impulses to the swallowing center in the brain. In response, muscles are stimulated to contract and raise the *larynx* (voice box). This pushes the *glottis,* the opening from the larynx into the trachea (windpipe), against a flap of tissue called the *epiglottis* ❷. These actions keep food out of the respiratory tract, directing it instead into the esophagus ❸.

Recall from the discussion on page 506 that the respiratory system also uses the mouth and pharynx. The elevation of the soft palate and the movement of the epiglottis over the trachea helps to keep the processes of breathing and swallowing separate.

Putting the Concept to Work

When you breathe through your mouth, air travels down your throat to your lungs. However, when you drink through your mouth, the liquid moving down your throat does *not* travel to your lungs. Why not?

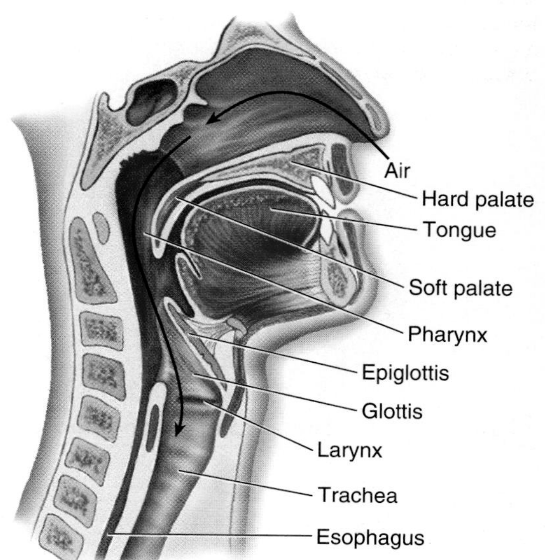

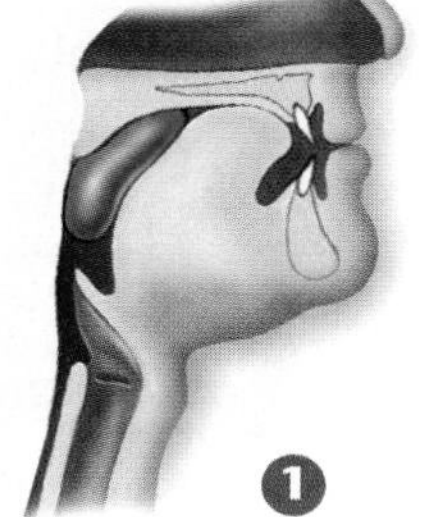

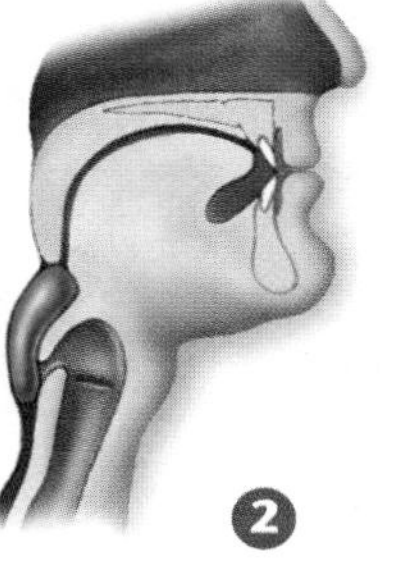

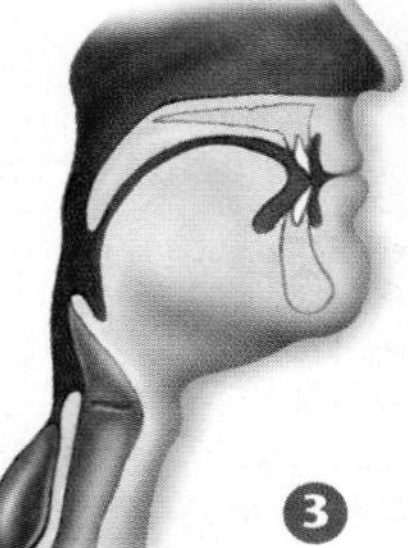

Figure 26.10 The human pharynx, palate, and larynx.

Swallowing triggers the closing of the epiglottis over the trachea, which keeps food and liquids from going down the windpipe.

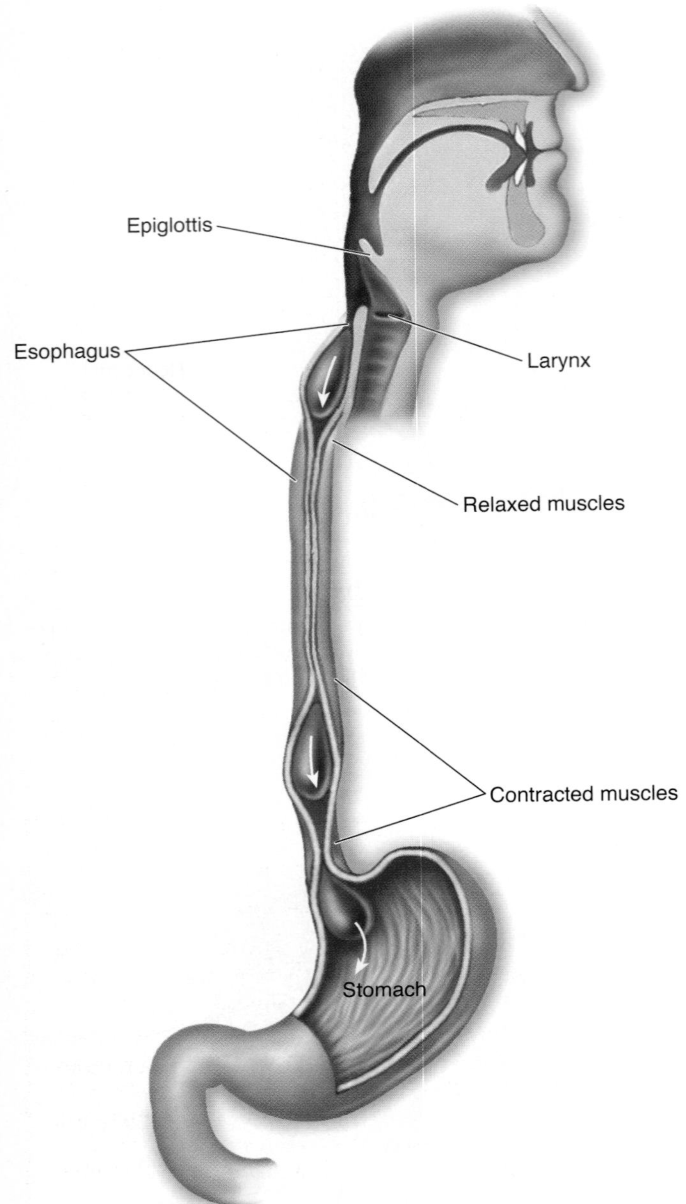

Figure 26.11 The esophagus and peristalsis.

26.5 The Esophagus and Stomach

LEARNING OBJECTIVE 26.5.1 Outline the structure and function of the esophagus and stomach.

Structure and Function of the Esophagus

Swallowed food enters a muscular tube called the **esophagus,** which connects the pharynx to the stomach. In adult humans, the esophagus is about 25 centimeters long; the upper third is enveloped in skeletal muscle, for voluntary control of swallowing, while the lower two-thirds is surrounded by involuntary smooth muscle. The swallowing center stimulates successive waves of contraction in these muscles that move food along the esophagus to the stomach. The muscles relax ahead of the food, allowing it to pass freely, and contract behind the food to push it along, as shown in figure 26.11. These rhythmic waves of muscular contraction are called **peristalsis;** they enable humans and other vertebrates to swallow even if they are upside down.

Stomach contents can be brought back up during vomiting, when the **sphincter** (a ring of circular smooth muscle between the stomach and esophagus) is relaxed and the contents of the stomach are forcefully expelled through the mouth. The relaxing of this sphincter can also result in the movement of stomach acid into the esophagus, causing an irritation called *heartburn.* Chronic and severe heartburn is a condition known as *acid reflux.*

Structure and Function of the Stomach

The **stomach** is a saclike portion of the digestive tract (figure 26.12). Its inner surface is highly convoluted, enabling it to fold up when empty and open out like an expanding balloon as it fills with food. Thus, while the human stomach has a volume of only about 50 milliliters when empty, it may expand to contain 2 to 4 liters of food when full.

The stomach contains an extra layer of smooth muscle for churning food and mixing it with *gastric juice,* an acidic secretion of the tubular gastric glands of the mucosa. The gastric glands lie at the bottom of deep depressions, the gastric pits shown in the enlargement in figure 26.12. These exocrine glands contain two kinds of secretory cells: *parietal cells,* which secrete hydrochloric acid (HCl); and *chief cells,* which secrete pepsinogen, a weak protease (protein-digesting enzyme) that requires a very low pH to be active. This low pH is provided by the HCl. Activated pepsinogen molecules then cleave each other at specific sites, producing a much more active protease, pepsin. This process of secreting a relatively inactive enzyme that is then converted into a more active enzyme outside the cell prevents the chief cells from digesting themselves. It should be noted that only proteins are partially digested in the stomach—there is no significant digestion of carbohydrates or fats there.

A solution with a low pH contains a higher concentration of hydrogen ions (H^+), as discussed on page 44. The HCl in the stomach dissociates creating a high concentration of H^+, which disrupts hydrogen bonding and causes proteins to denature, as described on page 55.

Action of Acid

The human stomach produces about 2 liters of HCl and other gastric secretions every day, creating a very acidic solution inside the stomach. The concentration of HCl in this solution is about 10 millimolar, corresponding to a pH of 2. Thus, gastric juice is about 250,000 times more acidic than blood, whose normal pH is 7.4. The low pH in the stomach helps denature food proteins, making them easier to

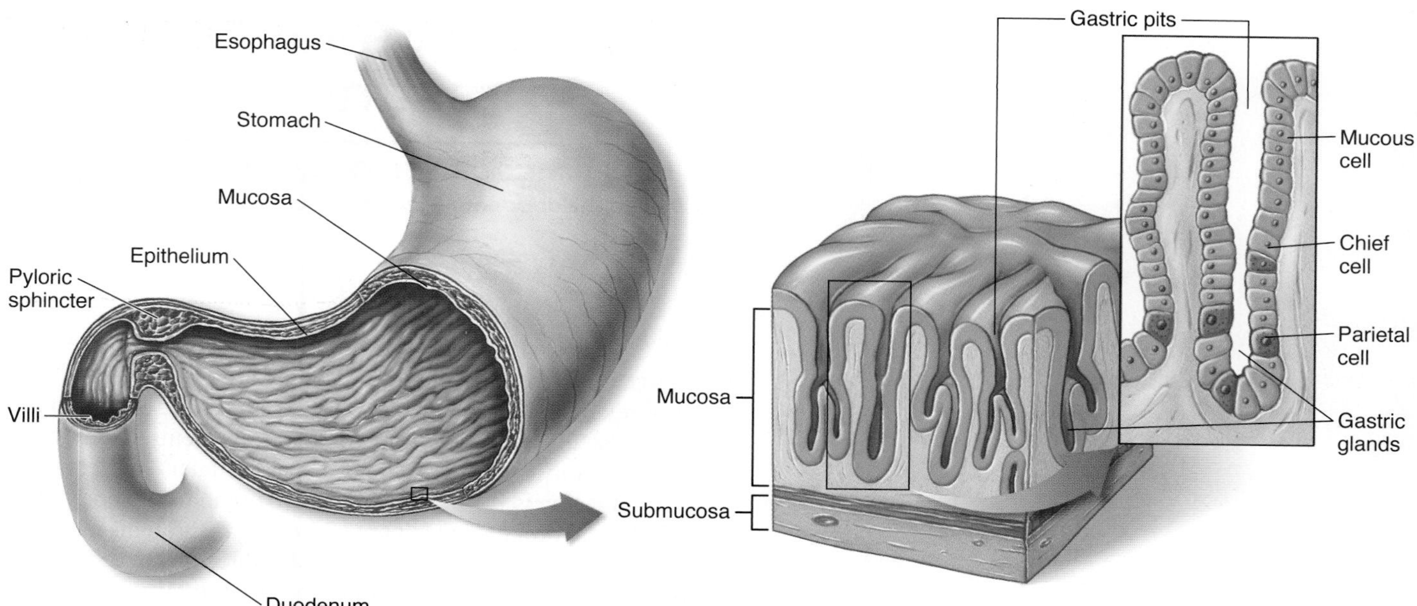

Figure 26.12 The stomach and gastric glands.

Food enters the stomach from the esophagus. The epithelial walls of the stomach are dotted with gastric pits, which contain glands that secrete hydrochloric acid (HCl) and the enzyme pepsinogen. The gastric glands consist of mucous cells, chief cells that secrete pepsinogen, and parietal cells that secrete HCl. Gastric pits are the openings of the gastric glands.

digest, and keeps pepsin maximally active. Active pepsin hydrolyzes food proteins into shorter chains of polypeptides that are not fully digested until the mixture enters the small intestine. The mixture of partially digested food and gastric juice is called **chyme.**

Ulcers

It is important that the stomach not produce too much acid. If it did, the body could not neutralize the acid later in the small intestine, a step essential for the final stage of digestion. Production of acid is controlled by hormones. These hormones are produced by endocrine cells scattered within the walls of the stomach. The hormone gastrin regulates the synthesis of HCl by the parietal cells of the gastric pits, permitting HCl to be made only when the pH of the stomach is higher than about 1.5.

Overproduction of gastric acid can occasionally eat a hole through the wall of the stomach. Such **gastric ulcers** are rare, however, because epithelial cells in the mucosa of the stomach are protected by a layer of alkaline mucus, and because those cells are rapidly replaced by cell division if they become damaged (gastric epithelial cells are replaced every two to three days). Over 90% of gastrointestinal ulcers are **duodenal ulcers,** which are ulcers of the small intestine. These may be produced when the mucosal barriers to self-digestion are weakened by an infection of the bacterium *Helicobacter pylori.* Modern antibiotic treatments can reduce symptoms and often cure the ulcer.

Leaving the Stomach

Chyme leaves the stomach at its base through the *pyloric sphincter* and enters the small intestine. This is where all terminal digestion of carbohydrates, fats, and proteins occurs, and where the products of digestion—amino acids, glucose, and fatty acids—are absorbed into the blood.

Putting the Concept to Work

Acid causes both ulcers and heartburn. Why do antibiotics cure one and not the other?

IN THE NEWS

Are Microbes Making Americans Fatter? The number of overweight Americans is skyrocketing. What is fueling this trend? Surely some of it is lifestyle. Today's "super-size-it" fast foods and "big gulp" drinks, coupled with lack of physical exercise, leave us consuming more calories without burning them off. It now appears, however, that this isn't the whole story. Researchers have recently stumbled onto a second potential cause of our collective weight problem. Your digestive system is teeming with bacteria, some 100 trillion of them, and it now appears that overweight people have a different assortment than lean people. There are two basic phyla of intestinal bacteria, *Firmicutes* and *Bacteriodetes*, and it turns out that obese people have a much higher proportion of firmicutes than lean people. When obese people are put on a diet and lose weight, the balance of bacteria shifts to that seen in lean people. The researchers discovered that overweight people gained weight not because they always ate more, but because their firmicutes are more efficient at breaking down polysaccharides into simple sugars, which the body stores as fat. In addition, firmicutes suppress your ability to produce a substance called "fasting-induced adipose factor" (Fiaf) that keeps fat cells from storing fat. By suppressing Fiaf, firmicutes cause the gates to your fat cells to stay open, so the excess sugars produced can be channeled directly into fat. Fast-food diets and lack of exercise will make anyone overweight, but firmicute intestinal microbes appear to accelerate the process. It would seem we are not only what we eat, but also who helps us eat it.

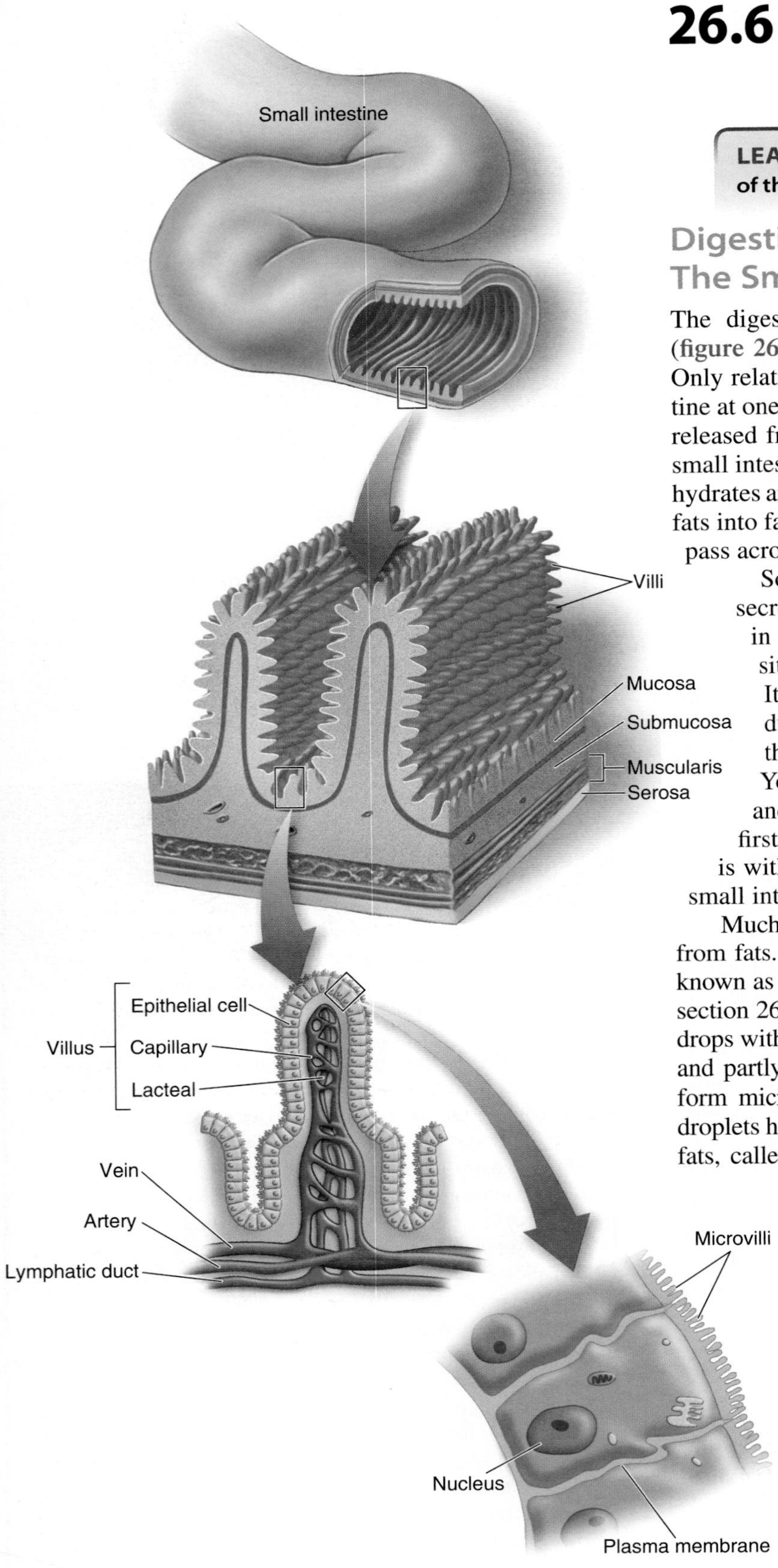

26.6 The Small and Large Intestines

LEARNING OBJECTIVE 26.6.1 Contrast the locations and roles of the duodenum, jejunum, ileum, and large intestine.

Digestion and Absorption: The Small Intestine

The digestive tract exits from the stomach into the **small intestine** (**figure 26.13**), where large molecules are broken down into small ones. Only relatively small portions of food are introduced into the small intestine at one time, to allow time for acid to be neutralized (using bicarbonate released from the pancreas and discussed later) and enzymes to act. The small intestine is the primary digestive organ of the body. Within it, carbohydrates are broken down into simple sugars, proteins into amino acids, and fats into fatty acids. Once these small molecules have been produced, they pass across the epithelial wall of the small intestine into the bloodstream.

Some of the enzymes necessary for these digestive processes are secreted by the cells of the intestinal wall. Most, however, are made in a large gland called the *pancreas* (discussed in section 26.7), situated near the junction of the stomach and the small intestine. It is one of the body's major exocrine glands (secreting through ducts). The pancreas sends its secretions into the small intestine through a duct that empties into its initial segment, the **duodenum.** Your small intestine is approximately 6 meters long—unwound and stood on its end, it would be far taller than you are! Only the first 25 centimeters, about 4% of the total length, is the duodenum. It is within this initial segment, where the pancreatic enzymes enter the small intestine, that the majority of digestion occurs.

Much of the food energy the vertebrate body harvests is obtained from fats. The digestion of fats is carried out by a collection of molecules known as *bile salts* secreted into the duodenum from the *liver* (discussed in section 26.7). Because fats are insoluble in water, they enter the intestine as drops within the watery chyme. The bile salts, which are partly lipid-soluble and partly water-soluble, work like detergents. They combine with fats to form microscopic droplets in a process called emulsification. These tiny droplets have greater surface areas upon which the enzyme that breaks down fats, called *lipase*, can work. This allows the digestion of fats to proceed more rapidly. The digested fats are first absorbed into lymphatic vessels called lacteals before they later enter the bloodstream.

Two areas make up the rest of the small intestine (96% of its length), the **jejunum** and the **ileum.** Digestion continues into the jejunum, but the ileum is devoted to absorbing water and the products of digestion into the bloodstream. The lining of the small intestine is folded into ridges, as shown in **figure 26.13**. The ridges are covered with fine fingerlike projections called **villi** (singular, **villus**), each too small to see with the naked eye. In turn, each of the cells covering a villus is covered on its outer surface by a field of cytoplasmic projections called **microvilli.** The enlargement of the villus shows epithelial cells lining the villus, and the further enlargement of these cells shows the microvilli on the surface side of the cells. Scanning and transmission electron micrographs in **figure 26.14** give you different perspectives of the microvilli. Both villi and microvilli greatly

Figure 26.13 The small intestine.

A cross section of the small intestine shows the structure of the villi and microvilli.

increase the absorptive surface of the lining of the small intestine. The average surface area of the small intestine of an adult human is about 300 square meters, more than the surface of many swimming pools!

The amount of material passing through the small intestine is startlingly large. An average human consumes about 800 grams of solid food, and 1,200 milliliters of water per day, for a total volume of about 2 liters. To this amount is added about 1.5 liters of fluid from the salivary glands, 2 liters from the gastric secretions of the stomach, 1.5 liters from the pancreas, 0.5 liters from the liver, and 1.5 liters of intestinal secretions. The total adds up to a remarkable 9 liters—more than 10% of the total volume of your body! However, although the flux is great, the *net* passage is small. Almost all these fluids and solids are reabsorbed during their passage through the small intestine—about 8.5 liters across the walls of the small intestine and 0.35 liters across the wall of the large intestine. Of the 800 grams of solids and 9 liters of liquids that enter the digestive tract each day, only about 50 grams of solids and 100 milliliters of liquids leave the body as feces.

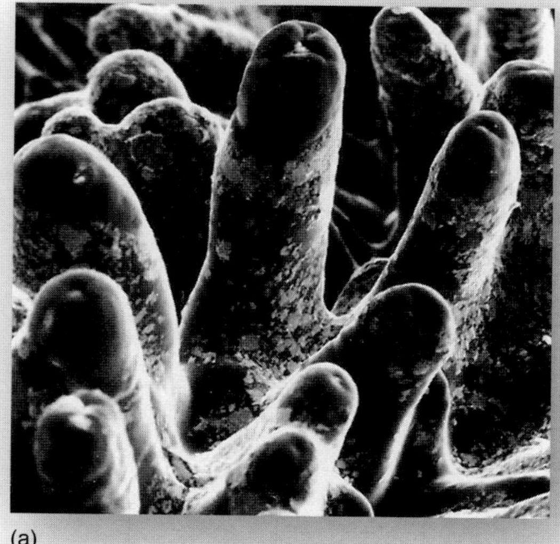

(a)

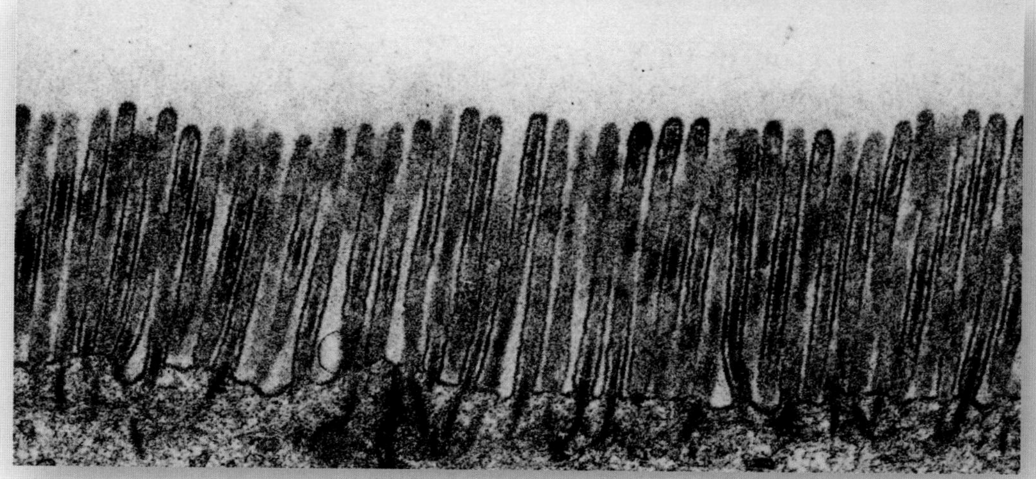

(b)

Figure 26.14 Microvilli in the small intestine.

(a) Microvilli, shown in a scanning electron micrograph, are very densely clustered, giving the small intestine an enormous surface area, which is very important for efficient absorption. (b) Intestinal microvilli as shown in a transmission electron micrograph.

Concentration of Solids: The Large Intestine

The **large intestine,** or **colon,** is much shorter than the small intestine, approximately 1 meter long, but it is called the large intestine because of its larger diameter. The small intestine empties directly into the large intestine at a junction where the cecum and the appendix are located, which are two structures no longer actively used in humans (see figure 26.5). No digestion takes place within the large intestine, and only about 6% to 7% of fluid absorption occurs there. The large intestine is not convoluted, lying instead in three relatively straight segments, and its inner surface does not possess villi. As a consequence, the large intestine has only one-thirtieth the absorptive surface area of the small intestine. Although some water, sodium, and vitamin K are absorbed across its walls, the primary function of the large intestine is to act as a refuse dump. Within it, undigested material, including large amounts of plant fiber and cellulose, is compacted and stored. Many bacteria live and actively divide within the large intestine, where they play a role in the processing of undigested material into the final excretory product, **feces.** Bacterial fermentation produces gas within the human colon at a rate of about 500 milliliters per day. This rate increases greatly after the consumption of beans or vegetable matter because the passage of undigested plant material (fiber) into the large intestine provides substrates for fermentation.

The final segment of the digestive tract is a short extension of the large intestine called the **rectum.** Compact solids within the colon pass through the rectum as a result of the peristaltic contractions of the muscles encasing the large intestine, and then out of the body through the **anus.**

Putting the Concept to Work

If you ingest 800 g (1.8 lb) of solid each day, and excrete only 50 g (0.1 lb), why don't you gain a *lot* of weight?

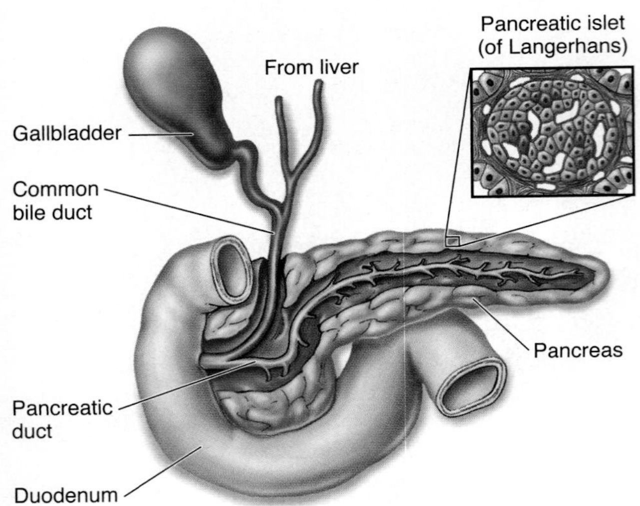

Figure 26.15 The pancreatic and bile ducts empty into the duodenum.

BIOLOGY & YOU

Vegans. We humans are omnivores, meaning we can eat a broad range of plant and animal tissues—but not all of us choose to do so. Some people don't like spinach and love steak, while others, called vegetarians, choose not to eat meat. Some become vegetarians because they judge it a more healthy diet—plants are low in saturated fats linked to heart disease. Others make the choice for ethical reasons, sensitive to the animal rights issues associated with livestock agriculture. Still others simply don't like meat. The most extreme form of vegetarian diet is the "vegan" diet. Vegans avoid all animal proteins. They don't eat red meat, poultry, fish, eggs, or milk. Instead, they obtain all protein and nutrients from grains, vegetables, fruits, legumes, nuts, and seeds. The vegan diet, mirroring that of our early human ancestors, is very challenging, because no single fruit, vegetable, or grain contains all the essential amino acids that humans require in their diet. Vegetal foods must be eaten in particular combinations to provide this necessary balance. Beans and rice together provide a balanced diet, but neither food does so when eaten alone. For calcium, which is usually obtained from milk, vegans must eat green leafy vegetables like broccoli or spinach. In practice it is not difficult to achieve this balance if a vegan eats a variety of plants.

26.7 Accessory Digestive Organs

LEARNING OBJECTIVE 26.7.1 Describe the functions of the pancreas, liver, and gallbladder.

The Pancreas

The **pancreas,** a large gland situated near the junction of the stomach and the small intestine (see figure 26.5), is one of the accessory organs that contribute secretions to the digestive tract. Fluid from the pancreas is secreted into the duodenum through the *pancreatic duct*, shown in figure 26.15. This fluid contains a host of enzymes that digest proteins, starch, and fats. Pancreatic enzymes digest proteins into smaller polypeptides, polysaccharides into shorter chains of sugars, and fats into free fatty acids and other products.

Pancreatic fluid also contains bicarbonate, which neutralizes the HCl from the stomach and gives the chyme in the duodenum a slightly alkaline pH. In addition to its exocrine role in digestion, the pancreas also functions as an endocrine gland, secreting several hormones into the blood that control the blood levels of glucose and other nutrients. These hormones are produced in the **islets of Langerhans,** clusters of endocrine cells scattered throughout the pancreas and shown in the enlarged view in figure 26.15. Two pancreatic hormones, insulin and glucagon, are discussed in chapters 27 and 30.

Endocrine glands release their products, hormones, directly into the bloodstream as described on page 584, while exocrine glands release their products into ducts that connect to nearby structures. The pancreatic hormones are discussed on page 590.

The Liver and Gallbladder

The **liver** is the largest internal organ of the body. In an adult human, the liver weighs about 1.5 kilograms and is the size of a football. The main exocrine secretion of the liver is **bile,** a fluid mixture consisting of *bile pigments* and *bile salts* that is delivered into the duodenum during the digestion of a meal. The bile salts work like detergents, dispersing large drops of fat into a fine suspension of smaller droplets. This breaking up, or emulsification, of the fat into droplets produces a greater surface area of fat upon which the lipase enzymes can act, and thus allows the digestion of fat to proceed more rapidly.

After it is produced in the liver, bile is stored and concentrated in the gallbladder (the green organ in figure 26.15). The arrival of fatty food in the duodenum stimulates the gallbladder to contract, causing bile to be injected into the duodenum through the common bile duct.

Regulatory Functions of the Liver

A large vein carries blood from the stomach and intestine directly to the liver, which is the first stop for substances absorbed from the gastrointestinal tract. The liver acts as a kind of purification plant. Ingested alcohol and other drugs are taken into liver cells and metabolized; this is why the liver is often damaged as a result of alcohol and drug abuse. The liver also removes toxins, pesticides, carcinogens, and other poisons, converting them into less toxic forms. The liver and all of the digestive organs work together (figure 26.16).

Putting the Concept to Work

If your liver ceases to function ("liver failure"), what happens that makes you seriously ill?

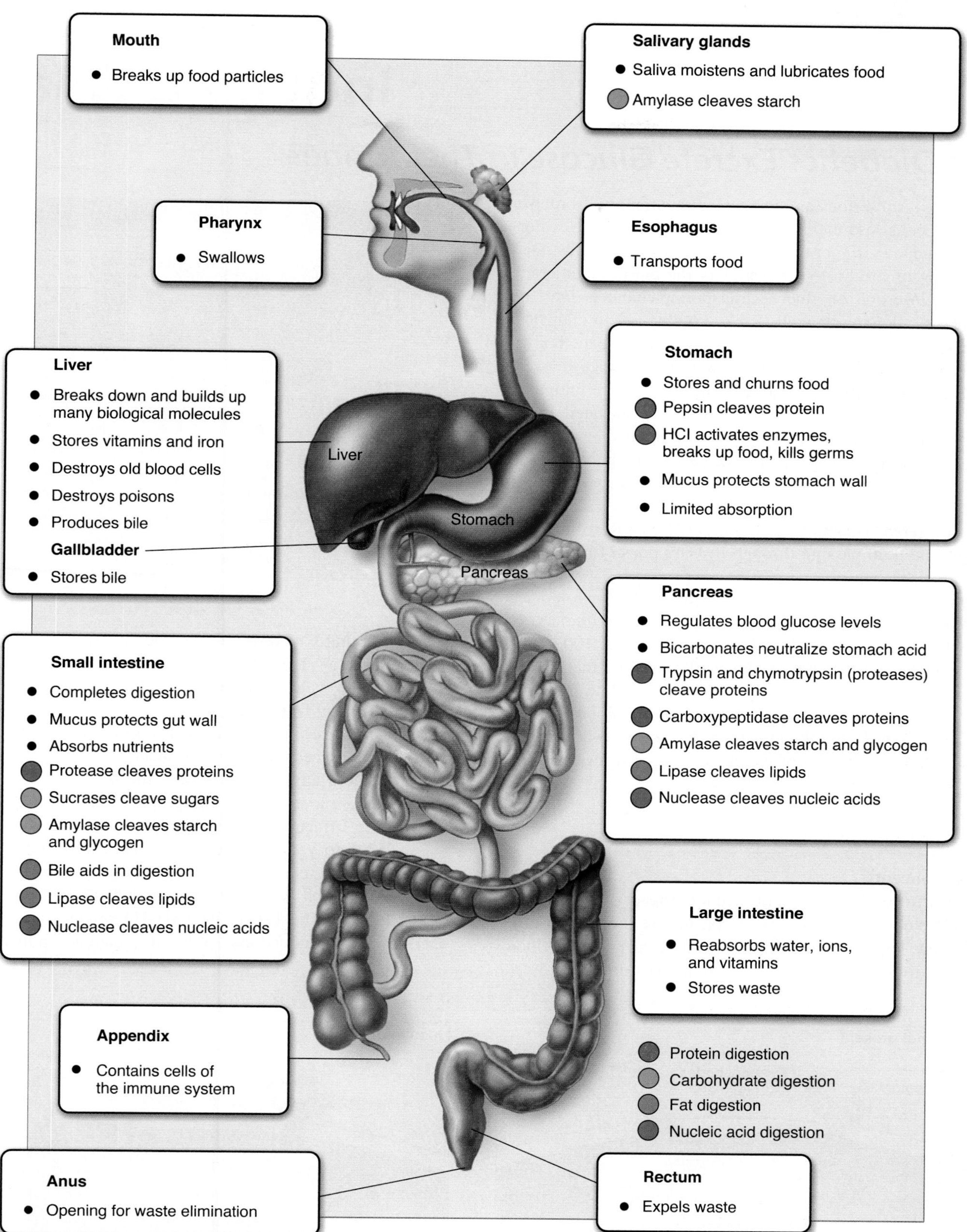
Mouth
Breaks up food particles
Salivary glands
Saliva moistens and lubricates food
Amylase cleaves starch
Pharynx
Swallows
Esophagus
Transports food
Liver
Breaks down and builds up many biological molecules
Stores vitamins and iron
Destroys old blood cells
Destroys poisons
Produces bile
Gallbladder
Stores bile
Liver
Stomach
Pancreas
Stomach
Stores and churns food
Pepsin cleaves protein
HCl activates enzymes, breaks up food, kills germs
Mucus protects stomach wall
Limited absorption
Pancreas
Regulates blood glucose levels
Bicarbonates neutralize stomach acid
Trypsin and chymotrypsin (proteases) cleave proteins
Carboxypeptidase cleaves proteins
Amylase cleaves starch and glycogen
Lipase cleaves lipids
Nuclease cleaves nucleic acids
Small intestine
Completes digestion
Mucus protects gut wall
Absorbs nutrients
Protease cleaves proteins
Sucrases cleave sugars
Amylase cleaves starch and glycogen
Bile aids in digestion
Lipase cleaves lipids
Nuclease cleaves nucleic acids
Large intestine
Reabsorbs water, ions, and vitamins
Stores waste
Appendix
Contains cells of the immune system
Protein digestion
Carbohydrate digestion
Fat digestion
Nucleic acid digestion
Anus
Opening for waste elimination
Rectum
Expels waste

Figure 26.16 The organs of the digestive system and their functions.

The digestive system contains some dozen different organs that act on the food that is consumed, starting with the mouth and ending with the anus. All of these organs must work properly for the body to effectively obtain nutrients.

Inquiry & Analysis

Why Do Diabetics Excrete Glucose in Their Urine?

Late-onset diabetes is a serious and increasingly common disorder in which the body's cells lose their ability to respond to insulin, a hormone which is needed to trigger their uptake of glucose. As illustrated below, the binding of insulin to a receptor in the plasma membrane causes the rapid insertion of glucose transporter channels into the plasma membrane, allowing the cell to take up glucose. In diabetics, however, glucose molecules accumulate in the blood while the body's cells starve for the lack of them. In mild cases, blood glucose levels rise to several times the normal value of 4 m*M;* in severe untreated cases, blood glucose levels may become enormously elevated, up to 25 times the normal value. A characteristic symptom of even mild diabetes is the excretion of large amounts of glucose in the urine. The name of the disorder, *diabetes mellitus*, means "excessive secretion of sweet urine." In normal individuals, by contrast, only trace amounts of glucose are excreted. The kidney very efficiently reabsorbs glucose molecules from the fluid passing through it. Why doesn't it do so in diabetic individuals?

The graph on the upper right displays so-called glucose tolerance curves for a normal person (*blue line*) and a diabetic (*red line*). After a night without food, each individual drank a test dose of 100 grams of glucose dissolved in water. Blood glucose levels were then monitored at 30-minute and one-hour intervals. The dotted line indicates the kidney threshold, the maximum concentration of blood glucose molecules (about 10 m*M*) that the kidney is able to retrieve from the fluid passing through it when all of its glucose-transporting channels are being utilized full-bore.

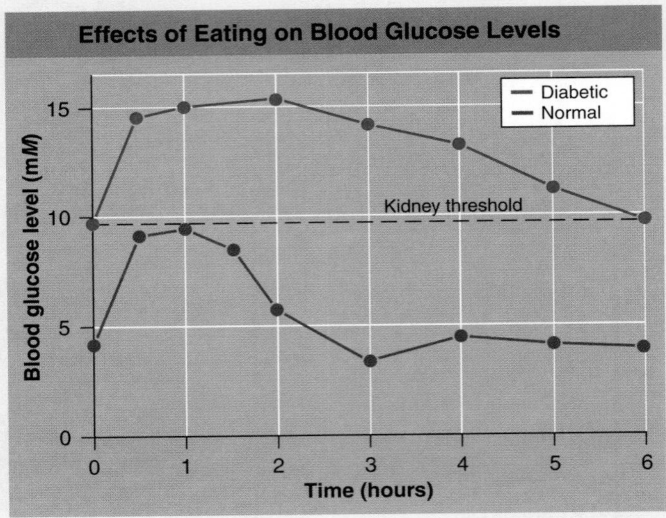

Analysis

1. **Applying Concepts**
   Reading a Curve. What is the immediate impact on the normal individual's blood glucose levels of consuming the test dose of glucose? How long does it take for the normal person's blood glucose level to return to the level before the test dose?
   Comparing Curves. Is the impact any different for the diabetic person? How long does it take for the diabetic person's blood glucose levels to return to the level before the test dose?
2. **Interpreting Data**
   a. Is there any point at which the normal individual's blood glucose levels exceed the kidney threshold?
   b. Is there any point at which the diabetic individual's blood glucose levels do *not* exceed the kidney threshold?
3. **Making Inferences**
   a. Why do you suppose the diabetic individual took so much longer to recover from the test dose?
   b. Would you expect the normal individual to excrete glucose? Explain. The diabetic individual? Explain.
4. **Drawing Conclusions** Why do diabetic individuals secrete sweet urine?

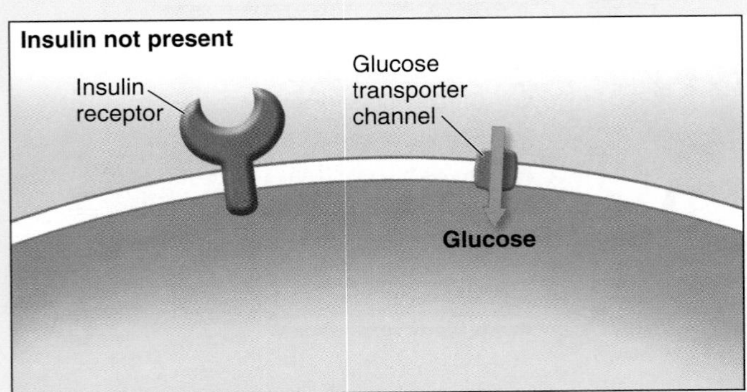

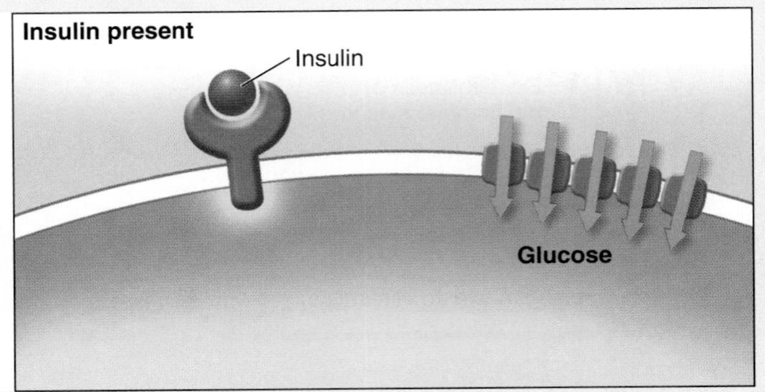

Summary of Learning Outcomes

Food Energy and Essential Nutrients

Food for Energy and Growth

26.1.1 Animals consume food as a source of energy and as a source of essential molecules and minerals. For humans, a balanced diet of fruits, vegetables, grains, proteins, and dairy is recommended, as indicated by the nutrition plate shown here from **figure 26.1.**

- The energy from food is either used up through metabolic activity (the BMR and exercise) or is stored as fat in fat cells. Fats have a higher energy content per gram, about 9.3 calories per gram, compared to 4.1 calories for carbohydrates and proteins. If a person consumes a lot of calories, especially in the form of fats, but doesn't burn off those calories through exercise, the energy is stored as fat. A measurement called a body mass index (BMI) is an easy guide to determining whether a person is overweight or obese.

26.1.2 Many animals must consume foods that contain essential amino acids, minerals, and vitamins that the body needs but cannot produce itself.

Digestion

Types of Digestive Systems

26.2.1 All animals are heterotrophs. Heterotrophs are divided into three groups based on what they eat. Herbivores eat exclusively plants, carnivores are meat eaters, and omnivores have diets that contain both plants and meat.

- Single-celled organisms and lower animal phyla, such as sponges, digest food intracellularly. Food is taken up by individual cells and is broken down inside the cells.
- All other animals digest food extracellularly. Digestive enzymes are released into a cavity or tract where they break down food. The products of digestion are then absorbed by cells in the body. The digestive cavity in flatworms and cnidarians, like the *Hydra* shown here from **figure 26.3**, is called the gastrovascular cavity.
- Theevolutionofaone-waydigestivetract has allowed specialization of the digestive tract, where different regions of the tract are involved in different digestive functions.

Vertebrate Digestive Systems

26.3.1 Vertebrate digestion occurs in a tubular gastrointestinal tract with specialized areas for different digestive functions. The size or structure of specialized digestive areas vary in different animal groups depending on the animal's diet.

The Mouth and Teeth

26.4.1 In vertebrates, food is first brought into the mouth. Reptiles and mammals tear and grind food with teeth. Birds break up food in the gizzard, a compartment of their digestive system. In the gizzard, food is churned and ground up with pebbles that the bird has swallowed. In other vertebrates, teeth are used to chew up food, breaking it into smaller pieces.

26.4.2 The chewed food mixes with saliva in the mouth. Saliva moistens and lubricates the food and it contains the enzyme salivary amylase that begins the digestion of starches. The moistened food is then swallowed, passing from the mouth into the esophagus. A flap called the epiglottis closes over the trachea so that the food passes down the esophagus and not into the windpipe.

The Esophagus and Stomach

26.5.1 Food is moved along the esophagus to the stomach by peristaltic waves of muscle contractions. A ring of smooth muscle, called a sphincter, closes off the esophagus from the stomach, keeping food from coming back up.

- In the stomach, muscle contractions churn up the food with gastric juice, which contains hydrochloric acid and pepsin, a protein-digesting enzyme activated by HCl. Gastric juice is produced by two gastric glands. These exocrine glands in the stomach lining contain two types of secretory cells: parietal cells that secrete HCl and chief cells that secrete pepsinogen. The low pH in the stomach due to the HCl activates pepsinogen to pepsin.
- Proteins are partially digested in the stomach by pepsin. The acidic conditions in the stomach help denature proteins so they are easier to digest in the small intestine. The partially digested food and gastric juice that leaves the stomach is called chyme.

The Small and Large Intestines

26.6.1 Most digestion occurs in the initial upper portion of the small intestine, called the duodenum. The acidic chyme from the stomach passes into the duodenum, where it is neutralized and mixed with other digestive enzymes. Some enzymes are secreted by the cells that line the walls of the intestine, but most enzymes and other digestive substances are produced in the pancreas or other accessory organs. The rest of the small intestine is involved in absorption of food molecules and water. The lining of the small intestine is folded into ridges which are covered with fingerlike projections called villi, shown here from **figure 26.13.** The surface of the cells that line the villi are themselves covered with cytoplasmic projections called microvilli. Villi and microvilli increase the surface area for absorption.

- The large intestine collects and compacts solid waste, releasing it through the rectum and anus.

Accessory Digestive Organs

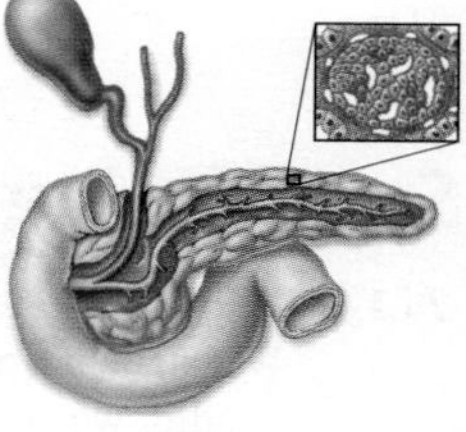

26.7.1 The pancreas, shown here from **figure 26.15**, produces protein-digesting enzymes, a starch-digesting enzyme, and a fat-digesting enzyme. The pancreatic fluid also contains bicarbonate, which neutralizes the acidic chyme.

- The liver produces bile (a mixture of bile pigments and bile salts), which breaks down fats. Bile is stored in the gallbladder and released into the small intestine. All of the organs of digestion work together.

Test Your Understanding

26.2.1 One-way passage of food through the digestive system of many animal groups allows
a. intracellular digestion.
b. specialization of different regions of the digestive system.
c. release of digestive enzymes into the gut.
d. extracellular digestion.

26.3.1 Organisms with longer digestive systems, which help break down foods that are difficult to digest, are usually
a. herbivores.
b. carnivores.
c. omnivores.
d. detritivores.

26.4.1 The purpose of a gizzard, like teeth, is to
a. hold on to prey.
b. begin the chemical digestion of food.
c. release enzymes.
d. begin the physical digestion of food.

26.4.2 When a mammal swallows food, the food is prevented from going up into the nasal cavity by the
a. esophagus.
b. tongue.
c. soft palate.
d. epiglottis.

26.5.1 The first site of protein digestion in the digestive system occurs in the
a. mouth.
b. esophagus.
c. stomach.
d. small intestine.

26.6.1 Which of the following statements is *false*?
a. Villi and microvilli improve the efficiency of absorption in the small intestine.
b. The surface area of the large intestine is greater than that of the small intestine.
c. Digestion occurs primarily in the duodenum.
d. About 6% to 7% of fluid absorption takes place in the colon.

26.6.1 Most of the absorption of food molecules takes place in the
a. stomach.
b. liver.
c. small intestine.
d. large intestine.

26.6.1 The purpose of the villi and microvilli in the small intestine is to
a. neutralize stomach acid.
b. produce bile.
c. produce digestive enzymes.
d. increase the surface area of the small intestine for absorption of nutrients.

26.6.1 The primary function of the large intestine is
a. the breakdown and absorption of fats.
b. the absorption of water.
c. the concentration of solid wastes.
d. the absorption of vitamin C.

26.7.1 The _______________ secretes digestive enzymes and bicarbonate solution into the small intestine to aid digestion.
a. pancreas
b. liver
c. gallbladder
d. All of the above.

Apply Your Understanding

26.4.1 "Don't talk with your mouth full" is parental advice that is important for not only social reasons (manners) but for medical reasons. Talking while eating can result in choking. Explain how this could occur.

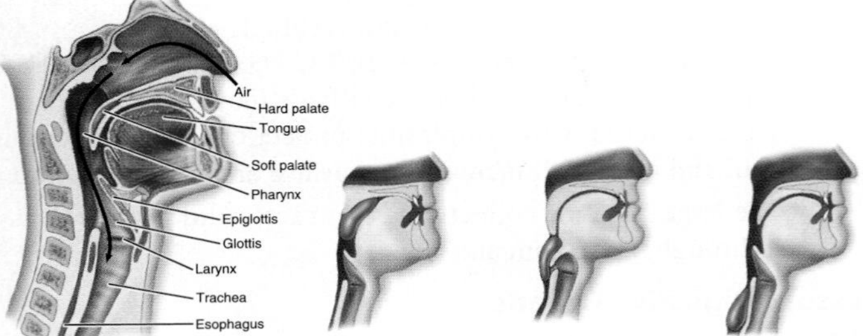

26.7.1 What are the functions of the tan-colored organ and the green-colored organ shown here?

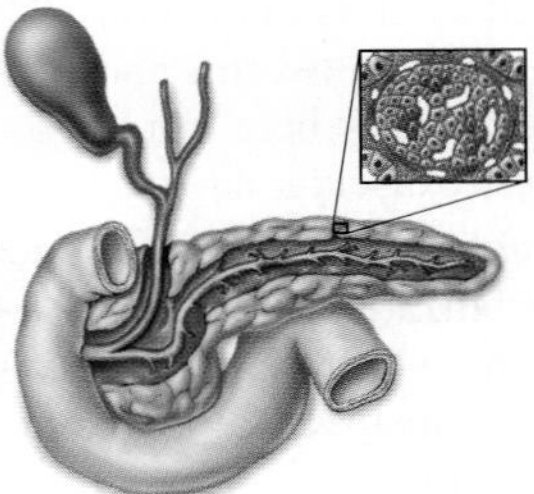

Synthesize What You Have Learned

26.1.1 Why is it so important for Popeye, and you, to eat your green leafy vegetables (spinach, chard, turnip and mustard greens, broccoli, cauliflower, cabbage)?

26.1.1 You're going on a backpacking trip with three friends. Lisa wants to pack trail snacks of chocolate cupcakes; Chris wants to take beef jerky. Andre insists that you should all pack GORP (good old raisins and peanuts—sometimes known as trail mix). They turn to you to decide. Explain which one is best for a quick snack to keep up your energy on a long hike, and why.

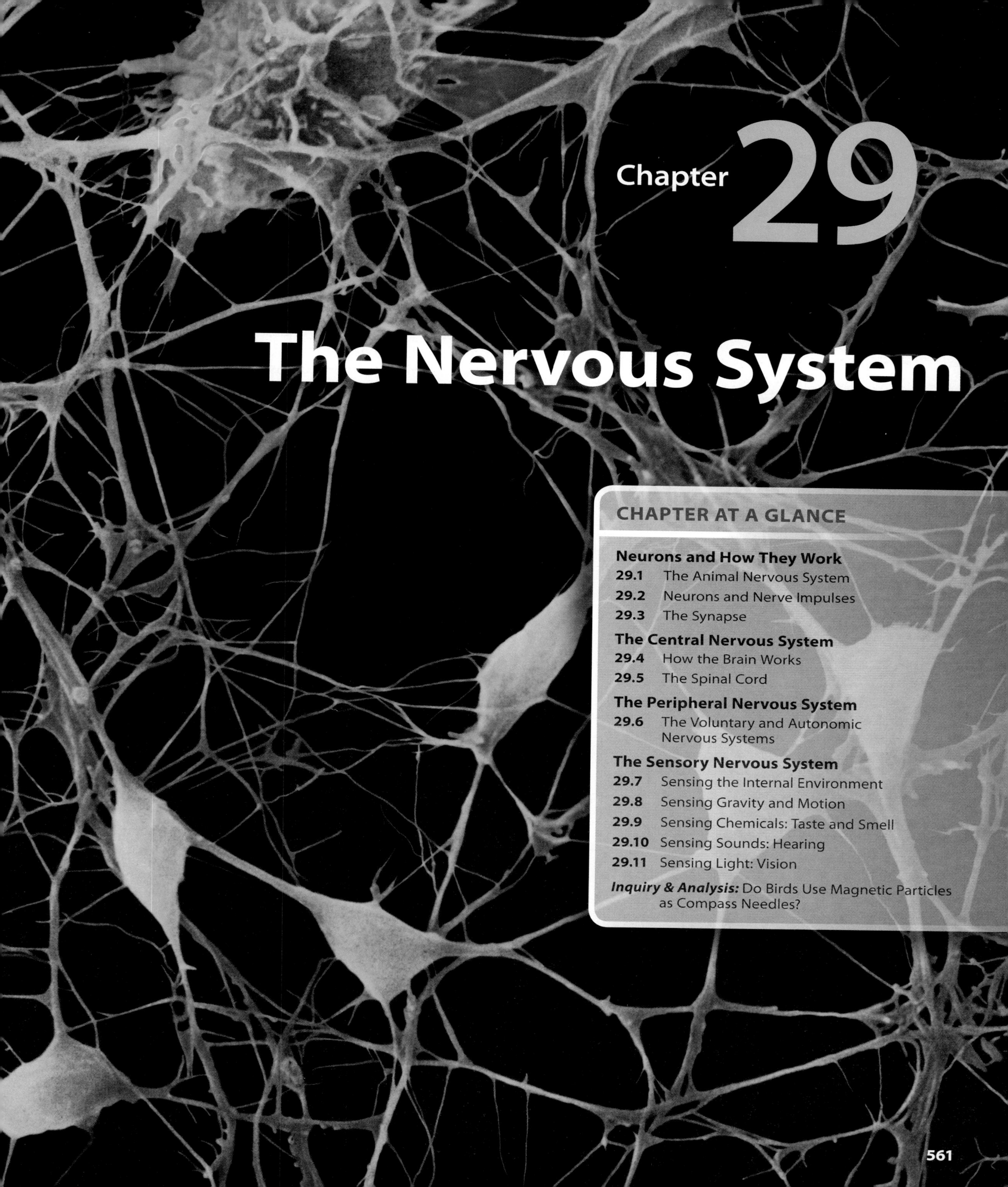

Chapter 29

The Nervous System

CHAPTER AT A GLANCE

Neurons and How They Work

29.1 The Animal Nervous System

29.2 Neurons and Nerve Impulses

29.3 The Synapse

The Central Nervous System

29.4 How the Brain Works

29.5 The Spinal Cord

The Peripheral Nervous System

29.6 The Voluntary and Autonomic Nervous Systems

The Sensory Nervous System

29.7 Sensing the Internal Environment

29.8 Sensing Gravity and Motion

29.9 Sensing Chemicals: Taste and Smell

29.10 Sensing Sounds: Hearing

29.11 Sensing Light: Vision

Inquiry & Analysis: Do Birds Use Magnetic Particles as Compass Needles?

Neurons and How They Work

29.1 The Animal Nervous System

LEARNING OBJECTIVE 29.1.1 **Identify the three types of neurons in the animal nervous system and describe their functions.**

An animal must be able to respond to environmental stimuli. To do this, it must have sensory receptors that can detect the stimulus and motor effectors that can respond to it. In most invertebrate phyla and in all vertebrate classes, sensory receptors and motor effectors are linked by way of the **nervous system** (figure 29.1). As described in chapter 23, the nervous system consists of neurons and supporting cells. One type of neuron, called **association neurons** (or **interneurons**), is present in the nervous systems of most invertebrates and all vertebrates. In vertebrates, these neurons are located in the brain and spinal cord, which together are called the **central nervous system (CNS),** represented by the yellow circle in figure 29.1. They help provide more complex reflexes and, in the case of the brain, higher associative functions, including learning and memory, which require integration of many sensory inputs.

There are two other types of neurons. **Sensory** (or **afferent**) **neurons** (❶ in figure 29.2) carry impulses from sensory receptors to the CNS. **Motor** (or **efferent**) **neurons** ❸ carry impulses away from the CNS to effectors—muscles and glands. The association neurons ❷ link these two types of neurons together in the CNS. Together, motor and sensory neurons constitute the **peripheral nervous system (PNS)** of vertebrates (the bracketed tan circles in figure 29.1).

Putting the Concept to Work

Do sensory nerves carry impulses toward or away from the CNS?

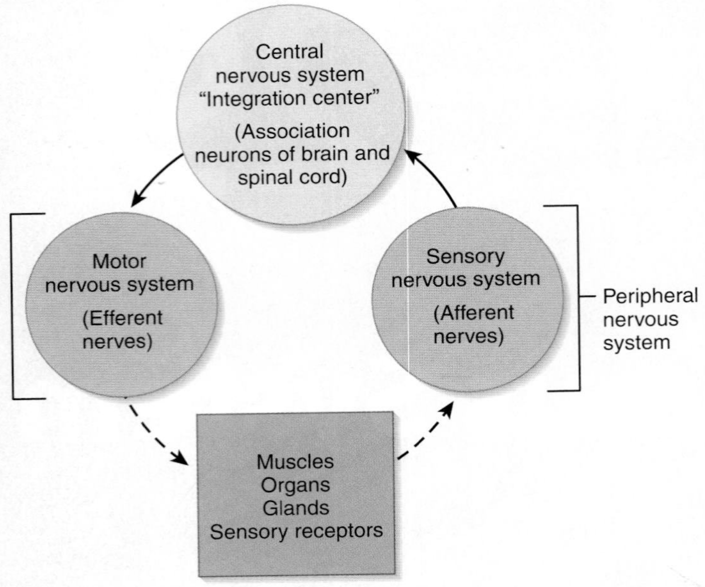

Figure 29.1 Organization of the vertebrate nervous system.

The central nervous system, consisting of the brain and spinal cord, issues commands via the motor nervous system and receives information from the sensory nervous system. The motor and sensory nervous systems together make up the peripheral nervous system.

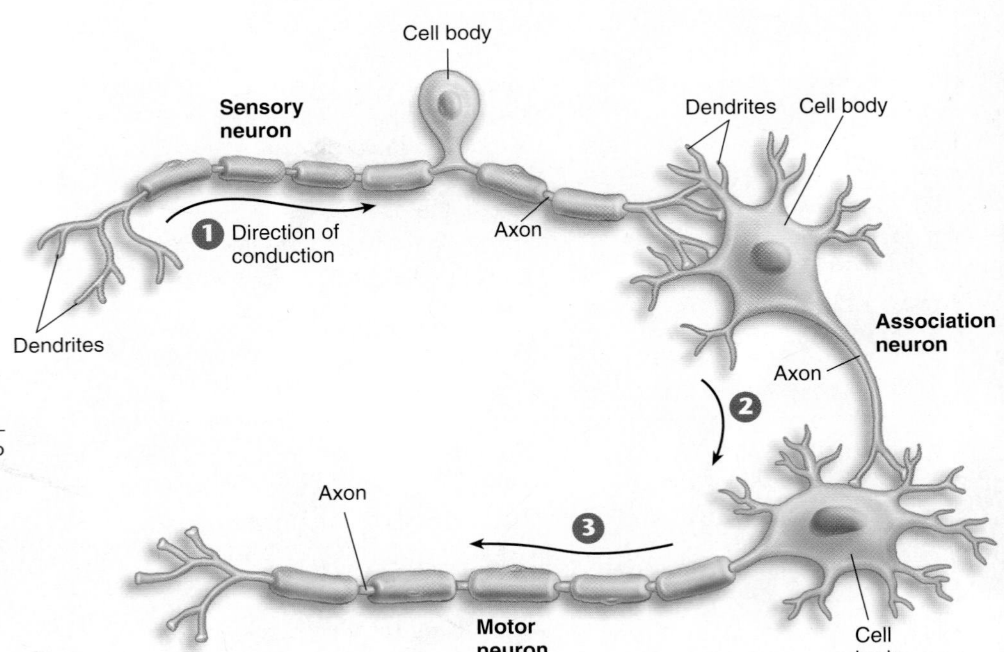

Figure 29.2 Three types of neurons.

Sensory neurons carry information about the environment to the brain and spinal cord. *Association neurons* are found in the brain and spinal cord and often provide links between sensory and motor neurons. *Motor neurons* carry impulses to muscles and glands (effectors).

29.2 Neurons and Nerve Impulses

LEARNING OBJECTIVE 29.2.1 Describe the basic structure of a neuron, and the functions of supporting cells, myelin, and nodes of Ranvier.

Neurons

The basic structural unit of the nervous system, whether central, motor, or sensory, is the nerve cell, or **neuron.** All neurons have the same basic structure as you can see by comparing the three cell types in figure 29.2 and the generalized cell in figure 29.3*a*. The *cell body* in figure 29.3*a* is the flat region of the neuron containing the nucleus. Short, slender branches called *dendrites* extend from one end of a neuron's cell body. Dendrites are input channels. Nerve impulses travel inward along them, toward the cell body. Motor and association neurons possess a profusion of highly branched dendrites, enabling those cells to receive information from many different sources simultaneously. Projecting out from the other end of the cell body is a single, long, tubelike extension called an *axon.* Axons are output channels. Nerve impulses travel outward along them, away from the cell body, toward muscles or glands, or to other neurons.

Most neurons are unable to survive alone for long; they require the nutritional support provided by supporting cells. More than half the volume of the human nervous system is composed of supporting cells and two of the most important kinds are **Schwann cells** and **oligodendrocytes.** These cells envelop the axons of neurons with a sheath of fatty material called myelin, which acts as an electrical insulator. Schwann cells produce myelin in the PNS, while oligodendrocytes produce myelin in the CNS. During development, these cells associate with the axon, as shown at the top in figure 29.3*b*, and begin to wrap themselves around the axon several times to form a **myelin sheath,** an insulating covering consisting of multiple layers of membrane. Axons that have myelin sheaths are said to be myelinated, and those that don't are unmyelinated. The myelin sheath is interrupted at intervals, leaving uninsulated gaps called **nodes of Ranvier** (the nodes are where the yellow underlying axon can be seen). At the node regions, the axon is in direct contact with the surrounding fluid. The nerve impulse jumps from node to node, speeding its travel down the axon. Multiple sclerosis, discussed in chapter 28, is a debilitating clinical disorder that results from the degeneration of the myelin sheath.

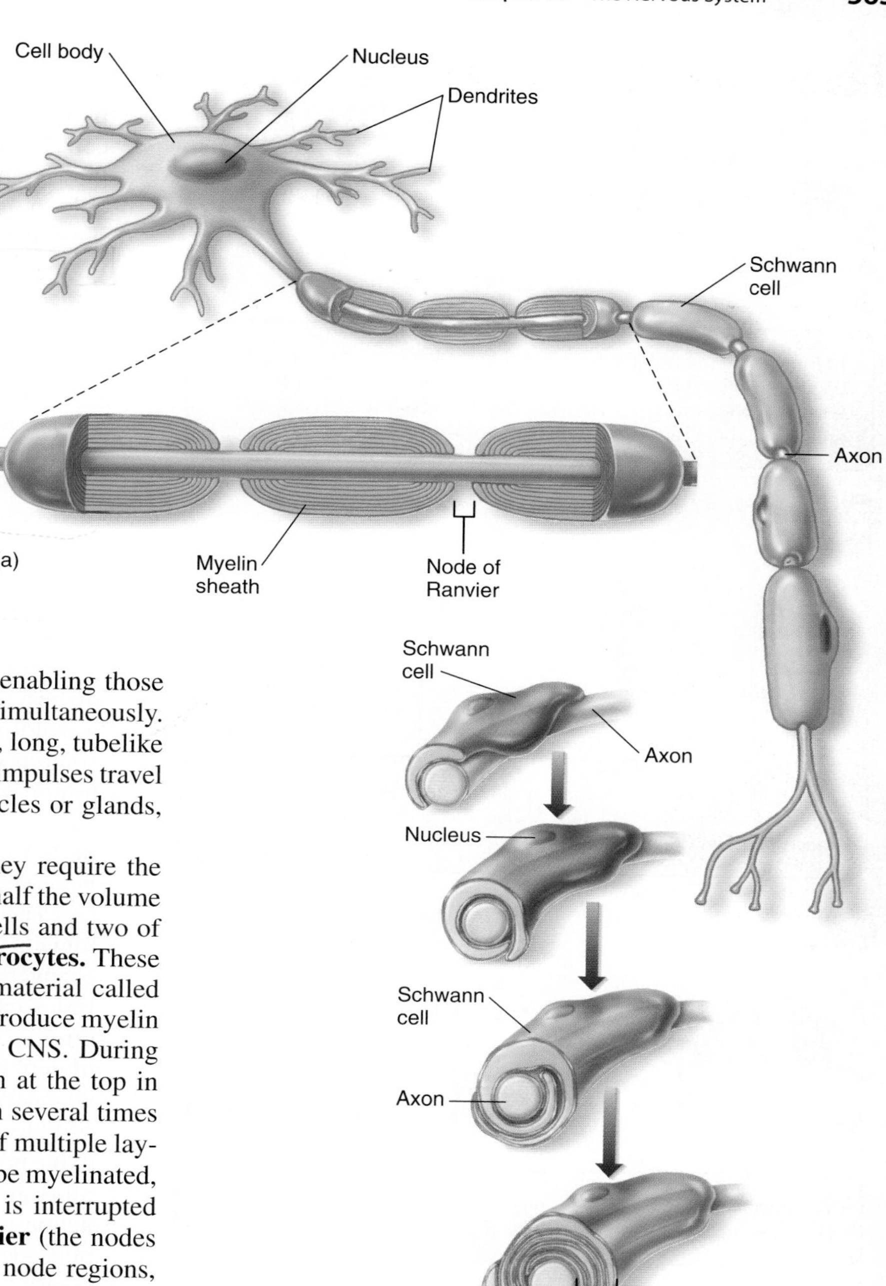

Figure 29.3 Structure of a typical neuron and formation of the myelin sheath.

(a) Extending from the cell body are many dendrites, which receive information and carry it to the cell body. A single axon transmits impulses away from the cell body. Many axons are encased by a myelin sheath, whose multiple membrane layers facilitate a more rapid conduction of impulses. The sheath is interrupted at regular intervals by small gaps called nodes of Ranvier. In the peripheral nervous system, myelin sheaths are formed by supporting Schwann cells. (b) The myelin sheath is formed by successive wrappings of Schwann cell membranes around the axon.

Putting the Concept to Work

Why does a disease that destroys myelin result in paralysis?

The Nerve Impulse

LEARNING OBJECTIVE 29.2.2 Explain how ion movements create an action potential and propagate a nerve impulse.

When a neuron is "at rest," not carrying an impulse, active transport proteins in the neuron's plasma membrane transport sodium ions (Na^+) out of the cell and potassium ions (K^+) in. This sodium-potassium pump, which

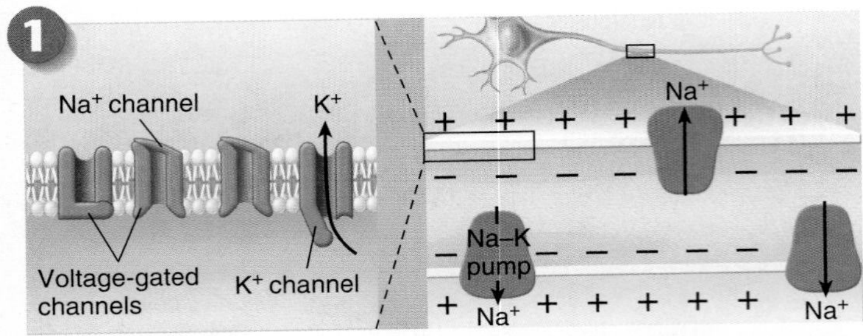

At the resting membrane potential, the inside of the axon is negatively charged because the sodium-potassium pump keeps a higher concentration of Na^+ outside. Voltage-gated ion channels are closed, but there is some leakage of K^+.

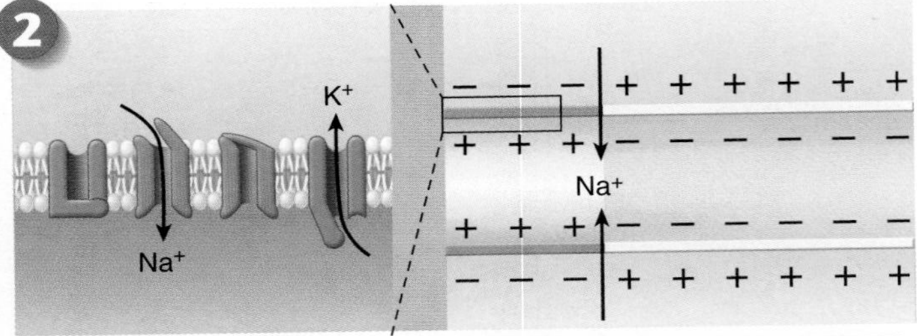

In response to a stimulus, the membrane depolarizes: voltage-gated Na^+ channels open, Na^+ flows into the cell, and the inside becomes more positive.

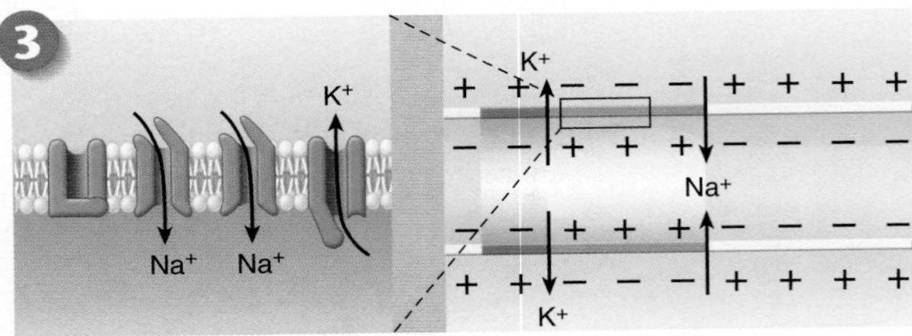

The local change in voltage opens adjacent voltage-gated Na^+ channels, and an action potential is produced.

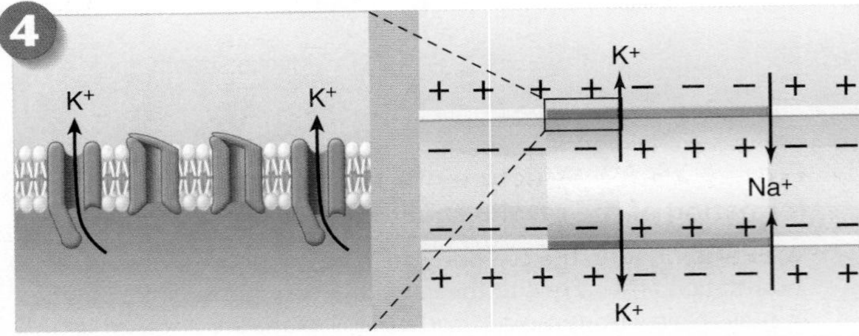

As the action potential travels farther down the axon, voltage-gated Na^+ channels close and K^+ channels open, allowing K^+ to flow out of the cell and restoring the negative charge inside the cell. Ultimately, the sodium-potassium pump restores the resting membrane potential.

Figure 29.4 How an action potential works.

was described in chapter 4, requires an expenditure of energy to function. Sodium ions cannot easily move back into the cell once they are pumped out, so the concentration of sodium ions builds up outside the cell. Similarly, potassium ions accumulate inside the cell, although they are not as highly concentrated because many potassium ions are able to diffuse out through open channels. The result is to make the outside of the neuron more positive than the inside, a condition called the *resting membrane potential*, indicated by the yellow coloring in panel 1 of figure 29.4. The resting plasma membrane is said to be "polarized."

Neurons are constantly expending energy to pump sodium ions out of the cell, in order to maintain the resting membrane potential. Using sophisticated instruments, scientists have been able to measure the voltage difference between the neuron interior and exterior as –70 millivolts (thousandths of a volt). The resting membrane potential is the starting point for a nerve impulse.

A nerve impulse travels along the axon and dendrites as an electrical current caused by ions moving in and out of the neuron through **voltage-gated channels** (that is, protein channels in the neuron membrane that open and close in response to an electrical voltage). The impulse starts when pressure or other sensory inputs disturb a neuron's plasma membrane, causing sodium channels on a dendrite to open (the purple channels in panel 2). As a result, sodium ions flood into the neuron from outside, down their concentration gradient, and for a brief moment a localized area inside of the membrane is "depolarized," becoming more positively charged in that immediate area of the axon (indicated by the pink coloring in panel 3).

The sodium channels in the small patch of depolarized membrane remain open for only about a half a millisecond. However, if the change in voltage becomes large enough, reaching **threshold potential,** it causes nearby voltage-gated sodium and potassium channels to open (panel 3). The sodium channels open first, which starts a wave of depolarization moving down the neuron. The opening of the gated channels causes nearby voltage-gated channels to open, like a chain of falling dominoes. This local reversal of voltage moving along the axon is called an **action potential.** An action potential follows an all-or-none law: A large enough depolarization produces either a full action potential or none at all, because the voltage-gated Na^+ channels open completely or not at all. Once they open, an action potential occurs. After a slight delay, potassium voltage-gated channels open and K^+ flows out of the cell down its concentration gradient, making the inside of the cell more negative. The increasingly negative membrane potential (colored green in panel 4) causes the voltage-gated sodium channels to snap closed again. This period of time after the action potential has passed and before the resting membrane potential is restored, is called the *refractory period.* A second action potential cannot fire during the refractory period; the resting potential must first be restored by the actions of the sodium-potassium pump.

The depolarization and restoration of the resting membrane potential takes only about 5 milliseconds. Fully 100 such cycles could occur, one after another, in the time it takes to say the word *nerve.*

Putting the Concept to Work

What is the difference between a resting potential, a threshold potential, and an action potential?

29.3 The Synapse

LEARNING OBJECTIVE 29.3.1 Describe a synapse, and explain how a neurotransmitter transmits a nerve impulse across it.

A nerve impulse travels along a neuron until it reaches the end of the axon, usually positioned very close to another neuron, a muscle cell, or gland. Axons, however, do not actually make direct contact with other cells. Instead, a narrow gap, 10 to 20 nanometers across, called the *synaptic cleft,* separates the axon tip and the target cell. This junction of an axon with another cell is called a **synapse.** The cell on the axon side of a synapse (on the left in figure 29.5) is called the **presynaptic neuron;** the cell on the receiving side of the synapse is called the **postsynaptic cell.**

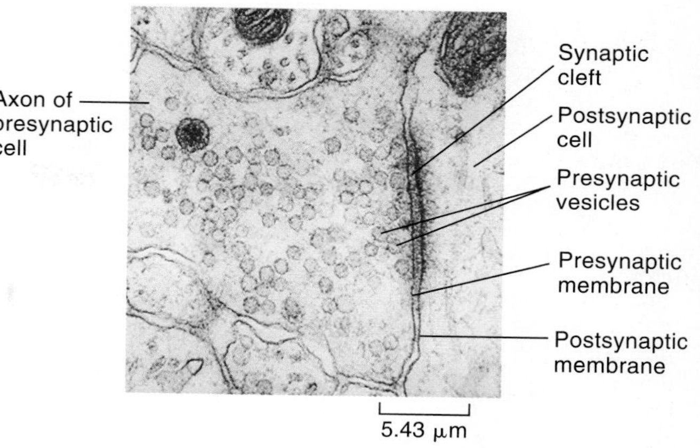

Figure 29.5 A synapse between two neurons.

This micrograph clearly shows the space between the presynaptic and postsynaptic membranes, which is called the synaptic cleft.

Neurotransmitters

When a nerve impulse reaches the end of an axon, its message must cross the synapse if it is to continue. Messages do not "jump" across synapses. Instead, they are carried across by chemical messengers called **neurotransmitters.** These chemicals are packaged in tiny sacs, or vesicles, at the tip of the axon. When a nerve impulse arrives at the tip, it causes the sacs to release their contents into the synapse, as shown in figure 29.6*a*. The neurotransmitters diffuse across the synaptic cleft and bind to receptors (the purple structures) in the postsynaptic membrane. The signal passes to the postsynaptic cell when the binding of the neurotransmitter opens special ion channels, allowing ions to enter the postsynaptic cell and cause a change in electrical charge across its membrane. The enlarged view of figure 29.6*a* shows how the channel opens and the ion (the yellow ball) enters the cell. Because these channels open when stimulated by a chemical, they are said to be *chemically gated.*

Why go to all this trouble? Why not just wire the neurons directly together? For the same reason that the wires of your house are not all connected but instead are separated by a host of switches. When you turn on one light switch, you don't want every light in the house to go on, the toaster to start heating, and the television to come on! If every neuron in your body were connected to every other neuron, it would be impossible to move your hand without moving every other part of your body at the same time. Synapses are the control switches of the nervous system. However, the control switch must be turned off at some point by getting rid of the neurotransmitter, or the postsynaptic cell would stay stimulated and keep firing action potentials. In some cases the neurotransmitter molecules diffuse away from the synapse. In other cases the neurotransmitter molecules are either reabsorbed by the presynaptic cell or degraded in the synaptic cleft.

Putting the Concept to Work

Why remove neurotransmitters from the synapse, if they are transmitting the impulse?

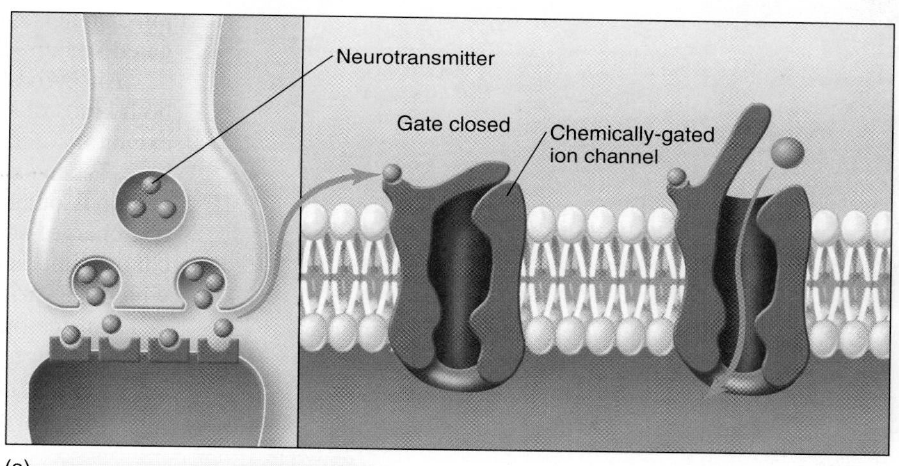

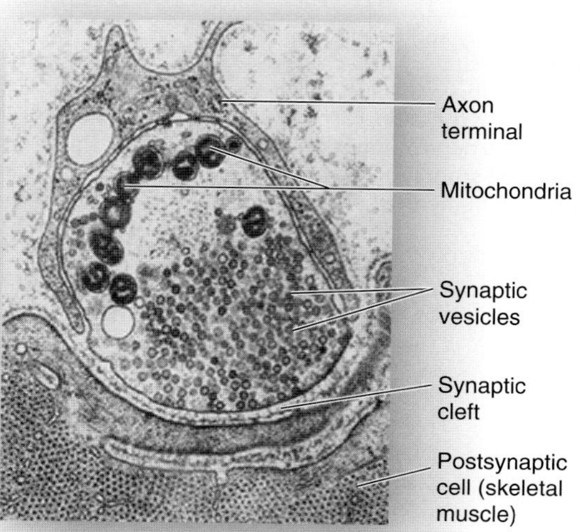

Figure 29.6 Events at the synapse.

(a) When a nerve impulse reaches the end of an axon, it releases a neurotransmitter into the synaptic cleft. The neurotransmitter molecules diffuse across the synapse and bind to receptors on the postsynaptic cell, opening ion channels. (b) A transmission electron micrograph of the tip of an axon filled with synaptic vesicles.

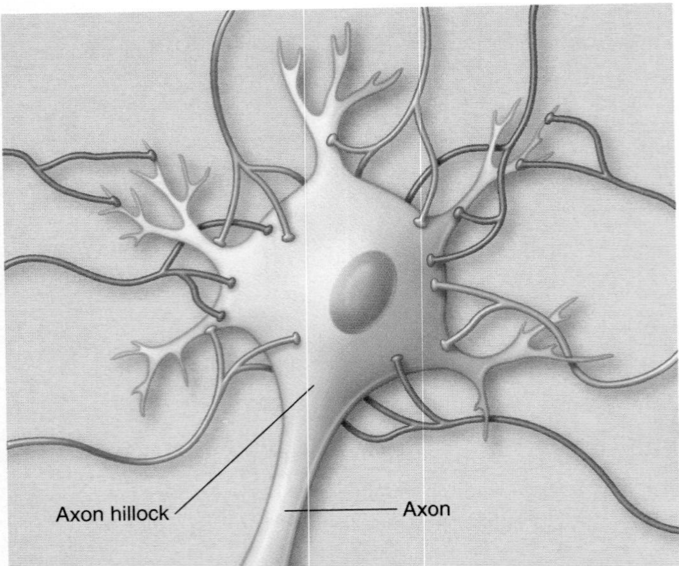

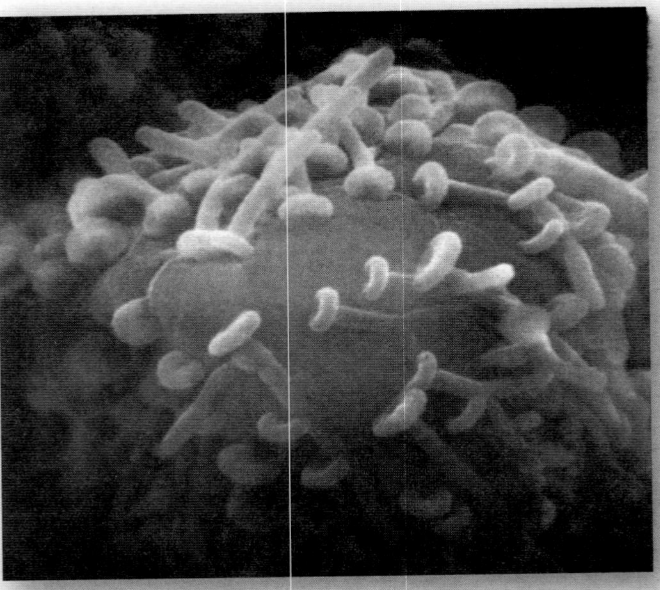

Figure 29.7 Integration.

Many different axons synapse with the cell body and dendrites of the postsynaptic neuron illustrated here. Excitatory synapses are shown in *red* and inhibitory synapses are shown in *blue*. The summed influence of their input at the base of the axon, called the axon hillock, determines whether or not a nerve impulse will be sent down the axon extending below. The scanning electron micrograph shows a neuronal cell body with numerous synapses.

Kinds of Synapses

LEARNING OBJECTIVE 29.3.2 **Contrast excitatory and inhibitory synapses, and explain how they together produce neural integration.**

The vertebrate nervous system uses dozens of different kinds of neurotransmitters, each recognized by specific receptors on receiving cells. They fall into two classes, depending on whether they excite or inhibit the postsynaptic cell.

In an *excitatory synapse,* the receptor protein is usually a chemically gated sodium channel. On binding with a neurotransmitter whose shape fits it, the sodium channel opens, allowing sodium ions to flood inward. If enough sodium ion channels are opened by neurotransmitters, an action potential begins.

In this case, the sodium channel opens due to the binding of a neurotransmitter, but once open, Na^+ travels into the cell by diffusion, down its concentration gradient as discussed on page 85.

In an *inhibitory synapse,* the receptor protein is a chemically gated potassium or chloride channel. Binding with its neurotransmitter opens these channels, leading to the exit of positively charged potassium ions or the influx of negatively charged chloride ions, resulting in a more negative interior in the receiving cell. This inhibits the start of an action potential, because the negative voltage change inside means that even more sodium ion channels must be opened to get a domino effect started among voltage-gated sodium channels to start an action potential.

An individual nerve cell, like the neuron in figure 29.7, can possess both kinds of synaptic connections to other nerve cells. In the drawing, the excitatory synapses are colored red and the inhibitory synapses are colored blue. When signals from both excitatory and inhibitory synapses reach the cell body of a neuron, the excitatory effects (which cause less internal negative charge) and the inhibitory effects (which cause more internal negative charge) interact with one another. The result is a process of **integration** in which the various excitatory and inhibitory electrical effects tend to cancel or reinforce one another. If the result of the integration is a large enough depolarization (where the inside of the cell becomes more positive), an action potential will fire. Neurons often receive many inputs. A single motor neuron in the spinal cord may have as many as 50,000 synapses on it!

Neurotransmitters and Their Functions

Acetylcholine (ACh) is the neurotransmitter released at the neuromuscular junction, the synapse that forms between a neuron and a muscle fiber. ACh forms an excitatory synapse with skeletal muscle but has the opposite effect on cardiac muscle, causing an inhibitory synapse.

Glycine and *GABA* are inhibitory neurotransmitters. This inhibitory effect is very important for neural control of body movements and other brain functions. Interestingly, the drug diazepam (Valium) causes its sedative and other effects by enhancing the binding of GABA to its receptors.

Biogenic amines are a group of neurotransmitters that include *dopamine,* important in controlling body movements, *norepinephrine* and the hormone *epinephrine*, both involved in the autonomic nervous system, and *serotonin,* which is involved in sleep and emotional states.

Putting the Concept to Work

Which type of synapse, excitatory or inhibitory, uses sodium channels?

The Central Nervous System

29.4 How the Brain Works

LEARNING OBJECTIVE 29.4.1 Describe the principal role of the cerebral cortex, the thalamus, the hypothalamus, the cerebellum, and the brain stem.

The structure and function of the vertebrate brain have long been the subject of scientific inquiry. Despite ongoing research, scientists are still not sure how the brain performs many of its functions. For instance, scientists continue to look for the mechanism the brain employs to store memories, and they do not understand how some memories can be "locked away," only to surface in times of stress. The brain is the most complex vertebrate organ ever to evolve, and it can perform a bewildering variety of complex functions.

The Cerebrum Is the Control Center of the Brain

Although vertebrate brains differ in the relative importance of different components, the human brain is a good model of how vertebrate brains function. About 85% of the weight of the human brain is made up of the cerebrum, the tan convoluted area in figure 29.8. The cerebrum is a large rounded area of the brain divided by a groove into right and left halves called cerebral hemispheres. The sectioned brain in figure 29.8 is cut along the center groove, with the left hemisphere removed, showing the right hemisphere. The cerebrum functions in language, conscious thought, memory, personality development, vision, and a host of other activities we call "thinking and feeling." The cerebrum, which looks like a wrinkled mushroom, is positioned over and surrounding the rest of the brain, like a hand holding a fist. Much of the neural activity of the cerebrum occurs within a thin, gray outer layer only a few millimeters thick called the **cerebral cortex** (*cortex* is Latin for "bark of a tree"). This layer is gray because it is densely packed with neuron cell bodies. The human cerebral cortex contains the cell bodies of more than 10 billion nerve cells (figure 29.9), roughly 10% of all the neurons in the brain. The wrinkles in the surface of the cerebral cortex increase its surface area (and number of cell bodies) threefold. Underneath the cortex is a solid white region of myelinated nerve fibers that shuttle information between the cortex and the rest of the brain.

The right and left cerebral hemispheres are linked by bundles of neurons called *tracts*. These tracts serve as information highways, telling each half of the brain what the other half is doing. Because these tracts cross over, in the area of the brain called the *corpus callosum* (the blue-colored band in figure 29.8), each half of the brain controls muscles and glands on the opposite side of the body. Therefore, a touch on the right hand is relayed primarily to the left cerebral hemisphere, which may then initiate a movement or some other type of response to the touch.

Researchers have found that the two sides of the cerebrum can operate as two different brains. For instance, in some people the tract between the two hemispheres has been cut by accident or surgery. In laboratory experiments, one eye of an individual with such a "split brain" is covered and a stranger is introduced. If the other eye is then covered instead, the person does not recognize the stranger who was just introduced!

Sometimes blood vessels in the brain are blocked by blood clots, causing a disorder called a *stroke*. During a stroke, circulation to an area in the brain is blocked and the brain tissue dies. A severe stroke in one side of the cerebrum often causes paralysis of the other side of the body.

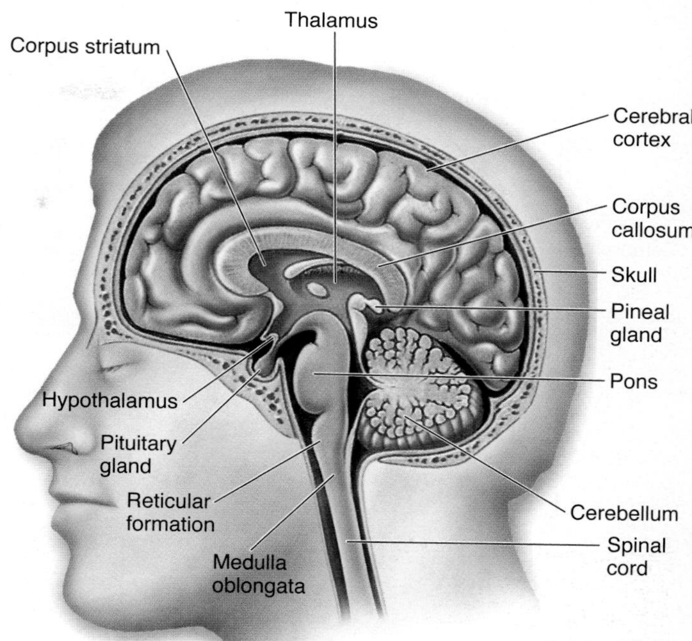

Figure 29.8 A section through the human brain.

The cerebrum occupies most of the brain. Only its outer layer, the cerebral cortex, is visible on the surface.

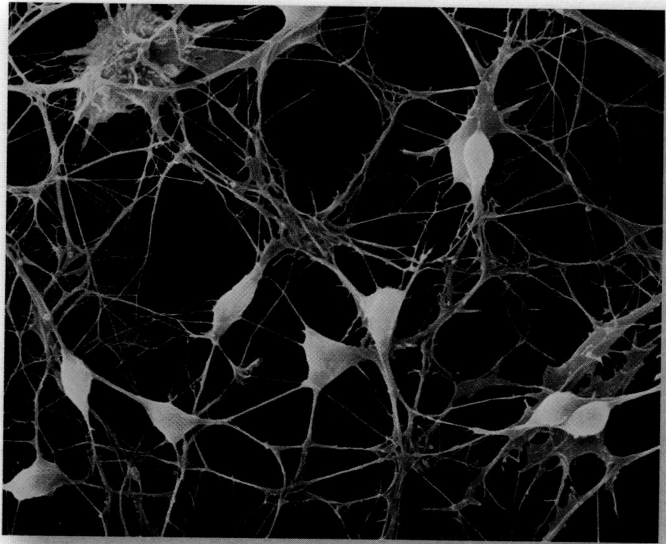

Figure 29.9 The cerebral cortex is a neural network of astonishing complexity.

The network of neurons seen here, magnified over a thousand times, is transmitting signals within the cerebral cortex, a layer of grey matter only a few millimeters thick on the brain's outer surface. Densely packed with neurons and highly convoluted, it is the site of higher mental activities, like your reading and understanding these words.

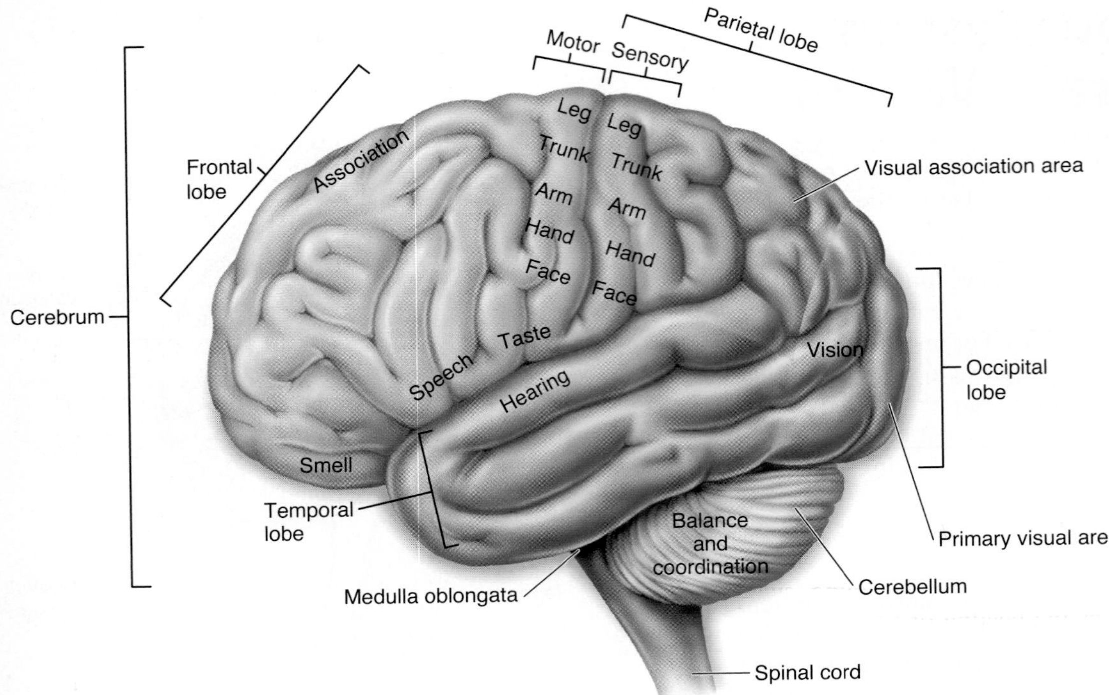

Figure 29.10 The major functional regions of the human brain.

Specific areas of the cerebral cortex are associated with different regions and functions of the body.

Figure 29.10 shows the general areas of the brain and the functions they control. The hemispheres of the cerebrum are divided into the frontal, parietal, occipital, and temporal lobes.

The Thalamus and Hypothalamus Process Information

Beneath the cerebrum are the thalamus and hypothalamus, important centers for information processing. The thalamus is the major site of sensory processing in the brain. Auditory (sound), visual, and other information from sensory receptors enter the thalamus and then are passed to the sensory areas of the cerebral cortex (indicated in figure 29.10). The thalamus also controls balance. Information about posture, derived from the muscles, and information about orientation, derived from sensors within the ear, combine with information from the cerebellum and pass to the thalamus. The thalamus processes the information and channels it to the appropriate motor center on the cerebral cortex.

The hypothalamus integrates all the internal activities of the body. It controls centers in the brain stem that in turn regulate body temperature, blood pressure, respiration, and heartbeat. It also directs the secretions of the brain's major hormone-producing gland, the pituitary gland. The hypothalamus is linked by an extensive network of neurons to other areas of the cerebral cortex. This network, along with parts of the hypothalamus and areas of the brain called the *hippocampus* and *amygdala,* make up the **limbic system.** The areas highlighted in green in figure 29.11 indicate the components of the limbic system. The operations of the limbic system are responsible for many of the most deep-seated drives and emotions of vertebrates, including pain, anger, sex, hunger, thirst, and pleasure, centered in the amygdala.

The role of the hypothalamus in the endocrine system is quite significant, as discussed on page 589. The hypothalamus directs the release of hormones from the pituitary gland, some of which are also produced in the hypothalamus.

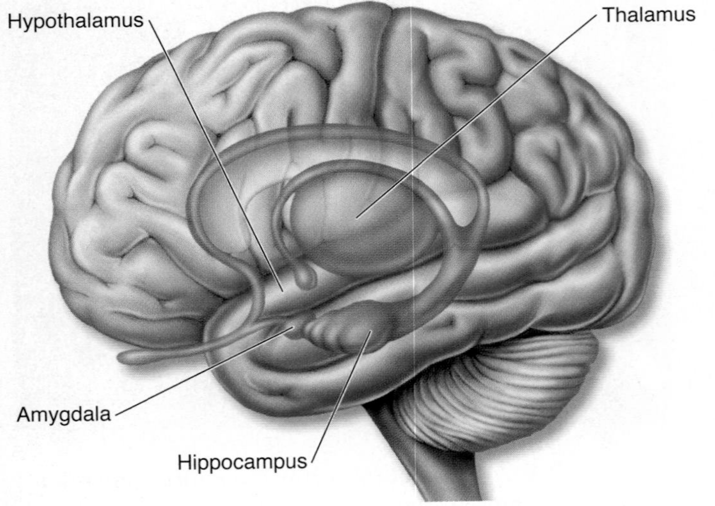

Figure 29.11 The limbic system.

The hippocampus and the amygdala are the major components of the limbic system, which controls our most deep-seated drives and emotions.

The limbic system is also the area of the brain affected by drugs such as cocaine, and the hippocampus is involved in memory.

The Cerebellum Coordinates Muscle Movements

Extending back from the base of the brain is a structure known as the **cerebellum.** The cerebellum controls balance, posture, and muscular coordination. This small, cauliflower-shaped structure, while well developed in humans and other mammals, is even more developed in birds. Birds perform more complicated feats of balance than we do, because they move through the air in three dimensions. Imagine the kind of balance and coordination needed for a bird to land on a branch, stopping at precisely the right moment without crashing into it.

The Brain Stem Controls Vital Body Processes

The **brain stem,** a term used to collectively refer to the midbrain, pons, and medulla oblongata, connects the rest of the brain to the spinal cord. This stalklike structure contains nerves that control your breathing, swallowing, and digestive processes, as well as the beating of your heart and the diameter of your blood vessels. A network of nerves called the *reticular formation* runs through the brain stem and connects to other parts of the brain. Their widespread connections make these nerves essential to consciousness, awareness, and sleep. One part of the reticular formation filters sensory input, enabling you to sleep through repetitive noises such as traffic yet awaken instantly when a telephone rings.

Language and Other Higher Functions

Although the two cerebral hemispheres seem structurally similar, they are responsible for different activities. The most thoroughly investigated example of this lateralization of function is language. The left hemisphere is the "dominant" hemisphere for language—the hemisphere in which most neural processing related to language is performed (figure 29.12).

While the dominant hemisphere for language is adept at sequential reasoning, like that needed to formulate a sentence, the nondominant hemisphere (the right hemisphere in most people) is adept at spatial reasoning, the type of reasoning needed to assemble a puzzle or draw a picture. It is also the hemisphere primarily involved in musical ability—a person with damage to the speech area in the left hemisphere may not be able to speak but may retain the ability to sing!

One of the great mysteries of the brain is the basis of memory and learning. There is no one part of the brain in which all aspects of a memory appear to reside. Although memory is impaired if portions of the brain, particularly the temporal lobes, are removed, it is not lost entirely. Many memories persist in spite of the damage, and the ability to access them gradually recovers with time. Therefore, investigators who have tried to probe the physical mechanisms underlying memory often have felt that they were grasping at a shadow.

Putting the Concept to Work

Contrast the limbic system with the reticular formation.

Figure 29.12 Different brain regions control various activities.

The colors indicate how the brain reacts in human subjects asked to listen to a spoken word, to read that same word silently, to repeat the word out loud, and then to speak a word related to the first. Regions of white, red, and yellow show the greatest activity.

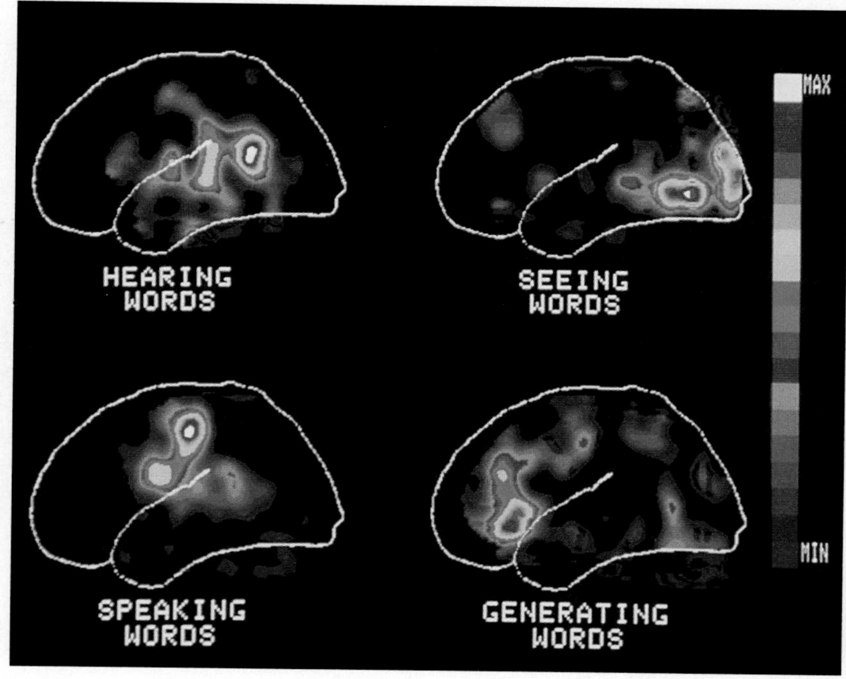

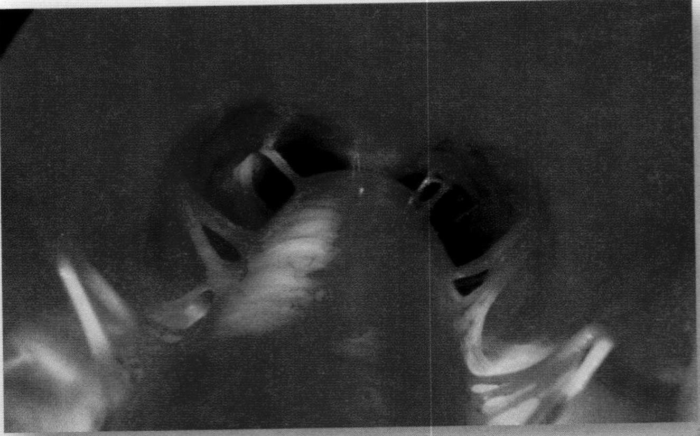

Figure 29.13 A view down the human spinal cord.

Pairs of spinal nerves can be seen extending out from the spinal cord. Along these nerves, the brain and spinal cord communicate with the body.

29.5 The Spinal Cord

LEARNING OBJECTIVE 29.5.1 Describe the structure of the spinal cord and explain its general function.

The **spinal cord** is a cable of neurons extending from the brain down through the backbone, which is the view in figure 29.13. The cross section through the spinal cord in figure 29.14 shows a darker gray area in the center that consists of neuron cell bodies, which form a column down the length of the cord. This column is surrounded by axons and dendrites, which make the outer edges of the cord white because they are coated with myelin. The spinal cord is surrounded and protected by a series of bones called the vertebrae. Spinal nerves pass out to the body from between the vertebrae. Messages between the body and the brain run up and down the spinal cord, like an information highway.

The vertebrae, individual bones stacked one on top of the other, make up the vertebral column as discussed on page 482. Because the vertebral column is made up of a series of bones, it is flexible, allowing the animal to flex its back, but it also protects the spinal cord.

In each segment of the spine, motor nerves extend out of the spinal cord to the muscles. Motor nerves from the spine control most of the muscles below the head. This is why injuries to the spinal cord often paralyze the lower part of the body. A muscle is paralyzed and cannot move if its motor neurons are damaged.

Spinal Cord Regeneration

In the past, scientists have tried to repair severed spinal cords by installing nerves from another part of the body to bridge the gap and act as guides for the spinal cord to regenerate. But most of these experiments have failed because the nerve bridges did not go from white matter to gray matter. Also, there is a factor that inhibits nerve growth in the spinal cord. After discovering that fibroblast growth factor stimulates nerve growth, neurobiologists tried gluing on the nerves, from white to gray matter, with fibrin that had been mixed with the fibroblast growth factor. Three months later, rats with the nerve bridges began to show movement in their lower bodies. In further analyses of the experimental animals, dye tests indicated that the spinal cord nerves had regrown from both sides of the gap. Many scientists are encouraged by the potential to use a similar treatment in human medicine. However, most spinal cord injuries in humans do not involve a completely severed spinal cord; often, nerves are crushed instead of severed. Also, although the rats with nerve bridges did regain some locomotory ability, tests indicated that they were barely able to walk or stand.

Figure 29.14 The vertebrate nervous system.

The spinal cord connects to the base of the brain, and nerves extend out from the spinal cord to all parts of the body.

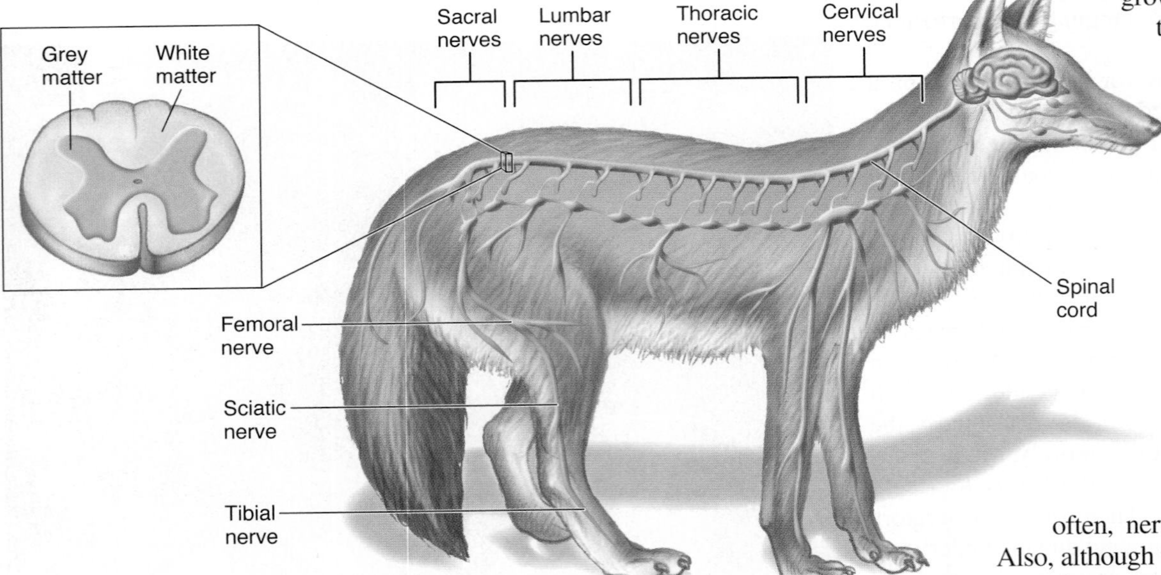

Putting the Concept to Work

Why can't a severed spine be repaired?

The Peripheral Nervous System

29.6 The Voluntary and Autonomic Nervous Systems

LEARNING OBJECTIVE 29.6.1 Contrast the voluntary and autonomic nervous systems, describing the opposing actions of the sympathetic and parasympathetic nervous systems.

As you learned in the opening discussion in section 29.1, the nervous system is divided into two main parts: the central nervous system (the pink boxes in figure 29.15) and the peripheral nervous system (the blue boxes). The motor pathways of the peripheral nervous system of a vertebrate can be further subdivided into the **somatic (voluntary) nervous system,** which relays commands to skeletal muscles, and the **autonomic (involuntary) nervous system,** which stimulates glands and relays commands to the smooth muscles of the body and to cardiac muscle. The voluntary nervous system can be controlled by conscious thought. You can, for example, command your hand to move. The autonomic nervous system, by contrast, cannot be controlled by conscious thought. You cannot, for example, tell the smooth muscles in your digestive tract to speed up their action. The central nervous system issues commands over both voluntary and autonomic systems, but you are conscious of only the voluntary commands.

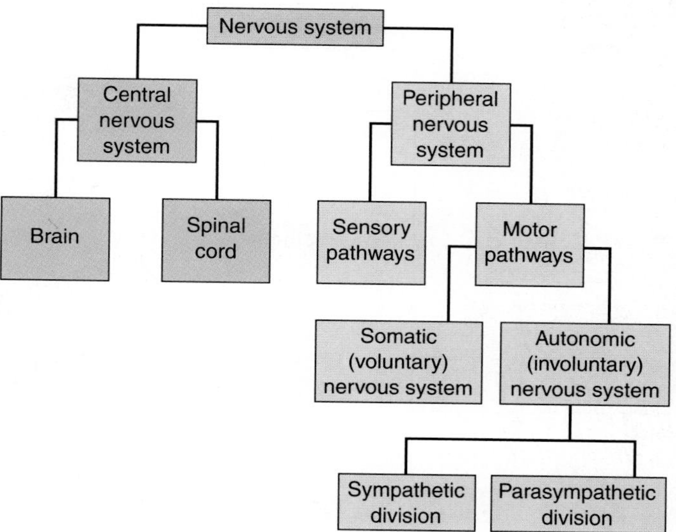

Figure 29.15 The divisions of the vertebrate nervous system.

The motor pathways of the peripheral nervous system are the somatic (voluntary) and autonomic nervous systems.

Voluntary Nervous System

Motor neurons of the voluntary nervous system stimulate skeletal muscles to contract in two ways. First, motor neurons may stimulate the skeletal muscles of the body to contract in response to conscious commands. For example, if you want to bounce a basketball, your CNS sends messages through motor neurons to the muscles in your arms and hands. However, skeletal muscle can also be stimulated as part of reflexes that do not require conscious control.

Reflexes Enable Quick Action. The motor neurons of the body have been wired to enable the body to act particularly quickly in time of danger—even before the animal is consciously aware of the threat. These sudden, involuntary movements are called reflexes. A **reflex** produces a rapid motor response to a stimulus because the sensory neuron bringing information about the threat passes the information directly to a motor neuron. One of the most frequently used reflexes in your body is blinking, a reflex that protects your eyes. If anything, such as an insect or a cloud of dust, approaches your eye, the eyelid blinks closed even before you realize what has happened. The reflex occurs before the cerebrum is aware the eye is in danger.

Because they involve passing information between few neurons, reflexes are very fast. Many reflexes never reach the brain. The "danger" nerve impulse travels only as far as the spinal cord and then comes right back as a motor response. Most reflexes involve a single connecting interneuron between the sensory neuron and the motor neuron. A few, like the knee-jerk reflex in figure 29.16,

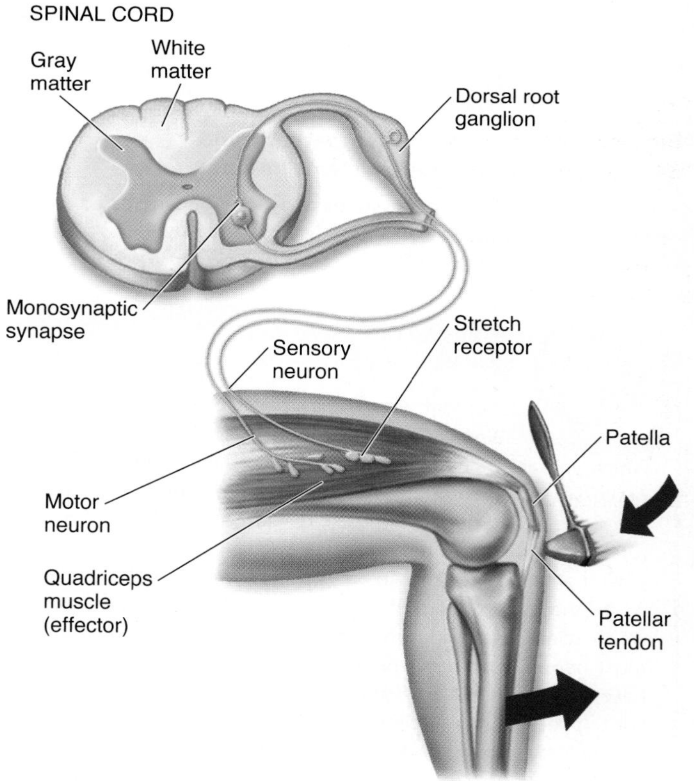

SPINAL CORD
Gray matter
White matter
Dorsal root ganglion
Monosynaptic synapse
Sensory neuron
Stretch receptor
Patella
Motor neuron
Quadriceps muscle (effector)
Patellar tendon

Figure 29.16 The knee-jerk reflex.

The most famous involuntary response, the knee jerk, is produced by activating stretch receptors in the quadriceps muscle. When a rubber mallet taps the patellar tendon, the muscle and stretch receptors in the muscle are stretched. A signal travels up a sensory neuron to the spinal cord, where the sensory neuron stimulates a motor neuron, which sends a signal to the quadriceps muscle to contract.

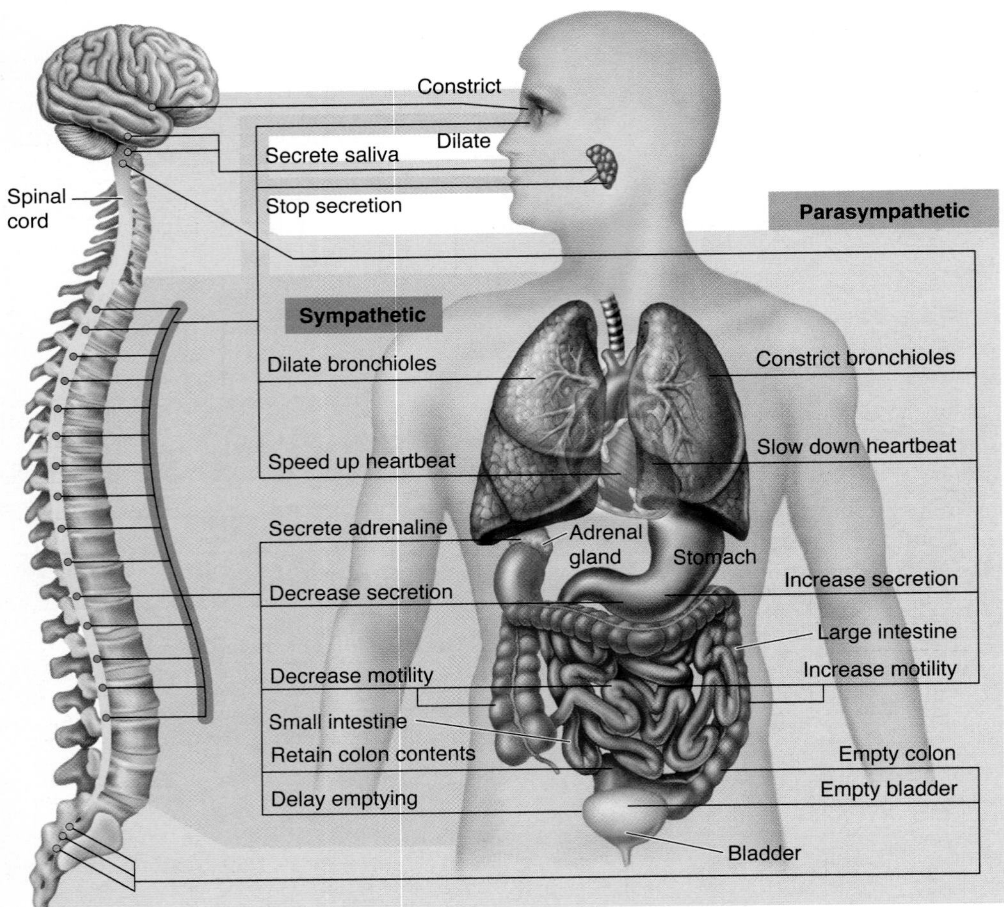

Figure 29.17 How the sympathetic and parasympathetic nervous systems interact.

A nerve path runs from both systems to every organ indicated except the adrenal gland, which is only innervated by the sympathetic nervous system.

are monosynaptic reflex arcs. You see in the figure that the sensory neuron, a stretch receptor embedded in a muscle, "senses" the stretching of the muscle when the tendon is tapped. This stretching could harm the muscle and so a nerve impulse is sent to the spinal cord where it synapses directly with a motor neuron—there is no interneuron between them. Similarly, if you step on something sharp, your leg jerks away from the danger; the prick causes nerve impulses in sensory neurons, which pass to the spinal cord and then to motor neurons, which cause your leg muscles to contract, jerking your leg up.

Autonomic Nervous System

Some motor neurons are active all the time. These neurons carry messages from the CNS that keep the body going even when it is not active. These neurons make up the autonomic nervous system. The autonomic nervous system carries messages to muscles and glands that work without the animal noticing.

The autonomic nervous system is the command network used by the CNS to maintain the body's homeostasis. Using it, the CNS regulates heartbeat and controls muscle contractions in the walls of the blood vessels. It directs the muscles that control blood pressure, breathing, and the movement of food through the digestive system. It also carries messages that help stimulate glands to secrete tears, mucus, and digestive enzymes.

The autonomic nervous system is composed of two divisions that act in opposition to one another. One division, the **sympathetic nervous system,** dominates in times of stress. It controls the "fight-or-flight" reaction, increasing blood pressure, heart rate, breathing rate, and blood flow to the muscles. The sympathetic nervous system is colored pink in **figure 29.17**, with neurons extending from the middle section of the spinal cord. Long motor neurons extend from the ganglia directly to each target organ. Another division, the **parasympathetic nervous system,** has the opposite effect. It conserves energy by slowing the heartbeat and breathing rate and by promoting digestion and elimination. The parasympathetic nervous system is colored in blue in the figure, with neurons extending from the upper and lower sections of the spinal cord.

Most glands, smooth muscles, and cardiac muscles get constant input from *both* systems. The CNS controls activity by varying the ratio of the two signals to either stimulate or inhibit the organ.

BIOLOGY & YOU

Biofeedback. Biofeedback is a technique in which you are trained to influence certain involuntary body processes under autonomic nervous system control, such as heart rate, blood pressure, muscle tension, and skin temperature. These processes are measured with electrodes and displayed on a monitor, providing you with "real-time" feedback on the internal workings of your body. How does biofeedback work? Scientists are not sure. It doesn't work for everyone, and most people who do benefit from biofeedback treatments have conditions that are brought on or made worse by stress. For this reason, many scientists believe that relaxation is key to successful biofeedback therapy. What is biofeedback good for? It shows considerable promise in treating urinary incontinence, which affects over 15 million Americans. Biofeedback is also becoming a possible treatment for attention deficit/hyperactivity disorder (ADHD).

Putting the Concept to Work

Which element of the autonomic nervous system—the sympathetic or parasympathetic—acts to slow the heartbeat?

The Sensory Nervous System

29.7 Sensing the Internal Environment

LEARNING OBJECTIVE 29.7.1 Describe how the body's sensory receptors respond to aspects of its internal environment.

Sensory receptors inside the body called **interoceptors** inform the CNS about the condition of the body. Much of this information passes to the hypothalamus, the part of the brain responsible for the body's homeostasis. The vertebrate body uses a variety of different sensory receptors to respond to different aspects of its internal environment.

Temperature change. Two kinds of nerve endings in the skin are sensitive to changes in temperature, one stimulated by cold, the other by warmth. By comparing information from the two, the CNS can learn what the temperature is and if it is changing.

Blood chemistry. Receptors in the walls of arteries sense CO_2 levels in the blood. The brain uses this information to regulate the body's respiration rate, increasing it when CO_2 levels rise above normal.

Pain. Damage to tissue is detected by special nerve endings within tissues, usually near the surface, where damage is most likely to occur. When these nerve endings are physically damaged or deformed, the CNS responds by reflexively withdrawing the body part and often by changing heartbeat and blood pressure.

Muscle contraction. Buried deep within muscles are sensory receptors called stretch receptors (see also pages 571–572). In each, the end of a sensory neuron is wrapped around a muscle fiber, like the receptor shown in figure 29.18. When the muscle is stretched, the fiber elongates, stretching the spiral nerve ending (like stretching a spring) and causing repeated nerve impulses to be sent to the brain. From these signals the brain can determine the rate of change of muscle length at any given moment. The CNS uses this information to control movements that require the combined action of several muscles, such as those that carry out breathing or locomotion.

Blood pressure. Blood pressure is sensed by neurons called baroreceptors with highly branched nerve endings within the walls of major arteries. When blood pressure increases, the stretching of the arterial wall, like the expansion of the artery in figure 29.19, causes the sensory neuron to increase the rate at which it sends nerve impulses to the CNS. When the wall of the artery is not stretched, the rate of firing of the sensory neuron goes down. Thus, the frequency of impulses provides the CNS with a continuous measure of blood pressure.

Touch. Touch is sensed by pressure receptors buried below the surface of the skin. There are a variety of different types, some specialized to detect rapid changes in pressure, others to measure the duration and extent to which pressure is applied, and still others sensitive to vibrations.

Putting the Concept to Work

How does the brain know whether an incoming sensory impulse is temperature, pressure, or pain?

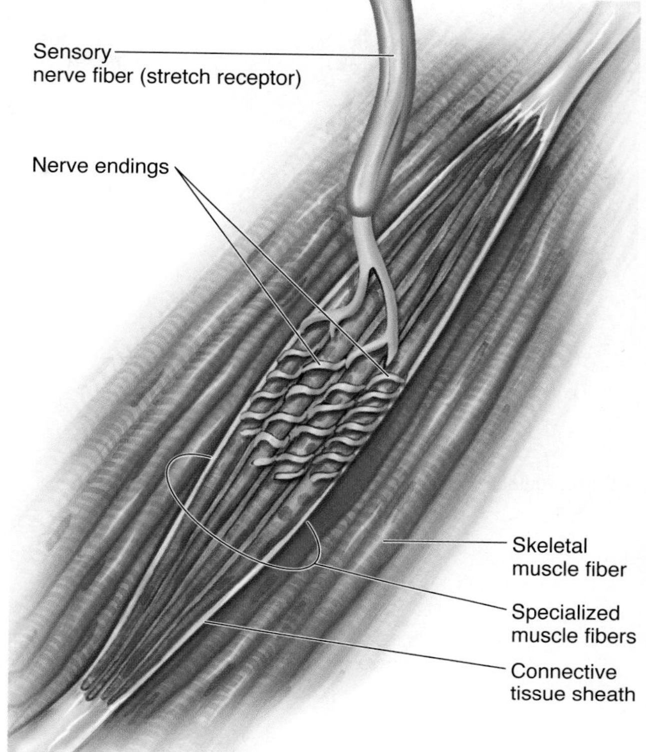

Figure 29.18 A stretch receptor embedded within skeletal muscle.

Stretching the muscle elongates the specialized muscle fibers, which deforms the nerve endings, causing them to send a nerve impulse out along the nerve fiber.

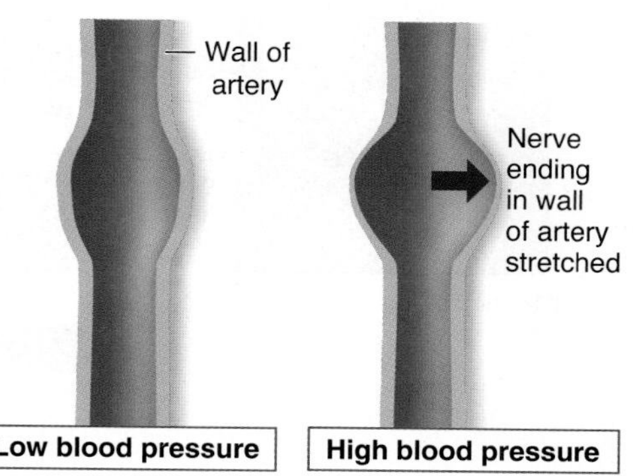

Figure 29.19 How a baroreceptor works.

A network of nerve endings covers a region where the wall of the artery is thin. High blood pressure causes the wall to balloon out there, stretching the nerve endings and causing them to fire impulses.

29.8 Sensing Gravity and Motion

LEARNING OBJECTIVE 29.8.1
Describe how the inner ear senses gravity and acceleration.

Two types of receptors in the ear inform the brain where the body is in three dimensions. This knowledge enables an animal to move freely and maintain its balance. Figure 29.20 shows the anatomy of the inner ear and the locations of these receptors.

Balance. To keep the body's balance the brain needs a frame of reference, and the reference point it uses is gravity. The sensory receptors that detect gravity are hair cells within the utricle and the saccule of the inner ear (figure 29.20 ❶). The tips of the hair cells project into a gelatinous matrix with embedded particles called **otoliths** ❷. To illustrate how these receptors work, imagine a pencil standing in a glass. No matter which way you tip the glass, the pencil rolls along the rim due to the pull of gravity, applying pressure to the lip of the glass. If you want to know the direction the glass is tipped, you need only ask where on the rim pressure is being applied. Similarly, otoliths in the utricle and saccule will shift in the matrix in response to the pull of gravity and stimulate hair cells. The brain uses information from the hair cells to determine vertical positioning.

Motion. The brain senses motion by employing a receptor in which fluid deflects cilia of hair cells in a direction opposite that of the motion. Within the inner ear are three fluid-filled **semicircular canals,** each oriented in a different plane at right angles to the other two (❶) so that motion in any direction can be detected. Protruding into the canal are groups of cilia from sensory hair cells. The cilia from each cell are arranged in a tentlike assembly called a *cupula,* shown in ❸, which is pushed when fluid in the semicircular canals moves in a direction opposite that of the head's movement. Because the three canals are oriented in all three planes, movement in any plane is sensed by at least one of them, and the brain is able to analyze body movements by comparing the sensory inputs from each canal.

The semicircular canals do not react if the body moves in a straight line, because the fluid in the canals does not move. That is why traveling in a car or airplane at a constant speed in one direction gives no sense of motion.

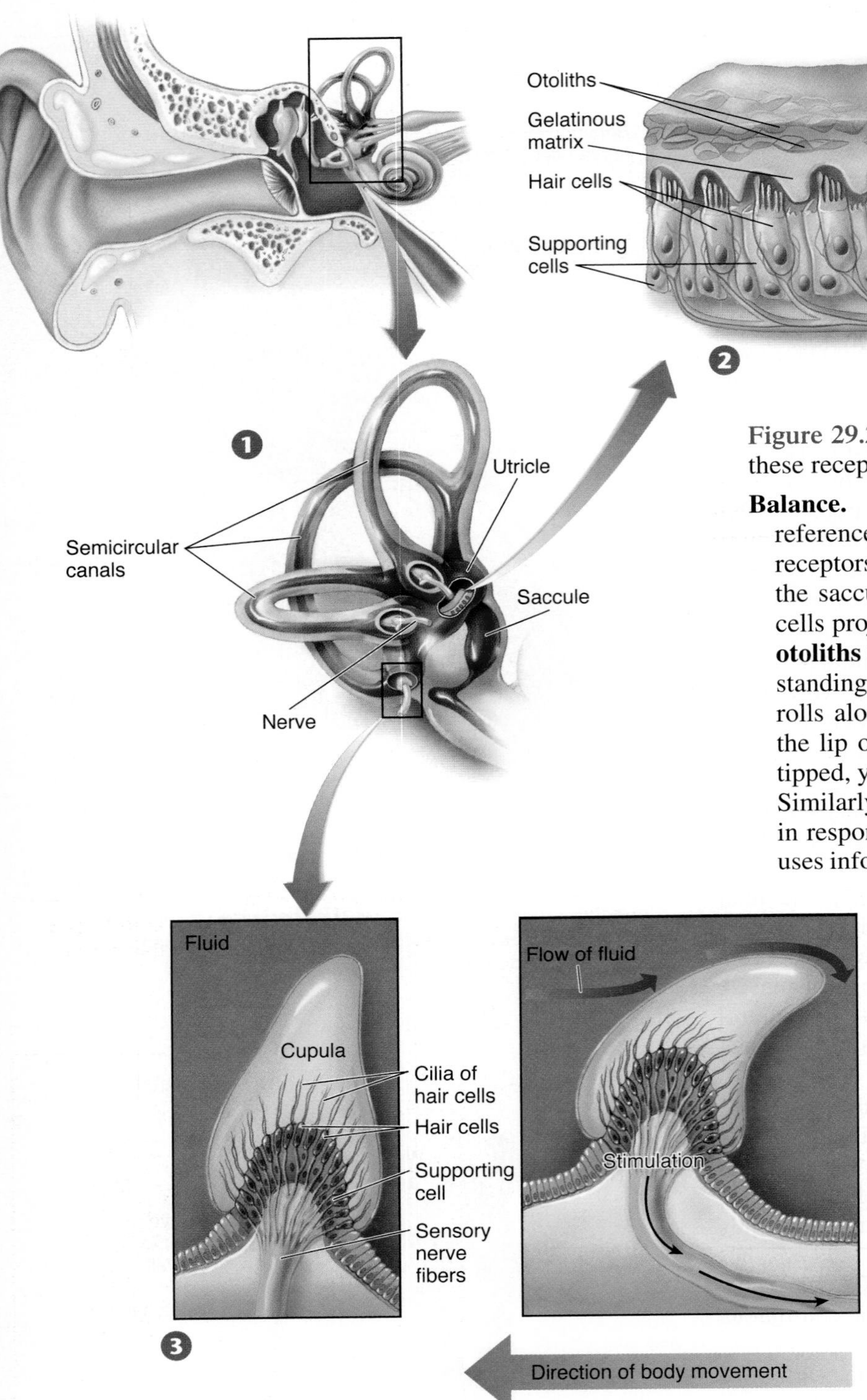

Figure 29.20 How the inner ear senses gravity and motion.

❶ The semicircular canals are part of the inner ear. ❷ Enlargement of a section of the utricle or saccule. Otoliths embedded in the gelatinous matrix move in response to the pull of gravity. ❸ The cupula within the semicircular canals are surrounded by fluid and contain hair cells. Movement in a particular direction causes fluid in the semicircular canal of that plane to move; the cupula is displaced, thereby stimulating the hair cells.

Putting the Concept to Work

Why does someone falling from a high window sense movement, while someone descending in an elevator does not?

29.9 Sensing Chemicals: Taste and Smell

LEARNING OBJECTIVE 29.9.1 Contrast the senses of taste and smell.

Vertebrates are able to detect many of the chemicals in air and in food.

Taste. Embedded within the surface of the tongue are *taste buds* located within *papillae*, which are the raised areas on the tongue in figure 29.21. Taste buds (the onion-shaped structures in the figure) contain many taste receptor cells, each of which has fingerlike microvilli that project into an opening called the taste pore. Chemicals from food dissolve in saliva and contact the taste cells through the taste pore. Salty, sour, sweet, bitter, and umami (a "meaty" taste) are perceived because chemicals in food are detected in different ways by taste buds. When the tongue encounters a chemical, information from the taste cells passes to sensory neurons, which transmit the signals to the brain.

Microvilli are hairlike extensions of the plasma membrane that increase the surface area of the cell. Epithelial cells that line the small intestine, as discussed on page 524, contain microvilli on the lumen surface of the cells that increase the surface area for absorption.

Smell. The nose contains chemically sensitive neurons whose cell bodies are embedded within the epithelium of the nasal passage, shown in cross section in figure 29.22. When they detect chemicals, these sensory neurons (the red cells in the enlarged view) transmit information to a location in the brain where smell information is processed and analyzed. Although humans can sense only five different tastes, they can detect thousands of different smells. It appears that as many as a thousand different genes may code for different receptor proteins for smell. The particular set of neurons that respond to a given odor might serve as a "fingerprint" that the brain can use to identify the odor. In many vertebrates (dogs are a familiar example), these neurons are far more sensitive than in humans.

Smell and taste are very important senses in telling an animal about its food. That is why when you have a bad cold and your nose is stuffed up, your food has little taste. Other receptors also play a role. For example, the "hot" sensation of foods such as chili peppers is detected by pain receptors, not chemical receptors.

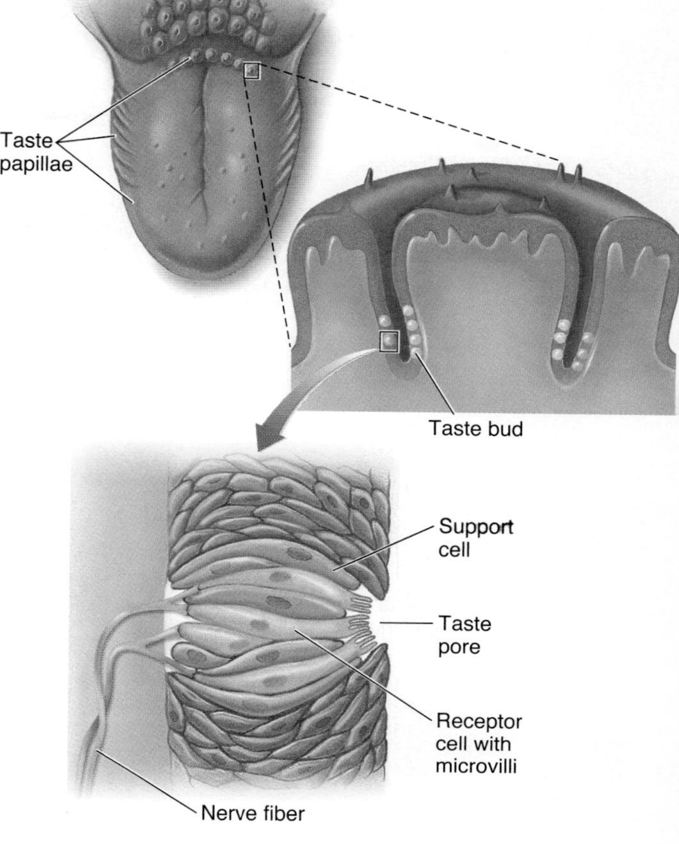

Figure 29.21 Taste.

Taste buds on the human tongue are typically grouped into projections called papillae. Individual taste buds are bulb-shaped collections of taste receptor cells that open out into the mouth through a taste pore.

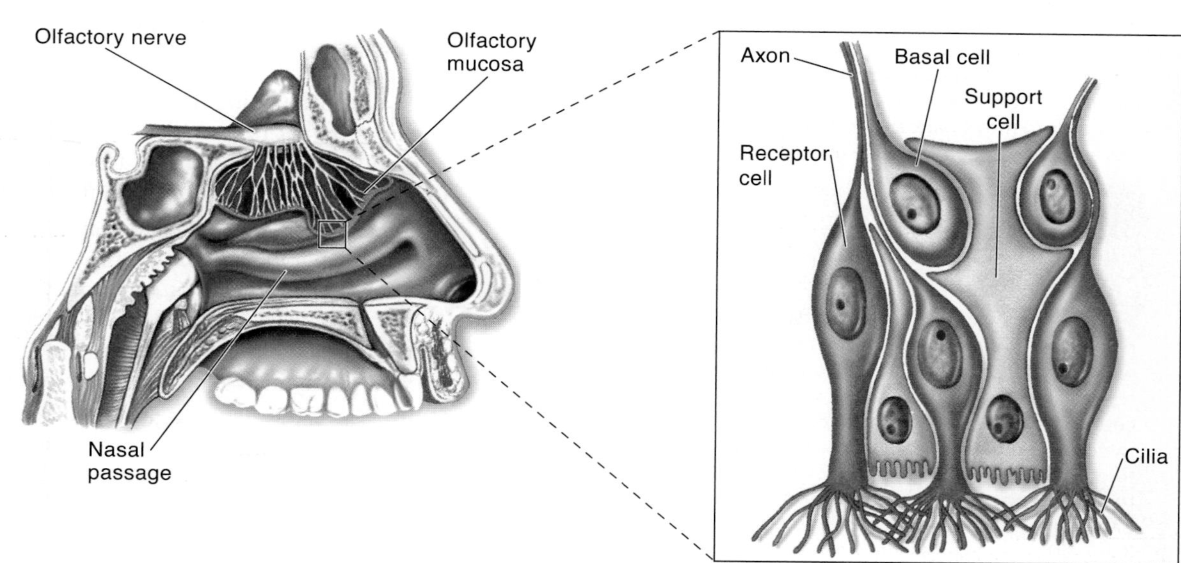

Figure 29.22 Smell.

Humans smell by using receptor cells located in the lining of the nasal passage. The receptor cells are neurons. Axons from these sensory neurons project back through the olfactory nerve directly to the brain.

Putting the Concept to Work

Why is your dog able to "smell" better than you can? Is it just because it has a bigger nose?

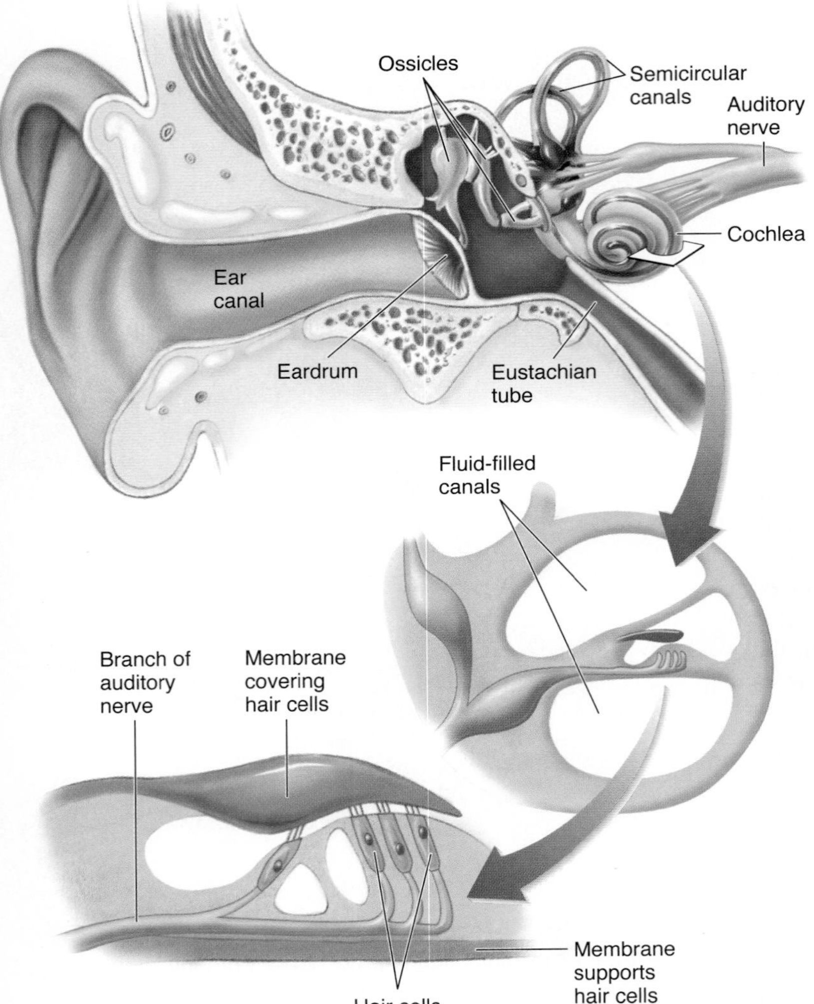

Figure 29.23 Structure and function of the human ear.

Sound waves passing through the ear canal beat on the eardrum, pushing a set of three small bones, or ossicles, against an inner membrane. This sets up a wave motion in the fluid filling the canals within the cochlea. The wave causes the membrane covering the hair cells to move back and forth against the hair cells, which causes associated neurons to fire impulses.

EVOLUTION

Hunting with Eyes Shut. A duckbilled platypus hunts at night, diving in streams to capture insect larvae with its eyes shut! It swims along steadily, wagging its bill from side to side, two or three sweeps per second, until electroreceptors in its bill sense tiny electrical currents generated by the muscle movements of its prey, an insect larva as it moves to evade the approaching platypus. It is easy to demonstrate this, once you know what is going on. Just drop a small 1.5 volt battery into the stream. A platypus will immediately orient to it and attack it, from as far away as 30 centimeters. In muddy murky waters, sensing the muscle movements of a prey individual is far superior to trying to see its body—which is how the platypus can hunt with its eyes shut.

29.10 Sensing Sounds: Hearing

LEARNING OBJECTIVE 29.10.1 Explain how sound receptors within the ear's cochlea differentiate between sounds of different frequencies and different intensities.

When you hear a sound, you are detecting the air vibrating—waves of pressure in the air beating against your ear, pushing a membrane called the eardrum in and out. As you can see in figure 29.23, on the inner side of the eardrum are three small bones, called ossicles, that act as a lever system to increase the force of the vibration. They transfer the amplified vibration across a second membrane to fluid within the inner ear. The fluid-filled chamber of the inner ear is shaped like a tightly coiled snail shell and is called the cochlea, from the Latin name for "snail." The middle ear, where the ossicles are located, is connected to the throat by the eustachian tube in such a way that there is no difference in air pressure between the middle ear and the outside. That is why your ears sometimes "pop" when landing in an airplane—the pressure is equalizing between the two sides of the eardrum. This equalized pressure is necessary for the eardrum to work.

The sound receptors within the cochlea are hair cells that rest on a membrane that runs up and down the middle of the spiraling chamber, separating it into two halves, the upper and lower fluid-filled canals in the enlarged view of the figure. The hair cells do not project into the fluid-filled canals of the cochlea; instead, they are covered by a second membrane (the darker blue membrane in the figure). When a sound wave enters the cochlea, it causes the fluid in the chambers to move. The moving fluid causes this membrane "sandwich" to vibrate, bending the hairs pressed against the upper membrane and causing them to send nerve impulses to sensory neurons that travel to the brain.

Sounds of different frequencies travel different distances down the length of the cochlea and cause different parts of the membrane to vibrate. Each area of the membrane fires a different set of sensory neurons—the identity of the sensory neuron being fired tells the CNS the frequency of the sound. Sound waves of higher frequencies, about 20,000 vibrations (or cycles) per second, also called hertz (Hz), don't travel very far into the cochlea and move the membrane in the area closest to the middle ear. Medium-length frequencies, about 2,000 Hz, travel farther and move the membrane in the area about midway down the length of the cochlea. The lowest-frequency sound waves, about 500 Hz, move the membrane near the tip of the cochlea.

The intensity of the sound is determined by how *often* the neurons fire. Our ability to hear depends upon the flexibility of the membranes within the cochlea. Humans cannot hear low-pitched sounds, below 20 Hz, although some vertebrates can. As children, we can hear high-pitched sounds, up to 20,000 cycles per second, but this ability decreases as we get older. Other vertebrates can hear sounds at far higher frequencies. Dogs readily hear sounds of 40,000 cycles per second and so respond to a high-pitched dog whistle that seems silent to a human.

Putting the Concept to Work

How does the ear distinguish a sound's frequency?

29.11 Sensing Light: Vision

Structure of the Vertebrate Eye

LEARNING OBJECTIVE 29.11.1 Diagram the structure of the human eye, explaining the functions of its elements.

The vertebrate eye works like a lens-focused camera. Light first passes through a transparent protective covering, the **cornea** (the light blue layer in figure 29.24), which begins to focus the light onto the rear of the eye. The beam of light then passes through the **lens,** which completes the focusing. The lens is attached by stringlike *suspensory ligaments* to **ciliary muscles.** When these muscles contract and relax, they change the shape of the lens and thus allow the eye to view objects that are far and near. The amount of light entering the eye is controlled by a shutter, called the **iris** (the colored part of your eye), between the cornea and the lens. The transparent zone in the middle of the iris, the **pupil,** gets larger in dim light and smaller in bright light. The pupil also gets smaller when the eye is viewing close objects.

The light that passes through the pupil is focused by the lens onto the back of the eye. An array of light-sensitive receptor cells lines the back surface of the eye, called the **retina.** The retina is the light-sensing portion of the eye. The vertebrate retina contains two kinds of photoreceptors, called **rods** and **cones,** which, when stimulated by light, generate nerve impulses that travel to the brain along a short, thick nerve pathway called the optic nerve. Rods, the taller, flat-topped cells in figure 29.25, are receptor cells that are extremely sensitive to light, and they can detect various shades of gray even in dim light. However, they cannot distinguish colors, and because they do not detect edges well, they produce poorly defined images. Cones, the pointed-topped cells, are receptor cells that detect color and are sensitive to edges so that they produce sharp images. The center of the vertebrate retina contains a tiny pit, called the **fovea,** densely packed with some 3 million cones. This area produces the sharpest image, which is why we tend to move our eyes so that the image of an object we want to see clearly falls on this area.

Putting the Concept to Work

How do ciliary muscles focus the eye?

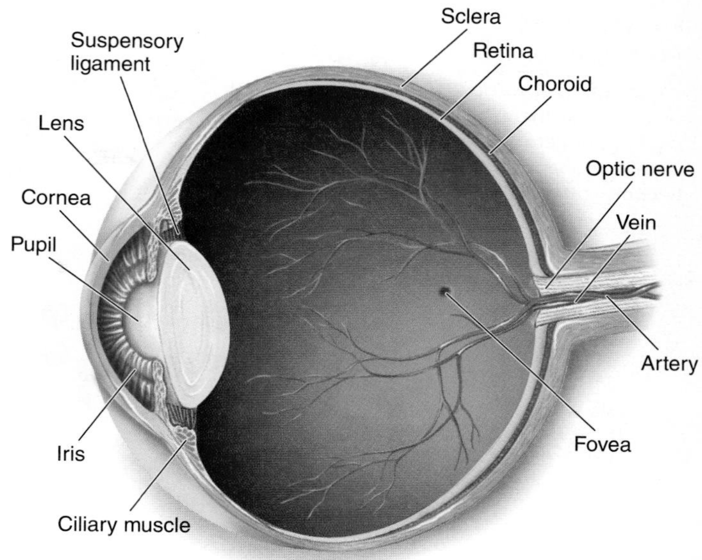

Figure 29.24 The structure of the human eye.

Light passes through the transparent cornea and is focused by the lens on the rear surface of the eye, the retina. The retina is rich in photoreceptors, with a high concentration in an area called the fovea.

How the Eye Senses Light

LEARNING OBJECTIVE 29.11.2 Explain how a photon of light initiates a sensory nerve impulse.

A rod or cone cell in the eye is able to detect a single photon of light. How can it be so sensitive? The primary sensing event of vision is the absorption of a photon of light by a pigment. The pigments in rods and cones are made from plant pigments called carotenoids. That is why eating carrots is said to be good for night vision—the orange color of carrots is due to the presence of carotenoids called carotenes. The visual pigment in the human eye is a fragment of carotene called *cis*-retinal. The pigment is attached to a protein called opsin to form a light-detecting complex called **rhodopsin.**

Pigments absorb certain wavelengths of light, as discussed on page 108. The primary photosynthetic pigment in plants is chlorophyll, which absorbs red and blue wavelengths, so that plants appear green.

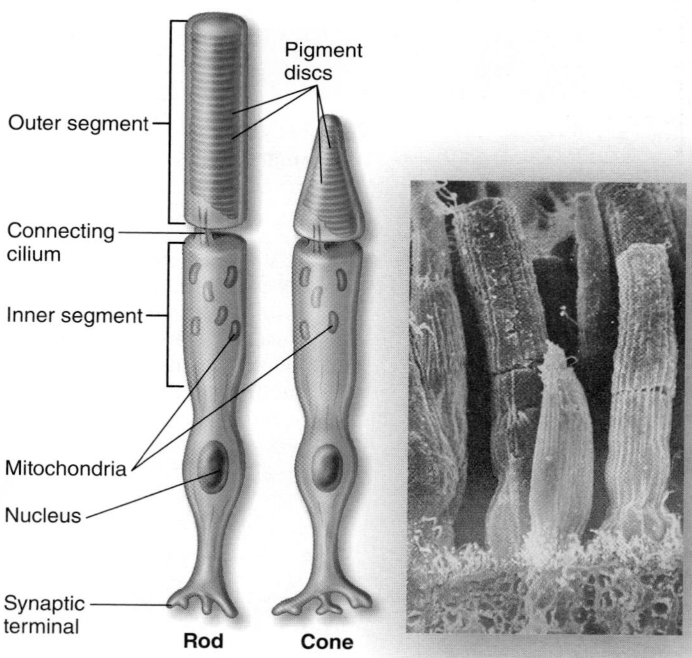

Figure 29.25 Rods and cones.

The broad tubular cell on the *left* is a rod. The shorter, tapered cell next to it is a cone. An electron micrograph of rods and cones is also shown.

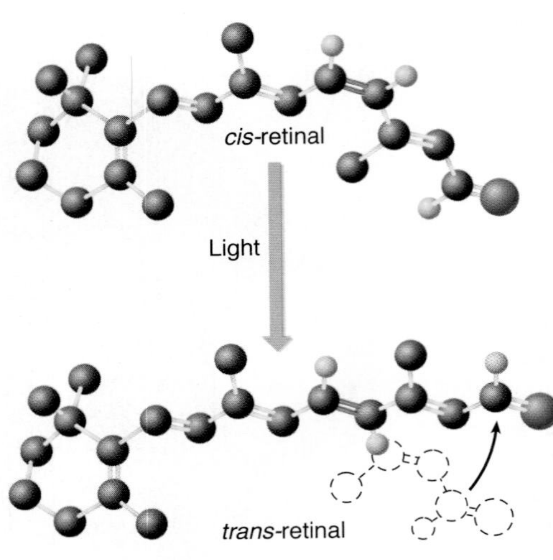

Figure 29.26 Absorption of light.

When light is absorbed by *cis*-retinal, the pigment undergoes a change in shape and becomes *trans*-retinal.

When it receives a photon of light, the pigment undergoes a change in shape. This change in shape must be large enough to alter the shape of the opsin protein attached to it. When light is absorbed by the *cis*-retinal pigment (the upper molecule in figure 29.26), the linear end of the molecule rotates sharply upward, straightening out that end of the molecule. The new form of the pigment is referred to as *trans*-retinal and the dashed outline in the figure shows the shape before it was stimulated by light. This radical change in the pigment's shape induces a change in the shape of the protein opsin to which the pigment is bound, initiating a chain of events that leads to the generation of a nerve impulse.

Each rhodopsin activates several hundred molecules of a protein called transducin. Each of these activates several hundred molecules of an enzyme whose product stimulates sodium channels in the photoreceptor membrane at a rate of about 1,000 per second. This cascade of events allows a single photon to have a large effect on the receptor.

Putting the Concept to Work

Why doesn't the eye run out of *cis*-retinal pigment?

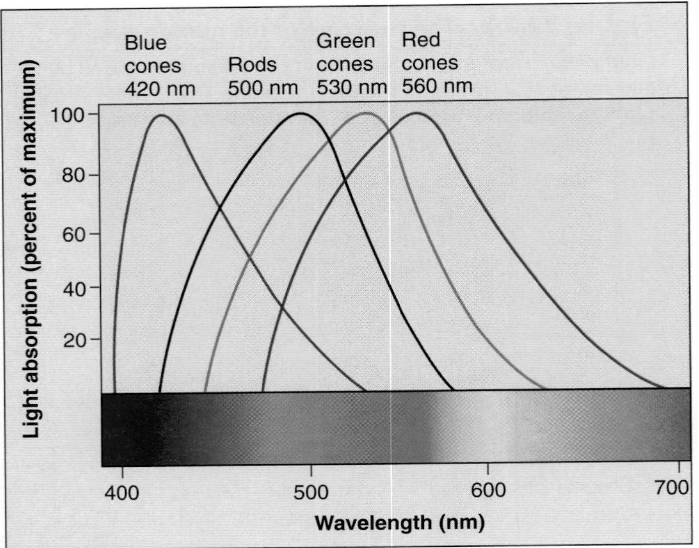

Figure 29.27 Color vision.

The absorption spectrum of *cis*-retinal is shifted in cone cells from the 500 nanometers characteristic of rod cells. The amount of the shift determines what color the cone absorbs: 420 nanometers yields blue absorption; 530 nanometers yields green absorption; and 560 nanometers yields red absorption. Red cones do not peak in the red part of the spectrum, but they are the only cones that absorb light in the far end of the spectrum.

Color Vision

LEARNING OBJECTIVE 29.11.3 Distinguish between rods and cones, and explain how cones produce color vision.

Three kinds of cone cells provide us with color vision. Each possesses a different version of the opsin protein (that is, one with a distinctive amino acid sequence and thus a different shape). These differences in shape affect the flexibility of the attached retinal pigment, shifting the wavelength at which it absorbs light. The absorption spectrum in figure 29.27 shows the wavelength of light that is absorbed by each cone and rod cell. In rods, light is absorbed at 500 nanometers. In cones, the three versions of opsin absorb light at 420 nanometers (blue-absorbing), 530 nanometers (green-absorbing), or 560 nanometers (red-absorbing). By comparing the relative intensities of the signals from the three types of cones, the brain can calculate the intensity of other colors.

Some people are not able to see all three colors, a condition referred to as *color blindness.* Color blindness is typically due to an inherited lack of one or more types of cones. People with normal vision have all three types of cones. People with only two types of cones lack the ability to detect the third color. For example, people with red-green color blindness lack red cones and have difficulty distinguishing red from green (figure 29.28). Color blindness is a sex-linked trait, and so men are far more likely to be color blind than women.

A sex-linked trait is controlled by a gene that is located on the X chromosome, as discussed on page 175. Because males carry only one X chromosome (the other sex chromosome is the Y chromosome), any gene that is carried on the X chromosome is expressed.

Most vertebrates, particularly those that are diurnal (active during the day), have color vision, as do many insects. Indeed, honeybees can see light in the near-ultraviolet range, which is invisible to the human eye. Color vision requires the presence of more

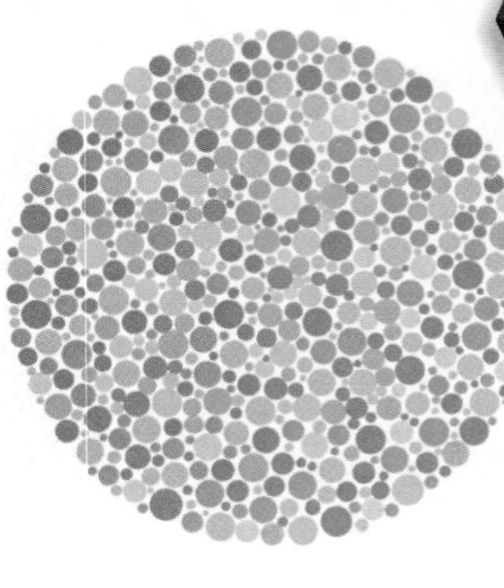

Figure 29.28 Test for color blindness.

People with normal color vision see the number 16, but people that are red-green color blind see just spots and no discernible number.

than one photopigment in different receptor cells, but not all animals with color vision have the three-cone system characteristic of humans and other primates. Fish, turtles, and birds, for example, have four or five kinds of cones; the "extra" cones enable these animals to see near-ultraviolet light. Many mammals (such as squirrels), on the other hand, have only two types of cones.

Putting the Concept to Work

Why can't rods produce color vision?

Conveying the Light Information to the Brain

LEARNING OBJECTIVE 29.11.4 Trace the path of light through the human eye.

The path of light through each eye is the reverse of what you might expect. The rods and cones are at the rear of the retina, not the front. If you track the path that light would take in figure 29.29, you will see that light passes through several layers of ganglion and bipolar cells before it reaches the rods and cones. Once the photoreceptors are activated, they stimulate bipolar cells, which in turn stimulate ganglion cells. The direction of nerve impulses in the retina is thus opposite to the direction of light.

Action potentials propagated along the axons of ganglion cells are relayed through structures called the *lateral geniculate nuclei* of the thalamus and projected to the occipital lobe of the cerebral cortex. There the brain interprets this information as light in a specific region of the eye's receptive field. The pattern of activity among the ganglion cells across the retina encodes a point-to-point map of the receptive field, allowing the retina and brain to image objects in visual space. In addition, the frequency of impulses in each ganglion cell provides information about the light intensity at each point, while the relative activity of ganglion cells connected (through bipolar cells) with the three types of cones provides color information.

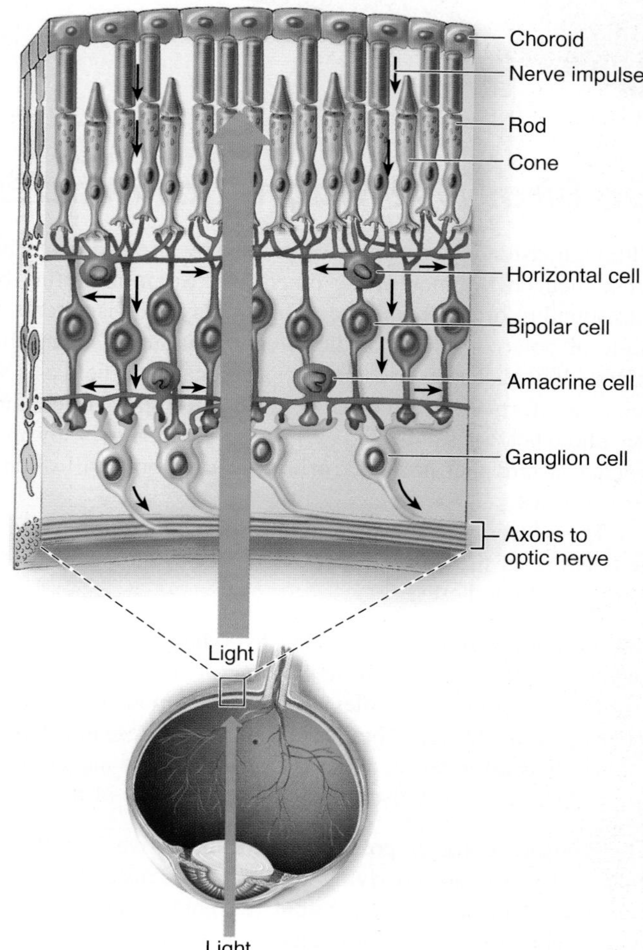

Figure 29.29 Structure of the retina.

The rods and cones are at the rear of the retina. Light passes over four other types of cells in the retina before it reaches the rods and cones. Nerve impulses then travel through the bipolar cells to the ganglion cells and on to the optic nerve (as indicated by the black arrows).

Binocular Vision

Primates (including humans) and most predators have two eyes, one located on each side of the face. When both eyes are trained on the same object, the image that each sees is slightly different because each eye views the object from a different angle. This slight displacement of the images permits **binocular vision,** the ability to perceive three-dimensional images and to sense depth or the distance to an object. Having their eyes facing forward maximizes the field of overlap in which this stereoscopic vision occurs, as seen by the overlapping blue triangles in the human in figure 29.30. The triangles are the field of view for each eye.

In contrast, prey animals generally have eyes located to the sides of the head, preventing binocular vision but enlarging the overall receptive field. Depth perception is less important to prey than detection of potential enemies from any angle. The eyes of the American woodcock, for example, are located at exactly opposite sides of its skull so that it has a 360-degree field of view without turning its head!

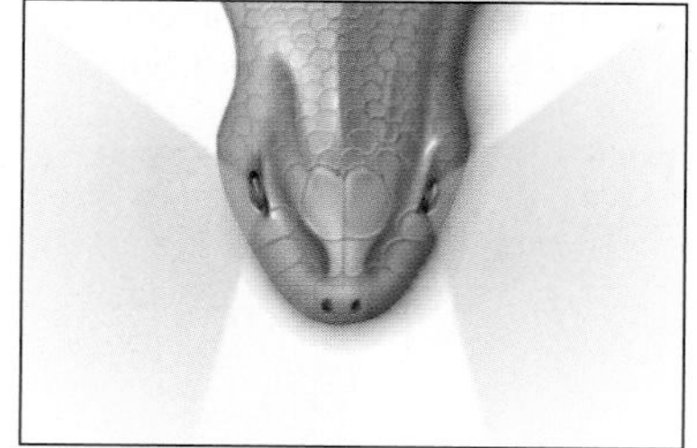

Figure 29.30 Binocular vision.

When the eyes are located on the sides of the head (as on the *left*), the two vision fields do not overlap and binocular vision does not occur. When both eyes are located toward the front of the head (as on the *right*) so that the two fields of vision overlap, depth can be perceived.

Putting the Concept to Work

Does light pass through a cone receptor from its pointed tip to its base, or up from its base and out through its tip?

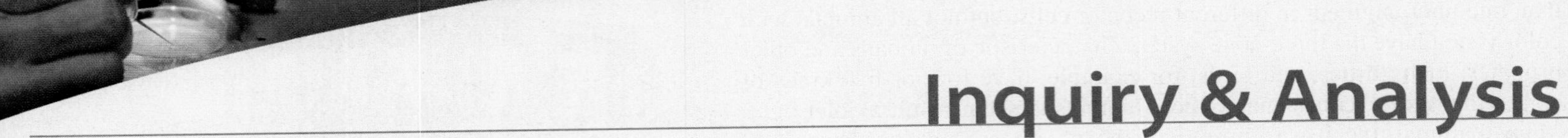

Inquiry & Analysis

Do Birds Use Magnetic Particles as Compass Needles?

Although vision is the primary sense used by all vertebrates, birds also sense their environment using other cues. Some migrating birds use infrasound to orient themselves. Others may use visual cues, like the angle of polarizing light or the direction of sunset. Many birds that migrate long distances use the earth's geomagnetic field as a source of compass information. If the magnetic field of a blind "orientation cage" (see photo below) is deflected by 120 degrees clockwise by an artificial magnet, a bird that normally orients to the north will orient toward the southeast.

The sensory system underlying the magnetic compass of these birds is one of the great mysteries of sensory biology. There are two competing hypotheses.

The magnetite hypothesis. One hypothesis is that crystals of the magnetic mineral magnetite within brain cells of migrating birds act as miniature compass needles. While trace amounts of magnetite are indeed present in some brain cells, intensive research has failed to confirm that information about the orientation of magnetite particles within these cells is transmitted to any other cells of the brain.

The photoreceptor hypothesis. An alternative hypothesis is that the primary process underlying the compass is instead a magnetically-sensitive chemical reaction within the photoreceptors of the bird's eyes. The alignment of photopigment molecules with the earth's magnetic field might alter the visual pattern in a way that could be used to obtain directional information.

Which hypothesis is correct? Experiments have shown that the magnetic detector used by birds in blind cages is light sensitive, as a photoreceptor compass should be—but this would also be true of a light-activated magnetite compass.

In 2004, University of California Irvine researchers devised a clever experiment to distinguish between the two hypotheses. They studied the way in which migrating European robins held in orientation cages use the magnetic field as a source of compass information to hop in the appropriate migratory direction. They found that the robins oriented 16 degrees north during the spring migration, the appropriate direction. To distinguish between the magnetite and photoreceptor hypotheses, the robins in the cages were exposed to oscillating low-level radio frequencies (7 MHz) that would disrupt the energy state of any light-absorbing photoreceptor molecules involved in sensing the magnetic field, but would not affect the alignment of magnetite particles.

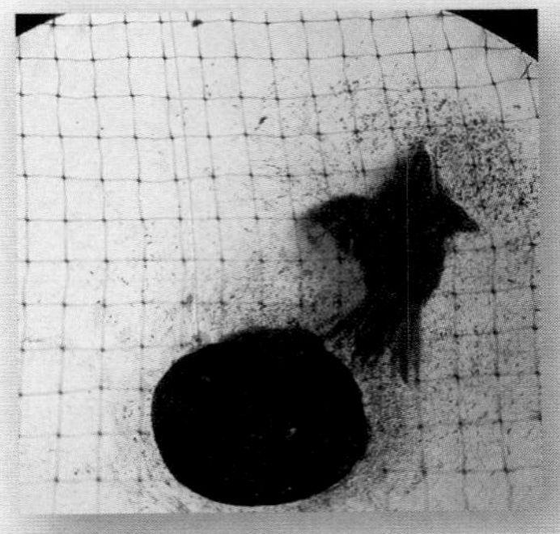

The chart above presents the results of this study. Each data entry is the mean of three recordings. For each recording, the bird was placed in a 35-inch conical orientation cage lined with coated paper, and the vector (the directional position of first contact with the paper) recorded relative to magnetic North (North = 360 degrees; East = 90 degrees; South = 180 degrees; West = 270 degrees).

Effect of Radio-Disruption on Orientation

Bird	Mean Heading (degrees): Geomagnetic field only	Mean Heading (degrees): Radio-disrupted
1	26	110
2	20	126
3	4	86
4	350	17
5	15	162
6	1	330
7	18	297
8	20	220
9	354	58
10	24	261
11	358	278
12	37	3

Mean vector 16°
360° N
270° W
E 90°
S 180°

Analysis

1. **Interpreting Data** Plot each column on a circle. For birds orienting to the geomagnetic field without radio interference, what is the greatest difference (expressed in degrees) between recorded vectors and the mean vector of 16 degrees? For birds orienting with 7 MHz radio interference?
2. **Making Inferences**
   a. For birds orienting to the geomagnetic field without radio interference, how many of the 12 birds oriented with an accuracy of +/– 30 degrees relative to the mean vector of 16 degrees? For birds orienting with 7 MHz radio interference, how many were +/– 30 degrees?
   b. If you were to select a bird at random, what is the probability that it would orient within +/– 30 degrees of the appropriate migration direction (16 degrees North) without radio interference? With radio interference?
3. **Drawing Conclusions** Is the ability of European robins to orient correctly with respect to geomagnetic fields disrupted by 7 MHz radio frequencies? Is it fair to conclude that the birds' compass sense involves a molecule sensitive to radio disruption, such as a photoreceptor? That it does not involve particles not sensitive to radio disruption?

Summary of Learning Outcomes

Neurons and How They Work

The Animal Nervous System

29.1.1 The nervous system is the communication network in the body. The animal nervous system is organized into a central nervous system that includes a brain and spinal cord and contains associative neurons, and a peripheral nervous system that contains sensory and motor neurons.

Neurons and Nerve Impulses

29.2.1 Neurons are cells that conduct electrical impulses but are supported by neuroglial cells, such as Schwann cells and oligodendrocytes. These cells closely associate with the axons, wrapping them in a fatty material called myelin.

29.2.2 Electrical signals begin in dendrites and travel down an axon. Nerve impulses result from the movement of Na^+ and K^+ ions across the plasma membranes through voltage-gated channels. The movement of Na^+ in one area of the membrane causes a change in electrical properties, called depolarization, which causes the opening of adjacent ion channels. If the depolarization is large enough it will trigger an action potential that will spread down the axon. The action of the Na^+/K^+ pumps restores the resting membrane potential.

The Synapse

29.3.1 A synapse is the junction of an axon with another cell. When a nerve impulse reaches the end of an axon, it triggers the release of neurotransmitters that pass across a small gap, called a synaptic cleft, between the axon and the postsynaptic cell. Neurotransmitter molecules bind to receptors on the postsynaptic cell causing chemically gated ion channels to open. Ions flow across the plasma membrane creating electrical impulses in the postsynaptic cell.

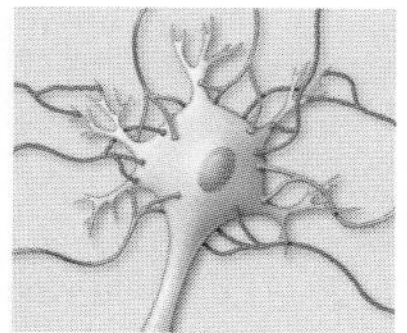

29.3.2 Depending on the type of ion that flows into the cell, the synapse is excitatory or inhibitory. All neural inputs are integrated in the postsynaptic cell, shown here from **figure 29.7**, producing an overall positive or negative change in membrane potential.

The Central Nervous System

How the Brain Works

29.4.1 The associative activity of the brain is centered in the cerebral cortex, which lies over the cerebrum and is the site of neural activities such as language, conscious thought, memory, personality development, and many other higher-level activities.

- The thalamus and hypothalamus, which lie underneath the cerebrum, process information and integrate bodily functions. Areas of the hypothalamus are also part of the limbic system, which is involved in deep-seated drives and emotions, such as pain, anger, sex, hunger, thirst, and pleasure.
- The cerebellum controls balance, posture, and muscular coordination. The brain stem controls vital functions, such as breathing, swallowing, heartbeat, and digestion. Language, memory, and learning are localized in the cerebrum. The processes of memory and learning are not as well understood.

The Spinal Cord

29.5.1 The spinal cord is a cable of neurons that extends from the brain down the back and is encased in the bony vertebrae of the backbone. Motor nerves carry impulses from the brain and spinal cord out to the body, and sensory nerves carry impulses from the body to the brain and spinal cord.

The Peripheral Nervous System

The Voluntary and Autonomic Nervous Systems

29.6.1 The voluntary nervous system relays commands between the CNS and skeletal muscles and can be consciously controlled; however, reflexes, such as the knee-jerk reflex shown here from **figure 29.16**, work without conscious control. The autonomic nervous system consists of opposing sympathetic and parasympathetic divisions that unconsciously relay commands between the CNS and muscles and glands.

The Sensory Nervous System

Sensing the Internal Environment

29.7.1 There are different kinds of interoceptors, but all function in informing the CNS about the internal condition of the body. For example, stretch receptors in muscles allow the CNS to control muscle movements, and baroreceptors in blood vessels provide the CNS with a continuous measure of blood pressure.

Sensing Gravity and Motion

29.8.1 Sensory receptors in the inner ear sense gravity and acceleration. The otolith sensory receptors detect gravity by the deflection of hair cells caused by the movement of otoliths in a gelatin-like matrix. Motion is detected by the deflection of hair cells in the cupula of the semicircular canals.

Sensing Chemicals: Taste and Smell

29.9.1 Chemicals are detected through the sense of taste, using taste buds on the tongue, and the sense of smell, using olfactory receptors that line the nasal passages. Different tastes and smells are detected because different chemicals stimulate different receptors on the tongue and the nasal passages.

Sensing Sounds: Hearing

29.10.1 Sound receptors detect vibrations of air through the deflection of hair cells in the inner ear. Sound waves cause the eardrum to vibrate. That vibration is amplified by bones in the middle ear, which displace fluid in the inner ear. This movement of fluid causes the deflection of hair cells.

Sensing Light: Vision

29.11.1 Sensory receptors in the eye use a lens to focus light on pigment-containing receptors.

29.11.2 Light striking the visual pigment retinal initiates a cascade of reactions that open sodium channels in the photoreceptor.

29.11.3 Rod cells detect the intensity of light, while cone cells detect different colors of light.

29.11.4 Light passes through layers of cells before reaching the rods and cones at the rear of the retina. Binocular vision allows for depth perception, but has a more limited field of view.

Test Your Understanding

29.1.1 Which of the following is *not* found in the peripheral nervous system?
a. axons
b. sensory neurons
c. association neurons
d. motor neurons

29.2.2 An action potential is caused by a quick depolarization of the membrane in a nerve cell resulting from
a. the influx of sodium ions.
b. the actions of the Na^+/K^+ pump.
c. the influx of potassium ions.
d. All of the above.

29.3.1 Neurotransmitters are released
a. from the postsynaptic cell.
b. into the synaptic cleft.
c. and bind to receptors on the presynaptic cell.
d. All of the above.

29.3.2 Excitatory neurotransmitters initiate an action potential in a postsynaptic neuron by opening
a. sodium ion gates in the postsynaptic cell.
b. potassium ion gates in the postsynaptic cell.
c. chloride ion gates in the postsynaptic cell.
d. calcium ion gates in the postsynaptic cell.

29.4.1 Integration of internal activities of the body is controlled by the
a. cerebrum.
b. cerebellum.
c. hypothalamus.
d. brain stem.

29.6.1 The purpose of the autonomic nervous system is to do all of the following *except*
a. stimulate glands.
b. relay messages to skeletal muscles.
c. relay messages to cardiac and smooth muscles.
d. regulate the body's homeostasis.

29.7.1 When arm muscles hurt after heavy exercise, the pain is detected by
a. neurotransmitters.
b. interoceptors.
c. associative neurons.
d. exteroceptors.

29.8.1 The ear senses different stimuli. Which of the following structures of the ear is associated with sensing motion and gravity?
a. cochlea
b. ear bones (the ossicles)
c. semicircular canals
d. eardrum

29.9.1 Which of the following is a chemical sensory system?
a. motion
b. stretch receptors
c. taste
d. vision

29.11.1 Which of the following statements is incorrect?
a. Vertebrates focus the eye by changing the shape of the lens.
b. Binocular vision allows for a better depth of perception.
c. Rod cells detect different colors and cones cells detect different shades of gray, allowing vision in dim light.
d. Light changes *cis*-retinal into *trans*-retinal.

Apply Your Understanding

29.3.1 At the synapse, a mutation in the structure of which component would effect whether or not a signal is transmitted, but not how strongly? Explain.

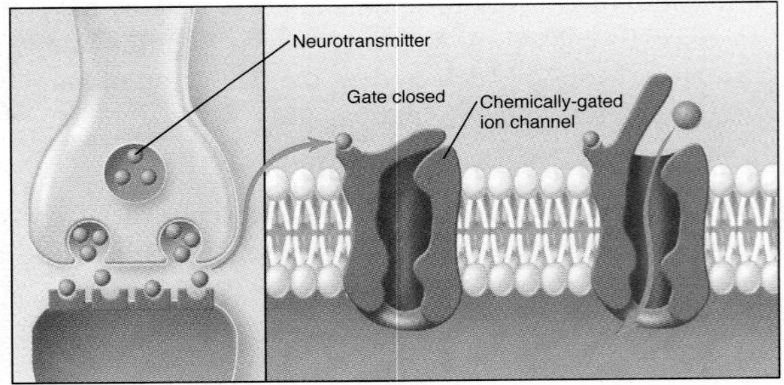

29.7.1 Your Aunt stood up suddenly at Sunday dinner and then fainted. Her fainting from standing up too quickly might involve a problem with what sensory receptor?

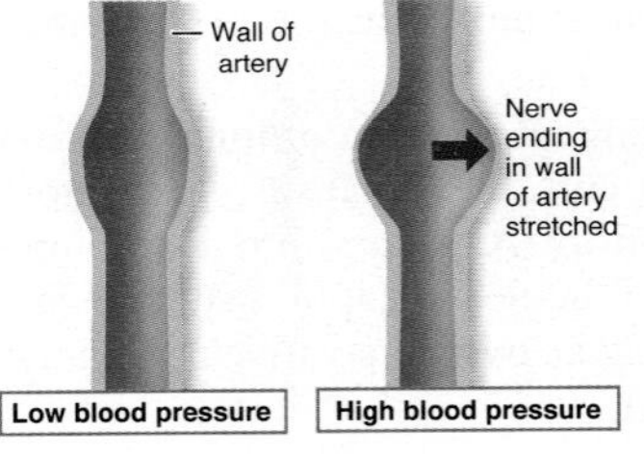

Synthesize What You Have Learned

29.2.2 Cyanide is a deadly poison that halts cellular respiration by inhibiting the mitochondrial enzyme cytochrome *c* oxidase. Chronic exposure to low levels of cyanide by those who use cassava roots as their primary food source in tropical Africa can eventually lead to permanent paralysis, as cyanide also disables the sodium potassium pump. Explain how this inhibition might lead to paralysis.

29.3.2 Botox, a derivative of the botulinum toxin that can cause fatal food poisoning, acts by inhibiting the release of acetylcholine at the neuromuscular junction. How could treating someone's face with a toxin produce desired cosmetic effects?

29.3.2 When an investigator stimulates an axon by touching it in the middle with an electrode, action potentials are generated in both directions. If instead the investigator stimulates the axon where it meets the cell body, the action potential goes only outward toward the axon terminal and not inward over the cell body. Can you explain what might be going on at the junction of the axon to the cell body that would prevent further passage of the action potential?

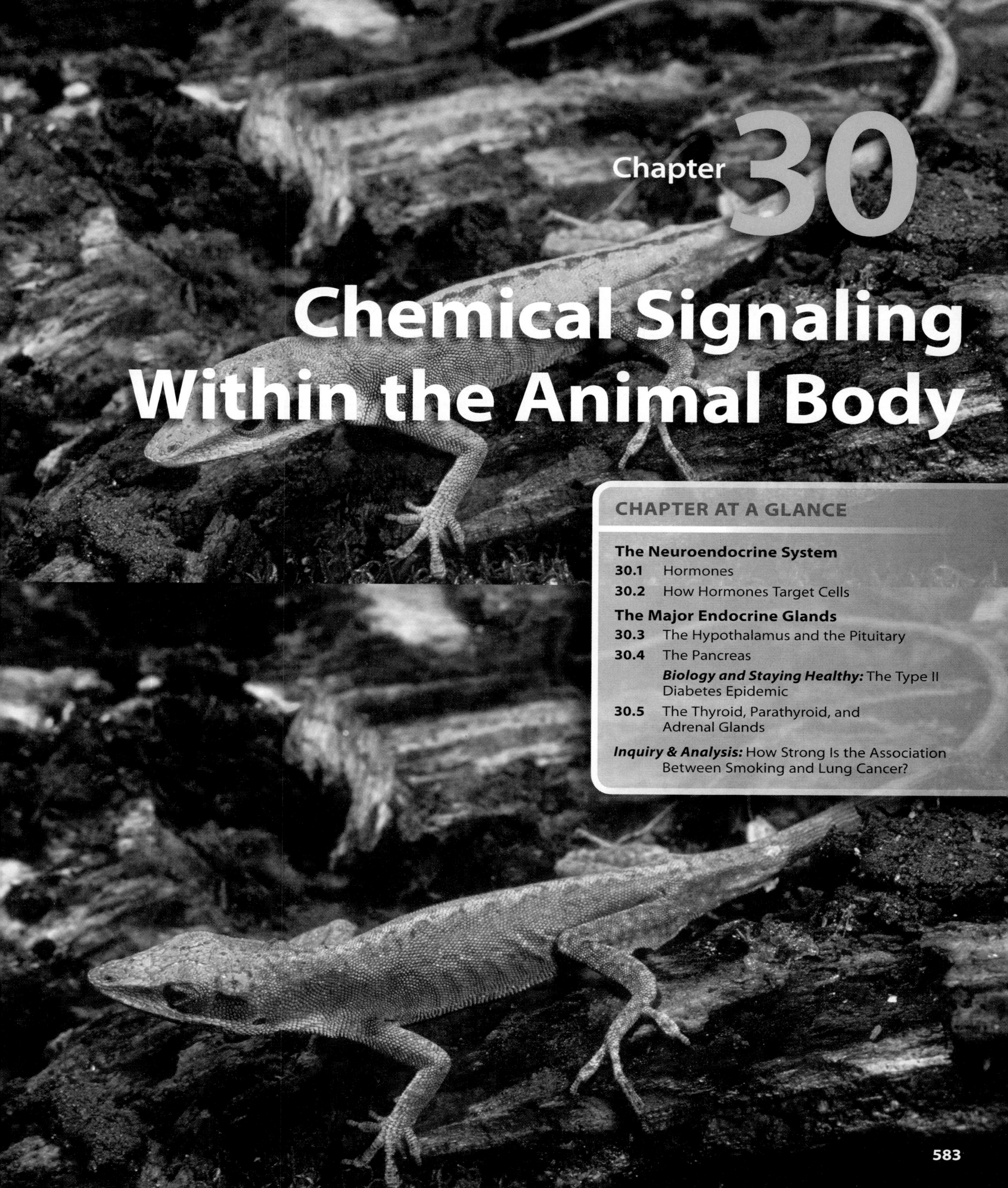

Chapter 30

Chemical Signaling Within the Animal Body

CHAPTER AT A GLANCE

The Neuroendocrine System

30.1 Hormones

30.2 How Hormones Target Cells

The Major Endocrine Glands

30.3 The Hypothalamus and the Pituitary

30.4 The Pancreas

Biology and Staying Healthy: The Type II Diabetes Epidemic

30.5 The Thyroid, Parathyroid, and Adrenal Glands

Inquiry & Analysis: How Strong Is the Association Between Smoking and Lung Cancer?

The Neuroendocrine System

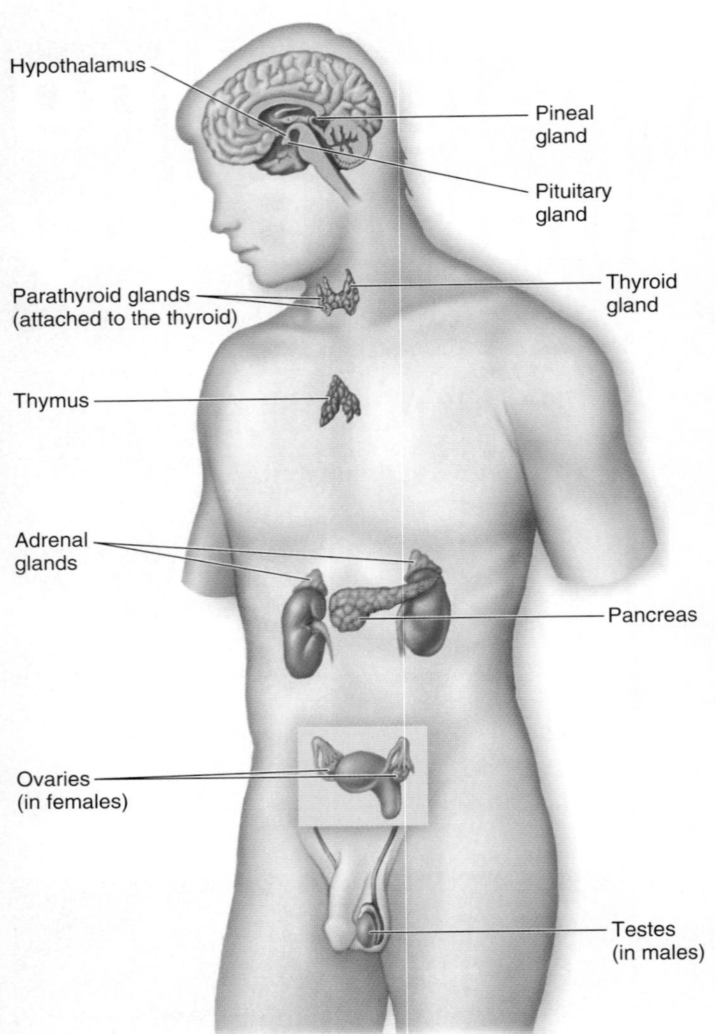

Figure 30.1 Major glands of the human endocrine system.

Hormone-secreting cells are clustered in endocrine glands. The pituitary and adrenal glands are each composed of two glands.

30.1 Hormones

LEARNING OBJECTIVE 30.1.1 **Explain the advantages of communication by hormones rather than nerves, and the role of the hypothalamus in coordinating this communication.**

A **hormone** is a chemical signal produced in one part of the body that is stable enough to be transported in active form far from where it is produced and that typically acts at a distant site. There are three big advantages to using chemical hormones as messengers rather than speedy electrical signals (like those used in nerves) to control body organs. First, chemical molecules can spread to all tissues via the blood (imagine trying to wire every cell with its own nerve!) and are usually required in only small amounts. Second, chemical signals can persist much longer than electrical ones, a great advantage for hormones controlling slow processes like growth and development. Third, many different kinds of chemicals can act as hormones, so different hormone molecules can be targeted at different tissues. For all these reasons, hormones are excellent messengers for signaling widespread, slow-onset, long-duration responses.

Hormones, in general, are produced by glands, most of which are controlled by the central nervous system. Because these glands are completely enclosed in tissue rather than having ducts that empty to the outside, they are called **endocrine glands** (from the Greek, *endon,* within). Hormones are secreted from them directly into the bloodstream (this is in contrast to **exocrine glands,** like sweat glands, which have ducts). Your body has a dozen principal endocrine glands (**figure 30.1**) that together make up the endocrine system.

The *endocrine system* and the *motor nervous system* are the two main routes the central nervous system (CNS) uses to issue commands to the organs of the body. The two are so closely linked that they are often considered a single system—the **neuroendocrine system.** The **hypothalamus** can be considered the main switchboard of the neuroendocrine system. The hypothalamus is continually checking conditions inside the body to maintain a constant internal environment, a condition known as homeostasis. Is the body too hot or too cold? Is it running out of fuel? Is the blood pressure too high? If homeostasis is no longer maintained, the hypothalamus has several ways to set things right again. For example, if the hypothalamus needs to speed up the heart rate, it can send a nerve signal to the medulla oblongata, or it can use a chemical command, causing the adrenal gland to produce the hormone epinephrine, which also speeds up the heart rate.

The Chain of Command

The hypothalamus issues commands to a nearby gland, the pituitary, which in turn sends chemical signals to the various hormone-producing glands of the body. The CNS regulates the body's hormones through a chain of command. The "releasing" hormones made by the hypothalamus cause the pituitary to synthesize a corresponding pituitary hormone, which travels to a distant endocrine gland and causes that gland to begin producing its particular endocrine hormone.

Putting the Concept to Work

What is the difference between endocrine and exocrine glands?

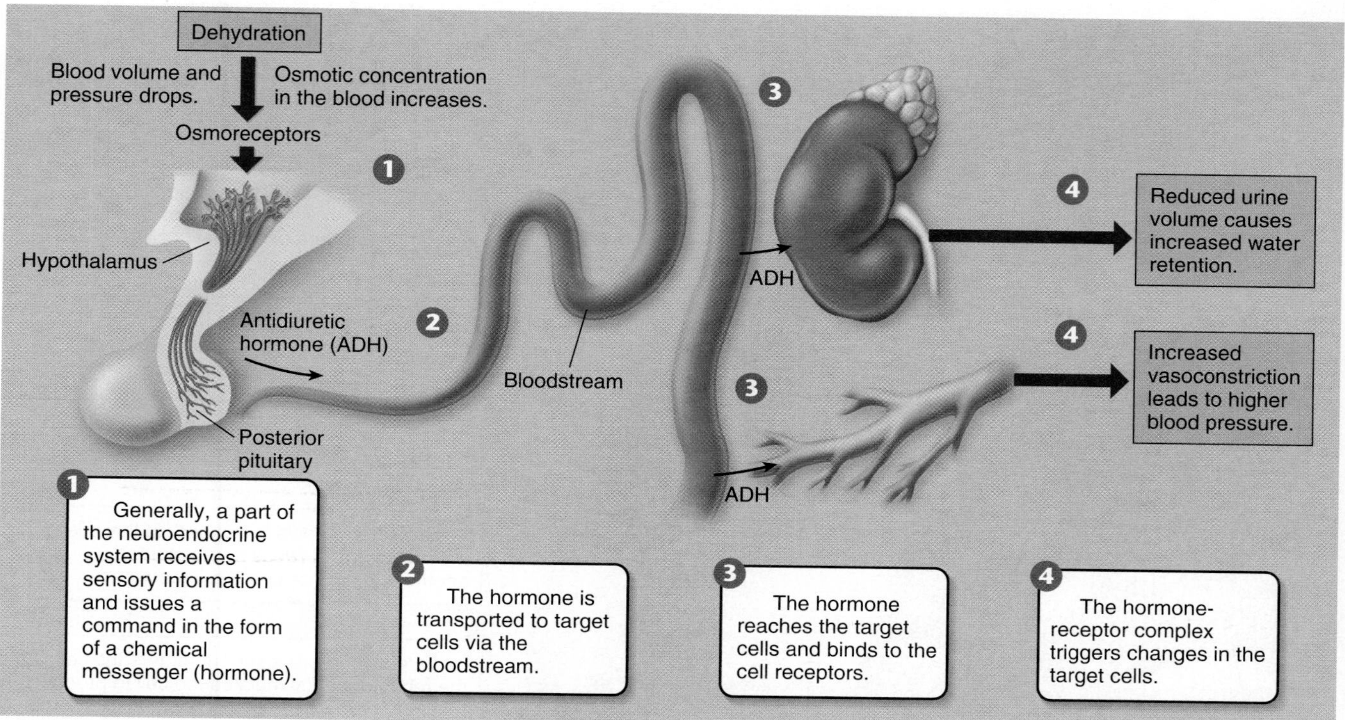

Figure 30.2 How hormonal communication works.

How Hormones Work

LEARNING OBJECTIVE 30.1.2 Delineate the four stages of hormonal signaling.

Hormones are effective messengers within the body mainly because a particular hormone can influence a specific target cell. How does the target cell recognize that hormone, ignoring all others? Embedded in the plasma membrane or within the target cell are receptor proteins that match the shape of the potential signal hormone like a hand fits a glove. The system is highly specific because cells that the body has targeted to respond to a particular hormone have receptor proteins shaped to fit that hormone and no other. Thus, chemical communication within the body involves *two* elements: a molecular signal (the hormone) and a protein receptor on or in target cells.

The path of communication taken by a hormonal signal can be visualized as the series of simple steps shown in the example in figure 30.2:

1. **Issuing the command.** Some hormones produced in cells in the hypothalamus are stored in the posterior pituitary and are released into the bloodstream in response to a signal from the brain.
2. **Transporting the signal.** The hormones travel through the bloodstream to the target cells.
3. **Hitting the target.** When a hormone encounters a cell with a matching receptor, called a target cell, the hormone binds to that receptor.
4. **Having an effect.** When the hormone binds to the receptor protein, the protein responds by changing shape, triggering a cell change.

Putting the Concept to Work

How do you suppose hormones made in the hypothalamus get to the pituitary to be released?

IN THE NEWS

Love-Enhancing Pharmaceuticals? Neuroscientists have developed many drugs that influence emotional states such as depression and anxiety, but how about love? They now report that when people look at photos of their lovers, this activates dopamine-related reward regions of the brain—the same regions stimulated by drugs such as nicotine and cocaine to produce euphoria, and by the hormone oxytocin to stimulate pair bonding. Other female mammals become attached to the nearest male if their brain is infused with oxytocin. Internet entrepreneurs have begun marketing oxytocin-laced sprays that claim to enhance dating success. The sprays are unlikely to be effective, but they point to a future when advances in neuroscience may transform love to an adjustable condition. What do you think of this?

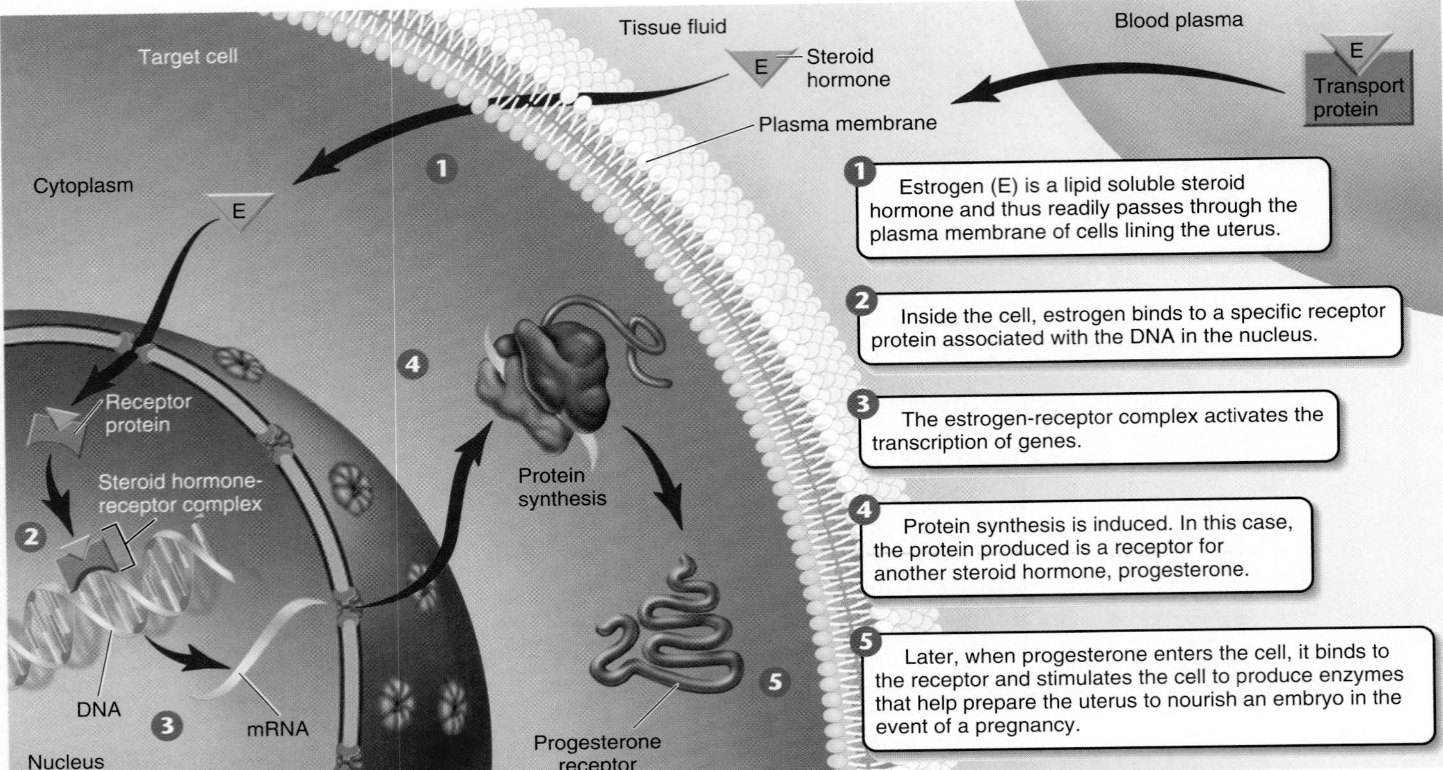
Tissue fluid
Blood plasma
Target cell
Steroid hormone
Transport protein
Plasma membrane
Cytoplasm
1 Estrogen (E) is a lipid soluble steroid hormone and thus readily passes through the plasma membrane of cells lining the uterus.
2 Inside the cell, estrogen binds to a specific receptor protein associated with the DNA in the nucleus.
3 The estrogen-receptor complex activates the transcription of genes.
4 Protein synthesis is induced. In this case, the protein produced is a receptor for another steroid hormone, progesterone.
5 Later, when progesterone enters the cell, it binds to the receptor and stimulates the cell to produce enzymes that help prepare the uterus to nourish an embryo in the event of a pregnancy.
Receptor protein
Steroid hormone-receptor complex
Protein synthesis
DNA
mRNA
Nucleus
Progesterone receptor

Figure 30.3 How steroid hormones work.

30.2 How Hormones Target Cells

Steroid Hormones Enter Cells

LEARNING OBJECTIVE 30.2.1 Describe the structure and mode of action of steroid hormones.

Some protein receptors designed to recognize hormones are located in the cytoplasm or nucleus of the target cell. The hormones in these cases are typically lipid-soluble **steroid hormones.** All steroid hormones are manufactured from cholesterol, a complex molecule composed of four rings. Steroids include the hormones that promote the development of secondary sexual characteristics such as testosterone, estrogen, and progesterone, discussed in detail in chapter 31.

Steroids, discussed on page 60, are a type of lipid. Because lipids are hydrophobic, steroids are able to cross the hydrophobic inner layer of the lipid bilayer, passing directly into the cell.

Steroid hormones like estrogen, "E" in figure 30.3, can pass across the lipid bilayer of the cell plasma membrane ❶ and bind to receptors within the cell and often, as in the case with estrogen, within the nucleus. The hormone-receptor complex then binds to the DNA in the nucleus ❷ and activates the gene for a progesterone receptor protein, which is transcribed ❸. The protein is synthesized ❹, and the receptor is available to bind progesterone when it enters the cell ❺, which itself activates another set of genes.

Anabolic steroids are synthetic compounds that resemble the male sex hormone testosterone. The injection of anabolic steroids into muscles activates growth genes and causes the muscle cells to produce more protein, resulting in bigger muscles and increased strength. However, anabolic

BIOLOGY & YOU

Performance-Enhancing Sports Supplements. Many athletes, coaches, and fans feel that the use of anabolic steroids and other substances to improve performance is unethical in sports. Steroids are actually illegal. On the other hand, no one would argue that taking vitamin supplements is unethical. There is a large array of products between these two extremes. Many substances widely marketed as "performance-enhancing dietary supplements" are discouraged by most coaches and have limited research on their safety or effectiveness. For example, it has been claimed that creatin improves sprinting and weight lifting, ephedrine improves strength and endurance, and glucosamine stimulates cartilage formation, but there is little evidence that such claims are true. On balance, when in doubt, don't take it.

steroids have many dangerous side effects, including liver damage, heart disease, and high blood pressure. Anabolic steroids are illegal, and athletes in many sports are tested for their use.

> **Putting the Concept to Work**
> **What does a steroid hormone do after it enters a cell?**

Peptide Hormones Act at the Cell Surface

> **LEARNING OBJECTIVE 30.2.2 Describe the structure and mode of action of peptide hormones.**

Other hormone receptors are embedded within the plasma membrane, with their recognition regions directed outward from the cell surface. **Peptide hormones**, like the one binding to the receptor in figure 30.4 ❶, are typically short peptide chains (although some are full-sized proteins). The binding of the peptide hormone to the receptor triggers a change in the cytoplasmic end of the receptor protein. This change then triggers events within the cell cytoplasm, usually through intermediate within-cell signals called **second messengers** ❷, which greatly amplify the original signal and result in changes in the cell ❸.

How does a second messenger amplify a hormone's signal? Second messengers activate enzymes. One of the most common second messengers is cyclic AMP (cAMP), and its actions are shown in figure 30.5. A single hormone molecule binding to a receptor in the plasma membrane can result in the formation of many second messengers in the cytoplasm. Each second messenger can activate many molecules of a certain enzyme, and sometimes each of these enzymes can in turn activate many other enzymes. Thus, second messengers enable each hormone molecule to have a tremendous effect inside the cell.

> **Putting the Concept to Work**
> **How do second messengers amplify hormone signals?**

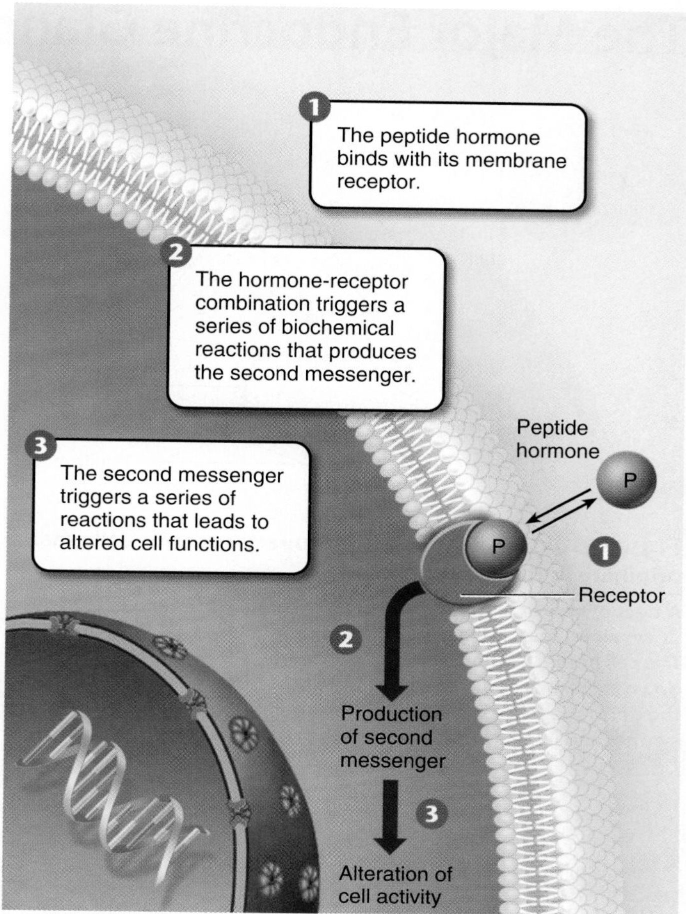

1 The peptide hormone binds with its membrane receptor.
2 The hormone-receptor combination triggers a series of biochemical reactions that produces the second messenger.
3 The second messenger triggers a series of reactions that leads to altered cell functions.
Peptide hormone
P
P
1
Hormone (first messenger)
Receptor
3 Protein kinases catalyze a wide variety of actions, depending on the nature of the first messenger. Because of the presence of a second messenger, the effect on the cell is greatly amplified.
Adenylyl cyclase
2
Production of second messenger
3
Alteration of cell activity

Figure 30.4 How peptide hormones work.

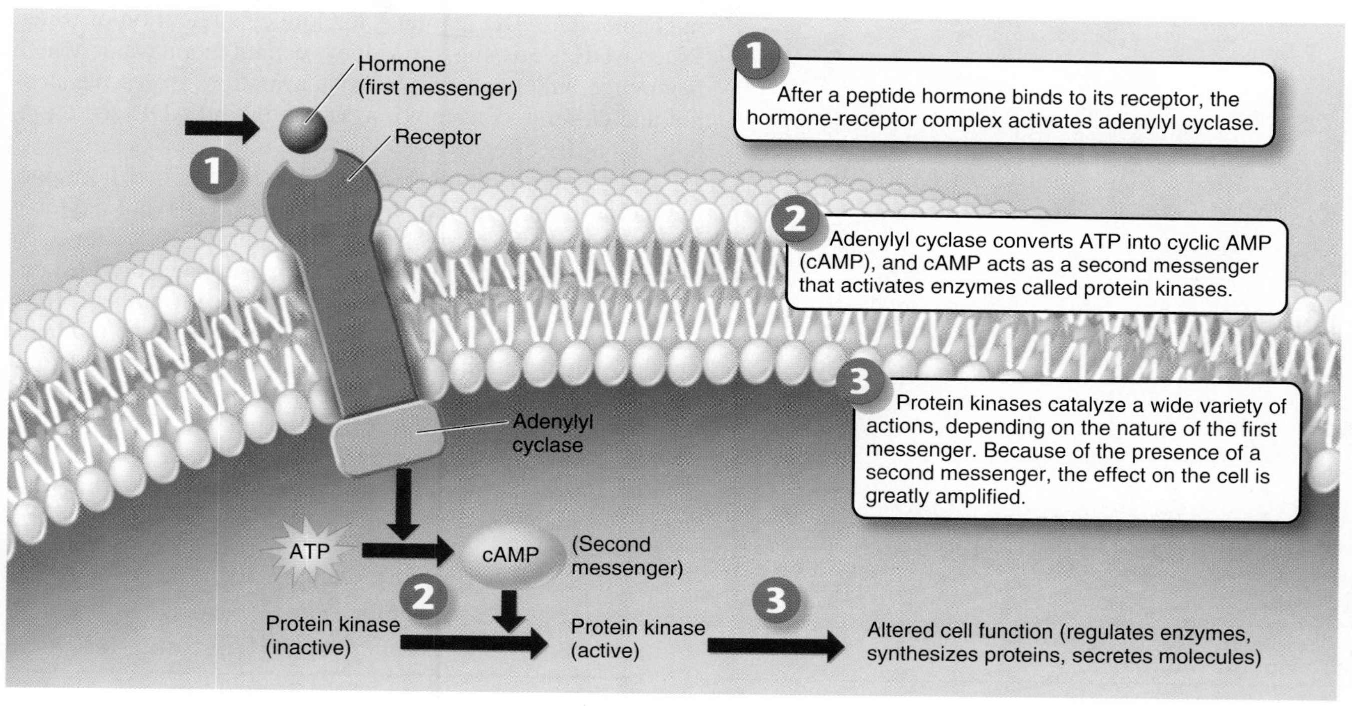

Protein kinase (inactive)

Figure 30.5 How second messengers work.

The Major Endocrine Glands

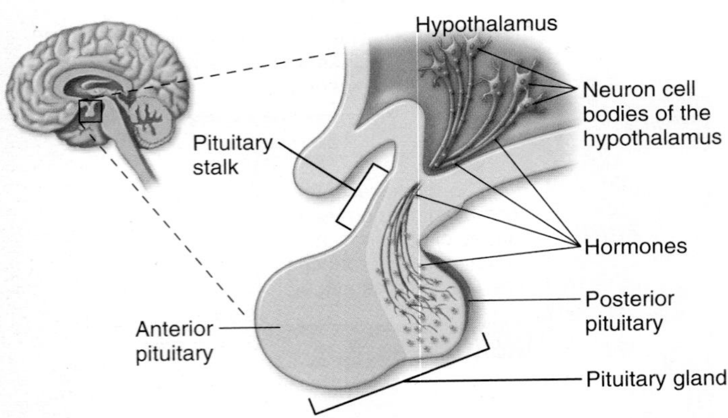

Figure 30.6 The posterior pituitary contains cells that originate in the hypothalamus.

A tract of nerve cells originates in the hypothalamus and extends down along the pituitary stalk and ends in the posterior pituitary. The cell bodies of the neurons produce hormones, which travel down the axons and are stored in the posterior pituitary. Thus, the hormones released from the posterior pituitary are actually synthesized in neurons in the hypothalamus.

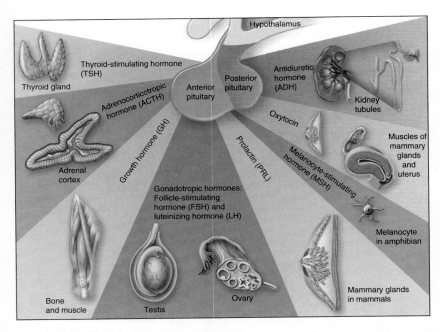

Figure 30.7 The role of the pituitary.

30.3 The Hypothalamus and the Pituitary

LEARNING OBJECTIVE 30.3.1 Contrast the posterior and anterior pituitary glands.

The hypothalamus, the "control center" of the neuroendocrine system, exerts its control by releasing hormones that influence the nearby **pituitary gland,** located in a bony recess in the brain just below the hypothalamus. The pituitary in turn produces hormones that influence the body's other endocrine glands. Hormones produced by the back portion of the pituitary, or *posterior lobe,* regulate water conservation, as well as milk letdown and uterine contraction in women; hormones produced by the front portion, or *anterior lobe,* regulate the other endocrine glands.

The Posterior Pituitary

The posterior pituitary contains axons that originate in cell bodies within the hypothalamus. The hormones released from the posterior pituitary are actually produced by neuron cell bodies located in the hypothalamus. The hormones are transported to the posterior pituitary through axon tracts and are stored and released from the posterior pituitary (**figure 30.6**).

The role of the posterior pituitary first became evident in 1912, when a remarkable medical case was reported: A man who had been shot in the head developed a surprising disorder—he began to urinate every 30 minutes, unceasingly. The bullet had lodged in his pituitary gland, and subsequent research demonstrated that surgical removal of the pituitary also produces these unusual symptoms. Pituitary extracts were shown to contain a substance that makes the kidneys conserve water, and in the early 1950s the peptide hormone vasopressin (now more commonly called **antidiuretic hormone, ADH**) was isolated. As you learned in chapter 27, ADH regulates the kidney's retention of water. When ADH is missing, the kidneys cannot retain water, which is why the bullet caused excessive urination. Excessive alcohol and caffeine consumption, which inhibit ADH secretion, have a similar effect.

The posterior pituitary also releases a second hormone, **oxytocin,** of very similar structure—both ADH and oxytocin are short peptides composed of nine amino acids. However, oxytocin has a very different function; it initiates uterine contraction during childbirth and milk release in mothers. Here is how milk release works: Sensory receptors in the mother's nipples, when stimulated by sucking, send messages to the hypothalamus, causing the hypothalamus to stimulate the release of oxytocin from the posterior pituitary. The oxytocin travels in the bloodstream to the breasts, where it stimulates contraction of the muscles around the ducts into which the mammary glands secrete milk.

Putting the Concept to Work

Why does pituitary injury lead to excessive urination?

The Anterior Pituitary

LEARNING OBJECTIVE 30.3.2 List seven peptide hormones that the anterior pituitary produces, and explain how the hypothalamus regulates their release.

The anterior pituitary gland produces seven major peptide hormones (figure 30.7), each controlled by a particular releasing signal secreted from the hypothalamus:

1. **Thyroid-stimulating hormone (TSH).** TSH stimulates the thyroid gland to produce the thyroid hormone thyroxine, which in turn stimulates oxidative respiration.
2. **Adrenocorticotropic hormone (ACTH).** ACTH stimulates the adrenal gland to produce a variety of steroid hormones. Some regulate the production of glucose; others regulate the balance of sodium and potassium ions in the blood.
3. **Growth hormone (GH).** GH stimulates the growth of muscle and bone throughout the body.
4. **Follicle-stimulating hormone (FSH).** FSH is significant in the female menstrual cycle by triggering the maturation of egg cells and stimulating the release of estrogen. In males, it stimulates cells in the testes, regulating development of the sperm.
5. **Luteinizing hormone (LH).** LH plays an important role in the female menstrual cycle by triggering ovulation, which is the release of a mature egg. It also stimulates the male gonads to produce testosterone.
6. **Prolactin (PRL).** Prolactin stimulates the breasts to produce milk, which is released in response to oxytocin.
7. **Melanocyte-stimulating hormone (MSH).** In reptiles and amphibians, MSH stimulates color changes in the epidermis (figure 30.8). The function of this hormone in humans is still poorly understood.

Follicle-stimulating hormone and luteinizing hormone (along with estrogen and progesterone that are produced elsewhere in the body) coordinate the female reproductive cycle, discussed in more detail on page 604.

How the Hypothalamus Controls the Anterior Pituitary

The hypothalamus controls production and secretion of the anterior pituitary hormones by means of a family of special hormones. Neurons in the hypothalamus secrete these releasing and inhibiting hormones into blood capillaries at the base of the hypothalamus. Figure 30.9 shows the relationship of neurons (colored blue in the figure) that extend from the hypothalamus into the posterior pituitary, where they deliver the hormones for storage and release, to other neurons of the hypothalamus (colored yellow in the figure), which produce releasing and inhibiting hormones and release them into capillaries. These capillaries drain into small veins that run within the stalk of the pituitary to a second bed of capillaries in the anterior pituitary.

Each releasing hormone delivered to the anterior pituitary by these capillaries regulates the secretion of a specific anterior pituitary hormone. For example, thyrotropin-releasing hormone (TRH) stimulates the release of TSH, and growth-hormone-releasing hormone (GHRH) stimulates the release of GH.

Putting the Concept to Work

Why doesn't the hypothalamus just release hormones directly into the bloodstream? Why bother with releasing hormones?

Figure 30.8 A hormone in action.

Melanocyte-stimulating hormone stimulates color changes in reptiles and amphibians The green anole (*Anolis carolinensis*) shown here in the upper photo has changed to a tan color in the lower photo, in response to an environmental cue.

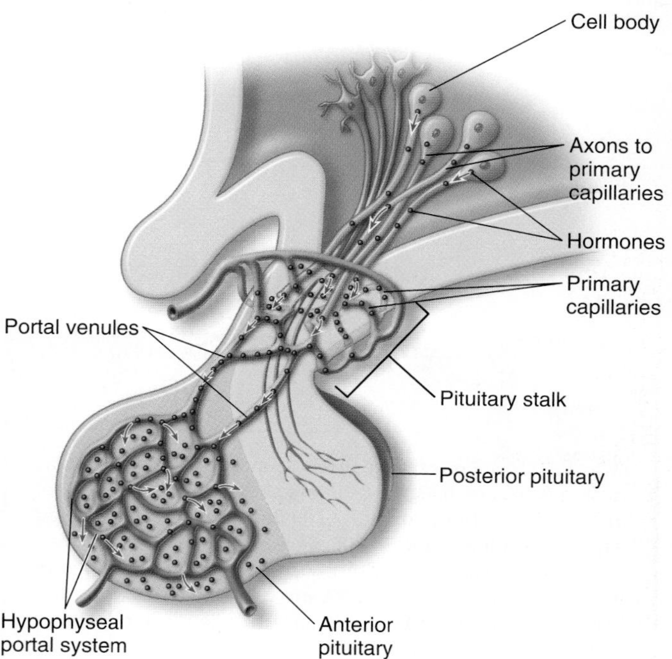

Figure 30.9 Hormonal control of the anterior pituitary gland by the hypothalamus.

Neurons in the hypothalamus secrete hormones that are carried by short blood vessels to the anterior pituitary gland, where they either stimulate or inhibit the secretion of anterior pituitary hormones.

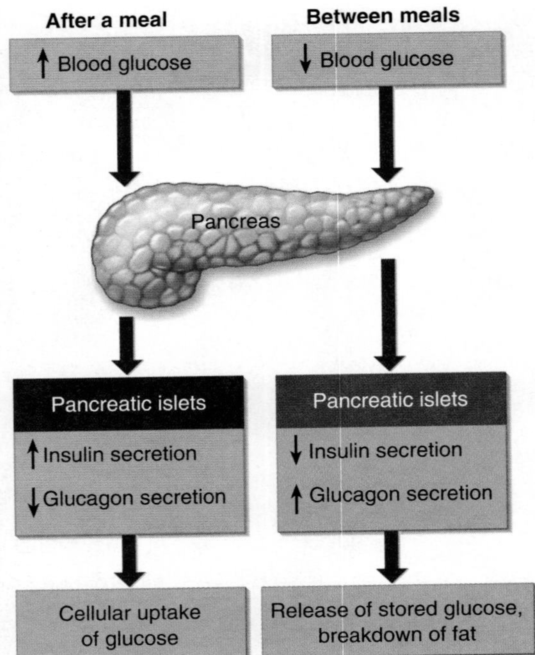

Figure 30.10 Insulin and glucagon secreted by the pancreas regulate blood glucose levels.

After a meal, an increased secretion of insulin by the beta cells of the pancreatic islets of Langerhans promotes the movement of glucose from blood into tissue cells. Between meals, an increased secretion of glucagon by the alpha cells of the pancreatic islets and decreased secretion of insulin cause the release of stored glucose and the breakdown of fat.

30.4 The Pancreas

LEARNING OBJECTIVE 30.4.1 Identify the hormones produced in the pancreas, and describe how they interact to regulate blood glucose levels.

The **pancreas** gland is located behind the stomach and is connected to the front end of the small intestine by a narrow tube. It secretes a variety of digestive enzymes into the digestive tract through this tube, and for a long time it was thought to be solely an exocrine gland. In 1869, however, a German medical student named Paul Langerhans described some unusual clusters of cells scattered throughout the pancreas. In 1893, doctors concluded that these clusters of cells, which came to be called islets of Langerhans, produced a substance that prevented diabetes mellitus. **Diabetes mellitus** is a serious disorder in which affected individuals' cells are unable to take up glucose from the blood, even though their levels of blood glucose become very high. Some individuals lose weight and literally starve; others develop poor circulation, sometimes resulting in amputation of limbs with restricted circulation. Diabetes is the leading cause of blindness among adults, and it accounts for one-third of all kidney failures. It is the seventh leading cause of death in the United States.

The islets of Langerhans in the pancreas produce two hormones that interact to govern the levels of glucose in the blood. These hormones are *insulin* and *glucagon.* Insulin is a storage hormone, designed to put away nutrients for leaner times. It promotes the accumulation of glycogen in the liver and triglycerides in fat cells. When food is consumed (left side of figure 30.10), beta cells in the islets of Langerhans secrete insulin, causing the cells of the body to take up and store glucose as glycogen and triglycerides to be used later. When body activity causes the level of glucose in the blood to fall as it is used as fuel (right side of figure 30.10), other cells in the islets of Langerhans, called alpha cells, secrete glucagon, which causes liver cells to release stored glucose and fat cells to break down triglycerides for energy use. The two hormones work together to keep glucose levels in the blood within a narrow range.

Over 26 million people in the United States, and over 246 million people worldwide, have **diabetes.** There are two kinds of diabetes mellitus. About 5% to 10% of affected individuals suffer from type I diabetes, an autoimmune disease in which the immune system attacks the islets of Langerhans, resulting in abnormally low insulin secretion. Called juvenile-onset diabetes, this type usually develops before age 20. Affected individuals can be treated by daily injections of insulin. Active research on the possibility of transplanting islets of Langerhans holds promise as a lasting treatment for type I diabetes.

In type II diabetes, the level of insulin in the blood is often higher than normal, but cells don't respond to insulin. This form of diabetes usually develops in people over 40 years of age. It is almost always a consequence of excessive weight; in the United States, 80% of those who develop type II diabetes are obese. The cells of some type II diabetics, overwhelmed with food, adjust their appetite for glucose downward, reducing their sensitivity to insulin by reducing their number of insulin receptors. To compensate, the pancreas pumps out ever-more insulin. Type II diabetes is usually treatable with diet and exercise, and most affected individuals do not need daily injections of insulin.

Putting the Concept to Work

Distinguish between type I and type II diabetes.

IN THE NEWS

Pancreatic Cancer. Among the most deadly of all cancers are malignant tumors of the pancreas. Each year in the United States, about 37,700 individuals are diagnosed with this condition, and 34,300 die from the disease. Less than 5% of those diagnosed with pancreatic cancer are still alive five years after diagnosis; 50% are dead within six months. Pancreatic cancer is sometimes called a "silent killer" because early pancreatic cancer often does not cause symptoms, so a tumor is often not diagnosed until it is far advanced. Unfortunately, we don't have much of an idea of what causes pancreatic cancer. It is more common in men over 60, and slightly more common in cigarette smokers, diabetics, and obese people, but there are no established guidelines for preventing pancreatic cancer.

Biology and Staying Healthy

The Type II Diabetes Epidemic

We Americans love to eat, but recently the Centers for Disease Control and Prevention released a report warning we are eating ourselves into a diabetes epidemic. Diabetes affected 7 million Americans in 1991. By the end of 2010, the number was over 26 million, more than 8% of all Americans, which is an alarming increase in just 19 years!

The same explosion of diabetes is being seen worldwide. Diabetes now affects 246 million people, and kills 3.8 million each year. Every 10 seconds one person dies of diabetes. In the same 10 seconds two more people develop the disease.

Diabetes is a disorder in which the body's cells fail to take up glucose from the blood. Tissues waste away as glucose-starved cells are forced to consume their own proteins. Diabetes is the leading cause of kidney failure, blindness, and amputation in adults. Almost all the increase in diabetes in the last decade is in the 90% of diabetics who suffer from type II, or "adult-onset," diabetes. These individuals lack the ability to use the hormone insulin.

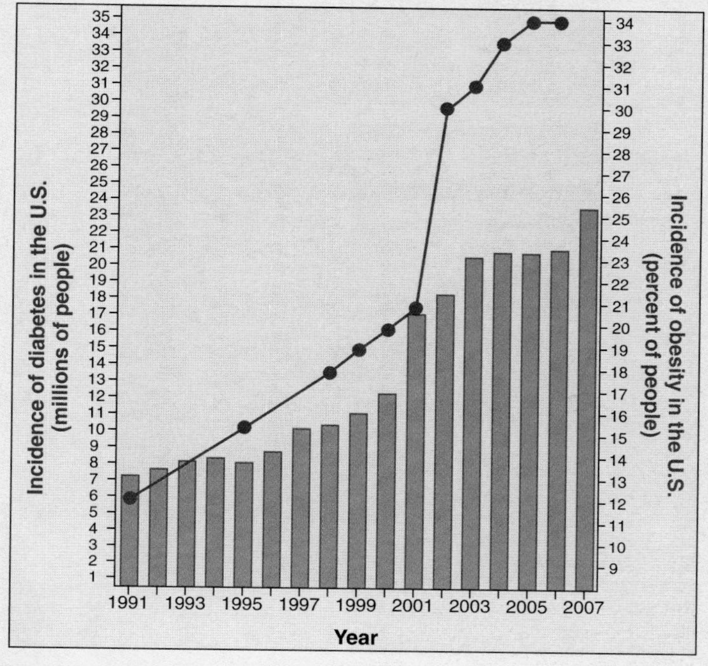

Your body manufactures insulin after a meal as a way to alert cells that higher levels of glucose are coming soon. The insulin signal attaches to special receptors on the cell surfaces, which respond by causing the cell to turn on its glucose-transporting machinery. Some individuals who suffer from type II diabetes have normal or even elevated levels of insulin in their blood, and normal insulin receptors, but for some reason the binding of insulin to their cell receptors does not turn on the glucose-transporting machinery like it is supposed to do. For 30 years researchers have been trying to figure out why not.

How does insulin act to turn on a normal cell's glucose transporting machinery? Proteins called IRS proteins (the names refer not to tax collectors, but to *insulin receptor substrate*) snuggle up against the insulin receptor inside the cell. When insulin attaches to the receptor protein, the receptor responds by adding a phosphate group onto the IRS molecules. Like being touched by a red-hot poker, this galvanizes the IRS molecules into action. Dashing about, they activate a variety of processes, including an enzyme that turns on the glucose-transporting machinery.

When the IRS genes are deliberately taken out of action in so-called knockout mice, type II diabetes results. Are defects in the genes for IRS proteins responsible for type II diabetes? Probably not. When researchers look for IRS gene mutations in inherited type II diabetes, they don't find them. The IRS genes are normal.

This suggests that in type II diabetes something is interfering with the action of the IRS proteins. What might it be? An estimated 80% of those who develop type II diabetes are obese, a tantalizing clue. Look at the graph. During the same time that diabetes has undergone its explosive increase, the obesity rate increased from 6% of the U.S. population to over 34%.

What is the link between diabetes and obesity? Recent research suggests an answer to this key question. A team of scientists at the University of Pennsylvania School of Medicine had been investigating why a class of drugs called thiazolidinediones (TZDs) helped combat diabetes. They found that TZDs cause the body's cells to use insulin more effectively, and this suggested to them that the TZD drug might be targeting a hormone.

The researchers then set out to see if they could find such a hormone in mice. In search of a clue, they started by looking to see which mouse genes were activated or deactivated by TZD. Several were. Examining them, they were able to zero in on the hormone they sought. Dubbed *resistin,* the hormone is produced by fat cells and prompts tissues to resist insulin. The same *resistin* gene is present in humans too. The researchers speculate that resistin may have evolved to help the body deal with periods of famine.

Mice given resistin by the researchers lost much of their ability to take up blood sugar. When given a drug that lowers resistin levels, these mice recovered the lost glucose-transporting ability.

Researchers don't yet know how resistin acts to lower insulin sensitivity, although blocking the action of IRS proteins seems a likely possibility.

Importantly, dramatically high levels of the hormone were found in mice obese from overeating. Finding this sort of result is like ringing a dinner bell to diabetes researchers. If obesity is causing high resistin levels in humans, leading to type II diabetes, then resistin-lowering drugs might offer a diabetes cure!

On the scent of something important, resistin researchers are now shifting their efforts from mice to humans. Much needs to be checked, as there are no guarantees that what works in a mouse will do so in the same way in a human. Still, the excitement is tangible.

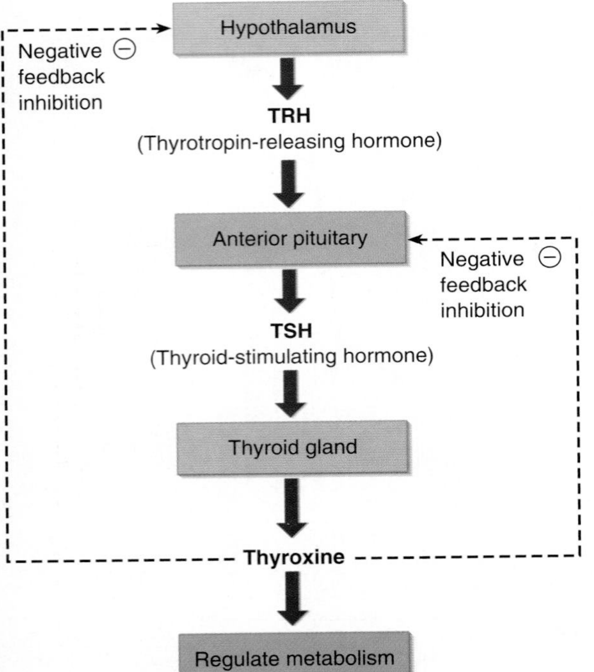

Figure 30.11 The thyroid gland secretes thyroxine.

(a) Thyroxine exerts negative feedback control of the hypothalamus and anterior pituitary. (b) A goiter is caused by a lack of iodine in the diet, which causes thyroxine secretion to decrease. As a result, there is less negative feedback, TSH is not inhibited from stimulating the thyroid gland, and the thyroid gland becomes enlarged.

IMPLICATION FOR YOU Do you think you would be able to treat this woman's goiter by administering iodine? Explain.

30.5 The Thyroid, Parathyroid, and Adrenal Glands

LEARNING OBJECTIVE 30.5.1 Locate the thyroid, parathyroid, and adrenal glands, identify the hormones they produce, and discuss how these hormones function.

The Thyroid: A Metabolic Thermostat

The **thyroid gland** is shaped like a shield (its name comes from *thyros,* the Greek word for "shield") and lies just below the Adam's apple in the front of the neck. The thyroid makes several hormones, the two most important of which are **thyroxine,** which increases metabolic rate and promotes growth, and **calcitonin,** which inhibits the release of calcium from bones.

Thyroxine regulates the level of metabolism in the body in several important ways. Without adequate thyroxine, growth is retarded. For example, children with underactive thyroid glands are not able to carry out carbohydrate breakdown and protein synthesis at normal rates, a condition called cretinism, which results in stunted growth. Mental retardation can also result, because thyroxine is needed for normal development of the central nervous system.

Negative feedback loops control many body functions, as discussed on page 532. In the case of hormone regulation, the hormone itself can be the response that feeds back to the effector (gland), increasing or decreasing its own production.

The thyroid is stimulated to produce thyroxine by the hypothalamus, which is inhibited by thyroxine via negative feedback. The dashed lines in **figure 30.11*a*** illustrate how thyroxine inhibits the release of TRH and TSH from the hypothalamus and anterior pituitary, respectively.

Thyroxine contains iodine, and if the amount of iodine in the diet is too low, the thyroid cannot make adequate amounts of thyroxine to keep the hypothalamus inhibited. The hypothalamus will then continue to stimulate the thyroid, which will grow larger in a futile attempt to manufacture more thyroxine. The greatly enlarged thyroid gland that results is called a goiter (**figure 30.11*b***). This need for iodine in the diet is why iodine is added to table salt.

Calcitonin, which is also produced by the thyroid and will be discussed later, plays a key role in maintaining proper calcium levels in the body.

The Parathyroids: Regulating Calcium

The **parathyroid glands** are four small glands attached to the thyroid. Small and unobtrusive, they were ignored by researchers until well into the last century. The first suggestion that the parathyroids produce a hormone came from experiments in which they were removed from dogs: The concentration of calcium in the dogs' blood plummeted to less than half the normal level. However, if an extract of the parathyroid gland was administered, calcium levels returned to normal. If an excess was administered, calcium levels in the blood became *too* high, and the bones of the dogs were literally dismantled by the extract. It was clear that the parathyroid glands were producing a hormone that acted on calcium, both its uptake into bones and release from bones.

The hormone produced by the parathyroids is **parathyroid hormone (PTH).** It is one of only two hormones in the body that is absolutely essential for survival (the other is aldosterone, a hormone produced by the adrenal glands, discussed below). PTH regulates the level of calcium in blood. Calcium ions are needed in muscle contraction—by initiating calcium release, nerve impulses cause muscles to contract. A vertebrate cannot live without the muscles that pump the heart and drive the body, and these muscles cannot function if calcium levels are not kept within narrow limits.

PTH acts as a fail-safe to make sure calcium levels never fall too low. If they do, as in **figure 30.12*a***, PTH is released into the bloodstream, travels to the bones, and acts on the osteoclast cells (the blue cells) within bones, stimulating them to dismantle bone tissue and release calcium into the bloodstream. PTH also acts on the kidneys to reabsorb calcium ions from the filtrate and leads to activation of vitamin D, necessary for calcium absorption by the intestine. A diet deficient in vitamin D leads to poor bone formation, a condition called rickets. The hormone calcitonin is released from the thyroid gland and acts in reverse of PTH. When calcium levels in the blood rise (**figure 30.12*b***), calcitonin activates osteoblast cells (the orange cells) to take up calcium, and rebuild bone.

Osteoblasts are bone cells that build new bone tissue and osteoclasts are bone cells that secrete enzymes that break down bone tissue. Both cell types are involved in bone remodeling as discussed on page 478.

The Adrenals: Two Glands in One

Mammals have two **adrenal glands,** one located just above each kidney (see **figure 30.1**). Each adrenal gland is composed of two parts: (1) an inner core, the **medulla,** which produces the hormones epinephrine (also called adrenaline) and norepinephrine; and (2) an outer shell, the **cortex,** which produces the steroid hormones cortisol and aldosterone.

The Adrenal Medulla: Emergency Warning Siren. The adrenal medulla releases **epinephrine** and **norepinephrine** in times of stress. These hormones act as emergency signals that stimulate rapid deployment of body fuel. The "alarm" response these hormones produce throughout the body is identical to the individual effects achieved by the sympathetic nervous system, but it is much longer lasting. Among their effects are accelerated heartbeat, increased blood pressure, higher levels of blood sugar, and increased blood flow to the heart.

The Adrenal Cortex: Inflammation, Stress, and Maintaining the Proper Amount of Salt. The adrenal cortex produces the steroid hormone cortisol. **Cortisol** (also called hydrocortisone) acts on many different cells in the body to maintain nutritional well-being. It stimulates carbohydrate metabolism and reduces inflammation. Synthetic derivatives of this hormone, such as prednisone, have widespread medical use as anti-inflammatory agents. Cortisol is also called the *stress hormone,* released in times of stress to help the body deal with acute stress. Problems arise when the body experiences chronic stress and cortisol levels remain high in the body. This can lead to problems with high blood pressure, reduced immune function, fat accumulation, and maintaining blood sugar, among others. These chronic effects of cortisol are unhealthy.

The adrenal cortex also produces **aldosterone.** Aldosterone acts primarily in the kidney to promote the uptake of sodium and other salts from the urine, which also increases the reabsorption of water. Aldosterone is, with PTH, one of the two endocrine hormones essential for survival. Removal of the adrenal glands is invariably fatal.

Putting the Concept to Work

What two hormones are so essential for human survival that you would die if they ceased to be produced? Why are they so important?

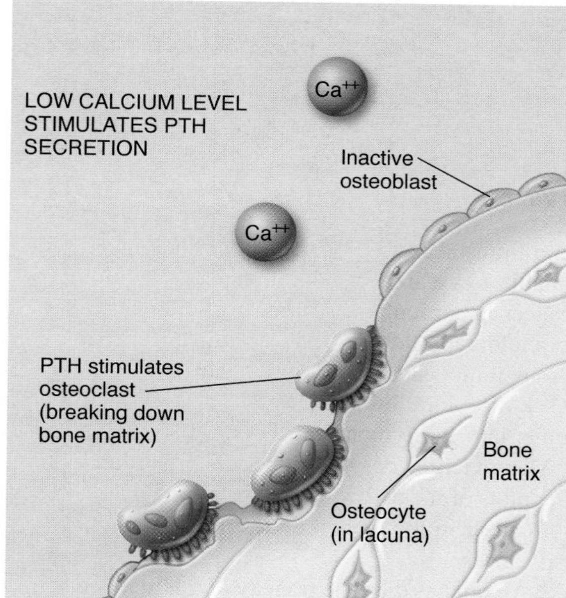

(a)

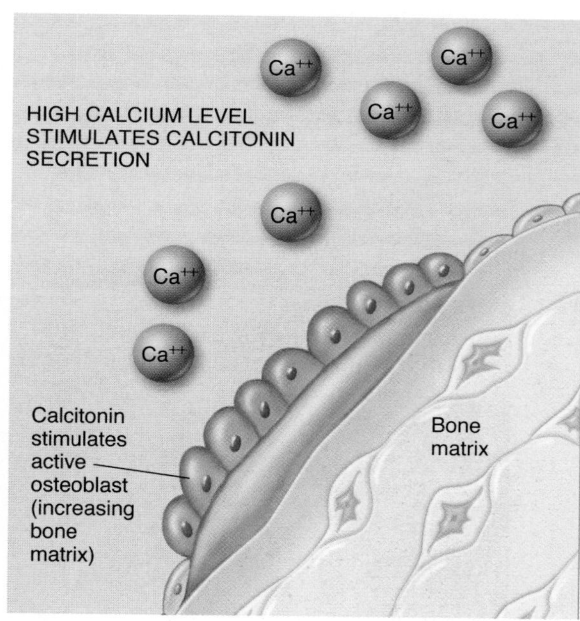

(b)

Figure 30.12 Maintenance of proper calcium levels in the blood.

(a) When calcium levels in the blood become too low, the parathyroid gland produces additional amounts of PTH, which stimulates the breakdown of bone, releasing calcium. (b) Conversely, abnormally high levels of calcium in the blood trigger the thyroid gland to secrete calcitonin, which inhibits the release of calcium from bone, and promotes the activity of osteoblasts to remove calcium from the blood and deposit it in bone.

Inquiry & Analysis

How Strong Is the Association Between Smoking and Lung Cancer?

About a third of all cases of cancer in the United States are directly attributable to cigarette smoking. The association between smoking and cancer is particularly striking for lung cancer. The lung you see in the photograph below, riddled with cancer, is that of a smoker. A cancerous tumor has almost completely taken over the top half, and the black discoloration is due to tars. Cancer cells can migrate from the lungs into the lymph and blood vessels and spread through the body. Many victims of lung cancer die of secondary tumors that form in other parts of the body, such as the brain. Over half a million people died of cancer in the United States in 2011; about 27% of them died of lung cancer.

All Americans die. The tragedy of this statistic is that so many die unnecessarily soon—fully 87% of the lung cancer deaths were cigarette smokers. Smoking is a popular pastime among Americans. In the United States, 21% of adults and 23% of teens smoke, and U.S. smokers consumed 389 billion cigarettes in 2005. The smoke emitted from these cigarettes contains some 3,000 chemical components, including vinyl chloride, benzo[*a*]pyrenes, and N-nitrosonornicotine, all potent mutagens. Smoking places these mutagens into direct contact with the tissues of the lungs, with cancer as the potential result.

How strong is the correlation between the number of cigarettes smoked per day and the incidence of lung cancer? To find out, a detailed study was made of the incidence of lung cancer among American men, and of the cigarettes smoked per day. The results are presented in the graph above.

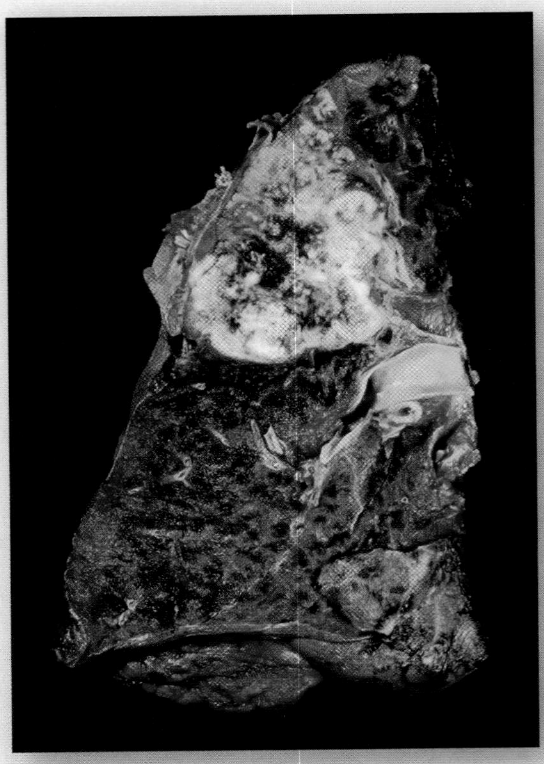

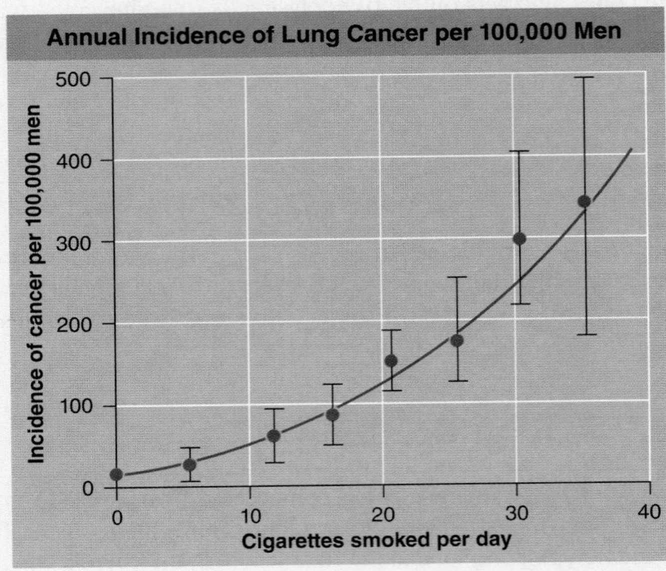

Analysis

1. **Applying Concepts** The vertical lines drawn through the points on the graph are "error bars." How much estimation error is associated with the estimate of cancer incidence among men smoking 20 cigarettes a day? 30 cigarettes?
2. **Interpreting Data**
   - **a.** If the incidence of cancer per 100,000 men is 100, what is the percent of men with cancer?
   - **b.** Do you see a trend in the magnitude of the error bars in the graph? What might account for this?
3. **Making Inferences**
   - **a.** There are 20 cigarettes in a pack. What is the incidence of cancer among "a-pack-a-day" smokers?
   - **b.** What is the incidence of lung cancer among nonsmokers?
   - **c.** Compare the risk of contracting lung cancer among individuals who smoke one pack a day to the risk among nonsmokers.
   - **d.** Is the relationship between cigarettes smoked per day and incidence of lung cancer linear? Why do you think the relationship is this way? What do you think this says about the risks of heavier smoking?
4. **Drawing Conclusions** Do these results support the hypothesis that cigarette smoking causes cancer? Do they prove it? Explain.

Summary of Learning Outcomes

The Neuroendocrine System

Hormones

30.1.1 Hormones are chemical signals produced in glands or other endocrine tissues and transported to distant sites in the body. Endocrine glands produce hormones and release them into the bloodstream.

30.1.2 Many endocrine glands and tissues are under the control of the central nervous system. The hypothalamus often causes the release of hormones from the pituitary gland. Hormones are effective signals because only cells that have receptors for that particular hormone respond to it. The hormone binds to the receptor on such a "target cell" and elicits a response in that cell, often a change in cellular activity or genetic expression.

How Hormones Target Cells

30.2.1 Steroid hormones are lipid-soluble molecules. They pass through the plasma membrane of the target cell and bind to receptors in the cytoplasm or nucleus. The hormone-receptor complex binds to DNA, causing a change in gene expression that alters cell function.

30.2.2 Peptide hormones are unable to pass through the plasma membrane. Instead, they bind to membrane protein receptors. The binding of the hormone, shown here from **figure 30.5,** causes a change in the internal side of the receptor which activates a second messenger. Second messengers, such as cyclic AMP, activate enzymes in the cell. The enzymes then trigger a change in cellular activity. The second messenger system is a cascade of reactions that amplifies the signal and facilitates the change in cellular activity.

The Major Endocrine Glands

The Hypothalamus and the Pituitary

30.3.1 The pituitary gland is actually two glands: the posterior and anterior pituitary glands. The posterior pituitary develops as an extension of the hypothalamus and contains axons that extend from cell bodies in the hypothalamus.

- The hormones released from the posterior pituitary are actually produced in the hypothalamus and transported by the axons to the posterior pituitary for storage and release. The hormones of the posterior pituitary include antidiuretic hormone (ADH), which regulates water retention in the kidneys, and oxytocin, which initiates uterine contractions during childbirth and milk release in the mother.

30.3.2 The anterior pituitary originates from epithelial tissue and produces the hormones it releases. Seven hormones are produced in the anterior pituitary. They are thyroid-stimulating hormone (TSH), adrenocorticotropic hormone (ACTH), growth hormone (GH), follicle-stimulating hormone (FSH), luteinizing hormone (LH), prolactin (PRL), and melanocyte-stimulating hormone (MSH). The hypothalamus controls the anterior pituitary. The hypothalamus produces hormones that are released into blood capillaries that surround the pituitary stalk. They travel a short distance to the anterior pituitary, as shown here from **figure 30.9.**

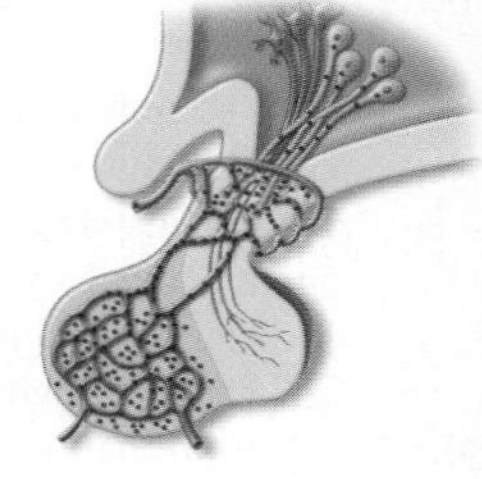

The Pancreas

30.4.1 The pancreas secretes two hormones—insulin and glucagon—into the blood. These hormones interact to maintain stable blood glucose levels. Insulin stimulates cell uptake of glucose from the blood. Glucagon stimulates the breakdown of glycogen to glucose. Two different types of cells in the islets of Langerhans produce insulin and glucagon.

- These hormones work opposite to each other. An increase in blood glucose levels triggers the release of insulin and a decrease in blood glucose levels triggers the release of glucagon. When insulin is not available or cells fail to respond to insulin, diabetes mellitus can result.

The Thyroid, Parathyroid, and Adrenal Glands

30.5.1 The thyroid gland is a shield-shaped organ that lies just beneath the Adam's apple in the front of the neck. The thyroid makes several hormones, but the two most important hormones produced by the thyroid are thyroxine, which increases metabolism and growth, and calcitonin, which stimulates calcium uptake by bones. Thyroxine is controlled by negative feedback. When enough of the hormone has been released, it feeds back to inhibit the hormone-production process.

- Underproduction of thyroxine can lead to serious health problems. The underproduction of thyroxine in children can stunt growth and lead to mental retardation. A lack of iodine inhibits the production of thyroxine. In the absence of adequate levels of thyroxine, the hypothalamus will continue to stimulate the thyroid gland, leading to the formation of a goiter.
- The parathyroid glands are four small glands that are attached to the thyroid. The parathyroids produce parathyroid hormone. PTH regulates the levels of calcium in the blood. Low calcium ion concentrations stimulate the release of PTH from the parathyroid glands. PTH acts on the bones to dismantle bone tissue, releasing Ca^{++} into the blood, shown here from **figure 30.12.** When Ca^{++} levels again increase, calcitonin is released from the thyroid and stimulates the uptake of Ca^{++} by bone cells and the synthesis of new bone tissue.

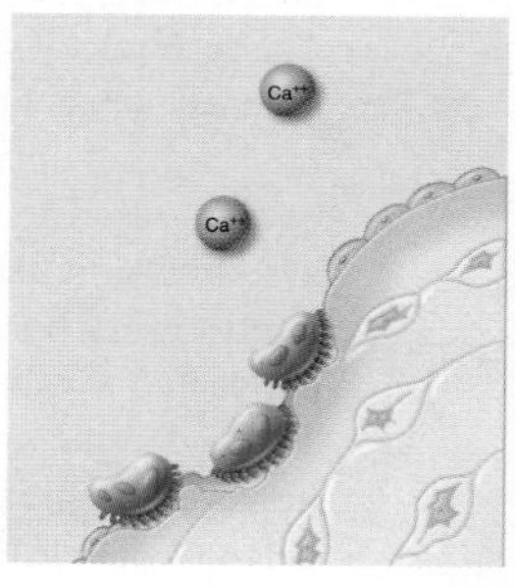

- The adrenal gland is actually two glands: The adrenal medulla is the inner core, and the adrenal cortex is the outer shell. The adrenal medulla secretes epinephrine and norepinephrine that stimulate an emergency response in the body. The adrenal cortex secretes cortisol, which is involved in inflammation and the regulation of glucose and stress responses. It also secretes aldosterone, which promotes the uptake of sodium and water from urine.

Test Your Understanding

30.1.1 One advantage chemical signaling has over electrical signaling is that
- **a.** reaction to stimuli can happen very quickly.
- **b.** although it takes large amounts of chemicals, the chemical signals are efficient.
- **c.** chemical signals stick around longer than electrical signals and can be used for slow processes.
- **d.** chemical signals are used only in response to external stimuli.

30.1.1 A coordination center for some of the endocrine system is the
- **a.** hypothalamus.
- **b.** adrenal gland.
- **c.** thyroid gland.
- **d.** pancreas.

30.1.2 Hormones are effective messengers in the body because they
- **a.** fit into receptors specifically shaped for them.
- **b.** are proteins.
- **c.** are released from synaptic vesicles.
- **d.** All of the above.

30.2.2 The action of steroid hormones is different from that of peptide hormones because
- **a.** peptide hormones must enter the cell to begin action, whereas steroid hormones must begin action on the external surface of the cell membrane.
- **b.** steroid hormones must enter the cell to begin action, whereas peptide hormones must begin action on the external surface of the cell membrane.
- **c.** peptide hormones produce a hormone-receptor complex that works directly on the DNA, whereas steroid hormones cause the release of a secondary messenger that triggers enzymes.
- **d.** None of the above.

30.3.1 The hormone that regulates water concentration in the urine is released from the
- **a.** thyroid gland.
- **b.** thymus.
- **c.** anterior pituitary gland.
- **d.** posterior pituitary gland.

30.3.2 _____ is the hormone that stimulates the adrenal gland to produce a number of steroid hormones.
- **a.** ACTH
- **b.** LH
- **c.** TSH
- **d.** MSH

30.4.1 Type I diabetes is caused by an abnormality in endocrine cells of the
- **a.** pancreas.
- **b.** thymus.
- **c.** adrenal glands.
- **d.** hypothalamus.

30.5.1 The release of the thyroid hormone calcitonin is triggered by
- **a.** too much glucose in the blood.
- **b.** too much sodium in the blood.
- **c.** too much calcium in the blood.
- **d.** too much iodine in the blood.

30.5.1 Epinephrine mimics the effects of the
- **a.** somatic nervous system.
- **b.** central nervous system.
- **c.** parasympathetic nervous system.
- **d.** sympathetic nervous system.

30.5.1 Which of the following hormones is released from the adrenal cortex during periods of stress?
- **a.** cortisol
- **b.** aldosterone
- **c.** epinephrine
- **d.** growth hormone

Apply Your Understanding

30.1.1 Some of the body systems are located primarily in one area of the body, or are obviously connected. The respiratory system, for instance, is located in the head and upper portion of the body. The skeletal system is articulated, almost every bone is connected to others. The endocrine system, however, is spread out, a batch of glands that do not appear connected with one another. Speculate on why this is so.

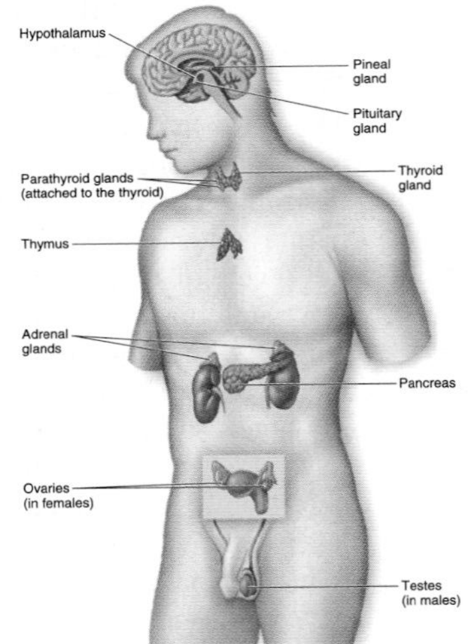

30.3.1 A hypothetical patient has a disorder in which the hypothalamus can no longer secrete its "inhibiting" hormones. Which of the anterior pituitary hormones will be affected?

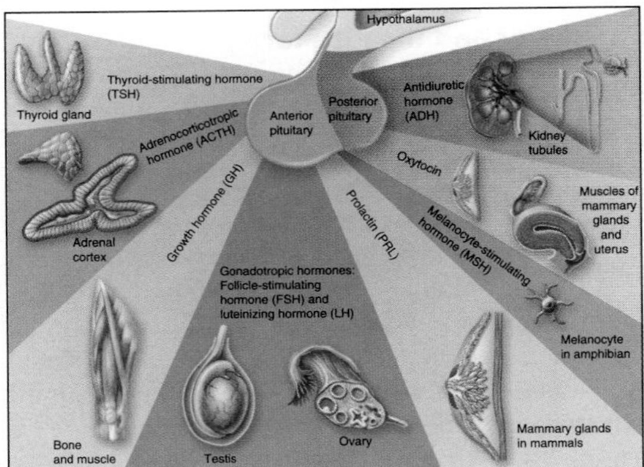

Synthesize What You Have Learned

30.2.1 The younger brother of your friend wants to be a sports star in high school. Although he is only in the eighth grade, he brags that he is taking steroids he gets from a friend in order to "bulk up" for next year. He asks if you have ever heard of any problems for kids his age—he only wants to take them "a couple of years" to get a football scholarship so his family can afford for him to go to college. How would you advise him?

30.5.1 Given that your bones are so very important, why would your body ever need a system that includes osteoclasts, which literally break down your bone tissue?

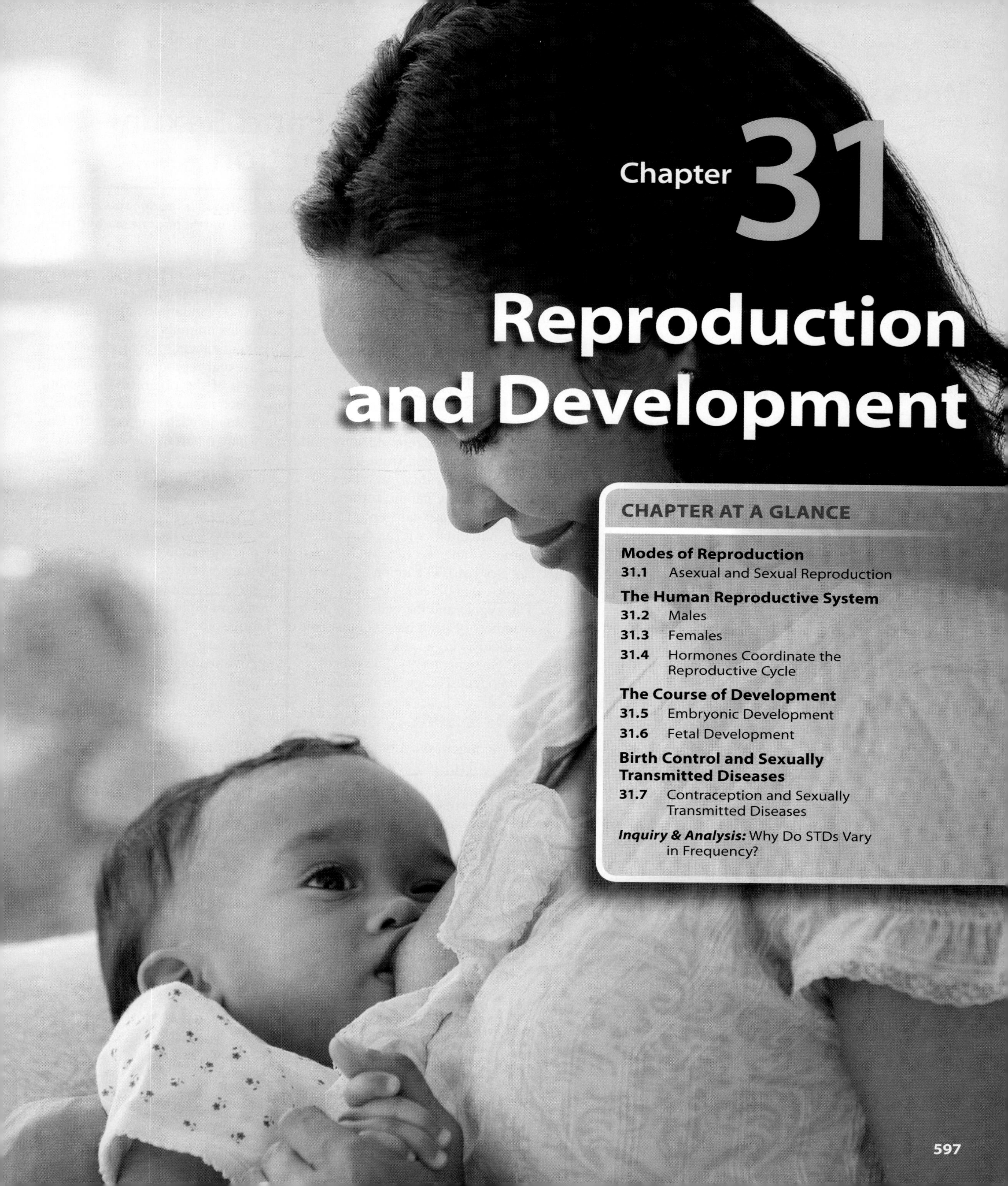

Chapter 31

Reproduction and Development

CHAPTER AT A GLANCE

Modes of Reproduction

31.1 Asexual and Sexual Reproduction

The Human Reproductive System

31.2 Males

31.3 Females

31.4 Hormones Coordinate the Reproductive Cycle

The Course of Development

31.5 Embryonic Development

31.6 Fetal Development

Birth Control and Sexually Transmitted Diseases

31.7 Contraception and Sexually Transmitted Diseases

Inquiry & Analysis: Why Do STDs Vary in Frequency?

Modes of Reproduction

31.1 Asexual and Sexual Reproduction

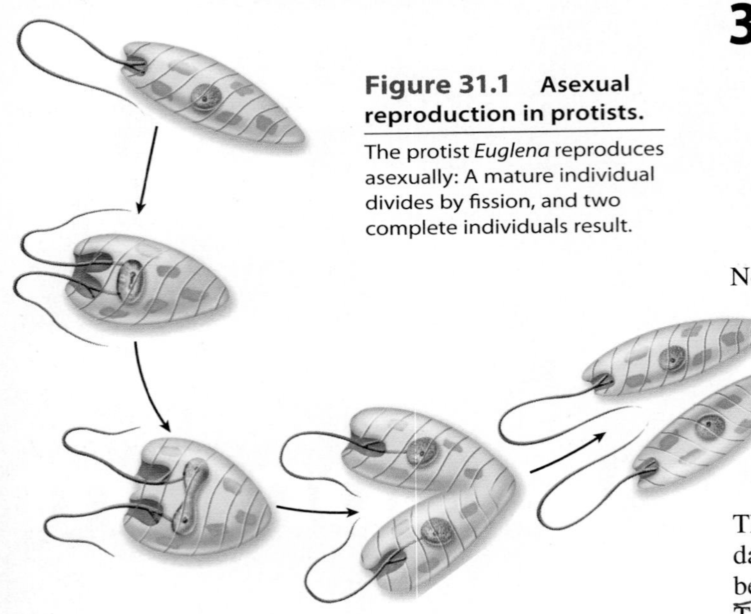

Figure 31.1 Asexual reproduction in protists.

The protist *Euglena* reproduces asexually: A mature individual divides by fission, and two complete individuals result.

LEARNING OBJECTIVE 31.1.1 Contrast asexual and sexual reproduction, discriminating between parthenogenesis, hermaphroditism, protogyny, and protandry.

Not all reproduction involves two parents. Asexual reproduction, in which the offspring are genetically identical to the parent, is the primary means of reproduction among protists, cnidarians, and tunicates, and also occurs in some more complex animals.

Through mitosis, genetically identical cells are produced from a single parent cell. This permits asexual reproduction to occur in the *Euglena* in figure 31.1 by division of the organism, or **fission.** The DNA replicates and cell structures, such as the flagellum, duplicate. The nucleus divides with identical nuclei going to each daughter cell. Cnidaria commonly reproduce by **budding,** where a part of the parent's body becomes separated from the rest and differentiates into a new individual. The new individual may become an independent animal or may remain attached to the parent, forming a colony.

Unlike asexual reproduction, sexual reproduction occurs when a new individual is formed by the union of *two* cells. These cells are called **gametes,** and the two kinds that combine are generally called *sperm* and *eggs* (or ova). The union of a sperm and an egg produces a fertilized egg, or **zygote,** that develops by mitotic division into a new multicellular organism. The zygote and the cells it forms by mitosis are diploid; they contain both members of each homologous pair of chromosomes. The gametes, formed by meiosis in the sex organs, or **gonads**—the *testes* and *ovaries*—are haploid (see chapter 9). The processes of spermatogenesis (sperm formation) and oogenesis (egg formation) are described in later sections.

Different Approaches to Sex

Parthenogenesis, a type of reproduction in which offspring are produced from unfertilized eggs, is common in many species of arthropods. Some species are exclusively parthenogenic, whereas others switch between sexual reproduction and parthenogenesis in different generations. In honeybees, for example, a queen bee mates only once and stores the sperm. She then can control the release of sperm. If no sperm are released, the eggs develop parthenogenetically into drones, which are males; if sperm are allowed to fertilize the eggs, the fertilized eggs develop into other queens or worker bees, which are female. Parthenogenesis also occurs among populations of some lizard genera.

Hermaphroditism, another variation in reproductive strategy, is when one individual has both testes and ovaries and so can produce both sperm and eggs. The hamlet bass in figure 31.2*a* are hermaphroditic,

(a)

(b)

Figure 31.2 Hermaphroditism and protogyny.

(a) The hamlet bass (genus *Hypoplectrus*) is a deep-sea fish that is a hermaphrodite. In the course of a single pair-mating, one fish may switch sexual roles as many as four times. Here, the fish acting as a male curves around its motionless partner, fertilizing the upward-floating eggs. (b) The bluehead wrasse *Thalassoma bifasciatium* is protogynous. Here a large male, or sex-changed female, is seen among females, which are typically much smaller.

producing both eggs and sperm. During mating each fish switches from producing eggs that are fertilized by its partner, to producing sperm that fertilize its partner's eggs. A tapeworm is hermaphroditic and can fertilize itself as well as cross-fertilize, a useful strategy because it is unlikely that there will be another tapeworm living inside the host. Most hermaphroditic animals, however, require another individual to reproduce. Two earthworms, for example, are required for reproduction—like the hamlet bass, each functions as both male and female. Each leaves the encounter with fertilized eggs.

Numerous fish genera include species in which individuals can change their sex in response to social or environmental conditions, a process called *sequential hermaphroditism.* Among coral reef fish, for example, both **protogyny** ("first female," a change from female to male) and **protandry** ("first male," a change from male to female) occur. In the protogynous bluehead wrasse in figure 31.2*b*, the sex change appears to be under social control. These fish commonly live in large groups, or schools, where successful reproduction is typically limited to one or a few large, dominant males. If those males are removed, the largest female rapidly changes sex and becomes a dominant male (the blue-headed fish in the photo).

Putting the Concept to Work

Give an example of a parthenogenic animal.

Sex Determination

LEARNING OBJECTIVE 31.1.2 Discuss sex determination in mammals.

In mammals, the sex is determined early in embryonic development. The reproductive systems of human males and females appear similar for the first 40 days after conception. During this time, the cells that will give rise to ova or sperm migrate to the embryonic gonads, which have the potential to become either ovaries in females or testes in males. If the embryo is XY, it is a male and will carry a gene on the Y chromosome whose protein product converts the gonads into testes (as on the left in figure 31.3). In females, who are XX, this Y chromosome gene and the protein it encodes are absent, and the gonads become ovaries (as on the right). Recent evidence suggests that the sex-determining gene may be one known as ***SRY*** (for "*s*ex-determining *r*egion of the *Y* chromosome"). The *SRY* gene appears to have been highly conserved during the evolution of different vertebrate groups.

Once testes form in the embryo, they secrete testosterone and other hormones that promote the development of the male external genitalia and accessory reproductive organs (indicated in the blue box in the figure). If testes do not form, the embryo develops female external genitalia and accessory reproductive organs. The ovaries do not promote this development of female organs because the ovaries are nonfunctional at this stage. In other words, all mammalian embryos will develop female sex accessory organs and external genitalia by default unless they are masculinized by the secretions of the testes.

Putting the Concept to Work

If genetic engineering could be used to transfer the *SRY* gene into an X chromosome, would a zygote carrying a normal X and this *SRY*-X be a female or a male? Explain.

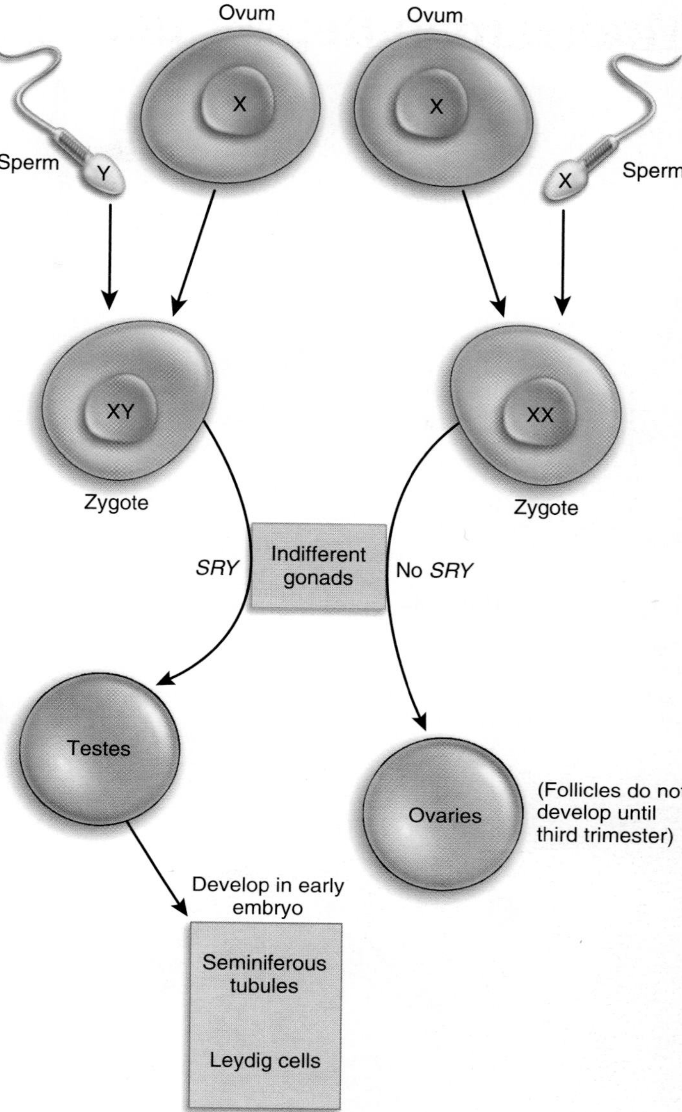

Figure 31.3 Sex determination.

Sex determination in mammals is made by a gene on the Y chromosome designated *SRY*. Testes are formed when the Y chromosome and *SRY* are present; ovaries are formed when they are absent.

The Human Reproductive System

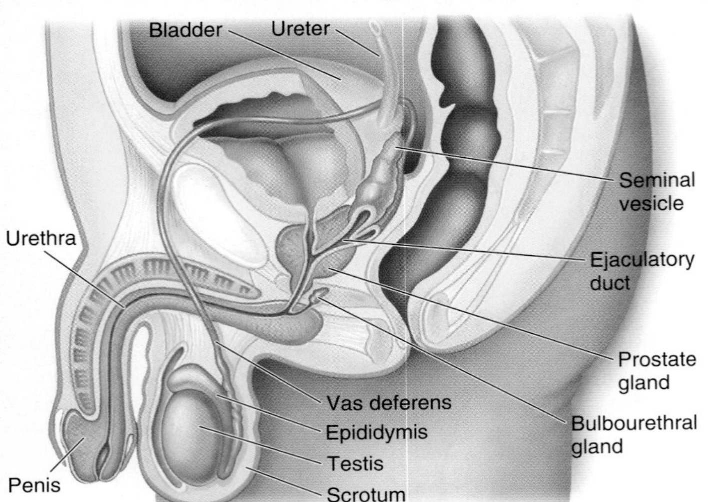

Figure 31.4 The male reproductive organs.

The testis is where sperm are formed. Cupped above the testis is the epididymis, a highly coiled passageway within which sperm complete their maturation. Extending away from the epididymis is a long tube, the vas deferens.

31.2 Males

LEARNING OBJECTIVE 31.2.1 Describe the male reproductive system, including where and how sperm are formed and delivered.

The human male gamete, or **sperm,** is highly specialized for its role as a carrier of genetic information. Produced by meiosis, sperm cells have 23 chromosomes instead of the 46 found in other cells of the male body. Sperm do not successfully complete their development at 37°C (98.6°F), the normal human body temperature. The sperm-producing organs, the **testes** (singular, **testis**), move during the course of fetal development into a sac called the scrotum (figure 31.4), which hangs between the legs of the male, maintaining the two testes at a temperature about 3°C cooler than the rest of the body. The testes contain cells that secrete the male sex hormone **testosterone.**

Male Gametes Are Formed in the Testes

An internal view of a testis in figure 31.5 ❶ shows that it is composed of several hundred compartments, each packed with large numbers of tightly coiled tubes called **seminiferous tubules** (seen in cross section in ❷). Sperm production, *spermatogenesis,* takes place inside the tubules. The process of spermatogenesis begins in germinal cells toward the outside

Figure 31.5 presents an overview of the process of meiosis during sperm development. Detailed descriptions of the stages of meiosis can be found on pages 150 through 153.

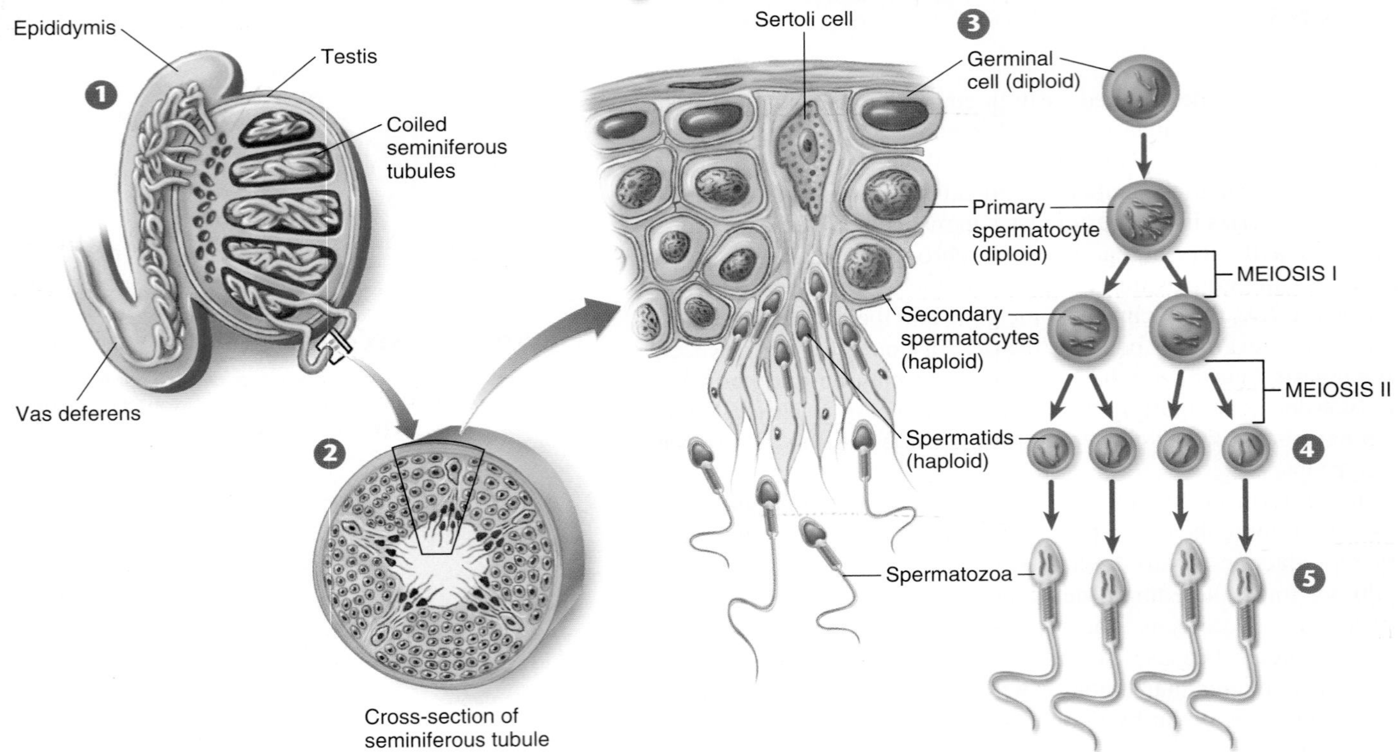

Figure 31.5 The testis and formation of sperm.

Inside the testis ❶, the seminiferous tubules ❷ are the sites of sperm formation. Germinal cells in the seminiferous tubules ❸ give rise to primary spermatocytes (diploid), which undergo meiosis to form haploid spermatids ❹. Spermatids develop into mobile spermatozoa, or sperm ❺. Sertoli cells are nongerminal cells within the walls of the seminiferous tubules. They assist spermatogenesis in several ways, such as helping to convert spermatids into spermatozoa.

of the tubule (shown in the enlarged view in ❸). As the cells undergo meiosis, they move toward the lumen of the tubule ❹, with spermatozoa being released into the tubule ❺. The number of sperm produced is truly incredible. A typical adult male produces several hundred million sperm each day of his life! Those that are not ejaculated from the body are broken down, and their materials are reabsorbed and recycled.

After a sperm cell is manufactured within the testes through intermediate stages of meiosis, it is delivered to a long, coiled tube called the **epididymis** (see figure 31.5), where it matures. A sperm cell is not motile when it arrives in the epididymis, and it must remain there for at least 18 hours before its motility develops. Mature sperm are relatively simple cells, consisting of a head, body, and tail (figure 31.6). The head encloses a compact nucleus and is capped by a vesicle called an *acrosome.* The acrosome contains enzymes that aid in the penetration of the protective layers surrounding the egg. The body and tail provide a propulsive mechanism: Within the tail is a flagellum, and inside the body are centrioles, which act as a basal body for the flagellum, and mitochondria, which generate the energy needed for flagellar movement.

From the epididymis, the sperm is delivered to another long tube, the **vas deferens.** When sperm are released, they travel through a tube from the vas deferens to the **urethra,** where the reproductive and urinary tracts join, emptying through the penis. Sperm is released in a fluid called **semen,** which also contains secretions mostly from the seminal vesicles and the prostate gland that provide metabolic energy sources for the sperm. Benign enlargement of the prostate occurs in 90% of men by age 70, but it can be cancerous. Prostate cancer is the second most common cancer in men and can be treated effectively if detected early during physical examinations, before it spreads.

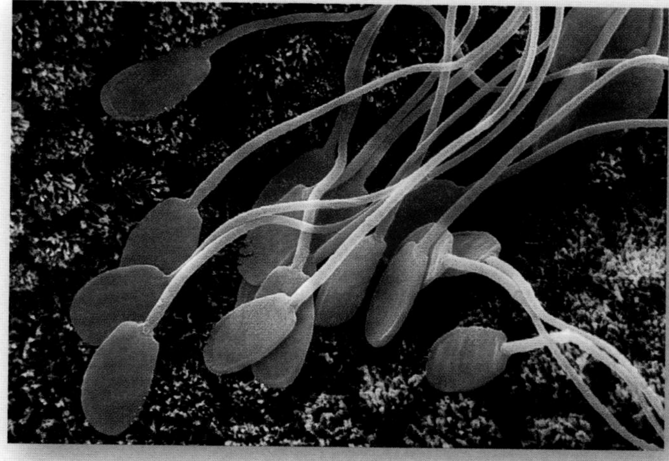

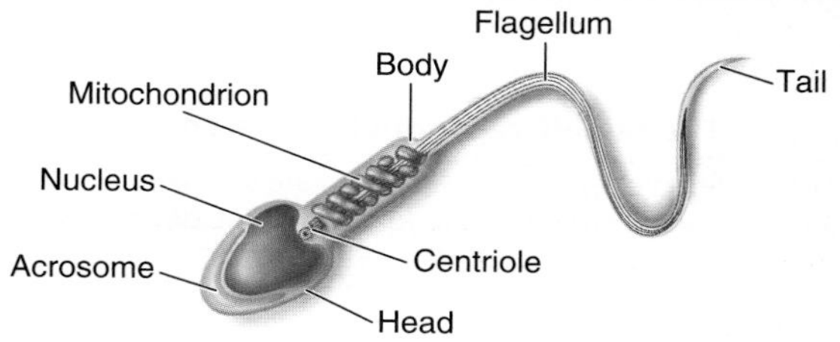

Figure 31.6 Human sperm cells.

Each sperm possesses a long tail that propels the sperm and a head that contains the nucleus. The tip, or acrosome, contains enzymes to help the sperm cell digest a passageway into the egg for fertilization.

Male Gametes Are Delivered by the Penis

In the case of humans and some other mammals, the **penis** is an external tube containing two long cylinders of spongy tissue side by side (figure 31.7). A third cylinder of spongy tissue contains in its center the urethra, through which both semen (during ejaculation) and urine (during urination) pass. Why this unusual design? The penis is designed to inflate. The spongy tissues that make up the three cylinders are riddled with small spaces between the cells, and when nerve impulses from the CNS cause the arterioles leading into this tissue to expand, blood collects within these spaces. Like blowing up a balloon, this causes the penis to become erect and rigid.

Erection can be achieved without any physical stimulation of the penis, but physical stimulation is required for semen to be delivered. Stimulation of the penis, as by repeated thrusts into the vagina of a female, leads first to the mobilization of the sperm. In this process, muscles encircling the vas deferens contract, moving the sperm along the vas deferens into the urethra. The bulbourethral glands also secrete a clear, slippery fluid that neutralizes the acidity of any residual urine and lubricates the head of the penis. Further penis stimulation then leads to **ejaculation,** the forceful ejection of 2 to 5 milliliters of semen. Within this small 5-milliliter volume are several hundred million sperm. Because there are extraordinarily high odds against any one individual sperm cell successfully completing the long journey to the egg and fertilizing it, successful fertilization requires a high sperm count. Males with fewer than 20 million sperm per milliliter are generally considered sterile.

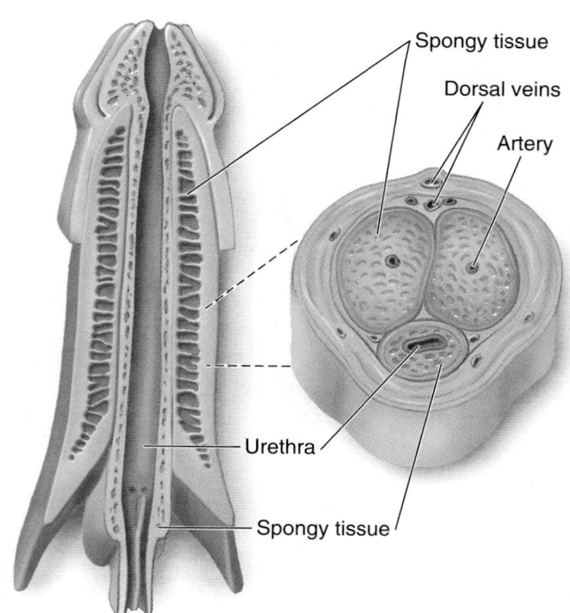

Figure 31.7 Structure of the penis.

(*Left*) longitudinal section; (*right*) cross section.

Putting the Concept to Work

What is the function of the prostate gland?

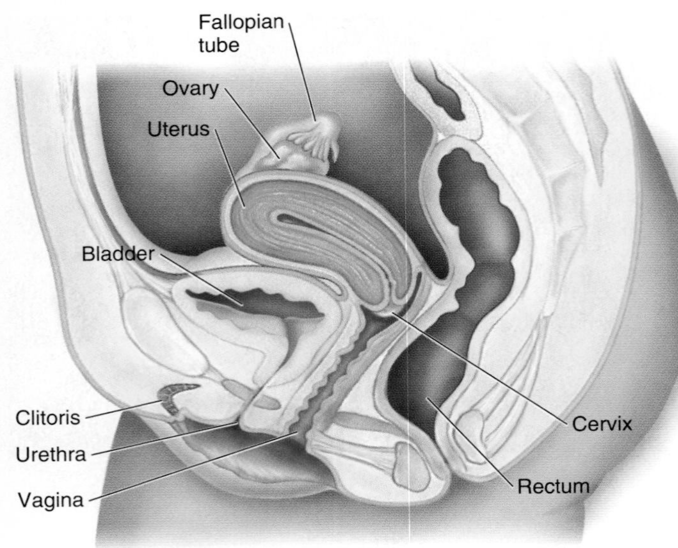

Figure 31.8 The female reproductive system.

The organs of the female reproductive system are specialized to produce gametes and to provide a site for embryonic development if the gamete is fertilized.

31.3 Females

LEARNING OBJECTIVE 31.3.1 Diagram the female reproductive system, describing where and how ova are formed and fertilized.

In females, eggs develop from cells called **oocytes,** located in the outer layer of compact masses of cells called **ovaries** within the abdominal cavity (figure 31.8). Recall that in males the gamete-producing cells are constantly dividing. In females all of the oocytes needed for a lifetime are already present at birth. During each reproductive cycle, one or a few of these oocytes are initiated to continue their development in a process called **ovulation;** the others remain in developmental holding patterns.

Usually Only One Female Gamete Matures Each Month

At birth, a female's ovaries contain some 2 million oocytes, all of which have begun the first meiotic division. At this stage they are called *primary oocytes* (❶ in figure 31.9). Each primary oocyte waits to receive the proper

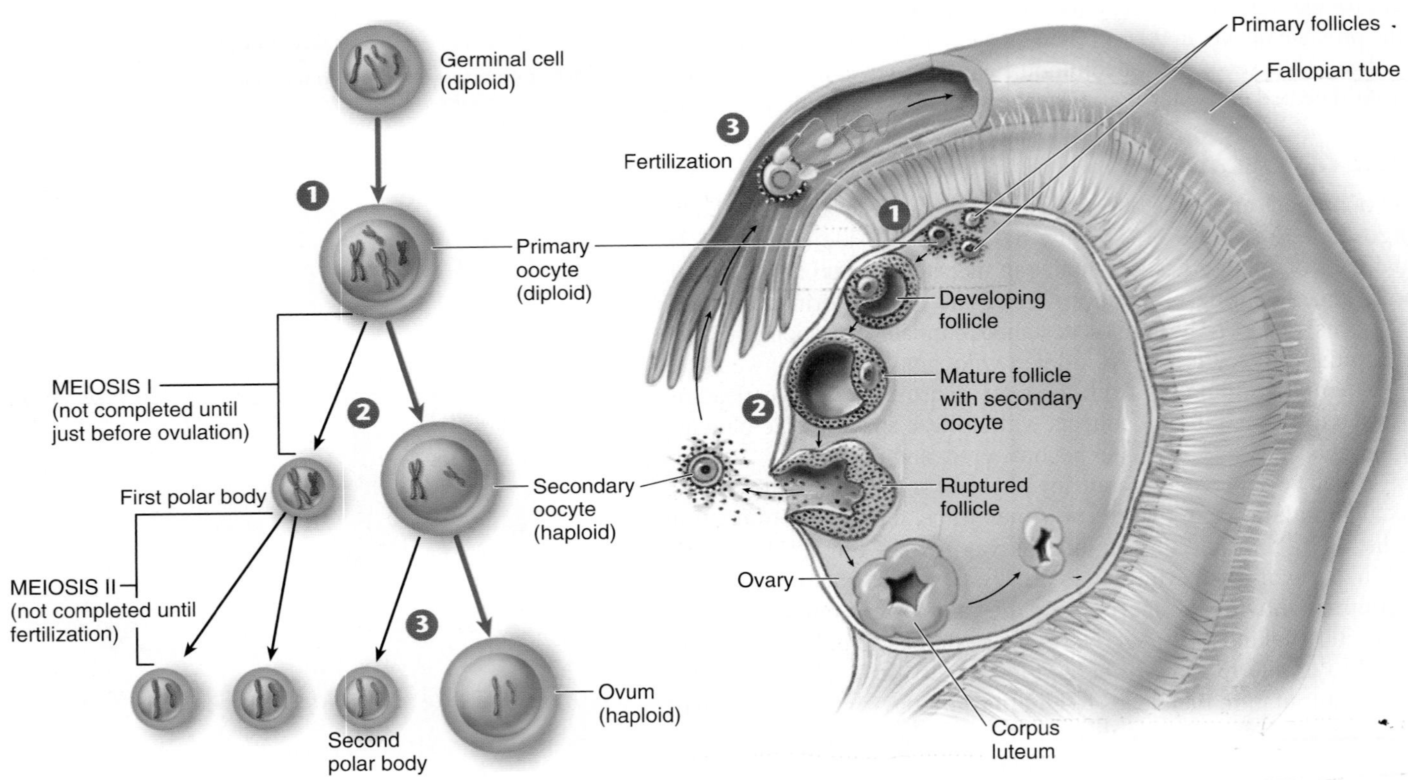

Figure 31.9 The ovary and formation of an ovum.

In this figure, the maturation of the ovum through meiosis is shown on the left, and the developmental journey of the ovum is on the right, with corresponding stages numbered on each. At birth, a human female's ovaries contain about 2 million egg-forming cells called oocytes, which have begun the first meiotic division and stopped. At this stage, they are called primary oocytes ❶, and their further development is halted until they receive the proper developmental signals, which are the hormones FSH and LH. Beginning at puberty, a monthly cycle of hormone secretion is established. When the hormones FSH and LH are released, meiosis resumes in a few oocytes, but only one oocyte usually continues to mature while the others regress. The primary oocyte (diploid) completes the first meiotic division, and one division product becomes a nonfunctional polar body. The other product, the secondary oocyte, is released during ovulation ❷, along with the polar body. The secondary oocyte does not complete the second meiotic division until fertilization ❸; that division yields two more nonfunctional polar bodies and a single haploid egg, or ovum. Fusion of the haploid egg with a haploid sperm during fertilization produces a diploid zygote.

developmental "go" signal before continuing on with meiosis. Until then, its meiosis remains arrested in prophase of the first meiotic division. Very few primary oocytes ever receive the awaited signal, which turns out to be the pituitary hormones FSH and LH, which were discussed in chapter 30.

With the onset of puberty, females mature sexually. At this time, the release of FSH and LH initiates the resumption of the first meiotic division in a few oocytes. The first meiotic division produces the *secondary oocyte* and a nonfunctional *polar body* ❷. In humans, usually only a single oocyte is ovulated and the others regress. In some instances more than one oocyte develops; if both are fertilized, they become fraternal twins. Approximately every 28 days after that, another oocyte matures and is ovulated, although the exact timing may vary from month to month. Only about 400 of the approximately 2 million oocytes a woman is born with mature and are ovulated during her lifetime.

Fertilization Occurs in the Oviducts

The **oviducts** (also called **fallopian tubes** or uterine tubes) transport eggs from the ovaries to the **uterus.** In humans, the uterus is a muscular, pear-shaped organ about the size of a fist that narrows to a muscular ring called the **cervix,** which leads to the vagina (figure 31.10*a*). Mammals other than primates have more complex female reproductive tracts, where part of the uterus divides to form uterine "horns." The uterus is lined with a stratified epithelial membrane, called the **endometrium.** The surface of the endometrium is shed approximately once a month during menstruation, while the underlying portion remains to generate a new surface during the next cycle.

After ovulation, smooth muscles lining the fallopian tubes contract rhythmically, moving the egg down the tube to the uterus in much the same way that food is moved down through your digestive system (see chapter 26), pushing it along by squeezing the tube behind it. The journey of the egg through the fallopian tube is a slow one, taking from five to seven days to complete. However, if the egg is not fertilized within 24 hours of ovulation, it loses its capacity to develop.

During sexual intercourse, sperm are deposited within the vagina, a thin-walled muscular tube about 7 centimeters long that leads to the mouth of the uterus. Using their flagella, sperm entering the uterus swim up to and enter the fallopian tubes. Sperm can remain viable within the female reproductive tract for up to six days. If sexual intercourse takes place five days before ovulation or one day after, a viable egg will be present high up in the fallopian tubes. Of the several hundred million sperm that are ejaculated, only a few dozen make it to the egg. Once they reach the egg, the sperm must penetrate through two protective layers that surround the secondary oocyte (figure 31.10*b* ❶): a layer of granulosa cells and a protein layer called the zona pellucida. Enzymes within the acrosome cap of the sperm help digest the second of these layers ❷. The first sperm to make it through the second layer stimulates the oocyte to block the entry of other sperm ❸ and to complete meiosis II. Meiosis II produces the **ovum** (plural, **ova**) and two more nonfunctional polar bodies (see figure 31.9 ❸). When the female haploid nucleus within the ovum combines with the male haploid nucleus, the egg is fertilized and becomes a zygote. The zygote then begins a series of cell divisions while traveling down the fallopian tube. After about six days, it reaches the uterus, attaches itself to the endometrial lining, and continues the long developmental journey that eventually leads to the birth of a child.

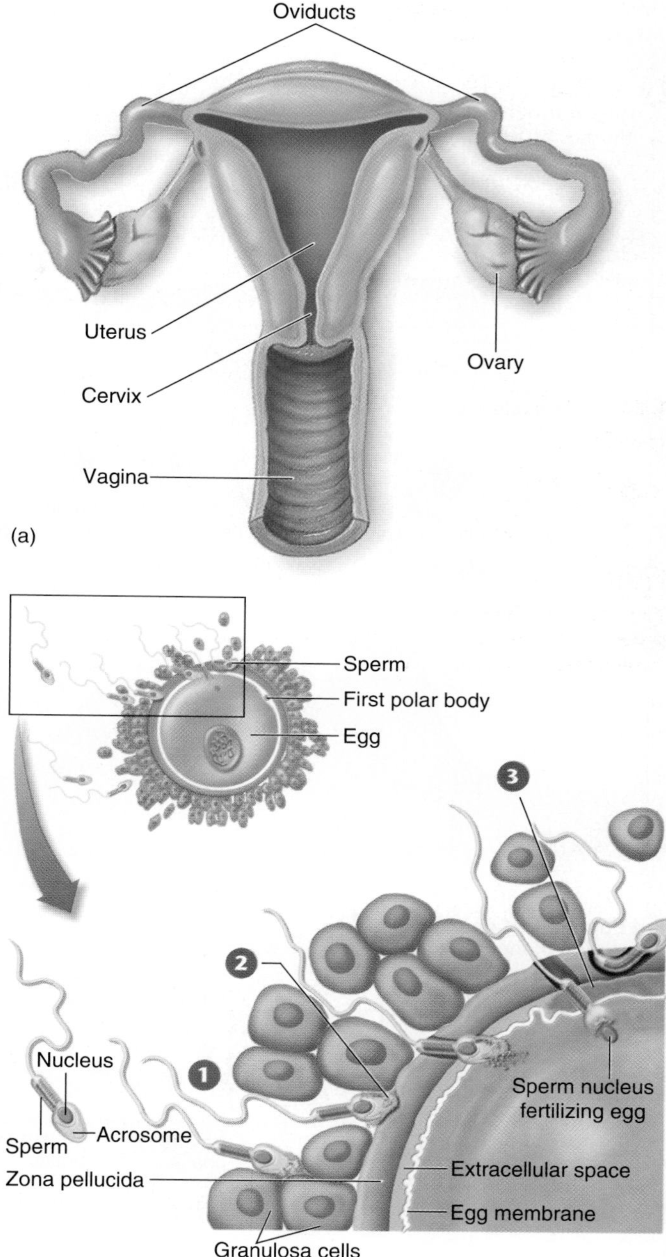

Figure 31.10 Fertilization occurs in the oviducts.

(a) The oviducts extend out from the uterus. Sperm are deposited in the vagina and travel to the oviducts. (b) Fertilization occurs in the oviduct when a sperm cell penetrates the outer layers of the egg cell.

Putting the Concept to Work

Where is the endometrium found? What does it do? When?

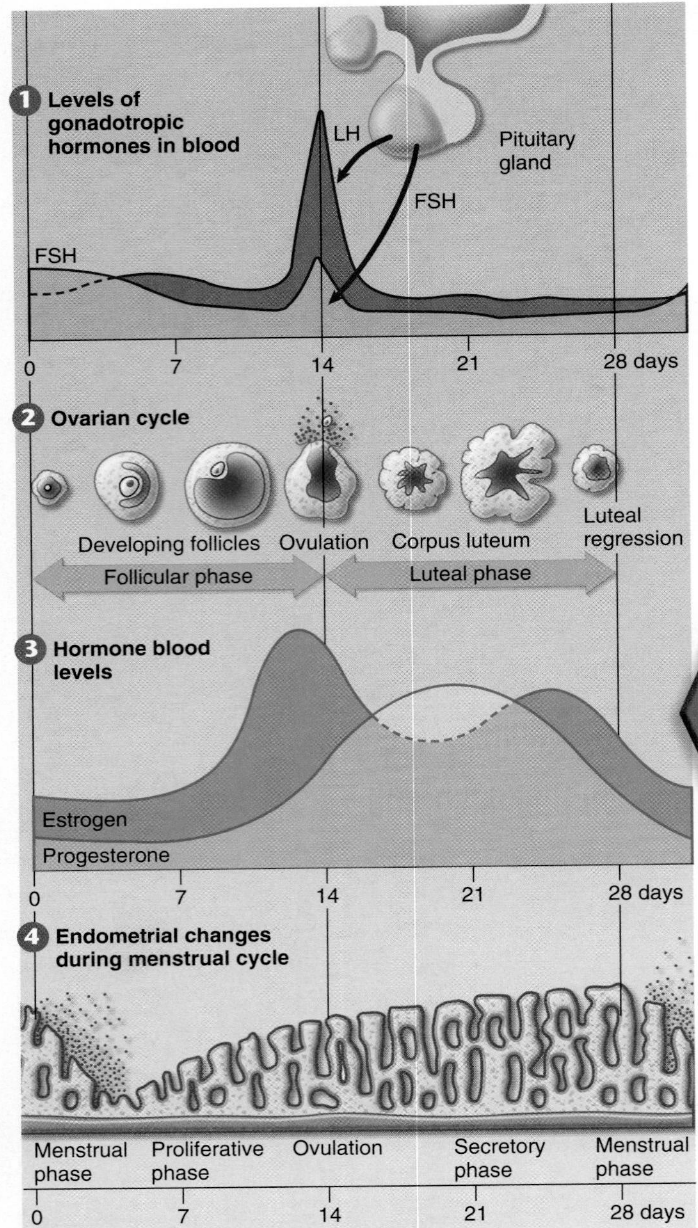

Figure 31.11 The human menstrual cycle.

Ovulation and the preparation of the uterine lining for implantation is controlled by a group of four hormones during the menstrual cycle.

IMPLICATION FOR YOU Men do not exhibit a reproductive cycle, and are able to donate sperm at any time of the month. Why do you think evolution has favored development of a menstrual cycle in women? Do you think it might have been possible to have evolved human females without a menstrual cycle? What is the basis of your conclusion?

31.4 Hormones Coordinate the Reproductive Cycle

LEARNING OBJECTIVE 31.4.1 Describe the two phases of the menstrual cycle, and explain how four hormones regulate them.

The female reproductive cycle, called a **menstrual cycle,** is composed of two distinct phases, the *follicular phase,* in which an egg reaches maturation and is ovulated, and the *luteal phase,* where the body continues to prepare for pregnancy. These phases are coordinated by a family of hormones. Hormones play many roles in human reproduction. Sexual development is initiated by hormones, released from the anterior pituitary and ovary, that coordinate simultaneous sexual development in many kinds of tissues. The production of gametes is another closely orchestrated process, involving a series of carefully timed developmental events. Successful fertilization initiates yet another developmental "program," in which the female body continues its preparation for the many changes of pregnancy.

Production of the sex hormones that direct all these processes is coordinated by the hypothalamus, which sends releasing hormones to the pituitary, causing it to produce particular sex hormones. Negative feedback, discussed in chapters 27 and 30, plays a key role in regulating these activities of the hypothalamus. When target organs receive a pituitary hormone, they begin to produce a hormone of their own, which circulates back to the hypothalamus, shutting down production of the pituitary hormone. In addition, *positive feedback* mechanisms play a role too. In these cases, a hormone circulates back to the hypothalamus and increases the production of a pituitary hormone.

The hypothalamus is the control center of the neuroendocrine system. As discussed on page 568, the hypothalamus integrates all internal activities in the body through neural connections. It also exerts control over the pituitary, as discussed on page 589.

Triggering the Maturation of an Egg

The first phase of the menstrual cycle, the follicular phase, corresponds to days 0 through 14 in figure 31.11. During this time, several follicles (an oocyte and its surrounding tissue is called a *follicle*) are stimulated to develop. This development is carefully regulated by hormones. The anterior pituitary, after receiving a chemical signal (GnRH) from the hypothalamus, starts the cycle by secreting small amounts of **follicle-stimulating hormone (FSH)** and **luteinizing hormone (LH)** ❶. These hormones stimulate follicular growth ❷ and the secretion of the female sex hormone **estrogen** ❸, more technically known as *estradiol,* from the developing follicles. Several follicles are stimulated to grow under FSH stimulation.

Estrogen is a steroid hormone, and as shown in figure 30.3 on page 586, steroid hormones are able to pass through the plasma membrane and bind to receptors inside the cell. The binding of estrogen to its receptor activates the transcription of a receptor protein for progesterone.

Initially, the relatively low levels of estrogen have a negative-feedback effect on FSH and LH secretion. The low but rising levels of estrogen in the bloodstream feed back to the hypothalamus, which responds to the rising estrogen by commanding the anterior pituitary to decrease production of FSH and LH. As FSH levels fall, usually only one follicle achieves maturity. Late in the follicular phase, estrogen levels in the blood have increased drastically, and these higher levels of estrogen begin to have a positive-feedback effect on FSH and LH secretion. The rise in estrogen levels signals the completion of the follicular phase of the menstrual cycle.

Preparing the Body for Fertilization

The second phase of the cycle, the luteal phase (days 14 through 28), follows smoothly from the first. In a positive-feedback response to high levels of estrogen, the hypothalamus causes the anterior pituitary to rapidly secrete large amounts of LH and FSH (see figure 31.11 ❶). The surge of LH is larger than the surge of FSH and can last up to 24 hours. The peak in LH secretion triggers ovulation: LH causes the wall of the follicle to burst, and the egg within the follicle is released into one of the fallopian tubes extending from the ovary to the uterus (see ❶ in figure 31.12).

After the egg's release and departure, estrogen levels decrease, and LH directs the repair of the ruptured follicle, which fills in and becomes yellowish. In this condition, it is called the *corpus luteum,* which is simply the Latin phrase for "yellow body." The corpus luteum soon begins to secrete the hormone **progesterone** (the light green curve in figure 31.11 ❸), in addition to small levels of estrogen. Increased levels of progesterone and estrogen have a negative-feedback effect on the secretion of FSH and LH, preventing further ovulations. Progesterone completes the body's preparation of the uterus for fertilization including the thickening of the endometrium (figure 31.11 ❹). If fertilization does *not* occur soon after ovulation, however, production of progesterone slows and eventually ceases, marking the end of the luteal phase. The decreasing levels of progesterone cause the thickened layer of blood-rich tissue to be sloughed off, a process that results in the bleeding associated with menstruation. **Menstruation,** or "having a period," usually occurs about midway between successive ovulations (shown in figure 31.11 at 28 days).

At the end of the luteal phase, neither estrogen nor progesterone is being produced. In their absence, the anterior pituitary can again initiate production of FSH and LH, thus starting another reproductive cycle. Each cycle begins immediately after the preceding one ends. A cycle usually occurs every 28 days, or a little more frequently than once a month, although this varies in individual cases. The Latin word for "month" is *mens,* which is why the reproductive cycle is called the menstrual cycle, or monthly cycle.

If fertilization does occur high in the fallopian tube (❷ in figure 31.12*a*), the zygote undergoes a series of cell divisions called cleavage ❸, while traveling toward the uterus. At the blastocyst stage, it implants in the lining of the uterus ❹. The tiny embryo secretes human chorionic gonadotropin (hCG), an LH-like hormone, which maintains the corpus luteum. By maintaining the corpus luteum, hCG keeps the levels of estrogen and progesterone high, thereby preventing menstruation, which would terminate the pregnancy. Because hCG comes from the embryo and not from the mother, it is hCG that is tested in all pregnancy tests.

As discussed on page 555, pregnancy tests use monoclonal antibodies which are produced using hCG as the antigen. The test strip is coated with the hCG monoclonal antibodies. If hCG is present in the urine, it will react with the antibodies and produce a positive result.

Putting the Concept to Work

When in the menstrual cycle does luteinizing hormone peak?

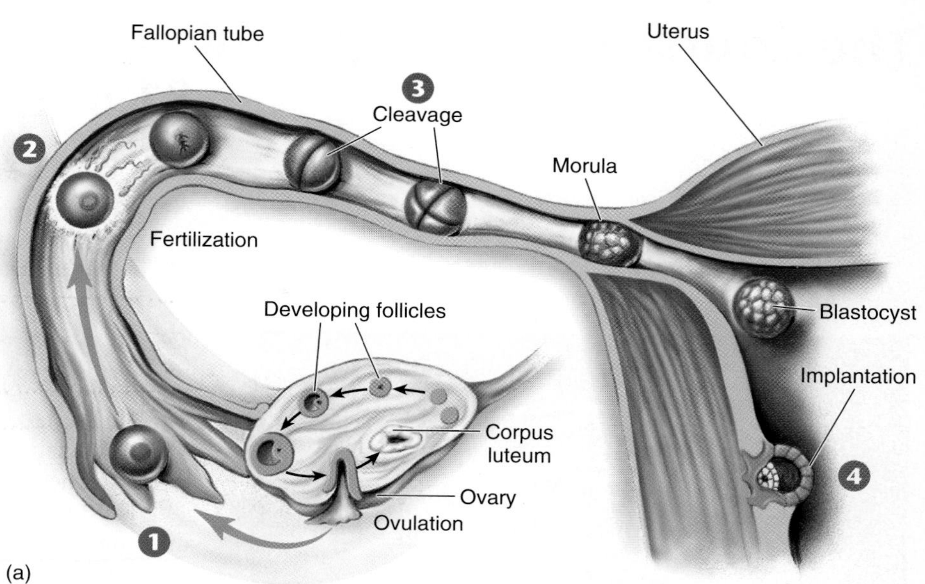

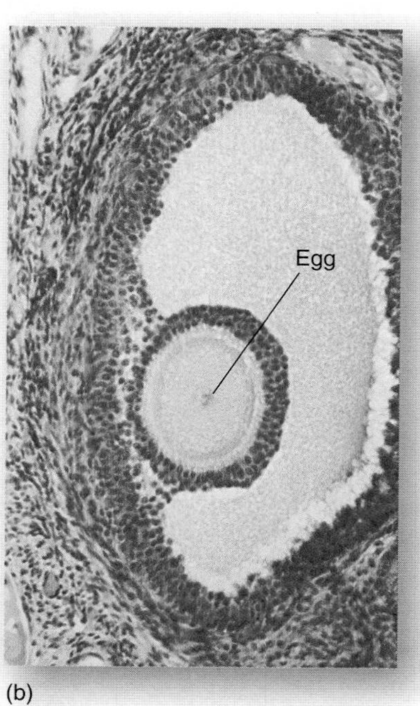

Figure 31.12 The journey of an ovum.

(a) Produced within a follicle and released at ovulation, an ovum is swept up into a fallopian tube ❶ and carried down by waves of contraction of the tube walls. Fertilization occurs within the tube ❷ by sperm journeying upward. Several mitotic divisions occur while the fertilized ovum undergoes cleavage and continues its journey down the fallopian tube ❸, becoming first a morula then a blastocyst. The blastocyst implants itself within the wall of the uterus ❹, where it continues its development. (b) A mature egg within an ovarian follicle. In each menstrual cycle, a few follicles are stimulated to grow under the influence of FSH and LH, but usually only one achieves full maturity and ovulation.

The Course of Development

31.5 Embryonic Development

LEARNING OBJECTIVE 31.5.1 Outline how the events of cleavage, gastrulation, and neurulation determine body architecture.

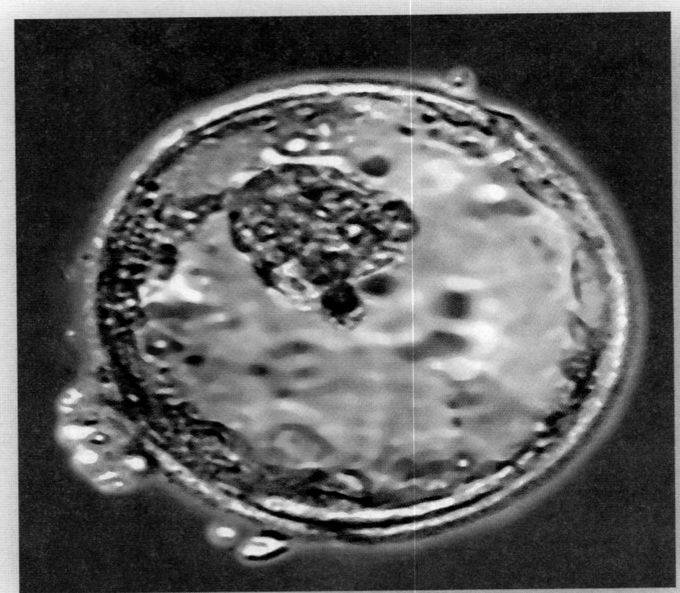

Cleavage: Setting the Stage for Development

Fertilization begins a carefully orchestrated series of developmental events. Table 31.1 traces the major stages of mammalian development, beginning with fertilization. Follow down the table as the stages of development are discussed here.

The first major event in human embryonic development is the rapid division of the zygote into a larger and larger number of smaller and smaller cells, becoming first 2 cells, then 4, then 8, and so on. The first of these divisions occurs about 30 hours after union of the egg and the sperm, and the second, 30 hours later. During this period of division, called **cleavage,** the overall size does not increase from that of the zygote. The resulting tightly packed mass of about 32 cells is called a **morula,** and each individual cell in the morula is referred to as a **blastomere.** The cells of the morula continue to divide, each cell secreting a fluid into the center of the cell mass. Eventually, a hollow ball of 500 to 2,000 cells is formed. This is the **blastocyst,** which contains a fluid-filled cavity called the **blastocoel** (figure 31.13*a*). Within the ball is an *inner cell mass* concentrated at one pole that goes on to form the developing embryo. The outer sphere of cells, called the *trophoblast,* releases the hCG hormone, discussed earlier.

During cleavage, the morula journeys down the mother's fallopian tube. On about the sixth day, the blastocyst has formed and reaches the uterus; it attaches to the uterine lining, and penetrates into the tissue of the lining. The blastocyst now begins to grow rapidly, initiating the formation of the membranes that will later surround, protect, and nourish it. One of these membranes, the **amnion,** will enclose the developing embryo, whereas another, the **chorion,** which forms from the trophoblast, will interact with uterine tissue to form the **placenta,** which will nourish the growing embryo (see figure 31.15). The placenta connects the developing embryo to the blood supply of the mother. Fully 61 of the cells at the 64-celled stage develop into the trophoblast and only 3 into the embryo proper.

(a)

(b)

Ectoderm	Epidermis, central nervous system, sense organs, neural crest
Mesoderm	Skeleton, muscles, blood vessels, heart, gonads
Endoderm	Lining of digestive and respiratory tracts; liver, pancreas

Figure 31.13 The beginnings of human development.

(a) A human blastocyst. The formation of the blastocyst occurs when the zygote undergoes cleavage producing a hollow ball of cells. An inner cell mass will later differentiate into the different tissues of the embryo. (b) The fate of the three primary germ layers.

Gastrulation: The Onset of Developmental Change

Ten to 11 days after fertilization, certain groups of cells move inward from the surface of the cell mass in a carefully orchestrated migration called **gastrulation.** First, the lower cell layer of the blastocyst cell mass differentiates into **endoderm,** one of the three primary embryonic tissues, and the upper layer into **ectoderm.** Just after this, much of the **mesoderm** arises by the invagination of cells that move from the upper layer of the cell mass *inward,* along the edges of a furrow that appears at the embryo midline, the primitive streak.

During gastrulation, about half of the cells of the blastocyst cell mass move into the interior of the human embryo. This movement largely determines the future development of the embryo. By the end of gastrulation, distribution of cells into the three primary germ layers has been completed. The ectoderm is destined to form the epidermis and neural tissue. The mesoderm is destined to form the connective tissue, muscle, and vascular elements. The endoderm forms the lining of the gut and its derivative organs (figure 31.13*b*).

Neurulation: Determination of Body Architecture

In the third week of embryonic development, the three primary cell types begin their development into the tissues and organs of the body. This stage in development is called **neurulation.**

The first characteristic vertebrate feature to form is the **notochord,** a flexible rod. Soon after gastrulation is complete, it forms from mesoderm tissue along the midline of the embryo, below its dorsal surface. After the notochord has been formed, the second characteristic vertebrate feature, the **neural tube,** forms from the region of the ectoderm that is located above the notochord and later differentiates into the spinal cord and brain. Just before the neural tube closes, two strips of cells break away and form the **neural crest.** These neural crest cells give rise to neural structures found in the vertebrate body.

While the neural tube is forming from ectoderm, the rest of the basic architecture of the human body is being rapidly determined by changes in the mesoderm. On either side of the developing notochord, segmented blocks of tissue form. Ultimately, these blocks, or **somites,** give rise to the muscles, vertebrae, and connective tissues. As development continues, more and more somites are formed. Within another strip of mesoderm that runs alongside the somites, many of the significant glands of the body, including the kidneys, adrenal glands, and gonads, develop. The remainder of the mesoderm layer moves out and around the inner endoderm layer of cells and eventually surrounds it entirely. As a result, the mesoderm forms two layers. The outer layer is associated with the body wall and the inner layer is associated with the gut. Between these two layers of mesoderm is the **coelom,** which becomes the body cavity of the adult.

By the end of the third week, over a dozen somites are evident, and the blood vessels and gut have begun to develop. At this point the embryo is about 2 millimeters (less than a tenth of an inch) long.

Putting the Concept to Work

What tissues do mesoderm cells give rise to in the adult body?

TABLE 31.1 Stages of Mammalian Development

	Stage (age)	Description
Sperm; Ovum	Fertilization (day 1)	The haploid male and female gametes fuse to form a diploid zygote.
Blastocyst; Inner cell mass; Trophoblast; Blastocoel	Cleavage (days 2–10)	The zygote rapidly divides into many cells, with no overall increase in size. These divisions affect future development, because different cells receive different portions of the egg cytoplasm and, hence, different regulatory signals.
Amniotic cavity; Ectoderm; Endoderm	Gastrulation (days 11–15)	The cells of the embryo move, forming three primary germ layers: ectoderm and endoderm form first, followed by the formation of mesoderm.
Primitive streak; Ectoderm; Mesoderm; Endoderm; Formation of extraembryonic membranes		
Neural groove; Notochord	Neurulation (days 16–25)	In all chordates, the first organ to form is the notochord; the second is the neural tube.
Neural crest; Neural tube; Notochord		During neurulation, the neural crest is produced as the neural tube is formed. The neural crest gives rise to several uniquely vertebrate structures such as sensory neurons, sympathetic neurons, Schwann cells, and other cell types.
	Organogenesis (days 26+)	Cells from the three primary cell layers combine in various ways to produce the organs of the body.

The First and Second Months: Organogenesis

LEARNING OBJECTIVE 31.5.2 Describe how the embryo takes shape.

In the fourth week of pregnancy, the body organs begin to form, a process called **organogenesis** (figure 31.14*a*). The eyes form, and the heart begins a rhythmic beating and develops four chambers. At 70 beats per minute, the little heart is destined to beat more than 2.5 billion times during a lifetime of about 70 years. More than 30 pairs of somites are visible by the end of the fourth week, and the arm and leg buds have begun to form. The embryo more than doubles in length during this week, reaching about 5 millimeters. By the end of the fourth week, the developmental scenario is far advanced, although most women are not yet aware that they are pregnant.

Figure 31.14 The developing human.

Photos (*top*) and illustrations (*bottom*) of a developing human show a four-week embryo (a), seven-week embryo (b), three-month fetus (c), and four-month fetus (d).

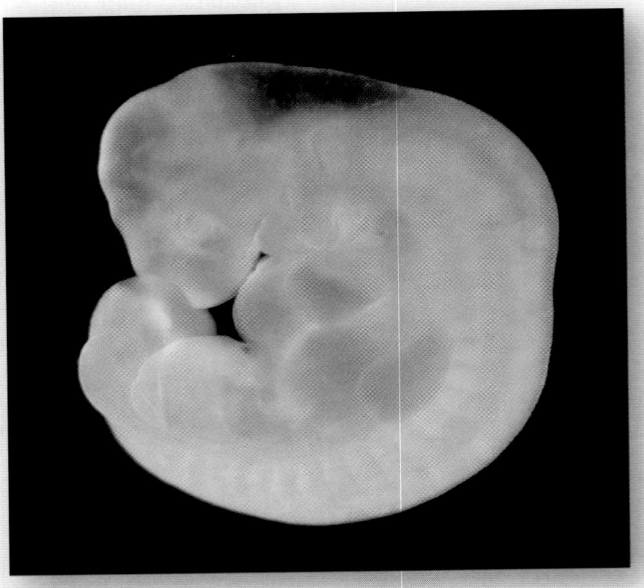

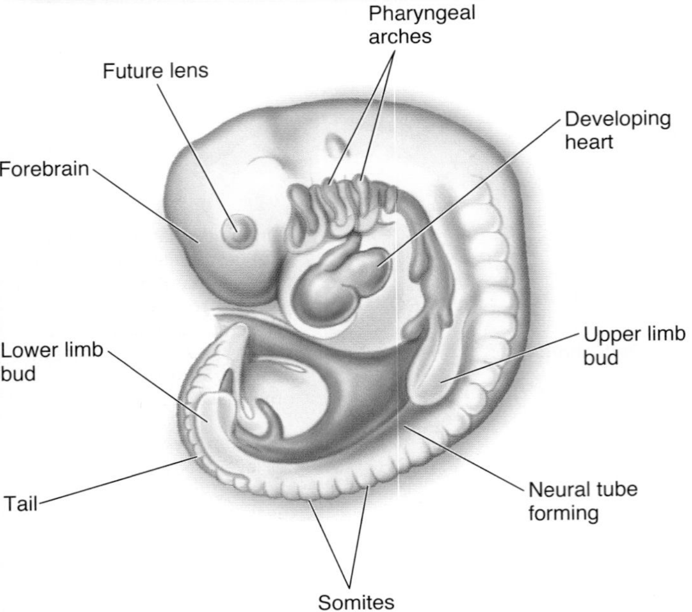

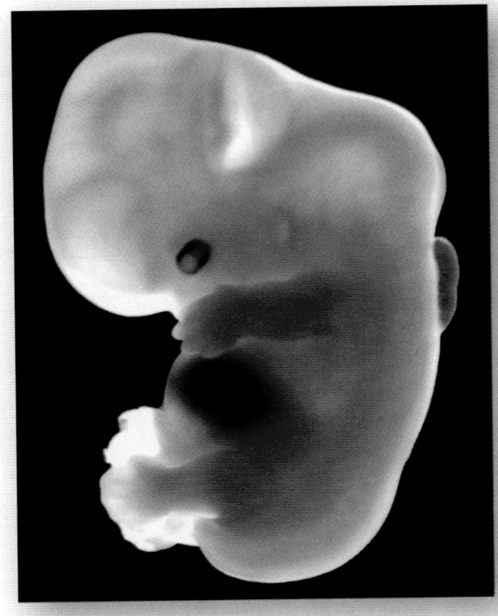

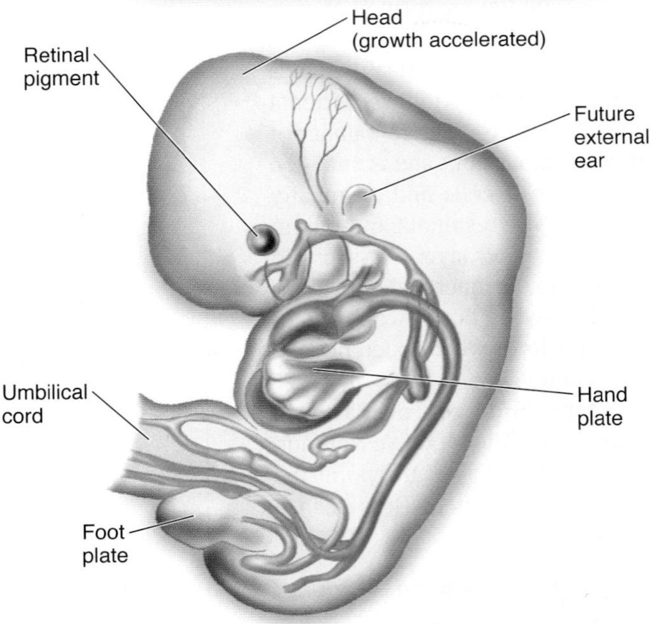

During the second month of pregnancy, great changes in morphology occur as the embryo takes shape (**figure 31.14*b***). The miniature limbs of the embryo assume their adult shapes. The arms, legs, knees, elbows, fingers, and toes can all be seen as well as a short, bony tail. The bones of the embryonic tail, an evolutionary reminder of our past, later fuse to form the coccyx, or tailbone. Within the body cavity, the major internal organs are evident, including the liver and pancreas. By the end of the second month, the embryo has grown to about 25 millimeters in length—it is 1 inch long. It weighs perhaps a gram and is beginning to look distinctly human.

Putting the Concept to Work

What happened to the tail you had as a two-month embryo?

BIOLOGY & YOU

Fetal Alcohol Syndrome. The first 8 weeks is a crucial time in human development because the proper course of events can be interrupted easily. For example, alcohol use by pregnant women during the first months of pregnancy is one of the leading causes of birth defects, producing fetal alcohol syndrome, in which the baby is born with a deformed face and often severe mental retardation. One in 250 newborns in the United States is affected with fetal alcohol syndrome.

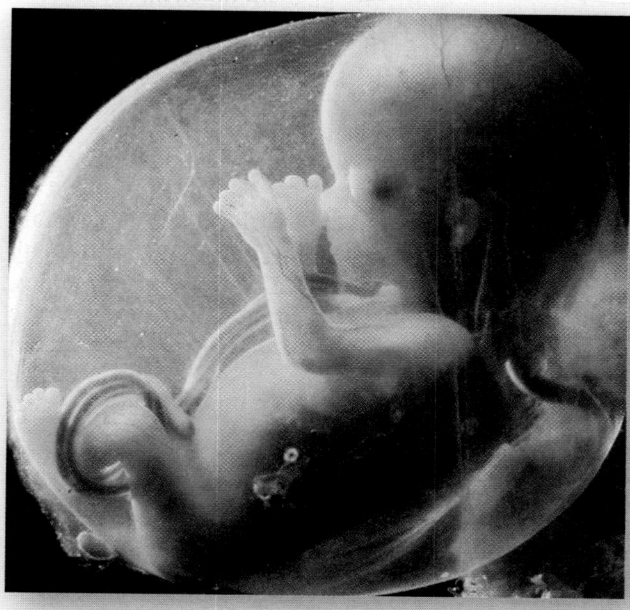

Development is essentially complete.

The developing human is now referred to as a fetus.

Facial expressions and primitive reflexes are carried out.

All of the major body organs have been established.

Arms and legs begin to move.

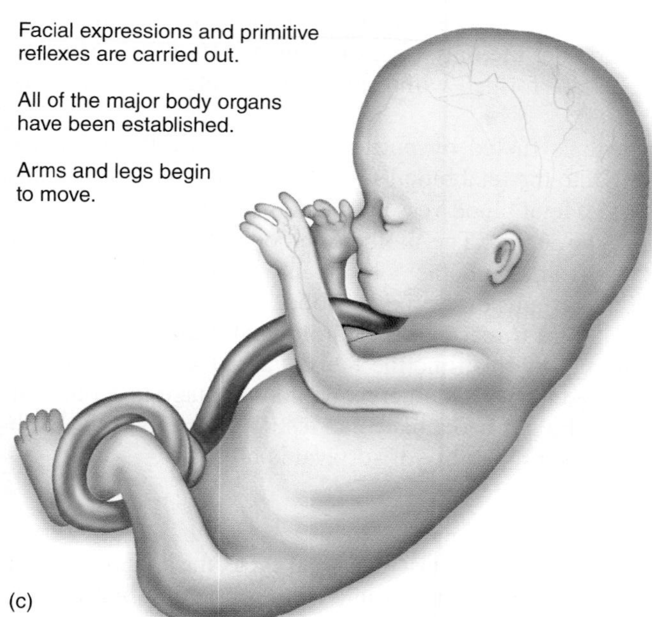

(c)

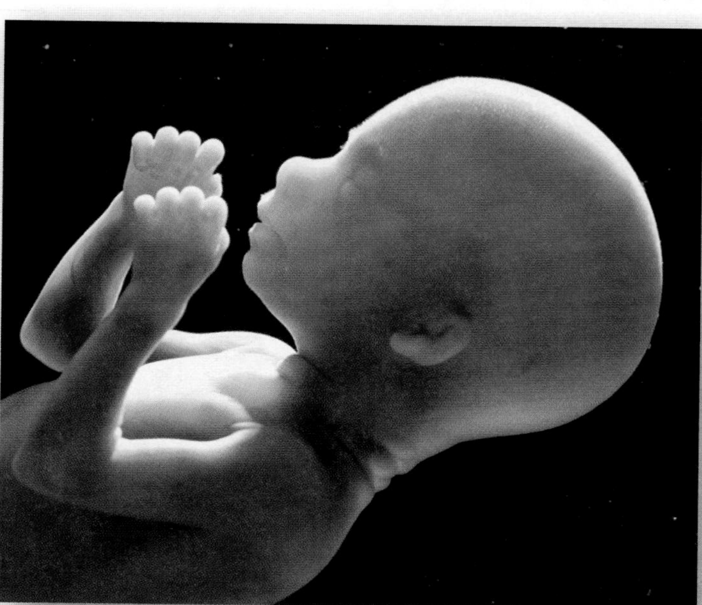

Bones actively enlarge.

Mother can feel baby kicking.

Following a period of rapid growth, the fetus is born.

Neurological growth continues after birth.

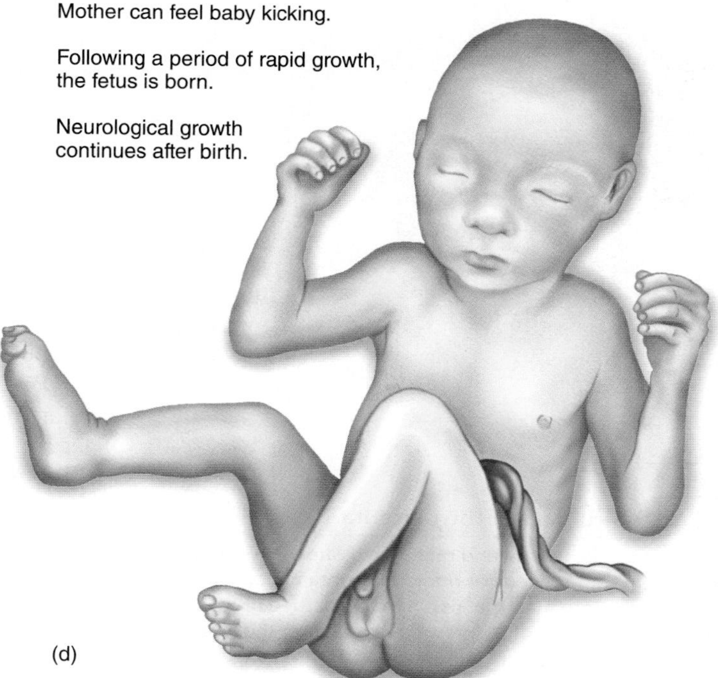

(d)

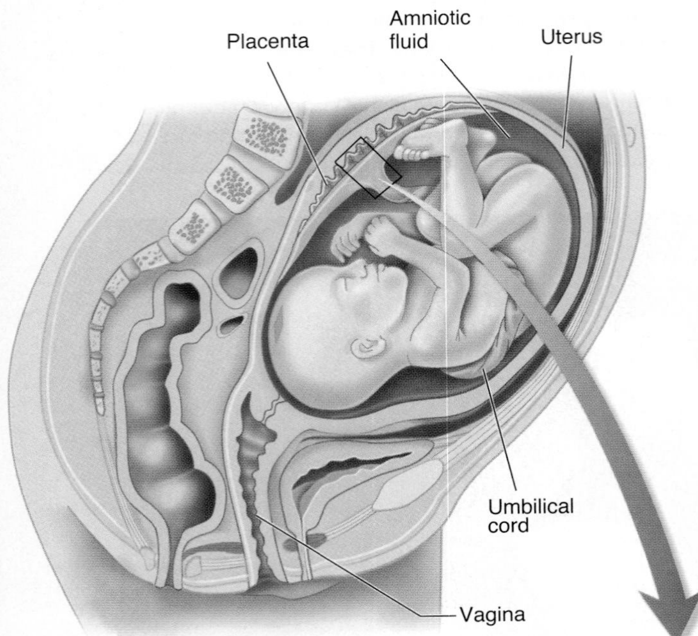

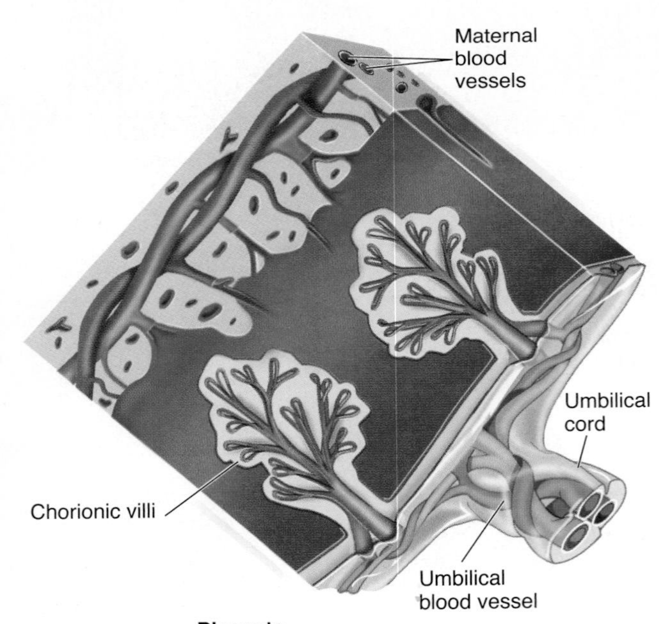

Figure 31.15 Structure of the placenta.

The placenta contains both fetal and maternal tissues. Extensions of the chorion membrane called chorionic villi contain fetal blood vessels and penetrate into maternal tissue that is bathed in the mother's blood. Oxygen and nutrients are able to enter the fetal blood from the maternal blood by diffusion. Waste substances enter the maternal blood from the fetal blood, also by diffusion.

31.6 Fetal Development

LEARNING OBJECTIVE 31.6.1 Outline the events that take place between the end of the second month and birth.

The Third Month: Completion of Development

Development of the embryo is essentially complete except for the lungs and brain. The lungs don't complete development until the third trimester, and the brain continues to develop even after birth. From this point on, the developing human is referred to as a **fetus** rather than an embryo. What remains is essentially growth. The nervous system and sense organs develop during the third month. The fetus begins to show facial expressions and carries out primitive reflexes such as the startle reflex and sucking. By the end of the third month, all of the major organs of the body have been established and the arms and legs begin to move (**figure 31.14*c***).

The Second Trimester: The Fetus Grows in Earnest

The second trimester is a time of growth. In the fourth (**figure 31.14*d***) and fifth months of pregnancy, the fetus grows to about 175 millimeters in length (almost 7 in. long), with a body weight of about 225 grams. Bone formation occurs actively during the fourth month. During the fifth month, the head and body become covered with fine hair. This downy body hair, called *lanugo,* is another evolutionary relic and is lost later in development. By the end of the fourth month, the mother can feel the baby kicking; by the end of the fifth month, she can hear its rapid heartbeat with a stethoscope. In the sixth month, growth accelerates. By the end of the sixth month, the baby is over 0.3 meter (1 ft) long and weighs 0.6 kilograms (about 1.5 lb)—and most of its prebirth growth is still to come. At this stage, the fetus cannot yet survive outside the uterus without special medical intervention.

The Third Trimester: The Pace of Growth Accelerates

The third trimester is a period of rapid growth. In the seventh, eighth, and ninth months of pregnancy, the weight of the fetus more than doubles. This increase in bulk is not the only kind of growth that occurs. Most of the major nerve tracts are formed within the brain during this period, as are new brain cells.

All of this growth is fueled by nutrients provided by the mother's bloodstream, passing into the fetal blood supply within the placenta. In the placenta (**figure 31.15**), fetal blood vessels extend from the umbilical cord into tissues that line the uterus. The mother's blood bathes this tissue so that nutrients can pass from the mother's blood into the fetal blood vessels without the two blood systems ever mixing blood.

By the end of the third trimester, the neurological growth of the fetus is far from complete, but by this time the fetus is about as large as it can get and still be delivered through the pelvis without damage to mother or child. As any woman who has had a baby can testify, it is a tight fit. Birth takes place as soon as the probability of survival is high.

Birth

At approximately 40 weeks from the last menstrual cycle, the process of birth begins as hormonal changes in the mother initiate the onset of **labor.** During labor and delivery the cervix gradually dilates (the opening becomes larger), the amnion ruptures causing amniotic fluid to flow out through the vagina (sometimes referred to as the "water breaking"), and uterine contractions become strong and regular, usually resulting in the expulsion of the fetus from the uterus. Hormones called **oxytocin** and **prostaglandins** work in a positive-feedback mechanism to stimulate and increase uterine contractions. The fetus is usually in a head-down position near the end of pregnancy. In a vaginal birth, the fetus is pushed down through the cervix and out through the vagina (figure 31.16). The umbilical cord is still attached to the baby, and a doctor, nurse, or parent clamps and cuts the cord. The baby transitions from living in a fluid environment to a gaseous one, and many of its organ systems undergo major changes. After the birth of the fetus, continuing uterine contractions expel the placenta and associated membranes, collectively called the "afterbirth." In some cases, such as when a vaginal delivery would cause harm to the fetus or the mother, the fetus and placenta are surgically removed from the uterus in a procedure called a *caesarian section (C-section).*

In the mother, hormones during late pregnancy prepare the *mammary glands* for nourishing the baby after birth. For the first couple of days after childbirth, the mammary glands produce a fluid called *colostrum,* which contains protein (including antibodies) and lactose but little fat. Then milk production is stimulated by the anterior pituitary hormone **prolactin,** usually by the third day after delivery. When the infant suckles at the breast (figure 31.17), the posterior pituitary hormone oxytocin is released, initiating milk release, or milk "letdown."

Postnatal Development

Growth continues rapidly after birth. Babies typically double their birth weight within a few months. Different organs grow at different rates, however, and the body proportions of infants are different than that of adults. The head, for example, is disproportionately large in newborns, but after birth it grows more slowly than the rest of the body. Such a pattern of growth, in which different components grow at different rates, is referred to as *allometric growth.*

The fact that the human brain continues to grow significantly for the first few years of postnatal life means that adequate nutrition and a safe environment are particularly crucial during this period.

Putting the Concept to Work

Distinguish between an embryo and a fetus.

Figure 31.17 A mother nursing her child.

It is difficult not to feel warmed by the look of wonder and delight seen on the face of a nursing mother.

Figure 31.16 Stages of childbirth.

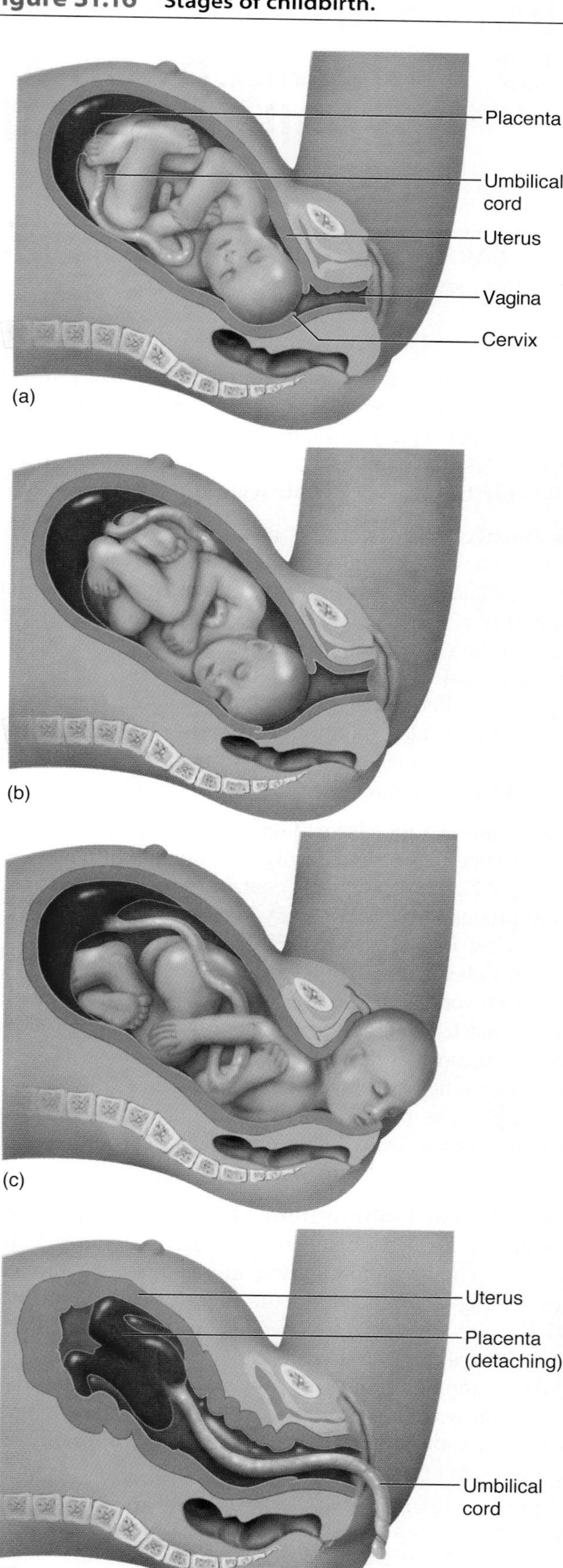

Birth Control and Sexually Transmitted Diseases

31.7 Contraception and Sexually Transmitted Diseases

LEARNING OBJECTIVE 31.7.1 Evaluate the effectiveness of five methods of contraception.

Contraception

Not all couples want to initiate a pregnancy every time they have sex, yet sexual intercourse may be a necessary and important part of their emotional lives together. The solution to this dilemma is to find a way to avoid reproduction without avoiding sexual intercourse, an approach that is commonly called **birth control,** or **contraception.**

Abstinence. The simplest and most reliable way to avoid pregnancy is not to have sex at all. Of all methods of birth control, this is the most certain—and the most limiting, because it denies a couple the emotional support of a sexual relationship. A variant of this approach is to avoid sex only on the days when successful fertilization is likely to occur. The rest of the sexual cycle is considered relatively "safe" for intercourse. This approach, called the rhythm method, or natural family planning when other indicators are also monitored, is satisfactory in principle but difficult in application because ovulation is not easy to predict and may occur unexpectedly. Failure rates are as high as 20% to 30%.

Prevention of Egg Maturation. A widespread form of birth control in the United States has been the daily ingestion of hormones, or **birth control pills** (figure 31.18*a*). These pills contain estrogen and progesterone, which shut down production of the pituitary hormones FSH and LH. The ovarian follicles do not ripen in the absence of FSH, and ovulation does not occur in the absence of LH. Other methods of hormone delivery include medroxy progesterone (Depo-Provera), which is injected every one to three months, the weekly birth control patch, which releases the hormones through the skin, and surgically implanted capsules that release hormones. Failure rates are less than 2%.

Emergency contraception, called **Plan B** or the "morning after pill," is a high-dose progesterone pill that can block ovulation if taken soon after unprotected sex. Its failure rate varies, and it should not be used as a primary method of birth control.

Prevention of Embryo Implantation. The insertion of a coil or other irregularly shaped object into the uterus is an effective means of birth control. The irritation in the uterus prevents the implantation of the descending embryo within the uterine wall. Such **intrauterine devices (IUDs)** are very effective because once inserted, they can be forgotten. They have a failure rate of less than 2%. A chemical means of preventing embryo implantation or ending an early pregnancy is **RU-486**. This pill blocks the action of progesterone, causing the endometrium to slough off. RU-486 must be administered under a doctor's care because of potentially serious side effects.

BIOLOGY & YOU

RU-486. Emergency contraception like the "morning after pill" (Plan B) should not be confused with the highly publicized RU-486 (Mifepristone). RU-486 is not an emergency contraceptive—it is not a contraceptive at all. It ends an unwanted pregnancy after conception. To be effective, RU-486 has to be administered within 49 days (or seven weeks) following the first day of the last menstrual period. A pregnancy terminated by RU-486 involves two drugs given two days apart. The first drug is RU-486 (Mifepristone), a synthetic steroid compound that works by blocking progesterone receptors in the uterus. Without progesterone stimulation, the endometrium degenerates and is sloughed off, ejecting the embryo with the shed lining of the uterus. Because RU-486 by itself is effective only 60% of the time in inducing removal of the embryo, a second medication, a prostaglandin called misoprostol, is given two days later to induce strong contractions of the uterus, forcing the embryo's expulsion. Because RU-486 has numerous side effects, some potentially severe (including sepsis, a severe infection of the bloodstream, and excessive bleeding), it must be administered by a doctor.

Sperm Blockage. Fertilization cannot occur without sperm. One way to prevent the delivery of sperm is to encase the penis within a thin rubber bag, or **condom** (figure 31.18*b*). In principle this method is easy to apply, but in practice it proves to be less effective due to incorrect use, with a failure rate of up to 15%. A second way to prevent the entry of sperm is to cover the cervix with a rubber dome called a **diaphragm** (figure 31.18*c*), inserted immediately before intercourse. Because the dimensions of individual cervices vary, diaphragms must be fitted by a physician. Failure rates average 20%.

Sperm Destruction. Another approach to birth control is to destroy the sperm within the vagina. Sperm can be destroyed with **spermicidal jellies, suppositories,** and **foams** applied immediately before intercourse. The failure rate varies widely, from 10% to 25%. The use of a spermicide with a condom or diaphragm increases the effectiveness over each method used independently.

Putting the Concept to Work

What is the failure rate of condoms? Of birth control pills?

Sexually Transmitted Diseases

LEARNING OBJECTIVE 31.7.2 Describe six significant STDs.

Sexually transmitted diseases (STDs) are diseases that spread from one person to another through sexual contact. AIDS, discussed in chapter 28, is a deadly viral STD. Other significant sexually transmitted diseases include:

Gonorrhea. The primary symptom of this disease, which is caused by the bacterium *Neisseria gonorrhoeae*, is discharge from the penis or vagina. It can be treated with antibiotics. If left untreated in women, gonorrhea can cause pelvic inflammatory disease (PID), a condition in which the fallopian tubes become scarred and blocked. PID can eventually lead to sterility.

Chlamydia. Caused by the bacterium *Chlamydia trachomatis,* this disease is sometimes called the "silent STD" because women usually experience no symptoms until after the infection has become established. Like gonorrhea, chlamydia can cause PID in women if left untreated.

Syphilis. Caused by the bacterium *Treponema pallidum,* this disease is one of the most potentially devastating STDs. Left untreated, the disease progresses to heart disease, mental deficiency, and nerve damage that may include loss of motor function or blindness.

Genital herpes. Caused by the herpes simplex virus type 2 (HSV-2), this disease is the most common STD in the United States. The virus causes red blisters on the penis or on the labia, vagina, or cervix that scab over.

Cervical cancer. About 70% of cervical cancer is caused by HPV (human papillomavirus), a sexually transmitted virus. Gardasil, a newly developed vaccine that blocks HPV in women not yet exposed to the virus, could cut worldwide deaths by about 290,000 women each year.

Putting the Concept to Work

Which STD is the most common in the United States?

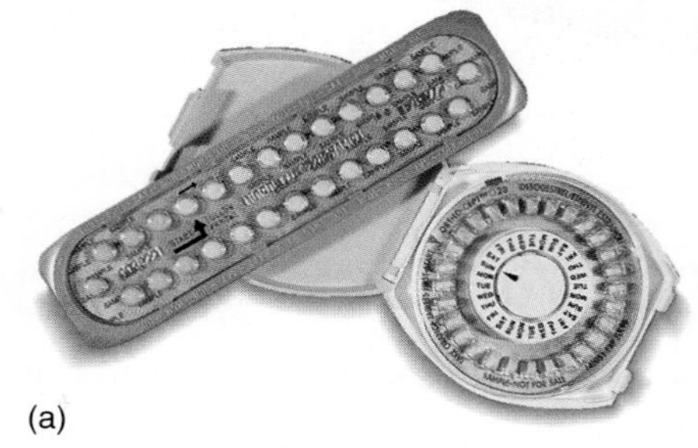

(a)

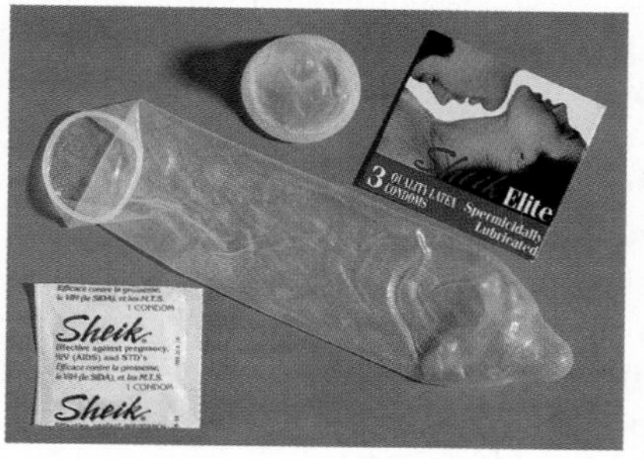

(b)

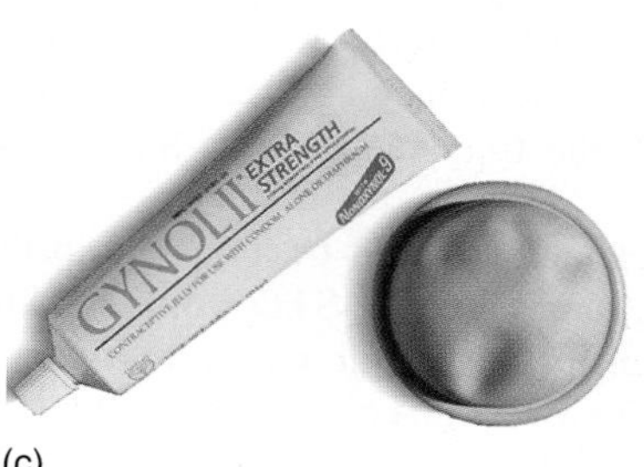

(c)

Figure 31.18 Three common birth control methods.

(a) Oral contraceptives; (b) condom; and (c) diaphragm and spermicidal jelly.

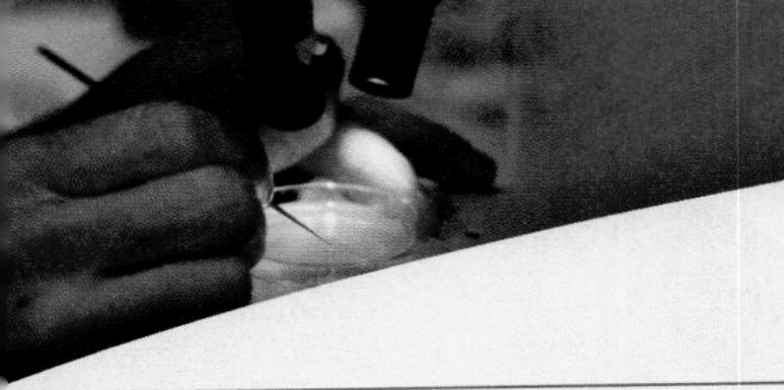

Inquiry & Analysis

Why Do STDs Vary in Frequency?

As a general rule, the incidence of a sexually transmitted disease is expected to increase with increasing frequencies of unprotected sexual contact. With the emergence of AIDS, intense publicity and education has lessened such dangerous behavior. Both the number of sexual partners and the frequency of unprotected sex have fallen significantly in the United States in the last decade. It would follow, then, that the frequencies of sexually transmitted diseases (STDs) like syphilis, gonorrhea, and chlamydia should also be falling.

However, the level of one STD sometimes rises while another falls. What are we to make of this? The simplest explanation of such a difference is that the two STDs are occurring in different populations, and one population has rising levels of sexual activity, while the other has falling levels. However, nationwide statistics encompass all population subgroups, and there is no reason to expect subgroups to contain different STDs. Certainly each major subgroup contains all three major STDs mentioned above. So this would seem an unlikely explanation for the frequency of one STD to be rising while another falls.

A second possible explanation would be a change in the infectivity of one of the STDs. A less infective STD would tend to fall in frequency in the population, for the simple reason that fewer sexual contacts result in infection. To assess this possibility, we must examine the individual STDs more closely.

Syphilis is most infective in its initial stage, but this stage lasts only about a month. Most transmissions occur during the much longer second stage, marked by a pink rash and sores in the mouth. The bacteria can be transmitted at this stage by kissing or shared liquids. Any drop in infectivity of this STD would be expected to shorten this stage—but no such shortening has been observed.

Gonorrhea can be transmitted by various forms of sexual contact with an infected individual at any time during the infection. There has been no drop in infectivity per sexual contact reported.

Chlamydia offers the most interesting possibility of changes in infectivity, because of its unusual nature. *Chlamydia trachomatis* is genetically a bacterium but is an obligate intracellular parasite, much like a virus in this respect—it can reproduce only inside human cells. The red structures in the photo are chlamydia bacteria inside human cells. Like gonorrhea, chlamydia is transmitted through vaginal, anal, or oral intercourse with an infected person. With chlamydia, the person may show no symptoms. Because the disease agent lives inside cells, its infectivity would not be expected to change unless the number of cells of an infected individual to which his or her sex partner would be exposed during intercourse were to change, a very unlikely possibility.

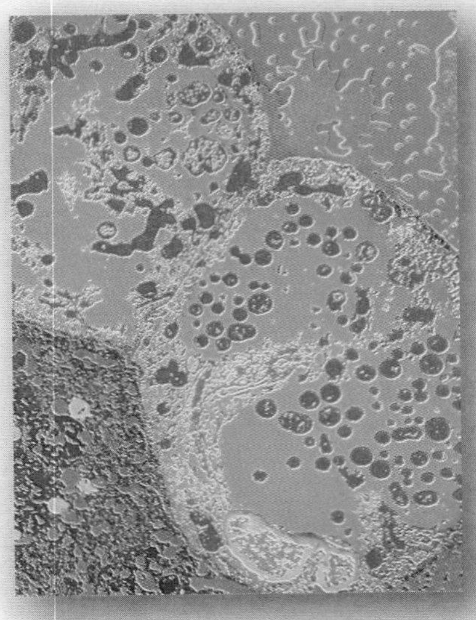

So a drop in infectivity doesn't seem very likely. There is, however, a third possible explanation for why the frequency of one STD in a population might rise while the frequency of another STD in that same population falls. To grasp this third possible explanation, we will need to examine carefully the trends in the incidence in the United States of gonorrhea, chlamydia, and syphilis. Detailed yearly statistics are reported in the graph above.

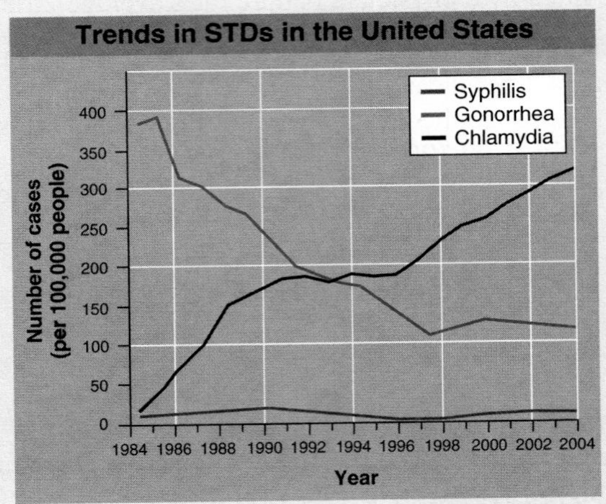

Analysis

1. **Making Inferences**
   - **a.** Gonorrhea: What is the incidence in 1985? In 2004? Has the frequency declined or increased? In general, are individuals aware they are infected when they transmit the STD?
   - **b.** Chlamydia: What is the incidence in 1985? In 2004? Has the frequency declined or increased? In general, are individuals aware they are infected when they transmit the STD?
2. **Drawing Conclusions** How might heightened public awareness explain why the trend in levels of gonorrhea differs from that of chlamydia?

Summary of Learning Outcomes

Modes of Reproduction

Asexual and Sexual Reproduction

31.1.1 Asexual reproduction through fission (as seen in **figure 31.1**) or budding is the primary means of reproduction among protists and some animals, but most animals reproduce sexually.

- In animals the most common mode of reproduction is sexual, but parthenogenesis and hermaphroditism are two variations. In parthenogenesis, offspring are produced from unfertilized eggs. In hermaphroditism, an individual has both testes and ovaries, producing both sperm and eggs. Some hermaphrodites can self-fertilize. In some species of animals, the social environment can cause a change in the sex of individuals, such as a female turning into a male when males are scarce, a process called sequential hermaphroditism.

31.1.2 In mammals, sex is genetically determined and appears during embryonic development. An embryo that is XY develops into a male and an XX embryo develops into a female.

The Human Reproductive System

Males

31.2.1 Male testes continuously produce large numbers of male gametes, sperm. The testes contain a large number of tightly coiled tubes called seminiferous tubules, where sperm develop in a process called spermatogenesis. As sperm develop and undergo meiosis, they move toward the lumen of the tubules, and from there they pass into the epididymis. Once matured, they are stored in the vas deferens. During sexual intercourse, sperm are delivered through the penis into the female.

Females

31.3.1 Female gametes, eggs or ova, develop in the ovary from oocytes. The ovaries are located in the lower abdomen. A female is born with some 2 million oocytes, all arrested during the first meiotic division. The hormones FSH and LH initiate the resumption of meiosis I in a few oocytes, but usually only one oocyte completes development in each monthly cycle.

- The egg ruptures from the ovary, called ovulation, and enters the fallopian tube. Sperm deposited in the vagina travel up through the cervix and uterus, shown here from **figure 31.10**, and into the fallopian tube, or oviduct, to reach the egg. Usually only one sperm cell penetrates the egg's protective layers. At this point, the oocyte completes meiosis II, and fertilization occurs. The fertilized egg, called a zygote, is transported to the uterus through the oviduct. The zygote attaches to the endometrial lining of the uterus where it completes development.

Hormones Coordinate the Reproductive Cycle

31.4.1 The human reproductive cycle, called a menstrual cycle, is divided into two phases, the follicular and luteal phases. The follicular phase begins with the secretion of FSH and LH, which stimulates the resumption of oocyte development and the secretion of estrogen. The estrogen acts as a negative-feedback signal to stop the secretion of FSH from the anterior pituitary.

- As the level of estrogen increases it begins to have a positive-feedback effect on FSH and LH. The luteal phase begins with a surge of LH, which causes ovulation and the formation of the corpus luteum. The corpus luteum begins secreting progesterone, which acts to prepare the uterus for implantation of the zygote.
- If fertilization does not occur, estrogen and progesterone levels drop and the endometrial lining of the uterus sloughs off, a process called menstruation, and a new cycle begins.
- If a zygote implants in the lining of the uterus (as seen in **figure 31.12**), estrogen and progesterone levels remain high due to the release of human chorionic gonadotropin (hCG) from the embryo. The uterus is maintained and no further egg maturation occurs.

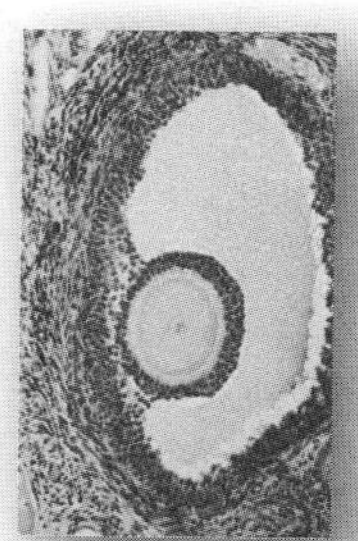

The Course of Development

Embryonic Development

31.5.1 The vertebrate embryo develops in three stages. The first stage, called cleavage, involves hundreds of cell divisions that eventually produce a hollow ball of cells called a blastocyst. The second stage, called gastrulation, involves the orchestrated movement of cells, forming the three germ layers: endoderm, ectoderm, and mesoderm. The third stage is neurulation, where the notochord and neural tube form.

31.5.2 Organs begin forming by the fourth week; by the end of the second month the embryo looks distinctly human. By the end of the third month, all major organs except the brain and lungs are developed (as seen in **figure 31.14**).

Fetal Development

31.6.1 Most of the key events in human development occur early in the first trimester. The second and third trimesters are periods of considerable growth, with the fetus receiving nourishment from the placenta.

- During labor and delivery, the fetus and placenta are expelled from the uterus. Hormones coordinate the production of milk in the mother for nourishing the newborn. Brain development continues in the baby after birth.

Birth Control and Sexually Transmitted Diseases

Contraception and Sexually Transmitted Diseases

31.7.1 Various birth control methods are available and work by preventing egg maturation, preventing embryo implantation, and blocking or killing sperm.

31.7.2 Sexually transmitted diseases are spread through sexual contact. AIDS is a deadly STD. Other STDs may not be as fatal as AIDS but are quite destructive, especially if left untreated.

Test Your Understanding

31.1.1 If offspring are not genetically identical to each other or to the parent, then the organism reproduces through
a. fission.
b. sexual reproduction.
c. budding.
d. All of the above.

31.1.1 In __________, an animal contains both ovaries and testes and can produce both eggs and sperm.
a. parthenogenesis
b. asexual reproduction
c. hermaphroditism
d. budding

31.1.2 In mammals, the embryonic gonads will develop into ovaries
a. if the *SRY* gene is expressed.
b. if both sex chromosomes are X.
c. if the sex chromosomes are X and Y.
d. within the first 40 days.

31.2.1 The __________ allows the temperature of the human male testes to be about 3°C cooler than the rest of the body.
a. seminiferous tubules
b. epididymis
c. vas deferens
d. scrotum

31.3.1 Oocyte development in human females requires the hormones
a. estrogen and testosterone.
b. FSH and LH.
c. progesterone and testosterone.
d. oxytocin and prolactin.

31.4.1 When pregnancy occurs, the endometrium is maintained by the
a. embryo releasing hCG.
b. decrease in levels of progesterone.
c. hypothalamus releasing GnRH.
d. increasing levels of FSH.

31.5.1 A human embryo has formed the three germ layers from which all tissues arise by the time
a. the blastula forms.
b. neurulation is complete.
c. the blastocyst forms.
d. gastrulation is complete.

31.5.1 In a developing human, the first tissues to begin forming are the
a. skeletal.
b. muscular.
c. neural.
d. digestive.

31.6.1 Contractions of the uterus during labor are stimulated by the hormone
a. estrogen.
b. prolactin.
c. oxytocin.
d. progesterone.

31.7.1 Which of the following is *not* a method of contraception?
a. destruction of the egg
b. prevention of egg maturation
c. sperm blockage
d. prevention of embryo implantation

Apply Your Understanding

31.1.2 Up until 40 days after conception, an embryo is neither male nor female. Explain what happens after that point in an embryo that carries the *SRY* gene.

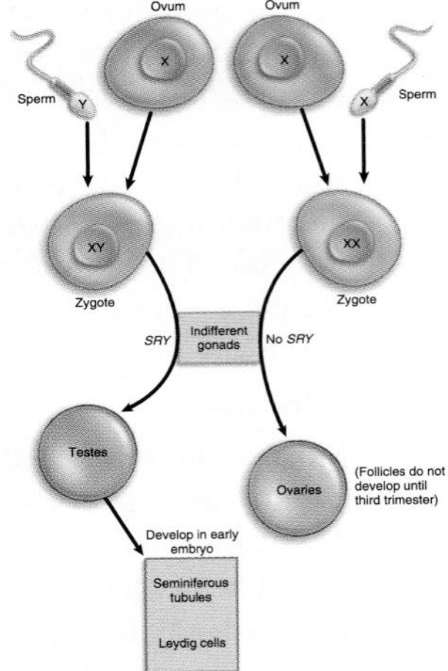

31.3.1 Sometimes a zygote implants in the fallopian tube rather than in the uterus. This is called an ectopic pregnancy (ectopic meaning "out of place"). It is necessary to terminate an ectopic pregnancy because it endangers the mother and the fetus cannot survive. Explain why the mother is in danger and why the fetus can't survive.

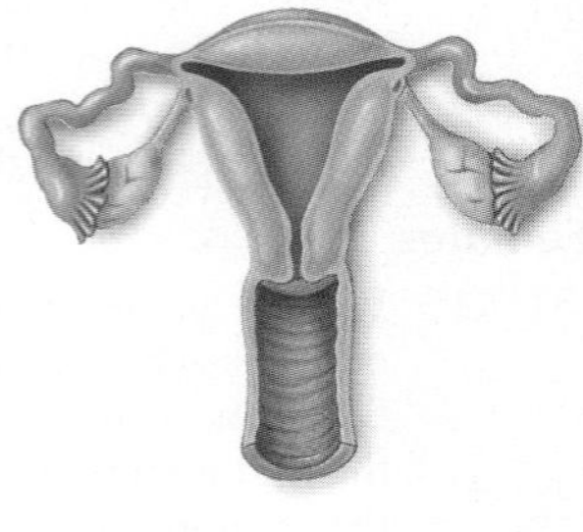

Synthesize What You Have Learned

31.1.1 Why are all the parents of parthenogenic offspring female?

31.2.1 Males produce their sperm throughout their lives, while females produce all their eggs at one time during sexual development. Would you expect most gene mutations in newborns to have originated from the father, or would you expect both parents to contribute a similar risk of mutation? Explain.

31.5.1 Oviparity (fertilized eggs deposited outside the mother's body to develop) is the rule in the animal kingdom. It is common in insects, fishes, amphibians, and reptiles, and universal in birds. Among mammals, the most primitive (the echidna and the platypus) are also oviparous. However, all mammals that evolved later (marsupials and placentals) are viviparous (young develop within the mother). What do you think was responsible for this major shift in reproductive strategy?

TABLE 13.1	Some Eukaryotic Genomes			
Organism		**Estimated Genome Size (Mbp)**	**Number of Genes (×1,000)**	**Nature of Genome**
Vertebrates				
	Homo sapiens (human)	3,200	20–25	The first large genome to be sequenced; the number of transcribable genes is far less than expected; much of the genome is occupied by repeated DNA sequences.
	Pan troglodytes (chimpanzee)	2,800	20–25	There are few base substitutions between chimp and human genomes, less than 2%, but many small sequences of DNA have been lost as the two species diverged, often with significant effects.
	Mus musculus (mouse)	2,500	25	Roughly 80% of mouse genes have a functional equivalent in the human genome; importantly, large portions of the noncoding DNA of mouse and human genomes have been conserved; overall, rodent genomes (mouse and rat) appear to be evolving more than twice as fast as primate genomes (human and chimpanzee).
	Gallus gallus (chicken)	1,000	20–23	One-third the size of the human genome; genetic variation among domestic chickens seems much higher than the genetic variation seen in humans.
	Fugu rubripes (pufferfish)	365	35	The *Fugu* genome is only one-ninth the size of the human genome, yet it contains 10,000 more genes.
Invertebrates				
	Caenorhabditis elegans (nematode)	97	21	The fact that every cell of *C. elegans* has been identified makes its genome a particularly powerful tool in developmental biology.
	Drosophila melanogaster (fruit fly)	137	13	*Drosophila* telomere regions lack the simple repeated segments that are characteristic of most eukaryotic telomeres. About one-third of the genome consists of gene-poor centric heterochromatin.
	Anopheles gambiae (mosquito)	278	15	The extent of similarity between *Anopheles* and *Drosophila* is approximately equal to that between human and pufferfish.
	Nematostella vectensis (sea anemone)	450	18	The genome of this cnidarian is much more like vertebrate genomes than nematode or insect genomes that appear to have become streamlined by evolution.
Plants				
	Oryza sativa (rice)	430	33–50	The rice genome contains only 13% as much DNA as the human genome, but roughly twice as many genes; like the human genome, it is rich in repetitive DNA.
	Populus trichocarpa (cottonwood tree)	500	45	This fast-growing tree is widely used by the timber and paper industries. Its genome, fifty times smaller than the pine genome, is one-third heterochromatin.
Fungi				
	Saccharomyces cerevisiae (brewer's yeast)	13	6	*S. cerevisiae* was the first eukaryotic cell to have its genome fully sequenced.
Protists				
	Plasmodium falciparum (malaria parasite)	23	5	The *Plasmodium* genome has an unusually high proportion of adenine and thymine. Scarcely 5,000 genes contain the bare essentials of the eukaryotic cell.

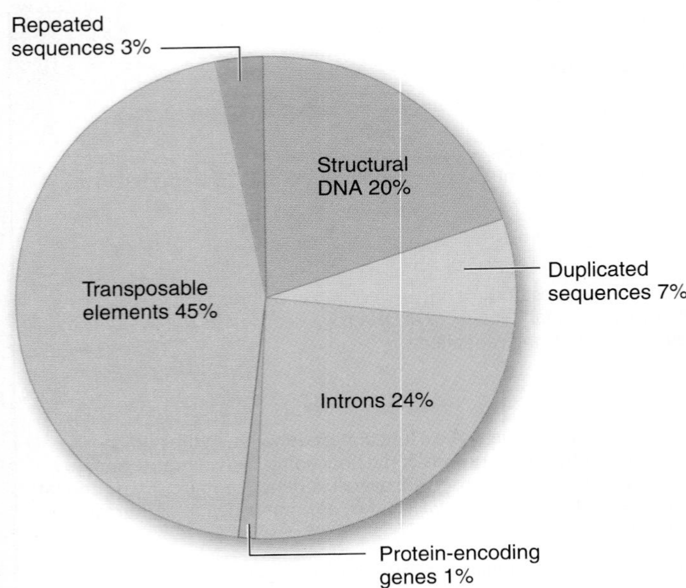

Figure 13.2 The human genome.

Very little of the human genome is devoted to protein-encoding genes, indicated by the light blue section in this pie chart.

13.2 The Human Genome

LEARNING OBJECTIVE 13.2.1 Describe the three major surprises discovered with the sequencing of the human genome.

On June 26, 2000, geneticists announced that the entire human genome had been sequenced. This effort presented no small challenge, as the human genome is huge—more than 3 billion base pairs, which is the largest genome sequenced to date. To get an idea of the magnitude of the task, consider that if all 3.2 billion base pairs were written down on the pages of this book, the book would be 500,000 pages long, and it would take you about 60 years, working eight hours a day, every day, at five bases a second, to read it all.

Reading the human genome for the first time, geneticists encountered three big surprises.

The Number of Genes Is Surprisingly Low

The human genome sequence contains only 20,000 to 25,000 protein-encoding genes, only 1% of the genome (figure 13.2). As you can see in table 13.1, this is scarcely more genes than in a nematode worm (21,000 genes), and not quite double the number in a fruit fly (13,000 genes). Researchers had confidently anticipated at least four times as many genes, because over 100,000 unique messenger RNA (mRNA) molecules can be found in human cells—surely, they argued, it would take as many genes to make them.

How can human cells contain more mRNAs than genes? Recall from chapter 12 that in a typical human gene, the sequence of DNA nucleotides that specifies a protein is broken into many bits called exons, scattered among much longer segments of nontranslated DNA called introns. Imagine this paragraph as a human gene: all the occurrences of the letter "e" could be considered exons, while the rest would be noncoding introns, which make up 24% of the human genome.

When a cell uses a human gene to make a protein, it first manufactures mRNA copies of the gene, then splices the exons together, getting rid of the intron sequences in the process. Now here's the turn of events researchers had not anticipated: The exon portions of human gene transcripts are often spliced together in different ways, called *alternative splicing*. As we discussed in chapter 12, each exon is actually a module; one exon may code for one part of a protein, another for a different part of a protein. When the exon transcripts are mixed in different ways, very different protein shapes can be built.

Alternative splicing, described on page 212 explains how fewer genes can encode many mRNA molecules. The mRNA shown in figure 12.10 consists of all the exons. You can imagine how a different mRNA would be produced if only half of the exons were used to make the mRNA.

With alternative splicing, it is easy to see how 25,000 genes can encode four times as many proteins. The added complexity of human proteins occurs because the gene parts are put together in new ways. Great music is made from simple tunes in much the same way.

Some Chromosomes Have Very Few Genes

In addition to the fragmenting of genes by the scattering of exons throughout the genome, there is another interesting "organizational" aspect of the genome. Genes are not distributed evenly over the genome. The small chromosome number 19 is packed densely with genes, transcription factors, and other functional elements.

Transcription factors are proteins involved in eukaryotic gene expression as discussed on page 216. Transcription cannot occur without the involvement of transcription factors.

BIOLOGY & YOU

Sequencing the Genome of a Cancer Patient. In 2008 scientists at Washington University in Saint Louis sequenced the entire genome of a cancer patient, a woman who had acute myeloid leukemia (AML). This was the first time all the genes of a cancer patient had been examined—a very important milestone because for the first time medical researchers could see exactly what genes had been changed to cause the cancer and aid its progression. The researchers discovered genetic mutations in the cells of the patient's cancerous tumor; mutations present in every tumor cell but not present in any other body cells. Two of these mutations were expected, as they had been linked to AML in many other patients. Importantly, however, there were eight other mutations, rare among humans and never before linked to AML. Important to her cancer, they are not at all predictive of AML in others. The key seems to be in how the mutated genes interact with each other, and with her other 20,000 genes. We know little of the complex ways genes interact, so the goal of predictive knowledge still eludes us. Trying to predict a cell's potential cancerous future by identifying altered genes has been likened to trying to understand "Hamlet" from a list of the words Shakespeare's play contains. The meaning comes from how those words are put together.

The much larger chromosome numbers 4 and 8, by contrast, have few genes, scattered like isolated hamlets in a desert. On most chromosomes, vast stretches of seemingly barren DNA fill the chromosomes between clusters rich in genes.

Most of the Genome Is Noncoding DNA

The third notable characteristic of the human genome is the startling amount of noncoding DNA it possesses. Only 1% to 1.5% of the human genome is coding DNA, devoted to genes encoding proteins. Each of your cells has about six feet of DNA stuffed into it, but of that, less than one inch is devoted to genes! Nearly 99% of the DNA in your cells seems to have little or nothing to do with the instructions that make you who you are (table 13.2).

There are four major types of noncoding human DNA:

Noncoding DNA Within Genes. As discussed earlier, a human gene is made up of numerous fragments of protein-encoding information (exons) embedded within a much larger matrix of noncoding DNA (introns). Introns make up 24% of the human genome—exons only 1%!

Structural DNA. Some regions of the chromosomes remain highly condensed, tightly coiled, and untranscribed throughout the cell cycle. These portions—about 20% of the DNA—tend to be localized around the centromere, or located near the telomeres, or ends, of the chromosome.

Repeated Sequences. Scattered about chromosomes are simple sequence repeats of two or three nucleotides like CA or CGG, repeated like a broken record thousands and thousands of times. These make up about 3% of the human genome. An additional 7% is devoted to other sorts of duplicated sequences. Repetitive sequences with excess C and G tend to be found in the neighborhood of translated genes, while A- and T-rich repeats dominate the nongene deserts. The light bands on chromosome karyotypes now have an explanation—they are regions rich in GC and genes. Dark bands signal neighborhoods rich in A and T which are thin on genes. Inspect the two human chromosomes shown in figure 13.3. Chromosome 8 contains many nongene areas that are indicated by the dark bands, while chromosome 19 is dense with genes and so it has few dark bands.

Transposable Elements. Fully 45% of the human genome consists of mobile parasitic bits of DNA called transposable elements. Discovered by Barbara McClintock in 1950 (she won the Nobel Prize in Physiology or Medicine in 1983 for her discovery), transposable elements are bits of DNA that are able to jump from one location on a chromosome to another—tiny molecular versions of Mexican jumping beans. Because they leave a copy of themselves behind when they jump, their numbers in the genome increase as generations pass. Nested within the human genome are over half a million copies of an ancient transposable element called *Alu*, composing fully 10% of the entire human genome. Often jumping right into genes, *Alu* transpositions cause many harmful mutations.

Transposable elements (also called transposons) are most harmful when they insert right in the middle of a gene, as discussed on page 199 and shown in table 11.1.

Putting the Concept to Work

The noncoding portions of human and mouse genomes have been conserved more than the coding portions. How might you explain this?

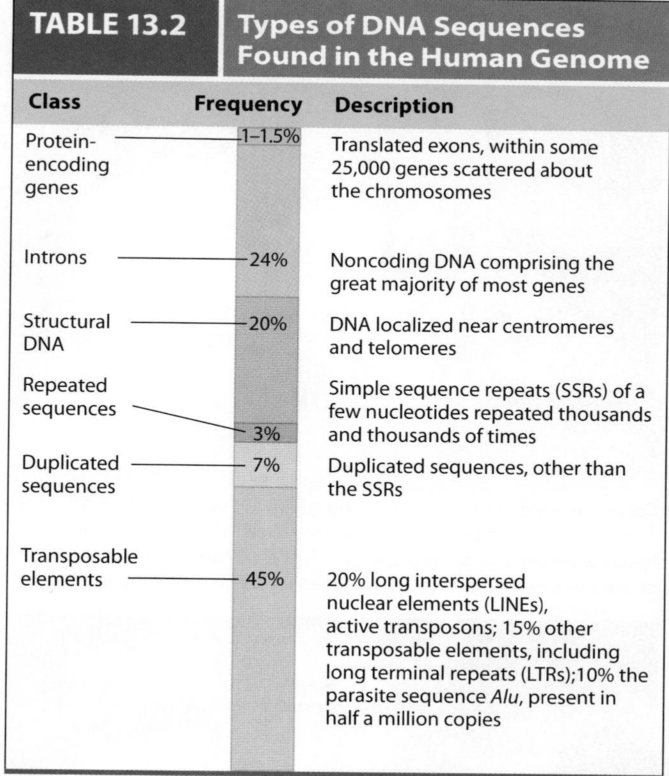

TABLE 13.2 Types of DNA Sequences Found in the Human Genome

Class	Frequency	Description
Protein-encoding genes	1–1.5%	Translated exons, within some 25,000 genes scattered about the chromosomes
Introns	24%	Noncoding DNA comprising the great majority of most genes
Structural DNA	20%	DNA localized near centromeres and telomeres
Repeated sequences	3%	Simple sequence repeats (SSRs) of a few nucleotides repeated thousands and thousands of times
Duplicated sequences	7%	Duplicated sequences, other than the SSRs
Transposable elements	45%	20% long interspersed nuclear elements (LINEs), active transposons; 15% other transposable elements, including long terminal repeats (LTRs);10% the parasite sequence *Alu*, present in half a million copies

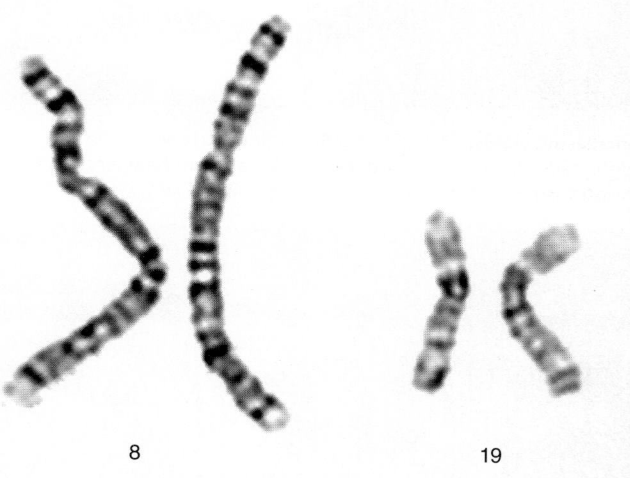

Figure 13.3 Banding on karyotyped chromosomes.

The dark bands are areas rich in A and T nucleotides, which indicate nontranslated areas. Lighter gene-heavy areas of the chromosome are rich in repetitive sequences containing C and G nucleotides.

Genetic Engineering

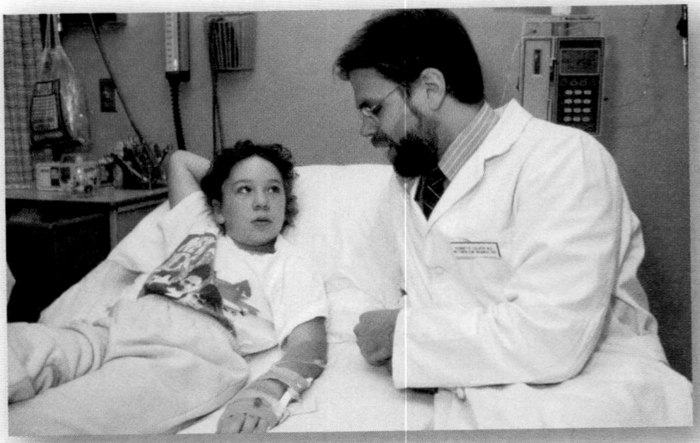

Curing disease. One of two young girls who were the first humans "cured" of a hereditary disorder by transferring into their bodies healthy versions of a defective gene. The transfer was successfully carried out in 1990, and twenty years later the girls remain healthy.

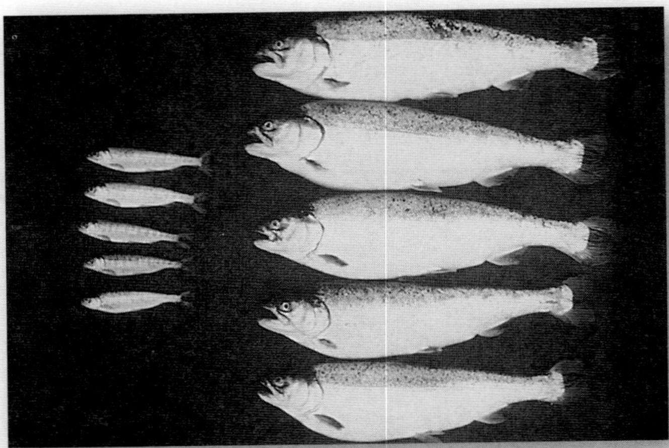

Increasing yields. The genetically engineered salmon on the *right* have shortened production cycles and are heavier than the nontransgenic salmon of the same age on the *left*.

Pest-proofing plants. The genetically engineered cotton plants on the *right* have a gene that inhibits feeding by weevils; the cotton plants on the *left* lack this gene, and produce far fewer cotton bolls.

Figure 13.4 Examples of genetic engineering.

13.3 A Scientific Revolution

In recent years, **genetic engineering**—the ability to manipulate genes and move them from one organism to another—has led to great advances in medicine and agriculture (figure 13.4). Most of the insulin used to treat diabetes is now obtained from bacteria that contain a human insulin gene. As we will learn in this chapter, cultivated plants and animals can be genetically engineered to resist pests, grow bigger, or grow faster.

Restriction Enzymes

LEARNING OBJECTIVE 13.3.1 Define restriction enzymes and explain how they are used to transfer genes between organisms.

The first stage in any genetic engineering experiment is to chop up the "source" DNA to get a copy of the gene you wish to transfer. This first stage is the key to successful transfer of the gene, and learning how to do it is what has led to the genetic revolution. The trick is in how the DNA molecules are cut. The cutting must be done in such a way that the resulting DNA fragments have "sticky ends" that can later be joined with another molecule of DNA.

This special form of molecular surgery is carried out by **restriction enzymes,** also called *restriction endonucleases*, which are special enzymes that bind to specific short sequences (typically four to six nucleotides long) on the DNA. These sequences are very unusual in that they are symmetrical—the two strands of the DNA duplex have the same nucleotide sequence, running in opposite directions! The sequence in figure 13.5, for example, is GAATTC. Try writing down the sequence of the opposite strand: it is CTTAAG—the same sequence, written backward. This sequence is recognized by the restriction enzyme *Eco*RI. Other restriction enzymes recognize other sequences.

What makes the DNA fragments "sticky" is that most restriction enzymes do not make their incision in the center of the sequence; rather, the cut is made to one side. In the sequence in figure 13.5 ❶, the cut is made on both strands between the G and A nucleotides, G/AATTC. This produces a break, with short, single strands of DNA dangling from each end. Because the two single-stranded ends are complementary in sequence, they could pair up and heal the break, with the aid of a sealing enzyme—*or* they could pair with *any other DNA fragment cut by the same enzyme,* because all would have the same single-stranded sticky ends. Figure 13.5 ❷ shows how DNA from another source (the orange DNA) also cut with *Eco*RI has the same sticky ends as the original source DNA. Any gene in any organism cut by the enzyme that attacks GAATTC sequences will have the same sticky ends, and can be joined to any other with the aid of a sealing enzyme called *DNA ligase* ❸.

As discussed on page 57, the two strands of DNA are held together through complementary base pairing of nucleotides. Base pairing is universal, whether the DNA resides in a bacterial cell or a human cell, and that is why restriction enzymes work on any DNA.

Putting the Concept to Work

Would a restriction enzyme that cut the sequence GAATTC between the A and the T be as useful in genetic engineering as one that cut the sequence between the G and the A? Explain.

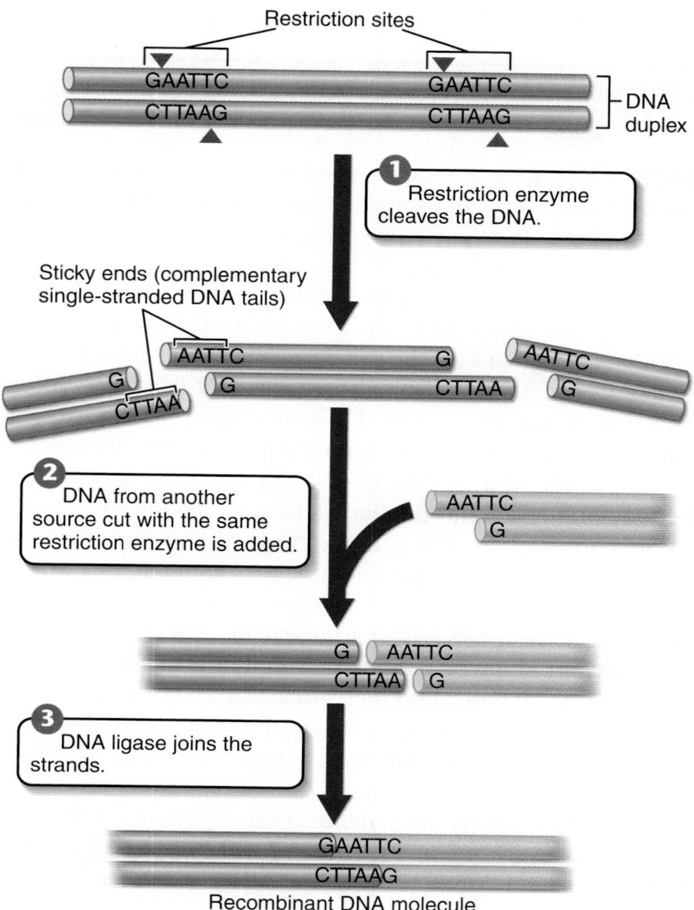

Figure 13.5 How restriction enzymes produce DNA fragments with sticky ends.

The restriction enzyme *Eco*RI always cleaves the sequence GAATTC between G and A. Because the same sequence occurs on both strands, both are cut. However, the two sequences run in opposite directions on the two strands. As a result, single-stranded tails are produced that are complementary to each other, or "sticky."

IMPLICATION FOR YOU Restriction enzymes evolved as a way for bacteria to destroy the DNA of invading viruses. Some 2,500 different restriction enzymes have been isolated from bacteria, using over 200 different 4- to 8-base recognition sequences. In each instance, the bacterium also contains an enzyme that adds a methyl group ($—CH_3$) to that same 4- to 8-base sequence. Why do you suppose bacteria always possess the pair of enzymes, and never just the restriction enzyme alone? *Hint:* There is a lot of viral DNA that the restriction enzyme has to "look through" to find the recognition sequence. Could something speed up this process?

Formation of cDNA

LEARNING OBJECTIVE 13.3.2 Explain why cDNA is necessary to produce eukaryotic proteins in bacteria.

As we have discussed, eukaryotic genes are encoded in segments called exons separated from one another by numerous nontranslated sequences called introns. The entire gene is transcribed by RNA polymerase, producing what is called the primary RNA transcript (figure 13.6). Before a eukaryotic gene can be translated into a protein, the introns must be cut out of this primary transcript. The fragments that remain are then spliced together to form the mRNA, which is eventually translated in the cytoplasm. When transferring eukaryotic genes into bacteria (discussed in section 13.4), it is necessary to transfer DNA that has had the intron information removed because bacteria lack the enzymes to carry out this processing. Bacterial genes do not contain introns. To produce eukaryotic DNA without introns, genetic engineers first isolate from the cytoplasm the processed mRNA corresponding to a particular gene. The cytoplasmic mRNA has *only* exons, properly spliced together. An enzyme called *reverse transcriptase* is then used to make a complementary DNA strand of the mRNA, from which there forms a double-stranded DNA molecule called complementary DNA, or **cDNA.**

Putting the Concept to Work

If you wished to produce a bacterial protein in a human cell culture, would you need to employ cDNA? Explain.

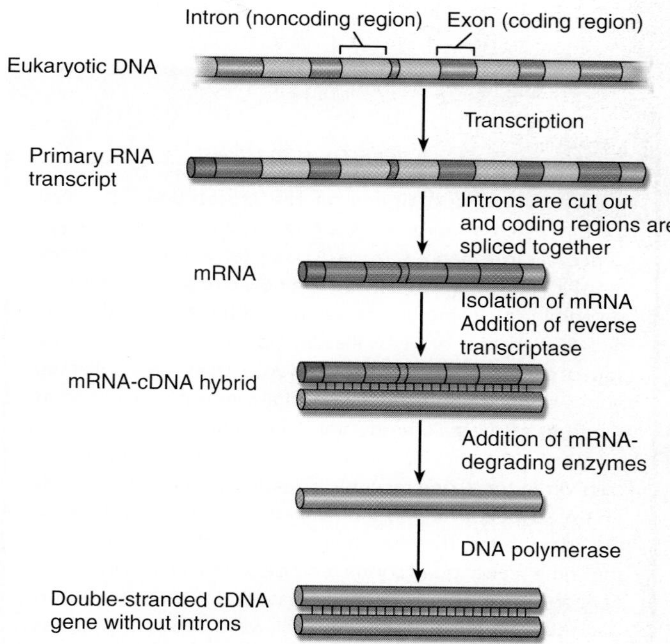

Figure 13.6 cDNA: Producing an intron-free version of a eukaryotic gene for genetic engineering.

In eukaryotic cells, a primary RNA transcript is processed into the mRNA, which is translated into a protein. In order to obtain a gene that bacteria will translate into the protein, the mRNA is isolated from eukaryotic cells and converted into cDNA. The cDNA is then transferred to bacterial cells, which can use it to direct the synthesis of the desired protein.

Probe 1 tags the same fragments of DNA in the rapist and the suspect but tags a different fragment of DNA in the victim. This probe indicates a match between the rapist and the suspect.

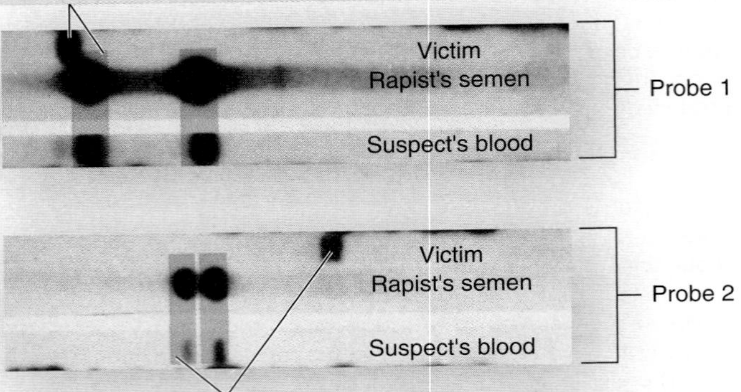

Like probe 1, probe 2 tags the same fragments of DNA in the rapist and the suspect but tags a different fragment of DNA in the victim. This probe indicates another match between the rapist and the suspect.

Figure 13.7 DNA fingerprints that led to conviction.

The two DNA probes seen here were used to characterize DNA isolated from the victim, the semen left by the rapist, and the suspect's blood. There is a clear match between the suspect's DNA and the DNA of the rapist's semen.

IN THE NEWS

Plant Witness for the Prosecution. The first case in which a murderer was convicted on plant DNA evidence was in Phoenix, Arizona. A pager left at the scene of the murder of a young woman led the police to a prime suspect. He admitted picking up the victim at a bar, but claimed she had robbed him of his wallet and pager. The crime scene squad examined the suspect's pickup truck and collected pods wedged by the front fender that were later identified as the fruits of the palo verde tree (*Cercidium spp.*). One squad member went back to the murder scene and found several palo verde trees, one recently damaged by a car. If the pods on the suspect's car could be linked to the damaged tree at the crime scene, they had their man. The detective heading the crime scene squad contacted a geneticist at the University of Arizona to establish evidence that would stand up in court that the pod indeed came from this very tree and no other. First, crucially, it was necessary to establish that individual palo verde trees have unique patterns of DNA. Sampling different palo verde trees at the murder scene and elsewhere quickly established that each palo verde tree is unique in its DNA pattern. Next, they compared the DNA pattern of a pod found on the suspect's truck to that of the damaged palo verde tree at the murder scene. They were the same. This placed the suspect at the scene of the murder beyond any doubt, and the suspect was convicted.

DNA Fingerprinting and Forensic Science

LEARNING OBJECTIVE 13.3.3 **Explain how DNA variation is used in forensic science to identify culprits in criminal investigations.**

DNA fingerprinting is a process used to compare samples of DNA. Because each person differs genetically from others in many ways, comparing DNA samples from two people can be used as a tool to tell them apart, much as detectives use fingerprints.

The process of DNA fingerprinting uses probes to fish out particular sequences to be compared from the thousands of other sequences in the human genome. Fragments of the subject's DNA are exposed to a "probe," a DNA fragment of a short, defined sequence that has been radioactively tagged so that it can be viewed. DNA fragments that have sequences complementary to the probes will bind the probes, which are then visible on autoradiographic film as dark bands. The resulting pattern of parallel bars on X-ray film resembles the line patterns of the universal price codes found on groceries, in essence a DNA "fingerprint" that can be used in criminal investigations and other identification applications.

Figure 13.7 shows the DNA fingerprints a prosecuting attorney presented in a rape trial in 1987. This trial was the first time DNA evidence was used in a court of law. Usually six to eight probes are used to identify the source of a DNA sample; two such probes are shown in **figure 13.7**. The probes are unique DNA sequences found in noncoding regions of human DNA that vary much more frequently from one individual to the next than do coding regions of the DNA. The chances of any two individuals, other than identical twins, having the same restriction pattern for these noncoding sequences varies from 1 in 800,000 to 1 in 1 billion, depending on the number of probes used. Since 1987, DNA fingerprinting has been admitted as evidence in thousands of court cases.

Putting the Concept to Work

If the suspect in the 1987 rape trial was innocent, what differences would you expect to see in the probes of figure 13.7?

PCR Amplification

LEARNING OBJECTIVE 13.3.4 **Explain how the tiny amount of DNA in a single hair can be enough for forensic analysis.**

Tiny DNA samples, as little as that found on a single human hair, can be magnified to many millions of copies by a process called **PCR** (for **polymerase chain reaction**). The use of DNA in forensic analysis often depends critically on PCR technology. In PCR, a double-stranded DNA fragment is heated so it becomes single-stranded; each of the strands is then copied by DNA polymerase to produce two double-stranded fragments. The fragments are heated again and copied again to produce four double-stranded fragments. This cycle is repeated many times, each time doubling the number of copies, creating enough DNA copies for analysis.

PCR is so powerful that a single hair will do. Biologists used to think that DNA was present only in the cells at the root of a hair. But we now know that hair follicle cells become incorporated into the growing shaft and their DNA is sealed in by the protein keratin.

Putting the Concept to Work

If a PCR cycle took 20 minutes, how long would it take to convert a single copy of a DNA fragment into a million copies?

13.4 Genetic Engineering and Medicine

LEARNING OBJECTIVE 13.4.1 Explain how genetic engineering has facilitated the production of medically important proteins.

Much of the excitement about genetic engineering has focused on its potential to improve medicine—to aid in curing and preventing illness. Major advances have been made in the production of proteins used to treat illness, and in the creation of new vaccines to combat infections.

Making "Magic Bullets"

Many genetic defects occur because our bodies fail to make critical proteins. Juvenile diabetes is such an illness. The body is unable to control levels of sugar in the blood because a critical protein, insulin, cannot be made. This failure can be overcome if the body can be supplied with the protein it lacks. The donated protein is in a very real sense a "magic bullet" to combat the body's inability to regulate itself.

Insulin is a type of chemical called a hormone that is produced in small quantities in one area of the body and is carried throughout the body in the bloodstream. Insulin, as discussed on pages 533 and 590, helps cells take up sugar from the blood.

Until recently, the principal problem with using regulatory proteins as drugs was in manufacturing the protein. Proteins that regulate the body's functions are typically present in the body in very low amounts, and this makes them difficult and expensive to obtain in quantity. With genetic engineering techniques, the problem of obtaining large amounts of rare proteins has been largely overcome. The cDNA of genes encoding medically important proteins are now introduced into bacteria. Because the host bacteria can be grown cheaply, large amounts of the desired protein can be easily isolated. In 1982 the U.S. Food and Drug Administration approved the use of human insulin produced from genetically engineered bacteria, the first commercial product of genetic engineering.

The use of genetic engineering techniques in bacteria has provided ample sources of therapeutic proteins, but the application extends beyond bacteria. Today hundreds of pharmaceutical companies around the world are busy producing other medically important proteins expanding the use of these genetic engineering techniques. A human gene added to the DNA of the mouse on the right in **figure 13.8** produces human growth hormone, allowing the mouse to grow larger than its twin.

The advantage of using genetic engineering is clearly seen with factor VIII, a protein that promotes blood clotting. A deficiency in factor VIII leads to hemophilia (discussed in chapter 10), an inherited disorder that is characterized by prolonged bleeding. For a long time, hemophiliacs received blood factor VIII that had been isolated from donated blood. Unfortunately, some of the donated blood had been infected with viruses such as HIV and hepatitis B, which were then unknowingly transmitted to those people who received blood transfusions. Today the use of genetically engineered factor VIII produced in the laboratory eliminates the risks associated with blood products obtained from other individuals.

Putting the Concept to Work

When a human gene is added to the DNA of a mouse, is it added as a DNA segment containing the gene, or as cDNA? Explain.

Eliminating Tooth Decay. The human mouth is home to billions of bacteria belonging to more than 300 species, but one species, *Streptococcus mutans*, is the major cause of tooth decay. It thrives on the organic film that coats tooth surfaces, and in the process of doing so produces lots of lactic acid, a corrosive chemical that gradually dissolves the protective enamel coating of the teeth. Genetic engineers have devised a way to block this path to the dentist's chair by replacing harmful *S. mutans* with a version of the species engineered to be more friendly to your mouth. To do this, they transferred into *S. mutans* a gene to increase production of an enzyme called urease. This enzyme converts urea, plentiful in the mouth, into ammonia, a base that neutralizes acid and creates conditions that enhance the buildup of tooth enamel. When the mouths of laboratory rats were colonized with this engineered form of *S. mutans*, they got far fewer cavities. Of course, this doesn't mean it will work with people. And even if it does, did anyone check the mouth odor of the rats?

Figure 13.8 Genetically engineered human growth hormone.

These two mice are genetically identical, but the large one has one extra gene: the gene encoding human growth hormone. The gene was added to the mouse's genome by genetic engineers and is now a stable part of the mouse's genetic makeup. In humans, growth hormone is used to treat various forms of dwarfism.

DNA and the Innocence Project

Every person's DNA is uniquely their own, a sequence of nucleotides found in no other person. Like a molecular social security number a billion digits long, the nucleotide sequence of an individual's genes can provide proof-positive identification of a rapist or murderer from DNA left at the scene of a crime—proof more reliable than fingerprints, more reliable than an eye witness, even more reliable than a confession by the suspect.

Never was this demonstrated more clearly than on May 16, 2006 in a Rochester, New York courtroom. There a judge freed convicted murderer Douglas Warney after ten years in prison.

The murder occurred on New Year's Day in 1996. The bloody body of William Beason, a prominent community activist, was found in his bed. Police called in all the usual suspects, in this case everyone known to be an acquaintance of the victim. Warney, an unemployed 34-year-old who had dropped out of school in the eighth grade, committed robberies, and worked as a male hustler, learned that detectives wanted to speak to him about the killing, and went to the police station for questioning. Within hours he was charged with murder.

Warney's interrogation was not recorded, but it resulted in a signed confession based on the words that the detective sergeant said Warney uttered, a confession that contained accurate details about the murder scene that had not been made public. Warney said that the victim was wearing a nightgown and had been cooking chicken in a pot, and that the murderer had used a 12-inch serrated knife. The case against him in court rested almost entirely on these vivid details. Even though Warney recanted his confession at his trial, the accuracy of his confession was damning. The details that Warney provided to the sergeant could have come only from someone who was present at the crime scene.

There were problems with his confession, brought out at trial. Three elements of the signed statement's account of that night were clearly not true. It said Warney had driven to the victim's house in his brother's car, but his brother did not own a car; it said Warney disposed of his bloody clothes after the stabbing in the garbage can behind the house, but the can, buried in snow from the day of the crime, did not contain bloody clothes; it named a relative of Warney as an accomplice, but that relative was in a secure rehabilitation center on that day.

The most difficult bit of evidence to match to the written confession was blood found at the scene that was not that of the victim. Drops of a second person's blood were found on the floor and on a towel. The difficult bit was that the blood was a different blood type than Warney's.

At trial, prosecutors pointed out that the blood could have come from the accomplice mentioned in the confession, and pounded away on the point that the details in the confession could only have come from first-hand knowledge of the crime.

After a short trial, Douglas Warney was convicted of the murder of William Beason and sentenced to 25 years.

When appeals failed, Mr. Warney in 2004 sought help from the Innocence Project, a non-profit legal clinic that helps identify wrongly-convicted individuals and secure their freedom. Set up at the Benjamin N. Cardozo School of Law in New York by lawyers Barry Scheck and Peter Neufeld, the Innocence Project specializes in using DNA technology to establish innocence.

The Innocence Project staff petitioned the court for additional DNA testing using new sensitive DNA probes, arguing that this might disclose evidence that would have resulted in a different verdict. The judge refused, ruling that the possibility that the blood found at the scene of the crime might match that of a criminal already in the state databank was "too speculative and improbable" to warrant the new tests.

Someone in the prosecutor's office must have been persuaded, however. Without notifying Warney's legal team, Project Innocence, or the court, this good Samaritan arranged for new DNA tests on the blood drops found at the crime scene. When compared to the New York State criminal DNA database, they hit a strong match. The blood was that of Eldred Johnson, in prison for slitting his landlady's throat in Utica two weeks before Beason was killed.

When confronted, the prisoner Johnson readily admitted to the stabbing of Beason. He said he was the sole killer, and had never met Douglas Warney.

This leaves the interesting question of how Warney's signed confession came to include such accurate information about the crime scene. It now appears he may have been fed critical details about the crime scene by the homicide detective leading the investigation, a Sergeant Gropp. It seems Gropp's partner had stepped out to get some papers when the confession was obtained. Sergeant Gropp died in March, 2006.

DNA testing has become a pillar of the American criminal justice system. It has provided key evidence that has established the guilt of thousands of suspects beyond any reasonable doubt—and, as you see here, also provided the evidence that our criminal justice system sometimes convicts and sentences innocent people. Over more than a decade, the Innocence Project and other similar efforts have cleared hundreds of convicted people, strong proof that wrongful convictions are not isolated or rare events. DNA testing opens a window of hope for the wrongly convicted.

A DNA Timeline

In 2000, Craig Venter of Celera, President Clinton, and Francis Collins of the Human Genome Project announce the human genome.

2006 Japanese cell biologist Shinya Yamanaka uses only four transcription factors to reprogram adult skin cells into embryonic stem cells, opening the possibility of ethical therapeutic cloning.

2000 Two teams, led by Craig Venter and Francis Collins, complete draft sequences of the human genome.

1998 Andrew Fire and Craig Mello discover RNA interference, leading to a Nobel Prize only eight years later.

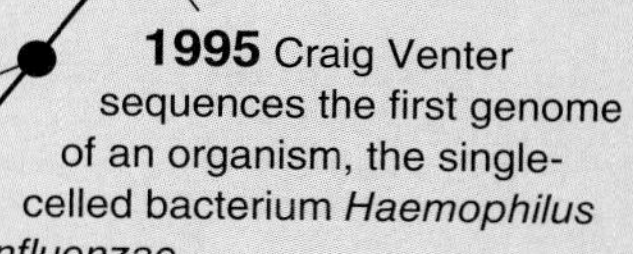

1996 Ian Wilmut uses the nucleus of an adult cell to successfully clone a sheep, "Dolly."

1995 Craig Venter sequences the first genome of an organism, the single-celled bacterium *Haemophilus influenzae*.

1992 Lawyers Barry Scheck and Peter Neufeld start the Innocence Project, whose efforts have cleared more than 120 wrongly convicted people through the use of DNA technology.

1985 British geneticist Alec Jeffreys invents DNA fingerprinting, the use of DNA in forensic analysis to match people to biological tissue found at crime scenes.

1983 Kary Mullis develops the polymerase chain reaction (PCR), allowing amplification and analysis of minute traces of DNA, such as that found in a single human hair.

1973 Herbert Boyer and Stanley Cohen invent genetic engineering, successfully inserting an amphibian RNA gene into a different organism.

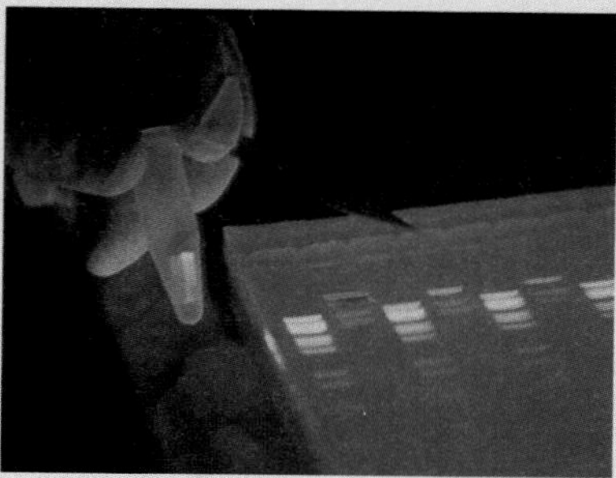

1964 Marshall Nirenberg and Har Khorana break the genetic code, learning which three-letter code words of DNA correspond to each amino acid in proteins.

1956 Vernon Ingram shows that sickle cell disease is due to a DNA mutation leading to a single amino acid change in the protein hemoglobin.

1953 James Watson and Francis Crick propose that the DNA molecule is a double helix, each strand's nucleotide sequence complementary to the other.

1952 Alfred Hershey and Martha Chase demonstrate that viruses inject DNA into bacteria to reproduce, not protein; this experiment convinces most biologists that DNA is the genetic material.

1950 Graduate student Ray Gosling, working in the lab of British biochemist Maurice Wilkins, obtains the first clear X-ray diffraction patterns of DNA; over the next two years, Rosalind Franklin and he produce ever-clearer pictures.

1944 American biochemist Oswald Avery purifies Griffith's transforming principle, and demonstrates conclusively that it is DNA, although this conclusion was not appreciated at first.

1928 British microbiologist Frederick Griffith discovers transformation of living bacteria by material from dead ones.

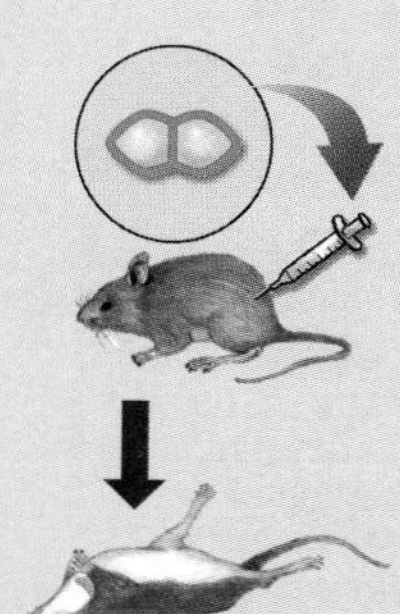

1869 German chemist Friedrich Miescher discovers DNA, called "nucleic acid" because it was isolated from sperm nuclei and is slightly acidic.

Powerful New Vaccines

LEARNING OBJECTIVE 13.4.2 Describe how a piggyback vaccine is constructed and used.

Another area of potential significance involves the use of genetic engineering to produce **subunit vaccines** against disease-causing viruses. Genes encoding part of the protein-polysaccharide coat of a virus like herpes simplex or hepatitis B are spliced into a fragment of the vaccinia (cowpox) virus genome (figure 13.9). The vaccinia virus, which is essentially harmless to humans, was used by British physician Edward Jenner more than 200 years ago in his pioneering vaccinations against smallpox. Vaccines produced in this way, also known as **piggyback vaccines,** elicit an immune response in the recipient against the coat of the disease-causing virus.

In 1995 the first clinical trials began for a new kind of vaccine, called a **DNA vaccine**. DNA containing a viral gene is injected into and taken up by the body, where the gene is expressed. The infected cells trigger a cellular immune response, in which blood cells known as killer T cells attack the infected cells. The first DNA vaccines spliced an influenza virus gene into a plasmid, which was then injected into mice. The mice developed strong cellular immune responses against influenza. The approach offers great promise.

In 2010 the first effective **cancer vaccines** were announced. A cancer vaccine is therapeutic rather than preventive, stimulating the immune system to attack a tumor in the same way invading microbes are attacked. The first cancer vaccine approved for clinical use employs proteins from prostate cancer cells to induce the immune system to attack prostate cancer tumors.

Putting the Concept to Work

Is a cancer vaccine also a piggyback vaccine?

Figure 13.9 Constructing a subunit, or piggyback, vaccine for the herpes simplex virus.

The harmless vaccinia virus can be used as a vector to carry a herpes simplex viral coat gene in a subunit, or piggyback, vaccine. Constructing this subunit vaccine begins with ❶ extracting the herpes simplex viral DNA and ❷ isolating a gene that codes for a protein on the surface of the virus. The cowpox viral DNA is extracted and cleaved ❸, and the herpes gene is combined with the cowpox DNA ❹. The recombinant DNA is inserted into a cowpox virus. Many copies of the recombinant virus, which have the outside coat of a herpes virus, are produced. When this recombinant virus is injected into a human ❺, the immune system produces antibodies directed against the coat of the recombinant virus ❻. The person therefore develops an immunity to the virus.

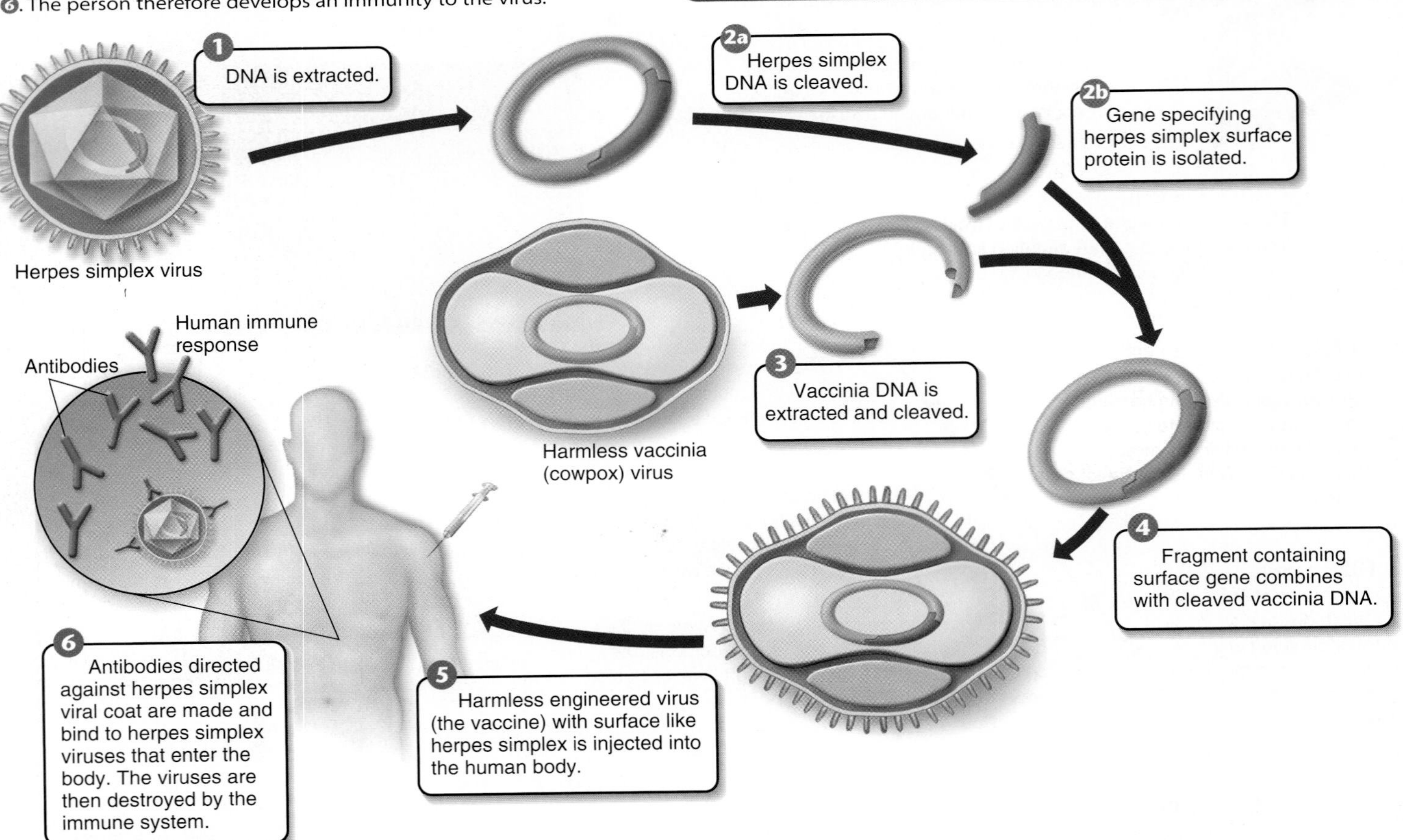

1 DNA is extracted.
Herpes simplex virus
2a Herpes simplex DNA is cleaved.
2b Gene specifying herpes simplex surface protein is isolated.
3 Vaccinia DNA is extracted and cleaved.
Harmless vaccinia (cowpox) virus
4 Fragment containing surface gene combines with cleaved vaccinia DNA.
5 Harmless engineered virus (the vaccine) with surface like herpes simplex is injected into the human body.
Human immune response
Antibodies
6 Antibodies directed against herpes simplex viral coat are made and bind to herpes simplex viruses that enter the body. The viruses are then destroyed by the immune system.

13.5 Genetic Engineering and Agriculture

LEARNING OBJECTIVE 13.5.1 Explain how genetic engineering is being used to increase food production.

Pest Resistance

An important effort of genetic engineers in agriculture has involved making crops resistant to insect pests without spraying with pesticides, a great saving to the environment. Consider cotton. Its fibers are a major source of raw material for clothing throughout the world, yet the plant itself can hardly survive in a field because many insects attack it. Over 40% of the chemical insecticides used today are employed to kill insects that eat cotton plants. The world's environment would greatly benefit if these thousands of tons of insecticide were not needed.

One successful alternative uses a kind of soil bacterium, *Bacillus thuringiensis* (Bt) that produces a protein that is toxic when eaten by crop pests. When the gene producing the Bt protein was inserted into the chromosomes of tomatoes, the plants began to manufacture Bt protein. While not harmful to humans, it makes the tomatoes highly toxic to hornworms (one of the most serious pests of commercial tomato crops) and cotton borers (the chief pests of cotton crops).

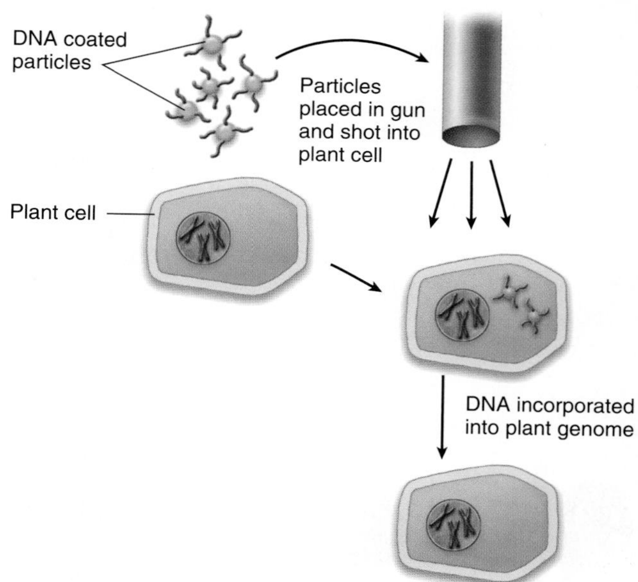

Figure 13.10 Shooting genes into cells.

A DNA particle gun, also called a gene gun, fires tungsten or gold particles coated with DNA into plant cells. The DNA coated particles pass through the cell wall and into the cell, where the DNA is incorporated into the plant cell's DNA. The gene encoded by the DNA is expressed.

Herbicide Resistance

A major advance has been the creation of crop plants that are resistant to the herbicide *glyphosate,* a powerful biodegradable herbicide that kills most actively growing plants. Glyphosate is used in orchards and agricultural fields to control weeds. Growing plants need to make a lot of protein, and glyphosate stops them from making protein by destroying an enzyme necessary for the manufacture of so-called aromatic amino acids (that is, amino acids that contain a ring structure). Humans are unaffected by glyphosate because we don't make aromatic amino acids—we obtain them from plants we eat! To make crop plants resistant to this powerful plant killer, genetic engineers screened thousands of organisms until they found a species of bacteria that could make aromatic amino acids in the presence of glyphosate. They then isolated the gene encoding the resistant enzyme and successfully introduced the gene into plants. They inserted the gene into the plants using DNA particle guns, also called gene guns. You can see in figure 13.10 how a DNA particle gun works. Small tungsten or gold pellets are coated with DNA (red in the figure) that contains the gene of interest and placed in the DNA particle gun. The DNA gun literally shoots the gene into plant cells in culture where the gene can be incorporated in the plant genome and then expressed. Plants that have been genetically engineered in this way are shown in figure 13.11. The two plants on top were genetically engineered to be resistant to glyphosate, the herbicide that killed the two plants at the bottom of the photo.

Figure 13.11 Genetically engineered herbicide resistance.

All four of these petunia plants were exposed to equal doses of an herbicide. The two on *top* were genetically engineered to be resistant to glyphosate, the active ingredient in the herbicide, whereas the two dead ones on the *bottom* were not.

Putting the Concept to Work

What sort of bacterial gene would enable bacterial cells to make aromatic amino acids in the presence of glyphosate?

More Nutritious Crops

LEARNING OBJECTIVE 13.5.2 Describe how researchers genetically engineered a more nutritious type of rice.

The cultivation of genetically modified (GM) crops of corn, cotton, soybeans, and other plants (**table 13.3**) has become commonplace in the United States. In 2010, 90% of soybeans in the United States were planted with seeds genetically modified to be herbicide resistant. The result has been that less tillage is needed and as a consequence soil erosion is greatly reduced. Pest-resistant GM corn in 2010 comprised over 86% of all corn planted in the United States, and pest-resistant GM cotton comprised 93% of all cotton.

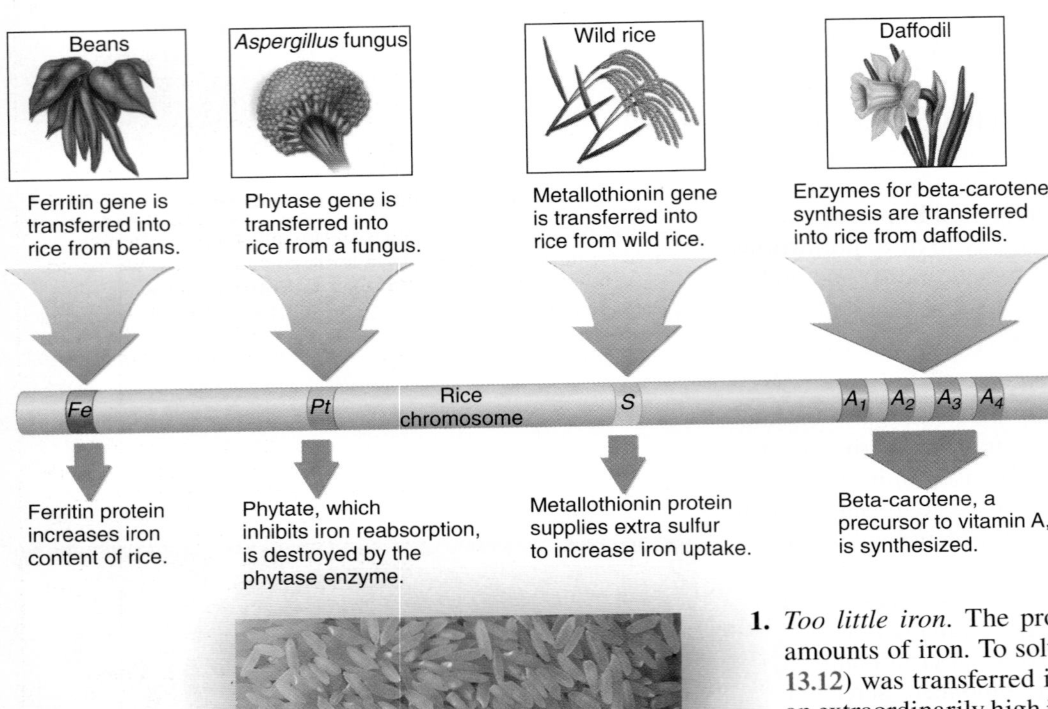
Beans
Aspergillus fungus
Wild rice
Daffodil
Ferritin gene is transferred into rice from beans.
Phytase gene is transferred into rice from a fungus.
Metallothionin gene is transferred into rice from wild rice.
Enzymes for beta-carotene synthesis are transferred into rice from daffodils.
Fe
Pt
Rice chromosome
S
A1 A2 A3 A4
Ferritin protein increases iron content of rice.
Phytate, which inhibits iron reabsorption, is destroyed by the phytase enzyme.
Metallothionin protein supplies extra sulfur to increase iron uptake.
Beta-carotene, a precursor to vitamin A, is synthesized.

Figure 13.12 Transgenic "golden" rice.

Golden rice goes a long way toward addressing serious nutritional deficiencies in one of the world's major food crops. The development of this transgenic rice by researchers is the first key step toward real progress. Many years will be required to breed the golden rice genes into lines adapted to local conditions.

IMPLICATION FOR YOU The "Free Rice Game" on the Internet (www.freerice.com) asks you quiz questions. For each answer you get right, 20 grains of rice are donated to the UN World Food Program to help end hunger. Since its inception in October 2007, over 50 billion grains of rice have been donated, about 20,000,000 grains a day. For each answer you get right, you then get a harder question to attempt. How many questions in a row do you think you can get right? (The average is four.)

The real promise of plant genetic engineering is to produce genetically modified plants with desirable traits that directly benefit the consumer. One recent advance, nutritionally improved "golden" rice, gives us a hint of what is to come. In developing countries, large numbers of people live on simple diets that are poor sources of iron and vitamin A. Iron deficiency affects about 30% of the world population, and an estimated 250 million children are deficient in vitamin A. These deficiencies are especially severe in developing countries where the major staple food is rice.

To solve the problem of dietary iron deficiency among rice eaters, gene engineers first asked why rice is such a poor source of dietary iron. The problem, and the answer, proved to have three parts:

1. *Too little iron.* The proteins of rice endosperm have unusually low amounts of iron. To solve this problem, a ferritin gene (Fe in **figure 13.12**) was transferred into rice from beans. Ferritin is a protein with an extraordinarily high iron content, and so it greatly increased the iron content of the rice.
2. *Inhibition of iron absorption by the intestine.* Rice contains an unusually high concentration of a chemical called phytate, which inhibits iron absorption in the intestine—it stops your body from taking up the iron in the rice. To solve this problem, a gene encoding an enzyme called phytase (Pt) that destroys phytate was transferred into rice from a fungus.
3. *Too little sulfur for efficient iron absorption.* The human body requires sulfur for the uptake of iron, and rice has very little of it. To solve this problem, a gene encoding a sulfur-rich protein (S) was transferred into rice from wild rice.

To solve the problem of vitamin A deficiency, the same approach was taken. First, the problem was identified. It turns out rice goes only partway toward making vitamin A; there are no enzymes in rice to catalyze the last four steps. To solve the problem, genes encoding these four enzymes (abbreviated A_1 A_2 A_3 A_4) were added to rice from a flower, the daffodil.

Putting the Concept to Work

Seven genes were transferred into GM golden rice. How could researchers ensure that the genes were expressed in the rice cells?

How Do We Measure the Potential Risks of Genetically Modified Crops?

LEARNING OBJECTIVE 13.5.3 **Assess whether GM foods are safe to eat, and whether GM crops are harmful to the environment.**

Is Eating Genetically Modified Food Dangerous? Many consumers worry that when genetic engineers introduce novel genes into genetically modified (GM) crops, there may be dangerous consequences for the food we eat. The introduction of glyphosate resistance into soybeans is an example. Is the soybean that results nutritionally different? No. But could introduced proteins like the enzyme making the GM soybeans glyphosate tolerant cause a fatal immune reaction in some people? Because the potential danger of allergic reactions is quite real, every time a protein-encoding gene is introduced into a GM crop it is necessary to carry out extensive tests of the introduced protein's allergen potential. No GM crop currently being produced in the United States contains a protein that acts as an allergen to humans. On this score, then, the risk of genetic engineering to the food supply seems to be slight.

Are GM Crops Harmful to the Environment? Those concerned about the widespread use of GM crops raise three legitimate concerns:

1. *Harm to Other Organisms.* Results from a small laboratory experiment suggested that pollen from Bt corn could harm larvae from the Monarch butterfly. While this preliminary report received considerable publicity, subsequent studies suggest little possibility of harm. Monarch butterflies lay their eggs on milkweed, not corn, and there is little if any milkweed growing in or near cornfields.
2. *Resistance.* All insecticides and herbicides used in agriculture share the problem that pests eventually evolve resistance to them, in much the same way that bacterial populations evolve resistance to antibiotics. To prevent this, farmers are required to plant at least 20% non-Bt crops alongside Bt crops to provide refuges where insect populations are not under selection pressure and in this way to slow the development of resistance. As a result, despite the widespread use of Bt crops like corn, soybeans, and cotton since 1996, there are as of yet only a few cases of insects developing resistance to Bt plants in the field. Unfortunately, the same restrictions have not been required for farmers using the herbicide glyphosate, leading to a different result: By the year 2010, glyphosate-resistant weeds had been reported by upset farmers in 22 states.
3. *Gene Flow.* How about the possibility that introduced genes will pass from GM crops to their wild or weedy relatives? For the major GM crops, there is usually no potential relative around to receive the modified gene from the GM crop. There are no wild relatives of soybeans in Europe, for example. Thus there can be no gene escape from GM soybeans in Europe, any more than genes can flow from you to your pet dog or cat. However—and this is a big however—for secondary crops only now being genetically modified, studies suggest that it will be difficult to prevent GM crops from interbreeding with surrounding relatives to create new hybrids.

Putting the Concept to Work

What would you recommend to farmers experiencing glyphosate-resistant weeds in their fields?

TABLE 13.3 Genetically Modified Crops

Rice 	Genes have been added to commercial rice from daffodils for vitamin A, and from beans, fungi, and wild rice to supply dietary iron; transgenic strains that are cold-tolerant are under development.
Wheat 	New strains of wheat, resistant to the herbicide glyphosate, greatly reduce the need for tilling and so reduce loss of topsoil.
Soybean  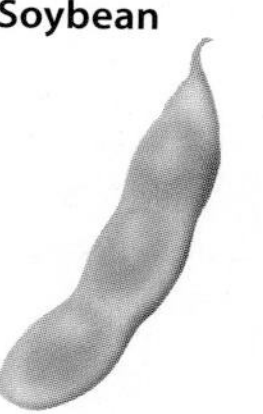	A major animal feed crop, soybeans tolerant of the herbicide glyphosate were used in over 90% of U.S. soybean acreage in 2010. Varieties are being developed that contain the *Bt* gene, to protect the crop from insect pests without chemical pesticides. The nutritional value of soybean crops is being improved by genetic engineers in several ways, including transgenic varieties with high tryptophan (soybeans are poor in this essential amino acid), reduced trans-fatty acids, and enhanced omega-3 (beneficial) fatty acids, common in fish oil but low in plants.
Corn 	Corn varieties resistant to insect pests (Bt corn) are widely planted (86% of U.S. acreage); varieties also tolerant of the herbicide glyphosate have been recently developed. Varieties that are drought-resistant are being developed, as well as nutritionally improved lines with high lysine, vitamin A, and high levels of the unsaturated fat oleic acid, which reduces harmful cholesterol and so prevents clogged arteries.
Cotton 	Cotton crops are attacked by cotton bollworm, budworm, and other lepidopteran insects; more than 40% of all chemical pesticide tonnage worldwide is applied to cotton. A form of the *Bt* gene toxic to all lepidopterans but harmless to other insects has transformed cotton to a crop that requires few chemical pesticides. Over 93% of U.S. acreage is Bt cotton.
Peanut 	The lesser cornstalk borer causes serious damage to peanut crops. An insect-resistant variety is under development by gene engineers to control this pest.
Potato 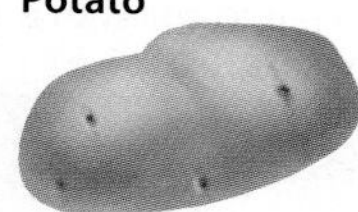	Verticillium wilt (a fungal disease) infects the water-conducting tissues of potatoes, reducing crop yields 40%. An antifungal gene from alfalfa reduces infections sixfold.
Canola 	Canola, a major vegetable oil and animal feed crop, is typically grown in narrow rows with little cultivation, requiring extensive application of chemical herbicides to keep down weeds. New glyphosate-tolerant varieties require far less chemical treatment. 93% of U.S. canola acreage planted is gene-modified canola.

The Revolution in Cell Technology

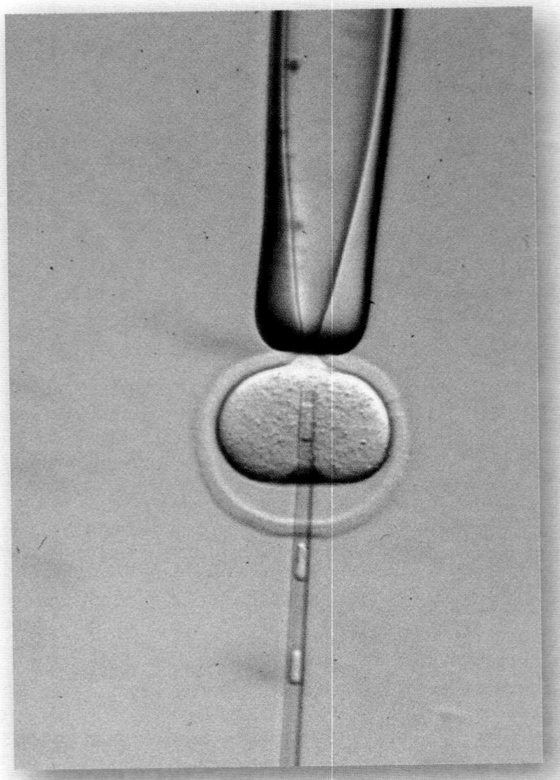

Figure 13.13 A cloning experiment.

In this photo, a nucleus is being injected from a micropipette *(bottom)* into an enucleated egg cell held in place by a pipette.

13.6 Reproductive Cloning

LEARNING OBJECTIVE 13.6.1 Describe experiments that have demonstrated the possibility of cloning animals from adult tissue.

One of the most active and exciting areas of biology involves recently developed approaches to manipulating animal cells. In this section, you will encounter three areas where landmark progress is being made in cell technology: reproductive cloning of farm animals, stem cell research, and gene therapy. Advances in cell technology hold the promise of revolutionizing our lives.

The idea of cloning animals was first suggested in 1938 by German embryologist Hans Spemann (called the "father of modern embryology"), who proposed what he called a "fantastical experiment": remove the nucleus from an egg cell (creating an enucleated egg) and put in its place a nucleus from another cell. When attempted many years later (figure 13.13), this experiment actually succeeded in frogs, sheep, monkeys, and many other animals. However, only donor nuclei extracted from early embryos seemed to work. After repeated failures using nuclei from adult cells, many researchers became convinced that the nuclei of animal cells become irreversibly committed to a developmental pathway after the first few cell divisions of the developing embryo.

Wilmut's Lamb

Then, in the 1990s, a key insight was made in Scotland by geneticist Keith Campbell, a specialist in studying the cell cycle of agricultural animals. Recall from chapter 8 that the division cycle of eukaryotic cells progresses in several stages. Campbell reasoned, "Maybe the egg and the donated nucleus need to be at the same stage in the cell cycle." This proved to be a key insight. In 1994 researchers succeeded in cloning farm animals from advanced embryos by first starving the cells, so that they paused at the beginning of the cell cycle. Two starved cells are thus synchronized at the same point in the cell cycle.

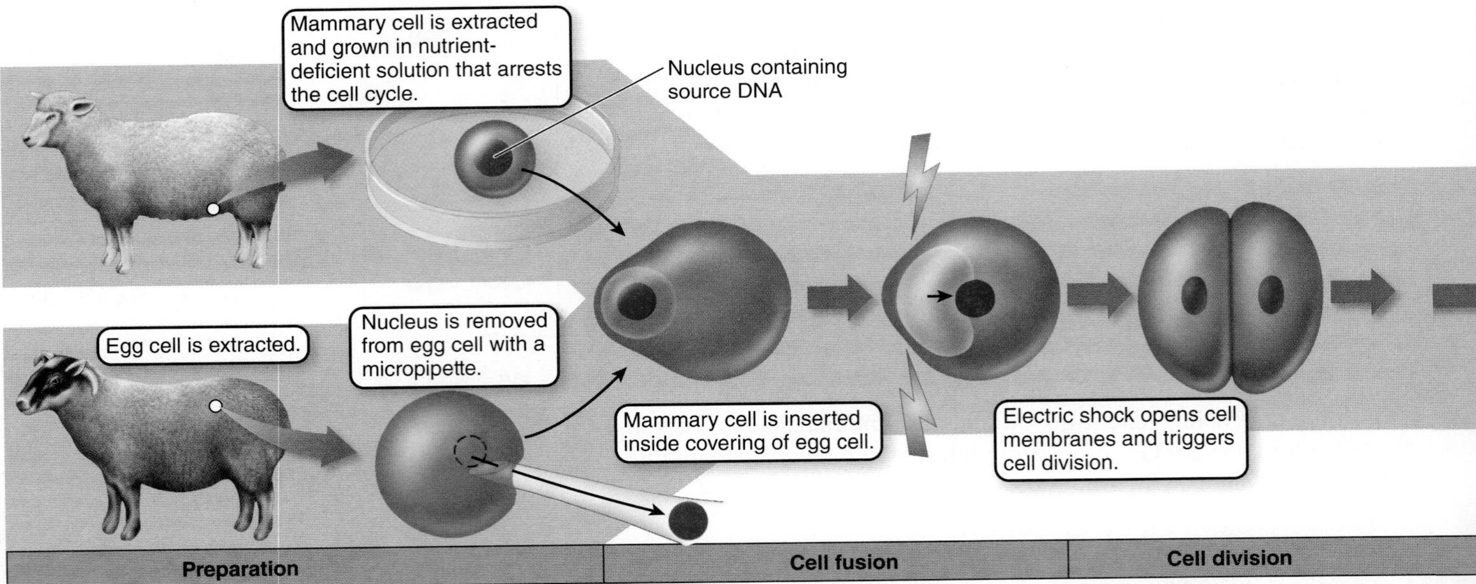

Mammary cell is extracted and grown in nutrient-deficient solution that arrests the cell cycle.
Nucleus containing source DNA
Egg cell is extracted.
Nucleus is removed from egg cell with a micropipette.
Mammary cell is inserted inside covering of egg cell.
Electric shock opens cell membranes and triggers cell division.
Preparation
Cell fusion
Cell division

Figure 13.14 Wilmut's animal cloning experiment.

Campbell's colleague Ian Wilmut then attempted the key breakthrough, the experiment that had been eluding researchers: He set out to transfer the nucleus from an adult differentiated cell into an enucleated egg, and to allow the resulting embryo to grow and develop in a surrogate mother, hopefully producing a healthy animal (**figure 13.14**). Approximately five months later, on July 5, 1996, the mother gave birth to a lamb. This lamb, "Dolly," was the first successful clone generated from an adult animal cell. Dolly grew into a healthy adult, and as you can see in the photo at the beginning of this chapter, she went on to have healthy offspring normal in every respect.

Progress with Reproductive Cloning

Since Dolly's birth in 1996, scientists have successfully cloned a wide variety of farm animals with desired characteristics, including cows, pigs, goats, horses, and donkeys, as well as pets like cats and dogs. Snuppy, the puppy in **figure 13.15**, was the first dog to be cloned. For most farm animals, cloning procedures have become increasingly efficient since Dolly was cloned. However, the development of clones into adults tends to go unexpectedly haywire. Almost none survive to live a normal life span.

The Importance of Gene Reprogramming

What is going wrong? It turns out that as mammalian eggs and sperm mature, their DNA is conditioned by the parent female or male, a process called reprogramming. Chemical changes are made to the DNA that alter when particular genes are expressed without changing the nucleotide sequences. In the years since Dolly, scientists have learned a lot about gene reprogramming, also called **epigenetics.** Epigenetics works by blocking the cell's ability to read certain genes. A gene is locked in the off position by adding a $—CH_3$ (methyl) group to some of its cytosine nucleotides. After a gene has been altered like this, the polymerase protein that is supposed to "read" the gene can no longer recognize it. The gene has been shut off.

We are only beginning to learn how to reprogram human DNA, so any attempt to clone a human is simply throwing stones in the dark, hoping to hit a target we cannot see. For this and many other reasons, human reproductive cloning is regarded as highly unethical.

Putting the Concept to Work

Why didn't gene reprogramming of gamete DNA prevent the successful cloning of Dolly?

Figure 13.15 Cloning the family pet.

This puppy named "Snuppy" is the first dog cloned. Beside him to the left, is the adult male dog who provided the skin cell from which Snuppy was cloned. The dog in the photo on the right was Snuppy's surrogate mother.

IMPLICATION FOR YOU Do you have a dog or cat? Do you think it would be ethical for you to have your dog or cat cloned when it grows old, so you can continue to enjoy its company for many more years? Then, in later years, do you clone the clone? What, if any, limits would you place on this process? Discuss.

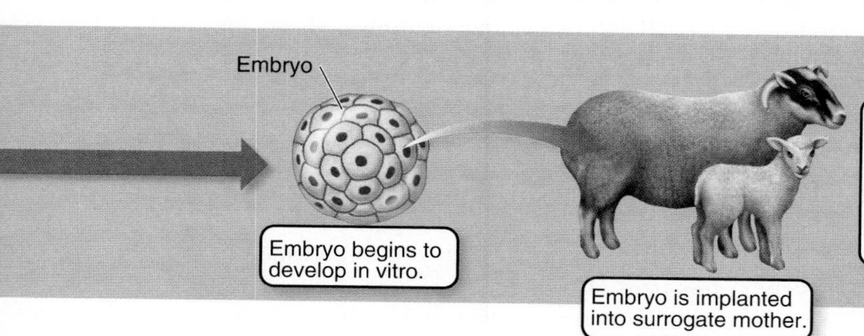

Embryo
Embryo begins to develop in vitro.
Embryo is implanted into surrogate mother.
After a five-month pregnancy, a lamb genetically identical to the sheep from which the mammary cell was extracted is born.
Development
Implantation
Birth of clone

Growth to adulthood

Figure 13.16 Human embryonic stem cells (×20).

This mass is a colony of undifferentiated human embryonic stem cells growing in tissue culture and surrounded by fibroblasts (elongated cells) that serve as a "feeder layer."

Figure 13.17 Promoting a cure for Parkinson's.

Michael J. Fox, with whom you may be familiar as a star of the *Back to the Future* film series and the TV show *Family Ties*, is a victim of Parkinson's disease, and a prominent spokesman for those who suffer from it. Here you see him testifying before the U.S. Senate (along with fellow advocate Mary Tyler Moore) on the need for vigorous efforts to support research seeking a cure.

13.7 Stem Cell Therapy

LEARNING OBJECTIVE 13.7.1 Describe how stem cells offer the possibility of replacing damaged human tissues.

You can see a mass of human embryonic stem cells in figure 13.16. Many are **totipotent**—able to form any body tissue, and even an entire adult animal. What is an embryonic stem cell, and why is it totipotent? To answer this question, we need to consider for a moment where an embryo comes from. At the dawn of a human life, a sperm fertilizes an egg to create a single cell destined to become a child. As development commences, that cell begins to divide, producing after four divisions a small mass of 16 **embryonic stem cells.** Each of these embryonic stem cells has all of the genes needed to produce a normal individual.

As development proceeds, some of these embryonic stem cells become committed to forming specific types of tissues, such as nerve tissues, and, after this step is taken, cannot ever produce any other kind of cell. For example, in nerve tissue they are then called *nerve stem cells.* Others become specialized to produce blood cells, others to produce muscle tissue, and still others to form the other tissues of the body. Each major tissue is formed from its own kind of tissue-specific **adult stem cell.** Because an adult stem cell forms only that one kind of tissue, it is not totipotent.

Using Stem Cells to Repair Damaged Tissues

Stem cells offer the exciting possibility of restoring damaged tissues. To understand how embryonic stem cells could be used to repair damaged tissue, follow along in figure 13.18. A few days after fertilization, an embryonic stage called the *blastocyst* forms ❶. Embryonic stem cells are harvested from its inner cell mass or from cells of the embryo at a later stage ❷. These embryonic stem cells can be grown in tissue culture (see figure 13.16) and in principle be induced to form any type of tissue in the body ❸. The resulting healthy tissue can then be injected into the patient where it will grow and replace damaged tissue ❹. Alternatively, where possible, adult stem cells can be isolated and when injected back into the body, can form certain types of tissue cells.

Both adult and embryonic stem cell transfer experiments have been carried out successfully in mice. Adult blood stem cells have been used to cure leukemia. Heart muscle cells grown from mouse embryonic stem cells have successfully replaced the damaged heart tissue of a living mouse. In other experiments, damaged spinal neurons have been partially repaired. In mouse brains, DOPA-producing neurons, whose progressive loss is responsible for Parkinson's disease, have been successfully replaced with embryonic stem cells, as have the islet cells of the pancreas, whose loss leads to juvenile diabetes. Because the course of development is broadly similar in all mammals, these experiments in mice suggest exciting possibilities for stem cell therapy in humans. The hope is that individuals with conditions such as Parkinson's disease (figure 13.17) might be partially or fully cured with stem cell therapy. As you might imagine, work proceeds intensively in this field of research.

There are ethical objections to using embryonic stems cells, but new experimental results hint at ways around this ethical maze. In 2007, researchers in two independent laboratories reported that they had engineered embryonic stemlike cells from normal adult human skin cells. The cells they created were pluripotent—they could differentiate into many different cell types. Whether pluripotency extends to totipotency is still being investigated. How were these cells transformed? The essential clue came six years earlier,

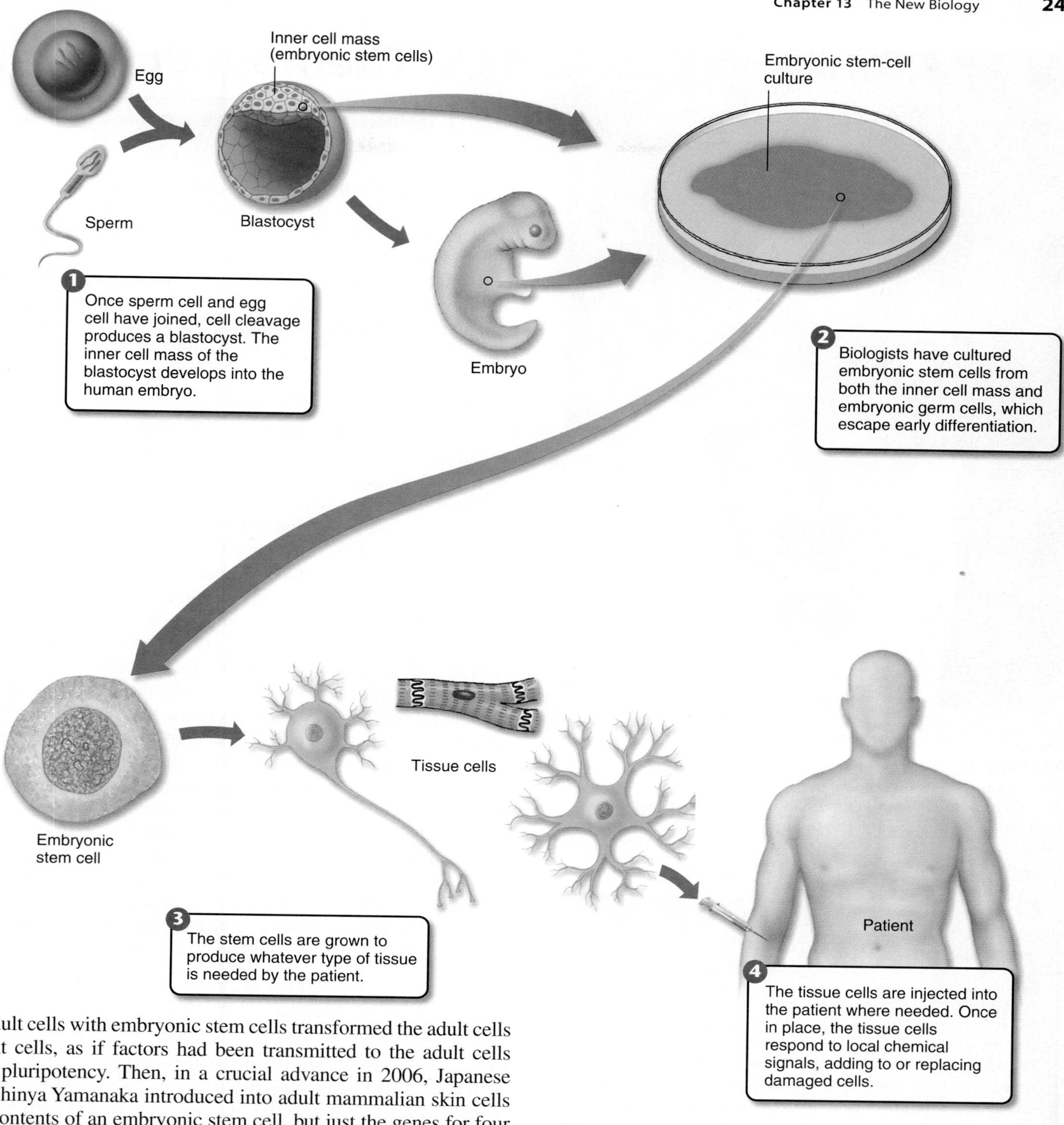

Egg
Inner cell mass
(embryonic stem cells)
Embryonic stem-cell
culture
Sperm
Blastocyst
1
Once sperm cell and egg cell have joined, cell cleavage produces a blastocyst. The inner cell mass of the blastocyst develops into the human embryo.
Embryo
2
Biologists have cultured embryonic stem cells from both the inner cell mass and embryonic germ cells, which escape early differentiation.
Embryonic
stem cell
Tissue cells
Patient
3
The stem cells are grown to produce whatever type of tissue is needed by the patient.
4
The tissue cells are injected into the patient where needed. Once in place, the tissue cells respond to local chemical signals, adding to or replacing damaged cells.

Figure 13.18 Using embryonic stem cells to restore damaged tissue.

Embryonic stem cells can develop into any body tissue. Methods are being developed for growing the tissue and using it in adults to repair damaged tissue, such as the brain cells of multiple sclerosis patients, heart muscle, and spinal nerves.

when fusing adult cells with embryonic stem cells transformed the adult cells into pluripotent cells, as if factors had been transmitted to the adult cells that conferred pluripotency. Then, in a crucial advance in 2006, Japanese cell biologist Shinya Yamanaka introduced into adult mammalian skin cells not the entire contents of an embryonic stem cell, but just the genes for four transcription factors. The genes were transferred into the skin cells carried piggyback on viruses. Once inside, these four factors induced a series of events that converted the adult skin cells to pluripotency. In effect, he had found a way to reprogram the adult cells to be embryonic stem cells. From proof of principle in a laboratory culture dish to actual medical application is still a leap, but the possibility is exciting.

Putting the Concept to Work

Can you see any ethical objection to treating Michael J. Fox's Parkinson's with pluripotent cells obtained from his skin?

Figure 13.19 Embryonic stem cells growing in cell culture.

These embryonic stem cells are derived from early human embryos and will grow indefinitely in tissue culture. When transplanted, they can sometimes be induced to form new cells of the adult tissue into which they have been placed. This suggests exciting therapeutic uses.

IN THE NEWS

Turning One Cell Type into Another. In 2008, doctors at Children's Hospital in Boston set out to cure type I diabetes, in which individuals lack the pancreatic beta cells needed to produce insulin. For two years they sifted through more than 1,000 transcription factors (proteins that tell cells which genes to turn on and off) to find ones that would turn the normal cells of the pancreas into beta cells. In the end they found that just three were needed to do the trick. When the three factors were injected into living mice whose islet cells had been destroyed, normal cells in the pancreas were turned into insulin-producing beta cells. The added insulin led to significant lowering of blood sugar levels, although not enough cells were transformed to cure diabetes. The new beta cells remained stable for many months. Although work needs to be done to improve efficiency, and a mouse is not a human, this result is proof in principle that adult cell transformation can work to cure tissue diseases.

13.8 Therapeutic Cloning

LEARNING OBJECTIVE 13.8.1 Distinguish between reproductive and therapeutic cloning.

While exciting, the therapeutic uses of stem cells to cure leukemia, type I diabetes, Parkinson's disease, damaged heart muscle, and injured nerve tissue were all achieved in experiments carried out using strains of mice without functioning immune systems. Why is this important? Because had these mice possessed fully functional immune systems, they almost certainly would have rejected the implanted stem cells as foreign. In humans with normal immune systems, their bodies might reject transplanted stem cells simply because they are from another individual.

Cloning to Achieve Immune Acceptance

Early in 2001 a research team at the Rockefeller University reported a way around this potentially serious problem. Their solution? They first isolated skin cells from a mouse, then using the same procedure that created Dolly, they created a 120-cell embryo from them. The embryo was then destroyed, its embryonic stem cells harvested and cultured (figure 13.19) for transfer to replace injured tissue. This procedure is called **therapeutic cloning.** Therapeutic cloning and the procedure that was used to create Dolly, called **reproductive cloning,** are contrasted in figure 13.20. You can see that steps 1 through 5 are essentially the same for both procedures, but the two methods proceed differently after that. In reproductive cloning, the blastocyst from step 5 is implanted in a surrogate mother in step 6a, developing into a baby that is genetically identical to the nucleus donor 7a. In therapeutic cloning, by contrast, stem cells from the blastocyst of step 5 are removed and grown in culture, step 6. These stem cells are developed into particular tissue types, such as pancreatic islet cells 7, and can then be injected or transplanted into a patient who needs them, such as a diabetic patient, where the new islet cells can begin producing insulin.

Therapeutic cloning, or, more technically, *somatic cell nuclear transfer,* successfully addresses the key problem that must be solved before embryonic stem cells can be used to repair damaged human tissues, which is immune acceptance. Because stem cells are cloned from the body's own tissues in therapeutic cloning, they pass the immune system's "self" identity check, and the body readily accepts them.

Gene Reprogramming to Achieve Immune Acceptance

In therapeutic cloning, the cloned embryo is destroyed to obtain embryonic stem cells. What is the moral standing of a six-day human embryo? Considering it a living individual, many people regard therapeutic cloning to be ethically unacceptable. Recent research discussed on the previous page suggests an alternative approach that avoids this problem: reprogramming adult cells into embryonic stemlike cells by introducing just a few genes into the adult cells. The genes are so-called transcription factors, turning on key genes that act to reverse the "shut off" epigenetic changes that have occurred during development of the adult cells.

Putting the Concept to Work

In what way(s) would gene reprogramming modify the experimental procedure illustrated in figure 13.20?

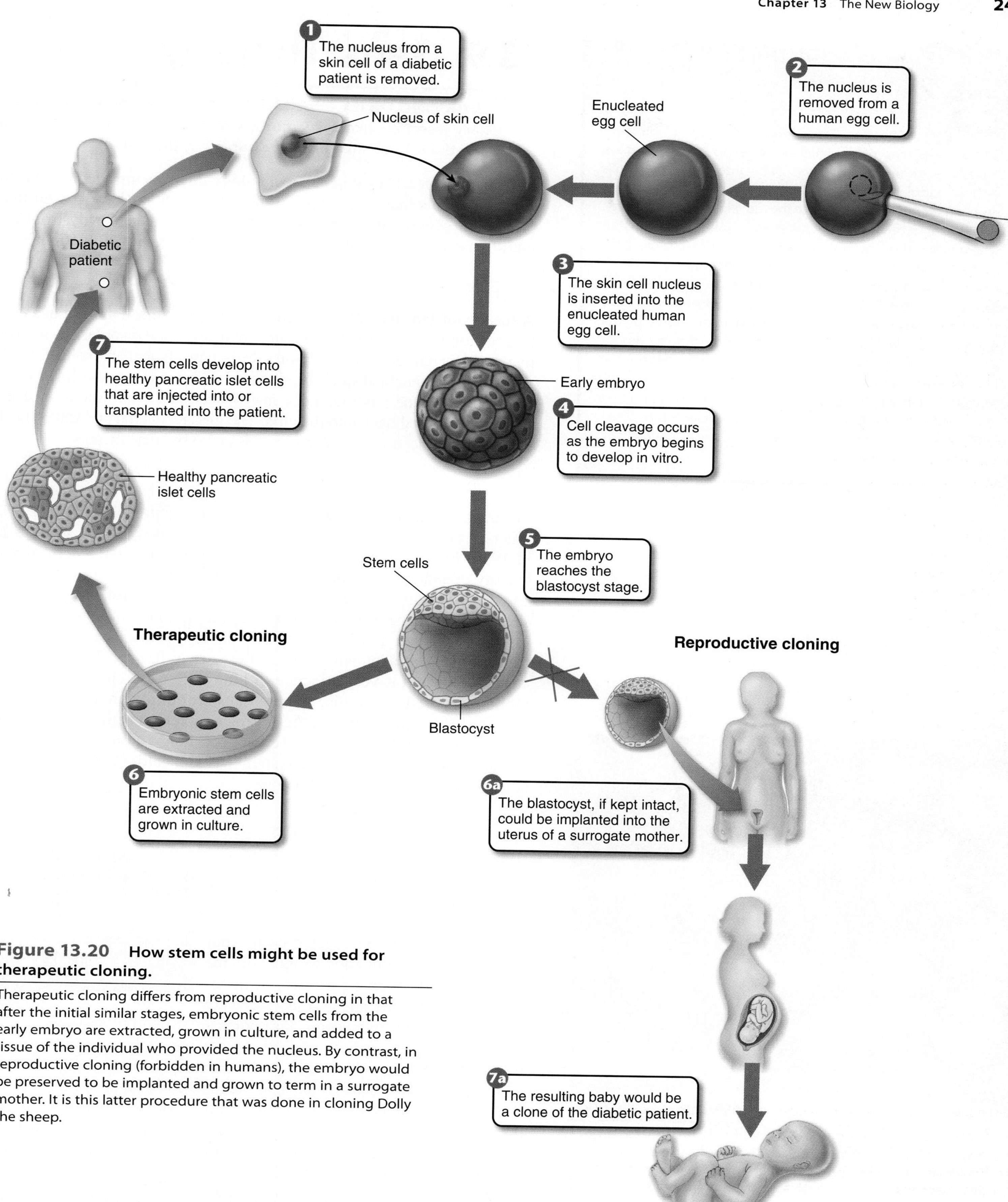

Figure 13.20 How stem cells might be used for therapeutic cloning.

Therapeutic cloning differs from reproductive cloning in that after the initial similar stages, embryonic stem cells from the early embryo are extracted, grown in culture, and added to a tissue of the individual who provided the nucleus. By contrast, in reproductive cloning (forbidden in humans), the embryo would be preserved to be implanted and grown to term in a surrogate mother. It is this latter procedure that was done in cloning Dolly the sheep.

IN THE NEWS

Shooting Genes into Cells. As you will learn on this page, one of the chief obstacles to successful gene therapy is getting the desired gene into a patient's cells without harming the patient. The usual virus vectors proved problematic, often leading to the development of cancer. In Germany a novel approach has been taken that picks up where plant bioengineers left off (figure 13.10, page 235). These researchers literally shoot the genes into a patient's tissue. Though plant bioengineers must use gold pellets to pierce the plant cell wall, the German researchers simply squirt the genes in across the plasma membranes of the patient's cells. Jet injection of "naked" genes (that is, without a protective virus coat) in a fine beam of water delivered at high pressure does not harm the genes and seems to be well tolerated by the tissue cells. Importantly, introducing genes into human tissues in this way is safe. Because the patient's DNA is not altered, there is no danger of cancer as there is with commonly used adenovirus vectors.

13.9 Gene Therapy

LEARNING OBJECTIVE 13.9.1 Explain attempts to cure hereditary disorders like cystic fibrosis by transferring a healthy gene into the cells of affected tissues, and why they failed.

The third major advance in cell technology involves introducing "healthy" genes into cells that lack them. For decades scientists have sought to cure often-fatal genetic disorders like cystic fibrosis, muscular dystrophy, and multiple sclerosis by replacing the defective gene with a functional one.

Early Success

A successful **gene transfer therapy** procedure was first demonstrated in 1990 (see section 13.3). Two girls were cured of a rare blood disorder due to a defective gene for the enzyme adenosine deaminase. Scientists isolated working copies of this gene and introduced them into bone marrow cells taken from the girls. The gene-modified bone marrow cells were allowed to proliferate, then were injected back into the girls. The girls recovered and stayed healthy. For the first time, a genetic disorder was cured by gene therapy.

The Rush to Cure Cystic Fibrosis

Researchers quickly set out to apply the new approach to one of the big killers, cystic fibrosis. The defective gene, labelled *cf*, had been isolated in 1989. Five years later, in 1994, researchers successfully transferred a healthy *cf* gene into a mouse that had a defective one—they in effect had cured cystic fibrosis in a mouse. They achieved this remarkable result by adding the *cf* gene to a virus that infected the lungs of the mouse, carrying the gene with it "piggyback" into the lung cells. The virus chosen as the "vector" was adenovirus (the red viruses in **figure 13.21**), a virus that causes colds and is very infective of lung cells. Very encouraged by these preliminary trials with mice, several labs set out to cure cystic fibrosis by transferring healthy copies of the *cf* gene into human patients the same way. But the gene-modified cells in the patients' lungs soon came under attack by the patients' own immune systems. The "healthy" *cf* genes were lost and with them any chance of a cure.

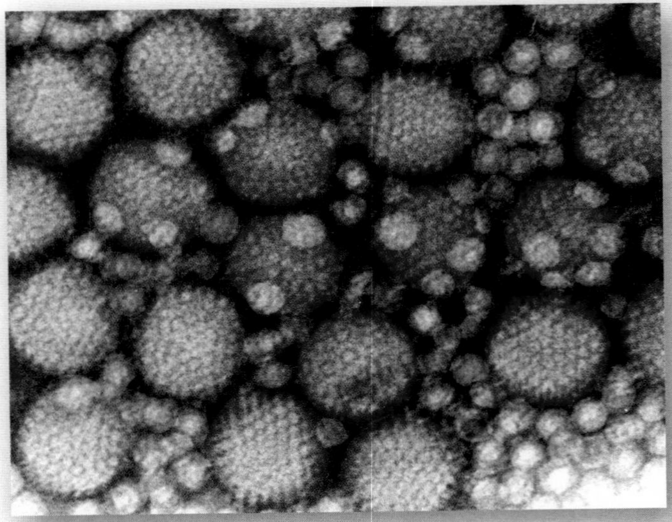

Figure 13.21 Adenovirus and AAV vectors (×200,000).

Adenovirus, the *red* virus particles above, has been used to carry healthy genes in clinical trials of gene therapy. Its use as a vector is problematic, however. AAV, the much smaller *bluish-green* virus particles seen in association with adenovirus here, lacks the many problems of adenovirus and is a much more promising gene transfer vector.

Problems with the Vector

In retrospect, although it was not obvious then, the problem with these early attempts seems predictable. Adenovirus causes colds. Do you know anyone who has never had a cold? When you get a cold, your body produces antibodies to fight off the infection, and so all of us have antibodies directed against adenovirus. We were introducing genes in a vector our bodies are primed to destroy.

The human immune response, discussed in chapter 28 on pages 548 to 553, primes the body after a first exposure to a virus in the primary immune response, allowing the secondary immune response to quickly fight subsequent infections by the same type of virus.

A second serious problem is that when the adenovirus infects a cell, it inserts its DNA into the human chromosome. Unfortunately, it does so at a random location. This means that the insertion events could cause mutations—if the viral DNA inserts into the middle of a gene, it could inactivate that gene. Because the spot where the adenovirus inserts is random, some of the mutations that result can be expected to cause cancer, an unacceptable consequence first reported in 1999.

In 2003, gene therapy clinical trials attempting to cure severe combined immune deficiency (SCID) were halted when 5 of the 20 patients in

Chapter 13

The New Biology

CHAPTER AT A GLANCE

Sequencing Entire Genomes

13.1 Genomics

13.2 The Human Genome

Genetic Engineering

13.3 A Scientific Revolution

13.4 Genetic Engineering and Medicine

Today's Biology: DNA and the Innocence Project

A Closer Look: A DNA Timeline

13.5 Genetic Engineering and Agriculture

The Revolution in Cell Technology

13.6 Reproductive Cloning

13.7 Stem Cell Therapy

13.8 Therapeutic Cloning

13.9 Gene Therapy

Inquiry & Analysis: Can Modified Genes Escape from GM Crops?

Sequencing Entire Genomes

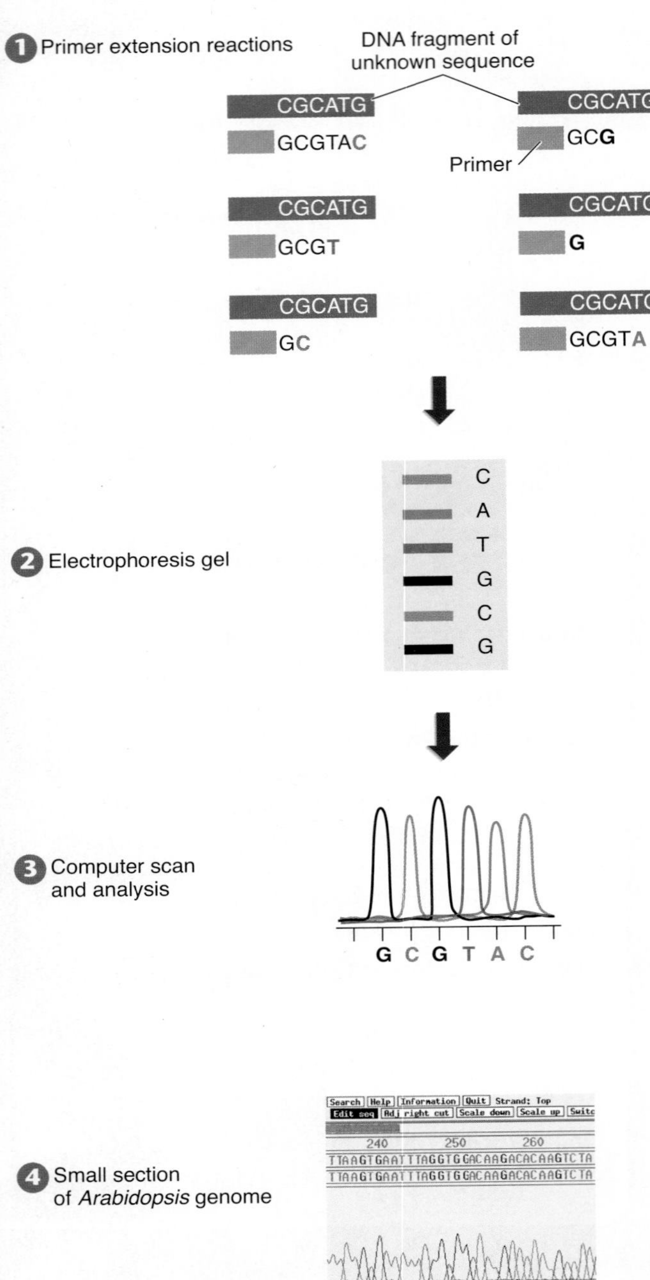

Figure 13.1 How to sequence DNA.

❶ DNA is sequenced by adding complementary bases to a single-stranded fragment. DNA synthesis stops when a chemical tag is inserted instead of a nucleotide, resulting in different sizes of DNA fragments. ❷ The DNA fragments of varying lengths are separated by gel electrophoresis, the smaller fragments migrating farther down the gel. (The letters indicate the chemical tags added in step 1 that stopped the replication process.) ❸ Computers scan the gel, from smallest to largest fragments, and display the DNA sequence as a series of colored peaks. ❹ Data from an automated DNA-sequencing run show the nucleotide sequence for a small section of the *Arabidopsis* (plant) genome.

13.1 Genomics

LEARNING OBJECTIVE 13.1.1 Describe the four stages of DNA sequencing.

The full complement of genetic information of an organism—all of its genes and other DNA—is called its **genome.** To study a genome the DNA is first sequenced, a process that allows each nucleotide of a DNA strand to be read in order. The first genome to be sequenced was a very simple one: a small bacterial virus called ϕ-X174 (ϕ is the Greek letter phi). Frederick Sanger, inventor of the first practical way to sequence DNA, obtained the sequence of this 5,375-nucleotide genome in 1977. This was followed by the sequencing of dozens of prokaryotic genomes. The recent advent of automated DNA sequencing machines has made it practical to sequence the DNA of much larger eukaryotic genomes, including our own (table 13.1).

Sequencing DNA

In sequencing DNA, the DNA of unknown sequence is first cut into fragments. Each DNA fragment is then copied (amplified), so there are thousands of copies of the fragment. The DNA fragments are then mixed with copies of DNA polymerase, copies of a primer (recall from chapter 11 that DNA polymerase can only add nucleotides onto an existing strand of nucleotides), a supply of the four nucleotide bases, and a supply of four different chain-terminating chemical tags. The chemical tags act as one of the four nucleotide bases in DNA synthesis, undergoing complementary base pairing. First, heat is applied to denature the double-stranded DNA fragments. The solution is then allowed to cool, allowing the primer (the lighter blue box in figure 13.1❶) to bind to a single strand of the DNA, and synthesis of the complementary strand proceeds. Whenever a chemical tag is added instead of a nucleotide base, the synthesis stops, as shown in the figure. For example, the terminating red "T" was added after three normal nucleotides and synthesis stopped. Because of the relatively low concentration of the chemical tags compared with the nucleotides, a tag that binds to G on the DNA fragment, for example, will not necessarily be added to the first G site. Thus, the mixture will contain a series of double-stranded DNA fragments of different lengths, corresponding to the different distances the polymerase traveled from the primer before a chain-terminating tag was incorporated (six are shown in ❶).

The series of fragments are then separated according to size by gel electrophoresis. The fragments become arrayed like the rungs of a ladder, each rung being one base longer than the one below it. Compare the lengths of the fragments in ❶ and their positions on the gel in ❷. The shortest fragment has only one nucleotide (G) added to the primer, so it is the lowest rung on the gel. In automated DNA sequencing, fluorescently colored chemical tags are used to label the fragments, one color for each type of nucleotide. Computers read the colors on the gel to determine the DNA sequence and display this sequence as a series of colored peaks (❸ and ❹). The development of automated sequencers in the mid-1990s made the sequencing of large eukaryotic genomes practical. A research institute with several hundred such instruments can sequence 100 million base pairs every day, with only 15 minutes of human attention!

Putting the Concept to Work

Would this procedure allow you to get the full nucleotide sequence of a DNA fragment containing an AUG triplet?

the trial developed leukemia. Apparently the vector had contained a small segment of DNA homologous to a leukemia-causing human gene. When the vector inserted there, the leukemia-causing genes were activated.

Success With New Vectors

Researchers are now investigating a much more promising vector, a tiny virus called *adeno-associated virus* (AAV—the smaller bluish-green viruses in **figure 13.21**) that has only two genes. To create a vector for gene transfer, researchers remove both of the AAV genes. The shell that remains is still quite infective and can carry genes into patients (**figure 13.22**). AAV does not elicit a strong immune response—cells infected with AAV are not eliminated by a patient's immune system.

In 2011, researchers using AAV as a vector succeeded in attempts to treat hemophilia, which you will recall from chapter 10 is a blood clotting disorder due to an X-linked recessive mutation. The researchers stripped out the AAV genes of the vector, replacing them with the relatively small *factor IX* gene, and then injected the recombinant vector into patients. After a single injection, four of the six patients were able to stop the usual injections of factor IX, costing $300,000 a year, and make adequate amounts of factor IX on their own for over 22 months (the other two patients continued to need injections, but less frequently). Trials using AAV as a vector are under way for a wide variety of disorders.

Also in 2011, researchers cured hemophilia in mice without using a vector at all. Instead, they used restriction enzymes to insert the corrective gene at the precise location of the defective one, using DNA-binding proteins called "zinc fingers" to guide the insertion. Trials are currently under way in dogs, a standard model for many treatments.

Putting the Concept to Work

Do you think the improved vector from the AAV clinical trials will work as a means of curing cystic fibrosis? Explain.

Figure 13.22 Using gene therapy to cure a retinal degenerative disease in dogs.

Researchers were able to use genes from healthy dogs to restore vision in dogs blinded by an inherited retinal degenerative disease. This disease also occurs in human infants and is caused by a defective gene that leads to early vision loss, degeneration of the retinas, and blindness. In the gene therapy experiments, genes from dogs without the disease ❶ were placed in an AAV vector ❷ and inserted into three-month-old dogs that were known to carry the defective gene ❸. All of the dogs had been blind since birth. Six weeks after the treatment, the dogs' eyes were producing the normal form of the gene's protein product, and by three months ❹, tests showed that the dogs' vision was restored.

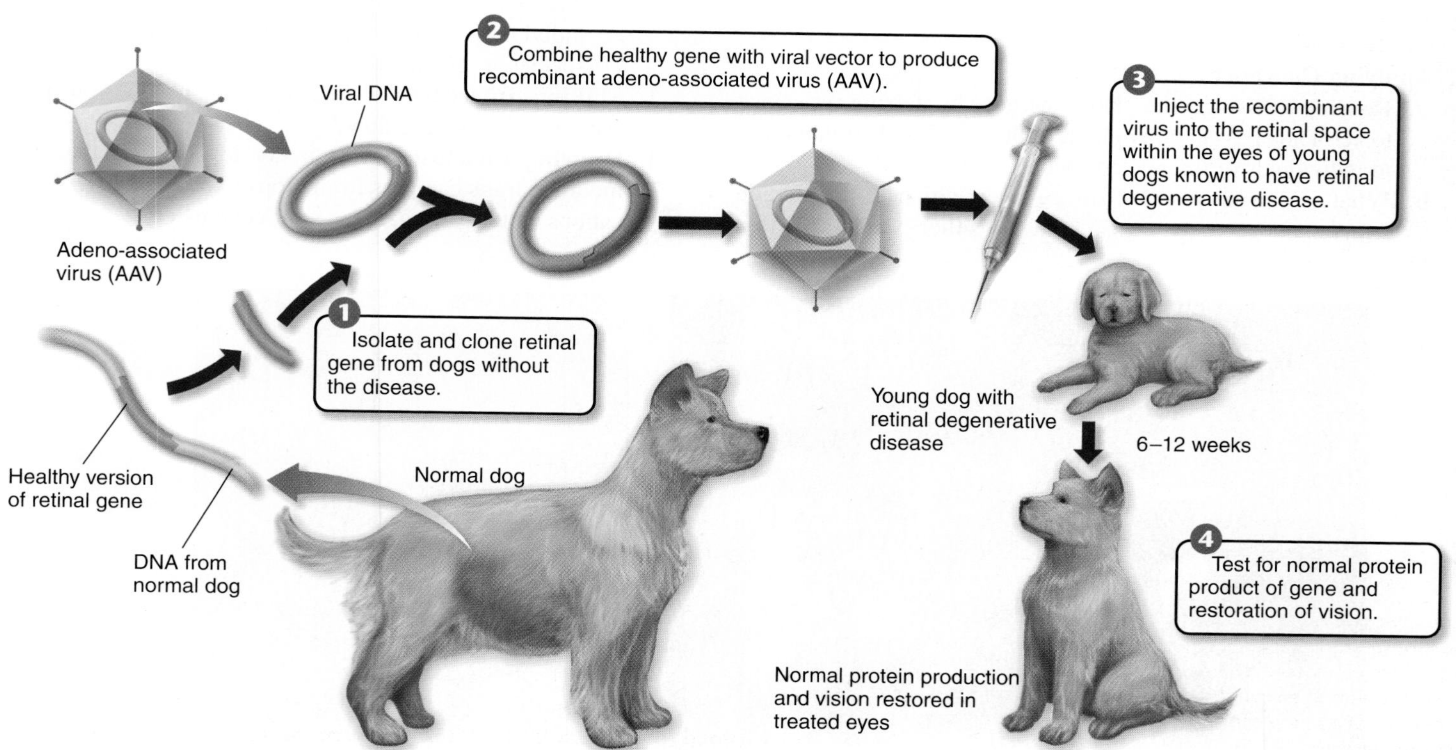
2
Combine healthy gene with viral vector to produce recombinant adeno-associated virus (AAV).
Viral DNA
3
Inject the recombinant virus into the retinal space within the eyes of young dogs known to have retinal degenerative disease.
Adeno-associated virus (AAV)
1
Isolate and clone retinal gene from dogs without the disease.
Young dog with retinal degenerative disease
6–12 weeks
Healthy version of retinal gene
Normal dog
DNA from normal dog
4
Test for normal protein product of gene and restoration of vision.
Normal protein production and vision restored in treated eyes

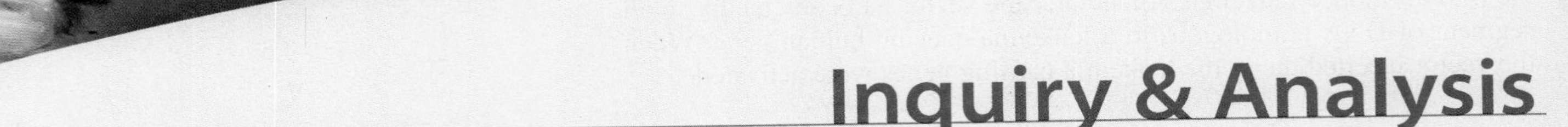

Inquiry & Analysis

Can Modified Genes Escape from GM Crops?

On page 237, the question of whether gene flow of GM crops posed a problem to the environment was discussed. A field experiment conducted in 2004 by the Environmental Protection Agency assessed the possibility that introduced genes could pass from genetically modified golf course grass to other plants. Investigators introduced a gene conferring herbicide resistance (the EPSP synthetase gene for resistance to glyphosate) into golf course bentgrass, *Agrostis stolonifera,* and then looked to see if the gene passed from the GM grass to other plants of the same species, and also if it passed to other related species.

The map at the bottom displays the setup of this elaborate field study. A total of 178 *A. stolonifera* plants were placed outside the golf course, many of them downwind. An additional 69 bentgrass plants were found to be already growing downwind, most of them the related species *A. gigantea*. Seeds were collected from each of these plants, and the DNA of resulting seedlings tested for the presence of the gene introduced into the GM golf course grass. In the graph, the upper red histogram (a **histogram** is a "bar graph" that sorts data into a series of discontinuous categories, the value of each bar representing the number of individuals in a category, or, as in this case, the average value of entries in that category) presents the relative frequency with which the gene was found in *A. stolonifera* plants located at various distances from the golf course. The lower blue histogram does the same for *A. gigantea* plants.

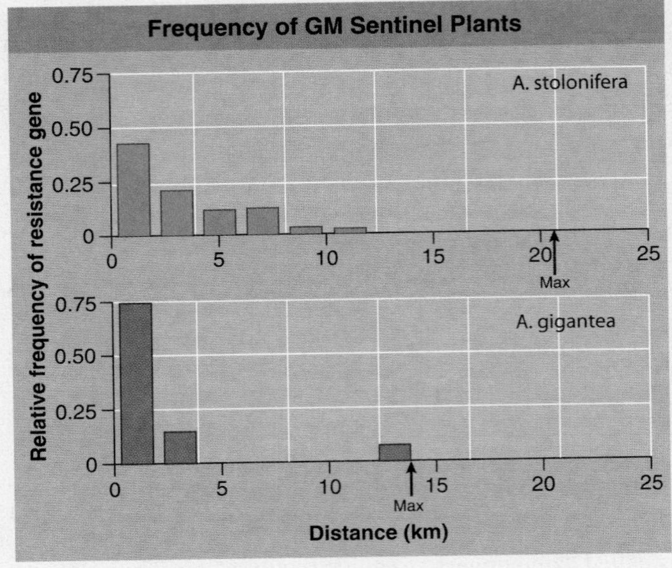

Analysis

1. **Applying Concepts**
   a. **Reading a Histogram.** Does the gene conferring resistance to herbicide pass to other plants of this species, *A. stolonifera*? to individuals of the related species *A. gigantea*?
   b. What is the maximal distance over which the herbicide resistance gene is transferred to other plants of this species? of the related species? what are these distances, expressed in miles (km $\times$ 0.62 = mile)?
2. **Interpreting Data**
   a. What general statement can be made about the effect of distance on the likelihood that the herbicide resistance gene will pass to another plant?
   b. Are there any significant differences in the gene flow to individuals of *A. stolonifera* and to individuals of the related species *A. gigantea*?
3. **Making Inferences** What mechanism do you propose to account for this gene flow?
4. **Drawing Conclusions** Is it fair to conclude that genetically modified traits can pass from crops to other plants? What qualifications would you place on your conclusion?

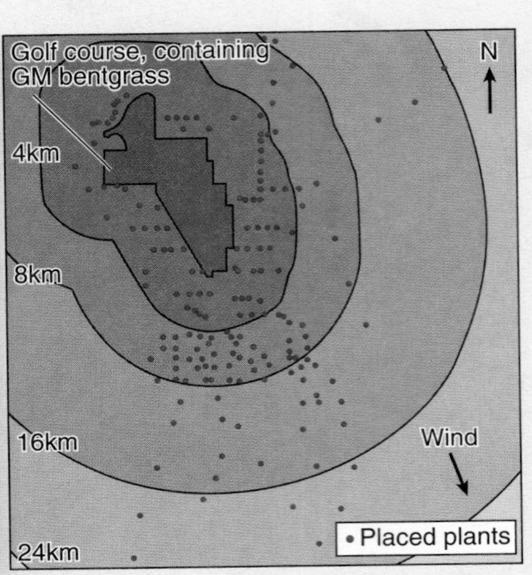

Appendix A

Answers to Test Your Understanding Questions

Chapter 1 *The Science of Biology*

1.1.1 a. kingdoms 1.2.1 c. cellular organization 1.3.1 b. atom, molecule, organelle, cell, tissue, organ, organ system, organism, population, species, community, ecosystem 1.3.2 d. emergent properties 1.4.1 b. evolution, energy flow, cooperation, structure determines function, and homeostasis 1.5.1-1 b. test each hypothesis, using appropriate controls, to rule out as many as possible 1.5.1-2 c. After sufficient testing, you can accept it as probable, being aware that it may be revised or rejected in the future 1.7.1 d. all living organisms consist of cells, and all cells come from other cells 1.7.2 c. is contained in a long molecule called DNA 1.7.4 c. Darwin

Chapter 2 *The Chemistry of Life*

2.1.1 b. an atom 2.2.1 c. an ion 2.3.1 d. ionic, covalent, and hydrogen 2.3.3-1 b. it can form four single covalent bonds 2.3.3-2 d. All of the above 2.4.1 a. hydrogen bonds between the individual water molecules 2.4.3 c. heat storage and heat of vaporization 2.4.4 a. cohesion 2.5.1-1 a. (1) acids and (2) bases 2.5.1-2 c. A buffer stops water from ionizing.

Chapter 3 *Molecules of Life*

3.1.1 b. proteins, carbohydrates, lipids, and nucleic acids 3.1.2 c. polypeptides 3.2.2 d. All of the above 3.2.5 c. structure, function 3.3.1 d. are information storage devices found in body cells 3.3.3 a. Adenine forms hydrogen bonds with thymine 3.4.1-1 a. structure and energy 3.4.1-2 a. glycogen 3.5.1-1 d. All of these are characteristics of fat molecules. 3.5.1-2 c. energy storage and some hormones

Chapter 4 *Cells*

4.1.1 a. cells are the smallest living things; nothing smaller than a cell is considered alive 4.2.1 d. prokaryotes, eukaryotes 4.4.1 b. a double lipid layer with proteins inserted in it, which surrounds every cell individually 4.5.1 a. a nucleolus 4.6.1 c. endoplasmic reticulum and the Golgi complex 4.7.1 d. mitochondria and the chloroplasts 4.8.1. b. cristae 4.9.1 d. slowly disperse throughout the water; this is because of diffusion 4.10.1 b. endocytosis and phagocytosis 4.11.2 c. energy and specialized pumps or carrier proteins

Chapter 5 *Energy and Life*

5.1.1 c. energy 5.2.1 d. says that energy can change forms, but cannot be created or destroyed 5.2.2 b. says that entropy, or disorder, continually increases in a closed system 5.3.1 a. exergonic and release energy 5.4.1 b. enzymes 5.4.2 c. temperature and pH 5.5.1-1 d. All of the above 5.5.1-2 c. an inhibitor molecule competes with the substrate for the active site on the enzyme 5.6.1-1 a. active site 5.6.1-2 a. the breaking of phosphate bonds in ATP

Chapter 6 *Photosynthesis: Acquiring Energy from the Sun*

6.1.1 c. photosynthesis 6.1.2 b. with molecules called pigments that absorb photons and use their energy 6.2.1-1 c. a small portion in the middle of the spectrum 6.2.1-2 a. red and blue 6.2.2 d. All of the above 6.3.1 c. go through the system only once; they are obtained by splitting a water molecule 6.3 b. chemiosmosis 6.3 a. electron transport system of photosystem I, Calvin cycle 6.4.1 c. build sugar molecules 6.5.1 b. use C_4 photosynthesis or CAM

Chapter 7 *How Cells Harvest Energy from Food*

7.1.1 a. breaking down the organic molecules that were consumed 7.2.1-1 c. substrate-level phosphorylation 7.2.1-2 b. glycolysis 7.2.1-3 b. makes ATP by splitting a molecule of glucose in half and capturing the energy 7.3.1 c. mitochondria of the cell and are broken down in the presence of O_2 to make more ATP 7.3.2 b. NAD^+, electron transport chain 7.4.2 d. during the electron transport chain 7.5.1-1 b. fermentation 7.5.1-2 a. pyruvate 7.6.1 c. each type of macromolecule is broken down into its subunits, which enter the oxidative respiration pathway

Chapter 8 *Mitosis*

8.1.1 a. copying DNA, then undergoing binary fission 8.2.1 c. the production of genetically identical daughter cells 8.3.1-1 c. most eukaryotes have between 10 and 50 pairs of chromosomes 8.3.1-2 c. carry information about the same traits located in the same places on the chromosomes 8.3.2 d. All of the above 8.4.1 b. metaphase 8.4.2 c. cytokinesis 8.4.3 d. interphase/DNA replication 8.5.1-1 a. growth factors 8.5.1-2 b. cancer

Chapter 9 *Meiosis*

9.1.1-1 d. the egg and sperm have only half the number of chromosomes found in the parents because of meiosis 9.1.1-2 d. 23 9.2.1 a. $1n$ gametes (haploid), followed by $2n$ zygotes (diploid) 9.3.1-1 a. homologous chromosomes exchange sections of chromosomes 9.3.1-2 b. Homologous chromosomes randomly orient themselves on the metaphase plate, called independent assortment. 9.3.1-3 a. prophase I 9.3.2 c. The duplicated sister chromatids separate 9.4.1-1 c. homologous chromosomes become closely associated 9.4.1-2 a. cells that are genetically identical to the parent cell/haploid cells 9.4.1-3 d. All of the above

Chapter 10 *Foundations of Genetics*

10.1.2 d. All of the above 10.2.1-1 a. all purple flowers 10.2.1-2 c. $^3/_4$ purple and $^1/_4$ white flowers 10.3.1 b. some factor, or information, about traits to their offspring and it may or may not be expressed 10.4.1 a. dihybrid cross 10.6.1-1 d. multiple genes 10.6.1-2 c. codominant traits 10.7.1 b. sex-linked eye color in fruit flies 10.8.1 d. All of the above. 10.11.1 b. chromosome karyotyping

Chapter 11 *DNA: The Genetic Material*

11.1.1 b. hereditary information can be added to cells from other cells 11.2.2 d. DNA 11.3.1-1 a. structure of DNA 11.3.1-2 c. the type of nitrogen base 11.3.1-3 d. adenine and guanine 11.4.1 b. TAACGTA 11.4.2 b. splits down the middle into two single strands, and each one then acts as a template to build its complement 11.4.3 a. a primer 11.5.1-1 c. by mutation or by transformation 11.5.1-2 a. germ-line tissues and are passed on to future generations

Chapter 12 *How Genes Work*

12.1.1-1 a. nRNA (nuclear RNA) 12.1.1-2 a. a promoter 12.2.1 c. transcription 12.3.1-1 d. a codon 12.3.1-2 c. a codon consists of three nucleotides 12.3.2 c. AUG 12.3.3 d. translation 12.4.1 d. All of the above 12.5.1 d. Some genes remain off as long as a repressor is bound 12.6.2 c. translating a gene as it is being transcribed

Chapter 13 *The New Biology*

13.1.1 c. genome 13.2.1 b. the exons used to make a specific mRNA can be rearranged to form different proteins. 13.3.1 c. restriction enzyme 13.3.2 b. exposing the mRNA of the desired eukaryotic gene to reverse transcriptase 13.3.3 c. DNA fingerprinting becomes more and more reliable as more probes are used 13.4.1 a. the drug to be produced in far larger amounts than in the past 13.5.1 a. increased yield 13.5.3 d. harm to the crop itself from mutations 13.8.1 a. immunological rejection of the tissue by the patient 13.9.1 c. viruses

Chapter 14 *Evolution and Natural Selection*

14.3.1-1 c. populations are capable of geometric increase, yet remain at constant levels 14.3.1-2 a. natural selection 14.4.1 b. seems to agree with Darwin's original ideas 14.5.1 d. adaptive radiation 14.6.2 a. homologous structures 14.8.1-1 c. no mutation within the population 14.8.1-2 a. 0.20 14.9.1 d. genetic drift 14.9.2 c. directional selection 14.13.1 d. reproductive isolation

Chapter 15 *Exploring Biological Diversity*

15.2.1 a. physical, behavioral, and molecular characteristics 15.3.1 a. the red fox is in the same family, but different genus than dogs and wolves 15.5.1-1 b. phylogeny 15.5.1-2 c. share a more recent common ancestor than those organisms that are farther apart 15.6.1-1 d. cell structure and DNA sequence 15.6.1-2 b. Archaea 15.6.1-3 d. are prokaryotes 15.7.1-1 c. Protista 15.7.1-2 b. multicellular 15.7.1-3 d. endosymbiosis of bacteria

Chapter 16 *Evolution of Microbial Life*

16.1.2 c. RNA 16.2.1 b. peptidoglycan 16.2.2 d. All the above 16.4.1 a. protein coats that contain DNA or RNA 16.4.2 c. birds 16.6.1 c. cysts 16.7.1 d. mushrooms 16.8.1-1 a. hyphae 16.8.1-2 a. both sexually and asexually 16.9.1 b. algae and fungi

Chapter 17 *Evolution of Plants*

17.1.1 c. dehydration 17.2.1 a. chloroplasts 17.3.1 b. they do not have specialized vascular tissue to transport water high 17.5.1 d. seeds 17.6.1 c. sporophyte 17.6.2 c. nourishment 17.7.1 c. ovules not completely covered by the sporophyte at pollination 17.8.1-1 c. fruits and flowers 17.8.1-2 a. pollination 17.8.2 b. the process of double fertilization

Chapter 18 *Evolution of Animals*

18.4.1 b. choanocytes 18.5.2 c. specialization of digestive tract 18.6.1 b. endoderm; mesoderm 18.6.5 c. deuterostome development 18.7.2 b. an animal with a sessile lifestyle, rather than one that moves through the environment 18.9.1-1 b. jaws 18.9.1-2 c. an internal skeleton made of cartilage 18.10.2 c. middle ear bones 18.11.1 d. thin hollow bones in the skeleton 18.12.1 c. hair

Chapter 19 *Populations and Communities*

19.1.1 a. population 19.4.2 c. carrying capacity 19.5.1 b. increased competition for food 19.6.1 a. short life span 19.8.1 d. community 19.9.3 c. resource partitioning 19.10.2 b. commensalism 19.11.3 b. decreasing competitive exclusion between prey species 19.12.1 a. aposematic coloration 19.14.1 c. secondary succession

Chapter 20 *Ecosystems*

20.1.2-1 c. producers 20.1.2-2 d. All of the above 20.2.1 d. amount of energy transferred to the top carnivores 20.3.1 a. from plants 20.4.1 b. combustion 20.5.1 c. ATP 20.7.1-1 d. desert conditions on the downwind side of a mountain due to increased moisture-holding capacity of the winds as the air heats up 20.7.1-2 b. decreases, temperature increases 20.10.1 d. the thermocline 20.11.1 c. tundra

Chapter 21 *Behavior and the Environment*

21.2.1 b. cannot be modified, because these behaviors seem built into the brain and nervous system 21.3.1 a. there is a clear link between presence or absence of a specific gene, a specific metabolic pathway, and a specific behavior 21.4.1 b. operant conditioning 21.7.1 c. reproductive fitness 21.8.1 d. foraging behavior 21.10.1 c. sexual selection 21.10.2 b. polyandry 21.12.1-1 c. reciprocity 21.12.1-2 b. kin selection 21.13.1 d. helpers at the nest

Chapter 22 *Human Influences on the Living World*

22.1.1 d. sulfur oxides as a major air pollutant 22.2.1 b. coal-powered industry 22.3.1 c. ozone levels 22.4.1 a. habitat loss 22.5.1 c. chlorofluorocarbons 22.6.1 a. environmental costs are hardly ever recognized as part of the economy 22.7.1 a. needed to preserve possible direct value from species, such as new medicines 22.8.1 c. increasing amounts of open space as countries develop 22.9.1-1 d. captive propagation 22.9.1-2 a. keystone species

Chapter 23 *The Animal Body and How It Moves*

23.1.1 c. the thoracic cavity 23.1.2 a. cells, tissues, organs, organ systems, organism 23.2.1 c. move the body 23.3.1 d. red blood cells 23.3.2 c. osteoblasts; osteoclasts 23.4.1 a. skeletal 23.5.1 b. neurotransmitters 23.6.2 b. axial skeleton 23.7.1 a. a single muscle can only pull and not push 23.7.2 c. to reset the myosin head so that it can reattach to the actin

Chapter 24 *Circulation*

24.1.1 c. A series of tubular hearts pump hemolymph into cavities of the body 24.1.2-1 d. All of the above are functions of the circulatory system 24.1.2-2 c. by passing warm blood near cold blood in the extremities to warm the blood 24.2.1 a. capillaries 24.3.2 d. erythrocyte 24.4.1-1 a. carries deoxygenated blood 24.4.1-2 d. Blood would flow back into the right ventricle. 24.4.1-3 b. lungs → veins → heart → arteries → arteriole → capillaries → venules → veins → heart → arteries → lungs 24.4.1-4 a. Only arteries carry oxygenated blood 24.4.1-5 b. a stethoscope

Chapter 25 *Respiration*

25.5.1 a. gills 25.2.1-1 b. fish gills 25.2.1-2 c. the animal's blood to be continually exposed to water of higher oxygen concentration 25.3.1-1 c. nostrils → nasal cavity → trachea → bronchus → alveoli 25.3.1-2 c. contracting the muscles around the thoracic cavity pulls your chest out 25.4.1-1 a. hemoglobin in red blood cells 25.4.1-2 b. as bicarbonate in the blood plasma 25.4.1-3 a. bicarbonate 25.4.1-4 b. active transport of carbon dioxide 25.5.1 d. All of the above

Chapter 26 *The Path of Food Through the Animal Body*

26.2.1 b. specialization of different regions of the digestive system 26.3.1 a. herbivores 26.4.1 d. begin the physical digestion of food 26.4.2 c. soft palate 26.5.1 c. stomach 26.6.1-1 b. The surface area of the large intestine is greater than that of the small intestine. 26.6.1-2 c. small intestine 26.6.1-3 d. increase the surface area of the small intestine for absorption of nutrients 26.6.1-4 c. the concentration of solid wastes 26.7.1 a. pancreas

Chapter 27 *Maintaining the Internal Environment*

27.1.1-1 b. homeostasis 27.1.1-2 d. negative feedback loop 27.1.2 b. glycogen to break down 27.2.1-1 a. pancreas 27.2.1-2 b. ants 27.3.1-1 b. nephron 27.3.1-2 a. glomerulus 27.3.2-1 c. loop of Henle 27.3.2-2 d. osmosis 27.4.1 d. urea

Chapter 28 *How the Animal Body Defends Itself*

28.8.1 a. sweat and oil glands 28.2.2-1 c. increase the number of immune system cells in an infected area 28.2.2-2 b. pathogenic bacteria do not grow well at high temperatures 28.3.1 a. T cells 28.4.1 b. have cell surface proteins that are different from the body's own cell surface receptors 28.5.1 d. destroy cells infected by pathogens 28.6.1 c. B cells 28.7.1 b. memory T and B cells 28.10.1 c. an autoimmune response 28.11.1 a. helper T cells

Chapter 29 *The Nervous System*

29.1.1 c. association neurons 29.2.2 a. the influx of sodium ions 29.3.1 b. into the synaptic cleft 29.3.2 a. sodium ion gates in the postsynaptic cell 29.4.1 c. hypothalamus 29.6.1 b. relay messages to skeletal muscles 29.7.1 b. interoceptors 29.8.1 c. semicircular canals 29.9.1 c. taste 29.11.1 c. Rod cells detect different colors and cone cells detect different shades of gray, allowing vision in dim light.

Chapter 30 *Chemical Signaling Within the Animal Body*

30.1.1-1 c. chemical signals stick around longer than electrical signals and can be used for slow processes 30.1.1-2 a. hypothalamus 30.1.2 a. fit into receptors specifically shaped for them 30.2.2 b. steroid hormones must enter the cell to begin action, whereas peptide hormones must begin action on the external surface of the cell membrane 30.3.1 d. posterior pituitary gland 30.3.2 a. ACTH 30.4.1 a. pancreas 30.5.1-1 c. too much calcium in the blood 30.5.1-2 d. sympathetic nervous system 30.5.1-3 a. cortisol

Chapter 31 *Reproduction and Development*

31.1.1-1 b. sexual reproduction 31.1.1-2 c. hermaphroditism 31.1.2 b. if both sex chromosomes are X 31.2.1 d. scrotum 31.3.1 b. FSH and LH 31.4.1 a. embryo releasing hCG 31.5.1-1 d. gastrulation is complete 31.5.1-2 c. neural 31.6.1 c. oxytocin 31.7.1 a. destruction of the egg

Chapter 32 *Plant Form and Function*

32.1.1 c. meristematic tissue 32.2.1 a. parenchyma cells 32.2.3 b. transports carbohydrates 32.3.1 d. at the pericycle 32.4.1-1 c. cambium 32.4.1-2 b. organization of vascular tissue 32.5.1 c. stomata 32.6.1 a. photosynthesis 32.7.1-1 b. translocation 32.7.1-2 d. osmosis

Chapter 33 *Plant Reproduction and Growth*

33.1.2-1 a. pollen 33.1.2-2 b. stigma 33.1.2-3 b. attract animal pollinators 33.2.1 d. oxygen and water 33.3.1 a. ovary 33.4.1 d. root 33.5.1 c. hormones 33.6.1 c. cells in plant stems to elongate 33.7.1 c. photoperiod 33.8.1 a. thigmotropism

Glossary

Terms and Concepts

A

absorption (L. *absorbere,* to swallow down) The movement of water and substances dissolved in water into a cell, tissue, or organism.

acid Any substance that dissociates to form H^+ ions when dissolved in water. Having a pH value less than 7.

acoelomate (Gr. *a,* not + *koiloma,* cavity) A bilaterally symmetrical animal not possessing a body cavity, such as a flatworm.

actin (Gr. *actis,* ray) One of the two major proteins that make up myofilaments (the other is myosin). It provides the cell with mechanical support and plays major roles in determining cell shape and cell movement.

action potential A single nerve impulse. A transient all-or-none reversal of the electrical potential across a neuron membrane. Because it can activate nearby voltage-sensitive channels, an action potential propagates along a nerve cell.

activation energy The energy a molecule must acquire to undergo a specific chemical reaction.

activator A regulatory protein that binds to the DNA and makes it more accessible for transcription.

active site The region of an enzyme surface to which a specific set of substrates binds, lowering the activation energy required for a particular chemical reaction and so facilitating it.

active transport The transport of a solute across a membrane by protein carrier molecules to a region of higher concentration by the expenditure of chemical energy. One of the most important functions of any cell.

adaptation (L. *adaptare,* to fit) Any peculiarity of structure, physiology, or behavior that promotes the likelihood of an organism's survival and reproduction in a particular environment.

adenosine triphosphate (ATP) A molecule composed of ribose, adenine, and a triphosphate group. ATP is the chief energy currency of all cells. Cells focus all of their energy resources on the manufacture of ATP from ADP and phosphate, which requires the cell to supply 7 kilocalories of energy obtained from photosynthesis or from electrons stripped from foodstuffs to form 1 mole of ATP. Cells then use this ATP to drive endergonic reactions.

adhesion (L. *adhaerere,* to stick to) The molecular attraction exerted between the surfaces of unlike bodies in contact, as water molecules to the walls of the narrow tubes that occur in plants.

aerobic (Gr. *aer,* air + *bios,* life) Oxygen-requiring.

allele (Gr. *allelon,* of one another) One of two or more alternative forms of a gene.

allele frequency The relative proportion of a particular allele among individuals of a population. Not equivalent to gene frequency, although the two terms are sometimes confused.

allopatric species (Gr. *allos,* other + *patra,* fatherland, country) Closely related species that do not live in the same geographical area.

allosteric interaction (Gr. *allos,* other + *stereos,* shape) The change in shape that occurs when an activator or repressor binds to an enzyme. These changes result when specific, small molecules bind to the enzyme, molecules that are not substrates of that enzyme.

alternation of generations A reproductive life cycle in which the multicellular diploid phase produces spores that give rise to the multicellular haploid phase and the multicellular haploid phase produces gametes that fuse to give rise to the zygote. The zygote is the first cell of the multicellular diploid phase.

altruism Self-sacrifice for the benefit of others; in formal terms, the behavior that increases the fitness of the recipient while reducing the fitness of the altruistic individual.

alveolus, *pl.* alveoli (L. *alveus,* a small cavity) One of the many small, thin-walled air sacs within the lungs in which the bronchioles terminate.

amino acid The subunit structure from which proteins are produced, consisting of a central carbon atom with a carboxyl group (—COOH), an amino group (—NH_2), a hydrogen, and a side group (R group); only the side group differs from one amino acid to another.

amniotic egg An egg that is isolated and protected from the environment by a more or less impervious shell. The shell protects the embryo from drying out, nourishes it, and enables it to develop outside of water.

anaerobic (Gr. *an,* without + *aer,* air + *bios,* life) Any process that can occur without oxygen. Includes glycolysis and fermentation. Anaerobic organisms can live without free oxygen.

anaphase In mitosis and meiosis II, the stage initiated by the separation of sister chromatids, during which the daughter chromosomes move to opposite poles of the cell; in meiosis I, marked by separation of replicated homologous chromosomes.

aneuploidy An abnormal number of chromosomes.

angiosperms The flowering plants, one of five phyla of seed plants. In angiosperms, the ovules at the time of pollination are completely enclosed by tissues.

anterior (L. *ante,* before) Located before or toward the front. In animals, the head end of an organism.

anther (Gr. *anthos,* flower) The part of the stamen of a flower that bears the pollen.

antibody (Gr. *anti,* against) A protein substance produced by a B cell lymphocyte in response to a foreign substance (antigen) and released into the bloodstream. Binding to the antigen, antibodies mark them for destruction by other elements of the immune system.

anticodon The three-nucleotide sequence of a tRNA molecule that is complementary to, and base pairs with, an amino acid-specifying codon in mRNA.

antigen (Gr. *anti,* against + *genos,* origin) A foreign substance, usually a protein, that stimulates lymphocytes to proliferate and secrete specific antibodies that bind to the foreign substance, labeling it as foreign and destined for destruction.

aorta (Gr. *aeirein,* to lift) The major artery of vertebrate systemic blood circulation; in mammals, carries oxygenated blood away from the heart to all regions of the body except the lungs.

apical meristem (L. *apex,* top + Gr. *meristos,* divided) In vascular plants, the growing point at the tip of the root or stem.

aposematic coloration An ecological strategy of some organisms that "advertise" their poisonous nature by the use of bright colors.

archaea A group of prokaryotes that are among the most primitive still in existence, characterized by the absence of peptidoglycan in their cell walls, a feature that distinguishes them from bacteria.

artery (L. *arteria,* artery) Any blood vessel that carries blood away from the heart.

arthropod (Gr. *arthros,* jointed + *podes,* feet) An animal of the phylum Arthropoda, which includes the arachnids, crustaceans, centipedes, millipedes, and insects.

asexual reproduction Reproducing without forming gametes. Asexual reproduction does not involve sex. Its outstanding characteristic is that an individual offspring is genetically identical to its parent.

atom **(Gr. *atomos,* indivisible)** A core (nucleus) of protons and neutrons surrounded by an orbiting cloud of electrons. The chemical behavior of an atom is largely determined by the distribution of its electrons, particularly the number of electrons in its outermost level.

atomic number The number of protons in the nucleus of an atom. In an atom that does not bear an electric charge (that is, one that is not an ion), the atomic number is also equal to the number of electrons.

autonomic nervous system **(Gr. *autos,* self + *nomos,* law)** The motor pathways that carry commands from the central nervous system to regulate the glands and nonskeletal muscles of the body. Also called the involuntary nervous system.

autosome **(Gr. *autos,* self + *soma,* body)** Any of the 22 pairs of human chromosomes that are similar in size and morphology in both males and females.

autotroph **(Gr. *autos,* self + *trophos,* feeder)** An organism that can harvest light energy from the sun or from the oxidation of inorganic compounds to make organic molecules.

axial skeleton The skeleton of the head and trunk of the human body containing 80 bones.

axon **(Gr., axle)** A process extending out from a neuron that conducts impulses away from the cell body.

B

B cell A lymphocyte that recognizes invading pathogens much as T cells do, but instead of attacking the pathogens directly, it marks them with antibodies for destruction by the nonspecific body defenses.

bacterium, ***pl.*** **bacteria** **(Gr. *bakterion,* dim. of *baktron,* a staff)** The most common type of prokaryotic organism. Cell walls contain peptidoglycan. Play many important ecological roles.

basal body In eukaryotic cells that contain flagella or cilia, a form of centriole that anchors each flagellum.

base Any substance that combines with H^+ ions thereby reducing the H^+ ion concentration of a solution. Having a pH value above 7.

bilateral symmetry **(L. *bi,* two + *lateris,* side; Gr. *symmetria,* symmetry)** A body form in which the right and left halves of an organism are approximate mirror images of each other.

binary fission **(L. *binarius,* consisting of two things or parts + *fissus,* split)** Asexual reproduction of a cell by division into two equal, or nearly equal, parts. Bacteria divide by binary fission.

binding site The site on a substrate or reactant that binds to an enzyme.

binomial system **(L. *bi,* twice, two + Gr. *nomos,* usage, law)** A system of nomenclature that uses two words. The first names the genus, and the second designates the species.

biomass **(Gr. *bios,* life + *maza,* lump or mass)** The total weight of all of the organisms living in an ecosystem.

biome **(Gr. *bios,* life + *-oma,* mass, group)** A major terrestrial assemblage of plants, animals, and microorganisms that occur over wide geographical areas and have distinct characteristics. The largest ecological unit.

blastocyst **(Gr. *blastos,* germ + *kystis,* bladder)** Embryonic stage in mammals that consists of a hollow ball of cells and inner cell mass surrounding a fluid-filled cavity.

buffer A substance that takes up or releases hydrogen ions (H^+) to maintain the pH within a certain range.

C

calorie **(L. *calor, heat*)** The amount of energy in the form of heat required to raise the temperature of 1 gram of water 1 degree Celsius.

calyx **(Gr. *kalyx,* a husk, cup)** The sepals collectively. The outermost flower whorl.

cancer Unrestrained invasive cell growth. A tumor or cell mass resulting from uncontrollable cell division.

capillary **(L. *capillaris,* hairlike)** A blood vessel with a very small diameter. Blood exchanges gases and metabolites across capillary walls. Capillaries join the end of an arteriole (small artery) to the beginning of a venule (small vein).

carbohydrate **(L. *carbo,* charcoal + *hydro,* water)** An organic compound consisting of a chain or ring of carbon atoms to which hydrogen and oxygen atoms are attached in a ratio of approximately 1:2:1. A compound of carbon, hydrogen, and oxygen having the generalized formula $(CH_2O)_n$, where n is the number of carbon atoms.

carcinogen **(Gr. *karkinos,* cancer + -gen)** Any cancer-causing agent.

cardiovascular system **(Gr. *kardia,* heart + L. *vasculum,* vessel)** The blood circulatory system and the heart that pumps it. Collectively, the blood, heart, and blood vessels.

carpel **(Gr. *karpos,* fruit)** A leaflike organ in angiosperms that encloses one or more ovules.

carrying capacity The maximum population size that a habitat can support.

Casparian strip In plants, a band that encircles the cell wall of root endodermal cells. Adjacent cells' strips connect, forming a layer through which water cannot pass; therefore, all water entering roots must pass through cell membranes and cytoplasm.

catabolism **(Gr. *katabole,* throwing down)** A process in which complex molecules are broken down into simpler ones.

catalysis **(Gr. *katalysis,* dissolution + *lyein, to loosen*)** The enzyme-mediated process in which the subunits of polymers are positioned so that their bonds undergo chemical reactions.

catalyst **(Gr. *kata,* down + *lysis,* a loosening)** A general term for a substance that speeds up a specific chemical reaction by lowering the energy required to activate or start the reaction. An enzyme is a biological catalyst.

cell **(L. *cella,* a chamber or small room)** The smallest unit of life. The basic organizational unit of all organisms. Composed of a nuclear region containing the hereditary apparatus within a larger volume called the cytoplasm bounded by a lipid membrane.

cell cycle The repeating sequence of growth and division through which cells pass each generation.

cellular respiration The process in which the energy stored in a glucose molecule is released by oxidation. Hydrogen atoms are lost by glucose and gained by oxygen.

central nervous system (CNS) The brain and spinal cord, the site of information processing and control within the nervous system.

centriole **(Gr. *kentron,* center of a circle + L. *ola,* small)** A cytoplasmic organelle located outside the nuclear membrane, identical in structure to a basal body; found in animal cells and in the flagellated cells of other groups; divides and organizes spindle fibers during mitosis and meiosis.

centromere **(Gr. *kentron,* center + *meros,* a part)** A constricted region of the chromosome joining two sister chromatids, to which the kinetochore is attached.

chemical bond The force holding two atoms together. The force can result from the attraction of opposite charges (ionic bond) or from the sharing of one or more pairs of electrons (a covalent bond).

chemiosmosis The cellular process responsible for almost all of the adenosine triphosphate (ATP) harvested from food and for all the ATP produced by photosynthesis.

chemoautotroph An autotrophic bacterium that uses chemical energy released by specific inorganic reactions to power its life processes, including the synthesis of organic molecules.

chiasma, ***pl.*** **chiasmata** **(Gr. a cross)** In meiosis, the points of crossing over where portions of chromosomes have been exchanged during synapsis. A chiasma appears as an X-shaped structure under a light microscope.

chlorophyll **(Gr. *chloros,* green + *phyllon,* leaf)** The primary type of light-absorbing pigment in photosynthesis. Chlorophyll *a* absorbs light in the violet-blue and the red ranges of the visible light spectrum; chlorophyll *b* is an accessory pigment to chlorophyll *a*, absorbing light in the blue and red-orange ranges. Neither pigment absorbs light in the green range, 500–600 nm.

chloroplast **(Gr. *chloros,* green + *plastos,* molded)** A cell-like organelle present in algae and plants that contains chlorophyll (and usually other pigments) and is the site of photosynthesis.

choanocyte **(Gr. *choane,* funnel + *kytos,* hollow vessel)** A type of flagellated cell that lines the body cavity of a sponge.

chromatid **(Gr. *chroma,* color + L. *-id,* daughters of)** One of two daughter strands of a duplicated chromosome that is joined by a single centromere.

chromatin **(Gr. *chroma,* color)** The complex of DNA and proteins of which eukaryotic chromosomes are composed.

chromosome **(Gr. *chroma,* color + *soma,* body)** The vehicle by which hereditary information is physically transmitted from one generation to the next. In a eukaryotic cell, long threads of DNA that are associated with protein and that contain hereditary information.

cilium, ***pl.*** **cilia** **(L. eyelash)** Refers to flagella that are numerous and organized in dense rows. Cilia propel cells through water. In human tissue, they move water or mucus over the tissue surface.

cladistics A taxonomic technique used for creating hierarchies of organisms based on derived characters that represent true phylogenetic relationship and descent.

class A taxonomic category ranking below a phylum (division) and above an order.

clone (Gr. *klon,* twig) A line of cells, all of which have arisen from the same single cell by mitotic division. One of a population of individuals derived by asexual reproduction from a single ancestor. One of a population of genetically identical individuals.

cnidarian (Gr. *knide*, nettle) An animal of the phylum Cnidaria, which includes hydra, jellyfish, corals, and sea anemones.

cnidocyte (Gr. *knide*, nettle + *kytos*, hollow vessel) Modified cell of cnidarians that holds the nematocyst.

codominance In genetics, a situation in which the effects of both alleles at a particular locus are apparent in the phenotype of the heterozygote.

codon (L. code) The basic unit of the genetic code. A sequence of three adjacent nucleotides in DNA or mRNA that codes for one amino acid or for polypeptide termination.

coelom (Gr. *koilos,* a hollow) A body cavity formed between layers of mesoderm and in which the digestive tract and other internal organs are suspended.

coenzyme A cofactor of an enzyme that is a nonprotein organic molecule.

coevolution (L. *co-,* together + *e-,* out + *volvere,* to fill) A term that describes the long-term evolutionary adjustment of one group of organisms to another.

cohesion (L. *cohaes,* to cohere) The molecular attraction between the surfaces of like bodies in contact, such as that between water molecules and other water molecules.

commensalism (L. *cum,* together with + *mensa,* table) A symbiotic relationship in which one species benefits while the other neither benefits nor is harmed.

community (L. *communitas,* community, fellowship) The populations of different species that live together and interact in a particular place.

competition Interaction between individuals for the same scarce resources. Intraspecific competition is competition between individuals of a single species. Interspecific competition is competition between individuals of different species.

competitive exclusion The hypothesis that if two species are competing with one another for the same limited resource in the same place, one will be able to use that resource more efficiently than the other and eventually will drive that second species to extinction locally.

complement system The chemical defense of a vertebrate body that consists of a battery of proteins that insert in bacterial and fungal cells, causing holes that destroy the cells.

concentration gradient The concentration difference of a substance as a function of distance. In a cell, a greater concentration of its molecules in one region than in another.

condensation The coiling of the chromosomes into more and more tightly compacted bodies begun during the G_2 phase of the cell cycle.

conjugation (L. *conjugare,* to yoke together) An unusual mode of reproduction in unicellular organisms in which genetic material is exchanged between individuals through tubes connecting them during conjugation.

consumer In ecology, a heterotroph that derives its energy from living or freshly killed organisms or parts thereof. Primary consumers are herbivores; secondary consumers are carnivores or parasites.

cortex (L. bark) In vascular plants, the primary ground tissue of a stem or root, bounded externally by the epidermis and internally by the central cylinder of vascular tissue. In animals, the outer, as opposed to the inner, part of an organ, as in the adrenal, kidney, and cerebral cortexes.

cotyledon (Gr. *kotyledon,* a cup-shaped hollow) Seed leaf. Monocot embryos have one cotyledon, and dicots have two.

countercurrent flow In organisms, the passage of heat or of molecules (such as oxygen, water, or sodium ions) from one circulation path to another moving in the opposite direction. Because the flow of the two paths is in opposite directions, a concentration difference always exists between the two channels, facilitating transfer.

covalent bond (L. *co-,* together + *valare,* to be strong) A chemical bond formed by the sharing of one or more pairs of electrons.

crista, *pl.* cristae (L. *crista,* crest) A folded extension of the inner membrane of a mitochondrion. Mitochondria contain numerous cristae.

crossing over An essential element of meiosis occurring during prophase when nonsister chromatids exchange portions of DNA strands.

cuticle (L. *cutis,* skin) A very thin film covering the outer skin of many plants.

cytokinesis (Gr. *kytos,* hollow vessel + *kinesis,* movement) The C phase of cell division in which the cell itself divides, creating two daughter cells.

cytoplasm (Gr. *kytos,* hollow vessel + *plasma,* anything molded) A semifluid matrix that occupies the volume between the nuclear region and the cell membrane. It contains the sugars, amino acids, proteins, and organelles (in eukaryotes) with which the cell carries out its everyday activities of growth and reproduction.

cytoskeleton (Gr. *kytos,* hollow vessel + *skeleton,* a dried body) In the cytoplasm of all eukaryotic cells, a network of protein fibers that supports the shape of the cell and anchors organelles, such as the nucleus, to fixed locations.

D

deciduous (L. *decidere,* to fall off) In vascular plants, shedding all the leaves at a certain season.

dehydration reaction Water-losing. The process in which a hydroxyl (OH) group is removed from one subunit of a polymer and a hydrogen (H) group is removed from the other subunit, linking the subunits together and forming a water molecule as a by-product.

demography (Gr. *demos,* people + *graphein,* to draw) The statistical study of population. The measurement of people or, by extension, of the characteristics of people.

deoxyribonucleic acid (DNA) The basic storage vehicle or central plan of heredity information. It is stored as a sequence of nucleotides in a linear nucleotide polymer. Two of the polymers wind around each other like the outside and inside rails of a circular staircase.

depolarization The movement of ions across a cell membrane that wipes out locally an electrical potential difference.

detritivore (L. *detri,* a rubbing away + *vorare,* to devour) An organism that feeds on or breaks down dead organisms.

deuterostome (Gr. *deuteros,* second + *stoma,* mouth) An animal in whose embryonic development the anus forms from or near the blastopore, and the mouth forms later on another part of the blastula. Also characterized by radial cleavage.

dicot Short for dicotyledon; a class of flowering plants generally characterized by having two cotyledons, netlike veins, and flower parts in fours or fives.

diffusion (L. *diffundere,* to pour out) The net movement of molecules to regions of lower concentration as a result of random, spontaneous molecular motions. The process tends to distribute molecules uniformly.

dihybrid (Gr. *dis,* twice + L. *hibrida,* mixed offspring) An individual heterozygous for two genes.

dioecious (Gr. *di,* two + *eikos,* house) Having male and female flowers on separate plants of the same species.

diploid (Gr. *diploos,* double + *eidos,* form) Having two sets of chromosomes ($2n$), in contrast to haploid (n).

directional selection A form of selection in which selection acts to eliminate one extreme from an array of phenotypes. Thus, the genes promoting this extreme become less frequent in the population.

disaccharide (Gr. *dis,* twice + *sakcharon,* sugar) A sugar formed by linking two monosaccharide molecules together. Sucrose (table sugar) is a disaccharide formed by linking a molecule of glucose to a molecule of fructose.

disruptive selection A form of selection in which selection acts to eliminate rather than favor the intermediate type.

diurnal (L. *diurnalis,* day) Active during the day.

domain In taxonomy, the level higher than kingdom. The three domains currently recognized are Bacteria, Archaea, and Eukarya.

dominant allele An allele that dictates the appearance of heterozygotes. One allele is said to be dominant over another if an individual heterozygous for that allele has the same appearance as an individual homozygous for it.

dorsal (L. *dorsum,* the back) Toward the back, or upper surface. Opposite of ventral.

double fertilization A process unique to the angiosperms, in which one sperm nucleus fertilizes the egg and the second one fuses with the polar nuclei. These two events result in the formation of the zygote and the primary endosperm nucleus, respectively.

E

ecdysis (Gr. *ekdysis,* stripping off) The shedding of the outer covering or skin of certain animals. Especially the shedding of the exoskeleton by arthropods.

echinoderm (Gr. *echinos*, sea urchin, hedgehog + *derma*, skin) An animal of the phylum Echinodermata, which includes the sea stars, sea urchins, sea cucumbers, and sand dollars.

ecology (Gr. *oikos*, house + *logos*, word) The study of the relationships of organisms with one another and with their environment.

ecosystem (Gr. *oikos*, house + *systema*, that which is put together) A community, together with the nonliving factors with which it interacts.

ectoderm (Gr. *ecto*, outside + *derma*, skin) One of three embryonic germ layers that forms in the gastrula; giving rise to the outer epithelium and to nerve tissue.

ectothermic Referring to animals whose body temperature is regulated by their behavior or their surroundings.

electron A subatomic particle with a negative electrical charge. The negative charge of one electron exactly balances the positive charge of one proton. Electrons orbit the atom's positively charged nucleus and determine its chemical properties.

electron transport chain A collective term describing the series of membrane-associated electron carriers embedded in the inner mitochondrial membrane. It puts the electrons harvested from the oxidation of glucose to work driving proton-pumping channels.

electron transport system A collective term describing the series of electron carriers embedded in the thylakoid membrane of the chloroplast. It puts the electrons harvested from water molecules and energized by photons of light to work driving proton-pumping channels.

element A substance that cannot be separated into different substances by ordinary chemical methods.

embryonic stem cell A cell that is derived from the inner cell mass of an early embryo and is able to develop into any tissue or to give rise to an adult organism when injected into a blastocyst.

emergent properties Novel properties in the hierarchy of life that were not present at the simpler levels of organization.

endergonic (Gr. *endon*, within + *ergon*, work) Reactions in which the products contain more energy than the reactants and require an input of usable energy from an outside source before they can proceed. These reactions are not spontaneous.

endocrine gland (Gr. *endon*, within + *krinein*, to separate) A ductless gland producing hormonal secretions that pass directly into the bloodstream or lymph.

endocytosis (Gr. *endon*, within + *kytos*, cell) The process by which the edges of plasma membranes fuse together and form an enclosed chamber called a vesicle. It involves the incorporation of a portion of an exterior medium into the cytoplasm of the cell by capturing it within the vesicle.

endoderm (Gr. *endon*, outside + *derma*, skin) One of three embryonic germ layers that forms in the gastrula; giving rise to the epithelium that lines internal organs and most of the digestive and respiratory tracts.

endoplasmic reticulum (ER) (L. *endoplasmic*, within the cytoplasm + *reticulum*, little net) An extensive network of membrane compartments within a eukaryotic cell; attached ribosomes synthesize proteins to be exported.

endoskeleton (Gr. *endon*, within + *skeletos*, hard) In vertebrates, an internal scaffold of bone or cartilage to which muscles are attached.

endosperm (Gr. *endon*, within + *sperma*, seed) A nutritive tissue characteristic of the seeds of angiosperms that develops from the union of a male nucleus and the polar nuclei of the embryo sac. The endosperm is either digested by the growing embryo or retained in the mature seed to nourish the germinating seedling.

endosymbiotic (Gr. *endon*, within + *bios*, life) theory A theory that proposes how eukaryotic cells arose from large prokaryotic cells that engulfed smaller ones of a different species. The smaller cells were not consumed but continued to live and function within the larger host cell. Organelles that are believed to have entered larger cells in this way are mitochondria and chloroplasts.

endothermic The ability of animals to maintain an elevated body temperature using their metabolism.

energy The capacity to bring about change, to do work.

enhancer A site of regulatory protein binding on the DNA molecule distant from the promoter and start site for a gene's transcription.

entropy (Gr. *en*, in + *tropos*, change in manner) A measure of the disorder of a system. A measure of energy that has become so randomized and uniform in a system that the energy is no longer available to do work.

enzyme (Gr. *enzymos*, leavened; *from en*, in + *zyme*, leaven) A protein capable of speeding up specific chemical reactions by lowering the energy required to activate or start the reaction but that remains unaltered in the process.

epidermis (Gr. *epi*, on or over + *derma*, skin) The outermost layer of cells. In vertebrates, the nonvascular external layer of skin of ectodermal origin; in invertebrates, a single layer of ectodermal epithelium; in plants, the flattened, skinlike outer layer of cells.

epigenetics The conditioning of gametic DNA by the parent; also called gene reprogramming.

epistasis (Gr. *epistasis*, a standing still) An interaction between the products of two genes in which one modifies the phenotypic expression produced by the other.

epithelium (Gr. *epi*, on + *thele*, nipple) A thin layer of cells forming a tissue that covers the internal and external surfaces of the body. Simple epithelium consists of the membranes that line the lungs and major body cavities and that are a single cell layer thick. Stratified epithelium (the skin or epidermis) is composed of more complex epithelial cells that are several cell layers thick.

erythrocyte (Gr. *erythros*, red + *kytos*, hollow vessel) A red blood cell, the carrier of hemoglobin. Erythrocytes act as the transporters of oxygen in the vertebrate body. During the process of their maturation in mammals, they lose their nuclei and mitochondria, and their endoplasmic reticulum is reabsorbed.

estrus (L. *oestrus*, frenzy) The period of maximum female sexual receptivity. Associated with ovulation of the egg. Being "in heat."

estuary (L. *aestus*, tide) A partly enclosed body of water, such as those that often form at river mouths and in coastal bays, where the salinity is intermediate between that of saltwater and freshwater.

ethology (Gr. *ethos*, habit or custom + *logos*, discourse) The study of patterns of animal behavior in nature.

eukaryote (Gr. *eu*, true + *karyon*, kernel) A cell that possesses membrane-bounded organelles, most notably a cell nucleus, and chromosomes whose DNA is associated with proteins; an organism composed of such cells. The appearance of eukaryotes marks a major event in the evolution of life, as all organisms on earth other than bacteria and archaea are eukaryotes.

eumetazoan (Gr. *eu*, true + *meta*, with + *zoion*, animal) A "true animal." An animal with a definite shape and symmetry and nearly always distinct tissues.

eutrophic (Gr. *eutrophos*, thriving) Refers to a lake in which an abundant supply of minerals and organic matter exists.

evaporation The escape of water molecules from the liquid to the gas phase at the surface of a body of water.

evolution (L. *evolvere*, to unfold) Genetic change in a population of organisms over time (generations). Darwin proposed that natural selection was the mechanism of evolution.

exergonic (L. *ex*, out + Gr. *ergon*, work) Any reaction that produces products that contain less free energy than that possessed by the original reactants and that tends to proceed spontaneously.

exocytosis (Gr. *ex*, out of + *kytos*, cell) The extrusion of material from a cell by discharging it from vesicles at the cell surface. The reverse of endocytosis.

exon (Gr. *exo*, outside) A segment of DNA that is both transcribed into RNA and translated into protein.

exoskeleton (Gr. *exo*, outside + *skeletos*, hard) An external hard shell that encases a body. In arthropods, comprised mainly of chitin.

experiment The test of a hypothesis. An experiment that tests one or more alternative hypotheses and those that are demonstrated to be inconsistent with experimental observation are rejected.

F

facilitated diffusion The transport of molecules across a membrane by a carrier protein in the direction of lowest concentration.

family A taxonomic group ranking below an order and above a genus.

feedback inhibition A regulatory mechanism in which a biochemical pathway is regulated by the amount of the product that the pathway produces.

fermentation (L. *fermentum*, ferment) A catabolic process in which the final electron acceptor is an organic molecule.

fertilization (L. *ferre*, to bear) The union of male and female gametes to form a zygote.

fitness The genetic contribution of an individual to succeeding generations, relative to the contributions of other individuals in the population.

flagellum, *pl.* flagella (L. *flagellum*, whip) A fine, long, threadlike organelle protruding from the surface of a cell. In bacteria, a single protein fiber capable of rotary motion that propels the cell through the water. In eukaryotes, an array of microtubules with a characteristic internal 9 + 2 microtubule structure that is capable of vibratory but not rotary motion. Used in locomotion and feeding. Common in protists and motile gametes. A cilium is a short flagellum.

food web The food relationships within a community. A diagram of who eats whom.

founder effect The effect by which rare alleles and combinations of alleles may be enhanced in new populations.

frequency In statistics, defined as the proportion of individuals in a certain category, relative to the total number of individuals being considered.

fruit In angiosperms, a mature, ripened ovary (or group of ovaries) containing the seeds.

G

gamete (Gr. wife) A haploid reproductive cell. Upon fertilization, its nucleus fuses with that of another gamete of the opposite sex. The resulting diploid cell (zygote) may develop into a new diploid individual, or in some protists and fungi, may undergo meiosis to form haploid somatic cells.

gametophyte (Gr. *gamete,* wife + *phyton,* plant) In plants, the haploid (n), gamete-producing generation, which alternates with the diploid ($2n$) sporophyte.

ganglion, *pl.* ganglia (Gr. a swelling) A group of nerve cells forming a nerve center in the peripheral nervous system.

gastrulation The inward movement of certain cell groups from the surface of the blastula.

gene (Gr. *genos,* birth, race) The basic unit of heredity. A sequence of DNA nucleotides on a chromosome that encodes a polypeptide or RNA molecule and so determines the nature of an individual's inherited traits.

gene expression The process in which an RNA copy of each active gene is made, and the RNA copy directs the sequential assembly of a chain of amino acids at a ribosome.

gene frequency The frequency with which individuals in a population possess a particular gene. Often confused with allele frequency.

genetic code The "language" of the genes. The mRNA codons specific for the 20 common amino acids constitute the genetic code.

genetic drift Random fluctuations in allele frequencies in a small population over time.

genetic map A diagram showing the relative positions of genes.

genetics (Gr. *genos,* birth, race) The study of the way in which an individual's traits are transmitted from one generation to the next.

genome (Gr. *genos,* offspring + L. *oma,* abstract group) The genetic information of an organism.

genomics The study of genomes as opposed to individual genes.

genotype (Gr. *genos,* offspring + *typos,* form) The total set of genes present in the cells of an organism. Also used to refer to the set of alleles at a single gene locus.

genus, *pl.* genera (L. race) A taxonomic group that ranks below a family and above a species.

germination (L. *germinare,* to sprout) The resumption of growth and development by a spore or seed.

gland (L. *glandis,* acorn) Any of several organs in the body, such as exocrine or endocrine, that secrete substances for use in the body. Glands are composed of epithelial tissue.

glomerulus (L. a little ball) A network of capillaries in a vertebrate kidney, whose walls act as a filtration device.

glycolysis (Gr. *glykys,* sweet + *lyein,* to loosen) The anaerobic breakdown of glucose; this enzyme-catalyzed process yields two molecules of pyruvate with a net of two molecules of ATP.

golgi complex Flattened stacks of membrane compartments that collect, package, and distribute molecules made in the endoplasmic reticulum.

granum, *pl.* grana A stacked column of flattened, interconnected disks (thylakoids) that are part of the thylakoid membrane system in chloroplasts.

gravitropism (L. *gravis,* heavy + *tropes,* turning) The response of a plant to gravity, which generally causes shoots to grow up and roots to grow down.

greenhouse effect The process in which carbon dioxide and certain other gases, such as methane, that occur in the earth's atmosphere transmit radiant energy from the sun but trap the longer wavelengths of infrared light, or heat, and prevent them from radiating into space.

guard cells Pairs of specialized epidermal cells that surround a stoma. When the guard cells are turgid, the stoma is open; when they are flaccid, it is closed.

gymnosperm (Gr. *gymnos,* naked + *sperma,* seed) A seed plant with seeds not enclosed in an ovary. The conifers are the most familiar group.

H

habitat (L. *habitare,* to inhabit) The place where individuals of a species live.

half-life The length of time it takes for half of a radioactive substance to decay.

haploid (Gr. *haploos,* single + *eidos,* form) Having only one set of chromosomes (n), in contrast to diploid ($2n$).

Hardy-Weinberg equilibrium After G. H. Hardy, English mathematician, and G. Weinberg, German physician. A mathematical description of the fact that the relative frequencies of two or more alleles in a population do not change because of Mendelian segregation. Allele and genotype frequencies remain constant in a random-mating population in the absence of inbreeding, selection, or other evolutionary forces. Usually stated as: If the frequency of allele A is p and the frequency of allele a is q, then the genotype frequencies after one generation of random mating will always be $(p + q)^2 = p^2 + 2pq + q^2$.

Haversian canal After Clopton Havers, English anatomist. Narrow channels that run parallel to the length of a bone and contain blood vessels and nerve cells.

helper T cell A class of white blood cells that initiates both the cell-mediated immune response and the humoral immune response; helper T cells are the targets of the AIDS virus (HIV).

hemoglobin (Gr. *haima,* blood + L. *globus,* a ball) A globular protein in vertebrate red blood cells and in the plasma of many invertebrates that carries oxygen and carbon dioxide.

hemolymph (Gr. *haima,* blood + L. *lympha,* water) Circulating fluid in the coelom of some invertebrates, such as insects.

herbivore (L. *herba,* grass + *vorare,* to devour) Any organism that eats only plants.

heredity (L. *heredis,* heir) The transmission of characteristics from parent to offspring.

heterokaryon (Gr. *heteros,* other + *karyon,* kernel) A fungal hypha that has two or more genetically distinct types of nuclei.

heterotroph (Gr. *heteros,* other + *trophos,* feeder) An organism that does not have the ability to produce its own food. *See also* autotroph.

heterozygote (Gr. *heteros,* other + *zygotos,* a pair) A diploid individual carrying two different alleles of a gene on its two homologous chromosomes.

histone (Gr. *histos,* tissue) A complex of small, very basic polypeptides rich in the amino acids arginine and lysine. A basic part of chromosomes, histones form the core around which DNA is wrapped.

homeostasis (Gr. *homeos,* similar + *stasis,* standing) The maintaining of a relatively stable internal physiological environment in an organism or steady-state equilibrium in a population or ecosystem.

homeotherm (Gr. *homeo,* similar + *therme,* heat) An organism, such as a bird or mammal, capable of maintaining a stable body temperature.

hominid (L. *homo,* man) Human beings and their direct ancestors. A member of the family Hominidae. *Homo sapiens* is the only living member.

homologous chromosome (Gr. *homologia,* agreement) One of the two nearly identical versions of each chromosome. Chromosomes that associate in pairs in the first stage of meiosis. In diploid cells, one chromosome of a pair that carries equivalent genes.

homology (Gr. *homologia,* agreement) A condition in which the similarity between two structures or functions is indicative of a common evolutionary origin.

homozygote (Gr. *homos,* same or similar + *zygotos,* a pair) A diploid individual whose two copies of a gene are the same. An individual carrying identical alleles on both homologous chromosomes is said to be homozygous for that gene.

hormone (Gr. *hormaein,* to excite) A chemical messenger, often a steroid or peptide, produced in a small quantity in one part of an organism and then transported to another part of the organism, where it brings about a physiological response.

hybrid (L. *hybrida,* the offspring of a tame sow and a wild boar) A plant or animal that results from the crossing of dissimilar parents.

hybridization The mating of unlike parents of different taxa.

hydrogen bond A molecular force formed by the attraction of the partial positive charge of one hydrogen atom of a water molecule with the partial negative charge of the oxygen atom of another.

hydrolysis reaction (Gr. *hydro,* water + *lyse,* break) The process of tearing down a polymer by adding a molecule of water. A hydrogen is attached to one subunit and a hydroxyl to the other, which breaks the covalent bond. Essentially the reverse of a dehydration reaction.

hydrophilic (Gr. *hydro,* water + *philic,* loving) Describes polar molecules, which form hydrogen bonds with water and therefore are soluble in water.

hydrophobic (Gr. *hydro,* water + *phobos,* hating) Describes nonpolar molecules, which do not form hydrogen bonds with water and therefore are not soluble in water.

hydroskeleton (Gr. *hydro,* water + *skeletos,* hard) The skeleton of most soft-bodied invertebrates that have neither an internal nor an external skeleton. They use the relative incompressibility of the water within their bodies as a kind of skeleton.

hypertonic (Gr. *hyper,* above + *tonos,* tension) A solution surrounding a cell that contains a higher concentration of solutes than does the cell.

hypha, *pl.* hyphae *(Gr. hyphe,* web) A filament of a fungus. A mass of hyphae comprises a mycelium.

hypothalamus (Gr. *hypo,* under + *thalamos,* inner room) The region of the brain under the thalamus that controls temperature, hunger, and thirst and that produces hormones that influence the pituitary gland.

hypothesis (Gr. *hypo,* under + *tithenai,* to put) A proposal that might be true. No hypothesis is ever proven correct. All hypotheses are provisional—proposals that are retained for the time being as useful but that may be rejected in the future if found to be inconsistent with new information. A hypothesis that stands the test of time—often tested and never rejected—is called a theory.

hypotonic (Gr. *hypo,* under + *tonos,* tension) A solution surrounding a cell that has a lower concentration of solutes than does the cell.

I

inbreeding The breeding of genetically related plants or animals. In plants, inbreeding results from self-pollination. In animals, inbreeding results from matings between relatives. Inbreeding tends to increase homozygosity.

incomplete dominance The ability of two alleles to produce a heterozygous phenotype that is different from either homozygous phenotype.

independent assortment Mendel's second law: The principle that segregation of alternative alleles at one locus into gametes is independent of the segregation of alleles at other loci. Only true for gene loci located on different chromosomes or those so far apart on one chromosome that crossing over is very frequent between the loci.

industrial melanism (Gr. *melas,* black) The evolutionary process in which a population of initially light-colored organisms becomes a population of dark organisms as a result of natural selection.

inflammatory response (L. *inflammare,* to flame) A generalized nonspecific response to infection that acts to clear an infected area of infecting microbes and dead tissue cells so that tissue repair can begin.

integument (L. *integumentum,* covering) The natural outer covering layers of an animal. Develops from the ectoderm.

interneuron A nerve cell found only in the CNS that acts as a functional link between sensory neurons and motor neurons. Also called association neuron.

interphase That portion of the cell cycle preceding mitosis. It includes the G_1 phase, when cells grow, the S phase, when a replica of the genome is synthesized, and a G_2 phase, when preparations are made for genomic separation.

interstitial fluid (L. *inter,* among + *sistere,* to stand) Fluid situated in the extracellular spaces of tissues.

intron (L. *intra,* within) A segment of DNA transcribed into mRNA but removed before translation. These untranslated regions make up the bulk of most eukaryotic genes.

ion An atom in which the number of electrons does not equal the number of protons. An ion carries an electrical charge.

ionic bond A chemical bond formed between ions as a result of the attraction of opposite electrical charges.

isolating mechanisms Mechanisms that prevent genetic exchange between individuals of different populations or species.

isotonic (Gr. *isos,* equal + *tonos,* tension) A solution having the same concentration of solutes as the cell.

isotope (Gr. *isos,* equal + *topos,* place) An atom that has the same number of protons but different numbers of neutrons.

J

joint The part of a vertebrate where one bone meets and moves on another.

K

karyotype (Gr. *karyon,* kernel + *typos,* stamp or print) The particular array of chromosomes that an individual possesses.

kinetic energy The energy of motion.

kinetochore (Gr. *kinetikos,* putting in motion + *choros,* chorus) A disk of protein bound to the centromere to which microtubules attach during cell division, linking chromatids to the spindle.

kingdom The chief taxonomic category. This book recognizes six kingdoms: Archaea, Bacteria, Protista, Fungi, Animalia, and Plantae.

L

lamella, *pl.* lamellae (L. a little plate) A thin, platelike structure. In chloroplasts, a layer of chlorophyll-containing membranes. In bivalve mollusks, one of the two plates forming a gill. In vertebrates, one of the thin layers of bone laid concentrically around the Haversian canals.

ligament (L. *ligare,* to bind) A band or sheet of connective tissue that links bone to bone.

linkage The patterns of assortment of genes that are located on the same chromosome. Important because if the genes are located relatively far apart, crossing over is more likely to occur between them than if they are close together.

lipid (Gr. *lipos,* fat) A loosely defined group of molecules that are insoluble in water but soluble in oil. Oils such as olive, corn, and coconut are lipids, as well as waxes, such as beeswax and earwax.

lipid bilayer The basic foundation of all biological membranes. In such a layer, the nonpolar tails of phospholipid molecules point inward, forming a nonpolar zone in the interior of the bilayers. Lipid bilayers are selectively permeable and do not permit the diffusion of water-soluble molecules into the cell.

littoral (L. *litus,* shore) Referring to the shoreline zone of a lake or pond or the ocean that is exposed to the air whenever water recedes.

locus, *pl.* loci (L. place) The position on a chromosome where a gene is located.

loop of Henle After F. G. J. Henle, German anatomist. A hairpin loop formed by a urine-conveying tubule when it enters the inner layer of the kidney and then turns around to pass up again into the outer layer of the kidney.

lymph (L. *lympha,* clear water) In animals, a colorless fluid derived from blood by filtration through capillary walls in the tissues.

lymphatic system An open circulatory system composed of a network of vessels that function to collect the water within blood plasma forced out during passage through the capillaries and to return it to the bloodstream. The lymphatic system also returns proteins to the circulation, transports fats absorbed from the intestine, and carries bacteria and dead blood cells to the lymph nodes and spleen for destruction.

lymphocyte (Gr. *lympha,* water + Gr. *kytos,* hollow vessel) A type of white blood cell. A cell of the immune system that either synthesizes antibodies (B cells) or attacks virus-infected cells (T cells).

lyse (Gr. *lysis,* loosening) To disintegrate a cell by rupturing its plasma membrane.

lysosome (Gr. *lysis,* loosening + *soma,* body) A membrane-bounded vesicle containing digestive enzymes that is produced by the Golgi apparatus in eukaryotic cells.

M

macromolecule (Gr. *makros,* large + L. *moliculus,* a little mass) An extremely large molecule. Refers specifically to carbohydrates, lipids, proteins, and nucleic acids.

macrophage (Gr. *makros,* large + *-phage,* eat) A phagocytic cell of the immune system able to engulf and digest invading bacteria, fungi, and other microorganisms, as well as cellular debris.

Malpighian tubules Blind tubules opening into the hindgut of terrestrial arthropods and functioning primarily as excretory organs.

marrow The soft tissue that fills the cavities of most bones and is the source of red blood cells.

mass flow The overall process by which materials move in the phloem of plants.

mass number The mass number of an atom consists of the combined mass of all of its protons and neutrons.

matrix (L. *mater,* mother) In mitochondria, the fluid in the interior space surrounded by the cristae that contains the enzymes and other molecules involved in oxidative respiration; more generally, that part of a tissue within which an organ or process is embedded.

megaspore (Gr. *megas,* large + *spora,* seed) In plants, a haploid reproductive cell that develops into a female gametophyte; in most groups, megaspores are larger than microspores.

meiosis (Gr. *meioun,* to make smaller) A special form of nuclear division that precedes gamete formation in sexually reproducing eukaryotes. It results in four haploid daughter cells.

Mendelian ratio After Gregor Mendel, Austrian monk. Refers to the characteristic 3:1 segregation ratio that Mendel observed, in which pairs of alternative traits are expressed in the F_2 generation in the ratio of three-fourths dominant to one-fourth recessive.

menstruation (L. *mens,* month) Periodic sloughing off of the blood-enriched lining of the uterus when pregnancy does not occur.

meristem (Gr. *merizein,* to divide) In plants, a zone of unspecialized cells whose only function is to divide.

mesoderm (Gr. *mesos,* middle + *derma,* skin) One of the three embryonic germ layers that form in the gastrula. Gives rise to muscle, bone, and other connective tissue; the peritoneum; the circulatory system; and most of the excretory and reproductive systems.

mesophyll (Gr. *mesos,* middle + *phyllon,* leaf) The photosynthetic parenchyma of a leaf, located within the epidermis. The vascular strands (veins) run through the mesophyll.

metabolism (Gr. *metabole,* change) The process by which all living things assimilate energy and use it to grow.

metaphase (Gr. *meta,* middle + *phasis,* form) The stage of mitosis characterized by the alignment of the chromosomes on a plane in the center of the cell.

metastasis, *pl.* metastases (Gr. to place in another way) The spread of cancerous cells to other parts of the body, forming new tumors at distant sites.

microevolution (Gr. *mikros,* small + L. *evolvere,* to unfold) Refers to the evolutionary process itself. Evolution within a species. Also called adaptation.

microspore (Gr. *mikros,* small + spora, seed) In plants, a haploid reproductive cell that develops into a male gametophyte.

microtubule (Gr. *mikros,* small + L. *tubulus,* little pipe) In eukaryotic cells, a long, hollow cylinder about 25 nanometers in diameter and composed of the protein tubulin. Microtubules influence cell shape, move the chromosomes in cell division, and provide the functional internal structure of cilia and flagella.

mimicry (Gr. *mimos,* mime) The resemblance in form, color, or behavior of certain organisms (mimics) to other more powerful or more protected ones (models), which results in the mimics being protected in some way.

mitochondrion, *pl.* mitochondria (Gr. *mitos,* thread + *chondrion,* small grain) A tubular or sausage-shaped organelle 1 to 3 micrometers long. Bounded by two membranes, mitochondria closely resemble the aerobic bacteria from which they were originally derived. As chemical furnaces of the cell, they carry out its oxidative metabolism.

mitosis (Gr. *mitos,* thread) The M phase of cell division in which the microtubular apparatus is assembled, binds to the chromosomes, and moves them apart. This phase is the essential step in the separation of the two daughter cell genomes.

mole (L. *moles,* mass) The atomic weight of a substance, expressed in grams. One mole is defined as the mass of 6.0222×10^{23} atoms.

molecule (L. *moliculus,* a small mass) The smallest unit of a compound that displays the properties of that compound.

mollusk (L. *molluscus,* soft) An animal of the phylum Mollusca, which includes snails and slugs, bivalves (such as clams and oysters), and cephalopods (octopuses, squids, and nautiluses).

monocot Short for monocotyledon; flowering plant in which the embryos have only one cotyledon, the flower parts are often in threes, and the leaves typically are parallel-veined.

monomers (Gr. *mono,* single + *meris,* part) Simple molecules that can join together to form polymers.

monosaccharide (Gr. *monos,* one + *sakcharon,* sugar) A simple sugar.

morphogenesis (Gr. *morphe,* form + *genesis,* origin) The formation of shape. The growth and differentiation of cells and tissues during development.

multicellularity A condition in which the activities of the individual cells are coordinated and the cells themselves are in contact. A property of eukaryotes alone and one of their major characteristics.

muscle (L. *musculus,* mouse) The tissue in the body of humans and animals that can be contracted and relaxed to make the body move.

muscle cell A long, cylindrical, multinucleated cell that contains numerous myofibrils and is capable of contraction when stimulated.

muscle spindle A sensory organ that is attached to a muscle and sensitive to stretching.

mutagen (L. *mutare,* to change) A chemical capable of damaging DNA.

mutation (L. *mutare,* to change) A change in a cell's genetic message.

mutualism (L. *mutuus,* lent, borrowed) A symbiotic relationship in which both participating species benefit.

mycelium, *pl.* mycelia (Gr. *mykes,* fungus) In fungi, a mass of hyphae.

mycology (Gr. *mykes,* fungus) The study of fungi. A person who studies fungi is called a mycologist.

mycorrhiza, *pl.* mycorrhizae (Gr. *mykes,* fungus + *rhiza,* root) A symbiotic association between fungi and plant roots.

myelin sheath (Gr. *myelos,* marrow) A fatty layer surrounding the long axons of motor neurons in the peripheral nervous system of vertebrates.

myofibril (Gr. *myos,* muscle + L. *fibrilla,* little fiber) An elongated structure in a muscle fiber, composed of myosin and actin.

myosin (Gr. *myos,* muscle + *in,* belonging to) One of two protein components of myofilaments. (The other is actin.)

N

natural selection The differential reproduction of genotypes caused by factors in the environment. Leads to evolutionary change.

nematocyst (Gr. *nema,* thread + *kystos,* bladder) A coiled, threadlike stinging structure of cnidarians that is discharged to capture prey and for defense.

nephron (Gr. *nephros,* kidney) The functional unit of the vertebrate kidney. A human kidney has more than 1 million nephrons that filter waste matter from the blood. Each nephron consists of a Bowman's capsule, glomerulus, and tubule.

nerve A bundle of axons with accompanying supportive cells, held together by connective tissue.

nerve impulse A rapid, transient, self-propagating reversal in electrical potential that travels along the membrane of a neuron.

neuromodulator A chemical transmitter that mediates effects that are slow and longer lasting and that typically involve second messengers within the cell.

neuromuscular junction The structure formed when the tips of axons contact (innervate) a muscle fiber.

neuron (Gr. nerve) A nerve cell specialized for signal transmission.

neurotransmitter (Gr. *neuron,* nerve + L. *trans,* across + *mitere,* to send) A chemical released at an axon tip that travels across the synapse and binds a specific receptor protein in the membrane on the far side.

neurulation (Gr. *neuron,* nerve) The elaboration of a notochord and a dorsal nerve cord that marks the evolution of the chordates.

neutron (L. *neuter,* neither) A subatomic particle located within the nucleus of an atom. Similar to a proton in mass, but as its name implies, a neutron is neutral and possesses no charge.

neutrophil An abundant type of white blood cell capable of engulfing microorganisms and other foreign particles.

niche (L. *nidus,* nest) The role an organism plays in the environment; realized niche is the niche that an organism occupies under natural circumstances; fundamental niche is the niche an organism would occupy if competitors were not present.

nitrogen fixation The incorporation of atmospheric nitrogen into nitrogen compounds, a process that can be carried out only by certain microorganisms.

nocturnal (L. *nocturnus,* night) Active primarily at night.

node of Ranvier After L. A. Ranvier, French histologist. A gap formed at the point where two Schwann cells meet and where the axon is in direct contact with the surrounding intercellular fluid.

nondisjunction The failure of homologous chromosomes to separate in meiosis I. The cause of Down syndrome.

nonrandom mating A phenomenon in which individuals with certain genotypes sometimes mate with one another more commonly than would be expected on a random basis.

notochord (Gr. *noto,* back + L. *chorda,* cord) In chordates, a dorsal rod of cartilage that forms between the nerve cord and the developing gut in the early embryo.

nucleic acid A nucleotide polymer. A long chain of nucleotides. Chief types are deoxyribonucleic acid (DNA), which is double-stranded, and ribonucleic acid (RNA), which is typically single-stranded.

nucleolus A region inside the nucleus where rRNA and ribosomes are produced.

nucleosome (L. *nucleus,* kernel + *soma,* body) The basic packaging unit of eukaryotic chromosomes, in which the DNA molecule is wound around a ball of histone proteins. Chromatin is composed of long strings of nucleosomes, like beads on a string.

nucleotide A single unit of a nucleic acid, composed of a phosphate, a five-carbon sugar (either ribose or deoxyribose), and a purine or a pyrimidine.

nucleus (L. kernel, dim. Fr. *nux,* nut) A spherical organelle (structure) characteristic of eukaryotic cells. The repository of the genetic information that directs all activities of a living cell. In atoms, the central core, containing positively charged protons and (in all but hydrogen) electrically neutral neutrons.

O

oligotrophic (Gr. *oligo*, little, few + *trophein*, to nourish) Containing a scarcity of organic material and nutrients, and having a high oxygen content; in reference to a body of water, such as a lake.

oncogene (Gr. *onkos*, protuberance, tumor + *genos*, decent) Any of a number of genes that when inappropriately activated can cause unrestrained cell growth (cancer).

oocyte (Gr. *oion,* egg + *kytos,* vessel) A cell in the outer layer of the ovary that gives rise to an ovum. A primary oocyte is any of the 2 million oocytes a female is born with, all of which have begun the first meiotic division.

operculum (L. cover) A flat, bony, external protective covering over the gill chamber in fish.

operon (L. *operis,* work) A cluster of functionally related genes transcribed onto a single mRNA molecule. A common mode of gene regulation in prokaryotes; it is rare in eukaryotes other than fungi.

order A taxonomic category ranking below a class and above a family.

organ (L. *organon,* tool) A complex body structure composed of several different kinds of tissue grouped together in a structural and functional unit.

organ system A group of organs that function together to carry out the principal activities of the body.

organelle (Gr. *organella,* little tool) A specialized compartment of a cell. Mitochondria are organelles.

organism Any individual living creature, either unicellular or multicellular.

osmoregulation The maintenance of a constant internal solute concentration by an organism, regardless of the environment in which it lives.

osmosis (Gr. *osmos,* act of pushing, thrust) The diffusion of water across a membrane that permits the free passage of water but not that of one or more solutes. Water moves from an area of low solute concentration to an area with higher solute concentration.

osmotic pressure The increase of hydrostatic water pressure within a cell as a result of water molecules that continue to diffuse inward toward the area of lower water concentration (the water concentration is lower inside than outside the cell because of the dissolved solutes in the cell).

osteoblast (Gr. *osteon,* bone + *blastos,* bud) A bone-forming cell.

osteoclast (Gr. *osteon*, bone + *klan*, to break) A bone-dissolving cell.

osteocyte (Gr. *osteon,* bone + *kytos,* hollow vessel) A mature osteoblast.

outcross A term used to describe species that interbreed with individuals other than those like themselves.

ovary (L. *ovum,* egg) (1) In animals, the organ in which eggs are produced. (2) In flowering plants, the enlarged basal portion of a carpel that contains the ovule(s); the ovary matures to become the fruit.

oviparous (L. *ovum,* egg + *parere,* to bring forth) Refers to reproduction in which the eggs are developed after leaving the body of the mother, as in reptiles.

ovulation The successful development and release of an egg by the ovary.

ovule (L. *ovulum,* a little egg) A structure in a seed plant that becomes a seed when mature.

ovum, *pl.* ova (L. egg) A mature egg cell. A female gamete.

oxidation (Fr. *oxider,* to oxidize) The loss of an electron during a chemical reaction from one atom to another. Occurs simultaneously with reduction. Is the second stage of the 10 reactions of glycolysis.

oxidative metabolism A collective term for metabolic reactions requiring oxygen.

oxidative respiration Respiration in which the final electron acceptor is molecular oxygen.

P

pancreas (Gr. *pan*, all + *kreas*, flesh) A gland located near the stomach that secretes digestive enzymes into the small intestine and hormones into the blood.

parasitism (Gr. *para,* beside + *sitos,* food) A symbiotic relationship in which one organism benefits and the other is harmed.

parthenogenesis (Gr. *parthenos,* virgin + Eng. *genesis,* beginning) The development of an adult from an unfertilized egg. A common form of reproduction in insects.

partial pressures (P) The components of each individual gas—such as nitrogen, oxygen, and carbon dioxide—that together constitute the total air pressure.

pathogen (Gr. *pathos,* suffering + Eng. *genesis,* beginning) A disease-causing organism.

pedigree (L. *pes,* foot + *grus,* crane) A family tree. The patterns of inheritance observed in family histories. Used to determine the mode of inheritance of a particular trait.

peptide (Gr. *peptein,* to soften, digest) Two or more amino acids linked by peptide bonds.

peptide bond A covalent bond linking two amino acids. Formed when the positive (amino, or NH_2) group at one end and a negative (carboxyl, or COOH) group at the other end undergo a chemical reaction and lose a molecule of water.

peristalsis (Gr. *peri,* around + *stellein,* to wrap) The rhythmic sequences of waves of muscular contraction in the walls of a tube.

pH Refers to the concentration of H^+ ions in a solution. The numerical value of the pH is the negative of the exponent of the molar concentration. Low pH values indicate high concentrations of H^+ ions (acids), and high pH values indicate low concentrations (bases).

phagocyte (Gr. *phagein,* to eat + *kytos,* hollow vessel) A cell that kills invading cells by engulfing them. Includes neutrophils and macrophages.

phagocytosis (Gr. *phagein,* to eat + *kytos,* hollow vessel) A form of endocytosis in which cells engulf organisms or fragments of organisms.

phenotype (Gr. *phainein,* to show + *typos,* stamp or print) The realized expression of the genotype. The observable expression of a trait (affecting an individual's structure, physiology, or behavior) that results from the biological activity of proteins or RNA molecules transcribed from the DNA.

pheromone (Gr. *pherein,* to carry + [hor]mone) A chemical signal emitted by certain animals as a means of communication.

phloem (Gr. *phloos,* bark) In vascular plants, a food-conducting tissue basically composed of sieve elements, various kinds of parenchyma cells, fibers, and sclereids.

phosphodiester bond The bond that results from the formation of a nucleic acid chain in which individual sugars are linked together in a line by the phosphate groups. The phosphate group of one sugar binds to the hydroxyl group of another, forming an—O—P—O bond.

phospholipid A macromolecule similar in structure to a fat, but having only two fatty acids attached to the glycerol backbone, with the third space linked to a phosphorylated molecule; contains a polar hydrophilic "head" end (phosphate group) and a nonpolar hydrophobic "tail" end (fatty acids).

photon (Gr. *photos,* light) The unit of light energy.

photoperiodism (Gr. *photos,* light + *periodos,* a period) A mechanism that organisms use to measure seasonal changes in relative day and night length.

photorespiration A process in which carbon dioxide is released without the production of ATP or NADPH. Because it produces neither ATP nor NADPH, photorespiration acts to undo the work of photosynthesis.

photosynthesis (Gr. *photos,* light + *-syn,* together + *tithenai,* to place) The process by which plants, algae, and some bacteria use the energy of sunlight to create from carbon dioxide (CO_2) and water (H_2O) the more complicated molecules that make up living organisms.

photosystem An organized complex of chlorophyll, other pigments, and proteins that traps light energy as excited electrons. Plants have two linked photosystems in the thylakoid membrane of chloroplasts.

phototropism (Gr. *photos,* light + *trope,* turning to light) A plant's growth response to a unidirectional light source.

phylogeny (Gr. *phylon,* race, tribe) The evolutionary relationships among any group of organisms.

phylum, *pl.* phyla *(Gr. phylon,* race, tribe) A major taxonomic category, ranking above a class.

physiology (Gr. *physis,* nature + *logos,* a discourse) The study of the function of cells, tissues, and organs.

pigment (L. *pigmentum,* paint) A molecule that absorbs light.

pili (pilus) Short flagella that occur on the cell surface of some prokaryotes.

pinocytosis (Gr. *pinein,* to drink + *kytos,* cell) A form of endocytosis in which the material brought into the cell is a liquid containing dissolved molecules.

pistil (L. *pistillum,* pestle) Central organ of flowers, typically consisting of ovary, style, and stigma; a pistil may consist of one or more fused carpels and is more technically and better known as the gynoecium.

pituitary gland (L. *pituitarius,* mucus) Endocrine gland at the base of the hypothalamus, composed of anterior and posterior lobes. Pituitary hormones affect a wide variety of processes in vertebrates.

plankton (Gr. *planktos,* wandering) The small organisms that float or drift in water, especially at or near the surface.

plasma (Gr. form) The fluid of vertebrate blood. Contains dissolved salts, metabolic wastes, hormones, and a variety of proteins, including antibodies and albumin. Blood minus the blood cells.

plasma membrane A lipid bilayer with embedded proteins that control the cell's permeability to water and dissolved substances.

plasmid (Gr. *plasma,* a form or something molded) A small fragment of DNA that replicates independently of the bacterial chromosome.

plasmodesmata (Gr. *plasma,* form + *desma,* bond) In plants, cytoplasmic connections between adjacent cells.

platelet (Gr. dim of *plattus,* flat) In mammals, a fragment of a white blood cell that circulates in the blood and functions in the formation of blood clots at sites of injury.

pleiotropy (Gr. *pleros,* more + *trope,* a turning) A gene that produces more than one phenotypic effect.

polar molecule A molecule with positively and negatively charged ends. One portion of a polar molecule attracts electrons more strongly than another portion, with the result that the molecule has electron-rich (–) and electron-poor (+) regions, giving it magnetlike positive and negative poles. Water is one of the most polar molecules known.

polarization The charge difference of a neuron so that the interior of the cell is negative with respect to the exterior.

pollen (L. fine dust) A fine, yellowish powder consisting of grains or microspores, each of which contains a mature or immature male gametophyte. In flowering plants, pollen is released from the anthers of flowers and fertilizes the pistils.

pollen tube A tube that grows from a pollen grain. Male reproductive cells move through the pollen tube into the ovule.

pollination The transfer of pollen from the anthers to the stigmas of flowers for fertilization, as by insects or the wind.

polygyny (Gr. *poly,* many + *gyne,* woman, wife) A mating system in which a male mates with more than one female.

polymer (Gr. *polus,* many + *meris,* part) A large molecule formed of long chains of similar molecules called monomers.

polymerase chain reaction (PCR) A process by which DNA polymerase is used to copy a sequence of DNA repeatedly, making millions of copies of the same DNA.

polymorphism (Gr. *polys,* many + *morphe,* form) The presence in a population of more than one allele of a gene at a frequency greater than that of newly arising mutations.

polynomial system (Gr. *polys,* many + [bi]nomial) Before Linnaeus, naming a genus by use of a cumbersome string of Latin words and phrases.

polyp A cylindrical, pipe-shaped cnidarian usually attached to a rock with the mouth facing away from the rock on which it is growing. Coral is made up of polyps.

polypeptide (Gr. *polys,* many + *peptein,* to digest) A general term for a long chain of amino acids linked end to end by peptide bonds. A protein is a long, complex polypeptide.

polysaccharide (Gr. *polys,* many + *sakcharon,* sugar) A sugar polymer. A carbohydrate composed of many monosaccharide sugar subunits linked together in a long chain.

population (L. *populus,* the people) Any group of individuals of a single species, occupying a given area at the same time.

posterior (L. *post,* after) Situated behind or farther back.

potential difference A difference in electrical charge on two sides of a membrane caused by an unequal distribution of ions.

potential energy Energy with the potential to do work. Stored energy.

predation (L. *praeda,* prey) The eating of other organisms. The one doing the eating is called a predator, and the one being consumed is called the prey.

primary growth In vascular plants, growth originating in the apical meristems of shoots and roots, as contrasted with secondary growth; results in an increase in length.

primary plant body The part of a plant that arises from the apical meristems.

primary producers Photosynthetic organisms, including plants, algae, and photosynthetic bacteria.

primary structure of a protein The sequence of amino acids that makes up a particular polypeptide chain.

primordium, *pl.* primordia (*L. primus,* first + *ordiri,* begin) The first cells in the earliest stages of the development of an organ or structure.

productivity The total amount of energy of an ecosystem fixed by photosynthesis per unit of time. Net productivity is productivity minus that which is expended by the metabolic activity of the organisms in the community.

prokaryote (Gr. *pro,* before + *karyon,* kernel) A simple organism that is small, single-celled, and has little evidence of internal structure.

promoter An RNA polymerase binding site. The nucleotide sequence at the end of a gene to which RNA polymerase attaches to initiate transcription of mRNA.

prophase (Gr. *pro,* before + *phasis,* form) The first stage of mitosis during which the chromosomes become more condensed, the nuclear envelope is reabsorbed, and a network of microtubules (called the spindle) forms between opposite poles of the cell.

protein (Gr. *proteios,* primary) A long chain of amino acids linked end to end by peptide bonds. Because the 20 amino acids that occur in proteins have side groups with very different chemical properties, the function and shape of a protein is critically affected by its particular sequence of amino acids.

protist (Gr. *protos,* first) A member of the kingdom Protista, which includes unicellular eukaryotic organisms and some multicellular lines derived from them.

proton A subatomic particle in the nucleus of an atom that carries a positive charge. The number of protons determines the chemical character of the atom because it dictates the number of electrons orbiting the nucleus and available for chemical activity.

protostome (Gr. *protos,* first + *stoma,* mouth) An animal in whose embryonic development the mouth forms at or near the blastopore. Also characterized by spiral cleavage.

pseudocoel (Gr. *pseudos,* false + *koiloma,* cavity) A body cavity similar to the coelom except that it forms between the mesoderm and endoderm.

punctuated equilibrium A hypothesis of the mechanism of evolutionary change that proposes that long periods of little or no change are punctuated by periods of rapid evolution.

purine (L. *purus,* pure + *urina,* urine) The larger of the two general kinds of nucleotide base found in DNA and RNA; a nitrogenous base with a double-ring structure, such as adenine or guanine.

pyrimidine (alter. of pyridine, from Gr. *pyr,* fire + *id,* adj. suffix + *ine*) The smaller of two general kinds of nucleotide base found in DNA and RNA; a nitrogenous base with a single-ring structure, such as cytosine, thymine, or uracil.

Q

quaternary structure of a protein A term to describe the way multiple protein subunits are assembled into a whole.

R

radial symmetry (L. *radius,* a spoke of a wheel + Gr. *summetros,* symmetry) The regular arrangement of parts around a central axis so that any plane passing through the central axis divides the organism into halves that are approximate mirror images.

radioactivity The emission of nuclear particles and rays by unstable atoms as they decay into more stable forms. Measured in curies, with 1 curie equal to 37 billion disintegrations a second.

radula (L. scraper) A rasping, tonguelike organ characteristic of most mollusks.

recessive allele An allele whose phenotype effects are masked in heterozygotes by the presence of a dominant allele.

recombination The formation of new gene combinations. In bacteria, it is accomplished by the transfer of genes into cells, often in association with viruses. In eukaryotes, it is accomplished by reassortment of chromosomes during meiosis and by crossing over.

reducing power The use of light energy to extract hydrogen atoms from water.

reduction (L. *reductio,* a bringing back; originally, "bringing back" a metal from its oxide) The gain of an electron during a chemical reaction from one atom to another. Occurs simultaneously with oxidation.

reflex (L. *reflectere,* to bend back) An automatic consequence of a nerve stimulation. The motion that results from a nerve impulse passing through the system of neurons, eventually reaching the body muscles and causing them to contract.

refractory period The recovery period after membrane depolarization during which the membrane is unable to respond to additional stimulation.

renal (L. *renes,* kidneys) Pertaining to the kidney.

repression (L. *reprimere,* to press back, keep back) The process of blocking transcription by the placement of the regulatory protein between the polymerase and the gene, thus blocking movement of the polymerase to the gene.

repressor (L. *reprimere,* to press back, keep back) A protein that regulates transcription of mRNA from DNA by binding to the operator and so preventing RNA polymerase from attaching to the promoter.

resolving power The ability of a microscope to distinguish two points as separate.

respiration (L. *respirare,* to breathe) The utilization of oxygen. In terrestrial vertebrates, the inhalation of oxygen and the exhalation of carbon dioxide.

resting membrane potential The charge difference that exists across a neuron's membrane at rest (about 70 millivolts).

restriction enzyme (restriction endonuclease) A special kind of enzyme that can recognize and cleave DNA molecules into fragments. One of the basic tools of genetic engineering.

retrovirus (L. *retro,* turning back) A virus whose genetic material is RNA rather than DNA. When a retrovirus infects a cell, it makes a DNA copy of itself, which it can then insert into the cellular DNA as if it were a cellular gene.

ribonucleic acid (RNA) A class of nucleic acids characterized by the presence of the sugar ribose and the pyrimidine uracil; includes mRNA, tRNA, rRNA, and siRNA.

ribose A five-carbon sugar.

ribosome A cell structure composed of protein and RNA that translates RNA copies of genes into protein.

RNA interference A type of gene silencing in which the mRNA transcript is prevented from being translated; small interfering RNAs (siRNAs) have been found to bind to mRNA and target its degradation prior to its translation.

RNA polymerase The enzyme that transcribes RNA from DNA.

root The usually descending axis of a plant, normally belowground, which anchors the plant and serves as the major point of entry for water and minerals.

S

saltatory conduction A very fast form of nerve impulse conduction in which the impulses leap from node to node over insulated portions.

sarcoma (Gr. *sarx,* flesh) A cancerous tumor that involves connective or hard tissue, such as muscle.

sarcomere (Gr. *sarx,* flesh + *meris,* part of) The fundamental unit of contraction in skeletal muscle. The repeating bands of actin and myosin that appear between two Z lines.

sarcoplasmic reticulum (Gr. *sarx,* flesh + *plassein,* to form, mold; L. *reticulum,* network) The endoplasmic reticulum of a muscle cell. A sleeve of membrane that wraps around each myofilament.

scientific creationism A view that the biblical account of the origin of the earth is literally true, that the earth is much younger than most scientists believe, and that all species of organisms were individually created just as they are today.

second messenger An intermediary compound that couples extracellular signals to intracellular processes and also amplifies a hormonal signal.

secondary growth In vascular plants, growth that results from the division of a cylinder of cells around the plant's periphery. Secondary growth causes a plant to grow in diameter.

secondary structure of a protein The folding and bending of a polypeptide chain, which is held in place by hydrogen bonds.

seed A structure that develops from the mature ovule of a seed plant. Contains an embryo and a food source surrounded by a protective coat.

selection The process by which some organisms leave more offspring than competing ones and their genetic traits tend to appear in greater proportions among members of succeeding generations than the traits of those individuals that leave fewer offspring.

self-fertilization The transfer of pollen from an anther to a stigma in the same flower or to another flower of the same plant.

sepal (L. *sepalum,* a covering) A member of the outermost whorl of a flowering plant. Collectively, the sepals constitute the calyx.

septum, *pl.* septa (*L. saeptum,* a fence) A partition or cross-wall, such as those that divide fungal hyphae into cells.

sex chromosomes In humans, the X and Y chromosomes, which are different in the two sexes and are involved in sex determination.

sex-linked characteristic A genetic characteristic that is determined by genes located on the sex chromosomes.

sexual reproduction Reproduction that involves the regular alternation between syngamy and meiosis. Its outstanding characteristic is that an individual offspring inherits genes from two parent individuals.

shoot In vascular plants, the aboveground parts, such as the stem and leaves.

sieve cell In the phloem (food-conducting tissue) of vascular plants, a long, slender sieve element with relatively unspecialized sieve areas and with tapering end walls that lack sieve plates. Found in all vascular plants except angiosperms, which have sieve-tube members.

soluble Refers to polar molecules that dissolve in water and are surrounded by a hydration shell.

solute The molecules dissolved in a solution. *See also* solution, solvent.

solution A mixture of molecules, such as sugars, amino acids, and ions, dissolved in water.

solvent The most common of the molecules in a solution. Usually a liquid, commonly water.

somatic cells (Gr. *soma,* body) All the diploid body cells of an animal that are not involved in gamete formation.

somite A segmented block of tissue on either side of a developing notochord.

species, *pl.* species (L. kind, sort) A group of interbreeding organisms that are reproductively isolated from all other such groups; a taxonomic unit ranking below a genus and designated by a two-part scientific name consisting of its genus and the species name.

sperm (Gr. *sperma,* sperm, seed) A sperm cell. The male gamete.

spindle The mitotic assembly that carries out the separation of chromosomes during cell division. Composed of microtubules and assembled during prophase at the centrioles of the dividing cell.

spore (Gr. *spora,* seed) A haploid reproductive cell, usually unicellular, that is capable of developing into an adult without fusion with another cell. Spores result from meiosis, as do gametes, but gametes fuse immediately to produce a new diploid cell.

sporophyte (Gr. *spora,* seed + *phyton,* plant) The spore-producing, diploid ($2n$) phase in the life cycle of a plant having alternation of generations.

stabilizing selection A form of selection in which selection acts to eliminate both extremes from a range of phenotypes.

stamen (L. thread) The part of the flower that contains the pollen. Consists of a slender filament that supports the anther. A flower that produces only pollen is called staminate and is functionally male.

steroid (Gr. *stereos,* solid + L. *ol,* from oleum, oil) A kind of lipid. Many of the molecules that function as messengers and pass across cell membranes are steroids, such as the male and female sex hormones and cholesterol.

steroid hormone A hormone derived from cholesterol. Those that promote the development of the secondary sexual characteristics are steroids.

stigma (Gr. mark) A specialized area of the carpel of a flowering plant that receives the pollen.

stoma, *pl.* stomata (Gr. mouth) A specialized opening in the leaves of some plants that allows carbon dioxide to pass into the plant body and allows water vapor and oxygen to pass out of them.

stratum corneum The outer layer of the epidermis of the skin of the vertebrate body.

stroma (Gr. *stroma,* anything spread out) In chloroplasts, the semiliquid substance that surrounds the thylakoids and that contains the enzymes needed to assemble organic molecules from CO_2.

style (Gr. *stylos,* column) In flowers, the slender column of carpel tissue that arises from the top of the ovary and through which the pollen tube grows.

substrate (L. *substratus,* strewn under) A molecule on which an enzyme acts.

substrate-level phosphorylation The generation of ATP by coupling its synthesis to a strongly exergonic (energy-yielding) reaction.

succession In ecology, the slow, orderly progression of changes in community composition that takes place through time. Primary succession occurs in nature on bare substrates, over long periods of time. Secondary succession occurs when a climax community has been disturbed.

sugar Any monosaccharide or disaccharide.

surface tension A tautness of the surface of a liquid, caused by the cohesion of the liquid molecules. Water has an extremely high surface tension.

surface-to-volume ratio Describes cell size increases. Cell volume grows much more rapidly than surface area.

symbiosis (Gr. *syn,* together with + *bios,* life) The condition in which two or more dissimilar organisms live together in close association; includes parasitism, commensalism, and mutualism.

sympatric species (Gr. *syn,* together with + *patra,* fatherland, country) Closely related species that occupy the same geographical area.

synapse (Gr. *synapsis,* a union) A junction between a neuron and another neuron or muscle cell. The two cells do not touch. Instead, neurotransmitters cross the narrow space between them.

synapsis (Gr. *synapsis,* contact, union) The close pairing of homologous chromosomes that occurs early in prophase I of meiosis. With the genes of the chromosomes thus aligned, a DNA strand of one homologue can pair with the complementary DNA strand of the other.

syngamy (Gr. *syn,* together with + *gamos,* marriage) Fertilization. The union of male and female gametes.

T

T cell A type of lymphocyte involved in cell-mediated immune responses and interactions with B cells. Also called a T lymphocyte.

taxon, *pl.* taxa (Gr. *taxis,* arrangement) A group of organisms at a particular level in a classification system.

taxonomy (Gr. *taxis,* arrangement + *nomos,* law) The science of the classification of organisms.

telophase (Gr. *telos,* end + *phasis,* form) The phase of cell division during which the spindle breaks down, the nuclear envelope of each daughter cell forms, and the chromosomes uncoil and decondense.

tendon (Gr. *tenon,* stretch) A strap of connective tissue that attaches muscle to bone.

tertiary structure of a protein The three-dimensional shape of a protein. Primarily the result of hydrophobic interactions of amino acid side groups and, to a lesser extent, of hydrogen bonds between them. Forms spontaneously.

testcross A cross between an individual of unknown genotype and a recessive homozygote. A procedure used to determine a dominant individual's genotype.

testis, *pl.* testes (L. witness) In animals, the sperm-producing organ.

theory (Gr. *theorein,* to look at) A well-tested hypothesis supported by a great deal of evidence.

thigmotropism (Gr. *thigma,* touch + *trope,* a turning) The growth response of a plant to touch.

thorax (Gr. a breastplate) The part of the body between the head and the abdomen.

thylakoid (Gr. *thylakos,* sac + *-oides,* like) A flattened, saclike membrane in the chloroplast of a eukaryote. Thylakoids are stacked on top of one another in arrangements called grana and are the sites of photosystem reactions.

tissue (L. *texere,* to weave) A group of similar cells organized into a structural and functional unit.

totipotent (L. *totus*, entire + *potent*, to be able, have power) The condition in which a cell has the potential to form any body tissue or an entire organism.

trachea, *pl.* tracheae (L. windpipe) In vertebrates, the windpipe.

tracheid (Gr. *tracheia,* rough) An elongated cell with thick, perforated walls that carries water and dissolved minerals through a plant and provides support. Tracheids form an essential element of the xylem of vascular plants.

transcription (L. *trans,* across + *scribere,* to write) The first stage of gene expression in which the RNA polymerase enzyme synthesizes an mRNA molecule whose sequence is complementary to the DNA.

translation (L. *trans,* across + *latus,* that which is carried) The second stage of gene expression in which a ribosome assembles a polypeptide, using the mRNA to specify the amino acids.

translocation (L. *trans,* across + *locare,* to put or place) In plants, the process in which most of the carbohydrates manufactured in the leaves and other green parts of the plant are moved through the phloem to other parts of the plant.

transpiration (L. *trans,* across + *spirare,* to breathe) The loss of water vapor by plant parts, primarily through the stomata.

transposon (L. *transponere,* to change the position of) A DNA sequence carrying one or more genes and flanked by insertion sequences that confer the ability to move from one DNA molecule to another. An element capable of transposition (the changing of chromosomal location).

trophic level (Gr. *trophos,* feeder) A step in the movement of energy through an ecosystem.

tropism (Gr. *trop,* turning) A plant's response to external stimuli. A positive tropism is one in which the movement or reaction is in the direction of the source of the stimulus. A negative tropism is one in which the movement or growth is in the opposite direction.

turgor pressure (L. *turgor,* a swelling) The pressure within a cell that results from the movement of water into the cell. A cell with high turgor pressure is said to be turgid.

U

unicellular Composed of a single cell.

urea (Gr. *ouron,* urine) An organic molecule formed in the vertebrate liver. The principal form of disposal of nitrogenous wastes by mammals.

urine (Gr. *ouron,* urine) The liquid waste filtered from the blood by the kidneys.

V

vaccination The injection of a harmless microbe into a person or animal to confer resistance to a dangerous microbe.

vacuole (L. *vacuus,* empty) A cavity in the cytoplasm of a cell that is bound by a single membrane and contains water and waste products of cell metabolism. Typically found in plant cells.

van der Waals forces Weak chemical attractions between atoms that can occur when atoms are very close to each other.

variable Any factor that influences a process. In evaluating alternative hypotheses about one variable, all other variables are held constant so that the investigator is not misled or confused by other influences.

vascular bundle In vascular plants, a strand of tissue containing primary xylem and primary phloem. These bundles of elongated cells conduct water with dissolved minerals and carbohydrates throughout the plant body.

vascular cambium In vascular plants, the meristematic layer of cells that gives rise to secondary phloem and secondary xylem. The activity of the vascular cambium increases stem or root diameter.

vein (L. *vena,* a vein) (1) In plants, a vascular bundle forming a part of the framework of the conducting and supporting tissue of a stem or leaf. (2) In animals, any blood vessel that carries blood toward the heart.

ventral (L. *venter,* belly) Refers to the bottom portion of an animal. Opposite of dorsal.

vertebrate An animal having a backbone made of bony segments called vertebrae.

vesicle (L. *vesicula,* a little ladder) Membrane-enclosed sacs within eukaryotic cells.

vessel element In vascular plants, a typically elongated cell, dead at maturity, that conducts water and solutes in the xylem.

villus, *pl.* villi (L. a tuft of hair) In vertebrates, fine, microscopic, fingerlike projections on epithelial cells lining the small intestine that serve to increase the absorptive surface area of the intestine.

virus (L. slimy liquid, poison) Any of a group of complex biochemical entities consisting of genetic material wrapped in protein; viruses can reproduce only within living host cells and are thus not considered organisms.

vitamin (L. *vita,* life + *amine,* of chemical origin) An organic substance that the organism cannot synthesize, but is required in minute quantities by an organism for growth and activity.

viviparous (L. *vivus,* alive + *parere,* to bring forth) Refers to reproduction in which eggs develop within the mother's body and young are born free-living.

voltage-gated channel A transmembrane pathway for an ion that is opened or closed by a change in the voltage, or charge difference, across the cell membrane.

W

water vascular system The system of water-filled canals connecting the tube feet of echinoderms.

wood Accumulated secondary xylem. Heartwood is the central, nonliving wood in the trunk of a tree. Hardwood is the wood of dicots, regardless of how hard or soft it actually is. Softwood is the wood of conifers.

X

xylem (Gr. *xylon,* wood) In vascular plants, a specialized tissue, composed primarily of elongate, thick-walled conducting cells, that transports water and solutes through the plant body.

Y

yolk (O.E. *geolu,* yellow) The stored substance in egg cells that provides the embryo's primary food supply.

Z

zygote (Gr. *zygotos,* paired together) The diploid ($2n$) cell resulting from the fusion of male and female gametes (fertilization).

Credits

Photographs

Chapter 0

Opener: © Getty RF; 0.2: © BananaStock/JupiterImages RF; 0.4: © Corbis RF; p. 5: © Corbis RF; p. 6: © Getty RF; 0.9(corn): © Corbis RF; 0.9 (duck): © Index Stock RF; 0.9(cell): © University of Wisconsin-Madison News & Public Affairs; 0.9(sunbather): © Corbis RF; 0.9(Darwin): © Huntington Library/Superstock; 0.9(runner): © Pete Saloutos/Corbis; 0.10: © Brand X Pictures/PunchStock RF; 0.11: © Corbis RF; 0.12: The McGraw-Hill Companies, Inc. Lars A. Niki, photographer; 0.13: NASA.

Chapter 1

Opener: © Digital Vision/Getty RF; 1.1(archaea): © R. Robinson/Visuals Unlimited; 1.1(bacteria): © Alfred Pasieka/SPL/Photo Researchers; 1.1(protista, plantae): © Corbis RF; 1.1(fungi, animalia): © Getty RF; 1.2: © Tom E. Adams/Visuals Unlimited; 1.3: © Corbis RF; 1.4(population, species left): © Raymond Gehman/Corbis; 1.4(goose, crane): © Jim Bailey; 1.4(species right): © Corbis RF; 1.4(community, ecosystem): © Winfried Wisniewski/zefa/Corbis; p. 20(top left): © Joe McDonald/Animals Animals; p. 20(bottom left): © Tom McHugh/Photo Researchers; p. 20(right): © Kenneth Fink/Photo Researchers; p. 20-21(eagle, ants, hippo): © Corbis RF; p. 21(moth): © George Grall/National Geographic/Getty Images; 1.6: © Digital Vision/Getty RF; 1.7 (top): © Stocktrek/age fotostock RF; 1.7(middle): © Tom Pepeira, photographer/Iconotec RF; 1.7 (bottom): © Digital Vision/Getty RF; 1.8: © Dennis Kunkel/Phototake; 1.11: © Leonard Lessin/Peter Arnold/Photolibrary; p. 30: © Michael & Patricia Fogden/Corbis; p. 31(bird): © Corbis RF; p. 31(sunset): © Tom Pepeira, photographer/Iconotec RF.

Chapter 2

Opener: © Digital Archive Japan/Alamy RF; 2.1: © Thinkstock Images/Jupiter RF; 2.7: Courtesy Todd M. Blodgett, MD, University of Pittsburgh Medical Center; 2.8b_2: © The McGraw-Hill Companies, Inc.; 2.9c: © Bettmann/Corbis; p. 39: © Geostock/Getty RF; 2.11c: © Digital Archive Japan/Alamy RF; p. 41: Courtesy Who Zoo (whozoo.org); 2.12b, 2.13a: © Corbis RF; 2.13b: © Hermann Eisenbeiss/National Audubon Society Collection/Photo Researchers; 2.15(top): © The McGraw-Hill Companies/Bob Coyle, photographer; 2.15(middle): © The McGraw-Hill Companies, Inc. Jacques Cornell, photographer; 2.15(bottom): © The McGraw-Hill Companies, Inc. Jill Braaten photographer; p. 45: © Gilbert S. Grant/National Audubon Society Collection/Photo Researchers; p. 46(both): © Photo Archives South Tyrol Museum of Archaeology—www.iceman.it; p. 48: © Hermann Eisenbeiss/National Audubon Society Collection/Photo Researchers.

Chapter 3

Opener: © Michael Viard/Peter Arnold/Photolibrary; 3.1(both): © The McGraw-Hill Companies, Inc.; 3.5a: © Corbis; 3.5b-c: © Getty RF; 3.5d: © Photodisc/Getty RF; 3.5e: © Phototake/Alamy; 3.5f: © Dennis Kunkel Microscopy, Inc.; 3.6: © The McGraw-Hill Companies, Inc. Gary He, photographer; 3.9a: © Dr. Gopal Murti/Visuals Unlimited; 3.13: © Michael Viard/Peter Arnold/Photolibrary; 3.15: © J.D. Litvay/Visuals Unlimited; Table 3.1(cow, potatoes, leaves): © Corbis RF; Table 3.1(sugarcane): © PhotoLink/Getty RF; Table 3.1(arm): © Getty RF; Table 3.1(lobster): © Scott Johnson/Animals Animals; 3.17a: © Getty RF; 3.17b: © C Squared Studios/Getty RF; p. 61: © Otto Greule Jr/Getty Images; p. 62: © Dr. David M. Phillips/Visuals Unlimited.

Chapter 4

Opener: © Manfred Kage/Peter Arnold/Photolibrary; 4.2: © Dr. Tony Brain & David Parker/Photo Researchers; p. 68(LM): © David M. Phillips/Visuals Unlimited; p. 68(TEM): © Microworks/Phototake; p. 68(SEM): © Stanley Flegler/Visuals Unlimited; 4.4a: © Andrew Syred/Photo Researchers; 4.4b: © Alfred Pasieka/Photo Researchers; 4.4c: © Microfield Scientific Ltd/Photo Researchers; 4.10: This image was published in "Medical Cell biology" by Charles J. Flickinger; Elsevier Health Science Books 1979; 4.12: © Biophoto Associates/Photo Researchers; 4.13: © Don W. Fawcett/Visuals Unlimited; 4.14: Courtesy Dr. Kenneth Miller, Brown University; 4.17: © Manfred Kage/Peter Arnold/Photolibrary; 4.20: Courtesy Dr. Birgit Satir, Albert Einstein College of Medicine; p. 86: © SIU/Visuals Unlimited.

Chapter 5

Opener: © Andrew Darrington/Alamy; 5.1a: © Nice One Productions/Corbis RF; 5.2: © Andrew Darrington/Alamy; 5.3 (both): © Keith Eng, 2008 RF.

Chapter 6

Opener: © Corbis RF; Table 6.1: © Beateworks/Corbis RF; p. 107: © Corbis RF; 6.4: © Andrew Syred/Photo Researchers; 6.6: © Corbis RF; p. 114: © Philip Sze/Visuals Unlimited.

Chapter 7

Opener: © John Gerlach/Animals Animals; 7.1: © BananaStock/PunchStock RF; 7.5: © John Gerlach/Animals Animals; p. 123(tree): © Corbis RF; p. 123(zebra, lion): © Getty RF; p. 123(hyena and vultures): © Photodisc/Getty RF; p. 123(butterflies): © Edward S. Ross; p. 129: © Corbis RF; p. 130: U.S. Fish & Wildlife Service.

Chapter 8

Opener: © Andrew S. Bajer; 8.1b: © Lee D. Simon/Photo Researchers; 8.4: © SPL/Photo Researchers; p. 138-139(all) & 8.6: © Andrew S. Bajer; 8.7a: © David M. Phillips/Visuals Unlimited; 8.8: © Cabisco/Visuals Unlimited; 8.9: © Moredun Animal Health LTD/SPL/Photo Researchers; p. 144: Courtesy Priv. Doz. Dr. Roland Zell; p. 146: © SPL/Photo Researchers.

Chapter 9

Opener: © Adrian T Sumner/SPL/Photo Researchers; 9.2: © MIXA/Getty RF; 9.4a: © MedicalRF.com/Corbis RF; 9.4b: © Creatas/PunchStock RF; 9.4c: © Wetzel and Company RF; p. 152-153(all): © C.A. Hasenkampf/Biological Photo Service; 9.7: © Adrian T Sumner/SPL/Photo Researchers; p. 156: Reprinted with permission from Science Vol. 311, no. 5759 20 January 2006. Image: Khodjakov. Copyright 2006 AAAS.

Chapter 10

Opener: © Richard Gross/Biological Photography; 10.1: © Digital Vision/PunchStock RF; 10.2: © Time & Life Pictures/Getty Images; 10.4: © Richard Gross/Biological Photography; 10.5: R. W. Van Norman/Visuals Unlimited; p. 164(meter): Look-alike Meter graphic © MyHeritage.com, used with permission; p. 164(Katie, Tom): © Dave M. Benett/Getty Images; p. 164(Suri): © Marcel Thomas/FilmMagic/Getty Images; 10.12a: Albert F. Blakeslee, Of Corn and Men: The Interacting Influence of Heredity and Environment Ñ Movements for Betterment of Men, or Corn, or Any Other Living Thing, One-sided Unless They Take Both Factors into Account, The Journal of Heredity, 1914, vol. 5 (11): 511-518, by permission of Oxford University Press; 10.15a-b: © Fred Bruemmer; p. 172: © RubberBall Productions/Getty RF; 10.16: © Corbis; 10.18: © CBS/Phototake; 10.22b: © Stockbyte/Veer RF; 10.25: The Field Museum #CSA118, Chicago; 10.26: Reproduced from Ishihara's Tests for Colour Deficiency published by Kanehara Trading, Tokyo, Japan. Tests for color deficiency cannot be conducted with this material. For accurate testing, the original plates should be used. 10.28: © Bettmann/Corbis; 10.29(both): © Stanley Flegler/Visuals Unlimited; 10.34: © Yoav Levy/Phototake; p. 185: Otto L. Mohr, Woolly Hair A Dominant Mutant Character in Man, Journal of Heredity 1932, v.23, pp.345-352 by permission of Oxford University Press; p. 186: © Time & Life Pictures/Getty Images.

Chapter 11

Opener: © Michael Dunning/Getty Images; p. 192: © Michael Dunning/Getty Images; 11.4(Franklin): © Science Source/Photo Researchers; 11.4a: From J.D. Watson, The Double Helix Atheneum, New York, 1968.

Cold Spring Harbor Lab; 11.4b: © A.C. Barrington Brown/Photo Researchers; 11.9: © David Scharf; p. 200: © Brand X Pictures/PunchStock RF; p. 201: © Corbis RF.

Chapter 12

Opener: N. Ban, P. Nissen, J. Hansen, P.B. Moore & T.A. Steitz, "The Complete Atomic Structure of the Large Ribosomal Subunit at 2.4 A Resolution," reprinted with permission from Science v. 289 #5481, p. 917. © American Association for the Advancement of Science; 12.2: R C Williams, "Use of polyline for adsorption of nucleic acids and enzymes to electron microscope specimen films," PNAS vol. 74, no.6 (1977); 2313; 12.6: N. Ban, P. Nissen, J. Hansen, P.B. Moore & T.A. Steitz, "The Complete Atomic Structure of the Large Ribosomal Subunit at 2.4 A Resolution," reprinted with permission from Science v. 289 #5481, p. 917. © American Association for the Advancement of Science; 12.11: Courtesy Dr. Oscar L. Miller; 12.16: Courtesy Dr. Victoria Foe.

Chapter 13

Opener: Courtesy The Roslin Institute, The University of Edinburgh; 13.3: The Colorado Genetics Laboratory, Denver, CO; 13.4(doctor): Courtesy Dr. Ken Culver, Photo by John Crawford, National Institutes of Health; 13.4(fish): Robert H. Devlin/Fisheries & Oceans Canada; 13.4(cotton): Courtesy Monsanto Company; 13.7: Courtesy Gen-Probe Transplant Diagnostics Inc.; 13.8: R.L. Brinster, School of Veterinary Medicine, University of Pennsylvania; p. 232, p. 233(DNA): © Getty RF; p. 233(Clinton): © AFP/Getty Images; p. 233(gel): Courtesy Bio-Rad Laboratories, Inc.; 13.11: Courtesy Monsanto Company; 13.12: Golden Rice Humanitarian Board: www.goldenrice.org; 13.13: © Getty Images; 13.14: Courtesy The Roslin Institute, The University of Edinburgh; 13.15(Snuppy and dad): © AP Photo/Hwang Woo-suk; 13.15(Snuppy's "mom"): © Seoul National University/Handout/Reuters/ Corbis; 13.16: © University of Wisconsin-Madison News & Public Affairs; 13.17: © Alex Wong/Getty Images; 13.19: © SUW-Madison News & Public Affairs University of Wisconsin-Madison, Photo by Jeff Miller; 13.21: C. Garon & J. Rose/NIAID/NIH; p. 246: © Getty RF; p. 248: Courtesy The Roslin Institute, The University of Edinburgh.

Chapter 14

Opener: © Doug Cheeseman/Peter Arnold/Getty Images; 14.1: © Huntington Library/Superstock; 14.2: From Darwin, the Life of a Tormented Evolutionist, by Adrian Desmond; 14.7: © Digital Vision/Getty RF; 14.8: © Mary Evans Picture Library/Photo Researchers; 14.9: © Doug Cheeseman/Peter Arnold/ Getty Images; 14.10(both): Courtesy Dr. Arkhat Abzhanov, Harvard School of Dental Medicine, Photographer: Dr. Peter Grant of Princeton University; 14.13: © Andy Crawford/Getty Images; 14.15: Courtesy Michael Richardson and Ronan O'Rahilly; 14.19: © Ted Daeschler/VIREO; 14.21a: © Dr. David M. Phillips/Visuals Unlimited; 14.23: Courtesy Dr. Victor A. McKusick; 14.26: Courtesy the University of Chicago Library/Dept. of Special Collections and Todd L. Savitt; 14.29(both): © Breck P. Kent/Animals Animals; p. 275(all): Michael W. Nachman, Hopi E. Hoekstra, and Susan L. D'Agostino, "The genetic basis of adaptive melanism in pocket mice," PNAS April 29, 2003 vol. 100 no. 9 5268-5273. © 2003 National Academy of Sciences, U.S.A.; 14.32b: Courtesy H. Rodd; p. 278: © Peter E. Smith/The Natural Sciences Image Library; 14.33a-b: © Corbis RF; 14.33c: © Porterfield/Chickering/Photo Researchers; 14.34(1): © Photolibrary/Getty RF; 14.34(2): © Rob & Ann Simpson/Visuals Unlimited; 14.34(3): © Suzanne L. Collins & Joseph T. Collins/National Audubon society Collection/Photo Researchers; 14.34(4): © Phil A. Dotson/National Audubon Society Collection/Photo Researchers.

Chapter 15

Opener: © Dave Watts/Visuals Unlimited; 15.1: © Time & Life Pictures/Getty Images; 15.3(corn, koala): © Corbis RF; 15.3(wheat): © Henry Ausloos/ Animals Animals; 15.3(brown bear): © PunchStock/ Getty RF; 15.5(horse): © Juniors Bildarchiv/Alamy RF; 15.5(donkey): © Photodisc/Getty RF; 15.5(mule): © Alamy RF; 15.8(cat, cheetah, lynx, tiger, lion, leopard): © Corbis RF; 15.8(puma, bobcat, ocelot, caracal, snow leopard, jaguar): © Getty RF; p. 293: © Jim Pickerell/Alamy; 15.11: © Dave Watts/Visuals Unlimited; p. 298(all): U.S. Fish & Wildlife Service.

Chapter 16

Opener: © Dwight R. Kuhn; p. 304(moon): NASA; p. 304(landscape): NASA/JPL/Cornell; Table 16.1(bacteria): © Kwangshin Kim/Photo Researchers; Table 16.1(chemoautotroph): © Dennis Kunkel Microscopy, Inc./Visuals Unlimited; 16.4: © Leonard Lessin/Peter Arnold/Photolibrary; 16.5: © Dwight R. Kuhn; p. 309(duck): © Index Stock RF; p. 309(chimp): © Getty RF; p. 309(bat): © Eric & David Hosling/ Corbis; p. 309(bird): © Tim Zurowski/Corbis; 16.7a: © Dept. of Microbiology, Biozentrum/Photo Researchers; 16.8: © Dennis Kunkel Microscopy, Inc.; 16.9a: © Ed Reschke/Peter Arnold/Getty Images; 16.9b: © Manfred Kage/Peter Arnold/Photolibrary; 16.10: © Stephen Durr RF; 16.11: © John D. Cunningham/ Visuals Unlimited; 16.13a-b: © Corbis RF; 16.15: © Bill Keogh/Visuals Unlimited; 16.16: © L. West/ Photo Researchers; 16.17a: © Image Source/Getty RF; 16.17b: © Gallo Images-Nigel Dennis/Digital Vision/ Getty RF; 16.18: © Science VU/Visuals Unlimited; 16.19: © Corbis RF; p. 320: © Sue Ford/Photo Researchers; p. 322: © Stephen Durr.

Chapter 17

Opener: © Corbis RF; 17.1: © Corbis RF; 17.2: © David M. Phillips/Photo Researchers; 17.4a: © Edward S. Ross; 17.4b: © Richard Gross/Biological Photography; 17.6: © Edward S. Ross; 17.7: Courtesy Hans Steur, The Netherlands; 17.8: © Ray Simons/Photo Researchers; 17.9a: © Edward S. Ross; 17.9b: © Corbis RF; 17.9c: © Kingsley R. Stern; 17.9d: © Edward S. Ross; 17.9e: © John Gates/Visuals Unlimited; 17.11: © Kingsley R. Stern; 17.13: © Alan and Linda Detrick/ Photo Researchers; 17.13(inset): © R.J. Delorit, Agronomy Publications; 17.14b: © Walter H. Hodge/ Peter Arnold/Photolibrary; 17.14c: © imagebroker/ Alamy RF; 17.14d: © Robert Gustafson/Visuals Unlimited; 17.16b: © Ed Pembleton Photography; p. 338: © blickwinkel/Alamy; p. 339: © Corbis RF; p. 340(both): © R.J. Delorit, Agronomy Publications.

Chapter 18

Opener: © James H. Robinson/Animals Animals; Table 18.1(bear, brittle star, butterfly, jellyfish): © Corbis RF; Table 18.1(cancer cells): © David M. Phillips/ Visuals Unlimited; Table 18.2(millipede): © Edward S. Ross; Table 18.2(turtles): © Cleveland P. Hickman; Table 18.2(frog egg): © Cabisco/Phototake; Table 18.2(Neuromuscular junctions): © Ed Reschke; p. 344(anemone): © Getty RF; p. 344(owl): © Corbis RF; p. 344(worm): © IT Stock Free/Alamy RF; 18.4a: © ImageState/Alamy RF; 18.4b, 18.5a: © Corbis RF; 18.5b: © Tom Adams/Visuals Unlimited; 18.8a: © T.E. Adams/Visuals Unlimited; 18.8b: © Stan Elems/ Visuals Unlimited; 18.10: © T.E. Adams/Visuals Unlimited; 18.11: © Larry Jensen/Visuals Unlimited; 18.12(bivalve): © Comstock Images/PictureQuest RF; 18.12(octopus): © Fred Bavendam/Peter Arnold/ Photolibrary; 18.13a: © David M. Dennis; 18.13b: © Darlyne A. Murawski/National Geographic/Getty Images; 18.14a: © Photostock - Dieter Heinemann/ Alamy RF; 18.14b: © Comstock Images/PictureQuest RF; 18.14c: © Alex Kerstitch/Visuals Unlimited; 18.14d: © James H. Robinson/Animals Animals; 18.16a: © Alex Kerstitch/Visuals Unlimited; 18.16b: © Andrew J. Martinez/Photo Researchers; 18.16c: © Daniel W. Gotshall; 18.17a: © Corbis RF; 18.17b: © Eric N. Olson/The University of Texas MD Anderson Cancer Center; 18.18a: © Laurie O'Keefe/ Photo Researchers; 18.18b: © Alex Kerstitch/Visuals Unlimited; 18.19: © Life File/Photodisc/Getty RF; 18.20: © Michael Long/Natural History Museum, London; 18.21: © Stephen Wilkes/Getty Images; 18.22: © E.R. Degginger/Animals Animals; 18.24: © Stephen Frink Collection/Alamy; 18.27: © Creatas/ PunchStock RF; p. 366-367: © Joe Tucciarone/ Interstellar Illustrations; 18.32a: © Sir Francis Canker Photography/Getty Images RF; 18.32b-c: © Corbis RF; 18.36: © John Reader/Photo Researchers; p. 372: © Sinclair Stammers/Photo Researchers; p. 373(shark): © Stephen Frink Collection/Alamy; p. 373 (kangaroo): © Charles Philip/Corbis.

Chapter 19

Opener: © ABPL/Gavin Thomson/Animals Animals; 19.1a: © Vanessa Vick/Photo Researchers; 19.1b,d: © Edward S. Ross; 19.1c: © Ken Lucas/Visuals Unlimited; 19.2: © Ingram Publishing/age Fotostock RF; 19.3: © Tom Pepeira, photographer/Iconotec RF; 19.7: © Design Pics/Getty RF; 19.8: © ABPL/Gavin Thomson/Animals Animals; 19.9a-b © Getty RF; p. 383: © Raymond Gehman/Corbis; 19.15: Negative # 37680. © Chip Clark, Smithsonian Institution; 19.16: © Corbis RF; 19.18a: © Tim Davis/Photo Researchers; 19.18b: © Digital Vision RF; 19.18c: © Corbis RF; 19.21a-d: Courtesy J.B. Losos; 19.23: © Merlin D. Tuttle, Bat Conservation International; 19.24: © Fred Bavendam/Minden Pictures; 19.25: © Getty RF; 19.26: © Graphic Science/Alamy; 19.27: Courtesy Rolf O. Peterson; 19.29a: © Tom J. Ulrich/Visuals Unlimited; 19.30: © Alex L. Fradkin/Stockbyte RF; 19.31: © Edward S. Ross; 19.32: © PictureQuest RF; 19.33: © John Macgregor/Peter Arnold/Getty Images; 19.34a: © Edward S. Ross; 19.34b: © Paul A. Opler; 19.35a-d: © Edward S. Ross; 19.36: © Peter Chew; 19.37: © Tom Bean; p. 400: © Jim Bailey; p. 401(wolf): © Ingram Publishing/age Fotostock RF; p. 401(wildebeest): © Getty Images RF; p. 401(frog): © PictureQuest RF.

Chapter 20

Opener: © Bill Ross/Corbis; 20.2a: © Dave G. Houser/ Corbis; 20.2b-c: © Corbis RF; 20.2d-e: © Edward S. Ross; 20.8: © Gerry Ellis/Minden Pictures; 20.19a: © Digital Vision/PictureQuest RF; 20.19b: © Getty RF; 20.20a: © David Fleetham/Alamy; 20.20b: Courtesy J. Frederick Grassle, Woods Hole Oceanographic Institution; 20.20c: © Kenneth L. Smith; 20.21: © Dwight R. Kuhn; 20.22b-c: © Corbis RF; 20.24: © Bill Ross/Corbis; 20.25: © Michael Graybill & Jan Hodder/Biological Photo Service;

20.26: © E.R. Degginger/Photo Researchers; 20.27: © S.J. Krasemann/Peter Arnold/Photolibrary; 20.28: © J. Weber/Visuals Unlimited; 20.29: © IFA/Peter Arnold/Photolibrary; 20.30: © Charlie Ott/The National Audubon Society Collection/Photo Researchers; 20.31: © Cliff LeSergent/Alamy RF; 20.32: © Tom McHugh/Photo Researchers; 20.33: © Frank Krahmer/Getty Images RF; 20.34: © E.R. Degginger/Animals Animals; p. 426: U.S. Forest Service.

Chapter 21

Opener: © Francois Gohier/Photo Researchers; 21.1: © Stone/Getty Images; 21.3: © William C. Dilger, Cornell University; 21.4a-b: Reprinted from Cell, v. 86, issue 2, J.R. Brown et al, "A Defect in Nurturing in Mice Lacking the Immediate Early Gene fosB," pp 297-308, 1996, with permission from Elsevier; 21.5: © Thomas McAvoy, Life Magazine/Time/Getty Images; 21.7: © Thomas & Pat Leeson/Photo Researchers; 21.8: Courtesy Bernd Heinrich; 21.9: © Nina Leen/Time & Life Pictures/Getty Images; 21.10: © David R. Frazier Photolibrary/Alamy RF; 21.11: © Bios(C. Thouvenin)/Peter Arnold/Photolibrary; Table 21.1(bird): © Eric & David Hosling/Corbis; Table 21.1(seals): © Marc Moritsch/National Geographic Image Collection; Table 21.1(herd): © Alamy RF; Table 21.2(frog): Courtesy James Traniello; Table 21.1(lions): © K. Ammann/Bruce Coleman Inc.; Table21.1(dog): © Francois Gohier/Photo Researchers; 21.14: © Dr. Don W. Fawcett/Visuals Unlimited; 21.15b: © Scott Camazine/Photo Researchers; 21.16a: © Stan Osolinski; 21.17: © Nigel Dennis/National Audubon Society Collection/Photo Researchers; 21.19: © David Hosking/Photo Researchers; 21.20: © Jim Pickerell/Alamy; p. 448: Alamy RF; p. 440(raven): Courtesy Bernd Heinrich; p. 440(sunbird): © Bios(C. Thouvenin)/Peter Arnold/Photolibrary.

Chapter 22

Opener: © Steve McCurry/Magnum Photos; 22.2: © Corbis RF; 22.3: © Rob & Ann Simpson/Visuals Unlimited; p. 456: © 1999 Ed Ely/Biological Photo Service; 22.7: NASA; 22.9: © Gary Griffen/Animals Animals; 22.10a: © Daniel Beltra/Getty Images; 22.10b: NASA; 22.10c: © Frans Lanting; 22.12: © Stephanie Maze/Woodfin Camp & Associates; 22.17a-b: Courtesy University of Wisconsin-Madison Arboretum; 22.18: U.S. Fish & Wildlife Service/Craig Koppie; 22.19: © Kennan Ward/Corbis; 22.20: © Merlin D. Tuttle, Bat Conservation International; 22.21: © Shaen Adey/Getty Images; 22.22: © Byron Augustin; 22.23a: © Corbis RF; 22.23b: © Creatas/PunchStock RF; 22.24: © Corbis RF; 22.25: © Steve McCurry/Magnum Photos; 22.26(both): Courtesy Nashua River Watershed Association; 22.27: © Neil Rabinowitz/Corbis; p. 470: NASA; p. 471(acid rain): © Rob & Ann Simpson/Visuals Unlimited; p. 471(ozone): NASA; p. 471(erosion): © Frans Lanting; p. 471(rhino): © Kennan Ward/Corbis.

Chapter 23

Opener: © Anthony Bannister/Animals Animals; 23.3: © Jim Merli/Visuals Unlimited; 23.4: © Alamy RF; 23.6a&b: © Dr. Michael Klein/Peter Arnold/Photolibrary; 23.7: © Anthony Bannister/Animals Animals; 23.11: © Cleveland P. Hickman; 23.12: © David M. Dennis; p. 484: © Corbis RF; p. 486(runner): © Pete Saloutos/Corbis; p. 486(eagle): © Digital Vision RF; p. 486(fish): © Digital Vision/Getty RF; p. 487: © Alamy RF; p. 488: © Dr. Michael Klein/Peter Arnold/Photolibrary.

Chapter 24

Opener: © David M. Phillips/Visuals Unlimited; 24.6: © David M. Phillips/Visuals Unlimited; 24.7: © Ed Reschke; 24.9: © Manfred Kage/Peter Arnold/Photolibrary; p. 500(mouse): © Rob Simpson/Visuals Unlimited; p. 500(elephant): © Getty RF.

Chapter 25

Opener: © Getty RF; 25.6: © Getty RF; 25.7: © Science Source/Photo Researchers; p. 512: © Mark Chivers/Robert Harding World Imagery/Getty Images.

Chapter 26

Opener: © Corbis RF; 26.7: © Corbis RF; 26.14a: © David M. Phillips/Visuals Unlimited; 26.14b: © Biophoto Associates/Photo Researchers.

Chapter 27

Opener: © Corbis RF; 27.2: © Corbis RF; p. 540: © Michael & Patricia Fogden.

Chapter 28

Opener: © Eye of Science/Photo Researchers; 28.1: © Getty RF; 28.4: © Manfred Kage/Peter Arnold/Photolibrary; 28.7d: From Alan S. Rosenthal, "Regulation of the Immune Response Ñ Role of the Macrophage," New England Journal of Medicine 303: 1153, 1980; 28.13: © Visuals Unlimited; 28.14: National Library of Medicine; 28.15: © Jean Claude Revy/Phototake; 28.16: © Oliver Meckes/Photo Researchers; 28.18: © Eye of Science/Photo Researchers; p. 559: © Oliver Meckes/Photo Researchers.

Chapter 29

Opener: © Dennis Kunkel Microscopy, Inc./Visuals Unlimited; 29.5: © Dennis Kunkel/Phototake; 29.6b: © John Heuser, Washington University School of Medicine, St. Louis, MO; 29.7: © E.R. Lewis, YY Zeevi, T.E. Everhart, U. of California/Biological Photo Service; 29.9: © Dennis Kunkel Microscopy, Inc./Visuals Unlimited; 29.12: Courtesy Dr. Marcus E. Raichle, Washington University, McDonnell Center for High Brain Function; 29.13: © Lennart Nilsson/Scanpix; 29.25: © Omokron/PhotoResearchers; 29.28: Reproduced from Ishihara's Tests for Colour Deficiency published by Kanehara Trading, Tokyo, Japan. Tests for color deficiency cannot be conducted with this material. For accurate testing, the original plates should be used. p. 580: © James L. Amos/Photo Researchers.

Chapter 30

Opener(both): © E.R. Degginger/Animals Animals; 30.8(both): © E.R. Degginger/Animals Animals; 30.11: © John Paul Kay/Peter Arnold/Photolibrary; p. 594: © Science Source/Photo Researchers.

Chapter 31

Opener: © JGI/Getty RF; 31.2a: © Chuck Wise/Animals Animals; 31.2b: © Fred McConnaughey/The National Audubon Society Collection/Photo Researchers; 31.6: © David M. Phillips/Photo Researchers; 31.12b: © Ed Reschke; 31.13a: © Cavallini James/Phototake; 31.14a-b: © Bradley Smith; 31.14c: © Lennart Nilsson/Scanpix; 31.14d: © Tissuepix/Photo Researchers; 31.17: © JGI/Getty RF; 31.18a-c: © The McGraw-Hill Companies, Inc. Bob Coyle, photographer; p. 614: © R. Dourmashkin, MD/Photo Researchers; p. 615(egg): © Ed Reschke; p. 615(fetus): © Lennart Nilsson/Scanpix.

Chapter 32

Opener: © Scott T. Smith/Corbis; 32.2: © Biophoto Associates/Photo Researchers; 32.3: © George Wilder/Visuals Unlimited; 32.4: © Larry Mellichamp/Visuals Unlimited; 32.5a: © Dr. Jeremy Burgess/Photo Researchers; 32.5b: © Andrew Syred/Photo Researchers; 32.6: © Scott T. Smith/Corbis; 32.7: Courtesy SUNY College of Environmental Science and Forestry; 32.8a: © Randy Moore/Visuals Unlimited; 32.9b: © Biodisc/Visuals Unlimited; 32.10a: © Ed Reschke; 32.10b: © Peter Arnold/Alamy; 32.11: © Patrick J. Lynch/Photo Researchers; 32.13a-b: © Ed Reschke; 32.16: © CBS/Phototake; 32.16a: © Michael P. Gadomski/Dembinsky Photo Associates; 32.16b: © Corbis RF; 32.16c: © Steven J. Baskauf; 32.16d: © Getty RF; 32.16e-f, 32.17a: © Corbis RF; 32.17b: © Pat Anderson/visuals Unlimited; 32.19: © Ed Reschke; 32.23: © Kingsley R. Stern; p. 632: © Corbis RF; p. 633: © George Wilder/Visuals Unlimited; p. 634(root tip): © Biodisc/Visuals Unlimited; p. 635(tree rings): © CBS/Phototake.

Chapter 33

Opener: © Adam Hart-Davis/SPL/Photo Researchers; 33.1c: © Jerome Wexler/Photo Researchers; 33.3a: © Corbis RF; 33.3b: Used with permission of www .laspilitas.com; 33.5a,c: © Alamy RF; 33.5b: USDA photo by Jack Dykinga; 33.5d: © Bill Bonner; 33.5e: © Corbis RF; 33.5f: © Adam Hart-Davis/SPL/Photo Researchers; 33.6(left): © Nigel Cattlin/Visuals Unlimited; 33.6(right): © Helmut Gritscher/Peter Arnold/Photolibrary; 33.13a: © Maryann Frazier/Photo Researchers; 33.13b: © Martin Shields/Photo Researchers; 33.13c: © John D. Cunningham/Visuals Unlimited; p. 648: © Jeff K. Conner; p. 649, 650(bee): © Corbis RF; p. 649-650(apple, tomatoes): © Alamy RF; p. 650(butterfly): Used with permission of www.laspilitas.com; p. 650(peach): USDA photo by Jack Dykinga; p. 650(berries): © Bill Bonner; p. 650(dandelion): © Corbis RF; p. 650(coconut): © Adam Hart-Davis/SPL/Photo Researchers.

Line Art

Chapter 23

Page 486 (graph): Schmidt Nielson, *Animal Physiology* 3/e, 1983, Fig 6.19, pg. 215. Reprinted with the permission of Cambridge University Press.

Chapter 24

Page 500 (graph): Schmidt Nielson, *Animal Physiology* 3/e, 1983, Fig 4.11, pg. 110. Reprinted with the permission of Cambridge University Press.

Chapter 25

Page 512 (bottom graph): Schmidt Nielson, *Animal Physiology* 3/e, 1983, Fig 3.7, pg. 79. Reprinted with the permission of Cambridge University Press.

Index

AAV (adeno-associated virus) vector, 244 *fig.*, 245, 245 *fig.*
ABA (abscisic acid), 643 *table*
Abdominal cavity, 474
ABO blood groups, 173
ABO system, 555, 555 *fig.*
Abscisic acid (ABA), 643 *table*
Abstinence as birth control method, 612
Acer rubrum, 621 *fig.*
Acetylcholine (ACh), 566
Acetyl-CoA, production of, 121, 121 *fig.*
ACh (acetylcholine), 566
Acid(s), 44
  abscisic, 643 *table*
  amino, 53, 53 *fig.*, 517, 526
  crassulacean, 113
  deoxyribonucleic. *See* DNA
  fatty, 60
  gastric, 522–523
  hydrochloric, heartburn and, 44
  lactic, 127, 127 *fig.*, 130
  nucleic, 50, 50 *fig.*, 56–57
  ribonucleic. *See* RNA
  2,4,5-Trichlorophenoxyacetic, 645
  uric, formation in body, 539, 539 *fig.*
Acid rain, 45, 453, 453 *fig.*
Acid reflux, 44, 522
Acinonyx jubatus, 269
Acne, 544
Acoelomates, 351, 352
Acquired immunodeficiency syndrome (AIDS). *See* AIDS
Acrasiomycota, 315 *table*
Acrosome, 601
ACTH (adrenocorticotropic hormone), 589
Actin, 52 *fig.*
Actin filaments, 80
Action potentials, 564
Activating enzymes, 209
Activation energy, 94, 94 *fig.*
Activators, 97, 97 *fig.*, 214, 214 *fig.*, 215, 215 *fig.*
Active site of enzyme, 95, 95 *fig.*
Active transport, 87
  ATP for, 99 *table*
Acute myelogenous leukemia (AML), human genome in, 226
Adaptation(s)
  environment and, 377, 377 *fig.*
  life history, 385, 385 *fig.*, 385 *table*
  natural selection and, 253 *fig.*, 253–254
  of plants, to terrestrial life, 324 *fig.*, 324–325
  within populations, 272–277, 272–277 *fig.*
Adaptive radiation, 257
Adenine, 192, 192 *fig.*
Adeno-associated virus (AAV) vector, 244 *fig.*, 245, 245 *fig.*
Adenosine diphosphate (ADP), 125, 126
Adenosine triphosphate (ATP), 87
  cellular activities powered by, 98, 99 *table*
  cellular respiration and, 98
  hydrolysis of, 485, 485 *fig.*
  production by chemiosmosis, 111, 125
  production by glycolysis, 118, 120
  production by Krebs cycle, 124–125
  production by photosynthesis, 98, 107
  structure of, 98, 98 *fig.*
ADH (antidiuretic hormone; vasopressin), 538, 588, 588 *fig.*
Adhesion, 43, 629
Adipose tissue, 477
ADP (adenosine diphosphate), 125, 126
Adrenal cortex, 593
Adrenal glands, 593
Adrenal medulla, 593
Adrenocorticotropic hormone (ACTH), 589
Adult stem cells, 240
Adventitious plantlets, angiosperm reproduction by, 636, 636 *fig.*
Afferent neurons, 480, 480 *fig.*, 562, 562 *fig.*
African Americans, sickle-cell anemia in, 168, 272 *fig.*, 272–273
African elephant, pulse rate of, 500
African lion, 369 *fig.*
African weaver bird, societies of, 446, 446 *fig.*
Agatston, Arthur, 129
Age(s), evolutionary, 360
Age distribution, 386
Agent Orange, 645
Age structure of population, 386, 386 *fig.*
Aging of human cells, 144
Agnathans, 363
Agricultural chemicals, 453, 453 *fig.*
Agriculture
  global warming and, 454
  organic farming and, 459
Agriculture, genetic engineering and, 235 *fig.*, 235–237, 236 *fig.*, 237 *table*
  for herbicide resistance, 235, 235 *fig.*
  for more nutritious crops, 236, 236 *fig.*, 237 *table*
  for pest resistance, 235
  potential risks of, 237, 246
Agrostis stolonifera, genetically modified, 246
AIDS, 309. *See also* HIV
  antiviral drugs for, 557
  curing with *delta* 32, 218
  mechanism of immune system attack in, 557, 557 *fig.*
Air, amount of, altitude and, 512
Air pollution, 45, 453
  melanism and, 274 *fig.*, 274–275, 275 *fig.*
Alarm calls, 442, 444, 444 *fig.*, 445
Alarm pheromones, 442, 442 *fig.*
Albinism, 178 *fig.*, 178–179
Alcohol. *See* Ethanol
Alder trees, 399 *fig.*
Aldosterone, 538, 593
Alfalfa butterfly, pollination by, 638 *fig.*
Algae
  brown, 315 *table*
  coralline, 315 *table*
  CO2 removal from air by, 111
  green, 315 *table*
  red, 315 *table*
  uses of, 314
Alleles, 164, 266
  frequencies of, 266, 266 *fig.*
Allergens, 556, 556 *fig.*
Allergies, 556, 556 *fig.*
All-nighters, 5
Allometric growth, 611
Allomyces, 318 *table*
Allopatric species, 390
Allosaurus, 361 *fig.*
Allosteric enzymes, 97, 97 *fig.*
Alternating leaf position, 627, 627 *fig.*
Alternation of generations, 326, 326 *fig.*
Alternative energy sources, 467, 467 *fig.*
Alternative hypotheses, 23
Alternative splicing, 212, 226
Altitude, amount of air and, 512
Altruism, 444 *fig.*, 444–445, 445 *fig.*
Alveolata, 315 *table*
Alveoli, 504, 504 *fig.*
Alzheimer's disease, cell cycle and, 135
Ambulocetus, 259
Amino acids, 53, 53 *fig.*
  essential, 517, 526
  linking of, 53, 53 *fig.*
Amino groups, 50 *fig.*
AML (acute myelogenous leukemia), human genome in, 226
Ammonia, formation in body, 539, 539 *fig.*
Ammonites, 360 *fig.*
Amniocentesis, 184, 184 *fig.*
Amnion, 606
Amniotic eggs of reptiles, 365, 365 *fig.*
Amoeba, 315 *table*
Amphibians, 364 *fig.*, 364–365
  characteristics of, 364, 364 *fig.*
  global decline in, 456
Amygdala, 568 *fig.*, 568–569
Amylase, salivary, 521
Anabaena, 307, 307 *fig.*
Anabolic steroids, 61, 586–587
Analogous structures, 260, 260 *fig.*
Anaphase I in meiosis I, 150, 150 *fig.*, 152
Anaphase II in meiosis II, 153
Anaphase in mitosis, 139
4-Androstenedione (andro), 61
Anemia, sickle-cell, 168, 272 *fig.*, 272–273
Aneuploidy, 176
Angiogenesis inhibitors, 143
Angiosperms, 332
  development of, 641, 641 *fig.*
  flowers and. *See* Flowers
  fruits and, 640, 640 *fig.*
  seeds and, 337, 337 *fig. See also* Seed(s)
Animal(s) (Animalia), 28 *fig.*, 294, 294 *fig.*, 295 *table,* 341–373, 473–487. *See also* Amphibians; Mammals (Mammalia); Vertebrates; *specific animals*
  bilateral symmetry in, 350 *fig.*, 350–351, 351 *fig.*
  body cavity evolution in, 352–356, 352–356 *fig.*
  body plan of, 344, 345 *fig.*, 474 *fig.*, 474–475, 475 *fig.*
  cloning of. *See* Cloning; Reproductive cloning; Therapeutic cloning
  defenses of, 395, 395 *fig.*, 543–559
  diversity of. *See* Biodiversity
  embryos of, 357–359, 357–359 *fig.*
  family tree of, 346 *fig.*, 346–347, 347 *fig.*
  general features of, 342–343 *table*
  key transitions in body plan of, 344, 345 *fig.*
  kingdom of, 16 *fig.*
  learning in, 433–435
  nervous system of, 562, 562 *fig.*
  pollination by, 391 *fig.*, 638, 638 *fig.*
  seed dispersal by, 640, 640 *fig.*
  simplest, 348 *fig.*, 348–349, 349 *fig.*
  viral infection of, 310
Animal societies, 446, 446 *fig.*
Anions, 36
Annelids (Annelida)
  body cavity of, 355, 355 *fig.*
  body water content regulation in, 534, 534 *fig.*
Anolis, 390, 390 *fig.*
Anolis carolinensis, 589 *fig.*
Anomaly histogram, 470
Anopheles gambiae, genome of, 225 *table*
Anopheles mosquitoes, 320
Ant
  pheromone trails and, 443 *fig.*
  societies of, 446
Antarctica, ozone hole and, 11, 11 *fig.*, 23, 23 *fig.*, 457, 457 *fig.*
Antenna complex of a photosystem, 108
Anterior, definition of, 350, 350 *fig.*

Anthers, 336, 336 *fig.*, 637, 637 *fig.*
Anthidiine bee, 397 *fig.*
Anthocerophyta, 327 *table*
Anthoceros, 327 *table*
Anthocyanins, 637
Anthophyta, 327 *table*
Antibodies, 548, 552
  diversity of, 552, 552 *fig.*
  in medical diagnosis, 555, 555 *fig.*
  monoclonal, 142, 143, 555
Anticodons, 209, 209 *fig.*
Antidiuretic hormone (ADH; vasopressin), 538, 588, 588 *fig.*
Antigen-presenting cells, 549, 549 *fig.*
Antipollution laws, 457
Anti-sense therapy, 219
Antiviral drugs for AIDS, 557
Antler regrowth, 475
Anura, 365
Anus, 525, 527 *fig.*
Aorta, human, 497 *fig.*, 498
Aortic semilunar valve, 497 *fig.*, 498
Apical meristems, 618, 618 *fig.*
Apicomplexa, 315 *table*
Apis mellifera mellifera. *See* Honeybee
Apis mellifera scutela, 398
Apoda, 365
Aposematic coloration, 395, 395 *fig.*
Appendicular skeleton, 282 *fig.*, 482
Appendix, 527 *fig.*
Apples, seed dispersal by, 640 *fig.*
Apricot, 639
Aquaporins, 82
Aquifers, 410
Arachnids (Arachnida), 356 *fig.*
Arachnocampa luminosa, 535
Archaea, 28, 28 *fig.*, 69, 294, 294 *fig.*, 295 *table,* 296, 296 *fig.*. *See also* Prokaryotes
  kingdom of, 16 *fig.*
  lifestyles of, 307, 307 *fig.*
Archaeopteryx, 368, 368 *fig.*
Ardipithicus ramidus, 370 *fig.*
Aristotle, 286
Arithmetic progression, 253, 253 *fig.*
Armadillo, 252, 252 *fig.*
Arrowgrass, 338
Arteries, 490, 492, 492 *fig.*, 493, 493 *fig.*
Arterioles, 492, 492 *fig.*, 493
Arthropods (Arthropoda), 356, 356 *fig.*. *See also* Arachnids (Arachnida); Centipedes; Crustaceans; Insects (Insecta)
  exoskeleton of, 356, 481 *fig.*, 481–482, 482 *fig.*
  invasion of land by, 360
  jointed appendages of, 356
  respiratory systems of, 504
Artificial selection, 20, 269
Ascaris lumbricoides, 353
Ascomycetes, 318 *table*
Asexual reproduction, 148, 148 *fig.*
  by angiosperms, 636, 636 *fig.*
  fungal, 317, 317 *fig.*
Asian flu, 311
Aspergillus, 318 *table*
Association neurons, 480, 480 *fig.*, 562, 562 *fig.*
Associative learning, 433
Asthma, 507
Atherosclerosis, 498
Atmosphere. *See also* Air pollution
  ozone hole and, 11, 11 *fig.*, 22–23, 23 *fig.*, 457, 457 *fig.*
Atmospheric circulation, sun and, 414, 414 *fig.*
Atom(s), 18, 18 *fig.*, 34, 34 *fig.*
Atomic numbers, 34, 34 *table*
ATP. *See* Adenosine triphosphate (ATP)
ATP synthase, 111, 125
Atrioventricular (AV) node, 499
Atrium
  left, of human heart, 497, 497 *fig.*
  right, of human heart, 497 *fig.*, 498
Australopithecus, 370, 370 *fig.*
Australopithecus aethiopicus, 370 *fig.*
Australopithecus afarensis, 370 *fig.*
Australopithecus africanus, 370 *fig.*
Australopithecus anamensis, 370 *fig.*
Australopithecus boisei, 370 *fig.*
Australopithecus robustus, 370 *fig.*
Australopithecus sediba, 370 *fig.*
Autoimmune diseases, 556
Autonomic nervous system, 571, 572, 572 *fig.*
Autosomes, 176
Autotrophs, 324, 404. *See also* Plant(s) (Plantae)
Auxin, 643 *table,* 644 *fig.*, 644–645, 645 *fig.*
Avastin, 143
Avery, Oswald, 191, 233
AV (atrioventricular) node, 499
Axial skeleton, 282 *fig.*, 482
Axils of leaves, 624
Axon(s), 480, 480 *fig.*, 480 *table,* 563, 563 *fig.*
Axopodia, 312
Azolla, 327 *table*

Bacillus thuringiensis (Bt), 235
Backbone, 359. *See also* Vertebrates
  of fishes, 363
  of theropods, 367
Bacteria, 28, 28 *fig.*, 69, 69 *fig.*, 294, 294 *fig.*, 295 *table,* 296, 296 *fig.* *See also* Prokaryotes
  beneficial, 391, 404
  capsule of, 69, 69 *fig.*
  cell walls of, 69, 69 *fig.*, 305–306
  gram-negative, 305–306
  gram-positive, 305–306
  kingdom of, 16 *fig.*
  lifestyles of, 307, 307 *fig.*
  overweight and, 523
  viral infection of, 310, 310 *fig.*
Bacteriodetes, 523
Bacteriophages, 308, 308 *fig.*, 310, 310 *fig.*
Bacteroides fragilis, 391
Bacteroides thetaiotaomicron, 391
Balancing selection, 270 *fig.*, 271, 271 *fig.*
  sickle-cell anemia and, 273, 273 *fig.*
Bamboo, 636 *fig.*
Banting, William, 129
Bark, 625
Barnacles, 388, 388 *fig.*
Basal body, 81, 81 *fig.*
Basal layer of skin, 545
Basal metabolic rate (BMR), 516
Base(s), 44
Base pairs, 57, 57 *fig.*, 192
  Base substitution, 199, 199 *table*
Basidiomycetes, 318 *table*
  as decomposers, 405 *fig.*
Basilosaurus, 259
Basophils, 496, 496 *fig.*
Bat, 369
  flying foxes as keystone species, 446, 466 *fig.*
  pollination by, 391 *fig.*
  vampire, 256
Bates, Henry, 396
Batesian mimicry, 396, 396 *fig.*
B cells, 496, 496 *fig.*, 548
  humoral immune response and, 549, 551 *fig.*, 551–552, 552 *fig.*
Bear as omnivore, 405 *fig.*
Beason, William, 232
Beaver, 388, 388 *fig.*
Bee. *See also* Honeybee
  anthidiine, 397 *fig.*
  killer, invasion of, 398
  melittin from, for cancer treatment, 139
  pollination by, 638 *fig.*
Beer, making, 319
Behavior, 429–449
  cost-behavior analysis of, 437, 437 *fig.*
  evolutionary forces shaping, 436–441
  genetic effects on, 432, 432 *fig.*
  instinctive, 430, 431, 431 *fig.*
  learning and, 433–435
  social, 442–447
  study of, 430, 430 *fig.*
Behavioral ecology, 436, 436 *fig.*
Behavioral genetics, 432, 432 *fig.*
Behavioral isolation, 279 *table,* 280
Belding's ground squirrel, 445
Berries, 640, 640 *fig.*
"Best-fit" line, 282
Bicuspid valve, 497, 497 *fig.*
Bilateral symmetry, 344, 345 *fig.*, 350 *fig.*, 350–351
  evolution of, 344
  in flatworms, 350–351, 351 *fig.*
Bilateria, 346, 346 *fig.*
Bile pigments, 526
Bile salts, 524
Binary fission, prokaryotic, 134, 134 *fig.*, 306
Binding site of enzyme, 95, 95 *fig.*
Binocular vision, 579, 579 *fig.*
Binomial(s), 287
Binomial system of classification, 286 *fig.*, 286–287, 287 *fig.*
Biochemical pathways, 96, 96 *fig.*. *See also* Glycolysis
Biodiversity, 16, 16 *fig.*, 285–299
  benefits of, 294, 295, 296
  classification of organisms and, 286–289
  importance of generating, 151
  loss of, 455, 455 *fig.*
  preserving, 460, 460 *fig.*
  theory of evolution and, 28, 28 *fig.*, 29 *fig.*
  threatened species and, 291
Biofeedback, 572
Biofilms, 307
Biogeochemical cycles, 409
Biological magnification, 453, 453 *fig.*
Biological species concept, 279, 279 *table*
  classification of organisms and, 289
Biological themes, 20–21. *See also* Energy flows; Evolution; Homeostasis
Biological time, clock of, 302, 302 *fig.*
Biomass, 406
Biomes, 376, 422 *fig.*, 422–425
Biosphere, 376
Biosynthesis, ATP for, 99 *table*
Birch trees, 626 *fig.*
Bird(s), 368. *See also specific birds*
  bird-killing cats and, 228
  body temperature of, 540
  characteristics of, 368, 368 *fig.*
  history of, 368, 368 *fig.*
  kin selection in, 445, 445 *fig.*
  magnetic compass of, 580
  seed dispersal by, 640 *fig.*
  singing of, 430 *fig.*, 434, 434 *fig.*
Bird flu, 311
Birth, 610–611, 611 *fig.*
Birth control, 612–613, 613 *fig.*
Birth control pills, 612, 613 *fig.*
Biston betularia, 274, 274 *fig.*, 275, 275 *fig.*
Bitter almond, 639
Bivalves, 354, 354 *fig.*
Black rhinoceros, 465, 465 *fig.*
Black walnut tree, 626 *fig.*
Blastocyst, 240, 606
Blastomere, 606
Blood, 493 *fig.*, 495–496
  carbon dioxide transport in, 508 *fig.*, 508–509
  circulation of. *See* Circulatory systems
  hemoglobin in, 496, 508, 508 *fig.*
  oxygen transport in, 508, 508 *fig.*
  pH of, in swimming fish, 130
  plasma of, 477, 495
Blood cells, 52, 81, 496, 496 *fig.*
Blood chemistry, sensory receptors for, 573
Blood clotting, 491
  evolution of, 263, 263 *fig.*
Blood glucose, regulation of, 533, 533 *fig.*
Blood groups, 173
Blood pressure
  diastolic, 498, 498 *fig.*
  measuring, 498, 498 *fig.*
  sensory receptors for, 573, 573 *fig.*
  systolic, 498, 498 *fig.*
Blood typing, 555, 555 *fig.*
Blood vessels, vertebrate, 490, 492–494, 492–494 *fig.*
Bluehead wrasse, 598 *fig.*, 599
B lymphocytes. *See* B cells
BMI (body mass index), 516, 516 *fig.*
BMR (basal metabolic rate), 516
Body cavity
  evolution of, 344, 345 *fig.*, 352–356, 352–356 *fig.*
  kinds of, 352, 352 *fig.*
Body mass index (BMI), 516, 516 *fig.*
Body plan of animals, 474 *fig.*, 474–475, 475 *fig.*
  key transitions in, 344, 345 *fig.*
Body temperature
  of birds, 540
  regulation of, 491, 491 *fig.*, 533, 533 *fig.*
  sensory receptors for, 573
Body water, regulation of. *See* Osmoregulation
Bonds, Barry, 61
Bonds, chemical. *See* Chemical bonds
Bone, 477. *See also* Skeleton(s)
  compact, 478, 478 *fig.*
  osteoporosis and, 478, 478 *fig.*
  spongy, 478, 478 *fig.*
Bonobos, language in, 443

Bony fishes, 298
Book. *See* Textbook
Bormann, Herbert, 426
Bottled water, 452
Bottleneck effect, 269
Bowman's capsule, 536
Boyer, Herbert, 233
Brachiopods, 361
Bradford, David, 456
Brain
  Alzheimer's disease and, 135
  functioning of, 567–569, 567–569 *fig.*
  size of, 370, 370 *fig.*, 371 *fig.*
  sleep and, 5
  transmission of light information to, 579, 579 *fig.*
Brain stem, 569
Branta canadensis, 19
Breathing, mechanics of, 507
Brewer's yeast, genome of, 225 *table*
Bristlecone pines, 334
Bristle worm, 355 *fig.*
Bronchus, 506, 506 *fig.*
Brosimum alicastrum, 379 *fig.*
Brown algae, 315 *table*
Bryophyta, 327 *table*
Bryozoans, 361
Bt *(Bacillus thuringiensis),* 235
Buffers, 44
Bumpus, H. C., 271
Bundle of His, 499, 499 *fig.*
Buttercup, 623 *fig.*
Butterflies
  plant defenses and, 395, 395 *fig.*
  pollination by, 638, 638 *fig.*

Cabbage butterfly, 395, 395 *fig.*
Caenorhabditis elegans, 353
  genome of, 225 *table*
Calcitonin, 592
Calcium
  atomic number and mass number of, 34 *table*
  regulation by parathyroid hormone, 593, 593 *fig.*
Callorhinus ursinus, 382 *fig.*
Calvin cycle, 107, 112
CAM (crassulacean acid metabolism), 113
Cambium
  cork, 625, 625 *fig.*
  vascular, 618
Cambrian period, 360
Campbell, Keith, 238
Canada goose, 19, 438
Canada lynx, 394 *fig.*
Cancer
  artificial chromosomes for treatment of, 174
  cell cycle and, 141, 141 *fig.*
  cervical, 613
  definition of, 141
  gene therapy vectors and, 244
  human genome in, 226
  of lung, smoking and, 10, 10 *fig.*, 200–201, 510–511, 511 *fig.*, 594
  melittin treatment for, 139
  metastases of, 141
  monoclonal antibodies for treatment of, 142, 143
  mutations causing, 200–201
  pancreatic, 590
  preventing the spread of, 143
  preventing the start of, 142–143, 234
  radioactive tracers to identify, 36, 36 *fig.*
  of skin, 201
  somatic mutations and, 200–201
Cancer vaccines, 234
Canola, genetically modified, 237 *table*
CAP (catabolite activator protein), 215, 215 *fig.*
Capillaries, 490, 492, 492 *fig.*, 493 *fig.*, 494, 494 *fig.*
Capillary action in plants, 629, 629 *fig.*
Capsids, 308, 308 *fig.*
Capsule, bacterial, 69, 69 *fig.*
Captive breeding programs, 465, 465 *fig.*
Carbohydrates, 50, 50 *fig.*, 58, 59 *table*
  complex, 58, 58 *fig.*
  diets low in, 129
  simple, 58, 58 *fig.*
  sources of, 516
  transport in vascular plants, 631
Carbon, atomic number and mass number of, 34 *table*
Carbon cycle, 411, 411 *fig.*
Carbon-14 dating, 36, 46
Carbon dioxide
  bottled water and, 452
  in Calvin cycle, 107
  energy consumption and, 467
  global warming and, 11, 11 *fig.*, 39, 411
  released by burning fossil fuels, 454, 467
  removal from air by photosynthesis, 111
  transport in blood, 508 *fig.*, 508–509
Carbon fixation, 112, 113 *fig.*
"Carbon footprint," 411
Carbonic anhydrase, 508
Carboniferous period, 360
Carbonyl groups, 50 *fig.*
Carboxyl groups, 50 *fig.*
Carcinomas, 141
Cardiac muscle, 479
Cardiovascular disease, 219, 498
Cardiovascular system. *See* Circulatory systems
Caribbean reef shark, 477 *fig.*
Carnivores (Carnivora), 123, 405, 405 *fig.*, 518
  top, 405, 408
Carpels, 332, 336, 336 *fig.*
Carrying capacity, 382, 382 *fig.*
Cartilage, 477, 477 *fig.*
Casparian strip, 622
Castor bean, 639
Cat
  bird-killing, 228
  family tree of, 291, 292 *fig.*
Catabolite activator protein (CAP), 215, 215 *fig.*
Catalina Island mahogany tree, 378 *fig.*
Catalysis, 94, 94 *fig.*
Cations, 36
Causation, correlation and, 12
$CD4^+$ cells, HIV and, 557
cDNA (complementary DNA), formation of, 229, 229 *fig.*
Cecum, 519
Cedar trees, 327 *table*
Cell(s), 65–89
  cell theory and, 66–67
  in culture, 156
  cytoplasm of, 70, 70 *fig.*, 71 *fig.*
  daughter, 134, 134 *fig.*
  diploid, 136, 136 *fig.*, 148, 148 *fig.*, 149, 149 *fig.*
  enzyme regulation by, 97, 97 *fig.*
  epithelial, 476
  eukaryotic. *See* Eukaryotic cells
  fat, 477
  first, 303
  germ-line, 149
  haploid, 148, 148 *fig.*, 149, 149 *fig.*
  hierarchy of complexity in, 18–19 *fig.*
  human, aging of, 144
  movement of, 81, 81 *fig.*
  plasma membrane of. *See* Plasma membrane
  prokaryotic, 69, 69 *fig.*
  protist, surface of, 312
  rise of, 302 *fig.*, 302–303, 303 *fig.*
  size of, 66, 66 *fig.*
  somatic, 135
  stem. *See* Stem cells
  visualizing, 68, 68 *fig.*
Cell body of neuron, 480, 480 *fig.*, 480 *table,* 563, 563 *fig.*
Cell crawling, 81
  ATP for, 99 *table*
Cell cycle
  Alzheimer's disease and, 135
  cancer and, 141, 141 *fig.*
  complex, 135
  eukaryotic, 135
  prokaryotic, 134, 134 *fig.*
  simple, 134, 134 *fig.*
Cell death, 140, 140 *fig.*
Cell division, 134–140
  cell death and, 140, 140 *fig.*
  chromosomes and, 136 *fig.*, 136–137, 137 *fig.*
  cytokinesis and, 140, 140 *fig.*
  eukaryote cell cycle and, 135
  interphase and, 138
  mitosis and. *See* Mitosis
  prokaryote cell cycle and, 134, 134 *fig.*
Cell plates, 140
Cell surface proteins, 73
Cell theory, 26, 26 *fig.*
Cellular counterattack, 544, 546 *fig.*, 546–547, 547 *fig.*
Cellular immune response, 549, 550, 550 *fig.*
Cellular organization as property of life, 17, 17 *fig.*, 26
Cellular respiration, 118–127
  ATP production by, 98
  of fat, 128, 128 *fig.*
  glycolysis in, 118, 120
  oxidation in, 118 *fig.*, 118–119
  of protein, 128, 128 *fig.*
  reduction in, 118 *fig.* 118
Cellular slime molds, 315 *table*
Cellulose, 58, 59 *table*
  ethanol production from, 468
Cell walls
  bacterial, 69, 69 *fig.*, 305–306
  eukaryotic, 70 *fig.*, 71, 71 *fig.*, 75 *table*
  of fungi, 316
  lacking, in animals, 342 *table*
  prokaryotic, 69, 69 *fig.*
Cenozoic era, 361
Centipedes, 356 *fig.*
Central canal of bone, 478, 478 *fig.*
Central dogma, 206, 206 *fig.*
Central nervous system (CNS), 562, 562 *fig.*, 567–570. *See also* Brain
Central vacuole
  eukaryotic, 70 *fig.*, 71, 71 *fig.*
  of plant cells, 77, 77 *fig.*
Centrioles, 81, 81 *fig.*
  eukaryotic, 70 *fig.*, 71, 71 *fig.*
Centromeres, 136, 136 *fig.*, 154, 155 *fig.*
Cephalopods, 354, 354 *fig.*
Cerebellum, 567 *fig.*, 569
Cerebral cortex, 567, 567 *fig.*
Cerebral hemispheres, 567
Cerebrum, 567 *fig.*, 567–568, 568 *fig.*
Cervical cancer, 613
Cervix, 603, 603 *fig.*
Cesarean section, 611
CF (cystic fibrosis), 86, 170, 170 *fig.*, 171, 180 *table*
  Hardy-Weinberg predictions and, 267
CFCs (chlorofluorocarbons), ozone hole and, 22–23, 23 *fig.*, 457
cf gene, 170, 170 *fig.*, 171
CFTR protein, 86
Chaetoceros, growth of, iron and, 114
Chambers, Dwain, 61
Chamguava schippi, 379 *fig.*
Chaparral, 425, 425 *fig.*
Character displacements, 390, 390 *fig.*
Chargaff, Erwin, 192
Chargaff's rule, 192
Chase, Martha, 191, 233
Cheetahs, 269
Chemical activation, ATP for, 99 *table*
Chemical bonds
  covalent, 38, 38 *fig.*, 40 *fig.*, 60 *fig.*
  hydrogen, 40, 40 *fig.*
  ionic, 37, 37 *fig.*
  peptide, 53, 53 *fig.*
Chemically gated channels, 565, 565 *fig.*
Chemical reactions
  of Calvin cycle, 107, 112
  coupled, 98
  energy and, 92, 94, 94 *fig.*
  of glycolysis, 120
  oxidation-reduction (redox), 118, 118 *fig.*
Chemiosmosis, 111, 125
Chemistry, 33–47
  atoms and, 34 *fig.*, 34 *table*, 34–35
  ions and, 36, 36 *fig.*
  isotopes and, 36, 36 *fig.*
  molecules and, 37–40
  of water, 42–45
Chicken, genome of, 225 *table*
Chief cells, 522
Chimpanzee
  genome of, 225 *table*
  HIV and, 309
Chitin, 59 *table*, 481
  in fungal cell walls, 316
Chlamydia, 613, 614
Chlamydia trachomatis, 613, 614
Chlamydomonas, 315 *table*
Chloride shift, 508
Chlorine, atomic number and mass number of, 34 *table*
Chlorofluorocarbons (CFCs), ozone hole and, 11, 11 *fig.*, 22–23, 23 *fig.*, 457
Chlorophyll, 106
  energy absorption by, 107
  light absorption by, 108, 108 *fig.*
  photosystems and. *See* Photosystems
Chlorophyta, 315 *table*
Chloroplasts, 70 *fig.*, 71, 71 *fig.*, 75 *table,* 78–79, 79 *fig.*, 105–107
Choanocytes of sponges, 348

Choanoflagellates, 315 *table*
Choanoflagellida, 315 *table*
Choanozoa, 315 *table*
Cholesterol, 60, 180 *table*
  in plasma membrane, 72, 73
  statins and, 84
Cholesterol-lowering drugs, 84
Chondrichthyes, 363, 363 *fig.*
Chondrocytes, 477
Chordates (Chordata), embryonic development of, 358 *fig.*, 359
Chorion, 606
Chorionic villus sampling, 184
Chromatids, sister, 150
Chromatin, 74, 74 *fig.*, 137
  gene regulation in eukaryotes and, 216, 216 *fig.*
Chromosomal theory of inheritance, 28, 28 *fig.*
Chromosomes, 28, 28 *fig.*, 135, 174–177
  artificial, for cancer treatment, 174
  coiling of, 137, 137 *fig.*
  eukaryotic, 74, 75 *table*
  homologous, 136, 136 *fig.*, 137 *fig.*
  human, 27 *fig.*, 176–177
  human gene distribution in, 226–227
  human karyotype and, 136, 137 *fig.*
  number of, 136
  sex, 175 *fig.*, 175–177, 177 *fig.*
  structure of, 137
Chthamalus stellatus, 388, 388 *fig.*
Chyme, 523
Chytridiomycetes, 318 *table*
Chytrids, 456
Cidaris, 372
Cilia, eukaryotic, 75 *table,* 81, 81 *fig.*
Ciliary muscles, 577, 577 *fig.*
Ciliates, 315 *table*
Ciliophora, 315 *table*
Circulation, body cavity design and, 352
Circulatory systems, 489–501
  closed, 490, 490 *fig.*
  of fishes, 363
  functions of, 491, 491 *fig.*
  human, 497–499
  of mollusks, 354
  open, 490, 490 *fig.*
  vertebrate, 475, 492 *fig.*, 492–494
Cisternae, 77
Clades, 290
Cladistics, 290 *fig.*, 290–291
Clam, 354
Classical conditioning, 433
Classification of organisms, 286–289
  approaches to, 294, 294 *fig.*
  binomial system for, 286 *fig.*, 286–287, 287 *fig.*
  biological species concept and, 289
  higher categories and, 288, 288 *fig.*
  Linnaean system for, 286–287, 294 *fig.*
  polynomial system for, 286
  species names and, 287, 287 *fig.*
"Clean coal," 454
Clear-cutting, 426
Cleavage, 357, 606
Cleavage furrows, 140, 140 *fig.*
Cleavage reactions, of glycolysis, 120
Clements, F. E., 387
Climate change. *See* Global change; Global warming
Climax communities, 399
Clinton, Bill, 233
Clonal selection, 553, 553 *fig.*
Clones, 553
Cloning
  reproductive. *See* Reproductive cloning
  therapeutic, 242, 242 *fig.*, 243 *fig.*
Closed circulatory systems, 490, 490 *fig.*
Clostridium botulinum, 306
Club mosses, 327 *table,* 330 *fig.*, 331
Clumped population distribution, 379 *fig.*, 380
Cnidarians (Cnidaria), 349, 349 *fig.*
Cnidocytes, 349
CNS (central nervous system), 562, 562 *fig.*, 567–570. *See also* Brain
Coal, "clean," 454
Coal gasification, 454
Coastal sequoia, 334, 334 *fig.*
Coccoloba coronata, 379 *fig.*
Coconut, 640, 640 *fig.*
Cocos nucifera, 640, 640 *fig.*
Codominance, 173, 173 *fig.*
Codons, 208
Coelom, 352, 474
Coelomates, 352. *See also* Annelids (Annelida); Arthropods (Arthropoda); Chordates (Chordata); Echinoderms (Echinodermata); Mollusks (Mollusca)
Cognitive behavior, 435, 435 *fig.*
Cohen, Stanley, 233
Cohesion-adhesion-tension theory, of water movement in plants, 628–629, 629 *fig.*
Cohesion of water molecules, 43, 43 *fig.*
  in plants, 629
Cohorts, 386
Coleoptile, 541 *fig.*, 641
Colias eurytheme, pollination by, 638 *fig.*
Collagen, 52, 52 *fig.*, 477
Collecting ducts, 536
Collenchyma cells of plant ground tissue, 619, 619 *fig.*
Collins, Francis, 233
Collins, James, 456
Colon, 525, 527 *fig.*
Colonial organisms, 313, 313 *fig.*
Color
  of flowers, 637, 648
  in guppies, 276 *fig.*, 276–277, 277 *fig.*
  of plants, 108, 108 *fig.*
Coloration
  defensive, 395, 395 *fig.*
  protective, selection and, 275
Color blindness, 179, 179 *fig.*, 578, 578 *fig.*
Color of flowers, 637, 648
Color vision, 578 *fig.*, 578–579
Colostrum, 611
Combustion in carbon cycle, 411, 411 *fig.*
Commensalism, 392, 392 *fig.*
Communication in social groups, 442 *fig.*, 442–443, 443 *fig.*
Communities, 19, 19 *fig.*, 376, 376 *fig.*, 404
  climax, 399
  competition in, 388–390
  holistic concept of, 387
  individualistic concept of, 387
  niches and, 388–390
  pioneering, 399
  stability of, 399
Community ecologists, 377
Compact bone, 478, 478 *fig.*
Companion cells, 621, 621 *fig.*
Compass sense, 438, 438 *fig.*
Competition, 388–390
  competitive exclusion and, 389, 389 *fig.*
  interspecific, 30, 388
  intraspecific, 388
  niche overlap and, 389
  realized niche and, 388, 388 *fig.*
  reduction by predation, 394, 394 *fig.*
  resource partitioning and, 390, 390 *fig.*
Competitive exclusion, 389, 389 *fig.*
Competitive inhibition, 97, 97 *fig.*
Complementary DNA (cDNA), formation of, 229, 229 *fig.*
Complement system, 547, 547 *fig.*
Complex carbohydrates, 58, 58 *fig.*
Complex cell cycle, 135
Complexity
  organization of life and, 18–19, 18–19 *fig.*
  as property of life, 17
Compound leaves, 626 *fig.*, 627
Compound microscopes, 68
Concentration gradient, 82
Conclusions in scientific process, 23
Condensation in interphase, 138
Conditioned stimulus, 433
Conditioning, classical and operant, 433
Condoms, 613, 613 *fig.*
Cone(s) (of eye), 577, 577 *fig.*, 578, 578 *fig.*
Conifer(s), 327 *table,* 334 *fig.*, 334–335, 335 *fig.*, 399 *fig.*
Conifer forests, 424, 424 *fig.*
Coniferophyta, 327 *table*
Conjugation, bacterial, 306, 306 *fig.*
Conjugation bridges, 306, 306 *fig.*
Connecting, for learning, 3
Connective tissue, 477–478. *See also* Bone; Skeleton(s)
  fibrous, 477
  immune, 477
  skeletal, 477, 477 *fig.*
  storage and transport, 477
  of vertebrates, 474, 474 *fig.*
ConnectPlus program, 8, 8 *fig.*
Connell, J. H., 388
Conscious planning in animals, 435, 435 *fig.*
Conservation, environmental, 458–463
Consumers, 404
Consumption, population growth and, 463, 463 *fig.*
Continuous data, 13
Continuous variation, 170, 170 *fig.*
Contraception, 612–613, 613 *fig.*
Contractile proteins, 52 *fig.*
Control experiments, 23
Controls in scientific process, 23
Convergent evolution, 260
Cooksonia, 324
Cooperation as biological theme, 21
Coral crab, 356 *fig.*
Coralline algae, 315 *table*
Coral snake, 396
Core ideas of biology, 26–29
  cell theory, 26, 26 *fig.*
  gene theory, 26, 26 *fig.*, 27 *fig.*
  theory of evolution, 28, 28 *fig.*, 29 *fig.*, 262 *fig.*, 262–263, 263 *fig.*
  theory of heredity, 28, 28 *fig.*
Coriandrum, 647 *fig.*
Cork cambium, 625, 625 *fig.*
Corn, 327 *table,* 622 *fig.*
  development of, 641 *fig.*
  ethanol production and, 468, 468 *fig.*
  genetically engineered, 237 *table*
Cornea, 577, 577 *fig.*
Coronary heart disease, gene silencing for, 219
Corpus callosum, 567, 567 *fig.*
Corpus luteum, 605
Correlation, causation and, 12
Correns, Karl, 174
Cortex of plant stems, 624, 624 *fig.*
Cortisol, 593
Cotton, genetically modified, 237 *table*
Cottonwood tree, genome of, 225 *table*
Cotyledons, 333, 639, 639 *fig.*
Countercurrent flow, 505, 505 *fig.*
Countercurrent heat exchange, 491, 491 *fig.*
Coupled reactions, 98
Courtship behavior, 441 *table*
Covalent bonds, 38, 38 *fig.*, 40 *fig.*
  in fats, 60 *fig.*
Covariance, 172
C phase, 135
C_3 photosynthesis, 107, 112
C_4 photosynthesis, 113, 113 *fig.*
Crab
  as detritivore, 405 *fig.*
  foraging behavior of, 448
Crane, Siberian, 438
Crassulacean acid metabolism (CAM), 113
Crawling, by cells, 81, 99 *table*
C-reactive protein (CRP), heart attacks and, 498
Creationists, 93
Crenicichla alta, 276, 276 *fig.*
Crick, Francis, 192, 233
Cristae, 78, 78 *fig.*
Critical thinking, 3
Crop plants. *See* Agriculture
Crossing over, 150, 150 *fig.*, 151
CRP (C-reactive protein), heart attacks and, 498
Cruise, Suri, 164
Cruise, Tom, 164
Crustaceans, 356 *fig.*
Cryptic coloration, 395, 395 *fig.*
C-section, 611
Cucurbita, 621 *fig.*
Cuenot, Lucien, 170
Culture, cells in, 156
Cupula, 574
Cutaneous respiration of amphibians, 364, 364 *fig.*
Cuticle of plants, 324, 620
Cyanide, 639
Cyanobacteria, 307, 307 *fig.*
Cycad(s), 327 *table,* 334, 334 *fig.*
Cycadophyta, 327 *table*
Cyst(s), protist formation of, 312
Cystic fibrosis (CF), 86, 170, 170 *fig.*, 171, 180 *table*
  Hardy-Weinberg predictions and, 267
Cytochrome c, 261, 261 *fig.*
Cytokinesis, 140, 140 *fig.*
Cytokinins, 643 *table*
Cytoplasm, eukaryotic, 70, 70 *fig.*, 71 *fig.*
Cytoplasmic transport, ATP for, 99 *table*
Cytosine, 192, 192 *fig.*
Cytoskeleton, eukaryotic, 70, 70 *fig.*, 71 *fig.*, 75 *table,* 80–81
Cytotoxic T cells, 548, 548 *table*

Danaus plexippus, 396, 396 *fig.*
Dandelion, 640, 640 *fig.*
Dandruff, 476
d'Arrigo, Angelo, 438
Darwin, Charles Robert
Beagle voyage of, 250 *fig.*, 250–251, 251 *fig.*
critics of, 262 *fig.*, 262–263, 263 *fig.*
Galápagos Islands research of, 251 *fig.*, 251–252, 252 *fig.*, 255–257, 255–257 *fig.*
natural selection theory of, 20
study of plants by, 644, 644 *fig.*
theory of evolution of. *See* Theory of evolution
Darwin, Francis, study of plants by, 644, 644 *fig.*
Daughter cells, 134, 134 *fig.*
DDT, 465
biological magnification of, 453, 453 *fig.*
Deamination, 128
Deciduous forests, 424, 424 *fig.*
Decomposers, 319, 405, 405 *fig.*
Deep-sea waters, 419, 419 *fig.*
Deer, population growth of, 383
Defense(s)
of animals, 395, 395 *fig.*, 543–559
as circulatory system function, 491
immune. *See* Immune response; Immune system
of plants, 395, 395 *fig.*
skin as first line of, 544 *fig.*, 544–545, 545 *fig.*
Defensive coloration, 395, 395 *fig.*
Defensive proteins, 52 *fig.*
Dehydration synthesis, 50–51, 51 *fig.*
Delbruck, Max, 202
Deletions, 199, 199 *table*
Delphinus delphis, 378
delta 32, 218
Demography, 386, 386 *fig.*
Dendrites, 480, 480 *fig.*, 480 *table,* 563, 563 *fig.*
Density-dependent effects, 384, 384 *fig.*
Density-independent effects, 384
Dental cavities, eliminating, 231
Deoxyribonucleic acid (DNA). *See* DNA
Dependent variables, 12
Derived characters, 290
Dermal tissue of vascular plants, 620, 620 *fig.*
Dermatophagoides, 556 *fig.*
Dermis, 544, 545 *fig.*
The Descent of Man (Darwin), 254
Desert(s), 423, 423 *fig.*
Desert pocket mouse, selection for melanism in, 275
Desmodus rotundus, 256
Detritivores, 405 *fig.*, 406
Deuterostomes
embryonic development of, 357 *fig.*, 357–359
evolution of, 344
Development
embryonic. *See* Embryonic development
fetal, 610–611
postnatal, 611
Devil's Hole pupfish, 378, 378 *fig.*
Devonian period, 360
Diabetes mellitus, 590
cell transformation for treatment of, 242
glucose excretion and, 528
insulin for, 590
obesity and, 11, 11 *fig.*, 523, 591
type I, 556, 590
type II, 590, 591
Diaemus youngi, 256
Diaphragm (contraceptive), 613, 613 *fig.*
Diaphragm (muscle), 506
Diastolic blood pressure, 498, 498 *fig.*
Diatoms, 315 *table*
uses of, 314
Diceros bicornis, 465, 465 *fig.*
2,4-Dichlorophenoxyacetic acid (2,4-D), 645
Dicots (dicotyledons), 337
development of, 641, 641 *fig.*
roots of, 622, 622 *fig.*
stems of, 624, 624 *fig.*
Dictyostelium, 315 *table*
Didinium, 393, 393 *fig.*
Diet
high-fat, 516
optimal, 516, 516 *fig.*
vegan, 526
Dietary supplements, 517
Diffusion, 82, 82 *fig.*
facilitated, 85, 85 *fig.*
selective, 85
Digestion
external, fungal, 317
extracellular, of cnidarians, 349
Digestive systems, 518–529, 527 *fig.*
esophagus and, 522, 522 *fig.*
gallbladder and, 526
liver and, 526
mouth and teeth of, 520 *fig.*, 520–521, 521 *fig.*
pancreas and, 526, 526 *fig.*
small and large intestines of, 524 *fig.*, 524–525, 525 *fig.*
stomach and, 522 *fig.*, 522–523, 523 *fig.*
swallowing and, 521, 521 *fig.*
types of, 518, 518 *fig.*
vertebrate, 475, 519–526, 527 *fig.*
Dihybrid cross, 167, 167 *fig.*
Dikaryotic hypha, 317
Dilger, William, 432
Dinoflagellates, 315 *table*
Dinosaurs, 361, 361 *fig.*
evolution of, 361, 366
extinction of, 367
Golden Age of, 366–367
plant-eating, 367
Diphylla edaudata, 256
Diploid cells, 136, 136 *fig.*, 148, 148 *fig.*, 149, 149 *fig.*
Diplomonads, 315 *table*
Dipodomys, 539
Directional selection, 270 *fig.*, 271, 271 *fig.*
Disaccharides, 58, 59 *table*
Diseases and disorders
Alzheimer's disease, 135
asthma, 507
autoimmune, 556
cardiovascular, 219
gene silencing therapy for, 219
gene therapy for, 244 *fig.*, 244–245, 245 *fig.*
genetic, 180 *fig.*, 180 *table*, 180–184
HIV/AIDS. *See* AIDS; HIV
malignant. *See* Cancer
sexually transmitted, 613, 614. *See also* AIDS; HIV
stem cell therapy for, 240 *fig.*, 240–241, 241 *fig.*
therapeutic cloning for, 242, 242 *fig.*, 243 *fig.*
viral, 309–311
Disruptive selection, 270 *fig.*, 271, 271 *fig.*
Diversity
of antibodies, 552, 552 *fig.*
genetic, sustaining, 465 *fig.*, 465–466
of human social behavior, 447
of life. *See* Biodiversity
DNA, 17, 26, 26 *fig.*, 189–203
amino acid encoding and, 168
Avery experiments and, 191
of chromosomes, 37 *fig.*, 137
double helix of, 26, 26 *fig.*, 27 *fig.*, 56 *fig.*, 57, 57 *fig.*, 192, 193 *fig.*
extraction of, 57 *fig.*
first cells and, 303
gene theory and, 26
Griffith experiment and, 190, 190 *fig.*
Hershey-Chase experiment and, 191, 191 *fig.*
Innocence Project and, 232, 233
Meselson-Stahl experiment and, 194, 195 *fig.*
mitochondrial, 78
noncoding, 227, 227 *table*
nucleotides in, 26
prokaryotic cell cycle and, 134, 134 *fig.*
replication of, 194–197
sequences of. *See* Genomes
sequencing of, 224, 224 *fig.*
structural, 227, 227 *table*
structure of, 192, 192 *fig.*, 193 *fig.*
timeline of, 233
DNA fingerprinting, 230, 239 *fig.*
DNA ligase, 197, 228
DNA polymerase, 196
DNA replication, 211 *fig.*
DNA vaccines, 234, 234 *fig.*
Doll, Richard, 200
Dolly (sheep), 239
Dolphin, 378
Domains of life, 28, 28 *fig.*, 295, 296 *fig.*, 296–297, 297 *fig.*
Dominant traits, 162 *table,* 162–163, 164 *table*
Dopamine, 566
Doping, 61
Dormancy
of plants, 647
of seeds, 333
Dorsal, definition of, 350, 350 *fig.*
Double covalent bonds, 38
Double fertilization, 638
Double helix, 26, 26 *fig.*, 27 *fig.*, 56 *fig.*, 57, 57 *fig.*, 192, 193 *fig.*
Doublings, 144
Down syndrome, 176 *fig.*, 176–177, 177 *fig.*
Dr. Atkins' Diet Revolution, 129
"Drift bottles," 416
Drosophila, directional selection and, 271, 271 *fig.*
Drosophila melanogaster, 174 *fig.*, 174–175
bithorax mutant of, 198 *fig.*
genome of, 225 *table*
Drug(s)
antiviral, for AIDS, 557
birth control pills, 612, 613 *fig.*
cholesterol-lowering, 84
melittin, 139
regulatory proteins as, 231, 231 *fig.*
Drupes, 640, 640 *fig.*
Duchenne muscular dystrophy, 180 *table*
Duck, behavioral isolation of, 280
Duckbilled platypus, 369 *fig.*, 576
Duodenal ulcers, 523
Duodenum, 524
Dust mite, 556 *fig.*

Eagle, 438
Earthworm, 355 *fig.*
circulatory system of, 490 *fig.*
digestive system of, 518, 518 *fig.*
hydraulic skeleton of, 481, 481 *fig.*
Ebbesmeyer, Curtis, 416
Ebola virus, 309
Ecdysozoans, 347, 347 *fig.*
ECG (electrocardiogram), 499, 499 *fig.*
Echidna, 360 *fig.*
Echinarachnius parma, 358 *fig.*
Echinoderms (Echinodermata), embryonic development of, 358, 358 *fig.*
Ecological footprint, 463, 463 *fig.*
Ecological isolation, 279 *table,* 280, 280 *fig.*
Ecological pyramids, 408, 408 *fig.*
Ecological succession, 399, 399 *fig.*
Ecology, 376–377. *See also* Communities; Ecosystems; Niches
behavioral, 436, 436 *fig.*
environmental challenge and, 377, 377 *fig.*
levels of ecological organization and, 376 *fig.*, 376–377
Ecosystems, 19, 19 *fig.*, 376, 403–427, 404. *See also* Communities; Niches
biodiversity and, 295
conservation of, 446, 466 *fig.*
ecological pyramids and, 408, 408 *fig.*
energy flows through, 404–407
freshwater, 420 *fig.*, 420–421, 421 *fig.*
human, 404
land, 422 *fig.*, 422–426
materials cycles in, 409–413
ocean, 418 *fig.*, 418–419
weather and, 414–417
Ectoderm, 346, 350, 350 *fig.*, 606, 606 *fig.*, 607 *table*
Edmondson, W. T., 469
Edward VII, King of England, 181
Effectors, 532, 532 *fig.*
Efferent neurons, 480, 480 *fig.*, 562, 562 *fig.*
Egg(s), 598. *See also* Ovum(a)
maturation of, prevention of, 612
of reptiles, 365, 365 *fig.*
Egg-laying mammals, 369 *fig.*
Electrocardiogram (ECG or EKG), 499, 499 *fig.*
Electromagnetic spectrum, 108, 108 *fig.*
Electron(s), 34, 34 *fig.*, 35, 35 *fig.*
energy carried by, 35, 35 *fig.*
Electronegativity, 40
Electron shells, 35, 35 *fig.*
Electron transport chain, 124
Electron transport system (ETS), 109, 109 *fig.*, 110
Elephant, pulse rate of, 500
Elevation, weather and, 415, 415 *fig.*

Embryo(s)
animal, 357–359, 357–359 *fig.*
implantation of, prevention of, 612
Embryonic development
of animals, 343 *table*
human, 606, 606 *fig.*, 606 *table*
of protostomes and deuterostomes, compared, 357 *fig.*, 357–359
Embryonic stem cells, 240, 240 *fig.*
ethics of research using, 240–241
Embryo sacs of flowers, 637
Emergent properties, 19, 376
Emigration, 268
Encephalartos transvenosus, 334 *fig.*
Endangered species, preserving, 464–466, 464–466 *fig.*
Endangered Species Act of 1983, 464
Endergonic reactions, 94, 94 *fig.*
Endler, John, 277
Endocrine disrupters, 645
Endocrine function, as circulatory system function, 491
Endocrine glands, 584, 584 *fig. See also specific glands and hormones*
Endocrine system, 584
of vertebrates, 475
Endocytosis, 84, 84 *fig.*
Endoderm, 346, 350, 350 *fig.*, 606, 606 *fig.*, 607 *table*
Endomembrane system, eukaryotic, 70 *fig.*, 71, 71 *fig.*
Endometrium, 603
Endonucleases, restriction, 228
Endoplasmic reticulum (ER), eukaryotic, 75 *table,* 76, 76 *fig.*, 77
Endoskeletons, 481, 481 *fig.*
of echinoderms, 358
human, 482, 482 *fig.*
Endosperm of seeds, 332 *fig.*, 333, 337, 337 *fig.*
Endospores, 306
Endosymbiosis, 79, 79 *fig.*, 297, 297 *fig.*
Energy, 91–101
absorption by chlorophyll, 107
activation, 94, 94 *fig.*
ATP and. *See* Adenosine triphosphate (ATP)
capture by photosystems, 107
carried by electrons, 35, 35 *fig.*
for cell disposal of damaged proteins, 88
chemical, conversion of light energy to. *See* Photosynthesis
chemical reactions and, 94, 94 *fig.*
definition of, 92
entropy and, 93
enzymes and, 95–97
finding cleaner sources of, 467 *fig.*, 467–468
flows of. *See* Energy flows
from food, 516 *fig.*, 516–517, 517 *fig.*
harvest from food, 117–131. *See also* Cellular respiration; Fermentation; Glycolysis; Krebs cycle
kinetic, 92, 92 *fig.*
laws of thermodynamics and, 93, 93 *fig.*
light. *See* Light; Sunlight
plants' capture from sunlight, 108 *fig.*, 108–109
potential, 35
renewable, 467, 467 *fig.*
Energy flows, 20
through ecosystems, 404–407
in living things, 92, 92 *fig.*
through trophic levels, 406, 406 *fig.*, 407 *fig.*
Energy-harvesting reactions, of glycolysis, 120
Enhancers, 216
Entropy, 93, 93 *fig.*
Envelope, viral, 308
Environment
adaptation challenges and, 377, 377 *fig.*
effects on alleles, 171, 171 *fig.*
environmental conservation and, 458–463
genetically modified crops and, 237, 459
pollution and. *See* Pollution
solving environmental problems and, 464–469
temperature and, global warming and. *See* Global warming
Environmental water cycle, 409 *fig.*, 410
Enzyme(s), 51, 52, 52 *fig.*, 95–97
actions of, 95 *fig.*, 95–96, 96 *fig.*
activating, 209
active site of, 95, 95 *fig.*
allosteric, 97, 97 *fig.*5111
attachment to substrates, 100
binding site of, 95, 95 *fig.*
"directed evolution" of RuBisCO and, 112
factors affecting activity of, 96, 96 *fig.*
regulation by cells, 97, 97 *fig.*
restriction, 228
structure of, 55, 55 *fig.*
Enzyme polymorphism, 282
Eosinophils, 496, 496 *fig.*
Epidermis, 544–545, 545 *fig.*
of plants, 620
of roots, 622, 622 *fig.*
Epididymis, 601
Epigenetics, 239
Epiglottis, 521, 521 *fig.*
Epinephrine, 566, 593
Epithelial tissues, of vertebrates, 474, 474 *fig.*, 476, 476 *fig.*
Epochs, 360
Equilibrium, 82
Equisetum, 327 *table*
Equisetum talmeteia, 330 *fig.*
ER (endoplasmic reticulum), eukaryotic, 75 *table,* 76, 76 *fig.*, 77
Eras, 360
Erosion in carbon cycle, 411
Erritzoe, Johannes, 278
Erythroblastosis, 555
Erythrocytes, 52 *fig.*, 496, 496 *fig.*
Escherichia coli, 215
Esophagus, 527 *fig.*
acid reflux and, 44
structure and function of, 522, 522 *fig.*
Essay on the Principle of Population (Malthus), 253
Essential amino acids, 517, 526
Estradiol, 60, 604
Estuaries, 418
Ethanol
as energy source, 567–568, 568 *fig.*
fermentation producing, 127, 127 *fig.*
production of, 468, 468 *fig.*
Ethics, of stem cell research, 240–241
Ethology, 431
Ethylene, 643 *table*
ETS (electron transport system), 109, 109 *fig.*, 110
Euglena, 315 *table,* 598, 598 *fig.*
Euglenozoa, 315 *table*
Eukaryotes (Eukarya), 28, 28 *fig.*, 296 *fig.*, 297, 297 *fig.*. *See also* Protists (Protista)
cells of. *See* Eukaryotic cells
origin of, 297, 297 *fig.*
prokaryotes compared with, 305, 305 *table*
Eukaryotic cells, 70 *fig.*, 70–81, 71 *fig.*
cytoplasm of, 70, 70 *fig.*, 71 *fig.*
cytoskeleton of, 70, 70 *fig.*, 71 *fig.*, 75 *table*, 80–81
endomembrane system of, 75 *table*, 76–77
nucleus of, 74, 74 *fig.*, 75 *table*
organelles of, 75 *table*, 78–79
plasma membrane of, 72–73, 75 *table*
Eulampis, 540
Eumetazoa, 346, 346 *fig.*, 348
Euparkeria, 365 *fig.*
European honeybee, 398
European hornet, 397 *fig.*
Eutrophication, 413
Eutrophic lakes, 420 *fig.*, 421
Evaporation, 410
Evolution, 249–283
adaptation within populations and, 272–277, 272–277 *fig.*
agents of, 268–271, 269 *table*
anatomical record of, 260, 260 *fig.*
as biological theme, 20
coevolution and, 391, 391 *fig.*
controversy over, 262 *fig.*, 262–263, 263 *fig.*
convergent, 260
creationists and, 93
definition of, 250
of dinosaurs, 361
"directed," 112
extraterrestrial, 304
fossil evidence of, 252
genetic change within populations and, 266 *fig.*, 266–267
key transitions in animal body plan and, 344, 345 *fig.*
molecular record of, 261, 261 *fig.*
natural selection and. *See* Natural selection
novel genes and, 303
of plants, 326, 326 *fig.*, 327 *table*
of primates, 370 *fig.*, 370–371, 371 *fig.*
sexual reproduction and, 151
species formation and, 279 *table*, 279–281, 280 *fig.*, 281 *fig.*
theory of. *See* Theory of evolution
of vertebrates, 360 *fig.*, 360–361, 361 *fig.*
of whales, 259
Evolutionary psychology, 447
Excitatory synapses, 566
Exercise, weight loss and, 129
Exergonic reactions, 94, 94 *fig.*
Exhalation, 507
Exocrine glands, 584, 584 *fig.*
Exocytosis, 84, 84 *fig.*
Exons, 212
Exoskeletons, 356, 481 *fig.*, 481–482, 482 *fig.*
Experiments, 22, 23
control, 23
Explorations, 9
Exponential growth model, 381 *fig.*, 381–382, 383
Extensor muscles, 483, 484 *fig.*
External digestion, fungal, 317
Extinctions
loss of biodiversity due to, 455, 455 *fig.*
mass, 361
rates of, 372
Extracellular digestion of cnidarians, 349
Extremophiles, 307
Eye
rods and cones of, 577, 577 *fig.*
transmission of light information to brain and, 579, 579 *fig.*
vertebrate, structure of, 577, 577 *fig.*

Facilitated diffusion, 85, 85 *fig.*
Factor IX gene, 245
Fad diets, 129
$FADH_2$, in Krebs cycle, 124
Falco peregrinus, 465, 465 *fig.*
Fallopian tubes, 603, 603 *fig.*
Families, 288, 288 *fig.*
Family trees. *See* Phylogenies (family trees)
"Fasting-induced adipose factor" (Fiaf), 523
Fat(s), 60, 60 *fig. See also* Lipid(s)
dietary, sources of, 516
Fat cells, 477
Fatty acids, 60
Feathers, 368, 368 *fig.*
Feces, 525
Fecundity, 386
Feedback inhibition, 97, 97 *fig.*
Fermentation, 127, 127 *fig.*
Ferns, 327 *table,* 331, 331 *fig.*
Fertilization, 148
in angiosperms, 337, 638, 638 *fig.*
double, 638
human, 605, 607 *table*
random, 151
self-, in flowers, 638
Fertilizers, phosphorus-containing, 413
Fetus, 610–611
Rh factor and, 555
Fever, 547
F_1 generation, 161, 161 *fig.*, 162–163
F_2 generation, 161, 161 *fig.*, 163, 163 *fig.*
Fiaf ("fasting-induced adipose factor"), 523
Fibers, 619
Fibrin, 495, 495 *fig.*
Fibrinogen in blood plasma, 495
Fibroblasts, 477
Fibrous connective tissue, 477
Filial imprinting, 433, 433 *fig.*
Filtration of body water, 534
Finches
character displacement among, 390, 390 *fig.*
Darwin's research on, 252, 252 *fig.*, 255–257, 255–257 *fig.*
disruptive selection and, 271, 271 *fig.*
theory of evolution and, 29 *fig.*
Fire, Andrew, 218, 233
Firmicutes, 523
First law of thermodynamics, 93, 93 *fig.*
Fir trees, 327 *table*
Fishes, 362 *fig.*, 362–363. *See also specific fishes*
blood pH of, 130
bony, 298, 363, 363 *fig.*

characteristics of, 362–363, 363 *fig.*
gills of, 362, 504, 504 *fig.*, 505, 505 *fig.*
hermaphroditic, 598 *fig.*, 598–599
Fission, 598
binary, 134, 134 *fig.*, 306
Fixed action pattern, 431, 431 *fig.*
Flagella, 81, 81 *fig.*
bacterial, 306
eukaryotic, 75 *table*, 305 *table*
movements of, 99 *table*
prokaryotic, 69, 69 *fig.*, 305 *table*
Flame cells, 351
Flatworms (Platyhelminthes), 350 *fig.*, 350–351, 351 *fig.*
body water content regulation in, 534, 534 *fig.*
circulatory system of, 491
flame cells of, 351
gastrovascular cavity of, 518
respiratory systems of, 504
Flemming, Walther, 136
Flexor muscles, 483, 484 *fig.*
Flowers
color of, 637, 648
edible, 326
egg formation in, 638
evolution of, 326, 336–337
fertilization and, 638, 639 *fig.*
monoecious, 637
pollen formation by, 637–638
pollination of, 332, 391 *fig.*, 638, 638 *fig.*
structure of, 637, 637 *fig.*
Fluid mosaic model, 72
Fluorescent dye, 156
Flying, efficiency of, 486
Flying foxes, 446, 466 *fig.*
Foams (contraceptive), 613
Follicles, 604
Follicle-stimulating hormone (FSH), 589, 603, 604, 605
Follicular phase of menstrual cycle, 604, 604 *fig.*
Food
energy and growth and, 516 *fig.*, 516–517, 517 *fig.*
energy harvest from, 117–131. *See also* Cellular respiration; Fermentation; Glycolysis; Krebs cycle
genetically modified, potential risks of, 237, 459
Food chain, 405, 405 *fig.*
length of, 123
Food vacuoles, 313
Food web, 406, 407 *fig.*
Foraging behavior, 437, 437 *fig.*, 441 *table*, 448
Foram(s), 315 *table*
Foraminifera, 315 *table*
Forensic science, DNA fingerprinting and, 230, 230 *fig.*
Forests. *See also* Tree(s); *specific trees*
acid precipitation and, 453, 453 *fig.*
clear-cutting, 426
conifer, 424, 424 *fig.*
deciduous, 424, 424 *fig.*
monsoon, 425, 425 *fig.*
tropical rain forests, 423, 423 *fig.*, 460, 460 *fig.*
Forgetting, 2–3
fosB gene, 432, 432 *fig.*
Fossils, theory of evolution and, 258, 258 *fig.*, 260
Founder effect, 269, 269 *fig.*
Fovea, 577, 577 *fig.*
Fox, Michael J., 240 *fig.*
Frame-shift mutations, 199
Franklin, Rosalind, 192, 233
Freely movable joints, 482
Frequency, definition of, 266
Freshwater ecosystems, 420 *fig.*, 420–421, 421 *fig.*
Frog
leopard, postzygotic isolating mechanisms and, 281, 281 *fig.*
poison dart, 395 *fig.*
Fruit(s), 326, 640, 640 *fig.*
evolution of, 326
seed dispersal in, 640, 640 *fig.*
Fruit fly. *See Drosophila; Drosophila melanogaster*
FSH (follicle-stimulating hormone), 589, 603, 604, 605
Fugu rubripes, genome of, 225 *table*
Fulgio, 315 *table*
Full, Robert, 41
Function, determination by structure, 21
Functional groups, 50, 50 *fig.*
Fundamental niche, 388
Fundulus heteroclitus, 282
Fungi, 28 *fig.*, 316–319
associations of, 319, 319 *fig.*
body of, 316 *fig.*, 316–317
commercial uses of, 319
as decomposers, 405 *fig.*
ecological roles of, 319
imperfect, 318 *table*
kinds of, 318 *fig.*, 318 *table*, 318–319
kingdom of, 16 *fig.*
nutrition of, 317, 317 *fig.*
reproduction by, 316 *fig.*, 317, 317 *fig.*
Funnel web spider, 356 *fig.*
Fur from endangered species, 464
Fur seal, 382 *fig.*

GABA, 566
Galápagos Islands, Darwin's research on, 251 *fig.*, 251–252, 252 *fig.*
Gallbladder, 526, 526 *fig.*
Gallus gallus, genome of, 225 *table*
Gamete(s), 598. *See also* Egg(s); Ovum(a); Sperm
of plants, 324
Gamete fusion, prevention of, 279 *table,* 281
Gametophyte, 325, 325 *fig.*
Gametophyte generation, 637
Gangliosides, 183
Gap junctions in cardiac muscle, 479
Gas exchange, 508 *fig.*, 508–509
Gastric acid, 44, 522–523
Gastric juice, 522
Gastric ulcers, 523
Gastropods, 354, 354 *fig.*
Gastrovascular cavity, 349, 490, 490 *fig.*
Gastrulation, 606 *fig.*, 606–607, 607 *table*
Gause, G. F., 389
Gecko, adhesive properties of, 41
Gene(s), 17, 26, 26 *fig.*, 164, 205–221
architecture of, 212, 212 *fig.*
central dogma and, 206 *fig.*, 208
human behavior and, 447
human social behavior and, 447
influence on traits, 168, 169 *table*
modified, escape from GM crops, 246
mutation of. *See* Mutation(s)
noncoding DNA within, 227, 227 *table*
novel, origin of, 303
number in human genome, 226, 226 *fig.*
oncogenes, 141
protecting, 200–201
proto-oncogenes, 141
transcription and. *See* Transcription
translation and. *See* Translation
tumor-suppressor, 141
Gene expression, 206, 211 *fig.*, 211–218
RNA-level control of, 218, 218 *fig.*
transcriptional control in eukaryotes, 216 *fig.*, 216–217
transcriptional control in prokaryotes, 214 *fig.*, 214–215, 215 *fig.*
Gene flow from genetically modified crops, 237
Gene pool, 266
Generations, alternation of, 326, 326 *fig.*
Gene silencing, 218, 219
Gene theory, 26, 26 *fig.*, 27 *fig.*
Gene therapy, 244 *fig.*, 244–245, 245 *fig.*
Genetic code, 208, 208 *fig.*
Genetic counseling, 184
Genetic disorders, 180 *fig.*, 180 *table,* 180–184
genetic counseling and, 184
screening for, 184, 184 *fig.*
Genetic diversity, sustaining, 465 *fig.*, 465–466
Genetic drift as agent of evolution, 268 *table,* 269, 269 *fig.*
Genetic engineering, 228 *fig.*, 228–237
agricultural applications of, 235 *fig.*, 235–237, 236 *fig.*, 237 *table*
cDNA formation and, 229, 229 *fig.*
definition of, 228
DNA fingerprinting and, 230, 230 *fig.*
medical applications of, 231, 231 *fig.*, 234, 234 *fig.*
restriction enzymes and, 228, 229 *fig.*
Genetics, 159–186. *See also* DNA
behavioral, 432, 432 *fig.*
codominance and, 173, 173 *fig.*
continuous variation and, 170, 170 *fig.*
environmental effects and, 171, 171 *fig.*
gene influence on traits and, 168, 169 *table*
incomplete dominance and, 171, 171 *fig.*
Mendelian, 160 *fig.*, 160–167, 161–163 *fig.*, 162 *table*, 164 *table*, 165–167 *fig.*
pleiotropic effects and, 170 *fig.*, 170–171
population. *See* Population genetics
race and, 293
Genetic screening, 184, 184 *fig.*
Gene transfer therapy, 244–245
initial attempts at, 244
new vectors for, 245, 245 *fig.*
problems with vectors for, 244–245
Genital herpes, 613
Genomes
definition of, 224
eukaryotic, 225 *table*
human. *See* Human genome
intelligent design evaluated using, 264–265
sequencing, 224–227
Genomics, 224, 225 *table*
Genotype, 164
Gentoo penguins, 23 *fig.*
Genus(era), 286
Geographical isolation, 279 *table,* 280, 281
Geometric progression, 253, 253 *fig.*
Geospiza
character displacement among, 390, 390 *fig.*
Darwin's research on, 251 *fig.*, 251–252, 252 *fig.*, 255–257, 255–257 *fig.*
Geospiza fortis, beak shape in, 256, 256 *fig.*
Germination, of seeds, 333, 639, 641, 641 *fig.*
Germ-line cells, 135, 149
Germ-line tissues, mutations in, 198–199
GH (growth hormone), 589
Giant red sea urchin, 358 *fig.*
Giardia intestinalis, 315 *table*
Gibberellins, 643 *table*
Gigantosaurus, 361 *fig.*
Gila monster, 476, 476 *fig.*
Gills of fishes, 362, 504, 504 *fig.*, 505, 505 *fig.*
Gingerich, Philip, 259
Ginkgo biloba, 334 *fig.*, 335
Ginkgophyta, 327 *table*
Ginkgo trees, 327 *table*
Glands, 476
Gleason, H. A., 387
Gleevec, 143
Global change, 452–457
ozone hole and, 11, 11 *fig.*, 22–23, 23 *fig.*, 457, 457 *fig.*
pollution and, 45, 452–454, 452–454 *fig.*
Global warming, 454
Calvin cycle and, 112
carbon dioxide and, 11, 11 *fig.*, 39, 411
controversy over, 470
melting of ice caps and, 39
El Niño and, 417
Glomerular filtrate, 537
Glomerulus, 536
Glottis, 521, 521 *fig.*
Glucagon, 533, 590, 590 *fig.*
Glucose, 58, 58 *fig.*
blood, regulation of, 533, 533 *fig.*
cellular respiration and, 118–127
excretion in urine, 528
Glycerol, 60
Glycine, 566
Glycogen, 58, 59 *table*
Glycolysis, 118, 120
Glyphosphate, genetic engineering of crops resistant to, 235, 235 *fig.*
Glyptodont, 252, 252 *fig.*
Gnetophytes (Gnetophyta), 327 *table,* 334 *fig.*, 334–335
Goiter, 592, 592 *fig.*
Golding, William, 446
Golgi bodies, 77, 77 *fig.*
Golgi complexes, 76 *fig.*, 77
eukaryotic, 75 *table*, 76 *fig.*, 77, 77 *fig.*
Gonad(s), 598. *See also* Ovaries; Testes
Gonorrhea, 613, 614
Goose, 19, 431 *fig.*, 438
Gosling, Ray, 233
Gould, James L., 443
Gould, John, 255

G_1 phase, 135
G_2 phase, 135
Gram(s), 13
Gram, Hans, 305
Gram-negative bacteria, 305–306
Gram-positive bacteria, 305–306
Grana, 79, 79 *fig.*, 106
Grant, Peter, 256
Grant, Rosemary, 256
Graphs, 12–14, 62
  histograms, 13, 13 *fig.*
  line, 13, 13 *fig.*
  pie charts, 13, 13 *fig.*, 282
  scales and units and, 12 *fig.*, 12–13
  using, 14, 14 *fig.*
  variables and, 12, 12 *fig.*
Grasslands, 424, 424 *fig.*
  dry, tropical, 423, 423 *fig.*
Gravitropism, 647, 647 *fig.*
Gravity, sensory receptors for, 574, 574 *fig.*
Gray squirrel, classification of, 288, 288 *fig.*
Green algae, 313
Green anole, 589 *fig.*
Greenhouse effect, 454, 454 *fig.*
Greenhouse gases. *See* Carbon dioxide
"Green living," 458
Griffith, Frederick, 190, 233
Grizzly bears as omnivores, 405 *fig.*
Ground beetle, 376 *fig.*
Ground meristem, 622, 622 *fig.*
Ground squirrel, 445
Ground tissue of plants, 619, 619 *fig.*
Groundwater, 410
  preserving, 460
Growth
  allometric, 611
  essential substances for, 517
  food and, 516 *fig.*, 516–517, 517 *fig.*
  of plants, 329, 618, 624 *fig.*, 624–625, 625 *fig.*
  as property of life, 17
  of trees, maximum, 628
Growth hormone (GH), 589
Guanine, 192, 192 *fig.*
Guard cells of plants, 325, 620, 620 *fig.*
  regulation of transpiration by, 630, 630 *fig.*
Guppies, color in, 276 *fig.*, 276–277, 277 *fig.*
Gymnosperms, 332, 334 *fig.*, 334–335, 335 *fig.*

Habitats, 404
  of animals, diversity of, 343 *table*
  loss of, 455, 455 *fig.*
  niche compared with, 388
  restoration of, 464, 464 *fig.*
Habituation, 433
Hadrosaurus, 367
Haeckel, Ernst, 376
Hagstrum, Jonathan, 439
Hair
  of mammals, 369
  woolly, 185
Hairy cap moss, 327 *table*, 328
Haldane, J. B. S., 445
Half-lives, 46
Hamilton, William D., 445
Hamlet bass, 598, 598 *fig.*
Haploid cells, 148, 148 *fig.*, 149, 149 *fig.*
Haplopappus gracilis, 136
Hardin, Garret, 459
Hardy-Weinberg equilibrium, 266 *fig.*, 266–267
Hares, 393–394, 394 *fig.*
Haversian canals, 478, 478 *fig.*
Hay fever, 556
Hayflick, Leonard, 144
Head, vertebrate, 359
Head and Shoulders shampoo, 476
Head louse, 392, 392 *fig.*, 404
Hearing, 576, 576 *fig.*
Heart
  of amphibians, 364–365
  contraction of, 499, 499 *fig.*
  human, 497–499, 497–499 *fig.*
  of sauropods, 366
  size and rate of, 500
  vertebrate, 492
Heart attacks, 498
Heartburn, 44, 522
Heart disease, coronary, gene silencing for, 219
Heart murmurs, 498
Heat
  production of, 99 *table*
  of vaporization, of water, 43
Helicase, 196
Helicobacter, 391
Helicobacter pylori, 523
Helix, 192
Helper T cells, 548, 548 *table,* 549
Hemicellulose, 468
Hemoglobin, 62
  high altitude and, 512
  transport of, 496, 508, 508 *fig.*
Hemolymph, 490
Hemophilia, 180 *table,* 181, 181 *fig.*
Henri, Victor, 100
Hepaticophyta, 327 *table*
HER1 and HER2, 142
Herbicides
  plant genetic engineering for resistance to, 235, 235 *fig.*
  synthetic auxins as, 645
Herbivores, 123, 405, 405 *fig.*, 518
Heredity. *See also* Genetics; Inheritance
  early ideas about, 160, 160 *fig.*
  Mendel's experiments on, 160–167, 161–163 *fig.*, 162 *table*, 164 *table*, 165–167 *fig.*
  as property of life, 17
Heritability of I.Q. scores, 172
Hermaphroditism, 598 *fig.*, 598–599
  in flatworms, 351
Herpes simplex infections, genital, 613
Herrick, James, 168
Hershey, Alfred, 191, 233
Heterocysts, 307
Heterotrophs, 123, 316, 342 *table,* 404. *See also* Fungi
Heterozygosity, 164, 166
Heterozygote advantage, 273
High definition televisions, 67
Hill, John, 200
Hippocampus, 568 *fig.*, 568–569
His, bundle of, 499, 499 *fig.*
Histamines, 556
Histograms, 13, 13 *fig.*
Histones, 137
HIV, 308, 308 *fig.*, 309, 557, 557 *fig.*. *See also* AIDS
HMS Beagle, Darwin's voyage on, 250 *fig.*, 250–251, 251 *fig.*
H1N1 flu, 311
H2N2 flu, 311
H3N2 flu, 311
H5N1 flu, 311
Hofstetter, Nancy, 383
Holistic concept of communities, 387
Holmes, Katie, 164
Homeostasis, 532 *fig.*, 532–533, 533 *fig.*
  as biological theme, 21
  as property of life, 17
Homo, 370–371
  early, 370 *fig.*, 370–371, 371 *fig.*
  increase in brain size of, 370, 370 *fig.*, 371 *fig.*
Homo erectus, 370 *fig.*, 370–371
Homo floresiensis, 371
Homo habilis, 370, 370 *fig.*
Homo heidelbergensis, 370 *fig.*
Homologous chromosomes (homologues), 136, 136 *fig.*, 137 *fig.*
Homologues, 136, 137 *fig.*
Homo neanderthalensis, 370 *fig.*, 371, 371 *fig.*
Homo rudolfensis, 370 *fig.*
Homo sapiens, 370 *fig.*, 371, 371 *fig.*
Homozygosity, 164, 166
Honeybee
  counting by, 434
  dance language of, 442 *fig.*, 442–443
  European, 398
  societies of, 446
Honeysuckle, 640 *fig.*
Hong Kong flu, 311
Hooke, Robert, 26, 66
Hormones, 60, 584–587. *See also specific hormones*
  action of, 585, 585 *fig.*
  of anterior pituitary, 588, 588 *fig.*, 589, 589 *fig.*
  peptide, 587, 587 *fig.*
  of plants, 642 *fig.*, 642–643, 643 *fig.*
  of posterior pituitary, 588, 588 *fig.*
  regulating kidneys, 538
  reproductive cycle coordination by, 604 *fig.*, 604–605, 605 *fig.*
  steroid, 586 *fig.*, 586–587
Hornet, European, 397 *fig.*
Hornwort, 327 *table,* 328
Horse chestnut tree, 626 *fig.*
Horsetail, 327 *table,* 330 *fig.*, 331
House dust mite, 556 *fig.*
Human(s)
  as agents of dispersal, 380, 380 *fig.*
  beneficial bacteria and, 391, 404
  circulatory system of, 497–499, 497–499 *fig.*
  digestive system of, 519–526, 527 *fig.*
  ecosystems of, 404
  environmental conservation and, 458–463
  evolution of, 370 *fig.*, 370–371, 371 *fig.*
  global change and, 452–457
  population growth of. *See* Population growth
  pulse rate of, 500
  social behavior of, 447, 447 *fig.*
  solving environmental problems and, 464–469
Human activity, mass extinction due to, 3615436
Human genome, 168, 225 *table,* 226–227, 233
  in acute myelogenous leukemia, 226
  gene distribution in, 226–227
  noncoding DNA in, 227, 227 *table*
  number of genes in, 226, 226 *fig.*
Human immunodeficiency virus. *See* AIDS; HIV
Human reproductive system, 600–605
  female, 602 *fig.*, 602–605
  hormonal coordination of, 604 *fig.*, 604–605, 605 *fig.*
  male, 600 *fig.*, 600–601, 601 *fig.*
  sexually transmitted diseases and, 613, 614
Hummingbird, 540
Humoral immune response, 549, 551 *fig.*, 551–552, 552 *fig.*
Hunter, John, 297 *fig.*
Huntington's disease, 180 *table,* 183, 183 *fig.*
Hydra, 349, 349 *fig.*
  circulatory system of, 490
  gastrovascular cavity of, 518, 518 *fig.*
Hydration shells, 43
Hydraulic skeletons, 481, 481 *fig.*
Hydrochloric acid, heartburn and, 44
Hydrocortisone, 593
Hydrogen, atomic number and mass number of, 34 *table*
Hydrogenated fats, 60
Hydrogen atoms, transfer of, 121
Hydrogen bonds, 40, 40 *fig.*
Hydrogen ions, 44
  buffers and, 44
  pH and, 44, 44 *fig.*
Hydrolysis, 51, 51 *fig.*
Hydrophilic molecules, 43
Hydrophobic molecules, 43
Hydrothermal vent systems, 419
Hydroxide ions, 44
Hydroxyapatite, 478
Hydroxyl groups, 50, 50 *fig.*
Hypercholesterolemia, 180 *table*
Hyperion (tree), 628
Hypertonic solutions, 83, 83 *fig.*
Hyphae of fungi, 316 *fig.*, 316–317
Hypoplectrus, 598 *fig.*
Hypothalamus, 567 *fig.*, 568, 568 *fig.*
  pituitary gland and, 589, 589 *fig.*
Hypotheses, 22–23, 25
  alternative, 23
  testing of. *See* Experiments
Hypothyroidism, congenital, 180 *table*
Hypotonic solutions, 83, 83 *fig.*

Ice, formation of, 42, 42 *fig.*
Ice caps, 39, 425, 425 *fig.*
Ice fishing, 421
Iceman, dating of, 46
ID (intelligent design), 263, 263 *fig.*, 264–265
Iguana, temperature adaptation and, 377 *fig.*
Iguanodon, 367
Ileum, 524
Immigration, 268
Immovable joints, 482
Immune connective tissue, 477, 477 *fig.*
Immune response
  antigen specificity of, 558
  cellular, 549, 550, 550 *fig.*
  humoral, 549, 551 *fig.*, 551–552, 552 *fig.*
  initiation of, 549, 549 *fig.*
  primary, 553, 553 *fig.*
  secondary, 553, 553 *fig.*
  specific, 544
  vaccination and, 553, 554, 554 *fig.*

Immune system
allergies and, 556, 556 *fig.*
autoimmune diseases and, 556
defense as circulatory system function and, 491
HIV attack on, 557, 557 *fig.*
of vertebrates, 475
Immunity, passive, 551
Imperfect fungi, 318 *table*
Imprinting, 433, 433 *fig.*, 438
Inbreeding, 269
Inchworm caterpillar, 395 *fig.*
Incomplete dominance, 171, 171 *fig.*
Independent assortment, 150, 150 *fig.*, 151
law of, 167, 167 *fig.*
Independent variable, 12
Indexes, 114
Individualistic concept of communities, 387
Industrial melanism, 274–275
Inflammatory response, 547
Influenza, 309
Asian, 311
bird, 311
new strains of, 311
pandemics and, 311
swine, 311
Influenza vaccine, 553, 554
Infrasounds, pigeons and, 439
Ingram, Vernon, 233
Ingroups, 290
Inhalation, 507
Inheritance. *See also* Gene(s); Gene theory; Genetics; Heredity
chromosomal theory of, 28, 28 *fig.*
polygenic, 170, 170 *fig.*
Inhibitory synapses, 566
Innate behavior, 430, 431, 431 *fig.*
Innate releasing mechanism, 431
Inner cell mass, 606
Innocence Project, 232, 233
Insects (Insecta), 356 *fig.*. *See also specific insects*
flower color and, 648
Malpighian tubules of, 535, 535 *fig.*
osmoregulation by, 535, 535 *fig.*
as pollinators, 638, 638 *fig.*, 648
societies of, 446
Insertion of muscles, 483, 484 *fig.*
Insertions in DNA, 199, 199 *table*
Instinct, interaction with learning, 434, 434 *fig.*
Instinctive behavior, 430, 431, 431 *fig.*
Insulin, 533, 533 *fig.*, 590, 590 *fig.*
Integrating center, 532, 532 *fig.*
Integration of inhibitory and excitatory effects, 566, 566 *fig.*
Integumentary system. *See also* Hair; Skin
of vertebrates, 475
Intelligence, environmental effects on I.Q. scores and, 172
Intelligent design (ID), 263, 263 *fig.*, 264–265
Interleukin(s)
interleukin-1, 549
interleukin-2, 550, 550 *fig.*
Intermediate filaments, 80
Intermembrane space, 78, 78 *fig.*, 124
Interneurons, 562, 562 *fig.*
Interoceptors, 573, 573 *fig.*
Interphase, 135
Interspecific competition, 30, 388
Interstitial fluid, 490
Intertidal region, 418, 418 *fig.*
Intestines
large, 525, 527 *fig.*
small, 524 *fig.*, 524–525, 525 *fig.*, 527 *fig.*
Intraspecific competition, 388
Intrauterine devices (IUDs), 612, 613 *fig.*
Introns, 212, 226
Invertebrates, 343 *table*
Involuntary nervous system, 571, 572, 572 *fig.*
Ion(s), 36, 36 *fig.*
in blood plasma, 495
Ionic bonds, 37, 37 *fig.*
I.Q. scores, environmental effects on, 172
Iris (of eye), 577, 577 *fig.*
Iron
atomic number and mass number of, 34 *table*
Ernest, 168
phytoplankton growth and, 114
Irreducible complexity fallacy, 263, 263 *fig.*
IRS proteins, 591
Irwin, Rebecca, 648
Islets of Langerhans, 526, 526 *fig.*
Isotonic solutions, 83, 83 *fig.*
Isotopes, 36, 36 *fig.*. *See also* Radioactive isotopes
IUDs (intrauterine devices), 612, 613 *fig.*
Ivy, 627 *fig.*

Jaws
evolution in fishes, 363
of theropods, 367
Jeffreys, Alec, 233
Jejunum, 524
Jellyfish, 349, 349 *fig.*
Jenner, Edward, 554, 554 *fig.*
Johnson, Eldred, 232
Joint(s), human, 482
Jurassic period, 360

Kalanchoë daigremontiana, 636, 636 *fig.*
Kangaroo, 369 *fig.*
Kangaroo rat, 30, 539
Kanzi (bonobo), 443
Karyokinesis. *See* Mitosis
Karyotype, 136, 137 *fig.*
kcals (kilocalories), 486
Kelp, 315 *table*
Kenyanthropus platyops, 370 *fig.*
Keratin, 52, 52 *fig.*
Kerr, Warwick Estevan, 398
Kettlewell, Bernard, 274
Key stimulus, 431, 431 *fig.*
Keystone species, preserving, 446, 466 *fig.*
Khorana, Har, 233
Kidneys, 535
function of, 537, 537 *fig.*
hormonal control of, 538
mammalian, 536 *fig.*, 536–537, 537 *fig.*
Kidney stones, 536
Killer bee invasion, 398
Killifish, 276
Kilocalories (kcals), 486
Kinetic energy, 92, 92 *fig.*
Kingdoms of life, 16, 16 *fig.*, 28, 288, 288 *fig.*, 294 *fig.*, 294–295, 295 *table*
Kingsnake, 396
Kin selection, 445, 445 *fig.*
Kleinfelter syndrome, 177
Knight, T. A., 160
Krebs cycle, 118–119, 121–125, 122 *fig.*
acetyl-CoA production and, 121, 121 *fig.*
ATP production from electrons and, 124–125
Kringle 2 gene, 256
K-selected adaptations, 385, 385 *fig.*, 385 *table*

lac operon, 214 *fig.*, 215
Lactic acid
fermentation producing, 127, 127 *fig.*
pH of fish blood and, 130
Lactose, 59 *table*
Lactuca canadensis, temporal isolation of, 280
Lactuca graminifolia, temporal isolation of, 280
Lagging strand, 197, 197 *fig.*
Lakes
eutrophic, 420 *fig.*, 421
oligotrophic, 420 *fig.*, 420–421
Lamellae, of gills, 505, 505 *fig.*
Lamprey, 363
Land, invasion by plants and animals, 360 *fig.*, 360–361, 361 *fig.*
Langerhans, Paul, 590
Language
brain and, 569, 569 *fig.*
in primates, 443, 443 *fig.*
Lanugo, 610
Large intestine, 525, 527 *fig.*
Larynx, 521, 521 *fig.*
Lateral geniculate nuclei, 579
Lateral line system of bony fishes, 363
Lateral meristems, 618, 618 *fig.*
Latitude, weather and, 415, 415 *fig.*
Law of independent assortment, 167, 167 *fig.*
Law of segregation, 167
Laws of thermodynamics, 93, 93 *fig.*
Leading strand, 197, 197 *fig.*
Leaf-cutter ant societies, 446
Learning, 3 *fig.*, 3–4, 433–435
as active process, 4, 4 *fig.*
animal cognition and, 435, 435 *fig.*
associative, 433
brain and, 569
imprinting and, 433, 433 *fig.*, 438
interaction with instinct, 434, 434 *fig.*
nonassociative, 433
rehearsal for, 3
studying to learn and, 4
LearnSmart program, 9, 9 *fig.*
Leaves, 626 *fig.*, 626–627, 627 *fig.*
photosynthesis in. *See* Photosynthesis
of vascular plants, 618, 618 *fig.*
Lectins, 639
Left atrium of human heart, 497, 497 *fig.*
Left ventricle of human heart, 497, 497 *fig.*
Legs
of amphibians, evolution of, 364, 364 *fig.*
of sauropods, 366
of theropods, 367
Legumes, 639
Leopard frog, postzygotic isolating mechanisms and, 281, 281 *fig.*
Lepus americanus, 393–394, 394 *fig.*
Letter on Corpulence (Banting), 129
Leukemia, acute myelogenous, human genome in, 226
Leukocytes, 52 *fig.*, 496, 496 *fig.*
crawling by, 81
LH (luteinizing hormone), 589, 603, 604, 605
Lichens, 319, 319 *fig.*
Life
diversity of. *See* Biodiversity
domains of, 28, 28 *fig.*, 295, 296 *fig.*, 296–297, 297 *fig.*
kingdoms of. *See* Kingdoms of life
organization of, 16–17, 16–17 *fig.*, 26, 26 *fig.*
origin of, 302 *fig.*, 302–303, 303 *fig.*
properties of, 17, 17 *fig.*
unity of, 28, 28 *fig.*
Life cycles
of plants, changing, 325, 325 *fig.*
sexual, 149, 149 *fig.*
Life history adaptations, 385, 385 *fig.*, 385 *table*
Light. *See also* Sunlight
visible, 108, 108 *fig.*
Light-dependent reactions, 107, 108, 111
Light microscopes, 68, 68 *fig.*
Light receptors, 577–579, 577–579 *fig.*
Likens, Gene, 426
Limbic system, 568 *fig.*, 568–569
Limenitis archippus, 396, 396 *fig.*
Line graphs, 13, 13 *fig.*
Linkage, 175
Linking for learning, 3
Linnaeus, Carolus, 286, 286 *fig.*, 287
Linneaen system of classification, 286 *fig.*, 286–287, 287 *fig.*
Lion, 369 *fig.*
ecological isolation of, 280, 280 *fig.*
Lipid(s), 50, 50 *fig.*, 60, 60 *fig.*
cellular respiration of, 128, 128 *fig.*
Lipid bilayer, 72
Lishman, Bill, 438
Liver, 524, 526, 527 *fig.*
Liverworts, 327 *table,* 328
Llama, 512
Lobe-finned fishes, 364 *fig.*
Locomotion, efficiency of methods of, 486
Locomotor organelles, protist, 312
Locust, 380 *fig.*
Locusta migratoria, 380 *fig.*
Logarithmic (log) scales, 12 *fig.*, 12–13, 44 *fig.*
Logistic growth equation, 382, 382 *fig.*
Long-term memory, 2
Lonicera, 640 *fig.*
Loop of Henle, 536
Lophotrochozoans, 347, 347 *fig.*
Lord of the Flies (Golding), 446
Lorenz, Konrad, 431, 433
Lumbricus terrestris, 355 *fig.*
Lung(s), 364, 504, 504 *fig.*
Lung cancer, smoking and, 10, 10 *fig.*, 200–201, 510–511, 511 *fig.*, 594
Luria, Salvadore, 202
Luteal phase of menstrual cycle, 604, 604 *fig.*
Luteinizing hormone (LH), 589, 603, 604, 605
Lycopersicon lycopersicum, 620 *fig.*
Lycophyta, 327 *table,* 330, 330 *fig.*, 331
Lycopod(s), 327 *table*
Lycopodium, 327 *table*
Lyell, Charles, 252
Lymphocytes, 477, 548

Lymph vessels, 490
Lynx canadensis, 394 *fig.*
Lysenko, Trofim, 646
Lysosomes, eukaryotic, 71, 75 *table,* 77
Lysozyme, 545

MacLeod, Colin, 191
Macromolecules, 49–63
formation of, 50–51, 51 *fig.*
organic. *See* Carbohydrates; Lipid(s); Nucleic acids; Protein(s)
Macrophages, 27 *fig.*, 477, 546, 546 *fig.*, 548 *table*
Magnetic field, compass sense and, 438, 438 *fig.*
Magnetite hypothesis, 580
Maidenhair tree, 334 *fig.*, 335
Malaria. *See also Plasmodium*
sickle-cell disease and, 182, 182 *fig.*, 273, 273 *fig.*
treatment window for, 320
Malassezia globosa, 476
Malnutrition, preventing, 516
Malpighian tubules, 535, 535 *fig.*
Malthus, Thomas, 253
Mammals (Mammalia). *See also* Human(s); *specific animals*
characteristics of, 369
egg-laying, 369 *fig.*
history of, 369, 369 *fig.*
kidneys of, 536 *fig.*, 536–537, 537 *fig.*
osmoregulation by, 535–538, 536 *fig.*, 537 *fig.*
placental, 369 *fig.*
pouched, 369 *fig.*
reproduction in. *See* Human reproductive system
respiratory system of, 506 *fig.*, 506–507
of today, 369, 369 *fig.*
Mammary glands, 369, 611
Mantle of mollusks, 354, 354 *fig.*
Map sense, 438
Marchantia, 327 *table*
Marginal meristems, 626
Marler, Peter, 434
Mars, life on, 304
Marsupials (Marsupialia), 369 *fig.*. *See also specific animals*
Masarid wasp, 397 *fig.*
Mass, 34
Mass extinctions, 361
Mass flow, 631
Mass numbers, 34, 34 *table*
Mast cells, 548 *table,* 556
Mating, nonrandom, as agent of evolution, 268 *table,* 269
Mating systems, 440
Matrix, mitochondrial, 78, 78 *fig.*
Krebs cycle reactions in, 124
Matter, 34
Maximal sustainable yield, 384, 384 *fig.*
McCarty, Maclyn, 191
McClintock, Barbara, 227
McClintock, Martha, 440
"McClintock effect," 440
McGwire, Mark, 61
McKormick, Robert, 251
Meadow buttercup, 623 *fig.*
Mechanical isolation, 279 *table,* 281
Medical diagnosis, antibodies in, 555, 555 *fig.*
Medusa, 349, 349 *fig.*
Meerkat, altruistic behavior in, 444 *fig.*
Megaspores, 332, 637
Meiosis, 147–157
crossing over and, 150, 150 *fig.*
definition of, 135
discovery of, 148
meiosis I, 150, 150 *fig.*, 152
meiosis II, 152–153, 153 *fig.*
mitosis differentiated from, 154 *fig.*, 154–155, 155 *fig.*
sexual life cycle and, 149, 149 *fig.*
Melamine, adulteration of milk with, 53
Melanin, 201
Melanism
industrial, 274–275
selection against, 275, 275 *fig.*
selection for, 274, 274 *fig.*, 275
Melanocytes, 201
Melanocyte-stimulating hormone (MSH), 589, 589 *fig.*
Melanoma, 201
Melittin, 139
Mello, Craig, 218, 233
Membrane attack complex, 547
Membrane proteins, 72–73
Memory
brain and, 569
forgetting and, 2–3
improving, 2
sleep and, 5
Memory B cells, 548, 548 *table,* 552
Memory T cells, 548, 548 *table*
Mendel, Gregor, 28
experiments of, 160–167, 161–163 *fig.*, 162 *table*, 164 *table*, 165–167 *fig.*
Mendelian segregation, 28
Menstrual cycle, 604, 604 *fig.*, 604–605, 605 *fig.*
preparation of body for fertilization and, 605, 605 *fig.*
triggering maturation of an egg and, 604 *fig.*, 604–605
Menstrual synchrony, 440
Menstruation, 605
Meristems, 618, 618 *fig.*
ground, 622, 622 *fig.*
marginal, 626
of vascular plants, 618, 618 *fig.*
Merops bullockoides, kin selection in, 445, 445 *fig.*
Mesoderm, 346, 350, 350 *fig.*, 606, 606 *fig.*, 607 *table*
Mesophyll, 627
Mesophyll cells, 105
Mesozoic era, 360–361
Metabolism as property of life, 17, 17 *fig.*
Metabolites
in blood plasma, 495
transport of, 99 *table*
Metaphase I in meiosis I, 150, 150 *fig.*, 152
Metaphase II in meiosis II, 153
Metaphase in mitosis, 138, 138 *fig.*, 139
Metastases, 141
Methanogens, 307
Metric units, 13
MHC proteins, 549, 549 *fig.*
Microfilaments, 80
Micrographs, 156
Microscopes, 68, 68 *fig.*
Microspheres, 303
Microspores, 332, 637
Microtubules, 80
formation of, 156
Microvilli, intestinal, 524 *fig.*, 524–525, 525 *fig.*
Middle ear of mammals, 369
Miescher, Friedrich, 233
Mifepristone, 612
Migrations, as agent of evolution, 268 *table,* 269
Migratory behavior, 438, 438 *fig.*, 441 *table*
Milk, melamine adulteration of, 53
Miller, Stanley, 302–303
Miller-Urey experiment, 302–303, 303 *fig.*
Mimicry, 396–397
proximity to model and, 396
Minerals, plant absorption of, 324
Misoprostol, 612
Mitral valve, 497, 497 *fig.*
Mitochondria
eukaryotic, 70, 70 *fig.*, 71 *fig.*, 75 *table*, 78, 78 *fig.*
matrix of, 78, 78 *fig.*, 124
Mitochondrial DNA (mtDNA), 78
Mitosis, 130–145, 138–139
in anaphase, 139
cell division and. *See* Cell division
definition of, 135
in fungi, 316
meiosis differentiated from, 154 *fig.*, 154–155, 155 *fig.*
in metaphase, 138, 138 *fig.*, 139
in prophase, 138–139
in telophase, 139
Mold, slime, 315 *table*
Molecular clocks, 261, 261 *fig.*
Molecules, 18, 18 *fig.*, 37–40. *See also* Carbohydrates; Lipid(s); Nucleic acids; Protein(s)
bonds in, 37–38, 40
hydrophilic, 43
hydrophobic, 43
organic. *See* Macromolecules
polar, 38, 40 *fig.*
Møller, Anders, 278
Mollusks (Mollusca), 354, 354 *fig.*, 360 *fig.*
body cavity of, 354, 354 *fig.*
Molting
evolution of, 344
in nematodes, 353
Monarch butterfly, 396, 396 *fig.*
Monoclonal antibodies, 142, 143, 555
Monocots (monocotyledons), 337
development of, 641, 641 *fig.*
stems of, 624, 624 *fig.*
Monocytes, 496, 496 *fig.*, 548 *table*
Monoecious flowers, 637
Monomers, 50
Monosaccharides, 58
Monosomics, 176
Monotremes, 369 *fig.*
Monsoon forests, 425, 425 *fig.*
Moore, Mary Tyler, 240 *fig.*
Moose, wolf predation on, 393 *fig.*
Morels, 318 *table*
Morgan, Thomas Hunt, 174
Mormon tea, 327 *table*
Mortality, 386
Morula, 606
Mosquito
genome of, 225 *table*
malaria and, 320
Moss(es), 327 *table*
conducting systems of, 328, 328 *fig.*
reproduction by, 325, 325 *fig.*
Motion receptors, 574
Motor nervous system, 584
Motor neurons, 480, 480 *fig.*, 562, 562 *fig.*
Mountain sequoia, 334
Mouse
embryo of, 359 *fig.*
genetic influences on behavior in, 432, 432 *fig.*
genome of, 225 *table*
pulse rate of, 500
selection for melanism in, 275
Mouth, 527 *fig.*
food processing in, 521
Movement
of animals, 343 *table*
body cavity design and, 352
of plants, 644 *fig.*, 644–645, 645 *fig.*
as property of life, 17
M phase, 135
mtDNA (mitochondrial DNA), 78
Müller, Fritz, 396
Müllerian mimicry, 396–397, 397 *fig.*
Mullis, Kary, 233
Multicellular organisms
complex, 342 *table*. *See also* Animal(s) (Animalia); Fungi; Plant(s) (Plantae)
protist, 313, 313 *fig.*
Multiple sclerosis, 556
Mummichog, 282
Muscle(s)
cardiac, 479
ciliary, 577, 577 *fig.*
diaphragm, 506
extensor and flexor, 483, 484 *fig.*
insertion of, 483, 484 *fig.*
origin of, 483, 484 *fig.*
skeletal, 479, 479 *fig.*, 483, 484 *fig.*
smooth, 479
of vertebrates, 475
Muscle contraction
ATP for, 99 *table*, 485, 485 *fig.*
sensory receptors for, 573, 573 *fig.*
sliding filament model of, 485, 485 *fig.*
Muscle fibers, 479, 479 *fig.*
Muscle tissue, 479, 479 *fig.*
of vertebrates, 474, 474 *fig.*
Muscular dystrophy, Duchenne, 180 *table*
Mushrooms, 316, 316 *fig.*, 318 *table*
edible and poisonous, 318, 318 *fig.*
Mus musculus, genome of, 225 *table*
Mussels, 394 *fig.*
Mutation(s), 141, 198–199
as agent of evolution, 268 *table*, 269
cancer and, 143
definition of, 198
frame-shift, 199
human heredity and, 180 *fig.*, 180 *table*, 180–183
phenotype determination by, 168
point, 199
random versus directed, 202
sex difference in rate of, 199
somatic, 200–201, 552
types of, 198 *fig.*, 198–199
Mutualism, 392, 392 *fig.*
Mycelium(a) of fungi, 316, 316 *fig.*
Mycobacterium tuberculosis, 307
Mycorrhizae, 319, 319 *fig.*, 324
Myelin sheath, 563, 563 *fig.*
Myofibrils, 479, 479 *fig.*
Myofilaments, 479, 479 *fig.*
contraction of, 485, 485 *fig.*

Myosin, 52 *fig.*
Myosin filaments, 483
Myrmecia spp., 136
Myxomycota, 315 *table*

NAD+, NADH formation from, 121
NADH
  formation from NAD+, 121
  in Krebs cycle, 124
NADPH (nicotinamide adenine dinucleotide phosphate), photosynthesis and, 107, 109, 111, 111 *fig.*
Na^+-K^+ (sodium-potassium) pump, 87, 87 *fig.*
Nashua River cleanup, 469, 469 *fig.*
National Collaborative Prenatal Project, 172
Natural killer (NK) cells, 546, 547 *fig.*, 548 *table*
Natural selection, 20, 253 *fig.*, 253–254
  enzyme polymorphism and, 282
  targets of, 275
Nautilus, 354
Neanderthals, 370 *fig.*, 371, 371 *fig.*
Neck of sauropods, 366
Nectar, 638
Negative feedback loops, 532, 532 *fig.*
Neisseria gonorrhoeae, 613
Nematocysts, 349
Nematodes (Nematoda)
  body cavity of, 353, 353 *fig.*
  digestive system of, 518, 518 *fig.*
  genome of, 225 *table*
Nematostella vectenis, genome of, 225 *table*
Nephridia, 534, 534 *fig.*
Nephrons, 536, 537 *fig.*
Nephrostomes, 534, 534 *fig.*
Nerve cord, 359
Nerve stem cells, 240
Nerve tissue, 480, 480 *fig.*, 480 *table*
  of vertebrates, 474, 474 *fig.*
Nervous system, 561–581
  autonomic (involuntary), 571, 572, 572 *fig.*
  central, 562, 562 *fig.*, 567–570. *See also* Brain
  neurons of. *See* Neurons
  parasympathetic, 572, 572 *fig.*
  peripheral, 562, 562 *fig.*
  somatic (voluntary), 571–572, 572 *fig.*
  sympathetic, 572, 572 *fig.*
  vertebrate, 475
Net primary productivity, 406
Neufeld, Peter, 232, 233
Neural tube, 607
Neuroendocrine system, 583–595. *See also* Endocrine glands; Hormones; *specific glands; specific hormones*
Neurons, 480, 480 *fig.*, 480 *table*, 563–564
  association (interneurons), 480, 480 *fig.*, 562, 562 *fig.*
  motor (efferent), 480, 480 *fig.*, 562, 562 *fig.*
  nerve impulses generated by, 563 *fig.*, 563–564, 564 *fig.*
  presynaptic, 565
  sensory (afferent), 480, 480 *fig.*, 562, 562 *fig.*
Neurotransmitters, 480, 565, 566
Neurulation, 607, 607 *table*
Neutrons, 34, 34 *fig.*
Neutrophils, 496, 496 *fig.*, 546
Newt, Oregon, 138 *fig.*
Niches, 257, 388–390
  competitive exclusion and, 389, 389 *fig.*
  fundamental (theoretical), 388
  habitat compared with, 388
  overlap of, 389
  realized, 388, 388 *fig.*
  resource partitioning and, 390, 390 *fig.*
Nicotiana tabacum, 620 *fig.*
Nicotinamide adenine dinucleotide phosphate (NADPH), photosynthesis and, 107, 109, 111, 111 *fig.*
Nicotine. *See* Smoking
9 + 2 arrangement, 81
El Niño, 417, 417 *fig.*
  global warming and, 417
Nirenberg, Marshall, 233
Nitrobacter, 412
Nitrogen, atomic number and mass number of, 34 *table*
Nitrogen cycle, 412, 412 *fig.*
Nitrogen fixation, 307, 412
Nitrogenous wastes, elimination of, 539, 539 *fig.*
Nitrosomonas, 412
NK (natural killer) cells, 546, 547 *fig.*, 548 *table*
Nodes of Ranvier, 563, 563 *fig.*
Nonassociative learning, 433
Noncoding DNA, 227, 227 *table*
Noncompetitive inhibition, 97, 97 *fig.*
Nondisjunction, 176, 176 *fig.*
Norepinephrine, 566, 593
Note taking, studying, 2, 2 *fig.*
Notochord, 359, 607
Nuclear membrane, eukaryotic, 74, 74 *fig.*
Nuclear pores, eukaryotic, 74, 74 *fig.*
Nucleic acids, 50, 50 *fig.*, 56–57
Nucleoid region, prokaryotic, 69, 69 *fig.*
Nucleolus, eukaryotic, 74, 74 *fig.*, 75 *table*
Nucleosomes, 137
Nucleotides, 26, 56, 56 *fig.*, 192, 192 *fig.*
Nucleus
  eukaryotic, 70, 70 *fig.*, 71 *fig.*, 74, 74 *fig.*, 75 *table*
  prokaryotic, 69
Nutrition
  as circulatory system function, 491
  of fishes, 363
  fungal, 317, 317 *fig.*
  protist, 312–313

Oak trees, 327 *table*
Obesity, 477
  bacteria and, 523
  diabetes and, 11, 11 *fig.*, 591
Observation in scientific process, 22, 22 *fig.*
Ocean(s)
  circulation patterns in, 416 *fig.*, 416–417
  global warming and, 454
Ocean ecosystems, 418 *fig.*, 418–419
Octopuses, 354
Oligodendrocytes, 563, 563 *fig.*
Oligotrophic lakes, 420 *fig.*, 420–421
Omnivores, 518
Oncogenes, 141
On the Origin of Species by Means of Natural Selection, or The Preservation of Favoured Races in the Struggle for Life (Darwin), 250
Oocytes, 602 *fig.*, 602–603
Oomycota, 315 *table*
Open circulatory systems, 490, 490 *fig.*
Open-sea surface, 418 *fig.*, 418–419
Operant conditioning, 433
Operons, 214 *fig.*, 215
Opposite leaf pairs, 627, 627 *fig.*
Opsin, 577
Optimal foraging theory, 437, 437 *fig.*, 448
Orbitals, 35, 35 *fig.*
Orders, 288, 288 *fig.*
Ordovician period, 361
Oreaster occidentalis, 358 *fig.*
Oregon newt, 138 *fig.*
Organ(s), 18, 18 *fig.*. *See also specific organs*
  complex, regrowth of, 475
  of vertebrates, 474
Organelles, 18, 18 *fig.*. *See also* Chloroplasts; Mitochondria
  eukaryotic, 70, 70 *fig.*, 71 *fig.*, 75 *table*
  locomotor, protist, 312
  prokaryotic, 69
Organ function, body cavity design and, 352
Organic farming, 459
Organic molecules, 50
Organism(s), 18, 18 *fig.*
  levels of complexity in, 18 *fig.*, 19
Organismic water cycle, 409 *fig.*, 410, 410 *fig.*
Organizing, for learning, 3
Organogenesis, 607 *table*, 608 *fig.*, 608–609
Organ systems, 18, 18 *fig.*
  of vertebrates, 475, 475 *fig.*
Origin of life, 302 *fig.*, 302–303, 302–304, 303 *fig.*
Origin of muscles, 483, 484 *fig.*
Ornithorhynchus anatinus, 297 *fig.*
Orrorin tugenensis, 370 *fig.*
Oryza sativa, genome of, 225 *table*
Osmolality, 538
Osmoregulation, 534 *fig.*, 534–539
  by invertebrates, 534, 534 *fig.*
  by vertebrates, 535–538, 536 *fig.*, 537 *fig.*
Osmosis, 82–83, 83 *fig.*
Osmotic pressure, 83
Osteichthyes, 298
Osteoblasts, 477, 478
Osteocytes, 478
Osteoporosis, 478, 478 *fig.*
Otoliths, 574, 574 *fig.*
Ötzi, 46
Outgroups, 290
Ovaries, 598
  of flowers, 336, 336 *fig.*, 637, 637 *fig.*
Overweight, 516, 516 *fig.*
  bacteria and, 523
Oviducts, 603, 603 *fig.*
Ovulation, 602
Ovules
  of flowers, 637 *fig.*, 638
  of seed plants, 332
Ovum(a), 602 *fig.*, 603. *See also* Egg(s)
  triggering maturation of, 604 *fig.*, 604–605
Oxalis oregana, 376 *fig.*
Oxidation, 118 *fig.*, 118–119
ß-Oxidation, 128
Oxidation-reduction (redox) reactions, 118, 118 *fig.*
Oxidative metabolism, 78
Oxpecker, 392, 392 *fig.*
Oxygen
  atomic number and mass number of, 34 *table*
  transport in blood, 508, 508 *fig.*
Oxytocin, 588, 588 *fig.*, 611
Oyster, 354
Oyster mushroom, 317 *fig.*
Ozone hole, 11, 11 *fig.*, 22–23, 23 *fig.*, 457, 457 *fig.*
Ozone therapy, 23

Pacemaker, sinoatrial node as, 499
Pain, sensory receptors for, 573
Paleozoic era, 360
Paley, William, 263
Palisade mesophyll, 627
Palmately compound leaves, 626 *fig.*, 627
Palmiero, Rafael, 61
Pancreas, 526, 526 *fig.*, 590, 590 *fig.*
Pancreatic cancer, 590
Pancreatic duct, 526, 526 *fig.*
Pandemics, 311
Pangaea, 361
Panthera leo, 369 *fig.*
Pan troglodytes, genome of, 225 *table*
Paper wasp, 356 *fig.*
Papillae, 575, 575 *fig.*
Parabasalids, 315 *table*
Paramecium, 393, 393 *fig.*
  body water content regulation in, 534, 534 *fig.*
  reproduction among, 313 *fig.*
Paramecium aurelia, 389, 389 *fig.*
Paramecium bursaria, 389, 389 *fig.*
Paramecium caudatum, 389, 389 *fig.*
Paraphrasing in note taking, 2
Parasitism, 392, 392 *fig.*
Parasympathetic nervous system, 572, 572 *fig.*
Parathyroid glands, 592–593, 593 *fig.*
Parathyroid hormone (PTH), 592–593, 593 *fig.*
Parazoa, 346, 346 *fig.*, 348
Parenchyma cells of plant ground tissue, 619, 619 *fig.*
Parent(s), children's resemblance of, 164
Parental behavior, 441 *table*
Parietal cells, 522
Parkinson's disease, stem cell therapy for, 240
Parthenogenesis, 598
Partial charges, 38
Passive immunity, 551
Pathways, biochemical, 96, 96 *fig.*. *See also* Glycolysis
Pavlov, Ivan, 433
Payen, Anselme, 100
PCR (polymerase chain reaction), 230, 230 *fig.*
Pea, Mendel's experiments on, 160–167, 161–163 *fig.*, 162 *table*, 164 *table*, 165–167 *fig.*
Peach, 639, 640 *fig.*
Peanuts, genetically modified, 237 *table*
Pearls, formation of, 354
Peat moss, 327 *table*
Pectoral girdle, human, 482

Pedigrees, 178–179
analyzing for albinism, 178 *fig.*, 178–179
analyzing for color blindness, 179, 179 *fig.*
Pelvic girdle, human, 482
Pelycosaur, 360, 360 *fig.*
Penguin, 23 *fig.*
Penicillium, 136, 318 *table*
Penis, 601, 601 *fig.*
Peppered moths, 274, 274 *fig.*, 275, 275 *fig.*
Peptide bonds, 53, 53 *fig.*
Peptide hormones, action of, 587, 587 *fig.*
Percent, 62
Peregrine falcon, 465, 465 *fig.*
Perforin, 546, 547 *fig.*
Pericycle, 622
Periderm, 625, 625 *fig.*
Periods, 360
Peripheral nervous system (PNS), 562, 562 *fig.*
Peristalsis, 522, 522 *fig.*
Periwinkle, 627 *fig.*
Permafrost, 425
Permian period, 360, 361
Pest resistance, plant genetic engineering for, 235
PET (positron-emission tomography), 36, 36 *fig.*
Petals, 336, 336 *fig.*
color of, 637
PET/CT (positron-emission tomography/computed tomography), 36, 36 *fig.*
Petioles, 626
p53 gene, lung cancer and, 510, 511
P generation, 161
pH, 44, 44 *fig.*
definition of, 62
enzyme activity and, 96, 96 *fig.*5110
of fish blood, 130
protein function and, 62
Phaeophyta, 315 *table*
Phagocytosis, 84, 84 *fig.*
Phagosomes, 313
Pharyngeal pouches, 359
Pharynx, 521, 521 *fig.*
human, 527 *fig.*
Phaseolus vulgaris, 647 *fig.*
Phenotype, 164
alteration by mutation, 168
protein determination of, 168
Phenylketonuria (PKU), 180 *table*
Pheromones, 442, 442 *fig.*
Pheromone trails, 442 *fig.*
Phloem, 329
water transport in, 632
Phosphate groups, 50 *fig.*
Phospholipids
in biological membranes, 60, 60 *fig.*
in plasma membrane, 72
Phosphorus
atomic number and mass number of, 34 *table*
in fertilizers, 413
Phosphorus cycle, 413, 413 *fig.*
Phosphorylation, substrate-level, 120
Photons, 108, 108 *fig.*
Photoperiodism, 646 *fig.*, 646–647
Photoreceptor hypothesis, 580
Photorespiration, 113, 113 *fig.*
Photosynthesis, 20, 103–115
ATP production by, 98, 107
C4, 113, 113 *fig.*
Calvin cycle (photosynthesis C3) and, 107, 112
CO2 removal from air by, 111
energy capture from sunlight and, 108 *fig.*, 108–109
light-dependent reactions of, 107, 108
light-independent reactions of, 107
overview of, 104–107
photorespiration and, 113, 113 *fig.*
photosystems and, 108 *fig.*, 108–111
Photosystems, 108 *fig.*, 108–109
antenna complex of, 108
conversion of light to chemical energy by, 110 *fig.*, 110–111, 111 *fig.*
energy absorption by, 107
energy capture by, 107
excitation of, 107
I, 109, 111, 111 *fig.*
II, 109, 110, 110 *fig.*
striking of, by light, 106
Phototrophs, 312–313
Phototropism, 644 *fig.*, 644–645, 645 *fig.*
Phylogenies (family trees), 290–292
of animals, 346 *fig.*, 346–347, 347 *fig.*
of cats, 291, 292 *fig.*
cladistics and, 290 *fig.*, 290–291
new molecular approach to, 347, 347 *fig.*
traditional taxonomy and, 291, 291 *fig.*, 292 *fig.*
traditional viewpoint on, 346
of vertebrates, 362 *fig.*
Phylum(a), 288, 288 *fig.*
Physcomitrella patens, 328
Phytochrome, 647
Phytoplankton, growth of, iron and, 114
Pickling, 53
Pie charts, 13, 13 *fig.*, 282
Pieris rapae, 395, 395 *fig.*
Pigeon, homing, 439
Piggyback vaccines, 234, 234 *fig.*
Pigments
bile, 526
plant, 108, 108 *fig.*
Pike cichlid, 276, 276 *fig.*
Pilus(i)
bacterial, 306
prokaryotic, 69, 69 *fig.*
Pimples, 544
Pine tree, 327 *table,* 626 *fig.*
Pinnately compound leaves, 626 *fig.*, 627
Pinocytosis, 84, 84 *fig.*
Pioneering communities, 399
Pisaster, 394, 394 *fig.*
Pisolithus, 319 *fig.*
Pistol shrimp, 392, 392 *fig.*
Pit(s), in plant secondary walls, 620, 621 *fig.*
Pith, 624, 624 *fig.*
Pituitary gland, 588–589
anterior, 588, 588 *fig.*, 589, 589 *fig.*
hypothalamic control of, 589, 589 *fig.*
posterior, 588, 588 *fig.*
PKU (phenylketonuria), 180 *table*
Placenta, 606
Placental mammals, 369 *fig.*
Planaria, 351 *fig.*
circulatory system of, 490, 490 *fig.*
gastrovascular cavity of, 518
Plan B, 612
Planning, conscious, in animals, 435, 435 *fig.*
Plant(s) (Plantae), 28 *fig.*, 294, 294 *fig.*, 295 *table,* 323–339, 617–633
adaptation to terrestrial life, 324 *fig.*, 324–325
crop. *See* Agriculture
defenses of, 395, 395 *fig.*
dormancy of, 647
evolution of, 326, 326 *fig.*, 327 *table*
flowers of. *See* Flowers
fruits of, 326, 640, 640 *fig.*
green color of, 108, 108 *fig.*
hormones of, 642 *fig.*, 642–643, 643 *fig.*
importance of, 324 *fig.*
kingdom of, 16 *fig.*
life cycle of, changing, 325, 325 *fig.*
mineral absorption by, 324
movement of, 644 *fig.*, 644–645, 645 *fig.*
nonvascular, 328, 328 *fig.*
photosynthesis in. *See* Photosynthesis
regeneration in, 642, 642 *fig.*
reproduction by, 325, 325 *fig.*, 636–641. *See also* Flowers; Seed(s)
roots of, 324
salt-tolerant, 338
seed. *See* Angiosperms; Gymnosperms; Seed(s)
tissue types of, 619–621, 619–621 *fig.*
tropisms in, 647, 647 *fig.*
vascular. *See* Angiosperms; Gymnosperms; Vascular plants
vernalization of, 646
water conservation by, 324 *fig.*, 324–325
Plantlets, adventitious, angiosperm reproduction by, 636, 636 *fig.*
Plasma, 477, 495
Plasma cells, 548, 548 *table*, 552
Plasma membrane
aquaporins and, 82
disease-causing defects of, 86
eukaryotic, 70, 70 *fig.*, 71 *fig.*, 72–73, 75 *table*
structure of, 72–73
transport across, 82–87
Plasminogen activator, in vampire bats, 256
Plasmodesmata, 621, 621 *fig.*
eukaryotic, 70 *fig.*, 71, 71 *fig.*
Plasmodial slime molds, 315 *table*
Plasmodium, 314, 315 *table*
genome of, 225 *table*
Plasmodium falciparum, genome of, 225 *table*
Platelet(s), 496, 496 *fig.*
Platyhelminthes. *See* Flatworms (Platyhelminthes)
Platypus anatinus, 297 *fig.*
Pleiotropic effects, 170 *fig.*, 170–171
Pleurotus ostreatus, 317 *fig.*
Plumpy'nut, 516
Pneumococcus, 190, 190 *fig.*, 191
PNS (peripheral nervous system), 562, 562 *fig.*
Poinsettia, 626 *fig.*
Point mutations, 199
Poison dart frog, 395 *fig.*
Poisonous mushrooms, 318, 318 *fig.*
Polar bear, melting of ice caps and, 39
Polar bodies, 602 *fig.*, 603
Polar ice caps, 39, 425, 425 *fig.*
Polar molecules, 38, 40 *fig.*
dissolving in water, 43, 43 *fig.*
Pollen, formation of, 637–638
Pollen grains, 332, 637
Pollen tubes, 638
Pollination, 332, 638, 638 *fig.*
by animals, 391 *fig.*, 638, 638 *fig.*
flower color and, 648
by insects, 638, 638 *fig.*
self-, 638
Pollinators, 391 *fig.*, 638, 638 *fig.*
Pollution, 452–454
acid rain and, 453, 453 *fig.*
chemical, 452, 452 *fig.*
global change and, 454, 454 *fig.*
global warming and, 45
reducing, 458, 458 *fig.*
Pollution taxes, 457
Polyandry, 440
Polygenic inheritance, 170, 170 *fig.*
Polygyny, 440
Polymer(s), 50
Polymerase chain reaction (PCR), 230, 230 *fig.*
Polynomial system of classification, 286
Polynucleotide chains, 56, 56 *fig.*
Polyp(s), 349
Polypeptides, 53, 53 *fig.*
Polysaccharides, 58, 58 *fig.*, 59 *table*
Polystichum munitum, 376 *fig.*
Polytrichum, 327 *table,* 328
Pomes, 640, 640 *fig.*
Population(s), 19, 19 *fig.*, 376, 378–386
demography and, 386, 386 *fig.*
life history adaptations and, 385, 385 *fig.*, 385 *table*
maximizing productivity of, 384, 384 *fig.*
Population cycles, 393 *fig.*, 393–394, 394 *fig.*
Population density, 381, 381 *fig.*
effects of, 384, 384 *fig.*
Population dispersion, 380, 380 *fig.*
Population distribution, 379–380
dispersal mechanisms and, 380, 380 *fig.*
types of, 379 *fig.*, 379–380, 380 *fig.*
Population ecologists, 377
Population genetics, 266–271
agents of evolution and, 268 *table*, 268–271
Hardy-Weinberg equilibrium and, 266 *fig.*, 266–267
Population growth, 381 *fig.*, 381–382
carrying capacity and, 382, 382 *fig.*
consumption level in developed world and, 463, 463 *fig.*
curbing, 461 *fig.*, 461–463
declining rate of, 462
of deer, 383
density and, 400
exponential growth model and, 381 *fig.*, 381–382, 383
human, 382
logistic growth model and, 382, 382 *fig.*
population pyramids and, 462 *fig.*, 462–463, 463 *fig.*, 463 *table*
Population ranges, 378, 378 *fig.*
Population size, 381
Populus trichocarpa, genome of, 225 *table*
Porter, William, 383
Positive feedback, human reproductive cycle and, 604
Positron-emission tomography (PET), 36, 36 *fig.*
Positron-emission tomography/computed tomography (PET/CT), 36, 36 *fig.*

Postanal tail, 359
Posterior, definition of, 350, 350 *fig.*
Postnatal development, 611
Postsynaptic cells, 565, 565 *fig.*
Postzygotic isolating mechanisms, 279 *table,* 281, 281 *fig.*
Potassium, atomic number and mass number of, 34 *table*
Potatoes, genetically modified, 237 *table*
Potential energy, 35
Pott, Percivall, 200
Pouched mammals, 369 *fig.*
p53 protein, lung cancer and, 510
Prairie(s), 424, 424 *fig.*
Precapillary sphincters, 492, 492 *fig.*
Precipitation
  acid, 45, 453, 453 *fig.*
  global warming and, 454
Predation, 393 *fig.*, 393–394
  predator-prey cycles and, 393 *fig.*, 393–394, 394 *fig.*
  reduction of competition by, 394, 394 *fig.*
Predator-prey cycles, 393 *fig.*, 393–394, 394 *fig.*
Predictions in scientific process, 23
Pregnancies
  high-risk, 184, 184 *fig.*
  Rh factor and, 555
  tests for, 555
Prenatal development, 606–611
  embryonic. *See* Embryonic development
  fetal, 610–611
Pressure-flow hypothesis, 631
Presynaptic cells, 565, 565 *fig.*
Presynaptic neurons, 565
Prey, predator-prey cycles and, 393 *fig.*, 393–394, 394 *fig.*
Prezygotic isolating mechanisms, 279 *table,* 280 *fig.*, 280–281
Primary cell walls of plant ground tissue, 619
Primary consumers, 405
Primary growth of plants, 329, 618, 624, 624 *fig.*
Primary immune response, 553, 553 *fig.*
Primary oocytes, 602, 602 *fig.*
Primary productivity, 406
Primary RNA transcript, 212, 212 *fig.*
Primary structure of proteins, 54, 54 *fig.*
Primary succession, 399, 399 *fig.*
Primates. *See also specific primates*
  evolution of, 370 *fig.*, 370–371, 371 *fig.*
  language in, 443, 443 *fig.*
Primers, 196
Priming reactions of glycolysis, 120
Principle of competitive exclusion, 389, 389 *fig.*
Principles of Geology (Lyell), 252
PRL (prolactin), 589, 611
Probability, 165
Problem solving, 435, 435 *fig.*
Procambium, 622, 622 *fig.*
Producers, 404, 405, 405 *fig.*
Progesterone, 605
Programmed cell death, 140, 140 *fig.*
Prokaryotes. *See also* Archaea; Bacteria
  cells of, 69, 69 *fig.*
  eukaryotes compared with, 305, 305 *table*
  reproduction by, 306, 306 *fig.*
  structure of, 305 *table*, 305–306
  transcriptional control in, 214 *fig.*, 214–215, 215 *fig.*
Prolactin (PRL), 589, 611
Promoters, 206, 214, 214 *fig.*5244
Prophase I in meiosis I, 150, 150 *fig.*, 152
Prophase II in meiosis II, 152, 153
Prophase in mitosis, 138–139
Prostaglandins, 611
Protandry, 599
Proteasomes, 88
Protective coloration, selection and, 275
Protein(s), 50, 50 *fig.*, 52 *fig.*, 52–55, 190
  amino acids and, 53, 53 *fig.*
  in blood plasma, 495, 495 *fig.*
  cell surface, 73
  cellular respiration of, 128, 128 *fig.*
  of complement system, 547, 547 *fig.*
  contractile, 52 *fig.*
  damaged, energy required for disposal of, 88
  defensive, 52 *fig.*
  denaturation of, 55, 55 *fig.*
  folding of, 55, 55 *fig.*
  membrane, 72–73
  pH and function of, 62
  phenotype determination by, 168
  structural, 52 *fig.*
  structure of, 54, 54 *fig.*
  synthesis of, 212, 212 *fig.*, 213 *fig.*, 220
  transmembrane, 73
  transport, 52 *fig.*
Protists (Protista), 26 *fig.*, 28 *fig.*, 294, 294 *fig.*, 295 *table. See also* Eukaryotes (Eukarya)
  biology of, 312 *fig.*, 312–315
  impact on humans, 314
  kinds of, 314, 314 *fig.*, 315 *table*
  kingdom of, 16 *fig.*
  osmoregulation by, 534, 534 *fig.*
  phylogenetic tree for, 314 *fig.*
Protoderm of root, 622, 622 *fig.*
Protogyny, 599
Proton(s), 34, 34 *fig.*
Protonephridia, 534
Proto-oncogenes, 141
Protostomes, 344
  embryonic development of, 344, 344 *fig.*
Pseudocoel, 352
Pseudocoelomates, 352, 352 *fig.*, 353, 353 *fig.*
Pseudopodia, protist, 312
Psilotum, 327 *table*
Pterophyta, 327 *table,* 330 *fig.*, 330–331
Pterosaurs (Pterosauria), 361, 363 *fig.*
PTH (parathyroid hormone), 592–593, 593 *fig.*
p53 tumor-suppressor protein, 143
Pufferfish, genome of, 225 *table*
Pulmonary arteries, human, 497 *fig.*, 498
Pulmonary semilunar valve, 497 *fig.*, 498
Pulmonary veins
  amphibian, 364
  human, 497, 497 *fig.*
Pulse rate, 500
Punnett squares, 165, 165 *fig.*
Pupfish, 378, 378 *fig.*
Pupil (of eye), 577, 577 *fig.*
Purines, 192
Purkinje fibers, 499, 499 *fig.*
Pyloric sphincter, 523
Pyrenestes ostrinus, 271, 271 *fig.*
Pyrimidines, 192
Pyrrhophyta, 315 *table*
Quaternary structure of proteins, 54, 54 *fig.*
Quercus phellos, 287, 287 *fig.*
Quercus rubra, 287, 287 *fig.*
Quinton, Paul, 86
Race, genetics and, 293
Radial cleavage, 357
Radial symmetry, 344, 345 *fig.*
  of cnidarians, 349
Radiata, 346, 346 *fig.*
Radioactive decay, 36
Radioactive isotopes
  dating of Iceman using, 46
  half-lives of, 46
  labeling of DNA and protein with, 191
  medical uses of, 36, 36 *fig.*
Radiolarians, 315 *table*
Radish, 630 *fig.*
Radula of mollusks, 354, 354 *fig.*
Rain
  acid, 45, 453, 453 *fig.*
  global warming and, 454
Rain forests, tropical, 423, 423 *fig.*
  destruction of, 460, 460 *fig.*
Rain shadows, 415, 415 *fig.*
Rana mucosa, 456
Ranavirus, 456
Random fertilization, 151
Random population distribution, 379, 379 *fig.*
Ranunculus, 623 *fig.*
Ranunculus acris, 623 *fig.*
Raphanus sativus, 630 *fig.*
Ratios, 46
Ravens, 435 *fig.*
Rb tumor-suppressor protein, 143
Reabsorption of water, 537
Reactants, 94, 94 *fig.*
Reading, establishing a purpose for, 3
Realized niche, 388, 388 *fig.*
Receptacles of flowers, 336, 336 *fig.*
Recessive traits, 162 *table,* 162–163, 164 *table*
Reciprocity, 444
Rectum, 525, 527 *fig.*
Red algae, 313, 315 *table*
Red blood cells, 52 *fig.*, 496, 496 *fig.*
Red maple, 621 *fig.*
Red oak, 287, 287 *fig.*
Redox cycle, 126
"Red tides," 314
Reduction division, 154, 154 *fig.*, 155 *fig.*
Reduction in cellular respiration, 118 *fig.* 118
Redwood sorrel, 376 *fig.*
Redwood trees, 327 *table*
  community of, 376 *fig.*
  maximum height of, 628
Reflexes, 571, 571 *fig.*
Refractory period, 564
Refuse utilizers, 123
Regeneration, 475
  in plants, 642, 642 *fig.*
  of spinal cord, 570
Regression line, 13, 282
Rehearsal, means of, 3, 3 *fig.*
Renal cortex, 536, 537 *fig.*
Renal medulla, 536, 537 *fig.*
Renewable energy, 467, 467 *fig.*
Renner, Otto, 632
Repeated sequences, 227, 227 *fig.*
Repetition, for learning, 3
Replication, 134, 134 *fig.*
Replication fork, 196–197
Repressors, 97, 97 *fig.*, 214 *fig.*, 214–215
Reproduction, 597–605
  approaches to sex and, 598 *fig.*, 598–599
  asexual. *See* Asexual reproduction
  contraception and, 612–613, 613 *fig.*
  in fungi, 316 *fig.*, 317, 317 *fig.*
  human. *See* Human reproductive system
  by plants, 325, 325 *fig.*, 636–641. *See also* Flowers; Seed(s)
  prokaryotic, 306, 306 *fig.*
  as property of life, 17
  sex determination and, 599, 599 *fig.*
  sexual. *See* Sexual reproduction
  vegetative, 636, 636 *fig.*
Reproductive behaviors, 440 *fig.*, 440–441, 441 *table*
Reproductive cloning, 238 *fig.*, 238–239
  of Dolly, 239
  importance of gene reprogramming and, 239
  progress since Dolly's birth, 239, 239 *fig.*
  therapeutic cloning compared with, 242, 243 *fig.*
  Wilmut's experiment in, 238 *fig.*, 238–239
Reproductive isolation, 279
Reproductive systems
  human. *See* Human reproductive system
  of vertebrates, 475
Reptiles, 365, 365 *fig.*. *See also* Dinosaurs
  characteristics of, 365, 365 *fig.*
  first, 360
Research. *See also* Scientific investigations
  using embryonic stem cells, ethics of, 240–241
Resistin, 591
Resolution, 68, 68 *fig.*
Resource(s), nonreplaceable, protecting, 459 *fig.*, 459–460
Resource partitioning, 390, 390 *fig.*
Respiration
  in carbon cycle, 411, 411 *fig.*
  cellular. *See* Cellular respiration
  as circulatory system function, 491
  cutaneous, of amphibians, 364, 364 *fig.*
Respiratory systems, 503–513
  of aquatic vertebrates, 505, 505 *fig.*
  of arthropods, 504
  of flatworms, 504
  gas exchange and, 508 *fig.*, 508–509
  lung cancer and, 200–201, 510–511, 511 *fig.*, 594
  mammalian, 506 *fig.*, 506–507
  types of, 504, 504 *fig.*
  of vertebrates, 475
Response to stimulation as property of life, 17
Resting membrane potential, 564, 564 *fig.*
Restriction endonucleases, 228
Restriction enzymes, 228
Reticular formation, 567 *fig.*, 569
Retina, 577, 577 *fig.*
Retinal, 108
cis-Retinal, 577–578, 578 *fig.*
Reverse transcriptase, 229

Reznick, David, 277
Rh factor, 555
Rhinoceros, 465, 465 *fig.*
Rhizomes, angiosperm reproduction by, 636, 636 *fig.*
Rhizopoda, 315 *table*
Rhizopogon, 319 *fig.*
Rhizopus, 318 *table*
Rhodophyta, 315 *table*
Rhodopsin, 577–578
Rhynia, 324
Ribonucleic acid. *See* RNA
Ribosomal RNA (rRNA), 74, 209, 209 *fig.*
Ribosomes, 209, 209 *fig.*
eukaryotic, 74, 75 *table*
prokaryotic, 69, 69 *fig.*
Rice
flood-tolerant, 644
genome of, 225 *table*
transgenic, 236, 236 *fig.*, 237 *table*
Ricin, 639
Right atrium, of human heart, 497 *fig.*, 498
Right ventricle, of human heart, 497 *fig.*, 498
Rivulus hartii, 276
RNA, 57, 57 *fig.*
of chromosomes, 137
first cells and, 303
ribosomal, 74, 209, 209 *fig.*
transfer, 209, 209 *fig.*
RNA interference, 218, 219
RNA polymerase, 206
Rock crab, 481 *fig.*
Rod(s) (of eye), 577, 577 *fig.*
Rodents (Rodentia), 369. *See also specific animals*
Rodhocetus, 259
Root(s), 324
adventitious, 623
of vascular plants, 618, 618 *fig.*, 622 *fig.*, 622–623, 623 *fig.*
water absorption by, 630, 630 *fig.*
Root cap, 622, 622 *fig.*
Root hairs, 620, 630, 630 *fig.*
Root pressure, 629
Rose, 327 *table*
Ross, Ronald, 320
Rough endoplasmic reticulum (rough ER), eukaryotic, 76, 76 *fig.*, 77
Roundworms
nematodes. *See* Nematodes (Nematoda)
pseudocoelomates, 352, 352 *fig.*, 353, 353 *fig.*
rRNA (ribosomal RNA), 74, 209, 209 *fig.*
r-selected adaptations, 385, 385 *fig.*, 385 *table*
RU486, 612
RuBisCO, 112
Ruminants, 519
Runners, angiosperm reproduction by, 636, 636 *fig.*
Running, efficiency of, 486
Rusts, 318 *table*

Saccharomyces cerevisiae, genome of, 225 *table*
Sago palm trees, 327 *table*
Sahelanthropus tchadensis, 370 *fig.*
Salamander, 456
digestive system of, 518, 518 *fig.*
Saliva, 521
Salivary amylase, 521
Salivary glands, 527 *fig.*
Salt (sodium chloride)
dissolution in water, 43, 43 *fig.*
ionic bond in, 37, 37 *fig.*
plants tolerating, 338
Salts in blood plasma, 495
Sand dollar, 358 *fig.*
Sand wasp, 397 *fig.*
Sanger, Frederick, 224
SA (sinoatrial) node, 499, 499 *fig.*
Sarcomeres, 485, 485 *fig.*
SARS (severe acute respiratory syndrome), 309
Saturated fats, 60, 60 *fig.*
Sauropods, 366
Savannas, 423, 423 *fig.*
Scales, on graphs, 12 *fig.*, 12–13
Scallops, 354
Scanning electron microscopes (SEMs), 68
Scaphinotus velutinus, 376 *fig.*
Scarlet kingsnake, 396
Scavengers, 123
Scheck, Barry, 232, 233
Schleiden, Matthias, 26, 66
Schwann, Theodor, 26, 66
Schwann cells, 563, 563 *fig.*
Science, as way of thinking, 10 *fig.*, 10–11
Scientific investigations, 22–24
limitations of science and, 24
method of, 22
scientific method and, 34
stages of, 22 *fig.*, 22–23, 23 *fig.*
Scientific method, 24
Scientific names, 287
Sciurus carolinensis, 288, 288 *fig.*
Sclereids, 619
Sclerenchyma cells of plant ground tissue, 619, 619 *fig.*
Scotch pine trees, 381 *fig.*
Scrotum, 600, 600 *fig.*
Sea anemone, genome of, 225 *table*
Seal, fur, 382 *fig.*
Sea otter, 435 *fig.*
Sears, Barry, 129
Sea star, 358 *fig.*
Sea turtle, 253, 253 *fig.*
Sea urchin, 358 *fig.*
Sebulex shampoo, 476
Sebum, 544
Secondary cell walls of plant ground tissue, 619
Secondary consumers, 405
Secondary growth of plants, 329, 618, 624–625, 625 *fig.*
Secondary immune response, 553, 553 *fig.*
Secondary oocytes, 602 *fig.*, 603
Secondary structure of proteins, 54, 54 *fig.*
Secondary succession, 399
Second law of thermodynamics, 93, 93 *fig.*
Second messengers, 587, 587 *fig.*
Secretion, body water regulation and, 535
Seed(s). *See also* Angiosperms; Gymnosperms
ancient, 333
dispersal in fruits, 640, 640 *fig.*
evolution of seed plants and, 326
germination of, 333, 639, 641, 641 *fig.*
poisonous, 639
structure of, 332 *fig.*, 332–333, 333 *fig.*
Seedless vascular plants, 330 *fig.*, 330–331
Segmentation, evolution of, 344, 344 *fig.*, 355
Segregation, law of, 167
Selection, 269–271, 270 *fig.*
as agent of evolution, 268 *table*, 269
artificial, 269
directional, 270 *fig.*, 271, 271 *fig.*
disruptive, 270 *fig.*, 271, 271 *fig.*
against melanism, 275, 275 *fig.*
natural. *See* Natural selection
protective coloration and, 275
stabilizing, 270 *fig.*, 271, 271 *fig.*, 273, 273 *fig.*
Selective diffusion, 85
Selective permeability, 85, 87
Self-fertilization, 638
Self-mimicry, 397, 397 *fig.*
Self-pollination, 638
Selsun Blue shampoo, 476
Semibalanus balanoides, 388, 388 *fig.*
Semicircular canals, 574
Seminiferous tubules, 600, 600 *fig.*
Sensors, 532, 532 *fig.*
Sensory nervous system, 573–579
gravity and motion and, 574, 574 *fig.*
hearing and, 576, 576 *fig.*
internal environment and, 573, 573 *fig.*
taste and smell and, 575, 575 *fig.*
vision and, 577–579, 577–579 *fig.*
Sensory neurons, 480, 480 *fig.*, 562, 562 *fig.*
Sensory receptors
for gravity and motion, 574, 574 *fig.*
internal, 573, 573 *fig.*
for taste and smell, 575, 575 *fig.*
Sepals of flowers, 336, 336 *fig.*
Sequential hermaphroditism, 599
Sequoiadendron gigantea, 334
Sequoia sempervirens, 334, 334 *fig.*, 376 *fig.*
Sequoia trees, 334, 334 *fig.*
Serengeti wildebeest, 381 *fig.*
Serotonin, 566
Serum albumin, 495
"Set point," 129
Severe acute respiratory syndrome (SARS), 309
Sex chromosomes, 176
chromosomal theory of inheritance and, 175, 175 *fig.*
nondisjunction involving, 177, 177 *fig.*
Sex determination, 599, 599 *fig.*
Sex hormones, 60
Sex-linked traits, 175, 175 *fig.*
Sex ratio of population, 386
Sexual life cycles, 149, 149 *fig.*
alternation of generations and, 149, 149 *fig.*
germ-line tissues and, 149
Sexually transmitted diseases (STDs), 613, 614. *See also* AIDS; HIV
Sexual reproduction, 148 *fig.*, 148–149, 149 *fig.*
in animals, 343 *table*
evolution and, 151
human. *See* Human reproductive system
by plants. *See* Flowers; Plant(s) (Plantae); Seed(s)
Sexual selection, 440, 440 *fig.*
Shallow waters, of ocean, 418, 418 *fig.*
Shark, 363, 363 *fig.*
Shark fin soup, 363
Shoot of vascular plant, 618, 618 *fig.*
Short-term memory, 2–3
Shoulder girdle, human, 482
Shrimp, pistol, 392, 392 *fig.*
Shrub tea, 327 *table*
Siberian crane, 438
Siberian tiger, 381 *fig.*
Sickle-cell anemia, 168, 272 *fig.*, 272–273
Sickle-cell disease, 180 *table,* 182, 182 *fig.*
Sieve cells, 621, 621 *fig.*
Sieve plates, 621, 621 *fig.*
Sieve-tube members, 621, 621 *fig.*
Sign stimulus, 431, 431 *fig.*
Simple carbohydrates, 58, 58 *fig.*
Simple cell cycle, 134, 134 *fig.*
Simple epithelium, 476
Simple leaves, 626 *fig.*, 626–627
Simple sugars, 58, 58 *fig.*
Simpson, George, 298
Single covalent bonds, 38
Single-loop blood circulation of fishes, 363
Sink, 631
Sinoatrial (SA) node, 499, 499 *fig.*
Sister chromatids, 136, 136 *fig.*, 150
Skeletal connective tissue, 477. *See also* Bone; Skeleton(s)
Skeletal muscle, 479, 479 *fig.*
actions of, 483, 484 *fig.*
Skeleton(s). *See also* Bone; Cytoskeleton; Endoskeletons; Exoskeletons
of birds, 368
types of, 481, 481 *fig.*
of vertebrates, 475
Skin, of reptiles, 365
Skin cancer, 201
Skinner, B. F., 433
Sleep, studying and, 5
Sliding filament model of muscle contraction, 485, 485 *fig.*
Slightly movable joints, 482
Slime molds, 315 *table*
Slugs, 354
Small intestine, 524 *fig.*, 524–525, 525 *fig.*, 527 *fig.*
Smallpox vaccination, 554, 554 *fig.*
Smell sense, receptors for, 575, 575 *fig.*
Smoking, lung cancer and, 10, 10 *fig.*, 200–201, 510–511, 511 *fig.*, 594
Smooth endoplasmic reticulum (smooth ER), eukaryotic, 76, 76 *fig.*, 77
Smooth muscle, 479
Snails, 354, 354 *fig.*
Snowshoe hare, 393–394, 394 *fig.*
Social behavior, 441 *table,* 442–447
altruistic, 444 *fig.*, 444–445, 445 *fig.*
animal societies and, 447, 447 *fig.*
communication, 442 *fig.*, 442–443, 443 *fig.*
human, 447, 447 *fig.*
Societies, animal, 446, 446 *fig.*
Society, civil, 446
Sociobiology, 447
Socorro isopod, 378, 378 *fig.*
Sodium, atomic number and mass number of, 34 *table*
Sodium chloride (salt)
dissolution in water, 43, 43 *fig.*
ionic bond in, 37, 37 *fig.*
plants tolerating, 338

Sodium-potassium (Na^+-K^+) pump, 87, 87 *fig.*
ATP for, 99 *table*
Soil(s), adaptations and, 377
Solenoids, 137, 137 *fig.*
Solid worms. *See* Flatworms (Platyhelminthes)
Solubility, 43, 43 *fig.*
Solutes, 83
Solutions
hypertonic, 83, 83 *fig.*
hypotonic, 83, 83 *fig.*
isotonic, 83, 83 *fig.*
of salt in water, 43, 43 *fig.*
Somatic cell(s), 135, 149
Somatic cell nuclear transfer, 242, 242 *fig.*, 243 *fig.*
Somatic mutations, 552
cancer and, 200–201
Somatic nervous system, 571–572, 572 *fig.*
Somatic rearrangement, 552, 552 *fig.*
Somatic tissue, mutations in, 199
Somites, 607
Sound receptors, 576, 576 *fig.*
Source, 631
South Beach Diet, 129
Soybeans
development of, 641 *fig.*
genetically modified, 237 *table*
Sparrow
population density of, 400
stabilizing (balancing) selection and, 271
Speciation, 279–281
biological species concept and, 279, 279 *table*
isolating mechanisms and, 280 *fig.*, 280 *table*, 280–281, 281 *fig.*
Species, 19, 19 *fig.*, 250, 376
allopatric, 390
coevolution of, 391, 391 *fig.*
commensalism and, 392, 392 *fig.*
definition of, 286
endangered, preserving, 464–466, 464–466 *fig.*
introduced, 455, 464
keystone, preserving, 446, 466 *fig.*
loss of biodiversity and, 361, 455, 455 *fig.*
mutualism and, 392, 392 *fig.*
names of, 287, 287 *fig.*
number of, 289
overexploitation of, 455
symbiosis among, 391–392, 392 *fig.*
sympatric, 390
threatened, 291
Specific epithet, 287
Spemann, Hans, 238
Sperm, 598, 600
blockage of, 613, 613 *fig.*
delivery by penis, 601
destruction of, 613
production of, 600 *fig.*, 600–601
Spermatogenesis, 600 *fig.*, 600–601
Spermicidal jellies, 613
Sphaeropteris, 327 *table*
Sphagnum, 327 *table*
S phase, 135
Sphincters
esophageal, 522
precapillary, 492, 492 *fig.*
pyloric, 523
Spinal cord, 570, 570 *fig.*
regeneration of, 570
Spindle fibers, 138–139
Spine. *See* Backbone; Vertebrates
Spiny anteater, 369 *fig.*
Spiracles, 504
Spiral cleavage, 357
Sponges (Porifera), 348, 348 *fig.*
Spongy bone, 478, 478 *fig.*
Spongy mesophyll, 627
Sporangia, 329, 329 *fig.*
Spores
fungal, 317, 317 *fig.*
of plants, 324
Sporophyte, 325, 325 *fig.*
Sporophyte generation, 637
Sporozoans, 315 *table*
Spring overturn, 421
Spruce trees, 327 *table*
Squash, 621 *fig.*
Squid, 354
SRY gene, 599, 599 *fig.*
Stabilizing selection, 270 *fig.*, 271, 271 *fig.*
sickle-cell anemia and, 273, 273 *fig.*
Stamens, 336, 336 *fig.*, 637, 637 *fig.*
Starch, 58, 59 *table*
Starfish, 394, 394 *fig.*
Starling, 380, 380 *fig.*, 438 *fig.*
Statins, 84
Statistical significance, 400
STDs (sexually transmitted diseases), 613
variation in frequency of, 614
Stem(s)
dicot and monocot, comparison of, 624, 624 *fig.*
primary growth of, 624, 624 *fig.*
secondary growth of, 624–625, 625 *fig.*
of vascular plants, 618, 618 *fig.*, 624 *fig.*, 624–625, 625 *fig.*
Stem cells, 240–243, 249 *fig.*
adult, 240
embryonic, 240, 240 *fig.*
ethical issues with, 240–241
nerve, 240
stem cell therapy using, 240 *fig.*, 240–241, 241 *fig.*
therapeutic cloning and, 242, 242 *fig.*, 243 *fig.*
totipotent, 240
Steroid(s), 60
anabolic, 61, 586–587
Steroid hormones, action of, 586 *fig.*, 586–587
Steward, F. C., 642
Stickleback fish, 431 *fig.*
Stigmas of flowers, 336, 336 *fig.*, 637, 637 *fig.*
Stipules, 626
Stoddart, Marion, 469
Stoma(ata)
of plants, 113, 113 *fig.*, 620, 620 *fig.*
regulation of transpiration by, 630, 630 *fig.*
Stomach, 527 *fig.*
acid in, 44, 522–523
of sauropods, 366
structure and function of, 522, 523 *fig.*
ulcers of, 523
Storage polysaccharides, 59 *table*
Stramenopila, 315 *table*
Stratified epithelium, 476
Strauss, Sharon, 648
Streptococcus, 191
Streptococcus mutans, 231
Streptococcus pneumoniae, 190, 190 *fig.*
Stress hormone, 593
Striations in skeletal muscle, 479
Stroke, 567
Stroma of chloroplasts, 79, 79 *fig.*, 106
Strongylocentrotus franciscanus, 358 *fig.*
Structural DNA, 227, 227 *table*
Structural polysaccharides, 59 *table*
Structural proteins, 52 *fig.*
Structure, function determined by, 21
Studying, 2–5
all-nighters and, 5
to learn, 4
learning and, 3, 3 *fig.*
learning as active process and, 4, 4 *fig.*
note taking for, 2, 2 *fig.*
remembering and forgetting and, 2–3
Study On The Fly application, 9
Styles of flowers, 336, 336 *fig.*, 637, 637 *fig.*
Stylets of nematodes, 353
Substrate(s), 94, 94 *fig.*
Substrate-level phosphorylation, 120
Subunit vaccines, 234, 234 *fig.*
Succession, ecological, 399, 399 *fig.*
Suckers, angiosperm reproduction by, 636
Sucrose, 58, 59 *fig.*
Sugars, 58, 58 *fig.*, 59 *fig.*
Sulfur, atomic number and mass number of, 34 *table*
Sun, atmospheric circulation and, 414, 414 *fig.*
Sunbird, 437 *fig.*
Sunlight
adaptations and, 377
latitude and, 415, 415 *fig.*
ozone hole and, 22–23, 23 *fig.*, 457, 457 *fig.*
photoperiodism and, 646 *fig.*, 646–647
photosynthesis and. *See* Photosynthesis
plant movement and, 644 *fig.*, 644–645, 645 *fig.*
plants' capture of energy from, 108 *fig.*, 108–109
skin cancer and, 201
Suppositories (contraceptive), 613
Suppressor T cells, 548, 548 *table*
Surfactant, 506
Survivorship curves, 386, 386 *fig.*
Suspensory ligaments, 577, 577 *fig.*
Sutton, Walter, 174
Swallowing, 521, 521 *fig.*
Sweet woodruff, 627 *fig.*
Swim bladder, 363, 363 *fig.*
Swimming, efficiency of, 486
Swine flu, 311
Sword fern, 376 *fig.*
Symbiosis, 21, 79
among species, 391–392, 392 *fig.*
Symmetry
bilateral, 344, 345 *fig.*
radial, 344, 345 *fig.*
Sympathetic nervous system, 572, 572 *fig.*
Sympatric species, 390
Synapses, 480
kinds of, 566, 566 *fig.*
Synapsis, 154, 154 *fig.*
Synaptic cleft, 565, 565 *fig.*
Syngamy, 148
Syphilis, 613, 614
Systems ecologists, 377
Systolic blood pressure, 498, 498 *fig.*

$t_{1/2}$, 156
2,4,5-T (2,4,5-trichlorophenoxyacetic acid), 645
T_4 (thyroxine), 592
Table salt. *See* Salt (sodium chloride)
Tachyglossus aculeatus, 369 *fig.*
Taiga, 424, 424 *fig.*
Tails
postanal, 359
of sauropods, 366
of theropods, 367
Tanning, skin cancer and, 201
Taraxacum officinale, 640, 640 *fig.*
Taricha granulosa, 138 *fig.*
Taste buds, receptors for, 575, 575 *fig.*
Taxon (taxa), 287
Taxonomy, 287
Tay-Sachs disease, 180 *table*, 183, 183 *fig.*
TB (tuberculosis), 307
T cells, 496, 496 *fig.*, 548
cellular immune response and, 549, 550, 550 *fig.*
Teeth
eliminating cavities and, 231
of theropods, 367
vertebrate, 520 *fig.*, 520–521, 521 *fig.*
Televisions, high definition, 67
Telomerase, 143, 144
Telomeres, 143, 144
Telophase I in meiosis I, 150, 152
Telophase II in meiosis II, 153
Telophase in mitosis, 139
Temperature. *See also* Heat
adaptations and, 377, 377 *fig.*
body, regulation of. *See* Body temperature
environmental, global warming and. *See* Global warming
enzyme activity and, 96, 96 *fig.*5110
Temperature regulation, as circulatory system function, 491, 491 *fig.*
Temperature response, 547
Temporal isolation, 279 *table*, 280
TEMs (transmission electron microscopes), 68
Tensile strength in plants, 629
Territoriality, 437, 437 *fig.*, 441 *table*
Tertiary consumers, 405
Tertiary structure of proteins, 54, 54 *fig.*
Testcross, 166, 166 *fig.*
Testes, 598
sperm production in, 600, 600 *fig.*
Testosterone, 60
increasing, for athletic performance, 61
Tetrahydrogesetrinone (THG), 61
Textbook, 6–7
features of, 7, 7 *fig.*
how to use, 6
Internet resources for, 8–9
when to use, 6
Thalamus, 567 *fig.*, 568, 568 *fig.*
Thalassoma bifasciatum, 598 *fig.*
Theoretical niche, 388
Theories, 23
rejected, 24, 24 *fig.*
Theory of evolution, 28, 28 *fig.*, 29 *fig.*
controversy over, 262 *fig.*, 262–263, 263 *fig.*

Therapeutic cloning, 28, 28 *fig.*, 242, 242 *fig.*, 243 *fig.*
reproductive cloning compared with, 242, 243 *fig.*
Thermacidophiles, 307, 307 *fig.*
Thermal stratification, 421, 421 *fig.*
Thermoacidophiles, 307, 307 *fig.*
Thermodynamics, 92
laws of, 93, 93 *fig.*
Theropods, 367
THG (tetrahydrogesetrinone), 61
Thiazolidinediones (TZDs), 591
Thigmotropism, 647, 647 *fig.*
Thoracic breathing of reptiles, 365
Thoracic cavity, 474, 506, 506 *fig.*
Threatened species, 291
Threshold potential, 564, 564 *fig.*
Thylakoids, 79, 79 *fig.*, 106
grana and, 106
penetration of surface by sunlight, 106
Thymine, 192, 192 *fig.*
Thyroid gland, 592, 592 *fig.*
Thyroid-stimulating hormone (TSH), 589, 592
Thyrotropin-releasing hormone (TRH), 592
Thyroxine (T_4), 592
Tiger
ecological isolation of, 280, 280 *fig.*
Siberian, 381 *fig.*
Tiktaalik, 364 *fig.*
Tinbergen, Niko, 431
Tissues
of animals, 343 *table*
evolution of, 344
of vertebrates, 474, 474 *fig.*, 476–480
T lymphocytes. *See* T cells
TMV (tobacco mosaic virus), 308, 308 *fig.*
Toadstools, 318 *table*
Tobacco, 620 *fig.*
smoking, lung cancer and, 10, 10 *fig.*, 200–201, 510–511, 511 *fig.*, 594
Tobacco mosaic virus (TMV), 308, 308 *fig.*
Tomato(es), 640 *fig.*
Tomato plant, 620 *fig.*
Tooth decay, eliminating, 231
Top carnivores, 405, 408
Topsoil, preserving, 459
Torpor, 540
Totipotency, 240
Touch, pressure receptors and, 573
Trace elements, 517
Tracers, 36, 36 *fig.*
Tracheae, mammalian, 506, 506 *fig.*
Tracheids, 620, 621 *fig.*
Tracts, 567
Traditional taxonomy, 291, 291 *fig.*, 292 *fig.*
"The Tragedy of the Commons" (Hardin), 459
Traits
gene influence on, 168, 169 *table*
Mendelian inheritance of, 174–177, 174–177 *fig.*
non-Mendelian inheritance of, 170 *fig.*, 170–173
sex-linked, 175, 175 *fig.*
Transcription, 206, 206 *fig.*, 211 *fig.*
control in eukaryotes, 216 *fig.*, 216–217
control in prokaryotes, 214 *fig.*, 214–215, 215 *fig.*
Transcription factors, 216, 216 *fig.*
Trans fats, 60
Transfer RNA (tRNA), 209, 209 *fig.*
Transformation, 190
Translation, 206, 206 *fig.*, 211 *fig.*
genetic code and, 208, 208 *fig.*
polypeptide formation and, 210, 210 *fig.*
rRNA and, 209, 209 *fig.*
tRNA and, 209, 209 *fig.*
Translocation, 631
Transmembrane proteins, 73
Transmission electron microscopes (TEMs), 68
Transpiration, 410, 629 *fig.*, 629–630
regulation of, 630, 630 *fig.*
Transport
across plasma membranes, 82–87
active, 87, 99 *table*
of carbohydrates in vascular plants, 631
of carbon dioxide, in blood, 508 *fig.*, 508–509
cytoplasmic, 99 *table*
of hemoglobin, 496, 508, 508 *fig.*
of oxygen, in blood, 508, 508 *fig.*
of water in plants, 632
Transport connective tissue, 477
Transport disaccharides, 59 *table*
Transport proteins, 52 *fig.*
Transposable elements, 227, 227 *table*
trans-retinal, 578, 578 *fig.*
"Traveler's diarrhea," 312
Tree(s). *See also* Forests; *specific trees*
maximum height of, 628
photosynthesis in, 104
Tree fern, 327 *table*
Trenberth, Kevin, 417
Treponema pallidum, 613
TRH (thyrotropin-releasing hormone), 592
Triassic period, 360
Triceratops, 367
2,4,5-Trichlorophenoxyacetic acid (2,4,5-T), 645
Trichomes of plants, 620, 620 *fig.*
Trichomonas vaginalis, 315 *table*
Tricuspid valve, 497 *fig.*, 498
Triglochin maritima, 338
Trilobites, 360 *fig.*, 361
Triple covalent bonds, 38
Trisomics, 176
Trivers, Robert, 444
tRNA (transfer RNA), 209, 209 *fig.*
Trophic levels, 123
energy flows through, 406, 406 *fig.*, 407 *fig.*
Trophoblast, 606
Tropical monsoon forests, 425, 425 *fig.*
Tropical rain forests, 423, 423 *fig.*
Tropisms, 647, 647 *fig.*
Truffles, 318 *table*
Trypanosomes, 315 *table*
TSH (thyroid-stimulating hormone), 589, 592
Tube feet of echinoderms, 358
Tuberculosis (TB), 307
Tubular secretion, 537
Tubulin, 80
Tumor-suppressor genes, 141
Tundra, 425, 425 *fig.*
Tunicates, 359 *fig.*
Turgidity, 630
Turner syndrome, 177
Tutt, J. W., 274
Twin studies of behavior, 432
Tyrannosaurus, 361 *fig.*, 367
Tyrosine kinases, 143
TZDs (thiazolidinediones), 591

Ubiquitin, 88
Ultrasound, fetal, 184, 184 *fig.*
Ultraviolet light
ozone hole and, 11, 11 *fig.*, 22–23, 23 *fig.*, 457, 457 *fig.*
skin cancer and, 201
Ulva, 315 *table*
Unconditioned stimulus, 433
Uniform population distribution, 379, 379 *fig.*, 380 *fig.*
Units, on graphs, 13
Unity of life, 28, 28 *fig.*
Unsaturated fats, 60, 60 *fig.*
Urea, formation in body, 539, 539 *fig.*
Ureters, 536, 536 *fig.*
Urey, Harold, 302–303
Uric acid, formation in body, 539, 539 *fig.*
Urinary bladder, 536, 536 *fig.*
Urinary system, of vertebrates, 475
Urine, glucose excretion in, 528
Urodela, 365
Uterine tubes, 603, 603 *fig.*
Uterus, 603, 603 *fig.*

Vaccines, 554, 554 *fig.*
cancer, 234
DNA, 234, 234 *fig.*
influenza, 553, 554
piggyback (subunit), 234, 234 *fig.*
safety of, 554, 554 *fig.*
Vacuoles, 77, 77 *fig.*
Vampire bats, 256
van Beneden, Pierre-Joseph, 148
van der Waals forces, 40, 41
van Helmont, Jan Baptista, 517
van Leeuwenhoek, Anton, 26
Van Valen, Lee, 372
Vaporization, heat of, of water, 43
Variables, 12, 23
Variance, 172
Vascular cambium, 618, 624–625, 625 *fig.*
Vascular plants, 329–331, 329–331 *fig.*
evolution of vascular tissue and, 329, 329 *fig.*
leaves of, 618, 618 *fig.*
meristems of, 618, 618 *fig.*
organization of, 618, 618 *fig.*
roots of, 618, 618 *fig.*
seed, 332 *fig.*, 332–333. *See also* Angiosperms; Gymnosperms; Seed(s)
seedless, 330 *fig.*, 330–331
shoots of, 618, 618 *fig.*
stems of, 618, 618 *fig.*
water movement in, 620 *fig.*, 620–621, 621 *fig.*, 628 *fig.*, 628–630
Vascular system of echinoderms, 358
Vascular tissue of plants, 620 *fig.*, 620–621, 621 *fig.*
evolution of, 326
Vas deferens, 601
Vasopressin (ADH; antidiuretic hormone), 538, 588, 588 *fig.*
Vectors, for gene therapy, 244–245, 245 *fig.*
Vegan diet, 526
Vegetative reproduction, 636, 636 *fig.*
Veins, 490, 492, 492 *fig.*, 493 *fig.*, 494, 494 *fig.*
Velociraptor, 361 *fig.*, 367
Venter, Craig, 233
Ventral, definition of, 350, 350 *fig.*
Ventricles
left, of human heart, 497, 497 *fig.*
right, of human heart, 497 *fig.*, 498
Venules, 492, 492 *fig.*
Vernalization, 646
Verne, Jules, 446
Vertebrates, 343 *table. See also* Backbone; *specific animals*
aquatic, respiratory systems of, 505, 505 *fig.*
circulatory systems of, 475, 492 *fig.*, 492–494
digestive systems of, 519–526, 527 *fig.*
embryonic development of, 359
evolution of, 360 *fig.*, 360–361, 361 *fig.*
eyes of, 577, 577 *fig.*
family tree of, 362 *fig.*
invasion of land by, 360, 360 *fig.*
organs of, 474
organ systems of, 475, 475 *fig.*
osmoregulation by, 535–538, 536 *fig.*, 537 *fig.*
societies of, 446, 446 *fig.*
teeth of, 520 *fig.*, 520–521, 521 *fig.*
tissues of, 474, 474 *fig.*, 476–480
Vesicles, 76, 76 *fig.*
eukaryotic, 70 *fig.*, 71, 71 *fig.*
Vespa crabro, 397 *fig.*
Vessel elements, 620, 621 *fig.*
Viceroy butterfly, Batesian mimicry in, 396, 396 *fig.*
Victoria, Queen of England, 181, 181 *fig.*
Vicuna, 512
Villus(i), small intestinal, 524 *fig.*, 524–525
Viral diseases, 309–311. *See also specific viruses and diseases*
Virtual Labs, 9
Viruses, 308–311
animal infection by, 310
bacterial infection by, 310, 310 *fig.*
diseases caused by, origin of, 309
emerging, 309
structure of, 308 *fig.*, 308–309
Visible light, 108, 108 *fig.*
Vision, 577–579, 577–579 *fig.*
binocular, 579, 579 *fig.*
color, 578 *fig.*, 578–579
transmission of light information to brain and, 579, 579 *fig.*
Vitamin(s), 517
Voltage-gated channels, 564
Voluntary nervous system, 571–572, 572 *fig.*
Volvox, 313, 313 *fig.*
von Frisch, Karl, 431, 442
von Humboldt, Alexander, 410
Vorticella, 312, 312 *fig.*

Waggle dance of honeybees, 442 *fig.*, 442–443
Wallace, Alfred Russel, 254
Warney, Douglas, 232
Warning coloration, 395, 395 *fig.*

Washington, Lake, cleanup of, 469, 469 *fig.*
Wasp
Müllerian mimicry in, 396–397, 397 *fig.*
paper, 356 *fig.*
Wastes
in blood plasma, 495
nitrogenous, elimination of, 539, 539 *fig.*
Water
absorption by roots, 630, 630 *fig.*
body, regulation of. *See* Osmoregulation
bottled, 452
hydrogen bonds in, 40, 40 *fig.*
movement in vascular plants, 620 *fig.*, 620–621, 621 *fig.*, 628 *fig.*, 628–630
plant conservation of, 324 *fig.*, 324–325
properties of, 42 *table*, 42–43
reabsorption of, 537
seed dispersal by, 640, 640 *fig.*
transport in plants, 632
Waterbug, 420 *fig.*
Water cycle, 409 *fig.*, 409–410
Water fern, 327 *table*
Water mold, 315 *table*
Water pollution, 453
Water supply, adaptations and, 377
Water vascular system of echinoderms, 358
Watson, James, 192, 233
Weather, 414–417. *See also* Global change; Global warming
latitude and elevation and, 415, 415 *fig.*
ocean circulation patterns and, 416 *fig.*, 416–417
sun and atmospheric circulation and, 414, 414 *fig.*
Website resources, 9, 9 *fig.*
Weight, 34
Weight loss, 129
Welwitschia, 327 *table*
Welwitschia mirabilis, 334 *fig.*, 335
Wenner, Adrian, 442
Went, Frits, 644–645, 645 *fig.*
West Nile virus, 309
Whales, evolution of, 259
Wheat, 327 *table*
genetically modified, 237 *table*
Whisk fern, 327 *table,* 330 *fig.*, 331
White blood cells, 52 *fig.*, 496, 496 *fig.*
crawling by, 81
White-fronted bee-eater, kin selection in, 445, 445 *fig.*
White-tailed deer, population growth of, 383
Whorls
of flowers, 336
leaf arrangement in, 627, 627 *fig.*
Wild lettuce, temporal isolation of, 280
Wilkins, Maurice, 192, 233
Willow oak, 287, 287 *fig.*
Wilmut, Ian, 233, 239
Wind, seed dispersal by, 640, 640 *fig.*
Winder, Ernst, 200
Wolves
as carnivores, 405 *fig.*
geographical isolation by roads, 281
predation by, 393 *fig.*
temperature adaptation and, 377 *fig.*
Wood, 329, 625
Woolly hair, 185
Worms. *See* Earthworm; Flatworms (Platyhelminthes); Nematodes (Nematoda); Roundworms

x axis, 12, 12 *fig.*, 62
X chromosome
chromosomal theory of inheritance and, 175, 175 *fig.*
nondisjunction involving, 177, 177 *fig.*
Xylem, 329, 620
water transport in, 632

Yamagiwa, Katsusaburo, 200
Yamanaka, Shinya, 233, 241
y axis, 12, 12 *fig.*, 62
Y chromosome
chromosomal theory of inheritance and, 175, 175 *fig.*
nondisjunction involving, 177
Yeasts, 318 *table*
beer making and, 319
Yellow jacket, 397 *fig.*

Zamecnik, Paul, 220
Zea mays. See Corn
Zebra as herbivore, 405 *fig.*
Z lines, 485, 485 *fig.*
Zone diet, 129
Zone of differentiation of root, 622–623
Zone of elongation of root, 622
Zygomycetes, 318 *table*
Zygote, 148, 598

Applications Index

ABO blood groups, 173
ABO system, 555, 555 *fig.*
Abstinence as birth control method, 612
Acid(s)
- gastric, 522–523
- hydrochloric, heartburn and, 44

Acid rain, 45, 453, 453 *fig.*
Acid reflux, 44, 522
Acne, 544
Acute myelogenous leukemia (AML), human genome in, 226
Adult stem cells, 240
African Americans, sickle-cell anemia in, 168, 272 *fig.*, 272–273
Agent Orange, 645
Agricultural chemicals, 453, 453 *fig.*
Agriculture, genetic engineering and, 235 *fig.*, 235–237, 236 *fig.*, 237 *table*
AIDS, 218, 309, 557, 557 *fig.*
Air pollution, 45, 274 *fig.*, 274–275, 275 *fig.*, 453
Albinism, 178 *fig.*, 178–179
Aldosterone, 538, 593
Allergies, 556, 556 *fig.*
Alternative energy sources, 467, 467 *fig.*
Alzheimer's disease, cell cycle and, 135
Amino acids, linking of, 53, 53 *fig.*
Amino groups, 50 *fig.*
Amniocentesis, 184, 184 *fig.*
Anabolic steroids, 61, 586–587
Anemia, sickle-cell, 168, 272 *fig.*, 272–273
Antarctica, ozone hole and, 11, 11 *fig.*, 23, 23 *fig.*, 457, 457 *fig.*
Antibodies
- in medical diagnosis, 555, 555 *fig.*
- monoclonal, 142, 143, 555

Antipollution laws, 457
Anti-sense therapy, 219
Antiviral drugs for AIDS, 557
Asian flu, 311
Asthma, 507
Atherosclerosis, 498
Atmosphere, ozone hole and, 11, 11 *fig.*, 22–23, 23 *fig.*, 457, 457 *fig.*
Autoimmune diseases, 556

Bee(s), killer, invasion of, 398
Beer making, 319
Binocular vision, 579, 579 *fig.*
Biofeedback, 572
Bird flu, 311
Birth control, 612–613, 613 *fig.*
Blood glucose regulation, 533, 533 *fig.*
Blood groups, 173
Blood pressure, 498, 498 *fig.*, 573, 573 *fig.*
Blood typing, 555, 555 *fig.*
Body mass index (BMI), 516, 516 *fig.*
Bone, osteoporosis and, 478, 478 *fig.*
Brain, Alzheimer's disease and, 135

Cancer
- cell cycle and, 141, 141 *fig.*
- cervical, 613
- definition of, 141
- human genome in, 226
- of lung, 10, 10 *fig.*, 200–201, 510–511, 511 *fig.*, 594
- metastases of, 141
- mutations causing, 200–201
- pancreatic, 590
- preventing the spread of, 143
- preventing the start of, 142–143, 234
- radioactive tracers to identify, 36, 36 *fig.*
- of skin, 201
- somatic mutations and, 200–201
- treatment of, 139, 142, 143, 174, 244

Cancer vaccines, 234
Carbohydrates, diets low in, 129
Carbon-14 dating, 36, 46
"Carbon footprint," 411
Carcinomas, 141
Cardiovascular disease, 219, 498
Cervical cancer, 613
Cesarean section, 611
Chlamydia, 613, 614
Chlorofluorocarbons (CFCs), ozone hole and, 11, 11 *fig.*, 22–23, 23 *fig.*, 457
Cholesterol-lowering drugs, 84
Chorionic villus sampling, 184
Chromosomes, artificial, for cancer treatment, 174
Classical conditioning, 433
"Clean coal," 454
Clear-cutting, 426
Climate change. *See* Global change; Global warming
Cloning, therapeutic, 242, 242 *fig.*, 243 *fig.*
Coal, "clean," 454
Coal gasification, 454
Conditioning, classical and operant, 433
Condoms, 613, 613 *fig.*
Conservation, environmental, 458–463
Consumption, population growth and, 463, 463 *fig.*
Contraception, 612–613, 613 *fig.*
Corn, 237 *table*, 468, 468 *fig.*
Coronary heart disease, gene silencing for, 219
Cotton, genetically modified, 237 *table*
Creationists, 93
Critical thinking, 3
CRP (C-reactive protein), heart attacks and, 498
C-section, 611
Cystic fibrosis (CF), 86, 170, 170 *fig.*, 171, 180 *table*, 267

Dandruff, 476
DDT, 453, 453 *fig.*, 465
Deer, population growth of, 383
Demography, 386, 386 *fig.*
Dental cavities, eliminating, 231
Diabetes mellitus, 590
- glucose excretion and, 528
- obesity and, 11, 11 *fig.*, 523, 591
- treatment of, 242, 590
- types I and II, 556, 590, 591

Diaphragm (contraceptive), 613, 613 *fig.*
Diastolic blood pressure, 498, 498 *fig.*
Dietary supplements, 517
Diets, 129, 516, 516 *fig.*
Diseases and disorders
- Alzheimer's disease, 135
- asthma, 507
- autoimmune, 556
- cardiovascular, 219
- gene silencing therapy for, 219
- gene therapy for, 244 *fig.*, 244–245, 245 *fig.*
- genetic, 180 *fig.*, 180 *table*, 180–184
- HIV/AIDS. *See* AIDS; HIV
- malignant. *See* Cancer
- sexually transmitted, 613, 614. *See also* AIDS; HIV
- stem cell therapy for, 240 *fig.*, 240–241, 241 *fig.*
- therapeutic cloning for, 242, 242 *fig.*, 243 *fig.*
- viral, 309–311

Diversity of human social behavior, 447
DNA fingerprinting, 230, 239 *fig.*
DNA vaccines, 234, 234 *fig.*
Dolly (sheep), 239
Doping, 61
Down syndrome, 176 *fig.*, 176–177, 177 *fig.*
Dr. Atkins' Diet Revolution, 129
Drug(s)
- antiviral, for AIDS, 557
- birth control pills, 612, 613 *fig.*
- cholesterol-lowering, 84
- melittin, 139
- regulatory proteins as, 231, 231 *fig.*

Duchenne muscular dystrophy, 180 *table*
Duodenal ulcers, 523

Ebola virus, 309
Ecological footprint, 463, 463 *fig.*
Electrocardiogram (ECG or EKG), 499, 499 *fig.*
Embryonic stem cells, 240 *fig.*, 240–241
Endangered species, preserving, 464–466, 464–466 *fig.*
Energy, finding cleaner sources of, 467 *fig.*, 467–468
Environment
- environmental conservation and, 458–463
- genetically modified crops and, 237, 459
- pollution and. *See* Pollution
- solving environmental problems and, 464–469
- temperature and, global warming and. *See* Global warming

Epigenetics, 239
Erythroblastosis, 555
Ethanol
as energy source, 567–568, 568 *fig.*
production of, 127, 127 *fig.*, 468, 468 *fig.*
Ethics of stem cell research, 240–241
Evolution, controversy over, 93, 262 *fig.*, 262–263, 263 *fig.*
Exercise, weight loss and, 129

Fad diets, 129
Fat(s), dietary, sources of, 516
Fertilizers, phosphorus-containing, 413
Fever, 547
Foams (contraceptive), 613
Food, genetically modified, potential risks of, 237, 459
Forensic science, DNA fingerprinting and, 230, 230 *fig.*
Forests
acid precipitation and, 453, 453 *fig.*
clear-cutting, 426
Forgetting, 2–3
Founder effect, 269, 269 *fig.*
Fungi, commercial uses of, 319
Fur from endangered species, 464

Gastric ulcers, 523
Gene(s)
modified, escape from GM crops, 246
protecting, 200–201
Gene flow from genetically modified crops, 237
Gene silencing, 218, 219
Gene therapy, 244 *fig.*, 244–245, 245 *fig.*
Genetic counseling, 184
Genetic disorders, 180 *fig.*, 180 *table*, 180–184
Genetic engineering, 228 *fig.*, 228–237
Genetic screening, 184, 184 *fig.*
Gene transfer therapy, 244–245
Genital herpes, 613
Genomes
human. *See* Human genome
intelligent design evaluated using, 264–265
Gleevec, 143
Global change, 452–457
ozone hole and, 11, 11 *fig.*, 22–23, 23 *fig.*, 457, 457 *fig.*
pollution and, 45, 452–454, 452–454 *fig.*
Global warming, 454
Calvin cycle and, 112
carbon dioxide and, 11, 11 *fig.*, 39, 411
controversy over, 470
melting of ice caps and, 39
El Niño and, 417
Glucose, blood, regulation of, 533, 533 *fig.*
Goiter, 592, 592 *fig.*
Gonorrhea, 613, 614
Greenhouse effect, 454, 454 *fig.*
"Green living," 458

Hay fever, 556
Head and Shoulders shampoo, 476
Head louse, 392, 392 *fig.*, 404
Heart, human, 497–499, 497–499 *fig.*
Heart attacks, 498
Heartburn, 44, 522
Heart disease, coronary, gene silencing for, 219
Heart murmurs, 498
Helicobacter pylori, 523
Hemophilia, 180 *table,* 181, 181 *fig.*
Herpes simplex infections, genital, 613
HIV, 308, 308 *fig.*, 309, 557, 557 *fig.*. *See also* AIDS
H1N1 flu, 311
H2N2 flu, 311
H3N2 flu, 311
H5N1 flu, 311
Hong Kong flu, 311
Hormones, steroid, 586 *fig.*, 586–587
anabolic, 61, 586–587
Human activity, mass extinction due to, 3615436
Human genome, 168, 225 *table,* 226–227, 233
Human immunodeficiency virus. *See* AIDS; HIV
Huntington's disease, 180 *table,* 183, 183 *fig.*
Hydrochloric acid, heartburn and, 44
Hydrocortisone, 593
Hypercholesterolemia, 180 *table*
Hypothyroidism, congenital, 180 *table*

Ice fishing, 421
Influenza, 309, 311
Influenza vaccine, 553, 554
Innocence Project, 232, 233
Insulin, 533, 533 *fig.*, 590, 590 *fig.*
Intelligence, environmental effects on I.Q. scores and, 172
Intelligent design (ID), 263, 263 *fig.*, 264–265
Intrauterine devices (IUDs), 612, 613 *fig.*
I.Q. scores, environmental effects on, 172

Kidney stones, 536
Killer bee invasion, 398
Kleinfelter syndrome, 177

Leukemia, acute myelogenous, human genome in, 226
Lung cancer, smoking and, 10, 10 *fig.*, 200–201, 510–511, 511 *fig.*, 594

Malaria, 182, 182 *fig.*, 273, 273 *fig.*, 320
Malnutrition, preventing, 516
Medical diagnosis, antibodies in, 555, 555 *fig.*
Melamine, adulteration of milk with, 53
Melanocyte-stimulating hormone (MSH), 589, 589 *fig.*
Melanoma, 201
Melittin, 139
Menstrual cycle, 604, 604 *fig.*, 604–605, 605 *fig.*
Menstrual synchrony, 440
Menstruation, 605
Metastases, 141
Mifepristone, 612
Milk, melamine adulteration of, 53
Misoprostol, 612
Monoclonal antibodies, 142, 143, 555
Mosquito, malaria and, 320
Multiple sclerosis, 556
Muscular dystrophy, Duchenne, 180 *table*
Mushrooms, edible and poisonous, 318, 318 *fig.*

Nashua River cleanup, 469, 469 *fig.*
National Collaborative Prenatal Project, 172
El Niño, 417, 417 *fig.*

Obesity, 11, 11 *fig.*, 477, 523, 591
Organic farming, 459
Osteoporosis, 478, 478 *fig.*
Overweight, 516, 516 *fig.*, 523
Oxytocin, 588, 588 *fig.*, 611
Ozone therapy, 23

Pancreatic cancer, 590
Pandemics, 311
Parathyroid hormone (PTH), 592–593, 593 *fig.*
Parkinson's disease, stem cell therapy for, 240
Peanuts, genetically modified, 237 *table*
Peregrine falcon, 465, 465 *fig.*
p53 gene, lung cancer and, 510, 511
Phenylketonuria (PKU), 180 *table*
Pigeon, homing, 439
Piggyback vaccines, 234, 234 *fig.*
Pimples, 544
Plan B, 612
Plumpy'nut, 516
Poisonous mushrooms, 318, 318 *fig.*
Polar ice caps, 39, 425, 425 *fig.*
Pollution, 452–454
Pollution taxes, 457
Polymerase chain reaction (PCR), 230, 230 *fig.*
Population growth, human, 382
Positron-emission tomography (PET), 36, 36 *fig.*
Positron-emission tomography/computed tomography (PET/CT), 36, 36 *fig.*
Potatoes, genetically modified, 237 *table*
p53 protein, lung cancer and, 510
Precipitation
acid, 45, 453, 453 *fig.*
global warming and, 454
Pregnancies
high-risk, 184, 184 *fig.*
Rh factor and, 555
tests for, 555
Progesterone, 605
Prolactin (PRL), 589, 611
p53 tumor-suppressor protein, 143

Race, genetics and, 293
Radioactive isotopes
dating of Iceman using, 46
medical uses of, 36, 36 *fig.*
Rain
acid, 45, 453, 453 *fig.*
global warming and, 454
Rain forests, tropical, destruction of, 460, 460 *fig.*
"Red tides," 314
Reproductive cloning, 238 *fig.*, 238–239
Resistin, 591
Rh factor, 555
Rice
flood-tolerant, 644
transgenic, 236, 236 *fig.*, 237 *table*
RNA interference, 218, 219
RU486, 612

Sebulex shampoo, 476
Selsun Blue shampoo, 476
"Set point," 129
Severe acute respiratory syndrome (SARS), 309
Sexually transmitted diseases (STDs), 613, 614
Sickle-cell anemia, 168, 272 *fig.*, 272–273
Sickle-cell disease, 180 *table,* 182, 182 *fig.*
Skin cancer, 201
Smallpox vaccination, 554, 554 *fig.*
Smoking, lung cancer and, 10, 10 *fig.*, 200–201, 510–511, 511 *fig.*, 594
Social behavior, human, 447, 447 *fig.*

Society, civil, 446
South Beach Diet, 129
Soybeans, genetically modified, 237 *table*
Spermicidal jellies, 613
Statins, 84
Stem cells, 240–243, 249 *fig.*
  adult, 240
  embryonic, 240, 240 *fig.*
  ethical issues with, 240–241
  stem cell therapy using, 240 *fig.*, 240–241, 241 *fig.*
  therapeutic cloning and, 242, 242 *fig.*, 243 *fig.*
Steroid hormones
  action of, 586 *fig.*, 586–587
  anabolic, 61, 586–587
Stomach ulcers, 523
Stress hormone, 593
Stroke, 567
Subunit vaccines, , 234, 234 *fig.*
Sunlight
  ozone hole and, 22–23, 23 *fig.*, 457, 457 *fig.*
  skin cancer and, 201
Suppositories (contraceptive), 613
Swine flu, 311
Syphilis, 613, 614
Systolic blood pressure, 498, 498 *fig.*

Tanning, skin cancer and, 201
Tay-Sachs disease, 180 *table,* 183, 183 *fig.*
Teeth, eliminating cavities and, 231
Televisions, high definition, 67
Therapeutic cloning, 28, 28 *fig.*, 242, 242 *fig.*, 243 *fig.*
  reproductive cloning compared with, 242, 243 *fig.*
Thiazolidinediones (TZDs), 591
Threatened species, 291
Thyroid-stimulating hormone (TSH), 589, 592
Thyrotropin-releasing hormone (TRH), 592
Thyroxine (T_4), 592
Tobacco, smoking, lung cancer and, 10, 10 *fig.*, 200–201, 510–511, 511 *fig.*, 594
Tooth decay, eliminating, 231
Topsoil, preserving, 459
Trans fats, 60
"Traveler's diarrhea," 312
Tuberculosis (TB), 307
Turner syndrome, 177
Twin studies of behavior, 432

Ulcers, peptic, 523
Ultrasound, fetal, 184, 184 *fig.*
Ultraviolet light
  ozone hole and, 11, 11 *fig.*, 22–23, 23 *fig.*, 457, 457 *fig.*
  skin cancer and, 201
Urban deer, 383

Vaccines
  cancer, 234
  DNA, 234, 234 *fig.*
  influenza, 553, 554
  piggyback (subunit), 234, 234 *fig.*
  safety of, 554, 554 *fig.*
Vasopressin (ADH; antidiuretic hormone), 538, 588, 588 *fig.*
Vegan diet, 526
Viral diseases, 309–311
Vitamins, 517

Washington, Lake, cleanup of, 469, 469 *fig.*
Water pollution, 453
Weight loss, 129
West Nile virus, 309
Wheat, genetically modified, 237 *table*
White-tailed deer, population growth of, 383
Woolly hair, 185

Yeasts, beer making and, 319

Zone diet, 129

Connections

Biology and Staying Healthy

Anabolic Steroids in Sports (p.61)
Fad Diets and Impossible Dreams (p.129)
Curing Cancer (p.142-143)
Protecting Your Genes (p.200-201)
Silencing Genes to Treat Disease (p.219)
Bird and Swine Flu (p.311)
The Author Works Out (p.484)
How Hormones Control Your Kidney's Functions (p.538)
The Type II Diabetes Epidemic (p.591)

Today's Biology

Ice, Carbon Dioxide and Polar Bears (p. 39)
Acid Rain (p.45)
Membrane Defects Can Cause Disease (p.86)
Does Environment Affect I.Q.? (p.172)
DNA and the Innocence Project (p.232)
Darwin and Moby Dick (p.259)
Putting Intelligent Design to the Test (p.264-265)
Race and Medicine (p.293)
Has Life Evolved Elsewhere? (p.304)
The War Against Urban Deer (p. 383)
Invasion of the Killer Bees (p.398)
The Great Pigeon Race Disaster of 1997 Suggests an Answer to an Enduring Mystery (p.439)
The Global Decline in Amphibians (p.456)

A Closer Look

Metabolic Efficiency and the Length of Food Chains (p.123)
The Redox Cycle (p.126)
Evolutionary Consequences of Sex (p.151)
A DNA Timeline (p.233)
Dinosaurs (p.366-367)

Author's Corner

Pulling an All-Nighter (p.5)
Where Are All My Socks Going? (p.25)
How Tropical Lizards Climb Vertical Walls (p.41)
Are Bird-Killing Cats Nature's Way of Making Better Birds? (p.278)

Applications (Apps)

Biology

Improving memory (p.2)
Ozone therapy (p.23)
Heartburn (p.44)
Statins (p.84)
The Greeks get it wrong (p.110)
Look-Alike meter (p.164)
Is your black Labrador puppy Homozygous? (p. 166)
Sickle-cell disease (p.168)
Almost all inherited mutations occur in males (p.199)
Sequencing the genome of a cancer patient (p.226)
Eliminating tooth decay (p.231)
How biodiversity benefits you
—direct economic value (p.294)
—economic services (p.295)
—ethical/aesthetic values (p.296)
Traveler beware (p.312)
Making your own beer (p.319)
Eating flowers (p.326)
Living exponentially (p.382)
Your little friends (p.391)
Your own personal ecosystem (p.404)
You and the water cycle (p.409)
You and the carbon cycle (p.411)
You and the nitrogen cycle (p.412)
You and the phosphorus cycle (p.413)
Putting thermal stratification to work: Ice fishing (p.421)
Fly away home (p.438)
The dormitory effect (p.440)
Is the Golden Rule scientific? (p.445)
Lord of the flies (p.446)
Do you use bottled water? (p.452)
Green living (p.458)
Organic farming (p.459)
Endangered species fur (p.464)
Dandruff (p.476)
Getting fat (p.477)
Asthma (p.507)
Hiccups (p.508)
Vitamin supplements: Nutrition in a pill? (p.517)
Vegans (p.526)
Kidney stones (p.536)
Pimples (p.544)
Passive immunity (p.551)
Erythroblastosis (p.555)
Biofeedback (p.572)
Performance-enhancing supplements (p.586)
Fetal Alcohol Syndrome (p. 609)
RU-486 (p. 612)
Deadly seeds (p.639)

Evolution

Computer games evolve (p.20)
Creationists & the law (p.93)
Global warming and the Calvin cycle (p.112)
Nanobees Attack Dividing Cells (p.139)
How vampires evolved (p.256)
Why cheetahs are all alike (p.269)
Natural selection for melanism in mice (p.275)
Where do new kinds of genes come from? (p.303)
Wandering mimics (p.396)
Do humans have instincts? (p.430)
Can apes use language? (p.443)
Evolutionary psychology (p.447)
Regrowing complex organs (p.475)
Why bother with blood? (p.491)
Putting Malphigian tubules to other uses (p.535)
The dry life of the kangaroo rat (p.539)
"Seeing" heat (p.565)
Hunting with Eyes Shut (p.576)
How tall can a tree grow? (p.628)

In The News

Deadly baby food (p.53)
High resolution TV (p.67)
Using algae to fix global warming (p.111)
Alzheimers disease linked to cell cycle (p.135)
Bloom's syndrome (p.152)
Adding an artificial chromosome to treat disease (p.174)
Silencing AIDS (p.218)
Plant witness for the prosecution (p.230)
Turning one cell type into another (p.242)
Shooting genes into cells (p.244)
Why doesn't natural selection eliminate cystic fibrosis? (p.267)
Why does a wolf not cross the road? (p.281)
The biodiversity crisis (p.291)
Seeds from the Time of Jesus: A 2,000 Year Nap (p.333)
Shark fin soup (p.363)
Beavers back in Britain (p.388)
Message in a bottle (p.416)
El niño and global warming (p.417)
Counting bee (p.434)
Clean coal (p.454)
Predicting and preventing heart attacks (p.498)
The peanut butter debate (p. 516)
Are microbes making Americans fatter? (p.523)
But is it safe? (p.553)
Love-enhancing pharmaceuticals? (p.585)
Pancreatic cancer (p.590)
Petal color (p.637)
Fighting hunger with flood-tolerant rice (p.644)
Vernalization (p.646)